AN APPROACH TO ELECTRICAL SCIENCE

An Approach to Electrical Science

HENRY G. BOOKER

CORNELL UNIVERSITY

McGRAW-HILL BOOK COMPANY, INC.

New York   Toronto   London

1959

AN APPROACH TO ELECTRICAL SCIENCE

THE MAPLE PRESS COMPANY, YORK, PA.

To all interested in learning or teaching
the basis of electrical science

PREFACE

Electrical science has been created by electrical engineers, by physicists, and by applied mathematicians. Over a period of many years the author has been in contact with all three of these groups of scientists, both in the field of teaching and in the field of research. The three groups approach electrical science from different points of view. Members of one group sometimes find themselves out of sympathy with the viewpoint of another group, often on the basis of insufficient study. Fairly prolonged contact with the approaches to electrical science used by all three groups has convinced the author that no one of the approaches is uniformly the "best." On any particular topic it is easy to prefer one of the approaches. But as one moves from topic to topic the "best" approach is sometimes that of the electrical engineer, sometimes that of the physicist, and sometimes that of the mathematician. If one forms the habit of assimilating all three approaches, it is sometimes possible to devise an approach better than any of the three.

In this book and in a sequel that is being written, conventional lines of demarcation among electrical engineering, physics, and mathematics are disregarded. The attempt is to present the theoretical basis of electrical science, using for each topic what the author regards as the "best" approach. In most cases this takes the form of a modification of one of the standard approaches in the light of the other two. In some cases, however, the author has been led to a presentation that would not be considered standard by an electrical engineer, a physicist, or a mathematician. In this process it has occasionally been appropriate to introduce terminology not listed by either the American or the British Standards Association.

Traditionally, electrical engineers begin the study of electrical science with Ohm's law, and many students in electrical engineering gain the impression that Ohm's law is the basis of the subject. If a similar procedure were adopted in mechanical science, one would begin by teaching uniform motion of a body sliding down a rough inclined plane, and one would give students the erroneous impression that therein lies the basis of mechanics. In mechanics, one starts with statics in order to build up the concept of force that is a prerequisite to understanding dynamics. The corresponding procedure in electrical science is to make use of electrostatics to build up the concept of a driving force for electric current. On this matter, the approach of physicists and mathematicians is good, but the same cannot always be said for the approach of electrical engineers. As a consequence, many electrical engineers never learn to describe satisfactorily the electromagnetic field that exists when a battery produces a steady current in a wire.

A case in which the approach of physicists falls short of what is desirable involves the concepts underlying the **D** and **H** vectors in a vacuum. A well-known book on college physics, widely used in American universities, states that the **D** vector "does not have any direct physical interpretation." Faraday knew better more than a century ago. It is the function of the **D** and **H** vectors to describe the geometry of the charge and current distributions associated with an electromagnetic field or with any dissected portion thereof. In electrostatics **D** gives the charge per unit area on the surfaces of the conductors and on the surface of any conductor used to replace an equipotential surface. The **H** vector gives the current per unit width on the bounding surface of a magnetic field or on any perfectly conducting sheet inserted between tubes of magnetic flux without cutting them. For a tube of magnetic flux, **H** gives the current per unit length that must flow toroidally round the tube in order to preserve the tube in existence by itself. Electrical engineers usually succeed in conveying more effectively than physicists the fundamental concept involved in the **H** vector because of the long-standing practice in engineering of measuring **H** in ampere-turns per unit length. However, even the engineers invite criticism by inserting the word "turns." Inclusion of this unnecessary word dates from the preklystron era, when every toroidal inductor had turns.

Criticism of mathematicians in electrical science is associated with the widespread use of complex numbers. If we agree to use vernacular language, the most important thing about a complex number is that it is not a number but a vector. Moreover, there is nothing complex about it except in so far as the idea has been complicated by use of the words "real" and "imaginary" in a way that bears no relation to the vernacular meanings. Most students first encounter complex numbers in high school in connection with the solution of quadratic equations. Unfortunately the teachers are often as much in the dark as the students about the significance of the language involved. Many students in electrical science graduate from reputable universities without realizing that the process of finding a complex root of a quadratic equation corresponds geometrically to arranging the three vectors associated with the three terms in the equation so as to form a triangle. Vector methods for handling oscillations without wrestling with the language of complex numbers have been developed by electrical engineers to some extent. However, the process has never been pushed to its logical conclusion because it would take a mathematician to do so. In the sequel to the present book an attempt will be made to derive the full benefit of vector analysis as a vehicle of thought in oscillation theory in contrast to the mere use of complex numbers as a tool for calculation.

The present book is designed to provide in one year the basis necessary for (1) study of electric networks involving any combination of inductors, capacitors, resistors, and vacuum tubes or (2) study of transmission lines or (3) study of electromagnetic theory. The main prerequisite is a knowledge of elementary mechanics. A knowledge of elementary algebra and geometry is, of course, also required. Moreover in the first half of the book (Parts 1 and 2) it is assumed that the student can differentiate and integrate x^n with respect to x for integral values of n, positive and negative. The few sections in the first half of the book where more calculus than this is required can easily be elided or used to whet the student's appetite for more calculus. Serious use of elementary calculus is not involved until the second half of the book (Parts 3 and 4). In the first half vector concepts are taken over from mechanics. In the second half use is made of vector algebra, but not of the divergence or curl operator. Thus, in universities where elementary mechanics and some calculus are taught in the first semester of the freshman year, Parts 1 and 2 could be used in the second semester of the freshman year, and Parts 3 and 4 in the first semester of the sophomore year. In areas of the world where some mechanics and some calculus are taught in high school, the book could be introduced at the beginning of the freshman year.

In electrical engineering departments the book may be regarded as giving a more thorough treatment of the physical basis of electrical science than has been traditional. In physics departments the book may be regarded as giving a more organized treatment of elementary network theory than is customary. A student in electrical science whose instruction in "physics" follows the lines of this book can start his "engineering" studies directly with alternating-current network theory; no restatement along "engineering" lines of the circuits section of the "physics" course would be necessary. In departments of applied mathematics the book may be regarded as bringing the elementary aspects of classical electricity and magnetism into touch with contemporary electrical science.

In many departments of electrical engineering a fairly sharp distinction exists between "circuit" theory and "field" theory, with a treatment of the former preceding a treatment of the latter. This book avoids the distinction between circuit theory and field theory and seeks to fit both approaches into a single integrated picture. Nevertheless the book is capable of being used as a one-semester course in field theory by the process of eliding the sections on circuit theory. The elided sections would still serve to show students how field theory is related to circuit theory. Used in this way the book can carry a student in one semester from the law of inverse squares to a point where he can study any book on electromagnetic theory that starts with Maxwell's equations in integrated form.

Some features that the book does not cover should perhaps be mentioned. The book treats the physics of dielectrics, metals, and ferromagnetic material only on a "model" basis. It is assumed that the quantum mechanical treatment of these matters is best handled in a course on solid-state physics at a later stage in the curriculum. The book does not deal with transistors for the same reason. The book does not provide as extensive a drill in resistive networks as is frequently found in elementary books on electrical engineering. Emphasis is given to Kirchhoff's laws by treating, at appropriate stages in the development of the subject, (1) networks of capacitors, (2) networks of resistors, and (3) networks of inductors. This lays great stress on Kirchhoff's laws without giving the student the impression that all circuit elements function more or less like resistors.

In some places the treatment of material may be considered unusual or even new. Mention should perhaps be made of the method of introducing the Poynting vector. The traditional introduction using Poynting's theorem has been abandoned because of the confusion produced when interpreting the Poynting vector in a static electromagnetic field. The procedure adopted in this book is more direct and is easily interpreted even in a static electromagnetic field. After the Poynting vector has been introduced in this way, a statement and proof of Poynting's theorem are quite desirable. Poynting's theorem is, however, omitted from the book because the associated vector calculus is considered too difficult.

Problems have been included at the end of the book, with summarizing exercises at the end of each chapter. The summarizing exercises are designed to assist the student to formulate summaries of the chapters in his own words. Those concerned about teaching students to write good technical English may be particularly interested in the summarizing exercises. The problems involve a wide range of difficulty with the easier ones indicated by stars.

The form of the book has been finalized in connection with courses taught to sophomore students in electrical engineering at Cornell University, although some of the ideas first took shape years ago in connection with applied mathematics courses taught to freshmen at the University of Cambridge. The background of the book contains, however, a feature that is not directly connected with university teaching. The thinking has been profoundly influenced by the cross-fertilization of ideas among mathematicians, physicists, and electrical engineers that was an integral part of the development of radar.

The author takes this opportunity to express his appreciation to the staff members of Cornell University whose cooperation has made the preparation of this manuscript possible.

Henry G. Booker

CONTENTS

xiii

PART 1

ELECTRIC FIELDS AND CIRCUITS
IN ELECTROSTATICS

CHAPTER 1

ELECTRIC FIELD OF POINT CHARGES

1.1. Introduction. All matter is made up of fundamental particles of which the most important are (1) the neutron, whose mass is 1.67×10^{-27} kg; (2) the proton, whose mass is also 1.67×10^{-27} kg; and (3) the electron, whose mass is 9.1×10^{-31} kg. The mass of the electron is less than that of a proton or a neutron by a factor 1,840. If any two of these particles are placed at a distance r apart, there is a force between the particles that is inversely proportional to the square of r. These forces may be divided into forces of gravitational origin and forces of electrical origin. The forces of electrical origin are tremendously strong compared with those of gravitational origin.

The law of gravitation states that, if two particles of masses m_1 and m_2 are at a distance r apart, then there is a gravitational force of attraction between the particles the magnitude of which is proportional to m_1 and m_2 and inversely proportional to r^2. If this gravitational force of attraction is denoted by F_g, then

$$F_g = \gamma_g \frac{m_1 m_2}{r^2} \tag{1.1}$$

where γ_g is the constant of gravitation. If m_1 and m_2 are measured in kilograms, r in meters, and F_g in newtons, then the value of the constant of gravitation is

$$\gamma_g = 6.67 \times 10^{-11} \tag{1.2}$$

There are forces acting among all massive particles in accordance with Eq. (1.1).

In some cases the force between a pair of elementary particles is wholly gravitational in nature. Thus the force between a neutron and another distant neutron is purely a gravitational attraction and is completely described by Eq. (1.1). Likewise the force between a neutron and a distant proton is purely a gravitational attraction and is completely described by Eq. (1.1). The same is true for the force between a neutron and an electron. For other pairs of elementary particles, however, the gravitational force is not the only force acting.

Let us consider the force between a pair of protons. This force is found to be repulsive instead of attractive. Moreover it is found to be

3

tremendously strong compared with what one would expect on the basis of gravitation only. The force of repulsion between two protons is 1.36×10^{36} times bigger than one would expect for the force of attraction if gravity were the only force involved. Thus, although protons have the same mass as neutrons, the force between a pair of protons is 1.36×10^{36} times bigger than that between a pair of neutrons at the same distance apart. Moreover for the protons the force is repulsive whereas for the neutrons it is attractive. It is quite clear therefore that a proton possesses something that a neutron does not possess. This is known as electric charge.

For a pair of electrons there is a force of repulsion equal to that for a pair of protons at the same distance apart. It is clear therefore that electrons, like protons, possess electric charge. However, there is a difference between the electric charge possessed by an electron and that possessed by a proton. This may be understood by considering the force between a proton and an electron. In magnitude, the force between a proton and an electron is the same as that between a pair of protons or a pair of electrons at the same distance apart. But whereas the force for a pair of protons or for a pair of electrons is repulsive, that for a proton and an electron is attractive. Thus, while both protons and electrons exhibit the phenomenon of electric charge, there is a difference between the phenomenon exhibited in a proton and that exhibited in an electron, and we shall have to find a convenient means of describing this difference.

Since the electrical forces between charged particles are so enormous compared with the gravitational forces, it might be wondered why gravitational forces are of any importance at all. Consider, for example, the Earth. The Earth contains an enormous number of neutrons, protons, and electrons. But the number of protons is almost exactly equal to the number of electrons. Thus a positively charged particle outside the Earth experiences a tremendous repulsion from the protons in the Earth but an almost identical attraction to the electrons in the Earth. This electrical repulsion and attraction on the particle outside the Earth are so exactly balanced that the difference may well be smaller than the gravitational attraction of the Earth on the particle. Thus although electrical forces between charged particles are strong, the possibility of both repulsions and attractions usually leads to a great deal of neutralization. With gravitational forces, on the other hand, only attractions are possible, and so all contributions are additive. There are thus many situations in which gravitational forces predominate in spite of the great strength of electrical forces.

The force of electrical origin between any pair of particles is summarized in the law of inverse squares of electrostatics. This law is concerned with the electric force of repulsion F_e between two particles at a distance r apart. Let one particle possess an electric charge represented numerically by Q_1 and the other particle possess a charge represented numerically by Q_2. The law states that the force of repulsion between the two particles is directly proportional to the charges of the two particles and inversely proportional to the square of the distance between them. The formula is

$$F_e = \gamma_e \frac{Q_1 Q_2}{r^2} \tag{1.3}$$

where γ_e is a constant known as the constant of electrostatics. If Q_1 and Q_2 have the same sign, the force of repulsion is positive, but if Q_1 and Q_2 have opposite signs, the force of repulsion is negative, and this signifies an attraction. If $Q_1 = Q$ and $Q_2 = Q$, there is a force of repulsion between the particles equal to $\gamma_e(Q^2/r^2)$. If $Q_1 = -Q$ and $Q_2 = -Q$, then there is also a force of repulsion between the two particles equal to $\gamma_e(Q^2/r^2)$. But if $Q_1 = Q$ and $Q_2 = -Q$, the force between the two particles is a repulsion $-\gamma_e(Q^2/r^2)$, and this signifies an attraction of magnitude $\gamma_e(Q^2/r^2)$. Thus the electrical forces between fundamental particles are described by Eq. (1.3) if we assign to protons and electrons charges of equal magnitude but of opposite signs.

1.2. The Unit of Electric Charge. The numerical magnitude of the constant γ_e depends upon the choice made for a unit of electric charge. It would be convenient if the unit of electric charge were chosen to be the charge on an electron or some convenient multiple thereof. Historically, however, scientists were making quite exact measurements of electric charge long before they recognized that they were dealing with electrons and protons. In consequence, a unit of charge known as the coulomb came into use, and this unit is the charge on 6.22×10^{18} protons. In terms of the coulomb, the charge on a proton is 1.60×10^{-19} coulomb, and the charge on an electron is -1.60×10^{-19} coulomb.

1.3. The Constant of Electrostatics. Having decided to use the coulomb as the unit of charge, we can now determine from figures already quoted the numerical value of the constant of electrostatics γ_e. Consider a pair of protons at distance r apart. Let each have a mass m and a charge e. From Eq. (1.1), the gravitational force of attraction between the protons is

$$F_g = \gamma_g \frac{m^2}{r^2} \tag{1.4}$$

From Eq. (1.3) the electrostatic repulsion between the charges is

$$F_e = \gamma_e \frac{e^2}{r^2} \tag{1.5}$$

Hence the ratio of the electrostatic force of repulsion to the gravitational force of attraction is

$$\frac{F_e}{F_g} = \frac{\gamma_e}{\gamma_g} \frac{e^2}{m^2} \tag{1.6}$$

We have already stated that the numerical value of this ratio is 1.36×10^{36}. Furthermore, numerical values have been given for the constant of gravitation γ_g, the mass of the proton m, and the charge of the proton e. Substitution of these numerical values into Eq. (1.6) gives for the numerical value of the constant of electrostatics

$$\gamma_e = 9.0 \times 10^9 \tag{1.7}$$

Use of this numerical value for γ_e in Eq. (1.3) assumes that force is measured in newtons, charge in coulombs, and distance in meters.

1.4. Application of the Law of Inverse Squares.   Suppose that we have a number of charged particles and that we are interested in calculating the total force acting on a particular particle.   The force on particle 1 due to particle 2 is calculated from Eq. (1.3).   In the same way the force on particle 1 due to particle 3 is calculated from Eq. (1.3).   When the forces on particle 1 due to each of the other particles separately have been calculated, these forces may then be combined by vector addition according to well-known mechanical principles.   In this way, the resultant force on particle 1 due to all the other charged particles may be calculated.

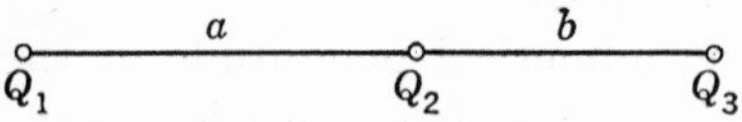

FIG. 1.1. Three charged particles in a straight line.

As an example, suppose that three particles carrying charges Q_1, Q_2, and Q_3 are arranged in order along a straight line as shown in Fig. 1.1. Let the distance between the particle carrying charge Q_1 and the particle carrying charge Q_2 be a and the distance between the particle carrying charge Q_2 and the particle carrying charge Q_3 be b.   Let us calculate in magnitude and direction the force on the particle carrying charge Q_2.

From the law of inverse squares [Eq. (1.3)], the force on Q_2 due to Q_1 is $\gamma_e(Q_1Q_2/a^2)$ in the direction from Q_1 to Q_2.   From the law of inverse squares the force on Q_2 due to Q_3 is $\gamma_e(Q_2Q_3/b^2)$ in the direction from Q_3 to Q_2.   Hence the total force on Q_2 is in the direction toward Q_3 and has the value

$$\gamma_e \frac{Q_1Q_2}{a^2} - \gamma_e \frac{Q_2Q_3}{b^2}$$

and this may be written as

$$\gamma_e Q_2 \left(\frac{Q_1}{a^2} - \frac{Q_3}{b^2} \right) \tag{1.8}$$

As a numerical example, let us calculate this force on the assumption that $Q_1 = 1,000$ $\mu\mu$coulombs,* $Q_2 = 2,000$ $\mu\mu$coulombs, and $Q_3 = 3,000$ $\mu\mu$coulombs, while $a = 10$ cm and $b = 20$ cm. If we are to use in expression (1.8) the numerical value of γ_e given in Eq. (1.7), then it is necessary to measure all charges in coulombs and all distances in meters. Hence into expression (1.8) we must substitute $Q_1 = 10^{-9}$ coulomb, $Q_2 = 2 \times 10^{-9}$ coulomb, $Q_3 = 3 \times 10^{-9}$ coulomb, $a = 10^{-1}$ m, $b = 2 \times 10^{-1}$ m, and $\gamma_e = 9.0 \times 10^9$. We thus calculate that the magnitude of the resultant force on Q_2 is 4.5×10^{-7} newton, or 0.45 μnewton.

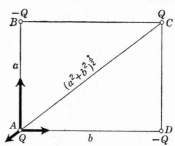

FIG. 1.2. Four charges at the corners of a rectangle.

As another example, suppose that, at the four consecutive corners of a rectangle of edges a and b, there are placed charges of strengths Q, $-Q$, Q, and $-Q$ as shown in Fig. 1.2. Let us calculate the force in magnitude and direction on one of the charges. We shall first calculate the components of the resultant force on this charge in directions parallel to the edges of the rectangle. From these two components the magnitude and the direction of the resultant can be calculated according to the principles of mechanics.

The component in the direction AD of the force on the charge at A consists of a force of attraction from the charge at D together with the component in the direction AD of the force of repulsion from the charge at C. There is no component in the direction AD of the force from the charge at B. From the law of inverse squares [Eq. (1.3)], the force of attraction on the charge at A from the charge at D is $\gamma_e(Q^2/b^2)$. The force of repulsion on the charge at A due to the charge at C is $\gamma_e Q^2/(a^2 + b^2)$. The component of this force in the direction AD is obtained by multiplying by the cosine of the angle CAD and changing the sign. The cosine of the angle CAD is $b/(a^2 + b^2)^{1/2}$. Hence the component in the direction AD of the resultant force on the charge at A is

$$\gamma_e \frac{Q^2}{b^2} - \gamma_e \frac{Q^2}{a^2 + b^2} \frac{b}{(a^2 + b^2)^{1/2}}$$

and this is equal to

$$\gamma_e Q^2 \left[\frac{1}{b^2} - \frac{b}{(a^2 + b^2)^{3/2}} \right] \qquad (1.9)$$

In the same way, the expression for the component in the direction AB of the resultant force on the charge at A is

$$\gamma_e \frac{Q^2}{a^2} - \gamma_e \frac{Q^2}{a^2 + b^2} \frac{a}{(a^2 + b^2)^{1/2}}$$

* μ denotes "micro," or 10^{-6}; $\mu\mu$ denotes "micromicro," or 10^{-12}.

and this is equal to

$$\gamma_e Q^2 \left[\frac{1}{a^2} - \frac{a}{(a^2 + b^2)^{3/2}} \right] \tag{1.10}$$

From the components of force given by expressions (1.9) and (1.10), the magnitude and direction of the resultant force upon the charge at A can be calculated.

As an additional example, suppose that two particles, each of mass m, are suspended under gravity from a common point by light strings each of length l. A total charge $2Q$ is divided equally between the two particles. As a result the system rests in equilibrium with the strings at an angle θ to the vertical as shown in Fig. 1.3. Let us calculate the magnitude of the charge Q in terms of the angle θ, the mass m of the particles, the acceleration g due to gravity, and the constant of electrostatics γ_e.

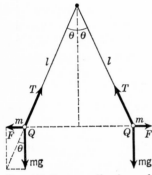

The distance between the two particles is $2l \sin \theta$. It follows from the law of inverse squares that the force of repulsion between the two particles on account of their charge is

$$F = \frac{\gamma_e Q^2}{(2l \sin \theta)^2} \tag{1.11}$$

FIG. 1.3. Two equally charged particles suspended from a common point.

In comparison with this force we neglect the gravitational force of attraction between the two particles, but we do not neglect the much larger force of gravitational attraction between the particles and the Earth.

From the principles of statics the system is in equilibrium when the resultant of the force F given by Eq. (1.11) and the weight mg of a particle are exactly balanced by the tension in the string attached to the particle. In equilibrium we therefore have

$$\tan \theta = \frac{F}{mg}$$

and if we substitute for F from Eq. (1.11), we derive

$$\tan \theta = \frac{1}{mg} \frac{\gamma_e Q^2}{(2l \sin \theta)^2} \tag{1.12}$$

Solution of this equation for Q gives

$$Q = \pm \left(\frac{4g}{\gamma_e} \right)^{1/2} (ml^2 \tan \theta \sin^2 \theta)^{1/2} \tag{1.13}$$

This equation expresses the charge on each particle in terms of the deviation angle θ and the other constants of the system.

An arrangement such as that illustrated in this example may be used to measure charge. To do so we measure the deviation angle θ and substitute it into Eq. (1.13) in order to derive the magnitude of the charge Q. Into Eq. (1.13) let us substitute the magnitudes of the acceleration due to gravity and of the constant of electrostatics. These values are $g = 9.81$ m/sec² and $\gamma_e = 9 \times 10^9$. We derive

$$Q = \pm 6.6 \times 10^{-5}(ml^2 \tan \theta \sin^2 \theta)^{\frac{1}{2}} \tag{1.14}$$

A typical value for the mass m of the particle might be 10 g ($= 10^{-2}$ kg), and a typical value for l might be 10 cm ($= 10^{-1}$ m). If the observed angular deviation θ were 30°, it would follow from Eq. (1.14) that the magnitude of the charge Q is 0.25 μcoulomb. It should be noted that the sign of the charge would not be determined. There is an instrument, known as the gold-leaf electroscope, that operates on these principles.

1.5. Electric Field. An electric point charge of strength Q placed at any point in space is said to be surrounded by an electric field. By this is meant the following: If a test charge of magnitude e is placed at any point in the region surrounding the given point charge Q, then the test charge e is acted upon by a force of electrical origin due to the presence of the given charge Q. The existence of this force, no matter where in the region surrounding the given charge Q the test charge e may be placed, is described by saying that the given point charge Q produces an electric field in the region surrounding it. According to the law of inverse squares the magnitude of the force on the test charge e when it is at distance r from the given point charge Q is

$$F = \gamma_e \frac{Qe}{r^2} \tag{1.15}$$

The force per unit charge acting on the test charge is

$$E = \frac{F}{e} \tag{1.16}$$

Substituting for F from Eq. (1.15) into Eq. (1.16) we deduce that the force per unit charge acting on the test charge is

$$E = \gamma_e \frac{Q}{r^2} \tag{1.17}$$

The direction of this force is radially outward as shown in Fig. 1.4.

We see from Eq. (1.17) that the force per unit charge acting on a test charge e in the presence of a given point charge Q depends upon the mag-

nitude of the given charge and upon the distance of the test charge from
the given point charge.   But it does not depend upon the magnitude of
the test charge e.   The force per unit charge acting on a test charge at a
particular point is a convenient measure of the strength of the electric
field at this point.   The force per unit charge acting on a test charge at a
particular point in an electric field has
both magnitude and direction.   It is a
vector known as the electric vector.

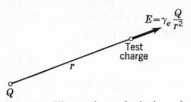

$$E = \gamma_e \frac{Q}{r^2}$$

The magnitude of the electric vector is
known as the electric field strength.
At a point in an electric field where
the electric vector is **E**, the force acting
on a test charge of magnitude e is

FIG. 1.4. Illustrating calculation of
radially outward electric vector due
to a positive point charge.

represented in magnitude and direction
by the vector $e\mathbf{E}$.   The electric vector
at a point in an electric field may be described as the vector representing
in magnitude and direction the force acting on a unit test charge at the
point.

If Q is positive, the quantity E appearing in Eq. (1.17) is the magnitude of the electric vector and is thus what is known as the electric field
strength.   Equation (1.17) shows that the electric field strength at distance r from the point charge of strength Q is directly proportional to Q
and inversely proportional to the square of the distance from the point
charge.   The direction of the electric vector is radially outward if Q is
positive but is radially inward if Q
is negative.   This situation is illustrated in Fig. 1.5.   In Fig. 1.5 the
direction of the lines gives at each
point of space the direction of the
force acting upon a positive test
charge at that point.   Such lines
are called lines of force and give at
each point in the electric field the
direction of the electric vector at
that point.   For a single point

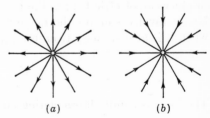

(a)   (b)

FIG. 1.5. The lines of force for a single
point charge (a) if the charge is positive,
(b) if the charge is negative.

charge, the lines of force are radially outward if the given point charge
is positive and radially inward if the given point charge is negative.

1.6. Calculation of Electric Fields.   To calculate the electric vector
at a point P due to a number of point charges, we imagine that a unit
test charge is placed at P.   We then calculate the forces exerted upon
the unit test charge from each of the given point charges using the law of
inverse squares.   These forces are then combined by vector addition in
accordance with the laws of mechanics as indicated in Fig. 1.6.   Thus the

electric vector at any point due to a number of point charges is the vector sum of the electric vectors due to the individual point charges.

As an example, suppose that, in a system of cartesian coordinates (x,y,z), two equal and opposite point charges Q and $-Q$ are placed at the points $(-a,0,0)$ and $(a,0,0)$ as shown in Fig. 1.7. Let us calculate the electric vector in magnitude and direction at all points of the x axis.

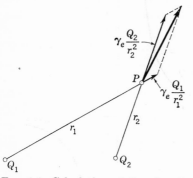

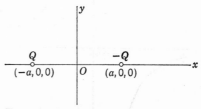

FIG. 1.6. Calculation of the electric field at a point P due to two point charges Q_1 and Q_2.

FIG. 1.7. A pair of equal and opposite point charges Q and $-Q$ at the positions $(-a,0,0)$ and $(a,0,0)$, respectively.

Place a unit test charge at the point $(x,0,0)$ on the x axis, distant x from the origin. The electric vector at this point is then the force acting on the unit test charge, and this is made up of a repulsion from the charge Q at the point $(-a,0,0)$ and an attraction to the charge $-Q$ at the point $(a,0,0)$. It is clear that the resultant force is in the direction of the positive x axis or in the reverse direction. Let us first consider a point on the x axis for which x is greater than a. The force of repulsion from the charge Q is, according to the law of inverse squares, $\gamma_e Q/(a+x)^2$. The force of attraction to the charge $-Q$ is in the same way $\gamma_e Q/(a-x)^2$. The resulting force on the test charge in the direction of the positive x axis is therefore

$$E = \frac{\gamma_e Q}{(a+x)^2} - \frac{\gamma_e Q}{(a-x)^2} \qquad (1.18)$$

In the same way it may be shown that if x lies between $-a$ and $+a$, so that the position of the unit test charge is between the two given charges Q and $-Q$, then the force on the unit test charge in the direction of the positive x axis is

$$E = \frac{\gamma_e Q}{(a+x)^2} + \frac{\gamma_e Q}{(a-x)^2} \qquad (1.19)$$

Likewise if x is less than $-a$, so that the unit test charge is to the left of the charge Q at $(-a,0,0)$, then the force on the unit test charge in the direction of the positive x axis is

$$E = - \frac{\gamma_e Q}{(a+x)^2} + \frac{\gamma_e Q}{(a-x)^2} \qquad (1.20)$$

On the basis of Eqs. (1.18) to (1.20), the electric field strength on the x axis is plotted as a function of x in Fig. 1.8. Where the ordinate is positive, the electric vector is in the direction from the positive charge

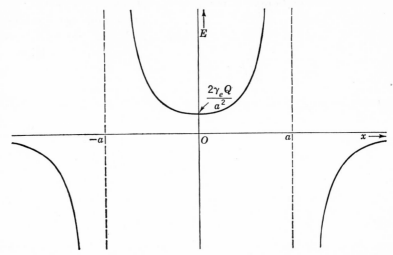

FIG. 1.8. The electric field in the x direction at points on the x axis in Fig. 1.7.

toward the negative charge. Where the ordinate is negative, the electric vector is in the opposite direction.

As another example suppose that, in a system of cartesian coordinates (x,y,z), two point charges Q and $-Q$ are again located at the points $(-a,0,0)$ and $(a,0,0)$. Let us now calculate the electric vector in magnitude and direction at all points on the y axis.

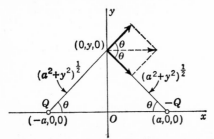

FIG. 1.9. Illustrating calculation of the electric field in the symmetrical plane between a pair of equal and opposite point charges.

Place a unit test charge at the point $(0,y,0)$ on the y axis, distant y from the origin as shown in Fig. 1.9. Such a point is equidistant from the two point charges. Consequently, the repulsive force experienced by the test charge from the charge Q is equal in magnitude to the attractive force experienced from the charge $-Q$. Hence the two forces combine vectorially to give an electric field parallel to the join of the charges shown in Fig. 1.9. By the law of inverse squares the repulsive force experienced by the test charge from the charge Q has magnitude $\gamma_e Q/(a^2 + y^2)$. The component of this in the direction of the resultant is obtained by multiplying by the cosine of the angle θ shown in Fig. 1.9. The magnitude of this cosine is $a/(a^2 + y^2)^{\frac{1}{2}}$. There is an equal component from the attractive force experienced by the test charge from the charge $-Q$. Hence the resultant electric field strength at the point $(0,y,0)$ is

$$E = \gamma_e \frac{Q}{a^2 + y^2} \frac{a}{(a^2 + y^2)^{\frac{1}{2}}} + \gamma_e \frac{Q}{a^2 + y^2} \frac{a}{(a^2 + y^2)^{\frac{1}{2}}}$$

$$= 2\gamma_e \frac{Qa}{(a^2 + y^2)^{\frac{3}{2}}} \tag{1.21}$$

The electric vector at all points on the y axis is in the direction of the x axis, and the variation of the magnitude with the distance y from the

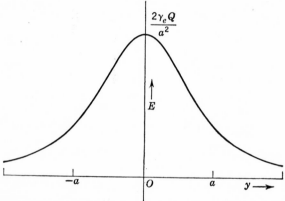

FIG. 1.10. Electric field strength in the symmetrical plane of a pair of equal and opposite point charges as a function of the distance from the point midway between the charges.

origin is given by Eq. (1.21). This electric field strength is plotted as a function of y in Fig. 1.10.

The electric field strength at the point $y = 0$ in Fig. 1.10 is the same as that at the point $x = 0$ in Fig. 1.8. The point referred to in both cases is the origin of the system of cartesian coordinates midway between the two charges. The electric field strength at this point is $2\gamma_e Q/a^2$. If $Q = 1,000$ $\mu\mu$coulombs (10^{-9} coulomb) and $a = 10$ cm (10^{-1} m), then the electric field at the mid-point between the two charges evaluates to 1,800 newtons/coulomb.

As a further example, suppose that, in a system of cartesian coordinates (x,y,z), two point charges Q and $-Q$ are once again placed at the points $(-a,0,0)$ and $(a,0,0)$, and let us calculate the electric vector in magnitude and direction at any point in the xy plane.

Place a unit test charge at the point $(x,y,0)$ in the xy plane. The forces of repulsion on this test charge from the charge Q and of attraction toward the charge $-Q$ are calculated from the law of inverse squares and combined vectorially as shown in Fig. 1.11. The magnitude of the force of repulsion on the unit test charge from the charge Q is, from the law of inverse squares,

$$\frac{\gamma_e Q}{(x+a)^2 + y^2}$$

The direction of the force is the direction of the vector $(x + a, y, 0)$.

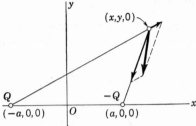

FIG. 1.11. Illustrating calculation of the electric field due to a pair of equal and opposite point charges.

The x and y components of the force of repulsion on the unit test charge from the charge Q are therefore

$$\frac{\gamma_e Q}{(x+a)^2 + y^2} \frac{x+a}{[(x+a)^2 + y^2]^{\frac{1}{2}}}$$

and

$$\frac{\gamma_e Q}{(x+a)^2 + y^2} \frac{y}{[(x+a)^2 + y^2]^{\frac{1}{2}}}$$

In the same way the x and y components of the force of attraction on the unit test charge from the charge $-Q$ are

$$-\frac{\gamma_e Q}{(x-a)^2 + y^2} \frac{x-a}{[(x-a)^2 + y^2]^{\frac{1}{2}}}$$

and

$$-\frac{\gamma_e Q}{(x-a)^2 + y^2} \frac{y}{[(x-a)^2 + y^2]^{\frac{1}{2}}}$$

The total x and y components of the electric vector at the point $(x,y,0)$ are therefore

$$E_x = \frac{\gamma_e Q(x+a)}{[(x+a)^2 + y^2]^{\frac{3}{2}}} - \frac{\gamma_e Q(x-a)}{[(x-a)^2 + y^2]^{\frac{3}{2}}} \qquad (1.22)$$

$$E_y = \frac{\gamma_e Q y}{[(x+a)^2 + y^2]^{\frac{3}{2}}} - \frac{\gamma_e Q y}{[(x-a)^2 + y^2]^{\frac{3}{2}}} \qquad (1.23)$$

From these equations the electric vector can be calculated in magnitude and direction at all points in the (x,y) plane. The lines of force of a pair of equal and opposite charges can then be drawn and are illustrated in Fig. 1.12.

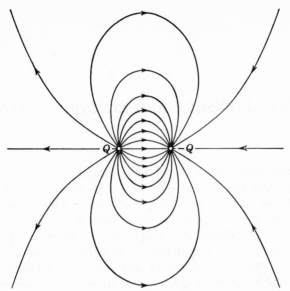

Fig. 1.12. The lines of force of a pair of equal and opposite point charges.

SUMMARIZING EXERCISES

1.1. Describe the law giving the gravitational force of attraction between two particles of masses m_1 and m_2 at a distance r apart, introducing the constant of gravitation γ_g. Write down the numerical value of γ_g.

1.2. Write down numerical values for the mass of a neutron, the mass of a proton, and the mass of an electron. Explain the facts concerning the forces acting between (a) a neutron and a neutron, (b) a proton and a proton, (c) an electron and an electron, and (d) a proton and an electron. From these statements deduce the existence of the phenomenon known as electric charge, and show that there are two sorts of electric charge. Explain why it is convenient to denote these two sorts of charge by opposite algebraic signs.

1.3. Two particles carrying charges of strengths Q_1 and Q_2 are located at a distance r apart in otherwise free space. Express the law of electrical force F between the particles in a form similar to the law of gravitation and involving the constant of electrostatics γ_e. State the numerical value of γ_e, assuming that r is measured in meters, F in newtons, and Q_1, Q_2 in coulombs. State the numerical values in coulombs of the charges on a proton and on an electron.

1.4. Explain what is meant by electric field strength. From the law of inverse squares calculate the electric field strength at a distance r from a positive point charge of strength Q in free space. Explain how the statement is modified if Q is negative.

1.5. Explain what is meant by the electric vector. If a number of point charges produce separately at a point P electric vectors that differ in magnitude and direction, explain how to calculate the resultant electric vector at P.

1.6. Explain what is meant by a line of force in an electrostatic field. Sketch the lines of force of (a) a single positive point charge, (b) a single negative point charge, and (c) a pair of equal and opposite point charges in free space.

CHAPTER 2

POTENTIAL ENERGY AND ELECTRIC POTENTIAL

2.1. Introduction. The concept of potential energy frequently used in connection with mechanical systems is of great value also for electrical systems. A coil spring is an example of a mechanical system involving potential energy. If a spring is compressed by application of a force, the force does work during the compression. When the spring is compressed, it possesses potential energy equal to the work done during compression. The potential energy of the compressed spring can again be made available by allowing the spring to expand. The work done by the spring during expansion is equal to the decrement of potential energy during the process. Of course these statements are strictly true only if frictional forces may be neglected. A system for which frictional forces are negligible is said to conserve energy and to be a "conservative system." For a conservative system, work done on it appears as increased potential energy of the system. This potential energy can be recovered by allowing the system to do work.

Consider a conservative mechanical system composed of a compressed coil spring, one end of which is fixed. Let the spring be compressed to the point where its length is x, and when so compressed let F be the force exerted by the spring upon whatever is maintaining the compression. Let the potential energy of the spring in this compressed condition be W. Now suppose that the object maintaining the compression of the spring moves a small distance, so that the length x of the spring increases to $x + dx$. During this process let the potential energy of the spring change from W to $W + dW$. If the increment dx in x is positive, then the increment dW in W must be negative, because the spring in expanding does work and consequently loses potential energy. Thus there is not a gain of potential energy dW during the placement but a loss of potential energy $-dW$. The work done by the spring during the displacement from x to $x + dx$ is $F\,dx$ because the force exerted by the spring is F and its point of application moves in the direction of F a distance dx. Now we are assuming that the system is conservative, which means that frictional forces may be neglected. It follows that the work done by the spring during expansion is equal to its loss of potential energy. In other words

$$F \, dx = -dW \tag{2.1}$$

Hence

$$F = -\frac{dW}{dx} \tag{2.2}$$

Thus the force exerted by the spring in the direction in which x increases is equal to the rate at which the potential energy of the spring decreases as it expands, measured per unit displacement of the point of application of the force.   If we know the function $W(x)$ giving the potential energy of the spring for different degrees of compression, then we can find the force exerted by the spring when its length is x merely by evaluating the negative derivation of the function $W(x)$ with respect to x.   Thus knowledge of the potential energy of a conservative system as a function of its configuration permits the force exerted by the system to be calculated merely by differentiation of the potential energy.

Equations (2.1) and (2.2) may be applied to any conservative system. If the system exerts at a certain point a force F, and if the point of application of this force moves through a small distance dx in the direction of F, then the work done is $F \, dx$.   If during this displacement the corresponding decrease in the potential energy of the system is $-dW$, then Eq. (2.1) is true, and from it follows Eq. (2.2).

To calculate the potential energy of the spring when compressed to length x, we have to calculate the total work that the spring would do in expanding to its uncompressed length x_0.   If the force F exerted by the spring were independent of the length of the spring, this work would be $F(x_0 - x)$.   For a normal spring, however, the force exerted by the spring depends upon its degree of compression.   Consequently the work done during expansion from length x to length x_0 must be calculated using an integral.   This gives for the potential energy of the spring when at length x

$$W = \int_x^{x_0} F \, dx \tag{2.3}$$

Equation (2.3) can be obtained by integrating Eq. (2.1) from x to x_0.

Equations (2.1) to (2.3) express in three equivalent forms what is known as the principle of work, or the principle of virtual work.

2.2. Potential Energy of a Pair of Point Charges of the Same Sign. Consider an electrical system composed of a pair of point charges of strengths Q_1 and Q_2.   For the present let us suppose that Q_1 and Q_2 have the same sign.   Then there is a force of repulsion between the two charges given by

$$F = \frac{\gamma_e Q_1 Q_2}{r^2} \tag{2.4}$$

If we push the two point charges together, work will have to be done against the repulsion between the charges.   This may be compared with the work done when compressing a spring.   Pushing the pair of point charges closer together stores potential energy.   This potential energy can be recovered by letting the point charges move apart again.   As the charges are allowed to move father apart, more energy is recovered from the system.   To recover all the available energy, it would be necessary to allow the distance between the charges to become infinite.   Thus a pair of point charges having the same sign behave somewhat like a compressed spring whose uncompressed length is infinite.   To calculate the potential energy of the pair of point charges when their separation is r, it is con-venient to picture one of the point charges as fixed, as shown in Fig. 2.1, and then to calculate the work done in allowing the other charge to move from distance r to an infinite dis-tance.   This is the total work that it

Fixed   Movable

Q_1 r Q_2 $\longrightarrow F$

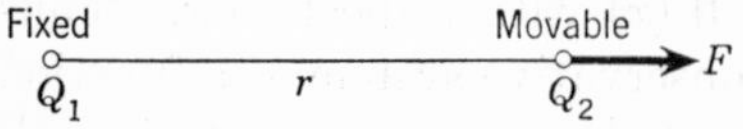

FIG. 2.1. Illustrating calculation of the potential energy of a pair of point charges.

is possible to get out of the two point charges when at separation r and is consequently their potential energy at this separation.   Hence the poten-tial energy W of two point charges Q_1 and Q_2 at separation r is

$$W = \int_r^\infty F \, dr \tag{2.5}$$

where the force F is given by Eq. (2.4).   Substituting from Eq. (2.4) into Eq. (2.5) we derive

$$W = \int_r^\infty \frac{\gamma_e Q_1 Q_2}{r^2} \, dr \tag{2.6}$$

$$= \gamma_e Q_1 Q_2 \int_r^\infty \frac{1}{r^2} \, dr$$

$$= \gamma_e Q_1 Q_2 \left[-\frac{1}{r} \right]_r^\infty$$

$$= \frac{\gamma_e Q_1 Q_2}{r} \tag{2.7}$$

Thus the potential energy of a pair of point charges is directly propor-tional to the product of the charges and inversely proportional to the dis-tance between them.   The expression (2.7) is the amount of work that can be obtained from a pair of point charges at separation r by allowing them to repel each other to an infinite separation.

In accordance with Eq. (2.2) it should be possible, from the expression (2.7) for the potential energy of the two point charges as a function of their separation, to obtain by differentiation the force between the charges.   This is done as follows:

$$F = -\frac{dW}{dr} \tag{2.8}$$

$$= -\gamma_e Q_1 Q_2 \frac{d}{dr}\frac{1}{r}$$

$$= -\gamma_e Q_1 Q_2 \left(-\frac{1}{r^2}\right)$$

$$= \gamma_e \frac{Q_1 Q_2}{r^2} \tag{2.9}$$

which is identical with Eq. (2.4), as it should be.

2.3. Potential Energy of a Pair of Point Charges of Opposite Signs.
Let us now consider the potential energy of a pair of point charges of strengths Q_1 and Q_2 when Q_1 and Q_2 have opposite signs. The force between the two charges is still given by Eq. (2.4), but it is now an attraction because Q_1 and Q_2 have opposite signs.

Let us suppose that, because of the finite size of the particles carrying the charges or for some other reason, the charges are unable to approach to a distance closer than r_0. If the charges are initially at distance r_0 apart, then to bring them to a larger distance r apart, it will be necessary to pull them apart against the attraction between them. Work will be required to do this, and this work is equal to the potential energy of the two particles at separation r. This potential energy can be recovered by permitting the two charges to move together again under their mutual attraction. The potential energy of the two charges at separation r is therefore

$$W = \int_r^{r_0} F\, dr \tag{2.10}$$

$$= \int_r^{r_0} \frac{\gamma_e Q_1 Q_2}{r^2}\, dr \tag{2.11}$$

$$= \gamma_e Q_1 Q_2 \int_r^{r_0} \frac{1}{r^2}\, dr$$

$$= \gamma_e Q_1 Q_2 \left[-\frac{1}{r}\right]_r^{r_0}$$

$$= \frac{\gamma_e Q_1 Q_2}{r} - \frac{\gamma_e Q_1 Q_2}{r_0} \tag{2.12}$$

As before, the force of attraction between the two charges can be derived from Eq. (2.12) by application of Eq. (2.8). In making this application the second term in Eq. (2.12) gives no contribution because it is independent of r.

In writing down the potential energy of a pair of charges of opposite signs it is usual to omit the constant term in Eq. (2.12), thereby making the expression identical with that for a pair of charges of the same sign given in Eq. (2.7). The addition or subtraction of a constant from the potential-energy function is, in fact, of no importance. The potential-energy function for a pair of charges at separation r is used to calculate the difference in energy for two different values of r. Consequently any constant added to the potential-energy function would cancel out when the difference of energy is calculated. It is normal practice to arrange the additive constant so that the potential energy of a pair of charges is zero when the charges are at an infinite distance apart whether the charges are of like sign or of unlike sign.

That the zero of potential energy of a system is arbitrary can be seen by considering the potential energy of a mass under gravity at a certain height. It does not matter whether the height is measured above ground level, above sea level, or above any other convenient level. What matters in practice is the change in potential energy arising from a change in height, and this is independent of the level from which height is measured.

We thus take the potential energy of two point charges Q_1 and Q_2 at a distance r apart to be given by Eq. (2.7) whatever the signs of the charges. The excess of the potential energy of the pair of charges when at separation r_1 over the potential energy when at separation r_2 is

$$\frac{\gamma_e Q_1 Q_2}{r_1} - \frac{\gamma_e Q_1 Q_2}{r_2} \tag{2.13}$$

2.4. Electric Potential or Voltage. Instead of describing an electric field by calculating the force exerted on a test charge at each point of the field, it is also possible to describe the electric field by calculating the potential energy of the test charge at each point of the field. For many purposes this second method is more convenient.

From Eq. (2.7) the potential energy of a test charge e at distance r from a point charge Q is

$$W = \gamma_e \frac{Qe}{r} \tag{2.14}$$

The potential energy of the test charge, measured per unit charge, is

$$\phi = \frac{W}{e} \tag{2.15}$$

Substitution for W from Eq. (2.14) into Eq. (2.15) gives for the potential energy of the test charge per unit charge

$$\phi = \gamma_e \frac{Q}{r} \tag{2.16}$$

We see from Eq. (2.16) that the potential energy of a test charge per unit charge in the presence of a given point charge Q depends upon the magnitude of the given charge and the distance of the test charge from the given point charge, but it does not depend upon the magnitude of the test charge e.   The potential energy per unit charge of a test charge at a particular point is known as the electric potential at that point.   At a point in an electric field where the electric potential is ϕ, the potential energy of a test charge of strength e is $e\phi$.   By putting $e = 1$ we see that the electric potential at any point is the potential energy of a unit test charge at that point.   Equation (2.16) shows that the electric potential at distance r from a point charge of strength Q is directly proportional to Q and inversely proportional to the distance from the charge.

We have seen that, from the potential energy W of a pair of point charges as a function of the distance r between them, we can derive the force F between them from Eq. (2.8).   If one of the point charges is a unit test charge, then the force F becomes numerically equal to the electric field strength E at the position of the test charge, and the potential energy W becomes numerically equal to the electric potential ϕ at the position of the test charge.   From Eq. (2.8) we therefore derive the relation

$$E = -\frac{d\phi}{dr} \tag{2.17}$$

This equation shows that if we know the electric potential ϕ of a point charge at all distances r from the point charge, we can derive by differentiation with respect to r the electric field strength of the point charge. Thus, by substituting from Eq. (2.16), which gives the electric potential ϕ of a point charge Q at distance r, into Eq. (2.17), we should derive the expression given in Eq. (1.17) for the electric field strength of a point charge Q.   Substitution from Eq. (2.16) into Eq. (2.17) gives

$$\begin{aligned}
E &= -\frac{d}{dr}\left(\gamma_e \frac{Q}{r}\right) \\
&= -\gamma_e Q \frac{d}{dr}\frac{1}{r} \\
&= \frac{\gamma_e Q}{r^2}
\end{aligned} \tag{2.18}$$

which is the same as Eq. (1.17), as it should be.

We see that the electric field strength may be derived from the electric potential by differentiation.   A description of the way in which the electric potential ϕ varies from point to point in an electric field is an alternative description of the phenomenon to that provided by the electric vector $\mathbf{E}$.   With the electric potential there is only one number associated with each point in space, whereas for the electric vector both the magnitude and direction have to be specified for each point.   This is sometimes expressed by saying that the electric potential ϕ is a scalar quantity whereas **E** is a vector quantity. The variation from point to point in space of the scalar electric potential ϕ is easier to describe than the variation from point to point of the vector field **E**. It is mainly for this reason that the electric potential is an important method of describing an electric field.

We can form an idea of the distribution of electric potential in an electric field by drawing equipotential surfaces. An equipotential surface is a

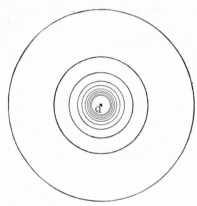

surface over which the electric potential has the same value. In the electric field of a single point charge, the electric potential is given by Eq. (2.16), and over a surface $r =$ constant this potential has the same value. The equipotential surfaces of a single point charge are thus spheres concentric with the charge, as shown in Fig. 2.2. The electric potential associated with any sphere concentric with the charge can be calculated from Eq. (2.16), and each sphere may then be marked with its appropriate electric potential.

FIG. 2.2. The equipotential surfaces of a single point charge.

It is usually convenient to draw equipotential surfaces at equal intervals of potential somewhat in the same way as contour maps are usually marked at equal intervals of height. If this is done for the field of a single point charge, the equipotential surfaces are much closer together near the point charge than they are farther away, as indicated in Fig. 2.2. The reason for this is illustrated in Fig. 2.3. In Fig. 2.3 is plotted the variation of the electric potential ϕ due to a single point charge Q as a function of distance r from the point charge. In accordance with Eq. (2.16) this curve is a rectangular hyperbola. In Fig. 2.3 we may mark equal intervals of electric potential and then deduce from the curve the radii of the corresponding equipotential surfaces. We see that the equipotential surfaces are closer together at points nearer the electric charge.

From the equipotential surfaces of an electric field it is possible to obtain a satisfactory picture of the electric field. From Eq. (2.17) we see that the field strength of a single point charge at distance r is the downward gradient of the curve in Fig. 2.3. This downward slope is indicated in Fig. 2.2 by the closeness of the equipotential surfaces in the same way that the slope of a hill on a contour map is indicated by the closeness of the contour lines. Moreover, the direction of the electric field at any point in space is perpendicular to the equipotential surface passing through that point for the following reason: If a test charge moves along an equipotential surface, its potential energy does not change. It follows from Eq. (2.2) that there is no force on the test charge along the equipotential surface. The force on the test charge must therefore be perpendicular to the surface. It follows that lines of electric force intersect equipotential surfaces at right angles. This is illustrated by comparing the lines of force in Fig. 1.5 with the corresponding equipotential surfaces in Fig. 2.2. We thus see that the electric field can be derived from the equipotential surfaces in much the same way that the downward gradient of hills is derived from contour lines on a contour map. The direction of the

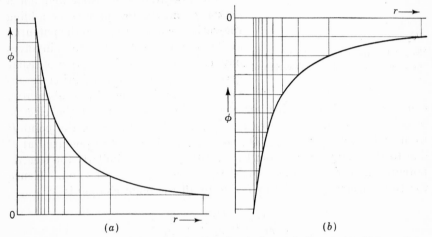

FIG. 2.3. The variation of electric potential of a single point charge with distance from the charge (a) if the charge is positive, (b) if the charge is negative.

electric vector at any point is the direction of steepest descent of the electric potential, while the decrease of potential per unit distance in this direction is the magnitude of the electric vector. This relation between the electric vector $\mathbf{E}$ and the electric potential ϕ is described by saying that the electric vector is the downward gradient of the electric potential, and this is written as an equation in the form

$$\mathbf{E} = -\operatorname{grad} \phi \qquad (2.19)$$

2.5. Units of Electric Potential and Electric Field Strength. Potential energy is measured in joules. Since electric potential is potential energy per unit charge, it may be measured in joules per coulomb. One joule per coulomb is known as a volt. Since the electric vector is the downward gradient of electric potential, electric field strength may be measured in volts per meter. This is an alternative to the unit newtons per coulomb previously used and is the one normally adopted.

2.6. The Electric Potential of a System of Point Charges. We have seen that the electric vector at a point P due to a number of point charges Q_1, Q_2, Q_3, . . . is obtained by evaluating the electric vector at the point P due to the point charges separately and then adding these contributions vectorially. In the same way the electric potential at the point P due to the point charges Q_1, Q_2, Q_3, . . . is calculated by evaluating at P the electric potential due to the separate point charges and then adding these contributions to obtain the total potential at P. Since electric potential is a scalar and not a vector quantity, the process of adding the various contributions to the potential at P to obtain the total potential involves only ordinary algebraic addition of scalar quantities. No vector addition is involved, and this is one of the substantial conveniences of describing an electric field by means of the electric potential. In Fig. 2.4, r_1, r_2, r_3, . . . are the distances of the point P from the point charges Q_1, Q_2, Q_3, ... The electric potential at P due to the charge Q_1 is, from Eq. (2.16), $\gamma_e Q_1/r_1$. Similarly the electric potential at P due to the point charge Q_2 is $\gamma_e Q_2/r_2$, and so on. Hence the total electric potential at P due to all the point charges is

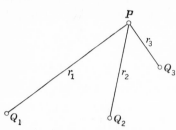

FIG. 2.4. Illustrating calculation of the electric potential of a system of point charges.

$$\phi = \gamma_e \frac{Q_1}{r_1} + \gamma_e \frac{Q_2}{r_2} + \gamma_e \frac{Q_3}{r_3} + \cdots$$

or

$$\phi = \gamma_e \left(\frac{Q_1}{r_1} + \frac{Q_2}{r_2} + \frac{Q_3}{r_3} + \cdots \right) \tag{2.20}$$

According to Eq. (2.20) the electric potential at an infinite distance from all the point charges is zero, and this is normally a convenient arrangement. However, it is always possible to add a constant to the electric potential at any point in an electric field as long as the same constant is added to the electric potential at all other points. A potential that has the same value at all points of the space has zero gradient and consequently produces no electric field in accordance with Eq. (2.19). We may therefore always add a constant to a potential function without affecting the electric field that it represents. It is normally convenient, however, to adjust the constant so that the potential at infinity is zero.

As an example of the calculation of electric potential let us calculate the potential at all points of the electric field of a pair of equal and opposite point charges Q and $-Q$. At a point distant r_1 from the point charge Q and r_2 from the point charge $-Q$ the electric potential is, according to Eq. (2.20),

$$\phi = \gamma_e \left(\frac{Q}{r_1} - \frac{Q}{r_2} \right)$$

or

$$\phi = \gamma_e Q \left(\frac{1}{r_1} - \frac{1}{r_2} \right) \qquad (2.21)$$

With the use of this equation the electric potential can be calculated at any point of the field. To calculate the equipotential surfaces it is convenient to rewrite Eq. (2.21) as

$$\frac{1}{r_1} - \frac{1}{r_2} = \frac{\phi}{\gamma_e Q} \qquad (2.22)$$

From this equation we see that the equipotential surface upon which the potential has the constant value ϕ is the locus of points such that the

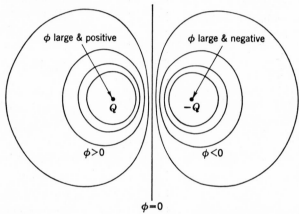

FIG. 2.5. The equipotential surfaces of a pair of equal and opposite point charges.

reciprocal of the distance from the point charge Q exceeds the reciprocal of the distance from the point charge $-Q$ by the constant value $\phi/\gamma_e Q$. The equipotential surface upon which $\phi = +\infty$ has the equation $r_1 = 0$. It is therefore an indefinitely small sphere enclosing the positive point charge. In the same way the equipotential surface upon which $\phi = -\infty$ has the equation $r_2 = 0$ and is therefore an indefinitely small sphere enclosing the negative point charge. The equipotential surface upon which $\phi = 0$ has the equation

$$\frac{1}{r_1} - \frac{1}{r_2} = 0$$

or

$$r_1 = r_2 \qquad (2.23)$$

This is the infinite sphere combined with the diametral plane that is symmetrically situated between the two point charges (see Fig. 2.5). The complete system of equipotential surfaces consists of a series of surfaces axially symmetrical about the lines through the point charges.

These intersect a plane through the point charges in a series of curves as shown in Fig. 2.5. The lines of force can be easily pictured from Fig. 2.5; they run from the positive point charge to the negative point charge in such a way that they everywhere cross the equipotential surfaces at right angles. These lines of force have already been illustrated in Fig. 1.12.

2.7. The Importance of Storing Energy by Electrical Means. There are many practical applications in which it is necessary to store energy for a short time and then release it. An example is a door-closing device. There are many mechanical devices for storing potential energy for a short period, one of these being a compressed spring.

From what has been said, it is clear that a pair of electric point charges is also a system that can be used for storing potential energy. The importance of electrical systems for storing potential energy lies in the possibility of designing them so that they have little inertia and so respond very quickly. If it is necessary to store energy for 1 μsec and then to release it 1 μsec later, an electrical method for storing the energy is needed.

2.8. How to Store Potential Energy Electrically in a Convenient "Package." By compressing the distance between a pair of like point charges, we have seen that it is possible to store potential energy and that, by allowing the distance between point charges to expand again, the energy can be recovered. Such a device is not, however, a convenient arrangement for storing potential energy. At a distance from the point charges large compared with their distance apart, the electric field is substantially that of a single point charge equal to the sum of the charges. The electric field of the device thus extends to a considerable distance, and a pair of such devices in close proximity would interact with each other undesirably.

An improved device for storing potential energy electrically can be obtained by using a pair of equal and opposite point charges. At a distance from the point charges large compared with their distance apart, the field of this device is comparatively small. Two such devices with zero net charge may therefore be placed in relatively close proximity without undue interaction. With such a device potential energy is stored by pulling the equal and opposite charges apart and is released by allowing them to move toward each other again.

A pair of equal and opposite point charges still have a field that is too diffuse to constitute a convenient practical package with which to store potential energy. A great improvement can be obtained by spreading the positive and negative charges more or less uniformly in two closely spaced parallel layers as indicated in Fig. 2.6b. With this arrangement the electric field is almost entirely confined to the space between the layers, the electric field elsewhere being comparatively weak. Two devices such as this can therefore be placed quite close together without undue interaction.

The convenient way of realizing this arrangement is to use a pair of closely spaced parallel metal plates.   The plates are charged by removing electrons from one plate and communicating them to the other plate.   We shall see that the electric charge on the plates automatically distributes itself over the surfaces facing each other in such a way that the electric field between the plates is strong and elsewhere is weak.   Such an arrangement is called a condenser because it condenses the electric field into the space between the plates.   It is also called a capacitor because of its capacity for storing potential energy.

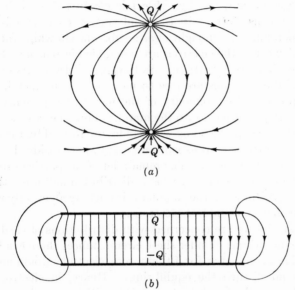

FIG. 2.6. (a) Electric field of a pair of equal and opposite point charges compared with (b) the electric field obtained by spreading the positive and negative charges more or less uniformly in two closely spaced parallel layers.

With a charge Q on one plate and a charge $-Q$ on the other plate there is a force of attraction between the plates qualitatively similar to that between a pair of equal and opposite point charges.   Potential energy may therefore be stored in the capacitor by pulling the plates apart, and this energy may be released again by allowing the plates to move toward each other again.   However, it is not necessary to move the plates of a capacitor in order to store or release energy.   All that is required is to move the electrons relative to the protons, and this can be achieved by moving only the electrons.   There is no point in moving the relatively heavy protons and no point whatever in moving the neutrons, which are uncharged.   Thus the plates of the capacitor can stay fixed in space as long as we have a means for moving electrons from one place to the other.   In fact the process of charging a capacitor stores potential energy in it which can be released by allowing the capacitor to discharge again. No motion of the plates is required, only of the electrons involved in the charging and discharging process. This is how the electrical engineer avoids high inertia in his systems and so is able to carry out operations millions of times faster than a mechanical engineer.

We shall encounter in due course a number of devices for moving electrons from one plate of a capacitor to the other. Among the simplest of these devices is a battery such as that used in a flashlight.

2.9. Conductors. An electrical conductor is a substance through which electric charge can move easily. Electric conductors exist in the solid, liquid, and gaseous states. In the solid state a conductor is usually a metal. A metal may be thought of as a substance in which the neutrons, protons, and most of the electrons are assembled into atoms that occupy fixed locations in a crystal lattice. In the space between these atoms the remainder of the electrons are free to move about the metal. If a free electron approaches the boundary of the metal, it experiences a strong force tending to pull it back into the metal. Thus the free electrons may be thought of as occupying a box whose sides are formed by the surfaces of the metal. The free electrons can move anywhere inside the metal but cannot easily escape from it. The remainder of the particles form a positive charge which may be thought of as distributed uniformly throughout the metal and which, when the conductor is uncharged, exactly neutralizes the negative charge of the free electrons.

In electrostatics we are concerned with distributions of electric charge that are in equilibrium. Under these circumstances there can be no electric field inside a conductor, for if there were, electrons would move and in doing so would disturb the equilibrium. Hence, in electrostatics, the electric field strength vanishes at all points within a conductor.

Since the electric field vanishes at all points within a conductor, no work is done in moving a test charge from one point in a conductor to another point in the same conductor. Hence the potential energy of a test charge does not vary as it is moved from one point to another point in the same conductor. The potential energy of the test charge is the same at all points within the conductor. Since electric potential ϕ is the potential energy of a unit test charge, it follows that the electric potential is the same at all points of the same conductor. The uniform electric potential experienced at all points of a given conductor is known as the potential of the conductor. At all points within a conductor whose potential is V the electric potential ϕ is given by

$$\phi = V \qquad (2.24)$$

In particular at all points on the surface of the conductor the electric potential ϕ has the constant value V. The surface of a conductor is therefore an equipotential surface upon which the electric potential is equal to the potential of the conductor.

Figure 2.7 illustrates a situation in which one conductor is at potential V_1 and another conductor is at potential V_2.   In these circumstances the electric potential throughout the one conductor is V_1 and the electric potential throughout the other conductor is V_2.   Thus the surface of the first conductor is an equipotential surface upon which the electric potential has the value V_1, and the surface of the second conductor is another equipotential surface upon which the electric potential has the value V_2.   Between the two conductors there are a series of equipotential surfaces upon which the electric potential has values varying from V_1 to V_2. There is thus an electric field between the two conductors for which the lines of force are the lines drawn from the one conductor to the other at right angles to the equipotential surfaces.   It follows that lines of electric

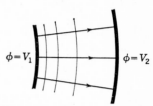

FIG. 2.7. The equipotential surfaces between two conductors at different potentials.

force leave and arrive at conductors perpendicular to the surface of the conductors.   There are no lines of force within the conductors and no gradient of potential there.

A situation such as that illustrated in Fig. 2.7 arises from electric charges distributed over the surfaces of the conductors.   We may see that the charge of a conductor resides on its surface by first considering a hollow conductor.   Let the potential of the hollow conductor be ϕ and let there be no charge in the interior of the conductor.   Then there can be no lines of force inside the conductor: a line of force cannot start from one point of the inner surface of the conductor and end in another point of the inner surface of the conductor, since the electric potential falls as we move along the line of force in the direction of the electric vector and the two ends of this line of force are at the same potential.   For the same reason it is not possible to have lines of force in the form of closed curves: the potential cannot fall as we go around the closed curve and yet come back to its starting value.   Hence there are no lines of force in the interior of a hollow charged conductor for which there is no charge in the hollow.   The potential throughout the interior of a hollow conductor is therefore uniform and equal to the potential of the conductor.   This is the same situation as would exist if the conductor were solid.   Hence a hollow conductor containing no charge in its interior may be replaced by a solid conductor without any change in the electric field.   Since it is obvious that the hollow conductor must carry its charge on the surface, it follows that the same is true of the solid conductor.

When a conductor is charged negatively, it has an excess of electrons, and this excess is spread over a thin layer on the surface of the conductor. When a conductor is charged positively, it has a deficit of electrons, and this deficit is spread over a thin layer covering the surface of the conductor; the protons thereby exposed near the surface form the positive surface charge on the conductor. The positive or negative surface charge on a conductor is distributed uniformly over the surface of the conductor only in certain simple situations. In general the charge per unit area on the surface of a conductor is different at different points on the conductor. The distribution depends upon the shape of the conductor and on the proximity of other conductors. It is necessary to consider what controls the distribution of electric charge over the surface of a conductor in any particular situation. Suppose that a particular conductor is to receive a negative charge. Suppose that to a particular point on the surface of the conductor we convey the necessary number of electrons to constitute the charge. At the moment when these electrons are held at the particular point on the surface of the conductor to which they are initially conveyed, the distribution of potential in space could be calculated by thinking of the electrons as constituting a negative point charge. Under these circumstances there would clearly be a distribution of electric potential over the surface of the conductor and throughout its interior. As soon as we release the electrons from the point to which they were initially conveyed, they will move over the surface of the conductor until this surface and the entire interior volume of the conductor reach the same potential. This is because, under equilibrium conditions, the surface of a conductor and its entire interior volume are at a common potential. The equilibrium distribution of electric charge over the surface of a conductor is thus controlled by the necessity for the surface of the conductor to be an equipotential surface. It is not easy in all cases to calculate what the equilibrium distribution of charge over the surface of a conductor is and what the equilibrium potential of the surface is. In some cases, however, a simple answer to this problem may be obtained by the method now to be described.

2.10. Replacement of an Equipotential Surface by a Conductor at the Same Potential. In any electrostatic field the equipotential surface upon which the electric potential has the fixed value V can be replaced by a thin conducting metal surface at the same potential V without affecting the field of either side of the surface. This follows from the fact that lines of force intersect equipotential surfaces at right angles. After the replacement has been made, there is no component of electric field parallel to the metal surface, and consequently there is no force available to redistributed charge in the metal surface. In the interior of the thin metal sheet the electric field strength vanishes, but elsewhere it is the same as before the metal sheet was put there. This situation is illustrated in

Fig. 2.8, using the field of a pair of equal and opposite charges Q and $-Q$. Replacement of the equipotential surface upon which the potential is V leaves the entire field unaffected except inside the metal sheet, where it now vanishes.

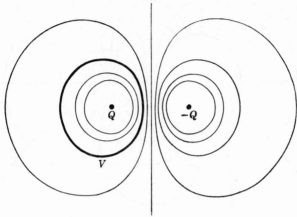

FIG. 2.8. Illustrating replacement of an equipotential surface by a metal sheet at the same potential.

After replacing an equipotential surface by a metal sheet at the same potential it is possible to abolish the electric field on one side of the surface without affecting the field on the other side.   Thus, if in Fig. 2.8 we were to remove the point charge $-Q$ after replacing the equipotential surface on which the potential is V by a metal sheet at potential V, we would obtain the situation illustrated in Fig. 2.9.   This is the field of a point charge Q inside a hollow conductor of a certain shape.   The process of removing the field in Fig. 2.8 outside the metal surface at potential V could be carried out in practice by joining this metal surface by a wire to the small conductor on which the charge $-Q$ may be supposed to reside.   In the same way in Fig. 2.8 we could remove the point charge $+Q$ after replacing the equipotential surface upon which the potential is V by a metal sheet at potential V.   We would then obtain the electric field illustrated in Fig. 2.10.   This is the electric field of a negative point charge in the

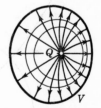

FIG. 2.9. Illustrating abolition of the electric field on one side of a metal sheet that replaces an equipotential surface (see Fig. 2.8).

presence of a conductor whose potential is V, the potential at infinity being taken as zero.

This procedure may be extended by replacing more than one equipotential surface by metal sheets.   Thus in Fig. 2.8 we could replace the equipotential surfaces upon which the potentials are V and $-V$ by metal

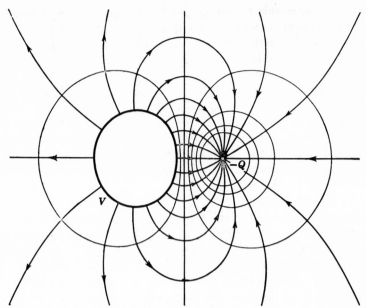

FIG. 2.10. Illustrating abolition of the electric field on one side of a metal sheet that replaces an equipotential surface (see Fig. 2.8).

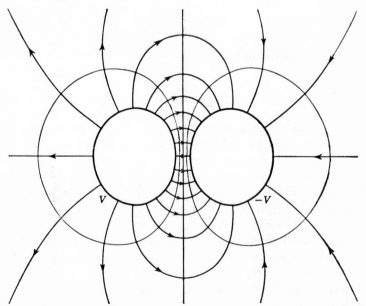

FIG. 2.11. Illustrating the replacement of two equipotential surfaces by metal sheets, retaining the field between the sheets.

sheets at the potentials V and $-V$, respectively. This would leave the entire field unaffected except in the interior of the sheets, where the field would be reduced to zero. After making the replacements we could then retain the electric field between the two sheets and abolish the rest of the field, thus obtaining the field shown in Fig. 2.11.

It is clear therefore that, if we have calculated the electric field for one problem in electrostatics, we can deduce from it the solutions of a number of other problems by replacing equipotential surfaces by metal sheets at the same potential. This is a technique that is particularly valuable for application to the electric field of point charges. We have seen how to calculate the electric field and the equipotential surfaces for any system of point charges. We now see that numerous other problems can be solved by taking the field of any system of point charges and replacing equipotential surfaces appropriately by metal sheets. In this way we may obtain the solution of a large number of problems concerning the electrostatic field of charged conductors.

2.11. The Electric Field of a Charged Spherical Conductor. As a simple example of the method of replacing an equipotential surface by a conducting sheet at the same potential, we may derive from the field of a single point charge the field of a charged spherical conductor.

Consider the electric field of a single point charge of strength Q. The electric potential at distance r from the point charge is

$$\phi = \gamma_e \frac{Q}{r} \tag{2.25}$$

Therefore the potential of the sphere $r = a$ is

$$V = \gamma_e \frac{Q}{a} \tag{2.26}$$

Let us now replace the equipotential surface $r = a$ by a thin metal sphere at the potential given by Eq. (2.26). This we can do without affecting the electric field either inside or outside the sphere $r = a$. Now let us abolish the electric field inside the sphere $r = a$ while retaining the electric field outside the sphere $r = a$. We then have the electric field of a metal sphere charged to the potential V given by Eq. (2.26). This field is illustrated in Fig. 2.12.

2.12. The Electric Field of a Spherical Capacitor. A spherical capacitor is a capacitor whose plates consist of a pair of concentric spherical metal conductors as indicated in Fig. 2.13. Let a be the radius of the inner conductor and b the radius of the outer conductor. Let us calculate the electric field produced between the plates of the capacitor when a given difference of potential is maintained between them.

To solve this problem we start with the electric field of a point charge Q whose position coincides with the common center of the two conductors.

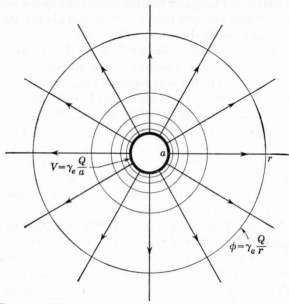

FIG. 2.12. The electric field of a charged spherical conductor.

We imagine initially that the conductors are absent. The electric potential of this point charge at distance r from the charge is

$$\phi = \gamma_e \frac{Q}{r} \tag{2.27}$$

The equipotential surfaces are spheres concentric with the point charge. The potential of the sphere $r = a$ is

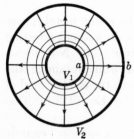

$$V_1 = \gamma_e \frac{Q}{a} \tag{2.28}$$

and of the sphere $r = b$ is

$$V_2 = \gamma_e \frac{Q}{b} \tag{2.29}$$

FIG. 2.13. The electric field of a spherical capacitor.

Let us now replace the sphere $r = a$ by a spherical conductor at potential V_1 given by Eq. (2.28). Let us also replace the equipotential surface $r = b$ by a spherical conductor at potential V_2 given by Eq. (2.29). Let us now abolish the field in the region $r < a$ and in the region $r > b$, leaving the field between the two spheres $r = a$ and $r = b$ unaffected. We thereby arrive at the field of a spherical capacitor whose inner conductor is of radius a and potential V_1 given by Eq. (2.28) and whose outer conductor is of radius b and potential V_2 given by Eq. (2.29). By subtraction of Eqs. (2.28) and (2.29) we see that the excess of the potential of the inner conductor over the potential of the outer conductor is

$$V = \gamma_e Q \left(\frac{1}{a} - \frac{1}{b} \right) \tag{2.30}$$

If the excess of potential of the inner conductor over that of the outer conductor is specified to be V, then Eq. (2.30) gives the strength Q of the point charge with which it is necessary to start in order to arrive at the required field in the spherical capacitor. This value of Q is

$$Q = \frac{V}{\gamma_e(1/a - 1/b)} \tag{2.31}$$

The electric field between the plates of the capacitor is therefore the same as would exist in the absence of the conductors due to a point charge at the common center whose strength Q is given by Eq. (2.31). This electric field is radially outward and inversely proportional to the square of distance from the common center. It is expressed by the equation

$$E = \gamma_e \frac{Q}{r^2} \tag{2.32}$$

where Q is given by Eq. (2.31).

In the process of abolishing the electric field inside the sphere $r = a$, the potential at all points within this sphere becomes uniform and equal to the value V_1 given by Eq. (2.28). Likewise, in the process of abolishing the electric field outside the sphere $r = b$ the potential at all points outside the sphere $r = b$ becomes uniform and equal to the value V_2 given by Eq. (2.29). For the spherical capacitor, therefore, the variation of electric potential ϕ with distance r from the common center is given by Eq. (2.27) for $a < r < b$, by Eq. (2.28) for $r < a$, and by Eq. (2.29) for $r > b$. This potential is plotted as a function of r in Fig. 2.14.

It will be observed that the distribution of potential with distance plotted in Fig. 2.14 is not such that the potential at infinity is zero. It will also be remembered, however, that a constant can always be added to or substracted from the potential at all points of space without altering the electric field that it represents. The electric field of the capacitor is given by the slope of the potential curve shown in Fig. 2.14, and this slope would be unaffected if the entire potential curve were moved upward or downward in the diagram. If desired, therefore, we can readjust the potential function of the spherical capacitor so as to make the potential zero at infinity by sliding the curve in Fig. 2.14 downward to the position shown in Fig. 2.15. This corresponds to subtracting from the potential at all points of space the constant value $\gamma_e Q/b$. This makes no difference to the potential difference between the two conductors and to the electric field between the two conductors.

It will be observed that what we have done is to arrive at the electric field of a spherical capacitor for a given difference of potential between the plates of the capacitor. We have not so far calculated the charges on the plates. Neither have we calculated the distribution of charge over each plate (although it is in fact obvious from the spherical symmetry of

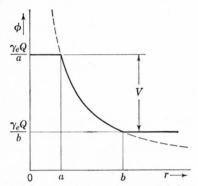

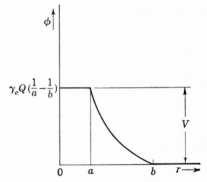

FIG. 2.14. Variation of potential in a spherical capacitor with distance from the common center.

FIG. 2.15. Variation of potential in a spherical capacitor with potential at infinity adjusted to zero.

the problem that the charge distribution over each plate is uniform in this case). In order to be able to calculate the charge on a conductor that is associated with a given electric field surrounding the conductor it is now convenient to introduce a concept known as electric flux density.

SUMMARIZING EXERCISES

2.1. Explain what is meant by the principle of virtual work.

2.2. Explain what is meant by the potential energy of a pair of charged particles. From the law of inverse squares, calculate the potential energy of a pair of point charges of strength Q_1 and Q_2 at distance r apart in free space, taking the potential energy of the pair to be zero when they are at an indefinitely large distance apart.

2.3. Describe what is meant by electric potential in an electrostatic field. State the unit in which electric potential is measured, and explain its relation to the coulomb.

2.4. Calculate the electric potential at distance r from a point charge of strength Q in free space, taking the potential to be zero at infinity.

2.5. Explain how to calculate the electric potential at a point due to a number of point charges of different strengths at different locations.

2.6. Explain what is meant by an equipotential surface. Prove that no work is done in moving a test charge in an equipotential surface, and that lines of force intersect equipotential surfaces at right angles.

2.7. Show that the equipotential surfaces of a single point charge are spheres concentric with the charge. Sketch the equipotential surfaces of a pair of equal and opposite point charges, showing that the potential on the plane bisecting the join of the point charges is equal to the potential at infinity. Relate these equipotential surfaces to the corresponding lines of force.

2.8. Explain what is meant by the statement that the electric vector at any point in an electrostatic field is the downward gradient of the electric potential.

2.9. Explain what is meant by a capacitor and why it is a convenient electrical means for storing potential energy.

2.10. Explain what is meant by a conductor of electricity. Describe the electric field within a conductor in electrostatics, and prove that the surface of the conductor is an equipotential surface. Explain why the charge on a conductor in electrostatics resides on its surface.

2.11. Prove that, in any electrostatic field, an equipotential surface at potential V may be replaced by a thin conducting surface at potential V without upsetting the field on either side of the surface.

2.12. A spherical capacitor consists of two concentric spherical conducting shells in free space, the smaller being of radius a and the larger of radius b. If the inner conductor is maintained at a potential V above the outer conductor, calculate the electric field at all points between the conductors. Describe the electric field existing (a) inside the inner conductor and (b) outside the outer conductor.

2.13. Explain why an electrostatic field is unaffected if the potential at all points of space is increased by a uniform amount.

CHAPTER 3

ELECTRIC FLUX

3.1. Introduction. An uncharged electric conductor is one that contains an equal number of protons and electrons. An uncharged system of conductors is one in which each conductor contains an equal number of protons and electrons and so is uncharged. The process of charging a system of conductors consists in removing electrons from some of the conductors and distributing them among the remainder of the conductors. In this process the total charge in the system remains constant, and this is known as the principle of conservation of charge.

Suppose that in the field of a system of charged conductors we draw a closed geometrical surface S as indicated in Fig. 3.1. Let us suppose that inside the closed geometrical surface S there is located a net charge Q. Then, in accordance with the principle of conservation of charge, there must be located outside the closed geometrical surface S a total charge $-Q$. Let us now suppose that we discharge the system. Then either the charge Q inside the surface S has to move outside the surface S and neutralize the charge $-Q$, or the charge $-Q$ has to move inside the surface S and neutralize the charge $+Q$. In either case we say that, in the discharging process, there is a flux of charge Q across the surface S from inside to outside. We could equally well say that there is a flux of charge $-Q$ across the surface S from outside to inside.

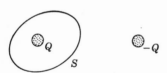

FIG. 3.1. Illustrating the principle of conservation of charge and Gauss' principle.

If in any electrostatic field we draw a closed geometrical surface S and if this surface encloses a total charge Q, the flux of charge out of S in discharging the system is Q. In discharging any electrostatic system the flux of charge out of any closed surface is equal to the initial charge within the surface. This is known as Gauss' principle.

It should be noted that, if a system of conductors is erected in the open air, then one of the conductors of the system is the Earth. The conductors as erected may carry a total charge Q, but this simply means that the surface of the Earth carries a charge $-Q$. In the same way, if a system of conductors is set up in a laboratory, the walls of the laboratory must be thought of as a conductor surrounding the system. The conductors as set up may carry a total charge Q, but this means that the walls of the laboratory carry a charge $-Q$. It is frequently convenient to allow for the walls of the laboratory or for the surface of the Earth in theoretical calculations by imagining that the given system of conductors is surrounded by an infinite spherical conductor. The potential of this infinite spherical conductor is often referred to as ground potential, and this potential is frequently taken as the zero of potential.

3.2. Electric Flux Density. Gauss' principle as stated above is more or less self-evident. However, it leads to important consequences in the study of electric fields if we contemplate a special method for discharging electrostatic systems. Ordinarily an electrostatic system would be discharged by connecting the various conductors by a metal wire. The

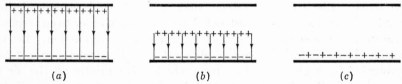

Fig. 3.2. Illustrating discharge of a parallel-plate capacitor by movement of the positive charge along the lines of electric force.

excess negative charge on one conductor would then flow along the wire until it neutralized the excess positive charge on another conductor. In applying Gauss' principle to the study of electric fields, however, it is not convenient to think of electrostatic systems as being discharged by wires. Instead we think of the distribution of charge on a positively charged conductor as being "unstuck" and moved bodily along the lines of electric force between the conductors until it neutralizes the negative charge at the opposite ends of these lines of force. Figure 3.2a illustrates a parallel-plate capacitor in which the upper plate is positively charged and the lower plate is negatively charged. Under these circumstances there is an electric field between the plates of the capacitor with the lines of electric force running from the positive plate to the negative plate as indicated in Fig. 3.2a. Let us now imagine that by some process it is possible to unstick the positive charge from the upper plate. Let it move bodily toward the negative plate as shown in Fig. 3.2b. During this process the region occupied by the electric field shrinks, since this is the region between the layers of positive and negative charge. Let this process continue until the positive charge coincides with the negative charge as shown in Fig. 3.2c. At this stage the positive charge neutralizes the negative charge on the lower plate and the capacitor is uncharged. This is a method of discharging the capacitor which, from a practical standpoint, is more complicated than that involved in connecting the plates by a wire, but which is nevertheless of greater interest in studying the original electric field.

The process of discharging a parallel-plate capacitor by the method illustrated in Fig. 3.2 could be simulated in a laboratory in the following way: In the first place it should be noticed that our original discussion of the law of inverse squares for a pair of point charges assumed that the two charges under discussion were the only two charges in space. This situation is described by saying that the medium surrounding the two point charges was assumed to be free space. In practice the medium surrounding the point charges might be air at normal temperature and pressure. The modifications arising from a medium between the charges other than free space will be considered in due course. So far, however, the medium between charges and between conductors has always been assumed to be free space. Electrostatic systems such as we have been considering would therefore have to be constructed in a vacuum in order to correspond accurately to the situations that we have had under discussion. Let us imagine therefore that the parallel-plate capacitor illustrated in Fig. 3.2 is surrounded by a glass envelope from which substantially all the air is pumped. We then have a vacuum tube of the type known as a diode. One conductor, or electrode, of a diode vacuum tube is normally provided with a heater by use of which this conductor can be made hot. This conductor is known as the cathode; the other conductor is known as the anode. With the heater turned off, we now charge the capacitor so that the anode has the positive charge and the cathode the negative charge. Now switch on the heater. For reasons to be discussed later this has the effect of unsticking the electrons from the cathode so that they move across to the anode. This discharges the capacitor in the manner indicated in Fig. 3.2 except that, in the experiment, it is the negative charge that moves across to the positive charge instead of the positive charge that moves across to the negative charge. In this experiment it is essential to have a vacuum between the plates of the capacitor in order that the electrons as they move across from the cathode to the anode do not collide with air molecules.

We are thus led to contemplate a method of discharging an electrostatic system in which the positive charge is unstuck from the positively charged conductors and allowed to move along the lines of force until it encounters and neutralizes the negative charge on a negatively charged conductor. The positive charge on a positively charged conductor is initially all at the same potential, since the surface of the conductor is an equipotential surface. It is convenient to imagine that, as the positive charge moves away from its conductor, the surface that it occupies continues to be an equipotential surface. In this way the surface occupied by the positive charge at any stage in this discharging process is one of the original equipotential surfaces of the field, and as the discharging process takes place, the positive charge occupies in succession the various equipotential surfaces of the original field.

This process is illustrated in Fig. 3.3 by means of a spherical capacitor. Figure 3.3a represents the capacitor in its initial charged condition with a positive charge on the outer surface of the inner conductor and a negative charge on the inner surface of the outer conductor. It is obvious from the spherical symmetry of the system in this particular case that the charges on the two conductors are distributed uniformly over their

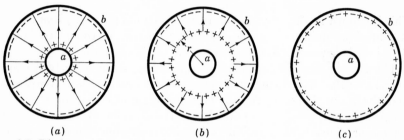

(a)   (b)   (c)

FIG. 3.3. Discharge of a spherical capacitor by displacement of the positive charge along radial lines of force.

surfaces. Thus the charge per unit area on the outer surface of the inner conductor (radius a) is

$$\frac{Q}{4\pi a^2} \tag{3.1}$$

and the charge per unit area on the inner surface of the outer conductor (radius b) is

$$-\frac{Q}{4\pi a^2} \tag{3.2}$$

These charges per unit area on the surfaces of the conductors are known as the charge densities of the conductors. We now contemplate a situation in which the positive charge on the inner conductor in Fig. 3.3a is separated from the conductor and expands radially outward so that each element of charge moves along a radial line of force. The geometrical shape of the positive charge is kept spherical so that it coincides with an equipotential surface at each stage during the discharging process. Figure 3.3b shows the situation when the positive charge has reached a radius r, and Fig. 3.3c shows the situation when the positive charge has arrived at the outer conductor and is neutralized by the negative charge on this conductor.

Let us consider the situation existing in Fig. 3.3b where the positive charge has reached a radius r. The total positive charge distributed round the sphere of radius r is equal to the total positive charge initially on the inner conductor, and this is Q. At the stage illustrated in Fig. 3.3b there is a total flux of charge Q taking place across a sphere of fixed radius r. This illustrates the application of Gauss' principle to the sphere of radius r: The total flux of charge across a sphere whose radius r is between a and b is equal to the total initial charge Q on the inner conductor. Since the sphere of radius r has an area $4\pi r^2$, the flux of electric charge per unit area of this sphere is

$$\frac{Q}{4\pi r^2} \tag{3.3}$$

This is known as the electric flux density at radius r. It gives the flux of charge per unit area across a sphere of radius r in the process of discharging the system along lines of force.

The electric flux density is a quantity that is particularly useful in calculating the charge density on the surface of a conductor. We observe that the expression (3.3) for the electric flux density at any distance r between a and b becomes identical with the charge density on the inner conductor given by expression (3.1) when r is equal to a. Thus the charge density on the surface of the inner conductor is equal to the electric flux density at a point just outside the inner conductor. This merely expresses the obvious fact that, in the discharge process along lines of force, the charge per unit area leaving the surface of a conductor is simply equal to the charge per unit area originally on the conductor. Likewise expression (3.2) for the charge density on the inner surface of the outer conductor is identical, except for sign, with the value of the electric flux density (3.3) when $r = b$. This expresses the fact that, in the discharge process along lines of force, the charge per unit area that arrives at the surface of a negatively charged conductor is equal in magnitude to the negative charge per unit area to be neutralized on that conductor. Thus at the surface of a positively charged conductor the charge density is equal to the outward electric flux density, and at a negatively charged conductor the charge density is equal in magnitude and opposite in sign to the inward electric flux density. It follows that, if we can calculate the electric flux density at all points in an electric field, we can calculate the charge densities on the surfaces of the conductors at all points merely by evaluating at the surfaces of the conductors the electric flux density.

The electric flux density at a point in an electric field has both magnitude and direction. The magnitude is the charge per unit area that crosses an equipotential surface passing through the point during the discharge process along lines of force. The direction is the direction of the flux, or flow, of positive charge during this discharge process, and this is the direction of the line of force through the point. It is convenient therefore to introduce at each point in an electric field a vector **D** whose direction is the direction of the electric vector **E** at the point and whose magnitude is the charge per unit area crossing an equipotential surface passing through the point.   The direction of the vector **D** at each point in the field is the direction at that point of the flux of charge involved in the discharging process, and the magnitude of the vector **D** gives the charge per unit area at each point crossing a surface perpendicular to the direction of **D**.   For the spherical capacitor illustrated in Fig. 3.3 the direction of **D** at each point between the plates is radially outward and the magnitude of **D** at distance r from the common center is given by expression (3.3) if $a < r < b$.   For $r < a$ and for $r > b$ the electric flux density is zero.

The special property of the electric flux density that makes it of considerable practical importance is that the outward electric flux density at the surface of a positively charged conductor is equal to the surface density of the charge on the conductor at that point.   At a negatively charged conductor the inward electric flux density is equal in magnitude and opposite in sign to the surface density of charge at that point of the conductor.   By making use of the vector character of **D** we can incorporate the statement for the positively charged conductor and the statement for the negatively charged conductor in a single statement as follows: The surface density of electric charge at a point of any conductor is equal to the outward normal component of the electric-flux-density vector just outside that point of the conductor.

The surface density of charge on a conductor, being the charge per unit area on the conductor, is measured in coulombs per square meter.   Likewise, the electric flux density D, being the charge per unit area passing the point during the discharge process along lines of force, is measured in coulombs per square meter.

3.3. The Electric Flux Density for a Single Point Charge.   The electric flux density at any point in the field of a single point charge can be calculated from that of the spherical capacitor discussed in the previous section by allowing the radius b of the outer conductor to tend to infinity and the radius a of the inner conductor to tend to zero.   The inner charged conductor then becomes a point charge of strength Q, and the outer conductor becomes the conductor at infinity.   It follows that the electric flux density for a single point charge Q is everywhere radially outward as shown in Fig. 3.4a, and its value at distance r from the point charge is

$$D = \frac{Q}{4\pi r^2} \qquad\qquad (3.4)$$

The significance of this statement is to be understood by imagining the point charge Q to be made up to a large number of smaller point charges (protons if positive, electrons if negative). The field of the point charge illustrated in Fig. 3.4a can then be destroyed by allowing the charge to expand radially and symmetrically as shown in Fig. 3.4b. When the charge has expanded to infinity, the field has been obliterated and the original electrostatic system discharged. The flux of charge involved in

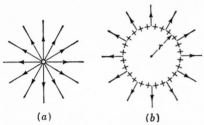

this process is clearly radial at all points, and the charge per unit area crossing a sphere of radius r is given by Eq. (3.4). Thus the electric flux density of a single point charge is inversely proportional to the square of the distance from the point charge. The reason for this is that, in the discharging process along lines of force, the

(a)   (b)

Fig. 3.4. Illustrating the field of electric flux density for a point charge.

charge Q originally concentrated at the point $r = 0$ is uniformly spread over a sphere or radius r in Fig. 3.4b and the area of this sphere is $4\pi r^2$. The inverse-square law for the electric flux density is therefore simply a consequence of the principle of conservation of charge.

We now see that there is a close relationship between the electric flux density D and the electric field strength E. At all points the direction of the vector representing the electric flux density and the vector representing the electric field strength are necessarily the same because the electric flux density arises from consideration of discharge along lines of force. Furthermore, for a single point charge, the magnitudes of the electric flux density and of the electric field strength are both inversely proportional to the square of distance from the point charge. By placing Eq. (3.4) alongside Eq. (1.17) we derive

$$D = \frac{Q}{4\pi r^2} \qquad E = \gamma_e \frac{Q}{r^2} \tag{3.5}$$

Comparison of these equations shows that, at all points in the field,

$$D = \frac{1}{4\pi\gamma_e} E \tag{3.6}$$

This equation states that, although the magnitudes of the electric flux density D and the electric field strength E vary from point to point in the field, their ratio maintains the constant value $1/4\pi\gamma_e$. From Eq. (1.7) the numerical value of this ratio is

$$\frac{1}{4\pi\gamma_e} = 8.854 \times 10^{-12} \tag{3.7}$$

Equation (3.6) can be written in the form

$$\mathbf{D} = \frac{1}{4\pi\gamma_e} \mathbf{E} \tag{3.8}$$

in which the quantities $\mathbf{D}$ and $\mathbf{E}$ represent the electric-flux-density vector and the electric vector in magnitude and direction. Equation (3.8) conveys the same information as Eq. (3.6) and in addition conveys the information that the direction of the electric-flux-density vector at any point is same as the direction of the electric vector at that point. Equation (3.8) implies that if the electric vector $\mathbf{E}$ has been calculated in magnitude and direction at all points of space, then the electric-flux-density vector $\mathbf{D}$ can be calculated at all points merely by multiplying the electric vector $\mathbf{E}$ by the constant $1/4\pi\gamma_e$. Alternatively if the electric-flux-density vector has been calculated in magnitude and direction at all points in space, then the electric vector can be derived by multiplying the electric-flux-density vector by the constant $4\pi\gamma_e$. If E is measured in volts per meter and D is measured in coulombs per square meter, then the numerical value of the constant $1/4\pi\gamma_e$ is that given in Eq. (3.7).

It is so common for the constant of electrostatics γ_e to appear in the combination $1/4\pi\gamma_e$ that it is convenient to introduce a new constant ϵ_v defined by the equation

$$\epsilon_v = \frac{1}{4\pi\gamma_e} \tag{3.9}$$

Use of the subscript v is intended to emphasize the fact that the space between charges and conductors considered so far is supposed to be a vacuum. Equation (3.8) then becomes

$$\mathbf{D} = \epsilon_v \mathbf{E} \tag{3.10}$$

and if E is measured in volts per meter and D in coulombs per square meter, then the numerical value of ϵ_v is, from Eqs. (3.7) and (3.9),

$$\epsilon_v = 8.854 \times 10^{-12} \tag{3.11}$$

Equations (3.10) and (3.11) describe how the electric-flux-density vector at any point is related to the electric vector at the same point in magnitude and direction.

From Eq. (3.9) the constant of electrostatics is given in terms of ϵ_v by the equation

$$\gamma_e = \frac{1}{4\pi\epsilon_v} \tag{3.12}$$

If the law of inverse squares expressed by Eq. (1.3) is stated in terms of the constant ϵ_v it becomes

$$F = \frac{1}{4\pi\epsilon_v} \frac{Q_1 Q_2}{r^2} \qquad (3.13)$$

and in the same way formula (2.7) for the potential energy for a pair of point charges becomes

$$W = \frac{1}{4\pi\epsilon_v} \frac{Q_1 Q_2}{r} \qquad (3.14)$$

Likewise Eq. (1.17) for the electric field strength of a point charge Q at distance r becomes

$$E = \frac{1}{4\pi\epsilon_v} \frac{Q}{r^2} \qquad (3.15)$$

and Eq. (2.16) for the electric potential of the point charge at distance r becomes

$$\phi = \frac{1}{4\pi\epsilon_v} \frac{Q}{r} \qquad (3.16)$$

The numerical value of ϵ_v to be used in Eqs. (3.12) through (3.16) is given by Eq. (3.11) provided that charge is measured in coulombs, distance in meters, force in newtons, potential energy in joules, potential in volts, and electric field strength in volts per meter. Use of this numerical value of ϵ_v in Eqs. (3.12) through (3.16) assumes that the space surrounding the charges is a vacuum and this is the reason for using the subscript v.

It should be noticed that a useful way of arriving at Eq. (3.15) for the electric field strength of a point charge is first to write down Eq. (3.4) for the electric flux density of the point charge and then to apply Eq. (3.10). The law of inverse squares for the electric flux density expressed by Eq. (3.4) is more self-evident than the law of inverse squares for the electric field strength expressed by Eq. (3.15). Equation (3.4) merely expresses the obvious fact that, in symmetrically discharging a point charge Q, there is a total flux of charge Q through a concentric sphere of radius r and this is spread uniformly over the surface $4\pi r^2$ of the sphere.

3.4. Gauss' Theorem. We have seen that the electric-flux-density vector **D** at a point P in an electric field gives the flux of charge per unit area crossing a surface through P at right angles to the direction of the flux when the system is discharged along the lines of force. The vector character of **D** is useful when it is desired to calculate the flux per unit area crossing a surface not at right angles to the direction of flux. In Fig. 3.5, **D** is the electric-flux-density vector at the point P in an electric field. A surface is drawn through P whose normal makes an angle θ with the direction of the flux, and dS is a small element of area of this surface

at the point P.   In Fig. 3.5 a surface is also drawn through P perpendicular to the direction of flux.   The projection of the element of area dS
onto the surface through P normal to the direction of the flux has area
$dS \cos \theta$.   The flux of charge crossing
the element of area dS during the discharge process is therefore

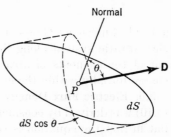

$$D(dS \cos \theta) \qquad (3.17)$$

Now expression (3.17) can also be
written as

$$(D \cos \theta) \, dS \qquad (3.18)$$

and this is the same as

$$D_n \, dS \qquad (3.19)$$

Fig. 3.5. Illustrating the calculation of the electric flux per unit
area across a surface whose normal
makes an angle θ with the direction
of the flux.

where D_n is the component of the electric-flux-density vector $\mathbf{D}$ in the
direction of the normal to dS.   This shows that the electric flux per
unit area crossing any surface, no matter what its orientation, is the
component of the electric-flux-density vector in the direction of the

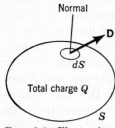

normal to the surface.   Thus, in discharging an
electrostatic system along lines of force, the electric-flux-density vector at any point P in the field
not only gives the flux of charge per unit area
crossing a surface through P normal to the direction of flux but also gives the electric flux density
per unit area crossing any surface through P by
simply taking the component along the normal
to the surface of the electric-flux-density vector
at P.

Fig. 3.6. Illustrating
Gauss' theorem.

By means of expression (3.19) it is possible to express Gauss' principle
as an integral involving the electric-flux-density vector $\mathbf{D}$.   When this is
done we arrive at what is known as Gauss' theorem.   In Fig. 3.6, S represents a closed geometrical surface enclosing a charge Q; dS represents
a small element of area of this closed surface at a position on the
surface where the electric-flux-density vector is $\mathbf{D}$.   A normal is drawn
to the element of area dS in the outward direction from the surface, and
D_n denotes the component of the electric-flux-density vector in the direction of this normal.   In discharging the system along lines of force, the
electric flux out of the closed surface S across the element of area dS is
given by expression (3.19).   The total electric flux out of the closed surface
S is obtained by adding up contributions from all the elements of area constituting the closed surface S, and this is represented by $\int D_n \, dS$.   Now

Gauss' principle states that this electric flux out of the closed surface S is equal to the electric charge Q initially within S. It follows that

$$\int D_n \, dS = Q \tag{3.20}$$

a result known as Gauss' theorem. It states that, in discharging an electrostatic system along lines of force, the sum of the electric fluxes out of the elements of area of a closed surface is equal to the electric charge initially within the closed surface.

3.5. Electric Flux Density for a System of Point Charges. Equation (3.10) was derived by considering the electric field of a single point charge, but in fact the equation is true for any electric field in free space. This can be seen by considering the electrostatic field of a system of point charges Q_1, Q_2, ... In Fig. 3.7, P is a point in the electric field of the system of point charges, and its distance from the point charge Q_1 is r_1, from Q_2 is r_2, and so on. dS is an element of area at P of a surface passing through P not necessarily normal to the electric-flux-density vector at P. If we contemplate discharge of the system along lines of force in the way previously considered, there exists at P an electric flux density represented in magnitude and direction by the vector $\mathbf{D}$. The component of this vector normal to a surface through P gives the electric flux

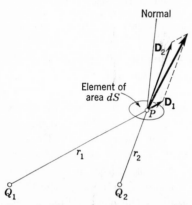

Fig. 3.7. Illustrating the vector addition of electric-flux-density vectors for a system of point charges.

per unit area crossing the surface at P. Let us now contemplate an alternative method for discharging the system. Let us suppose that each point charge is discharged in succession along its own lines of force. Let the electric flux density at P due to discharge of Q_1 be represented in magnitude and direction by the vector $\mathbf{D}_1$. In the same way let the electric flux density at P due to discharge of Q_2 along its line of force be represented in magnitude and direction by the vector $\mathbf{D}_2$, and likewise for the other point charges. The electric flux per unit area crossing any surface through P due to the separate point charges is given by the components along the normal to the surface at P of the vectors $\mathbf{D}_1$, $\mathbf{D}_2$, ... These fluxes add up to give the flux across the surface represented by the normal component of $\mathbf{D}$, and this is true for any surface passing through P. It follows that

$$\mathbf{D} = \mathbf{D}_1 + \mathbf{D}_2 + \cdots \tag{3.21}$$

where the addition on the right-hand side denotes vector addition. Equation (3.21) states that the electric-flux-density vector at any point in the field of a system of point charges is obtained by combining vectorially the electric-flux-density vectors at that point for the individual point charges. Now from Eq. (3.10) we have for the fields of the separate point charges

$$\mathbf{D}_1 = \epsilon_v \mathbf{E}_1 \qquad \mathbf{D}_2 = \epsilon_v \mathbf{E}_2 \qquad \cdots \qquad (3.22)$$

Substituting for $\mathbf{D}_1$, $\mathbf{D}_2$, . . . from Eqs. (3.22) into Eq. (3.21) we derive

$$\mathbf{D} = \epsilon_v (\mathbf{E}_1 + \mathbf{E}_2 + \cdots) \qquad (3.23)$$

Now if $\mathbf{E}$ is the resultant electric vector at P due to the point charges and $\mathbf{E}_1$, $\mathbf{E}_2$, . . . are the contributions from the separate point charges, then

$$\mathbf{E} = \mathbf{E}_1 + \mathbf{E}_2 + \cdots \qquad (3.24)$$

where the addition on the right-hand side is again vector addition. It follows from Eqs. (3.23) and (3.24) that

$$\mathbf{D} = \epsilon_v \mathbf{E} \qquad (3.25)$$

This shows that, for any system in free space, the directions of the electric-flux-density vector $\mathbf{D}$ and of the electric vector $\mathbf{E}$ are the same at all points of space and the ratio of the magnitude of the electric-flux-density vector to the magnitude of the electric vector is the constant ϵ_v whose magnitude is given by Eq. (3.11).

We thus see that, in any electrostatic field in free space, we can calculate the electric-flux-density vector at any point by calculating the electric vector at that point and multiplying by the constant ϵ_v given by Eq. (3.11). We also see that, in discharging the system along lines of force, the flux of electric charge per unit area at any point P of any surface drawn in the field is given by the component of the electric-flux-density vector $\mathbf{D}$ at P in the direction of the normal to the surface. Moreover for any closed surface drawn in any electrostatic field the flux of charge out of it in discharging the system is equal to the integral over the closed surface of the product of an element of area dS of the surface and the outward normal component D_n of the electric flux density at the element, that is,

$$\int D_n \, dS \qquad (3.26)$$

taken over the closed surface S. From Gauss' principle the integral (3.26) is equal to the total charge initially inside the closed surface S. This establishes the truth of Gauss' theorem [Eq. (3.20)] for a system of electric charges.

3.6. Calculation of the Surface Density of Charge on a Conductor.

While the field of electric flux density was introduced initially to describe the process of discharging electrostatic systems along lines of force, the main importance of the electric flux density is in connection with the calculation of the charge per unit area on the surfaces of conductors. Let P be a point just outside the surface of a positively charged conductor,

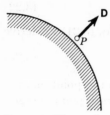

and let D be the electric flux density at P. The direction of the electric-flux-density vector at P is normally outward from the conductor as shown in Fig. 3.8 because the same is true of the electric vector **E**. In discharging the system along lines of force, the charge per unit area passing P normally outward is equal to the charge per unit area initially on the conductor near P. Hence the charge density on a conductor at any point is equal to the electric flux density just outside the conductor at that point. Close to the surface of a negatively charged conductor the electric flux density is directed normally inward, and so its outward normal component is negative. Thus in all cases the surface density of charge at any point of a conductor is equal to the outward normal component of the electric-flux-density vector close to the conductor at that point.

FIG. 3.8. Illustrating the relation between the electric flux density just outside the surface of a conductor and the charge per unit area on the conductor.

If therefore we know the electric field of a system of charge conductors, we can calculate the surface density of charge at any point of any conductor as follows. Let P be a point in the electric field close to the point on the conductor at which the surface density of charge is to be calculated. From the outward normal component of the electric vector at P we calculate the outward normal component of the electric-flux-density vector at P in accordance with Eq. (3.25) by multiplying the electric vector by the constant ϵ_v given by Eq. (3.11). This outward normal component of the electric-flux-density vector at P is then equal to the surface density of charge on the conductor close to P.

The total electric charge of any conductor is obtained by evaluating the integral (3.26) over the surface of the conductor, dS being an element of area of the surface of the conductor near which the outward normal component of the electric-flux-density vector is D_n. Since D_n is equal to the charge per unit area on the surface of the conductor, $D_n\, dS$ is the charge on the element of area dS, and so the integral (3.26) taken over the entire surface of the conductor is the total charge on the conductor.

These points may be illustrated in connection with the electric field of the charged conducting sphere of radius a illustrated in Fig. 2.12. We have already seen that the electric field of the charged sphere is the same as would exist in the absence of the sphere for a point charge Q at the center of the sphere, the value of Q being related to the potential of the sphere by Eq. (2.26). It follows that the electric field strength just outside the spherical conductor of radius a is, in accordance with the law of inverse squares [Eq. (3.15)],

$$E = \frac{1}{4\pi\epsilon_v} \frac{Q}{a^2} \tag{3.27}$$

Hence the electric flux density just outside the surface of the sphere is, from Eq. (3.25),

$$D = \epsilon_v E$$
$$= \frac{Q}{4\pi a^2} \tag{3.28}$$

This is therefore the charge per unit area on the surface of the sphere. In this particular case the charge per unit area is the same at all points of the spherical conductor, since expression (3.28) does not vary over the surface of the conductor. It was in any case obvious from the spherical symmetry of the problem that the surface density of charge over the conductor would be uniform in this case. The total charge on the spherical conductor is obtained by evaluating the integral (3.26) over the surface of the conductor. In this case, since the surface density of charge is uniform, evaluation of integral (3.26) simply requires the multiplication of the charge per unit area given by expression (3.28) by the area $4\pi a^2$ of the conductor. The total charge on the conductor is therefore Q. Equation (2.26) therefore relates the total charge on the spherical conductor to the potential V of the spherical conductor.

In connection with Fig. 2.12 it will be remembered that we arrived at the electric field of a spherical conductor at potential V by starting with the electric field of a point charge Q and replacing the equipotential surface of radius a by a conductor at the same potential. We now see that the result of this process is that the charge Q that was initially at the center now appears over the surface of the spherical conductor of radius a.

3.7. Calculation of the Electric Field of a System of Charged Conductors. We now see how to calculate the distribution of electric charge over a system of charged conductors if we know the electric field produced by the charged conductors. Calculation of the electric field of a system of charged conductors is not easy unless it can be achieved by using a previously known electric field and replacing equipotential surfaces by conductors at the same potential. This technique has been described in connection with Figs. 2.8 to 2.11. The procedure is as follows: (1) Calculate the electric field for some appropriate system of point charges. See, for example, Fig. 2.8. (2) Replace appropriate equipotential surfaces by conducting sheets at the same potentials, and abolish the electric fields inside the conductors so formed. See, for example, Fig. 2.11. (3) Calculate the charge per unit area at a point P of a conductor by multiplying the electric field at P by the constant ϵ_v given by Eq. (3.11). (4) Calculate the total charge on a conductor by taking the algebraic sum of the point charges previously within the conductor. The last point follows from the fact that the total charge on a conductor is equal to the integral (3.26) evaluated over the surface of the conductor, and by Gauss' theorem this is equal to the algebraic sum of the point charges within the surface before the surface was replaced by a conductor. Thus in Fig. 2.11 the total charges on the left-hand and right-hand conductors respectively are simply Q and $-Q$, the point charges from which the field was originally constructed.

If it is not possible to think of a simple distribution of charges, such as a system of point charges, which will lead to the required system of charged conductors by the above method, then the problem is usually difficult and possibly insoluble in terms of simple mathematical functions. Many interesting problems about the electric field of systems of charged conductors can, however, be solved by the above method, as will be seen in following chapters.

SUMMARIZING EXERCISES

3.1. Explain what is meant by the principle of conservation of charge.

3.2. Explain what is meant by the charge density on the surface of a conductor. The space between the conductors of a spherical capacitor is a vacuum, and it has inner radius a and outer radius b. The inner conductor carries a charge Q and the outer conductor a charge $-Q$. Evaluate the charge density on the inner conductor and the charge density on the outer conductor. If the capacitor is discharged symmetrically along lines of force, calculate the charge displaced across unit area of a sphere of radius r ($a < r < b$).

3.3. By considering the discharge of an electrostatic system along the lines of force, explain what is meant by the electric flux density D at any point in the field.

3.4. For a point charge of strength Q in free space, calculate the electric flux density D at distance r from the charge. From the law of inverse squares write down the value of the electric field strength E at the same point. Show that the relation between D and E may be written $D = \epsilon_v E$, where $\epsilon_v = 1/4\pi\gamma_e$ and γ_e is the constant of electrostatics. If D is measured in coulombs per square meter and E in volts per meter, calculate the numerical value of ϵ_v.

3.5. Explain what is meant by the electric-flux-density vector **D**. At a position in an electrostatic field where the electric-flux-density vector is **D** a geometrical element of area of magnitude dS is drawn. Let a normal be erected to this element of area and let the component along the normal of the electric-flux-density vector be D_n. If the system is discharged along lines of force, show that the flux of charge across the element of area is $D_n\,dS$.

3.6. State and prove Gauss' theorem.

3.7. Show that the surface density of charge at a point P of the surface of a conductor in an electrostatic field is equal to the outward normal component of the electric-flux-density vector at a point in the field close to P.

3.8. In the electrostatic field of a system of point charges, S denotes a closed equipotential surface on which the potential is V. The surface S is replaced by a conducting surface at potential V, and the field within S is abolished. Show that the charge residing on the surface of the introduced conductor is equal to the algebraic sum of the charges previously existing within this surface.

CHAPTER 4

CAPACITANCE

4.1. Introduction. We have seen the importance of a capacitor as a device for storing potential energy using an electric field that is largely confined to the region between the plates of the capacitor. Suppose that a given difference of potential V is maintained between the plates of a capacitor and that as a result the total charge on the positive plate is Q and on the negative plate is $-Q$. If the voltage between the plates is doubled, then the gradient of potential, and therefore the electric field, at all points is doubled. In consequence the electric flux density at all points is doubled, and in particular this is true close to the plates. Hence the charge per unit area on the plates is doubled, and this doubles the total charges on the plates. Thus the charges $\pm Q$ on the plates of a capacitor are proportional to the voltage V between the plates. The constant of proportionality, which depends upon the shape and size of the capacitor, is known as the capacitance of the capacitor. The capacitance C of a capacitor is the ratio of the magnitude of the charges on the plates to the magnitude of the potential difference between the plates and is defined by the equation

$$C = \frac{Q}{V} \tag{4.1}$$

The capacitance of a capacitor is measured in coulombs per volt; one coulomb per volt is known as a farad. The farad is an inconveniently large unit of capacitance, and use is commonly made of the microfarad or of the micromicrofarad. The latter unit is also known as a picofarad.

The capacitance of a capacitor is the quantity by which the voltage of the capacitor must be multiplied in order to obtain the magnitude of the charges on the plates. In some cases it is more convenient to work with the quantity by which the magnitude of the charges on the plates has to be multiplied in order to arrive at the voltage between the plates. This is the reciprocal of the capacitance and is known as the elastance of the capacitor. Elastance is measured in reciprocal farads. This unit is also known as a daraf, which is farad spelled backward.

4.2. Capacitance of a Sphere. Suppose that, in a laboratory, we erect a metal sphere of radius a (see Fig. 4.1). This sphere, together with the walls of the laboratory and other objects, forms a capacitor. We may idealize this situation by replacing the walls of the room by a spherical conductor of infinite radius.   By the capacitance of the sphere of radius a we mean the capacitance of the capacitor formed by this sphere and the enveloping sphere of infinite radius.

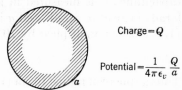

Charge = Q

Potential = $\dfrac{1}{4\pi\epsilon_v}\dfrac{Q}{a}$

We have already seen how to calculate the electric field of a charged spherical conductor.   Taking   the   potential   at infinity as zero, the potential of the conductor when its charge is Q is given by

Fig. 4.1. Illustrating the relation between the charge and the potential of a spherical conductor in free space.

Eq. (2.26).   If this equation is written in terms of the constant ϵ_v instead of the constant of electrostatics, it becomes, in accordance with Eq. (3.12),

$$V = \frac{1}{4\pi\epsilon_v}\frac{Q}{a} \tag{4.2}$$

Regarding the sphere of radius a and the infinite sphere as a capacitor, V is the excess of potential of the inner conductor over the outer conductor, Q is the charge on the inner conductor, and $-Q$ is the charge on the outer conductor.   From Eq. (4.1) the capacitance of this capacitor is the ratio of Q to V, that is, the ratio of the charge on the sphere to its potential, taking the potential at infinity as zero.   By calculating the ratio of Q to V from Eq. (4.2) and then substituting it into Eq. (4.1) we see that the capacitance of the sphere is

$$C = 4\pi\epsilon_v a \tag{4.3}$$

The capacitance of a sphere is thus proportional to its radius.   The larger the sphere, the more charge it holds for a given excess of potential over the potential at infinity.

To obtain a numerical value for the capacitance of a sphere of a given size we need to substitute the numerical value of ϵ_v given by Eq. (3.11) into Eq. (4.3).   It is in fact more convenient to notice from Eq. (3.12) that $4\pi\epsilon_v$ is the reciprocal of the constant of electrostatics, so that, from Eq. (1.7),

$$4\pi\epsilon_v = \frac{1}{9\times 10^9} \tag{4.4}$$

Substituting from Eq. (4.4) into Eq. (4.3) we deduce that

$$C = \frac{a}{9\times 10^9} \tag{4.5}$$

Use of the numerical value for the constant of electrostatics given by Eq. (1.7) implies that the radius a in Eq. (4.5) is measured in meters and the capacitance C is measured in farads. If C is measured in micromicrofarads instead of farads and a is still measured in meters, the expression (4.5) must be multiplied by 10^{12}, giving

$$C = 111a \qquad (4.6)$$

Thus a sphere of radius 10 cm (10^{-1} m) has a capacitance of approximately 11 $\mu\mu$farads.

By thinking of the Earth as one plate of the capacitor and the rest of the universe as the other plate (simulated by the sphere at infinity), we can talk about the capacitance of the Earth. Since the radius of the Earth is 6,370 km ($= 6.37 \times 10^6$ m), the capacitance of the Earth is about 700 μf. This illustrates vividly that the farad is an inconveniently large unit of capacitance.

4.3. Capacitance of a Small Metal Sphere above a Plane Conducting Earth. Let us suppose that, instead of erecting the conducting sphere of radius a in a laboratory, we erect it in the open air at a height h above the surface of the ground. For electrostatic purposes the Earth may be considered a good conductor. The sphere and the Earth therefore form a capacitor, and we can calculate the capacitance. To simplify the calculation, we take the radius a of the sphere to be small compared with the height h of the center of the sphere above the surface of the Earth, and we take the Earth to be flat (see Fig. 4.2).

Take the potential of the flat Earth as zero. We have to calculate the charge Q that must be communicated to the sphere in order to raise its potential to V. The ratio of Q to V is then the required capacitance. To obtain this information it is necessary to understand the complete electric field created by the presence of the charged sphere above the plane Earth. This problem illustrates the principles that we have outlined in Sec. 3.7 for calculating the electric field of a system of charged conductors.

To apply this method to the problem in hand, it is necessary to think of a system of point charges whose equipotential surfaces are such that one can be converted into the flat Earth and another can be converted into the small sphere of radius a with center at height h above the Earth. Let p be a geometrical plane coinciding with the surface of the Earth, and let C be the center of the small sphere. For the moment let us remove the Earth and the small metal sphere of radius a. Place a point charge Q at C and a point charge $-Q$ at the image of C in the plane p as shown in Fig. 4.3. The lines of force and equipotential surfaces for this pair of equal and opposite point charges can be drawn from Figs. 1.12 and 2.5. In connection with Fig. 2.5 we saw that the plane located symmetrically between the pair of equal and opposite point charges is a plane upon which the potential is the same as that on the sphere at infinity.   In Fig. 4.3 this symmetrical plane is the plane p.   If, therefore, we take the potential as zero at infinity, then the potential of the plane p in Figure 4.3 is zero. This plane can therefore be replaced by a plane conductor at zero potential as required in Fig. 4.2.

Now we also saw in conjunction with Fig. 2.5 that the equipotential surfaces close to the point charges are small spheres almost concentric with the point charges.   One of these equipotential surfaces in Fig. 4.3 therefore coincides closely with the surface of the small spherical conductor in Fig. 4.2.   This almost spherical equipotential surface of radius a in Fig. 4.3 can therefore be replaced by a conducting surface so that it becomes the small spherical conductor of Fig. 4.2.   We thus see that the electric field of the small charged sphere above the plane conducting

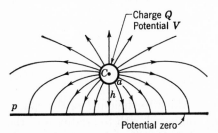

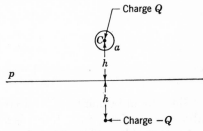

FIG. 4.2. Illustrating a capacitor formed by a small metal sphere above a plane conducting earth.

FIG. 4.3. Illustrating the relation between the electric field of a pair of equal and opposite point charges and the field of a small charged sphere above a plane conducting earth.

Earth shown in Fig. 4.2 is simply a portion of the field of a pair of equal and opposite point charges in free space, one at a position close to the center of the sphere and the other at the image of this point in the surface of the Earth.   Moreover it follows from rule 4 in Sec. 3.7 that, because the charge within the small spherical equipotential in Fig. 4.3 is Q, therefore the charge on the small spherical conductor in Fig. 4.2 is Q.   In the same way the charge on the plane Earth in Fig. 4.2 is $-Q$.

We now have to calculate the potential V of the sphere in Fig. 4.2 due to the charge Q on it.   This is the same thing as calculating the potential on the small spherical equipotential surface of radius a in Fig. 4.3. Now the electric potential ϕ at any point in Fig. 4.3 distant r_1 from the point charge Q and r_2 from the point charge $-Q$ is given by Eq. (2.21). If we now use the expression (3.12) for the constant of electrostatics, Eq. (2.21) becomes

$$\phi = \frac{Q}{4\pi\epsilon_v}\left(\frac{1}{r_1} - \frac{1}{r_2}\right) \tag{4.7}$$

On the small equipotential surface surrounding the point charge Q in Fig. 4.3 we can put approximately $r_1 = a$ and $r_2 = 2h$. With these values of r_1 and r_2 substituted into Eq. (4.7), this equation gives the electric potential V of the spherical conductor in Fig. 4.2. Hence

$$V = \frac{Q}{4\pi\epsilon_v}\left(\frac{1}{a} - \frac{1}{2h}\right) \tag{4.8}$$

This equation gives the potential V of the small spherical conductor in Fig. 4.2 when the charge on the sphere is Q and the charge on the flat Earth is $-Q$. Since the potential at infinity has been taken as zero and the flat Earth in Fig. 4.2 has the same potential, it follows that V is also the excess of potential of the small sphere in Fig. 4.2 over that of the plane Earth. The capacitance of the capacitor thus formed is consequently the ratio of Q to V derived from Eq. (4.8). The required capacitance is therefore

$$C = \frac{4\pi\epsilon_v}{1/a - 1/2h}$$

or
$$C = \frac{4\pi\epsilon_v a}{1 - a/2h} \tag{4.9}$$

Since we are thinking of a situation in which the height h of the sphere above the surface of the Earth is large compared with the radius a of the sphere, the denominator in the expression (4.9) for the capacitance is practically unity, and expression (4.9) is not substantially different from expression (4.3). Thus the capacitance of a charged spherical conductor in the presence of a plane conducting surface whose distance from the conductor is large compared with the radius of the sphere is substantially the same as the capacitance of the sphere in the presence of an infinite spherical conductor. This illustrates the fact that objects some distance from a conductor can be replaced by a sphere at infinity without altering substantially the magnitude of the charge that must be put upon the conductor to raise it to a given potential.

It should be noted that, although the capacitance of a spherical conductor is much the same whether it is in the presence of the plane Earth or in the presence of the infinite sphere, the lines of force are approximately the same only close to the sphere. With the infinite spherical conductor, the lines of force remain radial at all distances from the sphere, but with the plane Earth the lines of force are bent around as shown in Fig. 4.2.

If desired we can calculate the distribution of the negative charge $-Q$ over the plane Earth in Fig. 4.2 by application of rule 3 in Sec. 3.7. The procedure is to calculate the outward normal component of the electric vector at each point of the flat Earth and then multiply it by ϵ_v to obtain the charge per unit area of the conducting Earth. Calculation of the distribution of the vertical electric field over the plane Earth in Fig. 4.2 is identical with calculation of the vertical electric field over the plane p in Fig. 4.3 for the equal and opposite point charges Q and $-Q$. This we have already done in connection with Fig. 1.9, and the result is plotted in Fig. 1.10. Thus if the ordinates in Fig. 1.10 are multiplied by ϵ_v and y/a is reinterpreted as the ratio to h of the distance over the Earth from the point vertically below the center of the spherical conductor, then Fig. 1.10 gives the distribution of negative charge per unit area over the surface of the Earth in Fig. 4.2. Figure 1.10 shows that the negative charge density on the surface of the Earth is maximum at the point vertically below the center of the sphere and that at distances from this point large compared with h the charge density on the surface of the Earth is practically zero.

4.4. Capacitance of a Spherical Capacitor. Consider a capacitor consisting of a pair of concentric spherical metal sheets, the inner one being of radius a and the outer one of radius b as shown in Fig. 4.4. Let the capacitor be charged by transferring a charge Q from the outer conductor to the inner conductor, so that the inner conductor carries a charge Q and the inner surface of the outer conductor a charge $-Q$. Let V be the resulting excess of potential of the inner conductor over the outer conductor. We have already shown that the electric field between the plates of the capacitor is the same as would exist in this part of space for a point charge Q at

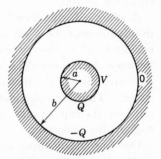

Fig. 4.4. A spherical capacitor.

the common center if the spherical conductors were not present. In this way we have calculated that the relation between V and Q is given by Eq. (2.30). If we express the result in terms of ϵ_v instead of in terms of the constant of electrostatics by means of Eq. (3.12), we derive

$$V = \frac{1}{4\pi\epsilon_v} Q \left(\frac{1}{a} - \frac{1}{b} \right) \tag{4.10}$$

The capacitance of the capacitor is the ratio of Q to V given by this equation. The capacitance of a spherical capacitor of inner radius a and outer radius b is therefore

$$C = \frac{4\pi\epsilon_v}{1/a - 1/b} \tag{4.11}$$

or

$$C = 4\pi\epsilon_v \frac{ab}{b - a} \tag{4.12}$$

If we allow b to tend to infinity in Fig. 4.4, the outer conductor becomes an infinite sphere, and then we have a charged sphere of radius a in otherwise free space. Thus, as b becomes indefinitely large compared with a, Eqs. (4.11) and (4.12) become identical with Eq. (4.3).

With the aid of a spherical capacitor we can illustrate the effect of designing capacitors with plates that are very close together. If the radius b of the outer conductor in Fig. 4.4 is only slightly greater than the radius a of the inner conductor, then the denominator $b - a$ in Eq. (4.12) becomes small, and consequently the capacitance of the capacitor becomes large. Thus, by making the separation between the plates of a capacitor small, we can make the equal and opposite charges on the plates large for a given potential difference between the plates. The ratio of the capacitance (4.12) to the capacitance (4.3) is $b/(b - a)$. Thus the effect of reducing the radius of the outer conductor from infinity to a value b slightly greater than a is to multiply the capacitance of an isolated sphere of radius a in free space by $b/(b - a)$, and the value of this ratio can easily be as big as 100.

A spherical capacitor has an important advantage and an important disadvantage. The advantage is that the electric field is completely enclosed within the outer conductor so that there can be no interaction between the interior fields of two adjacent spherical capacitors. The disadvantage lies in the fact that the interior of the inner conductor is waste space. Thus the spherical capacitor occupies an unreasonably large volume for its capacitance, and consequently it is inconvenient for most engineering purposes.

One important application of the spherical capacitor occurs, however, in the Van de Graaff high-voltage generator. The Van de Graaff generator is a large spherical capacitor whose inner radius is usually of the order of 1 m and whose outer radius is usually of the order of 10 m. The capacitor is provided with a conveyor belt mechanism for continuously transferring charge from the outer conductor to the inner conductor. In theory the charge on the inner conductor should build up indefinitely, provided that the inner conductor is supported in such a way that there is no leakage of charge back to the outer conductor. In practice, however, some leakage does exist, so that the voltage of the inner conductor ultimately reaches a value at which charge leaks back to the outer conductor as fast as it is conveyed from the outer conductor by the conveyor belt. By good design it is possible in this way to develop a potential of the inner conductor which differs from that of the outer conductor by more than a million volts.

4.5. Parallel-plate Capacitor. The capacitor that it is usually most convenient to use in practice consists of a pair of parallel plates, already illustrated in Fig. 2.6. As shown in Fig. 2.6, the lines of force between the plates are nearly parallel, and the electric field outside the region between the plates is quite small. To make simple calculations concerning a parallel-plate capacitor it is convenient to regard the lines of force between the plates as strictly parallel and the electric field outside the region between the plates as nonexistent, as indicated in Fig. 4.5. Under these circumstances the equipotential surfaces are planes parallel to the plates. They stop abruptly at the open edge of the capacitor if "fringing" is neglected.

A parallel-plate capacitor with fringing neglected may, if desired, be thought of as a portion of a spherical capacitor of large radius. Consider a spherical capacitor of large radius in which the inner and outer conductors are closely spaced. Draw a geometrical cone with vertex at the common center of the two spherical conductors and of sufficiently small angle so that the parts of the spherical conductors within the cone are practically plane. If we now remove the spherical conductors except for the

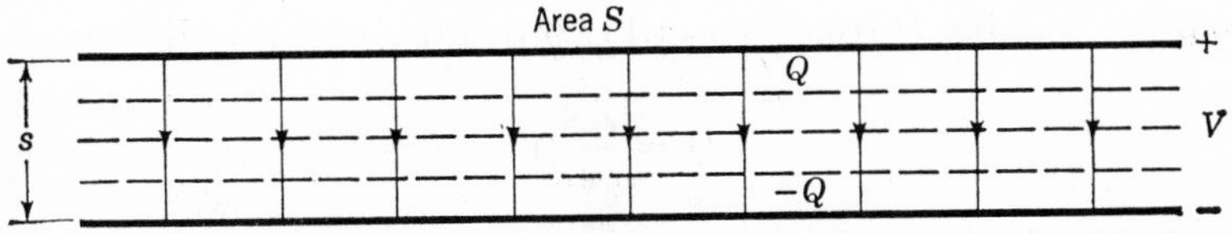

Fig. 4.5. The electric field of a parallel-plate capacitor neglecting fringing.

parts within the cone, we have an approximation to a parallel-plate capacitor. If the radii of the spheres are allowed to become indefinitely large, we can see that the strength of the electric field at all points between the plates of a parallel-plate capacitor is the same, provided that fringing is neglected. In electrical science the uniform electric field in a parallel-plate capacitor acts on particles possessing charge in the same way that in mechanics a uniform gravitational field acts on particles possessing mass.

In the parallel-plate capacitor shown in Fig. 4.5 let S be the area of the plates and s the separation between them. Let Q be the charge on the positive plate and $-Q$ the charge on the negative plate. Let V be the corresponding excess of potential of the positive plate over the negative plate. Since the electric field is uniform, the potential falls steadily from the positive plate to the negative plate with a uniform gradient. This gradient is obtained by dividing the total drop V of potential in passing from the positive plate to the negative plate by the total distance s between the plates. Thus the uniform electric field strength between the plates when fringing is neglected is

$$E = \frac{V}{s} \tag{4.13}$$

It follows from Eq. (3.25) that the electric flux density between the plates is uniform and is given by

$$D = \epsilon_v \frac{V}{s} \tag{4.14}$$

This is the amount of charge that would cross unit area of any equipotential surface between the plates of the capacitor if the capacitor were discharged by allowing the sheet of charge on the positive plate to move uniformly across the capacitor until it neutralized the sheet of negative charge on the negative plate as shown in Fig. 3.2.   Expression (4.14) also gives the amount of positive charge per unit area existing on the positive plate and the amount of negative charge per unit area on the negative plate.   By multiplying these charges per unit area by the total area S of either plate, we obtain the total charges Q and $-Q$ existing on the plates. Hence

$$Q = DS \tag{4.15}$$

By substituting for D from Eq. (4.14) into Eq. (4.15), we derive

$$Q = \frac{\epsilon_v S}{s} V \tag{4.16}$$

This gives the relation between the equal and opposite charges on the plates and the voltage between the plates.   The capacitance is the ratio of Q to V and so is

$$C = \frac{\epsilon_v S}{s} \tag{4.17}$$

This gives the capacitance of a parallel-plate capacitor in free space with plates of area S at a separation s, provided that fringing is neglected.   If C is measured in farads, S in square meters, and s in meters, then the numerical value of ϵ_v in Eq. (4.17) is given by Eq. (3.11).

As a numerical example, suppose that the area of the plates is 100 cm² ($= 10^{-2}$ m²) and the separation between the plates is 1 mm ($= 10^{-3}$ m). Then Eq. (4.17) shows that the capacitance of the capacitor, neglecting fringing, is

$$C = 8.854 \times 10^{-12} \frac{10^{-2}}{10^{-3}}$$

$$= 89 \ \mu\mu\text{f}$$

For a difference of potential of 1 volt between the plates, the charges on the plates are ± 89 $\mu\mu$coulombs.

The process of neglecting fringing in calculating the electric field of a parallel-plate capacitor is usually satisfactory provided that the separation between the plates is small compared with the linear dimensions of the plates. If the separation between the plates were large compared with their linear dimensions, the electric field would bear some resemblance to that of a pair of equal and opposite point charges.

In most practical cases a parallel-plate capacitor is constructed with a separation small compared with the linear dimensions of the plates, and calculation of its capacitance from Eq. (4.17) neglecting the effect of fringing is satisfactory. If unusual accuracy is required, it is then necessary either to make a more elaborate calculation allowing for fringing or

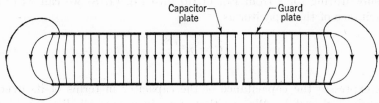

FIG. 4.6. Illustrating the use of guard plates to avoid fringing for a parallel-plate capacitor.

to construct the capacitor so as to avoid fringing. The latter can be achieved by using what are known as guard plates. The procedure is to construct the capacitor with plates whose linear dimensions are considerably greater than those necessary to provide the required capacitance, as shown in Fig. 4.6. The central portion of the enlarged plates forms the actual capacitor, while the remainder of the plates form guard plates. The result is that the fringing occurs at the edge of the guard plates instead of at the edge of the capacitor proper.

4.6. Multiple Parallel-plate Capacitors. To obtain large capacitances we need to use small separations and large plate areas. This leads to capacitors of inconvenient shape unless we fold them up into a more convenient package as shown in Fig. 4.7. This can be achieved by using a number of parallel metal plates with the odd-numbered

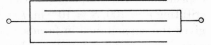

FIG. 4.7. Multiple parallel-plate capacitor.

plates connected metallically together to form one conductor of the capacitor and the even-numbered plates connected together to form the other conductor. This is simply a parallel-plate capacitor that has been folded back and forth upon itself so as to form a more convenient package.

Let s be the separation between adjacent plates and S the area of a plate. Let n be the number of spaces between plates. The arrangement is equivalent to a parallel-plate capacitor of area nS and separation s, and so, neglecting fringing, the capacitance is

$$C = n \frac{\epsilon_v S}{s} \tag{4.18}$$

A parallel-plate capacitor constructed in this way occupies a cylindrical volume whose normal cross section has area S and whose length is given by

$$l = ns \tag{4.19}$$

By substituting for s from Eq. (4.19) into Eq. (4.18) we can write the capacitance of the capacitor as

$$C = n^2 \frac{\epsilon_v S}{l} \tag{4.20}$$

This expresses the capacitance of the capacitor in terms of its over-all dimensions S and l. We see that, for given over-all dimensions, the capacitance is proportional to the square of the number of spaces into which the cylindrical volume is divided by insertion of equidistant plates occupying normal cross sections of cylinder, provided that alternate plates are connected to opposite terminals of the capacitor as shown in Fig. 4.7.

As a numerical example, suppose that we have a geometrical cube of edge 10 cm and that a pair of opposite faces are occupied by square metal sheets each of area 100 cm². Suppose that between these two metal sheets there are inserted similar parallel thin metal sheets at 1-mm intervals. Let the odd-numbered sheets be connected together to form one conductor of a capacitor and the even-numbered sheets be connected together to form the other conductor. The number of spaces between the plates is the number of 1-mm intervals in 10 cm, and this is 100. The capacitance of the capacitor is therefore obtained from Eq. (4.20) by substituting $n = 100$, $S = 10^{-2}$ m, $l = 10^{-1}$ m, and $\epsilon_v = 8.854 \times 10^{-12}$. This gives the capacitance in farads, and by multiplying by 10^6 we obtain the capacitance in microfarads. The resulting capacitance is 8.9 μf.

4.7. Capacitors of Variable Capacitance. The necessity frequently arises for using a capacitor whose capacitance can be adjusted. This can be achieved by adjusting the separation between the plates. However, except for capacitors of small maximum capacitance, this arrangement is usually inconvenient. An alternative arrangement is to use a capacitor of the type illustrated in Fig. 4.7 and to arrange for the odd-numbered plates to be capable of rotating on an axis perpendicular to the plates in such a way that the area of overlap of the two sets of plates is variable. It is this area of overlap that must be inserted into Eq. (4.20), thereby giving a variable capacitance.

4.8. The Vacuum Capacitivity. The constant ϵ_v that we have derived from the constant of electrostatics in accordance with Eq. (3.9) has a convenient interpretation in connection with parallel-plate capacitors. Draw a geometrical cube of unit edge in free space, and form a capacitor from two square metal sheets of unit edge coinciding with a pair of opposite faces of the cube (see Fig. 4.8).   Use guard plates to avoid fringing.   Since the area of the plates is unity and their separation is unity, Eq. (4.17) shows that the capacitance of the capacitor is ϵ_v. Hence the constant ϵ_v is the capacitance between metal plates coinciding with the opposite faces of a unit cube in free space provided that fringing is avoided.   Equation (3.11) shows that this capacitance is 8.854×10^{-12} farad or $8.854 \ \mu\mu f$.

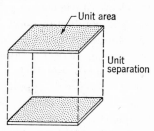

FIG. 4.8. A capacitor whose plates coincide with the opposite faces of a unit cube in free space.

To appreciate the units in which the constant ϵ_v is measured it is convenient to consider, not a unit cube, but a geometrical rectangular parallelepiped in free space whose edges are a, a, and l.   To a pair of opposite faces of area al attach metal plates as shown in Fig. 4.9, and use guard plates to avoid fringing.   The area of the plates of the capacitor shown in Fig. 4.9 is al, and the separation between them is a.   Equation (4.17) shows therefore that the capacitance of the capacitor is

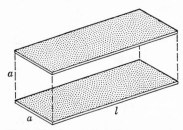

FIG. 4.9. A parallel-plate capacitor formed by attaching metal plates to a pair of opposite rectangular faces of a geometrical column of square cross section in free space.

$$C = \epsilon_v \frac{al}{a}$$

or
$$C = \epsilon_v l \qquad (4.21)$$

This capacitance is therefore independent of the dimension a but is directly proportional to the length l.   The constant ϵ_v is thus the capacitance per unit length of the capacitor shown in Fig. 4.9, and the unit in which it is measured is farad per meter.   The constant ϵ_v is thus the capacitance per unit length of a capacitor formed by attaching two rectangular plates to a pair of opposite faces of a geometrical column of square cross section in free space, fringing being avoided.   Equation (3.11) should therefore be written

$$\epsilon_v = 8.854 \times 10^{-12} \text{ farad/m} \qquad (4.22)$$

This numerical value of ϵ_v can also be read as $8.854 \ \mu\mu f/m$.

The constant ϵ_v will be called the vacuum capacitivity. It is a constant of proportionality involved in the calculation of the capacitance of all capacitors.

4.9. Use of Insulating Materials. Up to this point our discussions of the electrostatic field of point charges and of the electrostatic field between charged conductors have been based on the assumption that the region surrounding the point charges or the region between the conductors is free space. Strictly speaking, therefore, all systems so far discussed must be supposed to have been mounted in a vacuum tube. In many cases, however, it would make little difference if the region between the point charges or conductors were filled with some gas such as air at normal temperature and pressure. On the other hand substantial modifications are required if the region between the conductors is filled with some solid material such as porcelain or mica. In manufacturing a capacitor such as that illustrated in Fig. 4.7 it is frequently convenient to use layers of metal foil separated by layers of mica. Even if the capacitor is to have air between its plates, it is necessary to hold the plates in position by means of supports made, perhaps, of porcelain. It is necessary therefore to consider the electric field of a system of charged conductors under circumstances when the region between the conductors is not free space but is some solid, liquid, or gaseous substance.

We have seen that in electrostatics the electric field within a conductor is zero; an electric field in a conductor would cause a movement of charge that would proceed until the electric field at all points within the conductor had been reduced to zero. Thus a conductor is a substance that will not sustain within itself an electrostatic field without causing an electric current. It is clear therefore that it is not feasible to fill the volume between the plates of a capacitor with a conductor without discharging the capacitor. If the volume between the plates of a capacitor is to be filled with some substance that permits maintenance of the charges on the plates, it is essential that the substance be capable of sustaining within itself an electrostatic field without causing an electric current. A substance capable of sustaining an electrostatic field without causing an electric current is known as an insulator or as a dielectric.

A dielectric, like any other substance, must be composed of neutrons, protons, and electrons. But at the same time a dielectric must be such that, under the influence of an electrostatic field, it is not possible for protons and electrons to move through it so as to form an electric current. This occurs when the elementary particles are assembled into atoms or molecules in such a way that each atom or molecule contains an equal number of protons and electrons strongly bound together. Each atom or molecule then contains no total charge and consequently has no tendency to move under the electrostatic field. The dielectric must not

contain any loose protons or electrons that can wander independently
through the substance under the influence of an electric field, whereas
for a conductor it is essential that loose charged particles exist that can
drift through the substance under the influence of an electric field.

Let us consider a rectangular block of solid dielectric material in which
the atoms and molecules have fixed locations. Let us suppose that an
electric field is applied to the block in a direction parallel to an edge as
shown in Fig. 4.10. Under the influence of the electric field no atom will
move as a whole. There is, however, some distortion of the atoms. The
distribution of negative electrons surrounding the positive nucleus of an
atom is distorted under the electric field as illustrated in Fig. 4.11. The
negative electrons are pulled by the electric field in the direction opposite
that of the electric vector because they are negatively charged. The
electrons are displaced until the pull by the electric field is balanced by

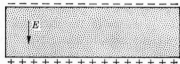

FIG. 4.10. Illustrating the electric polarization of a rectangular block of dielectric
by an electric field parallel to one edge.

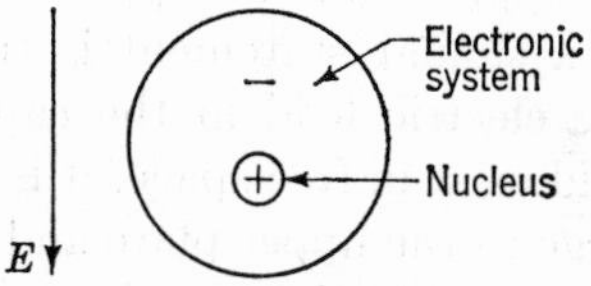

FIG. 4.11. Illustrating distortion of an
atom under the influence of an electric
field.

the force which binds them to the nucleus. If the electric field were
removed, the electronic system would return to its normal condition.
We thus see that, although progressive motion of electrons through a
dielectric is not possible, displacement of the electrons through a small
distance does occur. In a simple situation the displacement is proportional to the strength of the electric field that causes it. In Fig. 4.10 we
are therefore to imagine that the electrons associated with all atoms are
displaced in the direction opposite that of the electric vector by an
amount proportional to the strength of the electric field. This results
in an excess of electrons at the upper surface of the block and a deficit
of electrons at the lower surface. Under the influence of the electric
field, therefore, the upper surface of the block acquires a negative charge
and the lower surface a positive charge. When the electronic system
of an atom is distorted by application of an electric field as shown in
Fig. 4.11, the atom is said to be electrically polarized by the field. In
Fig. 4.10 the negative charge on the top surface of the dielectric and the
positive charge on the bottom surface are said to arise from polarization
of the dielectric by the applied electric field. These charges would disappear if the electric field were removed.

Let us now imagine that metal plates are fitted to the upper and lower surfaces of the dielectric block shown in Fig. 4.10, thereby forming a parallel-plate capacitor with a solid dielectric. Let us suppose that the electric field in the dielectric block is maintained by applying a suitable potential difference to the plates and that fringing is avoided. Since the electric field is downward, the upper plate is the high potential plate and the lower plate is the low potential plate. It will be necessary therefore to apply a positive charge to the upper plate and a negative charge to the lower plate. Let us suppose first of all that we apply to the upper and lower plates the positive and negative charges that would be required to maintain the electric field if the space between the plates were a vacuum. The effect of this is to polarize the dielectric and bring into play a negative charge on the upper surface of the dielectric and a positive charge on the lower surface as shown in Fig. 4.10. Thus the positive charge communicated to the upper plate is partly neutralized by the negative charge that appears on the upper surface of the dielectric due to polarization, and a similar statement is true for the lower plate. To maintain the same electric field in the capacitor in the presence of the dielectric as would exist in free space, it is necessary to communicate a larger positive charge to the upper plate and a larger negative charge to the lower plate. Electric field being the downward gradient of potential, maintenance of a given electric field between the plates of the capacitor implies maintenance of a given difference of potential between the plates. We thus see that to produce the same difference of potential between the plates of a capacitor in the presence of a dielectric as would exist in its absence requires that larger positive and negative charges be communicated to the plates. This implies, in accordance with Eq. (4.1), that the capacitance of the capacitor is increased by filling the space between the plates with a dielectric.

The upshot is that, with a uniform dielectric between the plates of a capacitor, the constant ϵ_v in the formula (4.17) for capacitance is replaced by a constant ϵ whose magnitude is larger than ϵ_v by an amount that depends upon the molecular constitution of the dielectric. The constant ϵ is called the capacitivity of the dielectric. Thus, if for any of the capacitors previously discussed we replace the free space between the plates by a uniform dielectric of capacitivity ϵ, then in the formula for capacitance we replace the capacitivity ϵ_v for a vacuum by the capacitivity ϵ for the dielectric. If a parallel-plate capacitor has plates of area S with a separation s between them and the region between the plates is filled with a dielectric of capacitivity ϵ, then the capacitance of the capacitor is

$$C = \frac{\epsilon S}{s} \qquad (4.23)$$

provided that fringing is avoided or neglected.

In the absence of a dielectric, the charge per unit area on the surface of a conductor at a point where the outward normal electric field strength is E is, in accordance with rule 3 of Sec. 3.7, $\epsilon_v E$. In the presence of a dielectric of capacitivity ϵ, the charge per unit area on the conductor has the larger value ϵE, the difference $(\epsilon - \epsilon_v)E$ being required to overcome the polarization charge on the surface of the dielectric in contact with the conductor. In rule 3 of Sec. 3.7, therefore, the vacuum capacitivity ϵ_v should in general be replaced by capacitivity ϵ of the dielectric in contact with the conductor.

If in any problem previously discussed the vacuum surrounding the point charge or between the charged conductors is filled by a uniform dielectric of capacitivity ϵ, then in all formulas the capacitivity ϵ_v for a vacuum is replaced by the capacitivity ϵ for the dielectric.' Consider, for example, the field of a single point charge Q in a uniform dielectric of capacitivity ϵ. By considering discharge of the point charge to infinity spherically along lines of force, we derive for the electric flux density at distance r from the point charge

$$D = \frac{Q}{4\pi r^2} \tag{4.24}$$

The corresponding electric field is then given by

$$E = \frac{1}{\epsilon} D \tag{4.25}$$

or

$$E = \frac{1}{4\pi\epsilon} \frac{Q}{r^2} \tag{4.26}$$

By integrating this electric field strength with respect to r from r to infinity we derive for the electric potential at distance r from the point charge

$$\phi = \frac{1}{4\pi\epsilon} \frac{Q}{r} \tag{4.27}$$

The formula for the force between two point charges Q_1 and Q_2 at distance r apart in a uniform dielectric of capacitivity ϵ is

$$F = \frac{1}{4\pi\epsilon} \frac{Q_1 Q_2}{r^2} \tag{4.28}$$

and the corresponding formula for the potential energy of the two charges is

$$W = \frac{1}{4\pi\epsilon} \frac{Q_1 Q_2}{r} \tag{4.29}$$

The ratio of the capacitivity of a dielectric to the capacitivity of free space is known as the dielectric constant of the dielectric. It is usually the dielectric constant of a dielectric that is quoted numerically, and this has to be multiplied by the vacuum capacitivity in order to obtain the capacitivity of the dielectric. Table 4.1 gives approximate numerical values for the dielectric constants of several substances commonly

TABLE 4.1

Substance	Dielectric constant ϵ/ϵ_v	Dielectric strength, volts/m
Air (at NTP).........	1.0006	3×10^6
Rubber..............	3.5	10^7
Porcelain............	5.0	1.1×10^7
Mica................	7	1.5×10^8
Paraffin.............	2.1	4×10^7

used as insulators. We see that, by using mica in place of air as the dielectric between the plates of a capacitor, the capacitance of the capacitor is increased by a factor of about 7.

The presence of dielectrics, especially dielectrics whose dielectric constant is substantially greater than unity, in the space between charged conductors raises a number of problems, most of which we shall not discuss. Mention will, however, be made of the fact that for each dielectric there is a maximum strength of electric field that the dielectric will sustain. If the electric field is too strong, the distortion of atoms illustrated in Fig. 4.11 becomes so great that electrons begin to part company from their atoms. The insulating properties of the dielectric then "break down," and there is a temporary discharge of the system through the dielectric. This is what happens when an electric spark passes through air. The maximum electric field strength that a dielectric will sustain without breaking down is known as its dielectric strength and depends upon the molecular structure of the dielectric. Approximate numerical values for dielectric strength are shown in Table 4.1. It will be noticed that much greater electric field strengths can be sustained by mica than by air. In using a capacitor it is necessary to ensure that the electric field strength in the capacitor does not exceed the dielectric strength of the dielectric. In designing capacitors it is desirable to avoid sharp points and sharp edges that would produce locally high electric fields and encourage breakdown of the dielectric. On the other hand, in designing a spark gap or a lightning arrester sharp points are used to produce locally high electric fields and so encourage breakdown.

SUMMARIZING EXERCISES

4.1. Explain what is meant by a dielectric, and define the terms capacitivity and dielectric constant. For a point charge of strength Q in a homogeneous dielectric of capacitivity ϵ, derive expressions for the electric flux density, the electric field strength, and the electric potential at distance r from the charge.

4.2. Define the capacitance of a capacitor and explain the unit in which it is measured. A parallel-plate capacitor has plates of area S with a separation s, and between the plates there is a homogeneous dielectric of capacitivity ϵ. Calculate the capacitance of the capacitor neglecting fringing.

4.3. The space between the plates of a spherical capacitor has inner radius a and outer radius b and is occupied by a homogeneous dielectric of capacitivity ϵ. Calculate the capacitance of the capacitor.

4.4. A conducting sphere of radius a is erected with its center at a height h above conducting horizontal ground. The radius of the sphere is small compared with its height above ground. A charge Q is transferred from the ground to the sphere. Explain how to derive the resulting electric field from the field of a pair of suitably placed point charges of strengths Q and $-Q$. Calculate by how much the potential of the sphere exceeds the potential of the ground.

4.5. A column of dielectric having length l and square cross section of edge a has conducting plates attached to a pair of opposite rectangular faces. The arrangement is used as a capacitor, and fringing is avoided. Calculate the capacitance of the capacitor, and show that the capacitance per unit length of the column is numerically equal to the capacitivity of the dielectric. State the unit in which capacitivity is measured.

4.6. Explain what is meant by the dielectric strength of a dielectric. Write down a numerical value for the dielectric strength of air at normal temperature and pressure.

CHAPTER 5

NETWORKS OF CAPACITORS

5.1. Introduction. An enormous number of problems in electrical science are solved by joining together by short pieces of metallic wire individual electrical devices such as capacitors. Other devices that are commonly included in such systems are resistors, inductors, transformers, vacuum tubes, and transistors. An arrangement of elements of this type connected together by short pieces of conducting wire is known as an electrical network. The design of an electrical network to achieve a specified purpose corresponds to designing a machine in mechanics by suitably connecting together such elements as springs, shock absorbers, weights, cogs, pulleys, levers, and servomechanisms. Just as there is an endless variety of machines that can be designed by the mechanical engineer, so there is an endless variety of networks that can be designed by the electrical engineer. At present we are in a position to discuss only networks of capacitors.

When a number of capacitors are mounted in close proximity, it is possible for lines of force to originate on a plate of one capacitor and terminate on a plate of another capacitor. Networks of capacitors are, however, usually mounted in such a way that lines of force originating on one plate of a capacitor terminate on the other plate of the same capacitor. Under these circumstances the charges on the two plates of an individual capacitor are equal and opposite. It is upon this assumption that we make elementary calculations concerning networks of capacitors.

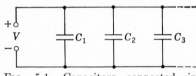

FIG. 5.1. Capacitors connected in parallel.

5.2. Capacitors Connected in Parallel. Capacitors connected as shown in Fig. 5.1 are said to be connected in parallel, or in shunt. Let us suppose that a battery of voltage V is connected to the terminals at the left and that we are interested in calculating the total amount of charge that has been passed through the battery when electrostatic equilibrium has been established. The metallic connection between all the upper plates of the capacitors ensures that, in electrostatic equilib-

72

rium, all these plates are at the same potential, and the same applies to the lower plates. Hence the voltage applied across each capacitor is the same and is equal to the voltage V of the battery.

Let C_1, C_2, . . . be the capacitances of the various capacitors. Since the same voltage V is applied across all capacitors, it follows from Eq. (4.1) that the charges on the upper plates of the capacitors are C_1V, C_2V, . . . , while the charges on the lower plates are $-C_1V$, $-C_2V$, ... It follows therefore that, for parallel connection, the charges of the capacitors are in the ratio of their capacitances.

The total charge supplied from the positive terminal of the battery is the sum of the charges on the upper plates of the capacitors and is therefore

$$(C_1 + C_2 + \cdots)V \tag{5.1}$$

and the charge supplied from the negative terminal of the battery is the negative of this. It follows from expression (5.1) that the total positive and negative charge supplied from the terminals of the battery is the same as would be supplied if there were connected across the battery a single capacitor of capacitance

$$C = C_1 + C_2 + \cdots \tag{5.2}$$

This is known as the equivalent capacitance of the group of capacitors connected in parallel. Equation (5.2) states that, if a number of capacitors are connected in parallel, they are equivalent to a single capacitor whose capacitance is the sum of the individual capacitances.

5.3. Capacitors Connected in Series. A group of capacitors connected by metallic wires as shown in Fig. 5.2 is said to be connected in series. Let a battery of voltage V be connected to the terminals shown in Fig. 5.2, and as a result let a charge Q be supplied from the posi-
tive terminal and $-Q$ from the negative terminal. In electrostatic equilibrium there is then a charge

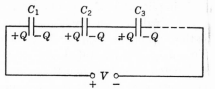

FIG. 5.2. Capacitors connected in series.

Q on the left-hand plate of the extreme left-hand capacitor and a charge $-Q$ on the right-hand plate of the extreme right-hand capaci-
tor. Since we are assuming that all lines of force from the left-hand plate on the first capacitor terminate on the right-hand plate on the same capacitor, it follows that there is the charge $-Q$ on the right-hand plate of the first capacitor. Now the conductor formed by the right-hand plate of the first capacitor, the left-hand plate of the second capaci-
tor, and the joining wire is an insulated conductor to which no total charge has been communicated. Hence the charge on the left-hand

plate of the second capacitor must be Q in order to balance the charge $-Q$ on the right-hand plate of the first capacitor. By continuing this argument, we see that the charges on the plates of the various capacitors are as shown in Fig. 5.2. Thus, with capacitors connected in series, it is the charges of the various capacitors that are the same, whereas with capacitors connected in parallel it is the voltages that are the same.

Let the capacitances of the various capacitors be $C_1, C_2, \ldots$. It follows from Eq. (4.1) that the voltages developed across these capacitors are $Q/C_1, Q/C_2, \ldots$. This implies that, when a number of capacitors are connected in series, the voltage across them divides in the ratio of the reciprocals of the capacitances. Since the reciprocal of capacitance is known as elastance, we may make this statement by saying that, when a number of capacitors are connected in series, the voltage across them divides in the ratio of their elastances.

The total voltage across the group of capacitors is obtained by adding the voltages across the individual capacitors. Hence the voltage of the battery is

$$V = \frac{Q}{C_1} + \frac{Q}{C_2} + \cdots$$

or

$$V = \left(\frac{1}{C_1} + \frac{1}{C_2} + \cdots \right) Q \tag{5.3}$$

The same voltage would be obtained if the battery were connected across a single capacitor of capacitance C such that

$$\frac{1}{C} = \frac{1}{C_1} + \frac{1}{C_2} + \cdots \tag{5.4}$$

This implies that if a number of capacitors are connected in series, they are equivalent to a single capacitor the reciprocal of whose capacitance is the sum of the reciprocals of the capacitances of individual capacitors. This may also be stated by saying that, if a number of capacitors are connected in series, then they are equivalent to a single capacitor whose elastance is the sum of the elastances of the individual capacitors.

It should be noted that, when a number of capacitors are connected in series, the equivalent elastance of the group exceeds the elastance of the capacitor of highest elastance in the group. This means that the equivalent capacitance of a group of capacitors connected in series is less than the capacitance of the smallest capacitor of the group.

5.4. More Complicated Networks of Capacitors. Figure 5.3 illustrates a battery of voltage V connected to a network of three capacitors of capacitances C_1, C_2, and C_3. Any one of the capacitors may be referred to as an element of the network. The battery which charged the system initially and which maintains a potential difference V between its

terminals may be referred to as a generator, or source. It may also be
called an element of the network. The connections between all elements
of the network are supposed to be metallic. A point in the network from
which two or more wires run to
different elements is referred to as
a node. The point A in Fig. 5.3
is a node because from it there
runs a wire to the battery and
a wire to a plate of capacitor C_1.
Likewise the point B is a node
because from it there run wires to
the plates of capacitors C_1, C_2, and

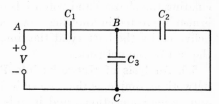

FIG. 5.3. A battery connected to a network of capacitors.

C_3. The point C is a node because from it run wires to the battery, to
capacitor C_2, and to capacitor C_3.

In an electrical network great importance attaches to closed geometrical
circuits drawn so as to coincide as closely as possible with the metallic
wires connecting the elements. In Fig. 5.3 we may start from node A,
pass along the wire to the left-hand plate of capacitor C_1, cross this
capacitor to the right-hand plate, and then proceed along the wire connecting it to node B. We may then proceed down the wire connecting
this node to the upper plate of capacitor C_3, pass across to the lower plate
of capacitor C_3, and then continue along the wire to node C. We may
then complete a closed geometrical circuit by passing along the wire to
the battery, through the battery, and so back to node A. Such a closed
geometrical circuit is referred to as a mesh of the network. For the network shown in Fig. 5.3 another mesh is obtained by starting from node B,
passing along the wire to the left-hand plate of capacitor C_2, crossing to
the right-hand plate, then passing round the wire to the lower plate of
capacitor C_3, crossing to the upper plate, and so returning via the wire
to node B.

A network of capacitors such as that shown in Fig. 5.3 constitutes a
system of conductors of special shape. There is a conductor associated
with each node of the network. For example, the conductor associated
with node B consists of the right-hand plate of capacitor C_1, the left-hand
plate of capacitor C_2, and the upper plate of capacitor C_3, all joined
together by conducting wires to node B. The network in Fig. 5.3 consists of three conductors associated with the nodes A, B, and C. It is
also in principle necessary to remember that the whole network is enclosed
by the "conductor at infinity." This conductor frequently takes the
form of a surrounding metal box or of a metal chassis upon which the
network is constructed. The potential of any conductor of the system
may be chosen to be zero. However, it is not uncommon for one node
of the network to be metallically connected with the metal box or chassis.

In this case, the node connected to the box or chassis is the one normally taken to be at zero potential.

For a network such as that shown in Fig. 5.3 one is interested in calculating the charges and potentials of each plate of each capacitor. One is also interested in knowing how much positive and negative charge was delivered by the battery at the time when the battery was connected to the rest of the network.

5.5. Analysis of Networks into Parallel and Series Connections. A network as simple as that shown in Fig. 5.3 can be analyzed into parallel and series connections, and in this way all the information about the network may be calculated. Thus capacitor C_2 is in parallel with capacitor C_3 and the two capacitors are equivalent to a single capacitor of capacitance

$$C_2 + C_3 \tag{5.5}$$

Moreover this pair of capacitors is connected in series with the capacitor

$$C_1 \tag{5.6}$$

It follows from Eq. (5.4) that the complete network of capacitors is equivalent to a single capacitor of capacitance C connected across the battery, where

$$\frac{1}{C} = \frac{1}{C_1} + \frac{1}{C_2 + C_3} \tag{5.7}$$

From Eq. (5.7) we deduce that

$$C = \frac{C_1(C_2 + C_3)}{C_1 + C_2 + C_3} \tag{5.8}$$

The positive charge supplied from the positive terminal of the battery is therefore

$$CV = \frac{C_1(C_2 + C_3)}{C_1 + C_2 + C_3} V \tag{5.9}$$

An equal negative charge is supplied from the negative terminal of the battery, and this, in accordance with our discussion of parallel connection, divides between the right-hand plate of capacitor C_2 and the lower plate of capacitor C_3 in the ratio C_2 to C_3. The charges on capacitors C_2 and C_3 are therefore obtained by taking the fractions

$$\frac{C_2}{C_2 + C_3} \quad \text{and} \quad \frac{C_3}{C_2 + C_3} \tag{5.10}$$

of the charge given by Eq. (5.9). The charge on capacitor C_2 is therefore

$$\frac{C_2}{C_2 + C_3} CV = \frac{C_1 C_2}{C_1 + C_2 + C_3} V \tag{5.11}$$

the positive charge being on the left-hand plate and the negative charge on the right-hand plate.   In the same way the charge on capacitor C_3 is

$$\frac{C_3}{C_2 + C_3} CV = \frac{C_1 C_3}{C_1 + C_2 + C_3} V \qquad (5.12)$$

the positive charge being on the upper plate and the negative charge on the lower plate.

The voltage across capacitor C_2 is the same as the voltage across capacitor C_3.   We may think of the network as consisting of a capacitor of capacitance given by expression (5.6) connected in series with a capacitor of capacitance given by expression (5.5).   It follows that the total voltage V of the battery divides into a voltage drop across C_1 and a common voltage drop across C_2 and C_3.   These two voltage drops respectively are in the inverse ratio of the capacitances (5.6) and (5.5) in accordance with our discussion of capacitors connected in series.   Hence the voltage drop across capacitor C_1 is

$$\frac{C_2 + C_3}{C_1 + C_2 + C_3} V \qquad (5.13)$$

and the common voltage drop across capacitors C_2 and C_3 is

$$\frac{C_1}{C_1 + C_2 + C_3} V \qquad (5.14)$$

We thus see that the charge on capacitor C_1 is given by Eq. (5.9), and the voltage drop across capacitance C_1 is given by expression (5.13), and we verify that the ratio of these is C_1.   Likewise the charge on capacitor C_2 is given by Eq. (5.11) and the voltage drop across it by Eq. (5.14), this charge and voltage being in the ratio C_2.   Again the charge on capacitor C_3 is given by Eq. (5.12) and the voltage drop across it by expression (5.14), these being in the ratio C_3.   The positive plates of capacitors C_1 and C_2 are the left-hand plates, while the positive plate of capacitor C_3 is the upper plate.

We thus obtain all the information about the network by thinking of it as a capacitor C_1 in series with a pair of capacitors C_2 and C_3 which are connected together in parallel.   This procedure is frequently the simplest way of analyzing a network, provided that the network is not too complicated.

While a network can always be analyzed into parallel and series connections, this procedure is too unorganized to use in complicated networks.   To arrive at a more systematic procedure for analyzing any network of capacitors, it is convenient first to restate the principles upon which the analysis is carried out in the form of two laws known as Kirchhoff's laws.

5.6. Kirchhoff's Conservation Law. Let us consider the network shown in Fig. 5.3, and let us assume that, before the battery is connected, all conductors are uncharged. This means in particular that the conductor consisting of the right-hand plate of capacitor C_1, the left-hand plate of capacitor C_2, and the upper plate of capacitor C_3, all joined by wires to node B, is initially uncharged. In the charging process this conductor is never touched, and consequently charge is neither given to it nor taken away from it. Even after the network has been charged, therefore, this conductor is uncharged. This does not mean that there are no charges on the plates connected to node B. What it means is that the algebraic sum of the charges on these plates is zero. This simply arises from the fact that, during the charging process, no net charge is either created or destroyed; charge is conserved in accordance with the principle of conservation of charge.

In the case of a conductor of the network that is touched during the charging process, the charge on the conductor does not remain zero but changes to whatever positive or negative value may be called for in the charging process. Consider, for example, the conductor associated with node C in the network shown in Fig. 5.3. When the battery is connected to the network, a negative charge is received by the conductor associated with node C, and this charge then divides between the right-hand plate of capacitor C_2 and the lower plate of capacitor C_3. Thus for a node that is touched during the charging process the algebraic sum of the charges on the plates connected to that node is equal to the charge received from the battery during the charging process.

We thus arrive at Kirchhoff's conservation law. The algebraic sum of the charges on the plates connected to any node of a network of capacitors is equal to the charge supplied to this node from the batteries or other sources of charge. In particular for a node to which no charge is communicated, the algebraic sum of the charges on the plates connected to this node is zero.

5.7. Kirchhoff's Circulation Law. We have seen that, in an electrostatic field, there is associated with each point in space a number known as the electric potential, which is the potential energy per unit charge of a test charge at the point. Associated with each point in space there is one and only one value of the electric potential. If we start from a point P in an electrostatic field and follow a closed curve returning to P, then the potential will in general change as we move round the curve but the final value of the potential will be the same as the initial value, this common value being the potential at the point P. If no friction is involved, the work done in taking a test charge round a closed curve and returning it to the starting point is zero. This corresponds to the fact that the work done in raising a mass against gravity and then returning it again to the initial level is zero provided that no friction is involved. Thus for any closed curve in any electrostatic field the change in potential in passing round the curve and returning to the starting point is zero.

This principle, which applies to any closed curve in an electrostatic field, applies in particular to the geometrical circuits in a network that we have called meshes. In the left-hand mesh of the network shown in Fig. 5.3 let us start from the point A and pass round the mesh in a clockwise sense, returning to the starting point. As we pass round the mesh from the left-hand plate of capacitor C_1 to the right-hand plate, there is a drop of potential. As we continue round the left-hand mesh and pass from the upper plate of capacitor C_3 to the lower plate, there is a further drop of potential. As we continue round the mesh past the point C and return to the starting point A, we pass through the battery where there is a rise of potential V. The total change of potential in going round the mesh and returning to the starting point is zero. The drop in potential across the capacitors C_1 and C_2 is balanced by the rise of potential as we pass through the battery.

For the right-hand mesh of the network shown in Fig. 5.3 there is no battery in the circuit. The excess of potential of the left-hand plate of the capacitor C_2 over the right-hand plate is the same as the excess of potential of the upper plate of capacitor C_3 over the lower plate. This fact may also be described by making a circuit of the right-hand mesh, starting from the point B, passing round the mesh, and returning to the starting point. As we pass from the left-hand plate of capacitor C_2 to the right-hand plate, there is a drop of potential. As we continue round the mesh and pass from the lower plate of capacitor C_3 to the upper plate of capacitor C_3, there is a rise of potential. The drop in potential as we pass through capacitor C_2 must be exactly balanced by the rise in potential as we pass through capacitor C_3 so that there is no net change of potential as we pass round the mesh and return to the starting point.

We thus arrive at Kirchhoff's circulation law. In going round a mesh of a network and returning to the starting point, the algebraic sum of the drops of potential is zero.

In applying Kirchhoff's circulation law it is wise to adopt some specific convention concerning the direction in which one moves around the meshes. A common convention is to move round all meshes in the clockwise sense, but at times it is convenient to depart from the convention.

5.8. Application of Kirchhoff's Laws. In using Kirchhoff's laws to ascertain all the charges and potentials in a given network of capacitors, there are several ways of arranging the analysis. The broad outline of the method is, however, as follows. Mathematical unknown quantities are introduced for the unknown charges and potentials of the network. To each node of the network we apply Kirchhoff's conservation law. To each mesh of the network we apply Kirchhoff's circulation law. We then have enough equations to solve for the unknown charges and potentials. Since only linear algebraic equations are involved, the mathematical process of solution is straightforward. However, there are both neat and clumsy ways of arranging this calculation. Network analysis is, in fact, as much an exercise in good organization as it is an exercise in electrical science.

There are two broad methods of attack. One is to introduce mathematical unknowns to describe the unknown charges on the plates of the capacitors. This is best done in such a way that Kirchhoff's conservation law is automatically satisfied. Equations for the unknowns are then obtained from Kirchhoff's circulation law. The other main method is to introduce mathematical unknowns to describe the potentials of the various nodes or conductors. Equations for the unknowns are then obtained by means of Kirchhoff's conservation law. One of these two methods of attack is usually simpler than the other in a particular case, and the simpler one is usually the one that involves the smaller number of mathematical unknowns.

5.9. The Charge Method. The charge method is the method in which the mathematical unknowns introduced are the charges on the plates of the various capacitors. There are two versions of this method, the uncontracted charge method and the contracted charge method. It is the latter that is to be recommended, but it is the former that we shall consider first.

Let us apply the uncontracted charge method to the network shown in Fig. 5.3. Let the charges of the capacitors be Q_1, Q_2, and Q_3, with the

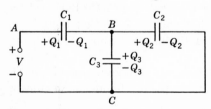

FIG. 5.4. Illustrating the uncontracted charge method.

positive plates assigned as shown in Fig. 5.4. Let us first apply Kirchhoff's conservation law to the various nodes. Application of the law to node A tells us merely that the charge supplied from the positive terminal of the battery is Q_1. Likewise application of Kirchhoff's conservation law to node C tells us merely that the charge supplied from the negative terminal of the battery is $-(Q_2 + Q_3)$. Application of Kirchhoff's conservation law to node B gives us, however, the following relation between the unknowns:

$$-Q_1 + Q_2 + Q_3 = 0 \tag{5.15}$$

Kirchhoff's conservation law has now been applied to each node, and we turn to application of Kirchhoff's circulation law.

To apply Kirchhoff's circulation law to the left-hand mesh in Fig. 5.4 we start from node A and proceed completely round the mesh in a clockwise sense. The drop in potential in passing through capacitor C_1 is Q_1/C_1. The drop in potential in passing through capacitor C_3 is Q_3/C_3. The rise in potential in going through the battery is V. Kirchhoff's circulation law for the left-hand mesh therefore leads to the equation

$$\frac{Q_1}{C_1} + \frac{Q_3}{C_3} - V = 0 \qquad (5.16)$$

In writing down an equation such as this it is necessary to pay careful attention to the signs of the potential differences. This care can be exercised by proceeding in the following manner: Starting out from node A and proceeding in a clockwise sense, we first encounter a plate of capacitor C_1. Write down the charge on the plate first encountered and divide it by the capacitance of the capacitor; this corresponds to the first term in Eq. (5.16). Then continue round the network in a clockwise sense until the next capacitor is encountered. Write down the charge on the plate first encountered and divide it by the capacitance of the capacitor; this corresponds to the second term in Eq. (5.16). By proceeding round the mesh in this way we can easily keep proper account of the algebraic signs and so write down the algebraic sum of the drops in potentials across the capacitors. Care is still necessary, however, to insert the voltages of the batteries with the appropriate signs.

For the right-hand mesh of Fig. 5.4 we start from node B and proceed in a clockwise sense. We first encounter the charge Q_2 on capacitor C_2, and the drop in potential in passing through this capacitor is therefore Q_2/C_2. Continuing round the mesh in a clockwise sense we next encounter the charge $-Q_3$ on capacitor C_3. The drop in potential in passing through this capacitor in the clockwise direction round the mesh is therefore $-Q_3/C_3$. There being no battery in this mesh, we equate the algebraic sum of the drops of potential in passing completely round the mesh to zero and so arrive at the equation

$$\frac{Q_2}{C_2} - \frac{Q_3}{C_3} = 0 \qquad (5.17)$$

for the right-hand mesh in Fig. 5.4.

Equations (5.15) to (5.17) now constitute three equations to determine the three unknown charges Q_1, Q_2, and Q_3. If we solve these equations for these unknowns, we then know the charges on all conductors of the system. The voltages across the capacitors are Q_1/C_1, Q_2/C_2, and Q_3/C_3. When the unknown charges have been calculated, therefore, we immediately derive the potential differences across the various capacitors and hence the potential of every conductor of the system. The results obtained are, of course, the ones already deduced by analyzing the network into parallel and series connections.

5.10. The Contracted Charge Method. Let us now turn to the contracted charge method, which is the recommended method when the charges are used for the mathematical unknowns. In the contracted

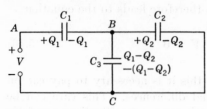

charge method for analyzing the network shown in Fig. 5.4 we introduce the unknown charges Q_1 and Q_2, but we do not introduce Q_3 as an unknown. The reason for this is that, in terms of Q_1 and Q_2, the charge Q_3 is immediately derived from Kirchhoff's conservation law, which we have expressed in the form

Fig. 5.5. Illustrating the contracted charge method.

of Eq. (5.15). In the contracted charge method, therefore, Fig. 5.4 is replaced by Fig. 5.5.

Having assigned charges to the plates of capacitors C_1 and C_2 as shown in Fig. 5.5, we can write down the charge on capacitor C_3 without introducing any further unknowns. This is done merely by realizing that, according to Kirchhoff's conservation law applied to node B, the total charge on the conductor associated with node B must be zero. Hence, if $-Q_1$ is the charge on the right-hand plate of capacitor C_1 and Q_2 is the charge on the left-hand plate of capacitor C_2, then the charge on the upper plate of capacitor C_3 must be $Q_1 - Q_2$ in order that the conductor associated with node B is as a whole uncharged. With the unknown charges labeled as shown in Fig. 5.5, we have only two mathematical unknowns for which to solve and so require only two mathematical equations with which to determine them. These equations are obtained by applying Kirchhoff's circulation law to the network.

Let us apply Kirchhoff's circulation law to the left-hand mesh in Fig. 5.5, starting from node A and passing round the mesh in a clockwise sense. We first encounter charge Q_1 on capacitor C_1, and consequently the drop in potential in passing through this capacitor is Q_1/C_1. Continuing round the mesh in a clockwise sense, we next encounter charge $Q_1 - Q_2$ on capacitor C_3, and therefore the drop in potential in passing through this capacitor is $(Q_1 - Q_2)/C_3$. We complete the circuit of the mesh by passing through the rise in potential V in the battery. Hence Kirchhoff's circulation law applied to the left-hand mesh of the network in Fig. 5.5 yields the equation

$$\frac{Q_1}{C_1} + \frac{Q_1 - Q_2}{C_3} - V = 0 \qquad (5.18)$$

In a similar manner we apply Kirchhoff's circulation law to the right-hand mesh in the network in Fig. 5.5. We start from node B and proceed round the mesh in a clockwise sense. We first encounter the charge Q_2 on capacitor C_2, and so the drop in potential on passing through this capacitor is Q_2/C_2. Continuing round the mesh in a clockwise sense, we next encounter the charge $-(Q_1 - Q_2)$ on capacitor C_3, and so the drop in potential in passing through this capacitor in the clockwise direction round the mesh is $-(Q_1 - Q_2)/C_3$. Kirchhoff's circulation law for the right-hand mesh of the network shown in Fig. 5.5 therefore gives

$$\frac{Q_2}{C_2} - \frac{Q_1 - Q_2}{C_3} = 0 \tag{5.19}$$

Equations (5.18) and (5.19) are a pair of linear algebraic equations for determining the unknown charges Q_1 and Q_2. When these have been determined, we know all charges of the network shown in Fig. 5.5 and hence all potentials.

It may be noted that Eqs. (5.18) and (5.19) can be obtained from Eqs. (5.16) and (5.17) by substituting for Q_3 from Eq. (5.15) into Eqs. (5.16) and (5.17). Thus the equations that we write down directly on the contracted charge method are the same as those obtained on the uncontracted charge method after carrying out the first stage in algebraic solution for the unknowns. What the contracted charge method does is to take into account Eq. (5.15) in labeling the diagram in the form shown in Fig. 5.5 instead of in the form shown in Fig. 5.4, thereby leading directly to Eqs. (5.18) and (5.19) on applying Kirchhoff's circulation law.

In order to solve Eqs. (5.18) and (5.19) for Q_1 and Q_2 we can conveniently rearrange the equations in the following form:

$$\left(\frac{1}{C_1} + \frac{1}{C_3}\right) Q_1 - \frac{1}{C_3} Q_2 = V \tag{5.20}$$

$$-\frac{1}{C_3} Q_1 + \left(\frac{1}{C_2} + \frac{1}{C_3}\right) Q_2 = 0 \tag{5.21}$$

Algebraic solution of these equations for Q_1 and Q_2 then gives

$$Q_1 = \frac{C_1(C_2 + C_3)}{C_1 + C_2 + C_3} V \tag{5.22}$$

$$Q_2 = \frac{C_1 C_2}{C_1 + C_2 + C_3} V \tag{5.23}$$

Equation (5.22) conveys the same information as Eq. (5.9), while Eq. (5.23) conveys the same information as Eq. (5.11). Using Eqs. (5.22) and (5.23) we may deduce that the charge on capacitor C_3 is

$$Q_1 - Q_2 = \frac{C_1 C_3}{C_1 + C_2 + C_3} V \tag{5.24}$$

and this equation conveys the same information as Eq. (5.12). The voltages across capacitors C_1, C_2, and C_3 are, respectively,

$$\frac{Q_1}{C_1} = \frac{C_2 + C_3}{C_1 + C_2 + C_3} V \tag{5.25}$$

$$\frac{Q_2}{C_2} = \frac{C_1}{C_1 + C_2 + C_3} V \tag{5.26}$$

$$\frac{Q_1 - Q_2}{C_3} = \frac{C_1}{C_1 + C_2 + C_3} V \tag{5.27}$$

Equation (5.25) conveys the same information as Eq. (5.13), while Eqs. (5.26) and (5.27) convey the same information as Eq. (5.14).

The main point of the approach used in the charge method is the use of the charges of the capacitors as the mathematical unknowns. The main point of the approach used in the contracted charge method is to reduce the number of unknown charges as far as possible by using the fact that any node that has not been connected to a battery has a total charge of zero. In the contracted charge method the unknown charges are arranged so that Kirchhoff's conservation law is already satisfied, and the equations to determine the unknown charges are then obtained from Kirchhoff's circulation law applied to the various meshes.

In choosing the unknown charges in the contracted charge method it is frequently convenient to adhere to a standard scheme. In Fig. 5.5 it will be noticed that the mathematical unknown Q_1 is the charge on that capacitor which is connected exclusively in the left-hand mesh. Likewise the other mathematical unknown Q_2 is the charge on the capacitor C_2 which is connected exclusively in the right-hand mesh. Furthermore it will be noticed that the signs have been arranged in such a way that we pass from the positive to the negative plate in moving round each mesh in a clockwise sense. The capacitor whose charge has been expressed in terms of a combination of Q_1 and Q_2 is the capacitor C_3 which is connected in both of the two meshes. In the contracted charge method it is convenient to introduce an unknown charge associated with each mesh of the network. This charge is the charge of a capacitor that is connected exclusively in the mesh under consideration. Moreover, the positive and negative plates of this capacitor are arranged so that movement from the positive to the negative plate is directed clockwise round the mesh. In terms of the unknown charges thus introduced, we can derive the charges of capacitors that are common to two meshes by means of Kirchhoff's conservation law. The equations required to determine the unknown charges are then written down from Kirchhoff's circulation law applied to the various meshes. While this particular method of organizing the unknown charges is not mandatory, it is wise to adopt some standard approach and the one described is a good one. It is advisable to preserve the standard method of approach even in a case when a particular mesh of a particular network does not contain a capacitor connected exclusively in that mesh. This can be done by the artifice of inserting exclusively in the mesh a capacitor of infinite capacitance; the voltage across this capacitor is zero, so that the charges and voltages of the network are unaffected by its insertion.

It will be noticed that, for the network that we have used for illustrating the charge method, this method, even in its contracted form, is less convenient but more organized than that based on analyzing the network into parallel and series connections. It is, however, easy to produce examples of networks in which the contracted charge method is considerably superior in every respect to any other method.

5.11. The Node-potential Method. In a network of capacitors all the plates connected to a particular node form a single conductor whose potential, relative to some agreed zero, can be determined. Associated with each node of the network is a conductor, and the potentials of these conductors are known as the node potentials of the network. In the node-potential method for calculating the various properties of a network of capacitors it is the potentials of the nodes that are used as the mathematical unknowns.

It is usually convenient to select the potential of one of the nodes as zero. If one of the nodes is connected to a metal chassis upon which the network is constructed or to a metal box within which the network is enclosed, it is usually convenient to make this node the one at zero potential. Using the network shown in Fig. 5.5 as an example, we select node C as the one at zero potential. Node A then has the potential V

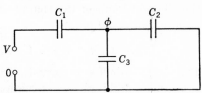

Fig. 5.6. Illustrating the node-potential method.

of the battery and is not an unknown potential. The only node whose potential requires calculation is node B. Let the potential of this node be ϕ. The potentials of the nodes are then as illustrated in Fig. 5.6.

It will be noticed that, in using the node potentials as the mathematical unknowns in the network shown in Fig. 5.6, only one unknown is required, namely, ϕ, whereas in the charge method, even in its contracted form, two unknown charges were involved. Thus the number of mathematical unknowns involved in the two methods is not necessarily the same.

To calculate the unknown potential ϕ in Fig. 5.6 we have available Kirchhoff's laws. Kirchhoff's circulation law states that in a complete circuit of any mesh we return to the initial potential. The truth of this law has already been assumed in the process of assigning to each node a unique potential. No matter what geometrical path we follow, whenever we return to the same node we return to the same potential. In the node-potential method, therefore, Kirchhoff's circulation law is automatically satisfied, and it is from Kirchhoff's conservation law that we obtain the equations necessary to determine the unknown node potentials.

To each node whose potential is unknown, we apply Kirchhoff's conservation law. For the network shown in Fig. 5.6 ϕ is the only unknown potential, and so it is only to the node having this potential that we need apply Kirchhoff's conservation law. Since the conductor associated with this node is supposed to have been initially uncharged and has not been touched during the charging process, it is still uncharged. Kirchhoff's conservation law applied to this node therefore states that the algebraic sum of the charge on the right-hand plate of capacitor C_1, on the left-hand plate of capacitor C_2, and on the upper plate of capacitor C_3 must be zero. For capacitor C_1 the excess of potential of the right-hand plate over the left-hand plate is $\phi - V$, and therefore the charge on the right-hand plate is $C_1(\phi - V)$. For capacitor C_2 the excess of potential of the left-hand plate over the right-hand plate is $\phi - 0$, and therefore the charge on the left-hand plate is $C_2(\phi - 0)$. For capacitor C_3 the excess of potential of the upper plate over the lower plate is $\phi - 0$, and therefore the charge on the upper plate is $C_3(\phi - 0)$. Equating to zero the algebraic sum of the charges on the plates associated with the node of potential ϕ, we obtain

$$C_1(\phi - V) + C_2(\phi - 0) + C_3(\phi - 0) = 0 \qquad (5.28)$$

This is Kirchhoff's conservation law applied to the node of unknown potential ϕ, and it gives an equation to determine this unknown potential. By solving Eq. (5.28) for ϕ we obtain

$$\phi = \frac{C_1}{C_1 + C_2 + C_3} V \qquad (5.29)$$

With the potentials of all the nodes now known, we know the potential differences across all the capacitors, and by multiplying these by the capacitances of the capacitors we obtain the charges on the capacitors. From Eq. (5.29) we can therefore derive all the information about the network shown in Fig. 5.6. For example, the charge on capacitor C_2 is

$$C_2\phi = \frac{C_1 C_2}{C_1 + C_2 + C_3} V \qquad (5.30)$$

This equation conveys the same information as Eq. (5.23) or (5.11).

It will be noticed that, in using Kirchhoff's conservation law to formulate Eq. (5.28), the procedure is to subtract from the potential of the node under consideration the potentials of each adjacent node and then multiply the differences by the corresponding capacitances. It is best to proceed in this way even if it is obvious that the potential of the node under consideration is less than the potential of some adjacent node. Thus, for example, for the network shown in Fig. 5.6 it is reasonably obvious, and it is in any case true, that the potential ϕ is less than the potential V, so that $\phi - V$ is negative. Thus the charge on the right-hand plate of capacitor C_1 is, in fact, negative, and the term $C_1(\phi - V)$ in Eq. (5.28) is negative. It is not, however, necessary to bear this in mind in writing down Eq. (5.28) provided that in each parenthesis of this equation the first potential written down is the potential of the node to which Kirchhoff's conservation law is being applied.

It will be noticed that, for the network that we have used as an example, the node-potential method is considerably superior to the charge method even in its contracted form. In the node-potential method only one mathematical unknown was required, and consequently only one linear equation was required to determine it. Whether the node-potential method of solving this particular network is superior to the method of analysis into parallel and series connections is debatable. The mathematical organization involved in the node-potential method is considerably superior, though it might be argued that, by analysis into parallel and series connections, one obtains a better insight into the functioning of the network.

5.12. Choice of Method. For any particular network a choice has to be made between the parallel-series method, the charge method, and the node-potential method. This choice can be made from the following considerations: If the way in which the network analyzes into parallel and series connections is immediately obvious to the eye as soon as the network is drawn out, the parallel-series method may well be a good choice. If, on the other hand, any serious thought is required to see how the network analyzes into parallel and series connections, then it will probably be better to choose either the charge or node-potential method. To decide between the charge and node-potential methods, draw out two diagrams of the network. On one diagram mark the unknowns

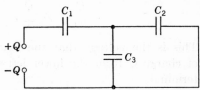

Fig. 5.7. Example of a network in which it is the charge Q transferred by the battery that is specified instead of the voltage of the battery.

required in the contracted charge method, and on the other mark the unknowns required in the node-potential method. The method to be preferred is the one that requires the smaller number of unknowns.

As an example, let us consider the problem illustrated in Fig. 5.7. This is the same network of capacitors previously considered, but instead of the voltage of the charging battery being specified, it is the total amount of charge Q that the battery transfers from the lower left-hand terminal to the upper left-hand terminal that is specified.   In terms of Q it is required to calculate the charges and potentials of all plates of the network.   It is immediately obvious that capacitors C_2 and C_3 are in parallel and that this parallel combination is in series with the capacitor C_1.   The parallel-series method would therefore be a good choice in this case.   The charge on the left-hand plate of capacitor C_1 is Q, and therefore the charge on the right-hand plate is $-Q$, and the excess of potential of the left-hand plate over the right-hand plate is

$$\frac{Q}{C_1} \tag{5.31}$$

Thinking of capacitors C_2 and C_3 as forming a single capacitor of capacitance $C_2 + C_3$, the charge of the combined capacitor is Q, and the potential difference across it is therefore

$$\frac{Q}{C_2 + C_3} \tag{5.32}$$

By multiplying this voltage by C_2 and C_3 we obtain the charges on the capacitors C_2 and C_3 respectively.   These charges are therefore

$$\frac{C_2}{C_2 + C_3} Q \quad \text{and} \quad \frac{C_3}{C_2 + C_3} Q \tag{5.33}$$

The positive plates of the capacitors are the left-hand plates for C_1 and C_2 and the upper plate for C_3.   The voltage across the left-hand terminals is the sum of the voltages across capacitors C_1 and C_2 and is therefore, from Eqs. (5.31) and (5.32),

$$\frac{Q}{C_1} + \frac{Q}{C_2 + C_3} = \frac{C_1 + C_2 + C_3}{C_1(C_2 + C_3)} Q \tag{5.34}$$

This is the voltage that the battery must have to cause the transfer of charge Q from the lower left-hand terminal to the upper left-hand terminal.

To illustrate the procedure for choosing between the charge method and the node-potential method, let us again consider the problem illustrated in Fig. 5.7.   In Fig. 5.8 the network has been drawn out twice. In Fig. 5.8a have been marked the charges on the plates.   For capacitor C_1 the charge on the left-hand plate is the given charge Q transferred by the battery during the charging process.   The charge on the right-hand plate is therefore $-Q$.   No unknown charges therefore have to be introduced in connection with capacitor C_1.   Let us introduce an unknown charge q for the left-hand plate of capacitor C_2. Then, by Kirchhoff's conservation law, the charge on the upper plate of capacitor C_3 is $Q - q$. The charges of all plates are therefore as shown in Fig. 5.8a and the only unknown charge is q. In Fig. 5.8b are marked the potentials of the nodes. Choose the potential of the lower left-hand terminal to be zero. Since it is the charge Q transferred by the battery that is prescribed, the potential of the upper left-hand terminal is an unknown potential ϕ_1. The potential of the remaining node is also unknown, and we denote it by ϕ_2. The potentials of all nodes in Fig. 5.8b have now been marked, and we see that there are two unknown node potentials, ϕ_1 and ϕ_2. Since one unknown q is required in the charge method and two unknowns ϕ_1 and ϕ_2 are required in the node-potential method, it follows that the charge method is to be preferred to the node-potential method in this case.

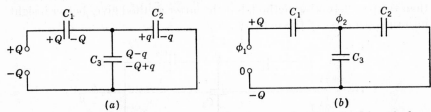

(a)   (b)

FIG. 5.8. Illustrating the choice between the charge and node-potential methods.

Using the charge method, we obtain the equation necessary to determine the unknown charge q from Kirchhoff's circulation law. Kirchhoff's circulation law applied to the left-hand mesh in Fig. 5.8a determines the voltage of the battery if we need to calculate this. It is application of Kirchhoff's circulation law to the right-hand mesh in Fig. 5.8a that gives the equation required to determine the unknown charge q. Starting at the upper left-hand corner of the right-hand mesh and proceeding clockwise round the mesh in the usual way, we derive the equation

$$\frac{q}{C_2} + \frac{-Q + q}{C_3} = 0 \tag{5.35}$$

Solution of this equation for q gives

$$q = \frac{C_2}{C_2 + C_3} Q \tag{5.36}$$

This is the charge on capacitor C_2. The charge on capacitor C_3 is

$$Q - q = \frac{C_3}{C_2 + C_3} Q \tag{5.37}$$

The voltage of the charging battery can be obtained by applying Kirchhoff's law to the left-hand mesh or, alternatively, from the fact that it is the sum of the voltages across capacitors C_1 and C_2. Using the second method, the voltage of the battery is

$$\frac{Q}{C_1} + \frac{q}{C_2} \tag{5.38}$$

and on substituting for q from Eq. (5.36) this becomes

$$\frac{C_1 + C_2 + C_3}{C_1(C_2 + C_3)} Q \tag{5.39}$$

Equations (5.36) and (5.37) convey the same information as expressions (5.33), while expression (5.39) conveys the same information as Eq. (5.34).

In this problem the node-potential method is clearly inferior to the charge method. The charge method is mathematically more systematic than the parallel-series method, but the latter method gives better insight into the operation of the network.

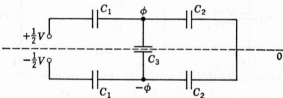

FIG. 5.9. A network that is symmetrical with respect to the dashed line.

5.13. Balanced Networks. Networks frequently possess symmetry properties that permit a reduction in the number of mathematical unknowns that must be introduced to describe the network. Such a network is called a balanced network, and it is usually convenient to take the potential on the plane of symmetry as zero. Figure 5.9 illustrates a balanced network, and the dashed line indicates the plane of symmetry. If we take the potential of this plane as zero, it follows that the potential of the node at the right-hand end of the network is zero. Moreover, application of a battery of voltage V to the left-hand terminals makes the potential of the upper terminal $\frac{1}{2}V$ and that of the lower terminal $-\frac{1}{2}V$. There are now two nodes whose potentials have not yet been evaluated. From the symmetry of the network these potentials may be taken as ϕ and $-\phi$, so that only one unknown is necessary to describe both potentials. Thus by taking advantage of the symmetry properties of the network shown in Fig. 5.9 only one unknown potential need be introduced in analyzing it. The equation necessary to determine this unknown is obtained from Kirchhoff's conservation law applied to the node of potential ϕ. If the conservation law is applied to the node of potential $-\phi$, the same equation is obtained.

It is always desirable to use any symmetry properties that a network may possess to reduce the number of mathematical unknowns as far as possible.

5.14. Standard Procedure for Analyzing Networks of Capacitors. From what has been said concerning the analysis of networks of capacitors we see that the procedure is as follows: (1) Decide whether the network is sufficiently simple to use the parallel-series method.   (2) If not, draw two diagrams of the network; mark the unknowns required in the charge method on one diagram and the unknowns required in the node-potential method on the other diagram.   Use the symmetry properties, if any, of the network to reduce the number of unknowns as far as possible.   (3) If the charge method involves the smaller number of unknowns, use it and derive equations for the unknowns by applying Kirchhoff's circulation law to the meshes.   (4) If the node-potential method involves the fewer number of unknowns, use it and obtain equations for the unknowns by applying Kirchhoff's conservation law to the nodes.   (5) Before solving the equations for the unknowns, decide which unknowns actually need to be determined in order to provide the required information about the network.

Although it is not advisable to choose between the charge and node-potential methods by casual inspection of the network, it is worthwhile to realize what features of a network favor the charge method and what features favor the node-potential method.   The main consideration involved is the relative number of meshes and nodes in the network. Figure 5.1 is an example of a network with many meshes and yet only two nodes.   Figure 5.2 is an example of a network with many nodes and yet only one mesh.   Now in the charge method there is a charge associated with each mesh, while in the node-potential method there is a potential associated with each node.   Hence a network with few meshes and many nodes is favorable to use of the charge method while a network with few nodes and many meshes is favorable to use of the node-potential method. However, another consideration affecting the relative number of mathematical unknowns involved in the charge and node-potential methods for a particular network is the way in which the charging process is specified. If the network is charged by batteries of given voltages, these given voltages reduce the number of unknown node potentials and thereby favor the node-potential method.   On the other hand, if the charging process is specified by the amounts of charge transferred by the various batteries, this reduces the number of unknown charges in the charge method and so favors this method.   To allow for all these considerations, it is best, as previously stated, to draw two diagrams of the network and to mark on one diagram the unknowns required in the charge method and on the other diagram the unknowns required in the node-potential method.   In this way the method involving the smaller number of mathematical unknowns can be reliably recognized.

SUMMARIZING EXERCISES

5.1. Prove that, if a number of capacitors whose capacitances are $C_1, C_2, \ldots, C_n$ are connected in parallel, the system can be used as a single capacitor of capacitance $C_1 + C_2 + \cdots + C_n$. Prove also that, if the capacitors are connected in series, the system can be used as a single capacitor of capacitance C where $1/C$ is equal to the sum of the reciprocals of the capacitances of the individual capacitors.

5.2. State and justify Kirchhoff's laws for a network of capacitors.

5.3. Explain how to calculate the charges and potentials in a network of charged capacitors using (a) the method of analysis into parallel and series connections, (b) the charge method, and (c) the node-potential method. Explain the advantages and disadvantages of the three methods.

5.4. Explain how the symmetry of a balanced network of capacitors can be used to reduce the number of unknowns required to describe it.

CHAPTER 6

COEFFICIENTS OF CAPACITANCE AND ELASTANCE FOR A NETWORK OF CAPACITORS

6.1. Introduction. Let us apply the principles that we have developed for analyzing networks of capacitors to the network shown in Fig. 6.1. In this network the central node, marked zero, is the node taken to have zero potential. Let charges Q_1, Q_2, and Q_3 be transferred to nodes 1, 2, and 3 from node 0, and as a result let the potentials of nodes 1, 2, and 3 be V_1, V_2, and V_3 respectively. The potential of node 0 is zero, and its charge is $-(Q_1 + Q_2 + Q_3)$. Applying Kirchhoff's conservation law to node 1 we obtain

$$Q_1 = C_{11}(V_1 - 0) + C_{12}(V_1 - V_2) + C_{13}(V_1 - V_3)$$

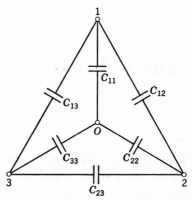

FIG. 6.1. Network for illustrating coefficients of capacitance and elastance.

In the same way by applying Kirchhoff's conservation law to nodes 2 and 3 we obtain, rspectively,

$$Q_2 = C_{22}(V_2 - 0) + C_{12}(V_2 - V_1) + C_{23}(V_2 - V_3)$$
$$Q_3 = C_{33}(V_3 - 0) + C_{13}(V_3 - V_1) + C_{23}(V_3 - V_2)$$

On collecting the terms in V_1, V_2, and V_3, these equations become

$$Q_1 = (C_{11} + C_{12} + C_{13})V_1 - C_{12}V_2 - C_{13}V_3 \qquad (6.1)$$
$$Q_2 = -C_{12}V_1 + (C_{22} + C_{23} + C_{12})V_2 - C_{23}V_3 \qquad (6.2)$$
$$Q_3 = -C_{13}V_1 - C_{23}V_2 + (C_{33} + C_{13} + C_{23})V_3 \qquad (6.3)$$

Equations (6.1) to (6.3) are the equations that determine the potentials V_1, V_2, and V_3 of the nodes when given charges Q_1, Q_2, and Q_3 are communicated to the nodes. Alternatively these equations give the charges

93

Q_1, Q_2, and Q_3 that must be communicated to the nodes in order to raise them to given potentials V_1, V_2, and V_3 above the potential of the central node.

Equations (6.1) to (6.3) relating the charges Q_1, Q_2, and Q_3 to the potentials V_1, V_2, and V_3 can be arranged in the form

$$Q_1 = c_{11}V_1 + c_{12}V_2 + c_{13}V_3 \qquad (6.4)$$
$$Q_2 = c_{21}V_1 + c_{22}V_2 + c_{23}V_3 \qquad (6.5)$$
$$Q_3 = c_{31}V_1 + c_{32}V_2 + c_{33}V_3 \qquad (6.6)$$

By comparing Eq. (6.4) with Eq. (6.1), Eq. (6.5) with Eq. (6.2), and Eq. (6.6) with Eq. (6.3) we see that the "diagonal" coefficients in Eqs. (6.4) to (6.6) are

$$c_{11} = C_{11} + C_{12} + C_{13} \qquad (6.7)$$
$$c_{22} = C_{22} + C_{23} + C_{12} \qquad (6.8)$$
$$c_{33} = C_{33} + C_{13} + C_{23} \qquad (6.9)$$

and the "nondiagonal" coefficients are

$$c_{12} = c_{21} = -C_{12} \qquad (6.10)$$
$$c_{23} = c_{32} = -C_{23} \qquad (6.11)$$
$$c_{31} = c_{13} = -C_{13} \qquad (6.12)$$

When the coefficients in Eqs. (6.4) to (6.6) have been calculated from the capacitances of the capacitors forming the network in accordance with Eqs. (6.7) to (6.12), we can apply any potentials to nodes 1, 2, and 3 and deduce the corresponding charges on nodes 1, 2, and 3 by means of Eqs. (6.4) to (6.6). The coefficients in Eqs. (6.4) to (6.6) are known as the coefficients of capacitance of the network.

Equations (6.4) to (6.6) are in a form convenient to use when the problem is to calculate the charges on nodes 1, 2, and 3 when the potentials of these nodes are given. If, however, it is the charges on the nodes that are given and the potentials that have to be calculated, then Eqs. (6.4) to (6.6) must be solved for V_1, V_2, and V_3 in terms of Q_1, Q_2, and Q_3. This solution is carried out by the ordinary process for solving linear algebraic equations and leads to equations of the form

$$V_1 = b_{11}Q_1 + b_{12}Q_2 + b_{13}Q_3 \qquad (6.13)$$
$$V_2 = b_{21}Q_1 + b_{22}Q_2 + b_{23}Q_3 \qquad (6.14)$$
$$V_3 = b_{31}Q_1 + b_{32}Q_2 + b_{33}Q_3 \qquad (6.15)$$

When the process of solution is carried out in detail, the coefficients in Eqs. (6.13) to (6.15) can be expressed in terms of those in Eqs. (6.4) to (6.6) and hence in terms of the capacitances of the capacitors forming the network.   From the process of solution it follows that

$$b_{12} = b_{21} \tag{6.16}$$
$$b_{23} = b_{32} \tag{6.17}$$
$$b_{31} = b_{13} \tag{6.18}$$

Thus the symmetry of the nondiagonal coefficients of capacitance expressed by Eqs. (6.10) to (6.12) leads to a corresponding symmetry of the nondiagonal coefficients in Eqs. (6.13) to (6.15).   The coefficients in Eqs. (6.13) to (6.15) are known as the coefficients of elastance of the network.   When the coefficients of elastance of a network have been calculated, we can apply any charges Q_1, Q_2, and Q_3 to nodes 1, 2, and 3 and deduce the corresponding potentials V_1, V_2, and V_3 from Eqs. (6.13) to (6.15).

The diagonal coefficients c_{11}, c_{22}, and c_{33} in Eqs. (6.4) to (6.6) are known as the coefficients of self-capacitance of the network, while the remaining coefficients in these equations are known as the coefficients of mutual capacitance.   Equations (6.10) to (6.12) show that the coefficients of mutual capacitance are numerically negative.   The coefficients b_{11}, b_{22}, and b_{33} in Eqs. (6.13) to (6.15) are known as the coefficients of self-elastance of the system, while the remaining coefficients in these equations are known as the coefficients
of mutual elastance.   If the network
were reduced to a single capacitor
connecting node 1 to node 0, then c_{11}
would be its capacitance and b_{11}
would be its elastance.   It should
be noted, however, that the reciprocal of a coefficient of capacitance
does not in general give the corresponding coefficient of elastance; the
relation between the coefficients of
capacitance and the coefficients of
elastance must be obtained either by
solving Eqs. (6.4) to (6.6) for V_1, V_2,
and V_3 so as to obtain equations of
the form (6.13) to (6.15) or alter-

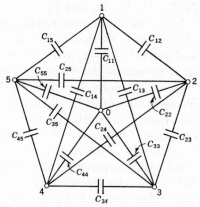

FIG. 6.2. More complicated network illustrating the coefficients of capacitance and elastance.

natively by solving Eqs. (6.13) to (6.15) for Q_1, Q_2, and Q_3 so as to obtain equations of the form (6.4) to (6.6).

The procedure that we have outlined in connection with the network shown in Fig. 6.1 could equally well be applied to the network shown in Fig. 6.2.   In this case there are five nodes in addition to the central node at zero potential.   We thus have five linear equations, instead of three, expressing the charges on nodes 1, 2, 3, 4, and 5 in terms of their potentials or alternatively expressing the potentials in terms of the charges. Corresponding to Eqs. (6.4) to (6.6) we have

$$Q_1 = c_{11}V_1 + c_{12}V_2 + c_{13}V_3 + c_{14}V_4 + c_{15}V_5 \qquad (6.19)$$
$$Q_2 = c_{21}V_1 + c_{22}V_2 + c_{23}V_3 + c_{24}V_4 + c_{25}V_5 \qquad (6.20)$$
$$Q_3 = c_{31}V_1 + c_{32}V_2 + c_{33}V_3 + c_{34}V_4 + c_{35}V_5 \qquad (6.21)$$
$$Q_4 = c_{41}V_1 + c_{42}V_2 + c_{43}V_3 + c_{44}V_4 + c_{45}V_5 \qquad (6.22)$$
$$Q_5 = c_{51}V_1 + c_{52}V_2 + c_{53}V_3 + c_{54}V_4 + c_{55}V_5 \qquad (6.23)$$

where $\qquad c_{11} = C_{11} + C_{12} + C_{13} + C_{14} + C_{15}$, etc. $\qquad (6.24)$

$$c_{12} = c_{21} = -C_{12}, \text{ etc.} \qquad (6.25)$$

Corresponding to Eqs. (6.13) to (6.15) we have

$$V_1 = b_{11}Q_1 + b_{12}Q_2 + b_{13}Q_3 + b_{14}Q_4 + b_{15}Q_5 \qquad (6.26)$$
$$V_2 = b_{21}Q_1 + b_{22}Q_2 + b_{23}Q_3 + b_{24}Q_4 + b_{25}Q_5 \qquad (6.27)$$
$$V_3 = b_{31}Q_1 + b_{32}Q_2 + b_{33}Q_3 + b_{34}Q_4 + b_{35}Q_5 \qquad (6.28)$$
$$V_4 = b_{41}Q_1 + b_{42}Q_2 + b_{43}Q_3 + b_{44}Q_4 + b_{45}Q_5 \qquad (6.29)$$
$$V_5 = b_{51}Q_1 + b_{52}Q_2 + b_{53}Q_3 + b_{54}Q_4 + b_{55}Q_5 \qquad (6.30)$$

where $\qquad\qquad\qquad b_{12} = b_{21}$, etc. $\qquad\qquad\qquad (6.31)$

Equations (6.26) to (6.30) are obtained by solving Eqs. (6.19) to (6.23) for V_1, V_2, V_3, V_4, and V_5.

From the above examples it may be seen that, for any charged network of capacitors, Kirchhoff's laws lead to linear equations relating the charges and potentials associated with the nodes. The equations can be written so as to express the charges in terms of the potentials, in which case the coefficients involved are the coefficients of capacitance. Alternatively the linear relations can be written so as to express the potentials in terms of the charges, in which case the coefficients involved are the coefficients of elastance. Both sets of coefficients can be expressed in terms of the capacitances of the capacitors constituting the network.

6.2. An Interpretation of the Coefficients of Capacitance and Elastance. Let us consider the network shown in Fig. 6.1. Let us suppose for the time being that node 1 is at unit potential and nodes 2 and 3 are at zero potential. In Eqs. (6.4) to (6.6) we then put

$$V_1 = 1 \qquad V_2 = 0 \qquad V_3 = 0 \qquad (6.32)$$

and obtain

$$Q_1 = c_{11} \qquad Q_2 = c_{21} \qquad Q_3 = c_{31} \qquad (6.33)$$

We thus see that the coefficients c_{11}, c_{21}, and c_{31} are numerically equal to the charges on nodes 1, 2, and 3 when node 1 is at unit potential and all the other nodes are at zero potential.   In the same way we can substitute into Eqs. (6.4) to (6.6)

$$V_1 = 0 \qquad V_2 = 1 \qquad V_3 = 0 \tag{6.34}$$

and obtain

$$Q_1 = c_{12} \qquad Q_2 = c_{22} \qquad Q_3 = c_{32} \tag{6.35}$$

Likewise if we substitute

$$V_1 = 0 \qquad V_2 = 0 \qquad V_3 = 1 \tag{6.36}$$

we obtain

$$Q_1 = c_{13} \qquad Q_2 = c_{23} \qquad Q_3 = c_{33} \tag{6.37}$$

We can summarize the information contained in Eqs. (6.32) to (6.37) by saying that the coefficient of capacitance c_{rs} is numerically equal to the charge on node r when unit potential is applied to node s and all other nodes are at zero potential.

In a similar way we can obtain an interpretation of the coefficients of elastance from Eqs. (6.13) to (6.15).   By putting

$$Q_1 = 1 \qquad Q_2 = 0 \qquad Q_3 = 0 \tag{6.38}$$

we obtain

$$V_1 = b_{11} \qquad V_2 = b_{21} \qquad V_3 = b_{31} \tag{6.39}$$

By putting

$$Q_1 = 0 \qquad Q_2 = 1 \qquad Q_3 = 0 \tag{6.40}$$

we obtain

$$V_1 = b_{12} \qquad V_2 = b_{22} \qquad V_3 = b_{32} \tag{6.41}$$

By putting

$$Q_1 = 0 \qquad Q_2 = 0 \qquad Q_3 = 1 \tag{6.42}$$

we obtain

$$V_1 = b_{13} \qquad V_2 = b_{23} \qquad V_3 = b_{33} \tag{6.43}$$

We can summarize the information contained in Eqs. (6.38) to (6.43) by saying that the coefficient of elastance b_{rs} is numerically equal to the potential on node r when node s carries unit charge and all other nodes are uncharged except the central one at zero potential.   Node 0 in fact carries a charge -1 due to the unit charge that has been transferred from it to node s.

Equations (6.10) to (6.12) can be summarized by means of the equation

$$c_{rs} = c_{sr} \tag{6.44}$$

the left- and right-hand sides being numerically equal and opposite to the capacitance of the capacitor in the network for which one plate is attached to node r and the other to node s.   Likewise Eqs. (6.16) to

(6.18) can be summarized by the single equation

$$b_{rs} = b_{sr} \qquad (6.45)$$

Equation (6.44) can now be interpreted by saying that the charge on node r when node s is at unit potential, all other nodes being at zero potential, is the same as the charge on node s when node r is at unit potential, other nodes being at zero potential. Likewise Eq. (6.45) can be interpreted by saying that the potential on node r when node s carries unit charge is the same as the potential on node s when node r carries unit charge, it being understood that all nodes not carrying the unit charge are uncharged except the central node at zero potential; node 0 carries a charge -1. These results constitute what is known as Green's reciprocal theorem for networks of capacitors.

6.3. The Principle of Superposition. The equations that we have developed relating the charges and potentials of the nodes of a network of capacitors are what are known mathematically as linear algebraic equations. No squares of the charges or potentials and no product terms in the charges and potentials are involved. The linearity of the equations relating the charges of the nodes to their potentials is the mathematical expression of a physical fact known as the principle of superposition.

Let us consider the network shown in Fig. 6.1 and make a study of the linear equations expressing the charges on the nodes in terms of the potentials of the nodes. These are Eqs. (6.4) to (6.6). Let us consider the following three circumstances:

1. Let the potential on node 1 be V_1 and the potentials on nodes 2 and 3 be zero. In these circumstances the charges on nodes 1, 2, and 3 are given by the first column on the right-hand side of Eqs. (6.4) to (6.6).

2. Let the potential on node 2 be V_2, and let the potentials on nodes 1 and 3 be zero. In these circumstances the charges on nodes 1, 2, and 3 are given by the second column on the right-hand side of Eqs. (6.4) to (6.6).

3. Let the potential of node 3 be V_3, and let the potentials of nodes 1 and 2 be zero. In these circumstances the charges on nodes 1, 2, and 3 are given by the third column on the right-hand side of Eqs. (6.4) to (6.6).

Now consider a situation in which a potential V_1 is applied to node 1, a potential V_2 to node 2, and a potential V_3 to node 3. In these circumstances the charges on nodes 1, 2, and 3 are given by Eqs. (6.4) to (6.6). These charges are, however, the sums of the charges obtained in the three situations (1), (2), and (3) discussed above. It follows therefore that the charges existing when the potentials of the nodes are (V_1, V_2, V_3) are obtained by superposing the charges in the cases when the potentials are $(V_1,0,0)$, $(0,V_2,0)$ and $(0,0,V_3)$. This is known as the principle of superposition and arises from the linearity of the equations relating the charges and potentials.

The principle of superposition also includes the following more obvious point. If a potential V_1 is applied to node 1 and zero potential to nodes 2 and 3, the charges on nodes 1, 2, and 3 are given by the first column of the right-hand side of Eqs. (6.4) to (6.6); these charges are V_1 times the charges given in Eqs. (6.33) appropriate to the situation in which unit potential is applied to node 1 and zero potential to nodes 2 and 3. It follows therefore that the charges on the nodes when the potentials are $(V_1,0,0)$ can be obtained by superposition of V_1 situations in each of which the potentials of the nodes are $(1,0,0)$. In the same way the charges on the nodes when the potentials are $(0,V_2,0)$ can be obtained by superposition of V_2 situations in each of which the potentials are $(0,1,0)$. Likewise the charges on the nodes when the potentials are $(0,0,V_3)$ can be obtained by superposition of V_3 situations in each of which the potentials on the nodes are $(0,0,1)$.

We thus see that the charges on the nodes when the potentials are (V_1,V_2,V_3) can be obtained by superposition of V_1 situations in which the potentials are $(1,0,0)$, V_2 situations in which the potentials are $(0,1,0)$, and V_3 situations in which the potentials are $(0,0,1)$. In the same way it follows from Eqs. (6.13) to (6.15) that the potentials on nodes 1, 2, and 3 when the charges are (Q_1,Q_2,Q_3) can be obtained by superposition of Q_1 situations in which the charges on nodes 1, 2, and 3 are $(1,0,0)$, Q_2 situations in which the charges are $(0,1,0)$, and Q_3 situations in which the charges are $(0,0,1)$.

6.4. Networks of Capacitors with Input and Output Terminals. It frequently happens that networks are constructed in such a way that only a few of the nodes are easily accessible. In Fig. 6.3 the dashed rectangular line represents a metal box whose potential we take to be the zero of potential. The network contains six nodes marked 0, 1, 2, 3, 4, and 5. Node 0 is connected to the enclosing metal box and is therefore at zero potential. Nodes 1 and 2 are connected through holes in the box to terminals that are accessible exterior to the box. Nodes 3, 4, and 5 are interior to the box and are inaccessible from the outside except by opening the box. We suppose that the network is initially uncharged. A charge can then be transferred from node 0 to node 1 or to node 2 or both. Since nodes 3, 4, and 5 are inaccessible and are initially uncharged, they necessarily remain uncharged.

An arrangement such as that shown in Fig. 6.3 might be used in the following way: A capacitor of capacitance C_L might be connected exterior to the box between nodes 2 and 0. A battery of given voltage might then be connected between nodes 1 and 0, and it might be required to calculate the resulting charge on the capacitor of capacitance C_L. In

these circumstances the battery connected between nodes 1 and 0 is
called a "source," while the capacitor connected externally between
nodes 2 and 0 is called the "load." Node 1 would be called the "input
terminal" of the network, and node 2 the "output terminal." Networks
that have a pair of accessible nodes in addition to the node at zero potential, the inaccessible nodes being uncharged, have some special properties
that we shall now study.

For a network such as that shown in Fig. 6.3 there are coefficients of
capacitance and coefficients of elastance that can be calculated in terms
of the capacitances of the individual capacitors of the network in the

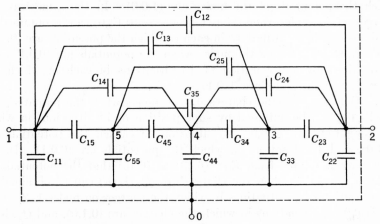

FIG. 6.3. Illustrating a network with accessible nodes (0, 1, and 2) and inaccessible
nodes (3, 4, and 5).

manner already studied. In fact the network shown in Fig. 6.3 is
identical with the network shown in Fig. 6.2. In Fig. 6.2 the network
was drawn so as to exhibit symmetry between nodes 1, 2, 3, 4, and 5.
In Fig. 6.3 the same network has been drawn in such a way as to draw a
distinction between the nodes 0, 1, and 2 now to be regarded as external
nodes and nodes 3, 4, and 5 now to be regarded as uncharged internal
nodes. The equations expressing the potentials of the nodes in terms of
their charges are therefore Eqs. (6.26) to (6.30). If these equations are
solved to express the charges of the nodes in terms of their potentials
we obtain Eqs. (6.19) to (6.23).

The special feature of which we have to take account is that nodes 3, 4,
and 5 are internal nodes and are therefore uncharged. This is expressed
by the equations

$$Q_3 = Q_4 = Q_5 = 0 \tag{6.46}$$

These equations make the left-hand sides of Eqs. (6.21) to (6.23) zero.
These three equations can therefore be solved for the potentials V_3, V_4,

and V_5 of the internal nodes in terms of the potentials V_1 and V_2 of the exterior terminals.   The expressions for V_3, V_4, and V_5 thereby obtained can then be substituted into Eqs. (6.19) and (6.20).   On collecting up the terms involving V_1 and V_2, we obtain equations of the form

$$Q_1 = a_{11}V_1 + a_{12}V_2 \tag{6.47}$$
$$Q_2 = a_{21}V_1 + a_{22}V_2 \tag{6.48}$$

These equations determine the charges Q_1 and Q_2 that must be transferred to the external terminals 1 and 2 from terminal 0 in order to raise these terminals to potentials V_1 and V_2, respectively, above that of terminal 0. In the course of carrying out the algebraic processes described, the coefficients a_{11}, a_{22}, a_{12}, and a_{21} would be determined in terms of the capacitances of the capacitors in the given network.   It would follow from Eq. (6.25) that

$$a_{12} = a_{21} \tag{6.49}$$

and that each is numerically negative.

Instead of discussing the network shown in Fig. 6.3 in terms of Eqs. (6.19) to (6.23), we can also discuss it in terms of Eqs. (6.26) to (6.30). Substituting into these equations from Eqs. (6.46), we see that the third, fourth, and fifth columns on the right-hand sides disappear.   Equations (6.28) to (6.30) then give the potentials V_3, V_4, and V_5 of the internal nodes in terms of the charges Q_1 and Q_2 applied to the exterior terminals. Equations (6.26) and (6.27) give the potentials V_1 and V_2 of the exterior terminals in terms of the charges Q_1 and Q_2 given to these terminals. Because of Eqs. (6.46) these two equations become

$$V_1 = b_{11}Q_1 + b_{12}Q_2 \tag{6.50}$$
$$V_2 = b_{21}Q_1 + b_{22}Q_2 \tag{6.51}$$

and, of course, Eq. (6.31) is still valid.

Equations (6.47) and (6.48) give the charges on the external terminals 1 and 2 in terms of their potentials.   Equations (6.50) and (6.51) give the potentials of the exterior terminals 1 and 2 in terms of their charges. Either pair of equations can be obtained from the other by algebraic solution.   In converting Eqs. (6.19) to (6.23) into Eqs. (6.47) and (6.48), and Eqs. (6.26) to (6.30) into Eqs. (6.50) and (6.51), we have eliminated the potentials of the internal nodes and obtained relations between the charges and potentials of the exterior terminals 1 and 2 only.   We see that these relations are what are described mathematically as linear.

Evaluation of the coefficients in Eqs. (6.47) and (6.48) or, alternatively, in Eqs. (6.50) and (6.51) is likely to be rather tiresome if the network is complicated.   In some cases it is helpful to use the following properties of the coefficients.   Consider the situation that exists when terminal 2 is

connected metallically to terminal 0. This situation is described as
one in which terminal 2 is "short-circuited" to terminal 0. It is represented mathematically by the equation $V_2 = 0$. If terminal 2 is short-
circuited and terminal 1 is raised to unit potential, then Eqs. (6.47) and
(6.48) show that the charges on terminals 1 and 2 are a_{11} and a_{21} respectively. Likewise if terminal 1 is short-circuited to terminal 0 and
terminal 2 is raised to unit potential, then Eqs. (6.47) and (6.48) show
that the charges on terminals 1 and 2 are a_{12} and a_{22} respectively. We
thus see that a_{11} is the charge on terminal 1 when this terminal is raised
to unit potential and terminal 2 is short-circuited to terminal 0. The
coefficient a_{22} is the charge on terminal 2 when this terminal is raised to
unit potential and terminal 1 is short-circuited to terminal 0. The
common value of the coefficients a_{12} and a_{21} is both (1) the charge on
terminal 1 when terminal 2 is raised to unit potential and terminal 1
is short-circuited to terminal 0 and (2) the charge on terminal 2 when
terminal 1 is raised to unit potential and terminal 2 is short-circuited to
terminal 0.

To study the significance of the coefficients in Eqs. (6.50) and (6.51),
it is convenient to consider a situation in which one or the other of the
terminals is uncharged. A terminal that is uncharged has not been
touched by any battery or other charged conductor. It has remained
isolated in space, a situation that is often described by saying that it is
"open-circuited." Let us suppose that terminal 2 is open-circuited and
that a unit charge is given to terminal 1. Then Eqs. (6.50) and (6.51)
show that, in these circumstances, the potentials of terminals 1 and 2
are b_{11} and b_{21} respectively. In the same way, if terminal 1 is open-
circuited and terminal 2 is given a unit charge, Eqs. (6.50) and (6.51)
show that the potentials of terminals 1 and 2 are b_{12} and b_{22} respectively.
We thus see that b_{11} is the potential of terminal 1 when terminal 2 is
open-circuited and unit charge is transferred from terminal 0 to terminal 1.
The coefficient b_{22} is the potential of terminal 2 when terminal 1 is open-
circuited and unit charge is transferred from terminal 0 to terminal 2.
The common value of the coefficients b_{12} and b_{21} is both (1) the voltage of
terminal 1 when this terminal is open-circuited and unit charge is transferred from terminal 0 to terminal 2 and (2) the voltage of terminal 2
when this terminal is open-circuited and a unit charge is transferred
from terminal 0 to terminal 1.

As an example, let us consider the network shown in Fig. 6.4. To
calculate the coefficients b_{11} and b_{21}, let us leave terminal 2 on open circuit
and transfer a unit charge from terminal 0 to terminal 1 as shown in
Fig. 6.5. The network then consists of two capacitors of capacitances
C_1 and C_3 connected in series, and the potential of terminal 2 is the
potential of the node between these two capacitors. The two capacitors

C_1 and C_3 connected in series are equivalent to a single capacitor whose capacitance is the reciprocal of $1/C_1 + 1/C_3$. Hence, with unit charge transferred from terminal 0 to terminal 1, the potential of this terminal is

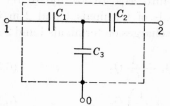

FIG. 6.4. Example of a network with one inaccessible node.

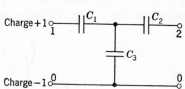

FIG. 6.5. Illustrating calculation of the coefficients b_{11} and b_{21} for the network shown in Fig. 6.4.

$1/C_1 + 1/C_3$. But the potential of terminal 1 when terminal 2 is open-circuited and unit charge is transferred from terminal 0 to terminal 1 is the coefficient b_{11}. Hence

$$b_{11} = \frac{1}{C_1} + \frac{1}{C_3} \qquad (6.52)$$

With terminal 2 on open circuit and capacitors C_1 and C_3 connected in series, a unit charge transferred from terminal 0 to terminal 1 results in a unit charge on capacitor C_3. Hence the potential of the upper plate of capacitor C_3 is $1/C_3$, and this is the potential of terminal 2 if this terminal is open-circuited. But the potential of terminal 2 when this terminal is open-circuited and a unit charge is transferred from terminal 0 to terminal 1 is the coefficient b_{21}. Hence

$$b_{21} = \frac{1}{C_3} \qquad (6.53)$$

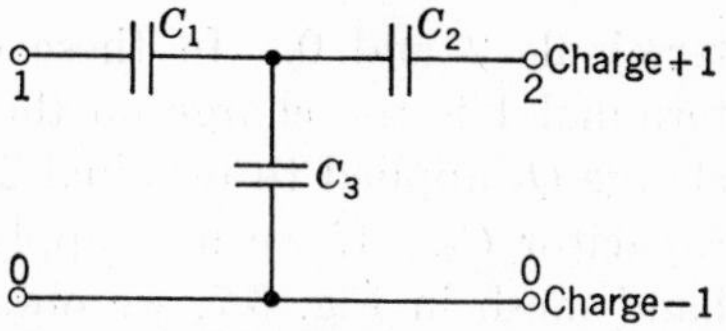

By leaving terminal 1 on open circuit and transferring a unit charge from terminal 0 to terminal 2 as shown in Fig. 6.6, we can derive in the same way the expressions

FIG. 6.6. Illustrating calculation of the coefficients b_{22} and b_{12} for the network shown in Fig. 6.4.

$$b_{22} = \frac{1}{C_2} + \frac{1}{C_3} \qquad (6.54)$$

$$b_{12} = \frac{1}{C_3} \qquad (6.55)$$

To derive Eqs. (6.54) and (6.55) it is not, in fact, necessary to repeat the process involved in the derivation of Eqs. (6.52) and (6.53). From the symmetry of the network we notice that the process of interchanging terminals 1 and 2 is equivalent to the process of interchanging capacitors

C_1 and C_2. Hence Eqs. (6.54) and (6.55) are obtained from Eqs. (6.52) and (6.53) by interchanging subscripts 1 and 2. We notice that this leads to the equality of the coefficients b_{12} and b_{21}, as it should. By substituting from Eqs. (6.52) to (6.55) into Eqs. (6.50) and (6.51) we see that the expressions for the potentials of terminals 1 and 2 in the network shown in Fig. 6.4 in terms of the charges on terminals 1 and 2 are

$$V_1 = \left(\frac{1}{C_1} + \frac{1}{C_2}\right) Q_1 + \frac{1}{C_3} Q_2 \tag{6.56}$$

$$V_2 = \frac{1}{C_3} Q_1 + \left(\frac{1}{C_2} + \frac{1}{C_3}\right) Q_2 \tag{6.57}$$

Equations (6.56) and (6.57) can also be derived as follows. Figure 6.7 shows the network of Fig. 6.4, with a battery of voltage V_1 applied between terminals 1 and 0 and a battery of voltage V_2 applied between

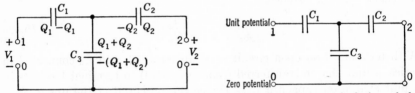

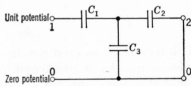

FIG. 6.7. Illustrating derivation of the relations between V_1, V_2, Q_1, and Q_2.

FIG. 6.8. Illustrating calculation of the coefficients a_{11} and a_{21} for the network shown in Fig. 6.4.

terminals 2 and 0. In these circumstances the charge Q_1 applied to terminal 1 is the charge on the left-hand plate of capacitor C_1 and the charge Q_2 applied to terminal 2 is the charge on the right-hand plate of capacitor C_2. If we now apply Kirchhoff's circulation law to the left-hand mesh in Fig. 6.7, we obtain Eq. (6.56), and if we apply it to the right-hand mesh, we obtain Eq. (6.57). In making this derivation it is convenient to circulate round the left-hand mesh in the clockwise sense and the right-hand mesh in the counterclockwise sense.

If, for the network shown in Fig. 6.4, it is desired to express the charges on the terminals in terms of the potentials of the terminals, we can achieve this by solving Eqs. (6.56) and (6.57) for Q_1 and Q_2, thereby obtaining

$$Q_1 = \frac{C_1}{C_1 + C_2 + C_3} [(C_2 + C_3)V_1 - C_2V_2] \tag{6.58}$$

$$Q_2 = \frac{C_2}{C_1 + C_2 + C_3} [-C_1V_1 + (C_1 + C_3)V_2] \tag{6.59}$$

These are the Eqs. (6.47) and (6.48) for the network shown in Fig. 6.4. Alternatively we can arrive at Eqs. (6.58) and (6.59) by direct calculation of the coefficient appearing in Eqs. (6.47) and (6.48) as follows: To calculate the coefficients a_{11} and a_{21}, we short-circuit terminal 2 to terminal 0 in Fig. 6.4 and apply a unit potential to terminal 1 as shown in Fig. 6.8. The charge on the left-hand plate of capacitor C_1 is then a_{11}, and the charge on the right-hand plate of capacitor C_2 is the coefficient a_{21}. With terminals 2 and 0 short-circuited, capacitor C_2 is in parallel with capacitor C_3, and this combination is in series with capacitor C_1. The equivalent capacitance between terminals 1 and 0 in these circumstances is

$$\frac{1}{1/C_1 + 1/(C_2 + C_3)} \tag{6.60}$$

and this can be rewritten as

$$\frac{C_1(C_2 + C_3)}{C_1 + C_2 + C_3} \tag{6.61}$$

With unit potential applied to terminal 1, the charge on terminal 1 is expression (6.61), and hence

$$a_{11} = \frac{C_1(C_2 + C_3)}{C_1 + C_2 + C_3} \tag{6.62}$$

With terminal 2 short-circuited to terminal 0 and unit potential applied to terminal 1, the combined charge on the right-hand plate of capacitor C_2 and the lower plate of capacitor C_3 is the negative of expression (6.60) or (6.61). The fraction of this charge that is on the right-hand plate of capacitor C_2 is $C_2/(C_2 + C_3)$. Hence the charge on the right-hand plate of capacitor C_2 is

$$-\frac{C_2}{C_2 + C_3}\frac{C_1(C_2 + C_3)}{C_1 + C_2 + C_3} \tag{6.63}$$

and this can be rewritten as

$$-\frac{C_1 C_2}{C_1 + C_2 + C_3} \tag{6.64}$$

But this is the charge on terminal 2 when this terminal is short-circuited and a unit potential is applied to terminal 1. Hence,

$$a_{21} = -\frac{C_1 C_2}{C_1 + C_2 + C_3} \tag{6.65}$$

To obtain the coefficients a_{22} and a_{12}, we can interchange terminals 1 and 2 in the above argument as shown in Fig. 6.9, and this is equivalent to interchanging capacitors C_1 and C_2. By interchanging subscripts 1 and 2 in Eqs. (6.62) and (6.65) we derive

$$a_{22} = \frac{C_2(C_1 + C_3)}{C_1 + C_2 + C_3} \tag{6.66}$$

$$a_{12} = -\frac{C_1 C_2}{C_1 + C_2 + C_3} \tag{6.67}$$

We notice that a_{12} is equal to a_{21} and that the common value is negative.

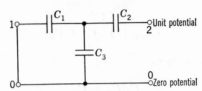

Fig. 6.9. Illustrating calculation of the coefficients a_{22} and a_{12} for the network shown in Fig. 6.4.

By substituting from Eqs. (6.62) and (6.65) to (6.67) into Eqs. (6.47) and (6.48) we derive Eqs. (6.58) and (6.59).

SUMMARIZING EXERCISES

6.1. For a charged network of capacitors, show that the relations between the charges and potentials associated with the nodes are linear algebraic equations. Explain what is meant by the coefficients of capacitance c_{rs} and the coefficients of elastance b_{rs} (a) when $r = s$ and (b) when $r \neq s$. Explain why $c_{rs} = c_{sr}$, and why $b_{rs} = b_{sr}$.

6.2. Give an interpretation of the coefficients of capacitance of a network of capacitors by considering a situation in which all the nodes are at zero potential except one. Likewise, give an interpretation of the coefficients of elastance of a network of capacitors by considering a situation in which the charges associated with all the nodes are zero except two.

6.3. Explain the physical significance of Green's reciprocal theorem for networks of capacitors.

6.4. For a network of capacitors, explain what is meant by the principle of superposition.

6.5. Explain what is meant by a network of capacitors that has input and output terminals. With all capacitors initially uncharged, a charge Q_1 is transferred to the input terminal from the terminal at zero potential and a charge Q_2 is transferred to the output terminal from the terminal at zero potential. The resulting voltage appearing at the input terminal is V_1 and that at the output terminal is V_2. Describe, in terms of certain coefficients, the relations between Q_1, Q_2, V_1, and V_2.

CHAPTER 7

USE OF EQUIVALENT NETWORKS

7.1. Introduction. We have seen that evaluation of the coefficients a_{11}, a_{22}, and a_{12} in Eqs. (6.47) and (6.48) or alternatively of the coefficients b_{11}, b_{22}, and b_{12} in Eqs. (6.50) and (6.51) involves a substantial calculation for a comparatively complicated network such as that shown in Fig. 6.3. There is, however, a substantial advantage accruing from the performance of this calculation. Suppose that, for the network shown in Fig. 6.3, a series of pairs of potentials are applied in succession to terminals 1 and 2 and that the corresponding charges on terminals 1 and 2 have to be calculated. One way of doing this would be to apply Kirchhoff's laws to the network, to eliminate the mathematical variables in which we are not interested, and so to deduce the quantities required. When a new pair of potentials was applied to terminals 1 and 2, we could repeat the whole process from the beginning. After this process had been repeated a number of times, it would become apparent that, although each new pair of potentials presented a new problem, nevertheless there was a close connection between successive calculations. We would then search for a method of solution that avoided starting the problem from the beginning every time the potentials of terminals 1 and 2 were changed. This would lead us to the procedure of calculating for the network the coefficients a_{11}, a_{22}, and a_{12} in Eqs. (6.47) and (6.48). We would then be able to alter the potentials V_1 and V_2 of terminals 1 and 2 in any way and immediately calculate the corresponding charges Q_1 and Q_2. Likewise, if it is the charges on terminals 1 and 2 that are specified and the potentials that have to be calculated, this calculation can easily be repeated for any number of pairs of charges as soon as the coefficients b_{11}, b_{22}, and b_{12} in Eqs. (6.50) and (6.51) have been calculated. Thus the coefficients a_{11}, a_{22}, and a_{12} or, alternatively, the coefficients b_{11}, b_{22}, and b_{12} completely describe the network no matter what charges or potentials may be applied to the external terminals. These coefficients change if the network changes, but they do not alter with changes in the charges and potentials applied externally.

By electrical measurements made externally on the network it is possible to deduce the coefficients a_{11}, a_{22}, and a_{12} or, alternatively, the corresponding coefficients b_{11}, b_{22}, and b_{12}. For example, by putting unit potential on terminal 1 and zero potential on terminals 2 and 0 we see from Eqs. (6.47) and (6.48) that the charges on terminals 1 and 2 under these circumstances are a_{11} and a_{21} (which is equal to a_{12}). Hence, by putting unit potential on terminal 1 and zero potential on terminals 2 and 0 and measuring the charges on terminals 1 and 2, we derive the two coefficients a_{11} and a_{12}. In the same way, by putting unit potential on terminal 2 and zero potential on terminals 1 and 0, we can measure the charge on terminal 2 and derive the coefficient a_{22}. By measuring at the same time the charge on terminal 1, we can verify the fact that a_{12} is equal to a_{21}. By using unit and zero charges on the terminals instead of unit and zero potentials, we can determine the coefficients b_{11}, b_{22}, and b_{12} in accordance with Eqs. (6.50) and (6.51). It is important to notice, however, that when we have determined the three coefficients a_{11}, a_{22}, and a_{12} or, alternatively, the three corresponding coefficients b_{11}, b_{22}, and b_{12}, there is nothing more that we can determine about the network purely from electrostatic measurements made external to the enclosing metal box. There are in fact numerous networks that lead to the same a and b coefficients, and these cannot be distinguished from one another by electrostatic measurements made external to the box.

The fact that there are in general a number of networks having the same a and b coefficients leads to the important concept of equivalent networks. All networks of capacitors enclosed in a metal box equipped with external terminals 0, 1, and 2 are said to be equivalent if they lead to the same a and b coefficients. Equivalent networks cannot be distinguished from one another by means of electrostatic measurements made external to the box.

The concept of equivalent networks is important for the following reason: Suppose that two networks are known to be equivalent in the sense described. Then they have the same a and b coefficients, so that the relations between the potentials and charges of the two exterior terminals are the same for both networks. Let us suppose further that one of the networks is complicated and the other network is simple. Then it follows that, in any discussion of the exterior behavior of the complicated network, we can use instead the simple network.

7.2. The Equivalent T and π Networks. Let us suppose that a complicated network is to be replaced by a simple equivalent network, and let us ask how simple the simple network could be. The complicated network is specified by the three coefficients a_{11}, a_{22}, and a_{12} or, alternatively, by the three corresponding coefficients b_{11}, b_{22}, and b_{12}. Three quantities are thus involved in specifying the exterior behavior of the complicated network. The simple network must therefore possess at least three parameters that can be adjusted to produce the right a and b coefficients. It should therefore be possible, for the complicated network of capacitors, to devise an equivalent simple network involving only three capacitors. Suitable equivalent networks involving three adjustable capacitors are shown in Fig. 7.1. By suitable choice of the capacitances of the capacitors in either of the networks shown in Fig. 7.1 it is possible to produce a network that, as far as external behavior is concerned, is identical with that of a much more complicated network such as that shown in Fig. 6.3. The networks shown in Fig. 7.1 can be redrawn in the form shown in Fig. 7.2. In this form the geometrical configurations of the capacitors suggest the letters T and π. If for a given complicated net-

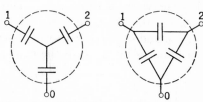

FIG. 7.1. Simple equivalent networks involving three capacitors.

work an equivalent network is formed of the type shown on the left in Fig. 7.2, this is called the equivalent T network for the given network. If on the other hand the equivalent network is formed as shown on the right in Fig. 7.2 this is called the equivalent π network for the given network.

Let us calculate the equivalent T network for a given complicated network. For the complicated network we suppose that the coefficients b_{11}, b_{22}, and b_{12} have been calculated. Now these coefficients, for a network of the type shown on the left-hand side of Fig. 7.2, have already

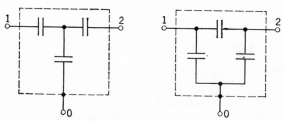

FIG. 7.2. T and π networks.

been calculated in connection with Fig. 6.4 and are given by Eqs. (6.52), (6.54), and (6.55). These equations therefore indicate how the capacitances C_1, C_2, and C_3 for the network shown in Fig. 6.4 must be related to the coefficients b_{11}, b_{22}, and b_{12} of the complicated network if the networks are to be equivalent. By solving Eqs. (6.52), (6.54), and (6.55) for C_1, C_2, and C_3 we obtain

$$C_1 = \frac{1}{b_{11} - b_{12}} \tag{7.1}$$

$$C_2 = \frac{1}{b_{22} - b_{12}} \tag{7.2}$$

$$C_3 = \frac{1}{b_{12}} \tag{7.3}$$

It follows that the network shown in Fig. 7.3 is the equivalent T network of any network of capacitors whose b coefficients are b_{11}, b_{22}, and b_{12}. Application of Kirchhoff's laws to the network shown in Fig. 7.3 leads to Eqs. (6.50) and (6.51).

In the same way it is possible to derive the equivalent π network of a given network of capacitors. This is shown in Fig. 7.4. We suppose that, for the given complicated network of capacitors, the coefficients a_{11}, a_{22}, and a_{12} have been calculated. In terms of these coefficients the capacitances involved in the equivalent π network are as shown in Fig.

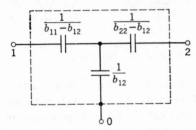

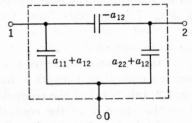

FIG. 7.3. Equivalent T network of a network of capacitors.

FIG. 7.4. Equivalent π network of a network of capacitors.

7.4. This is proved by applying Kirchhoff's conservation law to terminal 1, obtaining

$$Q_1 = (a_{11} + a_{12})(V_1 - 0) + (-a_{12})(V_1 - V_2) \qquad (7.4)$$

and to terminal 2, obtaining

$$Q_2 = (a_{22} + a_{12})(V_2 - 0) + (-a_{12})(V_2 - V_1) \qquad (7.5)$$

These two equations immediately simplify to Eqs. (6.47) and (6.48), thereby showing that the network in Fig. 7.4 has the same a coefficients as the given complicated network. The capacitor of capacitance $-a_{12}$ in Fig. 7.4 in fact has a positive capacitance, since a_{12} is numerically negative.

For any network whose a coefficients have been calculated, the relation between the charges and potentials of the external terminals 1 and 2 is represented mathematically by Eqs. (6.47) and (6.48), and these are also the equations appropriate to the π network shown in Fig. 7.4. Likewise for any network whose b coefficients have been calculated, the relation between the charges and potentials of the external terminals 1 and 2 is represented by Eqs. (6.50) and (6.51), and these are also the equations appropriate to the T network shown in Fig. 7.3. In studying the external properties of the given network, we can use either Eqs. (6.47) and (6.48) or Eqs. (6.50) and (6.51) or use either the equivalent T network shown in Fig. 7.3 or the equivalent π network shown in Fig. 7.4. In each case the same relation is implied between the potentials V_1 and V_2 of terminals 1 and 2 and the corresponding charges Q_1 and Q_2.

7.3. The Thévenin and Norton Equivalent Circuits for Networks of Capacitors. Let us consider a network of capacitors enclosed in a box at zero potential (terminal 0) and having a pair of external terminals 1 and 2. Let us suppose that the a and b coefficients for the network have been calculated. The relation between the charges and potentials of the exterior terminals is then given either by Eqs. (6.47) and (6.48) or by Eqs. (6.50) and (6.51). These relations can be expressed as equivalent networks for the original network as shown either in Fig. 7.3 or in Fig. 7.4. With these equivalent networks any changes can be made in the potentials of terminals 1 and 2 and the corresponding changes in the charges of terminals 1 and 2 are identical with those for the original network. Let us now suppose, however, that we are faced with a simpler problem

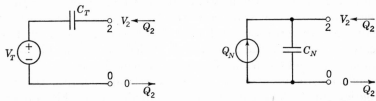

FIG. 7.5. The Thévenin equivalent circuit.   FIG. 7.6. The Norton equivalent circuit.

in which either the charge or the potential of terminal 1 is held fixed and we wish to study under these circumstances what the relation is between the charge and potential on terminal 2. To do this we could replace the given network by the equivalent T network shown in Fig. 7.3 or by the equivalent π network shown in Fig. 7.4. This simpler problem can, however, be solved with the aid of a simpler equivalent network. There are, in fact, two simpler equivalent networks available to describe the relation between the charge and potential of terminal 2 provided that either the charge or the potential of terminal 1 has a fixed value. One of these is shown in Fig. 7.5 and is known as the Thévenin equivalent network, or circuit. The other is shown in Fig. 7.6 and is known as the Norton equivalent network, or circuit.

In each of these equivalent networks the upper terminal on the right-hand side is terminal 2 of the original network, and the lower terminal on the right-hand side is terminal 0 of the original network, that is, the metal box at zero potential. In the Thévenin equivalent circuit there is a capacitor of capacitance C_T, known as the Thévenin capacitance, whose value has to be calculated in terms of the properties of the original network. In the Norton equivalent circuit there is a capacitor of capacitance C_N, known as the Norton capacitance, whose value likewise has to be determined in terms of the properties of the original network.

In the Thévenin equivalent circuit there is a battery of voltage V_T, known as the Thévenin voltage, whose value has to be calculated in terms of the properties of the original network and in terms of the constant charge or voltage maintained at terminal 1. In the Norton equivalent circuit there is a battery that has transferred in the direction of the vertical arrow a charge Q_N, known as the Norton charge, which has to be calculated in terms of the properties of the original network and the constant charge or voltage maintained at terminal 1.

Let us now suppose that, with the given charge or voltage maintained at terminal 1 of the original network, a charge Q_2 is transferred from terminal 0 to terminal 2 of the original network and that as a result the potential of terminal 2 is V_2. We need to calculate for the original network the way in which V_2 varies with Q_2. It is a fact that this calculation for the original network can equally well be made for the network shown in Fig. 7.5 or for the network shown in Fig. 7.6 provided that the elements in these equivalent networks have been properly evaluated. We now have to verify the truth of this statement and find out how to evaluate V_T and C_T in the Thévenin equivalent circuit and likewise how to evaluate Q_N and C_N in the Norton equivalent circuit.

To begin with let us write down the relation between Q_2 and V_2 appropriate to the Thévenin equivalent circuit. From Fig. 7.5 we see that the charge Q_2 applied to terminal 2 appears on the right-hand plate of capacitor C_T, and consequently there is a charge $-Q_2$ on the left-hand plate. We also notice that the excess of the voltage of the right-hand plate over the left-hand plate is the voltage V_2 of terminal 2 less the Thévenin voltage V_T. Thus the voltage developed across the capacitor C_T evaluates to $V_2 - V_T$, and the corresponding charge is Q_2. Hence

$$V_2 - V_T = \frac{Q_2}{C_T} \tag{7.6}$$

This is the relation between Q_2 and V_2 indicated by the Thévenin equivalent circuit. Let us also write down the relation between Q_2 and V_2 corresponding to the Norton equivalent circuit. In Fig. 7.6 the excess of the voltage of the upper plate of the capacitor C_N over that of the lower plate is V_2. Moreover the charge applied to the upper plate is the sum of the charge Q_2 applied to terminal 2 and the charge Q_N supplied by the Norton battery. Hence the charge on the capacitor C_N is $Q_2 + Q_N$, and the corresponding voltage is V_2, so that

$$Q_2 + Q_N = C_N V_2 \tag{7.7}$$

This is the relation between Q_2 and V_2 appropriate to the Norton equivalent circuit.

Now let us inquire what the relation between Q_2 and V_2 is for the original network.   Two cases arise according as the charge Q_1 on terminal 1 is kept constant as the relation between Q_2 and V_2 is varied, or the voltage V_1 of terminal 1 is kept constant as the relation between Q_2 and V_2 is varied.   Let us first consider the case in which Q_1 is kept constant.   Assuming that the b coefficients of the network have been calculated, the relation between Q_2 and V_2 for a given constant value of Q_1 is given by Eq. (6.51).   This equation can be rewritten in either of the forms

$$V_2 - b_{21}Q_1 = \frac{Q_2}{1/b_{22}} \tag{7.8}$$

$$Q_2 + \frac{b_{21}}{b_{22}} Q_1 = \frac{1}{b_{22}} V_2 \tag{7.9}$$

These rearrangements of Eq. (6.51) have been chosen so as to put this equation as nearly as possible in the forms (7.6) and (7.7) respectively. By comparing Eq. (7.6) with Eq. (7.8) we see that they are the same equation provided that

$$V_T = b_{21}Q_1 \tag{7.10}$$

$$C_T = \frac{1}{b_{22}} \tag{7.11}$$

By comparing Eq. (7.7) with Eq. (7.9) we see that the two equations are identical provided that

$$Q_N = \frac{b_{21}}{b_{22}} Q_1 \tag{7.12}$$

$$C_N = \frac{1}{b_{22}} \tag{7.13}$$

It follows that, for a given charge Q_1 applied to terminal 1 of the original network, the relation (6.51) between Q_2 and V_2 is the same as the relation (7.6) for the Thévenin equivalent circuit provided that the Thévenin voltage V_T is given by Eq. (7.10) and the Thévenin capacitance C_T is given by Eq. (7.11).   It likewise follows that the relation (6.51) between Q_2 and V_2 is identical with the relation (7.7) for the Norton equivalent circuit provided that the Norton charge Q_N is given by Eq. (7.12) and the Norton capacitance C_N is given by Eq. (7.13).   We have thus proved the validity of the Thévenin and Norton equivalent circuits for the case when the charge Q_1 on terminal 1 of the original network is held constant. Moreover we have established formulas for the elements in these equivalent circuits in terms of the b coefficients of the original network and the constant charge Q_1 applied to terminal 1 of the original network.

Let us now consider the case in which it is the potential V_1 of terminal 1 in the original network that is held constant.   Assuming that the a coefficients of the original network have been calculated, the relation between Q_2 and V_2 when V_1 is held constant is given by Eq. (6.48). This equation can be rearranged in either of the forms

$$V_2 - \left(-\frac{a_{21}}{a_{22}} V_1 \right) = \frac{Q_2}{a_{22}} \tag{7.14}$$

$$Q_2 + (-a_{21}V_1) = a_{22}V_2 \tag{7.15}$$

These two rearrangements were chosen so as to bring Eq. (6.48) into the forms of Eqs. (7.6) and (7.7) respectively. By comparing Eq. (7.6) with Eq. (7.14) we see that they are identical provided that

$$V_T = -\frac{a_{21}}{a_{22}} V_1 \tag{7.16}$$

$$C_T = a_{22} \tag{7.17}$$

Likewise by comparing Eq. (7.7) with Eq. (7.15) we see that they are identical provided that

$$Q_N = -a_{21}V_1 \tag{7.18}$$
$$C_N = a_{22} \tag{7.19}$$

Thus, provided the voltage V_1 of terminal 1 of the original network is held constant, the relation (6.48) between Q_2 and V_2 is identical with the relation (7.6) for the Thévenin equivalent circuit provided that the Thévenin voltage V_T is given by Eq. (7.16) and the Thévenin capacitance C_T is given by Eq. (7.17). Likewise the relation (6.48) between Q_2 and V_2 is identical with the corresponding relation (7.7) for the Norton equivalent circuit provided that the Norton charge Q_N is given by Eq. (7.18) and the Norton capacitance C_N is given by Eq. (7.19). We have thus established the validity of the Thévenin and Norton equivalent circuits for the case when the voltage V_1 of terminal 1 of the original network is held constant. Moreover we have obtained expressions for the elements in the Thévenin and Norton equivalent circuits in terms of the a coefficients of the original network and the constant voltage V_1 maintained at terminal 1.

7.4. Evaluation of the Elements in Thévenin and Norton Equivalent Circuits. If the b coefficients of the original network have been calculated, then the values of V_T and C_T in the Thévenin equivalent circuit and the values of Q_N and C_N in the Norton equivalent circuit are given by Eqs. (7.10) to (7.13) in the case when it is the charge Q_1 on terminal 1 of the original network that is kept constant. Likewise if the a coefficients of the original network have been calculated, then the values of V_T, C_T, Q_N, and C_N in the Thévenin and Norton equivalent circuits are given by Eqs. (7.16) to (7.19) if it is the voltage V_1 on terminal 1 of the original network that is kept constant. If, however, the a and b coefficients of the original network have not been calculated, then there is another method for evaluating V_T, C_T, Q_N, and C_N that may be more convenient.

For the original network let us apply to terminal 1 the given charge Q_1, or alternatively the given voltage V_1, and let us leave terminal 2 on open circuit. Let us calculate the voltage V_2 of terminal 2 in these circumstances. To do this we shall use the Thévenin equivalent circuit illustrated in Fig. 7.5. With terminal 2 on open circuit, no charge is conveyed to terminal 2, and consequently there is no charge on the right-hand plate of capacitor C_T. This capacitor is therefore uncharged, and so there is no difference of potential between its plates. In these circumstances the voltage of terminal 2 is simply the Thévenin voltage V_T. We have thus shown that the Thévenin voltage V_T is the potential of terminal 2 when this terminal is left on open circuit. We therefore arrive at the following procedure for calculating the Thévenin voltage V_T: Using the original network, leave terminal 2 on open circuit and apply to terminal 1 either the given charge Q_1 or alternatively the given voltage V_1. For these circumstances calculate the voltage of terminal 2. This is then the Thévenin voltage V_T to be used in the Thévenin equivalent circuit of Fig. 7.5.

A similar procedure can be devised for calculating the Norton charge Q_N appropriate to the Norton equivalent circuit illustrated in Fig. 7.6. For the original network let us apply to terminal 1 the given charge Q_1, or alternatively the given voltage V_1, and let us short-circuit terminal 2 to terminal 0. In these circumstances a charge leaves terminal 2 and passes through the short circuit to terminal 0. Let us calculate this charge using the Norton equivalent circuit shown in Fig. 7.6. With terminal 2 connected metallically to terminal 0 in Fig. 7.6 transfer of the charge Q_N in the direction of the vertical arrow results in an equal charge Q_N leaving terminal 2 and passing through the short circuit to terminal 0. The charge that leaves terminal 2 when this terminal is short-circuited to terminal 0 is therefore the Norton charge Q_N. We therefore arrive at the following procedure for calculating the Norton charge Q_N: Using the original network, short-circuit terminal 2 to terminal 0 and then apply to terminal 1 either the given charge Q_1 or alternatively the given voltage V_1. Calculate the resulting charge leaving terminal 2 and passing through the short circuit to terminal 0. This charge is the Norton charge Q_N to be used in the Norton equivalent circuit illustrated in Fig. 7.6.

Let us now turn our attention to evaluation of C_T and C_N. From Eqs. (7.10) and (7.16) we observe that, if the charge Q_1, or alternatively the voltage V_1, applied to terminal 1 is reduced to zero, so also is the Thévenin voltage V_T. In other words if no source is applied to terminal 1 of the original network, then the Thévenin voltage V_T in Fig. 7.5 is to be short-circuited. Under these circumstances the Thévenin capacitance C_T is connected directly between terminals 2 and 0. It follows that the Thévenin capacitance C_T is the equivalent capacitance between terminals 2 and 0 when no source is applied between terminals 1 and 0 of the original network. Thus, instead of using either Eq. (7.11) or (7.17) to calculate the Thévenin capacitance C_T, we can use the following procedure: With no source applied between terminals 1 and 0, we evaluate the equivalent capacitance between terminals 2 and 0. This capacitance is then the Thévenin capacitance C_T to be used in the Thévenin equivalent circuit illustrated in Fig. 7.5.

In the procedure just described for calculating the Thévenin capacitance C_T it is important to understand what is implied by the statement that no source is applied between terminals 1 and 0 of the original network. If we are studying the relation between Q_2 and V_2 under circumstances when it is the charge Q_1 applied to terminal 1 of the original network that is kept constant, then no source implies that Q_1 is zero. This means that terminal 1 is left on open circuit and is uncharged. On the other hand if we are studying the relation between Q_2 and V_2 under circumstances when it is the voltage V_1 applied to terminal 1 of the original network that is kept constant, then no source implies that V_1 is zero. This means that terminal 1 is short-circuited to terminal 0. Thus if the Thévenin equivalent circuit illustrated in Fig. 7.5 is to describe the relation between Q_2 and V_2 under circumstances when Q_1 is kept constant, then the Thévenin capacitance C_T is the equivalent capacitance between terminals 2 and 0 when terminal 1 is left on *open circuit*. But if the Thévenin equivalent circuit of Fig. 7.5 is to describe the relation between Q_2 and V_2 under circumstances when V_1 is kept constant, then the Thévenin capacitance C_T is the equivalent capacitance between terminals 2 and 0 when terminal 1 is *short-circuited* to terminal 0. These two different values for the Thévenin capacitance C_T can, of course, also be calculated from the two different formulas (7.11) and (7.17).

Again we observe from Eqs. (7.12) and (7.18) that, if the fixed charge Q_1, or alternatively the fixed voltage V_1, applied to terminal 1 of the original network is reduced to zero, so also is the Norton charge Q_N to be used in the Norton equivalent circuit illustrated in Fig. 7.6. If Q_N in Fig. 7.6 is zero, this means that no charge is transferred by the source. This means further that the source is disconnected, or in other words that it is open-circuited. The Norton equivalent circuit then simply consists of the capacitor of capacitance C_N connected between terminals 2 and 0. It follows that the Norton capacitance C_N is the equivalent capacitance between terminals 2 and 0 when no source is applied at terminal 1 of the original network. Thus, instead of using either Eq.

(7.13) or (7.19) to calculate the Norton capacitance C_N, we can use the following procedure: When no source is applied at terminal 1, we calculate the equivalent capacitance between terminals 2 and 0. This capacitance is then the Norton capacitance C_N to be used in the Norton equivalent circuit illustrated in Fig. 7.6.

It should be noticed that the procedure just described for calculating C_N is in fact identical with the corresponding procedure previously described for calculating C_T. It follows that the Thévenin and Norton capacitances are identical in value. This can be verified by comparing Eq. (7.11) with Eq. (7.13) or Eq. (7.17) with Eq. (7.19).

7.5. Relations between the Thévenin and Norton Equivalent Circuits. We have just drawn attention to the fact that the Thévenin capacitance C_T is, in fact, identical with the Norton capacitance C_N. This is not the only simple relation that exists between the Thévenin and Norton equivalent circuits. A more complete statement is made by the equations

$$C_T = C_N = \frac{Q_N}{V_T} \tag{7.20}$$

the validity of which we shall now investigate. If desired, the truth of Eqs. (7.20) can be established from Eqs. (7.10) to (7.13) or alternatively from Eqs. (7.16) to (7.19). It is merely a matter of substituting into Eqs. (7.20) the appropriate expressions for V_T, C_T, Q_N, and C_N. The truth of Eqs. (7.20) can, however, be derived without explicit reference to the a and b coefficients of the original network.

We have seen that removal of the source from terminal 1 of the original network makes V_T zero in Fig. 7.5 and Q_N zero in Fig. 7.6. In these circumstances C_T is the equivalent capacitance between terminals 2 and 0 in Fig. 7.5 while C_N is the same thing in Fig. 7.6, and this establishes the equality of the two capacitances.

To establish the second equality in Eqs. (7.20) we remember that the Thévenin voltage V_T is the voltage of terminal 2 when left on open circuit. Let us use the Norton equivalent circuit to calculate the voltage of terminal 2 when left on open circuit. If terminal 2 in Fig. 7.6 is on open circuit, it acquires no charge when the source is connected to terminal 1 of the original network, so that Q_2 is zero. It follows therefore that V_2 in Fig. 7.6 is identical with V_T when Q_2 is zero. Hence V_T is the voltage across the Norton capacitance C_N when this capacitor is charged only by the Norton charge Q_N. Hence C_N is the ratio of Q_N to V_T, and this is the statement made in the second equality in Eqs. (7.20). Thus both the Thévenin and Norton capacitances are equal to the ratio of the Norton charge to the Thévenin voltage.

Equations (7.20) imply that, among the four quantities V_T, C_T, Q_N, and C_N, there are two relations. It follows therefore that, in calculating the elements in the Thévenin and Norton equivalent circuits, there is necessity only to evaluate either C_T or C_N and either V_T or Q_N. The other two quantities can then be derived from Eqs. (7.20).

The significance of the relations (7.20) and also of the Eqs. (7.6) and (7.7) relating Q_2 to V_2 for the Thévenin and Norton equivalent circuits is summarized in Fig. 7.7. In this diagram the sloping straight line is a plot of the way in which the charge Q_2 communicated to terminal 2 varies with the voltage of terminal 2 when a source of given voltage or charge is maintained at terminal 1. The intercepts on the voltage and charge axes in Fig. 7.7 are marked as V_T and Q_N, while the slope of the line has the common value of C_T and C_N. If the equation of the sloping straight line in Fig. 7.7 is written down in accordance with standard formulas in analytical geometry, we arrive at either Eq. (7.6) or (7.7). Thus the sloping straight line in Fig. 7.7 describes the relation between V_2 and Q_2 involved in either the Thévenin or Norton equivalent circuit. In particular we verify from Fig. 7.7 that

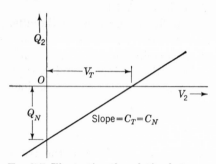

FIG. 7.7. Illustrating the relation between the charge and the voltage at the terminals of the Thévenin and Norton equivalent circuits shown in Figs. 7.5 and 7.6.

V_T is the value of V_2 when $Q_2 = 0$, that is, when terminal 2 is on open circuit. Likewise we verify from Fig. 7.7 that Q_N is the negative of the value of Q_2 for which $V_2 = 0$, and this means that Q_N is the charge that leaves terminal 2 when this terminal is short-circuited to terminal 0 and the given source is applied at terminal 1. In Fig. 7.7 the relations (7.20) simply express an obvious geometrical property of the triangle formed by the sloping straight line with the axes of coordinates.

7.6. Thévenin and Norton Equivalent Circuits for Networks of Capacitors Having Many Sources. In discussing the Thévenin and Norton equivalent circuits we have considered a network of capacitors to which is applied only one source, namely, that between terminals 1 and 0. The Thévenin and Norton equivalent circuits are, however, applicable when many sources are connected into the network, some of them having constant voltage and some constant charge. Let us therefore consider a network, such as that shown in Fig. 6.2, to some nodes of which are applied fixed charges, and to other nodes of which are applied fixed potentials. In particular let node 0 be maintained at zero potential. Let us suppose that one particular node, which we will take as node 2, is singled out for special treatment. To this node we shall apply a variable charge Q_2 and calculate the corresponding potential V_2, all other nodes being maintained at either a constant charge or a constant potential. In discussing this situation it is necessary to write down equations for the network from Kirchhoff's laws and to eliminate mathematical variables from them until we arrive at a linear equation relating Q_2, V_2, and the fixed charges or voltages of the sources. This linear relation between Q_2 and V_2 can be represented graphically as shown in Fig. 7.7 or as an equivalent circuit as shown in Fig. 7.5 or 7.6 and this establishes the applicability of the Thévenin and Norton equivalent circuits to this more complicated situation.

We still deduce from Fig. 7.5 that the Thévenin voltage V_T is the voltage of terminal 2 when on open circuit. Likewise we still deduce from Fig. 7.6 that the Norton charge Q_N is the charge that leaves terminal 2 when this terminal is short-circuited to terminal 0. Furthermore it still remains true from Figs. 7.5 and 7.6 that C_T and C_N are each equal to the equivalent capacitance between terminals 2 and 0 when all sources are removed. Removal of the sources requires that we short-circuit the constant-voltage sources and open-circuit the constant-charge sources.

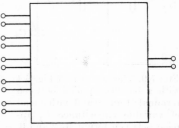

FIG. 7.8. Illustrating a network in which many nodes are accessible through exterior terminals.

Relations (7.20) are still true, so that from the values of V_T and C_T the values of Q_N and C_N could immediately be derived or vice versa. In this way we are able to apply the Thévenin and Norton equivalent circuits shown in Figs. 7.5 and 7.6 to a situation that we shall illustrate with the aid of Fig. 7.8.

Suppose that we have a network of capacitors and that some, but not necessarily all, of the nodes are accessible through terminals as shown in Fig. 7.8. Suppose that the terminals are arranged in pairs so as to be convenient for transferring charge from one terminal to another or for maintaining a difference of potential between two terminals of a pair. One pair of terminals is to be treated in a special way, and this has been drawn on the right in Fig. 7.8. We are interested in transferring a charge Q_2 between this pair of terminals and calculating the corresponding voltage V_2 between them. Moreover we are interested in having Q_2 take a series of values and in calculating the charge-voltage relationship for the right-hand pair of terminals in Fig. 7.8. This calculation is to be made for certain specified conditions at the left-hand pairs of terminals. At each pair of terminals on the left we shall maintain constant either the voltage between the pair of terminals or alternatively the amount of charge transferred between the pair of terminals. From what has been said it follows that the relation between the charge Q_2 and the voltage V_2 at the right-hand terminals in Fig. 7.8 can be calculated by replacing the entire network, together with the sources applied to the left-hand terminals in Fig. 7.8, by a Thévenin equivalent circuit as shown in Fig. 7.5 or by a Norton equivalent circuit as shown in Fig. 7.6. Moreover the Thévenin voltage V_T required in Fig. 7.5 is the voltage appearing at the right-hand terminals of Fig. 7.8 when these terminals are left on open circuit. Likewise the Norton charge Q_N required in Fig. 7.6 is the charge that leaves the positive terminal on the right-hand side of Fig. 7.8 and enters the negative terminal when these terminals are short-circuited. The

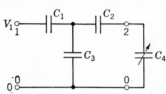

FIG. 7.9. The network of Fig. 6.4 with a battery applied between terminals 1 and 0 and with a load of variable capacitance C_4 applied between terminals 2 and 0.

ratio of the Norton charge Q_N to the Thévenin voltage V_T gives the Thévenin capacitance C_T and the Norton capacitance C_N in accordance with Eqs. (7.20). Alternatively the common value of C_T and C_N can be derived by calculating the equivalent capacitance across the terminals on the right-hand side of Fig. 7.8 when the sources applied to the left-hand terminals in Fig. 7.8 are removed; removal of the sources on the left-hand side of Fig. 7.8 implies short-circuiting each pair of terminals to which a constant-voltage source is applied and open-circuiting each pair of terminals for which the transferred charge is kept constant.

7.7. Application of the Thévenin and Norton Equivalent Circuits. The most straightforward application of a Thévenin or Norton equivalent circuit occurs when a network such as that shown in Fig. 6.4 has a battery connected between terminals 1 and 0 and a load capacitor of capacitance C_4 between terminals 2 and 0 as shown in Fig. 7.9. Under these circumstances the battery charges the load capacitor C_4 through the network and we are interested in calculating the resulting charge and voltage on the load capacitor. Suppose that the load capacitor has a variable capacitance and that we are interested in seeing how the charge and voltage of the load capacitor vary with its capacitance. Then it is convenient to replace the network shown in Fig. 6.4 together with the source applied between terminals 1 and 0 with a Thévenin or Norton equivalent circuit, as shown in Fig. 7.10 or 7.11 respectively. Instead of applying the load capacitor of variable capacitance C_4 to the original network and source as shown in Fig. 7.9, we apply it to the equivalent Thévenin circuit as shown in Fig. 7.10 or alternatively to the equivalent Norton circuit as shown in Fig. 7.11. From the network shown in Fig. 7.10 it is easy to calculate the charge and voltage on the variable capacitor C_4 provided that the Thévenin voltage V_T and the Thévenin capacitance C_T have been evaluated. It is equally simple to calculate the charge and voltage on the variable capacitance C_4 from the network shown in Fig. 7.11 provided that the Norton charge Q_N and the Norton capacitance C_N have previously been evaluated.

For the network shown in Fig. 6.4 we have already calculated the a and b coefficients; the a coefficients are given by Eqs. (6.62) and (6.65) to (6.67) while the b coefficients are given by Eqs. (6.52) to (6.55). We could therefore calculate the elements in the equivalent Thévenin circuit in Fig. 7.10 and in the equivalent Norton circuit shown in Fig. 7.11 by substituting these a and b coefficients either into Eqs. (7.10) to (7.13) or into Eqs. (7.16) to (7.19) according as it is the charge or the voltage that is

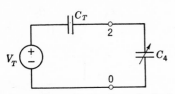

FIG. 7.10. Thévenin circuit equivalent to the network of Fig. 7.9.

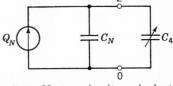

FIG. 7.11. Norton circuit equivalent to the network of Fig. 7.9.

to be kept constant at terminal 1. It is more common, however, to meet a situation in which we need to calculate the elements either in the equivalent Thévenin circuit shown in Fig. 7.10 or in the equivalent Norton circuit shown in Fig. 7.11 under circumstances when the a and b coefficients of the given network have not been calculated and are not specifically required. We can then proceed in the manner now to be described.

To calculate V_T and C_T or alternatively Q_N and C_N, it is necessary to decide whether it is the voltage of terminal 1 that is kept constant as the load capacitor C_4 is varied or the charge on terminal 1 that is kept constant as the load capacitor C_4 is varied. Let us suppose that it is the voltage on terminal 1 that is kept constant and that the constant value is V_1. Then the network of Fig. 6.4 together with the source applied at terminal 1 and the load applied at terminal 2 forms the complete network shown in Fig. 7.9, and we wish to calculate the elements of the equivalent circuit shown in Fig. 7.10 or alternatively of the equivalent circuit shown in Fig. 7.11.

First let us calculate the common value of C_T in Fig. 7.10 and C_N in Fig. 7.11. Since it is the voltage of terminal 1 that is to be kept constant as the load C_4 varies, we short-circuit terminal 1 to terminal 0, thereby forming the network shown in Fig. 7.12. The common value of C_T and C_N is the equivalent capacitance between terminals 2 and 0 for the network shown in Fig. 7.12. Since the capacitor C_1 is in parallel with the capacitor C_3 and this combination is in series with capacitor C_2, we derive

$$C_T = C_N = \frac{1}{1/C_2 + 1/(C_1 + C_3)} \qquad (7.21)$$

and this simplifies to

$$C_T = C_N = \frac{C_2(C_1 + C_3)}{C_1 + C_2 + C_3} \qquad (7.22)$$

Now let us calculate the Thévenin voltage V_T for the arrangement shown in Fig. 7.9. The Thévenin voltage is the voltage of terminal 2 when left on open circuit. It is therefore the voltage of terminal 2 in the network shown in Fig. 7.13. For the network shown in Fig. 7.13 terminal

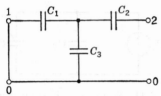

FIG. 7.12. Network for calculating the Thévenin and Norton capacitances for the arrangement shown in Fig. 7.9.

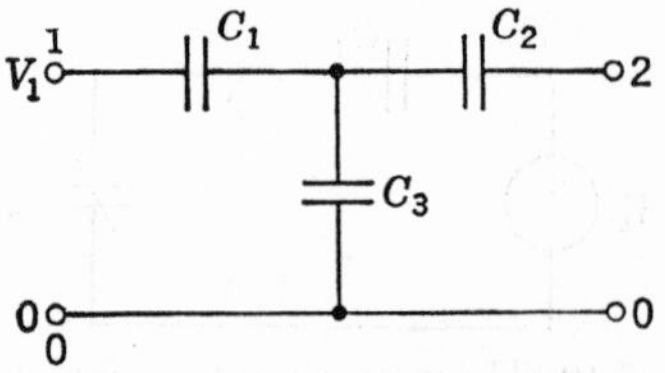

FIG. 7.13. Network for calculating the Thévenin voltage for the arrangement shown in Fig. 7.9.

2 is insulated, and consequently no charge is carried by the right-hand plate of capacitor C_2. The same is therefore true for the left-hand plate, and there is no difference of potential between the plates of this capacitor. The network therefore simply consists of capacitor C_1 in series with capacitor C_3, and the required Thévenin voltage is the voltage on the node between capacitor C_1 and capacitor C_3. Now the voltage V_1 divides between the two capacitors C_1 and C_3 connected in series inversely as their capacitances. Hence the voltage across the capacitor C_3 is the fraction $C_1/(C_1 + C_3)$ of the voltage across the pair of capacitors. It follows that the required Thévenin voltage is

$$V_T = \frac{C_1}{C_1 + C_3} V_1 \qquad (7.23)$$

We can therefore calculate the charge and voltage on the variable load capacitor C_4 in Fig. 7.9 by using the circuit shown in Fig. 7.10 with the value (7.23) for V_T and the value (7.22) for C_T.

If alternatively it is desired to use the Norton equivalent circuit shown in Fig. 7.11, then it is necessary to calculate Q_N. Since we have already calculated the Thévenin voltage V_T and the Thévenin capacitance C_T, the Norton charge Q_N may be calculated, in accordance with Eqs. (7.20), by multiplying expression (7.22) by expression (7.23). However, if we had decided initially to use the Norton equivalent circuit rather than the

Thévenin equivalent circuit, we would be interested in making a direct calculation of the Norton charge Q_N. This we would do as follows: The

Norton charge is the charge that leaves terminal 2 when this terminal is short-circuited to terminal 0. It is therefore the negative of the charge on the right-hand plate of capacitor C_2 in the network shown in Fig. 7.14. The Norton charge Q_N is therefore the charge of the left-hand plate of capacitor C_2 in Fig. 7.14. The network in Fig. 7.14 involves two capacitors of capacitances C_2 and C_3 connected

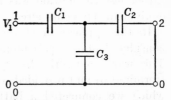

FIG. 7.14. Network for calculating the Norton charge for the arrangement shown in Fig. 7.9.

in parallel, and this pair is connected in series with the capacitor of capacitance C_1. The equivalent capacitance between terminals 1 and 0 is therefore

$$\frac{1}{1/C_1 + 1/(C_2 + C_3)} \qquad (7.24)$$

and this simplifies to

$$\frac{C_1(C_2 + C_3)}{C_1 + C_2 + C_3} \qquad (7.25)$$

The charge on the left-hand plate of capacitor C_1 is therefore

$$\frac{C_1(C_2 + C_3)}{C_1 + C_2 + C_3} V_1 \qquad (7.26)$$

and this charge divides between the left-hand plate of capacitor C_2 and the upper plate of capacitor C_3 in the ratio C_2 to C_3. The charge on the left-hand plate of capacitor C_2 is therefore

$$\frac{C_2}{C_2 + C_3} \frac{C_1(C_2 + C_3)}{C_1 + C_2 + C_3} V_1 \qquad (7.27)$$

Since this is the required Norton charge, we deduce that

$$Q_N = \frac{C_1 C_2}{C_1 + C_2 + C_3} V_1 \qquad (7.28)$$

We notice that this is, in fact, the product of expressions (7.22) and (7.23), as it should be in accordance with Eqs. (7.20). We can therefore calculate the charge and voltage on the variable load capacitor of capacitance C_4 in the arrangement shown in Fig. 7.9 by using the Norton equivalent circuit shown in Fig. 7.11, using the value (7.28) for Q_N and the value (7.22) for C_N.

In handling the arrangement shown in Fig. 7.9 it is a matter of choice whether we use the equivalent Thévenin circuit shown in Fig. 7.10 or the equivalent Norton circuit shown in Fig. 7.11. In this particular case rather less calculation was involved in evaluating the elements for the equivalent Thévenin circuit.

In the application of the Thévenin and Norton equivalent circuits considered above we commenced with the network shown in Fig. 6.4. This was a network already enclosed in a metal box at zero potential (terminal 0) and provided with two other external terminals 1 and 2, to which we connected a battery and a load capacitor. Thévenin and Norton equivalent circuits can, however, be applied in other circumstances. Suppose, for example, we were given the network shown in

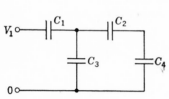

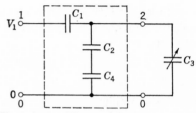

FIG. 7.15. Illustrating a network for which Thévenin and Norton equivalent circuits are derived.

FIG. 7.16. Illustrating the network shown in Fig. 7.15 redrawn so as to make the capacitor C_3 a load capacitor.

Fig. 7.15 and asked to calculate the charge and voltage on the capacitor C_4 for a series of values of this capacitance, with a fixed voltage V_1 applied between the terminals on the left. We could immediately reduce this problem to the one already solved by picturing the capacitors C_1, C_2, and C_3 as enclosed in a box, with capacitor C_4 as a load capacitor. This illustrates the fact that it is possible to apply the Thévenin and Norton equivalent circuits in the following way: Suppose that we have any network of capacitors energized by sources of constant voltage or constant charge connected to the network in specified ways. Now select any capacitor of the network and suppose that we are interested in calculating the charge and voltage on this capacitor for various values of its capacitance. This selected capacitor can then be regarded as a load capacitor, and the rest of the network, together with its sources, can be replaced by an equivalent Thévenin or Norton circuit.

As an example, let us suppose that the network of capacitors is that shown in Fig. 7.15 and that to it is applied a voltage V_1 as indicated. Let us further suppose that the selected capacitor is C_3 and that we are interested in calculating the charge and voltage of this capacitor for various values of the capacitance C_3, the voltage V_1 remaining constant. By redrawing the network as shown in Fig. 7.16 we see that the capacitors C_1, C_2, and C_4 can be regarded as in a box with external terminals 0, 1, and 2.   Between terminals 1 and 0 is applied the constant voltage V_1, and between terminals 2 and 0 is connected the variable load capacitor C_3. The network shown in Fig. 7.16 can therefore be reduced to the Thévenin form shown in Fig. 7.17 or to the Norton form shown in Fig. 7.18 according to preference.   The capacitances C_T and C_N are the equivalent capacitances across the right-hand terminals in the network shown in Fig. 7.19. It follows that

$$C_T = C_N = C_1 + \frac{1}{1/C_2 + 1/C_4} \qquad (7.29)$$

The Thévenin voltage V_T to be used in Fig. 7.17 is calculated from the network shown in Fig. 7.20.   The Thévenin voltage is the excess of volt-

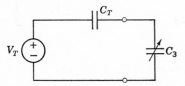

Fig. 7.17. Equivalent Thévenin circuit for the arrangement shown in Fig. 7.16.

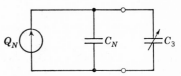

Fig. 7.18. Equivalent Norton circuit for the arrangement shown in Fig. 7.16.

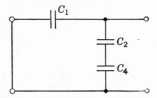

Fig. 7.19. Network for calculating the Thévenin and Norton capacitances for the arrangement shown in Fig. 7.16.

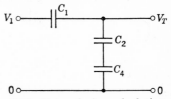

Fig. 7.20. Network for calculating the Thévenin voltage for the arrangement shown in Fig. 7.16.

age of the upper right-hand terminal of the network shown in Fig. 7.20 over that of the lower right-hand terminal and is therefore

$$V_T = \frac{C_1}{C_1 + \dfrac{1}{1/C_2 + 1/C_4}} V_1 \qquad (7.30)$$

The network shown in Fig. 7.16 is therefore equivalent to that shown in Fig. 7.17 provided that the value of V_T is given by Eq. (7.30) and the value of C_T by Eq. (7.29).   If alternatively we wish to use the Norton equivalent circuit shown in Fig. 7.18, then we have to calculate the Norton charge Q_N.   This is the charge that moves down the short circuit on the right of the network shown in Fig. 7.21 when the voltage V_1 is applied at the left. The Norton charge is therefore simply the charge on the left-hand plate of the capacitor C_1 in Fig. 7.21 and is therefore

$$Q_N = C_1 V_1 \tag{7.31}$$

The arrangment shown in Fig. 7.16 is therefore equivalent to the circuit shown in Fig. 7.18 provided that Q_N has the value given by Eq. (7.31) and C_N the value given by Eq. (7.29).

Let us now return to the network shown in Fig. 7.15 and select the capacitor C_2 instead of the capacitor C_3; we want to know the charge and

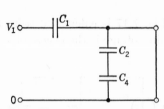

FIG. 7.21. Network for calculating the Norton charge Q_N for the arrangement shown in Fig. 7.16.

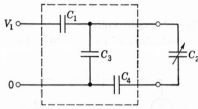

FIG. 7.22. The network of Fig. 7.15 redrawn to make capacitor C_2 a load capacitor.

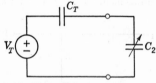

FIG. 7.23. The equivalent Thévenin circuit for the arrangement shown in Fig. 7.22.

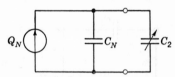

FIG. 7.24. The equivalent Norton circuit for the arrangement shown in Fig. 7.22.

voltage of the capacitor C_2 for a series of values of this capacitance and for a fixed voltage V_1 applied at the left of the network. In this case we can use the Thévenin and Norton equivalent circuits by redrawing the network of Fig. 7.15 as shown in Fig. 7.22. We can now replace the network shown in Fig. 7.22 by the equivalent Thévenin circuit shown in Fig. 7.23 or by the equivalent Norton circuit shown in Fig. 7.24 according to preference. To calculate C_T and C_N we use the network shown in Fig. 7.25 and derive

$$C_T = C_N = \frac{1}{1/C_4 + 1/(C_1 + C_3)} \tag{7.32}$$

or on simplification

$$C_T = C_N = \frac{C_4(C_1 + C_3)}{C_1 + C_3 + C_4} \tag{7.33}$$

To derive the Thévenin voltage V_T we use the network shown in Fig. 7.26

and calculate the voltage across the right-hand terminals when on open circuit.   We derive

$$V_T = \frac{C_1}{C_1 + C_3} V_1 \qquad (7.34)$$

The arrangement shown in Fig. 7.22 is therefore equivalent to that shown in Fig. 7.23 provided that V_T has the value given by Eq. (7.34) and C_T

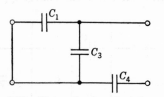

FIG. 7.25. Network for deriving the Thévenin and Norton capacitances for the arrangement shown in Fig. 7.22.

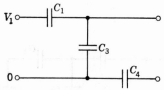

FIG. 7.26. Network for calculating the Thévenin voltage V_T for the arrangement shown in Fig. 7.22.

has the value given by Eq. (7.33).   If we are using the Norton equivalent circuit shown in Fig. 7.24, we calculate the Norton charge Q_N using the network shown in Fig. 7.27.   We require the charge that moves down the short circuit at the right-hand side of Fig. 7.27 when the voltage V_1 is applied at the left-hand side.   This is the charge on the right-hand plate of capacitor C_4.   By thinking of the network as a capacitor C_3 in parallel with the capacitor C_4, this pair being in series with the capacitor C_1, we derive for the charge on the right-hand plate of capacitor C_4

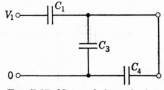

FIG. 7.27. Network for calculating the Norton charge Q_N for the arrangement shown in Fig. 7.22.

$$\frac{C_4}{C_3 + C_4} \frac{1}{1/C_1 + 1/(C_3 + C_4)} V_1 \qquad (7.35)$$

On simplification we derive

$$Q_N = \frac{C_1 C_4}{C_1 + C_3 + C_4} V_1 \qquad (7.36)$$

Hence the arrangement shown in Fig. 7.22 is equivalent to that shown in Fig. 7.24 provided that Q_N has the value given by Eq. (7.36) and C_N has the value given by Eq. (7.33).

In all the above applications of the Thévenin and Norton equivalent circuits it is the voltage V_1 of the source that has been kept constant. Let us now consider an example in which it is the charge Q_1 of the source that is kept constant.   Let us suppose that a given charge Q_1 is transferred from the lower left-hand terminal to the upper left-hand terminal as indicated in Fig. 7.28.   Let us select capacitor C_2 and ask what the charge and voltage on this capacitor are for various values of its capacitance and for a fixed value of Q_1.   As before, we rearrange the network as shown in Fig. 7.29.   The network shown in Fig. 7.29 can again be replaced by the equivalent Thévenin circuit shown in Fig. 7.23 or by the equivalent Norton circuit shown in Fig. 7.24, but new values must now be calculated for the elements in these equivalent circuits, since it is the charge Q_1 that

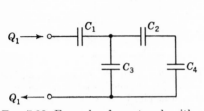

Fig. 7.28. Example of a network with a constant-charge source.

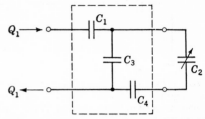

Fig. 7.29. The network shown in Fig. 7.28 redrawn to make capacitor C_2 the load capacitor.

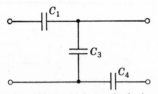

Fig. 7.30. Network for calculating the Thévenin and Norton capacitances for the arrangement shown in Fig. 7.29.

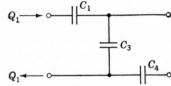

Fig. 7.31. Network for calculating the Thévenin voltage for the arrangement shown in Fig. 7.29.

is now kept constant as the capacitance of the load capacitor C_2 is varied. To calculate the new value for C_T and C_N we use the network shown in Fig. 7.30 in which the terminals on the left have now been open-circuited instead of short-circuited.   The required capacitance is the equivalent capacitance across the right-hand terminals in Fig. 7.30 and is therefore

$$C_T = C_N = \frac{1}{1/C_3 + 1/C_4} \qquad (7.37)$$

The new value for the Thévenin voltage V_T to be used in Fig. 7.23 is the excess of voltage of the upper right-hand terminal over that of the lower right-hand terminal of the network shown in Fig. 7.31.   Since there is no voltage across capacitor C_4, the charge on capacitor C_3 is Q_1.   The required voltage is therefore

$$V_T = \frac{Q_1}{C_3} \qquad (7.38)$$

The arrangement shown in Fig. 7.29 is therefore equivalent to that shown in Fig. 7.23 provided that V_T has the value given by Eq. (7.38) and C_T the value given by Eq. (7.37). If we use the equivalent Norton circuit shown in Fig. 7.24, the new value for the Norton charge Q_N is calculated from the

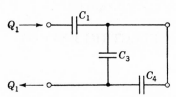

FIG. 7.32. Network for calculating the Norton charge for the arrangement shown in Fig. 7.29.

network shown in Fig. 7.32. The required charge is the charge on the right-hand plate of capacitor C_4 in Fig. 7.32, and hence

$$Q_N = \frac{C_4}{C_3 + C_4} Q_1 \qquad (7.39)$$

The arrangement shown in Fig. 7.29 is therefore equivalent to that shown in Fig. 7.24 provided that Q_N has the value given by Eq. (7.39) and C_N has the value given by Eq. (7.37).

SUMMARIZING EXERCISES

7.1. Explain what is meant by the statement that one network of capacitors possessing input and output terminals is equivalent to a second network of capacitors possessing input and output terminals. Describe circumstances in which it is convenient to make use of the concept of equivalent networks.

7.2. Explain what is meant by the equivalent T and π networks of a given network of capacitors possessing input and output terminals.

7.3. A network of capacitors possesses a pair of output terminals. It is energized either by transferring charge from one node to another or by connecting a battery between one node and another or both. Explain what is meant by the Thévenin and Norton equivalent circuits for the arrangement.

7.4. A network of capacitors is contained in a box from which protrude pairs of terminals connected to nodes of the network. One pair of terminals is used as a pair of output terminals. The other pairs of terminals are used to energize the network. For some of these pairs of terminals this is achieved by transferring a prescribed amount of charge from one terminal of the pair to the other, while across other pairs of terminals are connected batteries of prescribed voltage. It is required to evaluate the elements in the Thévenin and Norton equivalent circuits for the arrangement. Explain how this can be achieved by measurement without opening the box to examine the contents. Explain how to use the same method for calculating theoretically the elements in the Thévenin and Norton equivalent circuits in terms of the elements of the network and the given energizing sources.

7.5. Describe circumstances under which it is convenient to replace a network of capacitors and energizing sources by a Thévenin or Norton equivalent circuit.

CHAPTER 8

ELECTRIC ENERGY

8.1. Introduction. It will be remembered that capacitors were originally introduced as a convenient method of storing potential energy by electrical means. This could be done by varying the spacing between a pair of equal and opposite point charges, but a more compact electric field is produced by placing the equal and opposite charges on the plates of a capacitor (see Fig. 2.6). However, although we have calculated the potential energy of a pair of point charges [Eq. (2.7)], we have not so far calculated the potential energy stored in a capacitor that has given geometrical dimensions and carries a given charge or voltage.

8.2. Energy of a Charged Capacitor. Consider a capacitor of any size and shape with any arrangement of dielectric material, and let C be its capacitance. Let a charge Q be transferred from one plate to the other, so that the positive plate carries a charge Q and the negative plate a charge $-Q$. Let V be the resulting excess of potential of the positive plate over the negative plate. To charge the capacitor in this way a certain amount of energy W is used, and this energy can be recovered by discharging the capacitor. We wish to calculate W in terms of Q and V.

Electric potential is potential energy per unit charge. In consequence it might be thought at first sight that the energy of the capacitor is VQ on the grounds that a charge Q has been transferred through a potential difference V. This, however, would be an overestimate of the energy of the capacitor for the following reason: Let us suppose that the total charge Q is transferred from one plate to the other in small amounts. When the capacitor has been nearly charged, the potential difference between the plates is nearly V, and transfer of a small amount of charge at this stage would be through a voltage of nearly V. But near the beginning of the charging process the potential difference between the plates is nearly zero, and small amounts of charge transferred at this stage are transferred through a potential difference a great deal less than V. The mean potential difference through which charge is transferred during the charging process is therefore some fraction of V, and in consequence the energy in the capacitor when finally charged is some fraction of VQ. To calculate the potential energy stored in the capacitor when charged, we have to allow for the fact that small amounts of charge transferred at different stages during the charging process are transferred through successively increasing differences of potential.

Let us consider a stage in the charging process at which the potential difference between the plates of the capacitor is a fraction x of the final voltage V. At this stage in the charging process the potential difference between the plates is xV and the charges on the plates are xQ and $-xQ$. Now let us increase the charge on the positive plate by an amount $dx\,Q$ and increase the negative charge on the negative plate by an equal amount. This involves transferring an amount of charge $dx\,Q$ through a rise of potential xV. The work done is therefore

$$(xV)(dx\,Q) \tag{8.1}$$

To charge the capacitor completely, transfers of charge have to be made until the fraction x has increased from zero to unity. The total work done in charging the capacitor is therefore

$$W = \int_0^1 (xV)(dx\,Q) \tag{8.2}$$

In this equation V and Q are constants, being the final voltage and charge of the capacitor. They can therefore be brought in front of the integral sign, and Eq. (8.2) can be written as

$$W = VQ \int_0^1 x\,dx \tag{8.3}$$

The value of the integral in this equation is $\tfrac{1}{2}$, and consequently the formula for the potential energy of a capacitor whose voltage is V and charge is Q is

$$W = \tfrac{1}{2}VQ \tag{8.4}$$

The energy of the charged capacitor is therefore as though the charge Q were transferred through a potential difference $\tfrac{1}{2}V$, which is the average of the initial value zero and the final value V.

Since the ratio of Q to V is the capacitance C of the capacitor, formula (8.4) for the potential energy of a charged capacitor can be written in any one of the following equivalent forms:

$$W = \tfrac{1}{2}VQ = \tfrac{1}{2}CV^2 = \frac{1}{2C}Q^2 \tag{8.5}$$

We notice that, for a capacitor of given capacitance, the potential energy stored is proportional to the square of its voltage and also proportional to the square of its charge. We also notice that for a given voltage V the stored potential energy is proportional to the capacitance C, but for a given charge Q the stored potential energy is inversely proportional to the capacitance C. If the voltage between the plates of a capacitor is maintained constant and the plates are pushed closer together, additional charge must be supplied by the battery maintaining the constant potential, and consequently the potential energy stored in the capacitor increases. If, however, the charge of the capacitor is kept constant, then it must be that the capacitor is not connected to any source of energy, and as the plates are pulled apart, the energy of the system increases in the same way as for a pair of equal and opposite point charges.

It will be noted that, even for capacitors of comparatively high capacitance and for comparatively high voltages between the plates of the capacitor, the potential energy stored is not high. To store 1 joule in a 1-μf capacitor requires, in accordance with one of the Eqs. (8.5), a potential difference of 1,414 volts.

8.3. Energy of a Network of Capacitors. Let us now consider how to calculate the energy stored in a charged network of capacitors such as that shown in Fig. 6.1 or 6.2. Let nodes 1, 2, . . . be raised to potentials V_1, V_2, . . . , and let the corresponding charges on these nodes be, respectively, Q_1, Q_2, ... In terms of these potentials and charges we wish to calculate the potential energy stored by the network. At a certain stage during the charging process let the potentials and charges of the nodes be a fraction x of their final values. Now increase the charges of the nodes by additional small fractions dx of their final values. This involves bringing charges $dx\ Q_1$, $dx\ Q_2$, . . . up to potentials xV_1, xV_2, . . . , respectively. The work done is

$$(xV_1)(dx\ Q_1) + (xV_2)(dx\ Q_2) + \cdots \qquad (8.6)$$

To charge the network we have to allow x to go from 0 to 1, and the total work done is therefore

$$W = \int_0^1 [(xV_1)(dx\ Q_1) + (xV_2)(dx\ Q_2) + \cdots] \qquad (8.7)$$

Since V_1, Q_1, V_2, Q_2, . . . are constants in this equation, it can be rewritten as

$$W = (V_1Q_1 + V_2Q_2 + \cdots) \int_0^1 x\ dx \qquad (8.8)$$

thereby giving

$$W = \tfrac{1}{2}(V_1Q_1 + V_2Q_2 + \cdots) \qquad (8.9)$$

We thus see that the total potential energy stored in the network is obtained by multiplying each node potential by the corresponding node charge, summing for all nodes and dividing by 2.

Let us suppose that we are dealing with a network of capacitors for which the coefficients of capacitance c_{rs} and the coefficients of elastance b_{rs} have been calculated. In terms of these coefficients it is possible to express the potential energy of the network, given by Eq. (8.9), either entirely in terms of the potentials of the nodes or entirely in terms of the charges of the nodes. The charges are expressed in terms of the potentials by means of the equations

$$Q_1 = c_{11}V_1 + c_{12}V_2 + \cdots$$
$$Q_2 = c_{21}V_1 + c_{22}V_2 + \cdots \qquad (8.10)$$
$$\cdots \cdots \cdots \cdots \cdots \cdots$$

Substituting for the charges in terms of the potentials from Eqs. (8.10) into Eq. (8.9) and remembering that c_{rs} equals c_{sr}, we obtain

$$W = \tfrac{1}{2}(c_{11}V_1{}^2 + c_{22}V_2{}^2 + \cdots + 2c_{12}V_1V_2 + \cdots) \qquad (8.11)$$

This expresses the potential energy of the system in terms of the potentials of the nodes and the coefficients of capacitance of the network. Alternatively we can use the coefficients of elastance to express the potentials of the nodes in terms of their charges by means of the equations

$$V_1 = b_{11}Q_1 + b_{12}Q_2 + \cdots$$
$$V_2 = b_{21}Q_1 + b_{22}Q_2 + \cdots \qquad (8.12)$$
$$\cdots \cdots \cdots \cdots \cdots \cdots \cdots$$

Substituting for the potentials in terms of the charges from Eqs. (8.12) into Eq. (8.9) and remembering that b_{rs} equals b_{sr}, we obtain

$$W = \tfrac{1}{2}(b_{11}Q_1{}^2 + b_{22}Q_2{}^2 + \cdots + 2b_{12}Q_1Q_2 + \cdots) \qquad (8.13)$$

This expresses the potential energy of the system in terms of the charges of the nodes and the coefficients of elastance of the network. Equations (8.9), (8.11), and (8.13) for a network of capacitors correspond to Eqs. (8.5) for a single capacitor.

A considerable simplification takes place in the calculation of the potential energy of a charged network if there are a number of nodes that are uncharged. Consider networks such as those shown in Figs. 6.3 and 6.4 in which there are only two accessible nodes (nodes 1 and 2) other than the node at zero potential (node 0). All internal nodes are then uncharged, and Eq. (8.9) reduces to

$$W = \tfrac{1}{2}(V_1Q_1 + V_2Q_2) \qquad (8.14)$$

Thus the total potential energy stored within the box is obtained by multiplying the voltages applied to the exterior terminals by their corresponding charges, adding, and dividing by 2. By using the a and b coefficients of the network defined by Eqs. (6.47), (6.48), (6.50), and (6.51), the expression (8.14) for the potential energy stored within the box can be expressed entirely in terms of the potentials of the exterior terminals or entirely in terms of their charges. By substituting from Eqs.

(6.47) and (6.48) into Eq. (8.14) we derive

$$W = \tfrac{1}{2}(a_{11}V_1{}^2 + 2a_{12}V_1V_2 + a_{22}V_2{}^2) \tag{8.15}$$

Likewise by substituting from Eqs. (6.50) and (6.51) into Eq. (8.14) we derive

$$W = \tfrac{1}{2}(b_{11}Q_1{}^2 + 2b_{12}Q_1Q_2 + b_{22}Q_2{}^2) \tag{8.16}$$

Equation (8.15) expresses the potential energy stored in the box in terms of the potentials of the exterior terminals, while Eq. (8.16) expresses the potential energy stored in the box in terms of the charges on the exterior terminals.

As an example, consider the network shown in Fig. 6.4 and suppose that a potential V_1 is applied to terminal 1 and a potential V_2 is applied to terminal 2. We wish to calculate the total potential energy stored in the box. The a coefficients for this network have already been calculated and are given by Eqs. (6.62) and (6.65) to (6.67). It follows from Eq. (8.15) that the potential energy stored in the box is

$$W = \frac{1}{2(C_1 + C_2 + C_3)} [C_1(C_2 + C_3)V_1{}^2 - 2C_1C_2V_1V_2 + C_2(C_1 + C_3)V_2{}^2] \tag{8.17}$$

8.4. Maximizing the Potential Energy Stored in a Selected Capacitor of a Network. Let us suppose that we have a given network of capacitors such as that shown in Fig. 7.15 and that a fixed voltage V_1 is applied between the terminals on the left. Let us suppose that we are interested in adjusting the capacitance of capacitor C_2 in order to maximize the potential energy stored in this capacitor. We then rearrange the network as shown in Fig. 7.22 and replace it either by the Thévenin equivalent circuit shown in Fig. 7.23 or by the Norton equivalent circuit shown in Fig. 7.24. Let us elect to use the Thévenin equivalent circuit and assume that an appropriate calculation has been made of the Thévenin voltage V_T [Eq. (7.34)] and the Thévenin capacitance C_T [Eq. (7.33)]. The problem is then to adjust the capacitance of capacitor C_2 in Fig. 7.23 in order to maximize the potential energy stored in this capacitor.

The voltage V_T in Fig. 7.23 divides between the capacitors C_T and C_2 in the inverse ratio of the capacitances. Hence the voltage developed across capacitor C_2 is

$$\frac{C_T}{C_T + C_2} V_T \tag{8.18}$$

Using one of the Eqs. (8.5), we deduce for the potential energy stored in capacitor C_2

$$\frac{1}{2} C_2 \left(\frac{C_T}{C_T + C_2} V_T \right)^2 \tag{8.19}$$

and this can be written as

$$\frac{1}{2}\,C_T V_T^{\,2}\,\frac{y}{(1+y)^2} \qquad (8.20)$$

where

$$y = \frac{C_2}{C_T} \qquad (8.21)$$

The expression (8.20) for the energy stored in capacitor C_2 is plotted as a function of the ratio of C_2 to C_T in Fig. 8.1. By differentiating expression (8.20) with respect to y for a maximum we see that the maximum occurs where $y = 1$ and that the maximum value is $\frac{1}{8}C_T V_T^{\,2}$. Thus, for a fixed value of the voltage V_1 in Fig. 7.22, the potential energy stored in capacitor C_2 is maximized by making the capacitance C_2 equal to the Thévenin capacitance C_T in Fig. 7.23.

If we had elected to use the Norton equivalent circuit shown in Fig. 7.24 instead of the Thévenin equivalent circuit shown in Fig. 7.23, we would have demonstrated in a similar manner that the potential energy stored in capacitor C_2

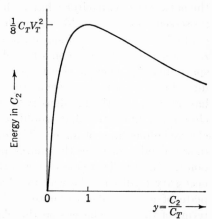

Fig. 8.1. Illustrating the variation of the energy stored in capacitor C_2 in Fig. 7.23 with the magnitude of the capacitance C_2.

is maximized by making this capacitance equal to C_N, which is, of course, identical in value with C_T. With the help of Eqs. (7.20) the energy stored in the load capacitor when this energy is at a maximum can be written in any of the equivalent forms

$$\frac{1}{8}\,C_T V_T^{\,2} = \frac{1}{8}\frac{Q_N^{\,2}}{C_N} = \frac{1}{8}\,V_T Q_N \qquad (8.22)$$

We can see that the elements in the Thévenin and Norton equivalent circuits now possess the following additional interpretation. Figure 7.8 represents a network of capacitors with a number of external pairs of terminals. To the terminals on the left are attached sources involving fixed potential differences or fixed transfers of charge. For this arrangement we can work out the Thévenin voltage V_T, the Thévenin capacitance C_T, the Norton charge Q_N, and the Norton capacitance C_N. Now attach to the terminals on the right in Fig. 7.8 a load capacitor of variable capacitance C_L. The potential energy stored in this load capacitor is a maximum when C_L is adjusted to be equal to the common value of the Thévenin and Norton capacitances C_T and C_N. Moreover, when this adjustment has been made, the energy stored in the load is given by any of the equivalent expressions (8.22).

For example, to maximize the potential energy stored in capacitor C_2 in the arrangement shown in Fig. 7.15, C_2 should have the value given by Eq. (7.33). To maximize the potential energy stored in capacitor C_2 in the arrangement shown in Fig. 7.28, C_2 should have the value given by Eq. (7.37).

8.5. The Building-block Method for Visualizing Electric Fields. In the networks of capacitors that we have been studying, each capacitor has possessed an electric field, although little explicit reference to it has been made. At each point of space there has been an electric vector **E** giving the force per unit charge on a test charge at that point. At each point of space there has been an electric potential ϕ giving the potential energy per unit charge on a test charge at that point. At each point of space there has been an electric flux density **D** giving in magnitude and direction the charge per unit area that would pass this point if the system were discharged along lines of force. The outward normal component of **D** close to any conductor gives the charge per unit area on the conductor at this point. In our discussion of networks of capacitors, however, it was not necessary to discuss the way in which the charge was distributed over a plate of a particular capacitor. The entire analysis was conducted in terms of the total charges on the plates of the various capacitors. Likewise it was not necessary for us to discuss the distribution of electric potential in space. Only the potentials on the various conductors or nodes were involved. We are now going to reemphasize the **D**, **E**, and ϕ fields in the space between conductors and to make use of what we have learned about capacitors in parallel and in series to understand these fields further. In this further discussion of the electric field between the conductors it will not be necessary to assume that the conductors have the special shapes implied in a network of capacitors. The charged conductors may have any shape and are to be pictured as surrounded by the conductor at infinity, the potential of which it is usually convenient to take as zero.

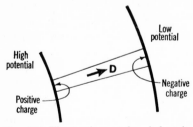

FIG. 8.2. Illustrating a tube of electric flux.

Since the electric potential falls as we move along a line of force in the direction of the electric vector, lines of force run from a conductor at one potential to another conductor at lower potential as indicated in Fig. 8.2. The electric flux density **D** is directed along these lines in the same direction. A group of such lines drawn through a small closed curve in the field form a tube known as a tube of electric flux. Tubes of electric flux therefore run from a conductor at one potential to a conductor at a lower potential. At the high-potential end of the tube the charge on the conductor is positive and, measured per unit area, is the electric flux density at this end of the tube. At the low-potential end of the tube the charge is negative and, measured per unit area, is equal in magnitude to the electric flux density at this end of the tube. During a process of discharge along lines of force, the positive charge at the high-potential end of the tube moves along the tube until it finally neutralizes the negative charge at the low-potential end of the tube, or vice versa. The charges at opposite ends of a tube of flux are therefore equal in magnitude and opposite in sign. If all the tubes of electric flux that constitute the entire field are drawn, the tubes pair off equal elements of positive and negative charge on the conductors.

The product of the electric flux density at any point of a tube and the normal cross section of the tube at that point is the flux of electric charge that passes this cross section of the tube during the process of discharge along tubes of flux. Hence the product of the electric flux density at any point of a tube and the normal cross section of the tube at that point remains constant as we move along the tube. This product is equal to the positive charge at the high-potential end of the tube and is equal and opposite to the negative charge at the low-potential end. As we move along a tube, the normal cross section is inversely proportional to electric flux density, and so from the variation in cross section of the tube we can judge the strength of the electric flux density at each point. If the tubes of flux for the entire field are drawn so as to commence on equal elements of positive charge, then the strength

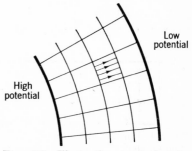

Fig. 8.3. Illustrating analysis into building blocks by tubes of electric flux and equipotential surfaces.

of the electric flux density at any point can be judged from the extent to which the tubes are crowded at that point.

Let us now mark out in the electric field between the conductors not only the tubes of electric flux but also the equipotential surfaces as shown in Fig. 8.3. The equipotential surfaces intersect the tubes of flux at right angles and divide the entire electric field into "building blocks," each consisting of a short portion of a thin tube of electric flux cut off between two close equipotential surfaces forming normal cross sections of the tube. In each building block the electric field is that of a parallel-plate capacitor as indicated in Fig. 8.3. Moreover, the electric field in each building block is the electric field in a parallel-plate capacitor with no fringing whatever, because adjacent building blocks prevent fringing. Each building block may therefore be thought of as an ideal parallel-plate capacitor, and the entire electric field may be regarded as a large number of ideal parallel-plate capacitors fitted together in building-block fashion as shown in Fig. 8.3. The building blocks distributed along a particular tube of flux constitute the tube of flux. The building blocks distributed between two equipotential surfaces form the field of the capacitor that would be created if the two equipotential surfaces were replaced by conductors at the appropriate potentials.

If an individual building block is thought of as an ideal parallel-plate capacitor, the electric field strength E within it gives the voltage per unit distance between the plates of the capacitor, and the magnitude of the electric flux density D within it gives the positive and negative charges per unit area on the plates of the capacitor. Thus the D and E fields at any point of an electric field are the charge per unit area and voltage per unit distance for a local parallel-plate capacitor that would produce the local field.

The building blocks distributed between equipotential surfaces constitute ideal parallel-plate capacitors connected in parallel. The building blocks distributed along a single tube of flux constitute ideal parallel-plate capacitors connected in series. The entire field may therefore be thought of as a number of small, ideal parallel-plate capacitors appropriately connected in parallel and in series. The capacitance of a large capacitor can be calculated from the capacitances of its building blocks by application of the usual formulas for capacitors connected in parallel and in series. Fringing does not have to be taken into account in calculating the capacitance of an individual building block because fringing is prevented by the existence of adjacent building blocks.

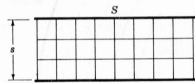

FIG. 8.4. Illustrating the analysis into building blocks of a large parallel-plate capacitor for which fringing is neglected.

As an example, let us consider the field of large parallel-plate capacitor whose plates are of area S with a separation s between them. For simplicity, let us suppose that fringing for this large capacitor can be neglected. Then the tubes of flux and the equipotential surfaces are as shown in Fig. 8.4. Let us suppose that the tubes of flux are drawn so that each has unit cross-sectional area and that the equipotential surfaces are drawn so that adjacent ones have a unit separation. Each building block is then a parallel-plate capacitor with unit dimensions for which fringing does not have to be taken into account. Its capacitance is therefore the capacitivity ϵ of the medium. Between any adjacent pair of equi-potential surfaces there are S building blocks, connected in parallel, each consisting of a capacitor of capacitance ϵ. Within any tube of flux there are s building blocks connected in series, each consisting of a capacitor of capacitance ϵ. Now S capacitors each of capacitance ϵ connected in parallel form a capacitor of capacitance ϵS, and if s of these capacitors are connected in series, the resulting capacitance is $\epsilon S/s$. This therefore is the capacitance of the large parallel-plate capacitor when fringing is neglected, as, of course, we already know.

8.6. Distribution of Potential Energy in an Electric Field. At a point in an electrostatic field where the electric flux density is D and the electric field strength is E, let us consider a building block bounded by the surface of a tube of electric flux of unit cross-sectional area cut off by a pair of equipotential surfaces at unit distance apart. The volume of this build-ing block is unity. If the field in this building block is thought of as that of an ideal parallel-plate capacitor whose plates coincide with the flat ends of the building block, then the charges on the plates are $\pm D$ and the voltage between the plates is E. It follows from Eq. (8.4) that the potential energy stored in the building block is $\frac{1}{2}ED$. This energy is stored in a building block of unit volume, so that the potential energy stored per unit volume in the electrostatic field at a place where the electric field strength is E and the electric flux density is D is $\frac{1}{2}ED$. If each building block in the field is thought of as an ideal parallel-plate capacitor, we see that potential energy is stored in each building block. Hence potential energy is distributed throughout the electrostatic field at the rate $\frac{1}{2}ED$ per unit volume. The entire energy of the field can be evaluated by calculating it at the rate $\frac{1}{2}ED$ per unit volume, using for each element of volume the values of E and D at the position of the element.

Since the ratio of the electric flux density at a point in the field to the electric field strength at the same point is the capacitivity ϵ of the medium at that point, the expression for the potential energy w per unit volume of the field at that point can be written in any of the following equivalent forms:

$$w = \tfrac{1}{2}ED = \tfrac{1}{2}\epsilon E^2 = \frac{1}{2\epsilon}D^2 \qquad (8.23)$$

These equations for the energy per unit volume at a point in an electric field are to be compared with Eqs. (8.5) for the total energy of a capacitor.

The way in which potential energy is distributed throughout an elec-trostatic field tells us how much energy would be derived by discharging a portion of the field. Thus, suppose that a pair of equipotential surfaces were replaced by conductors at the appropriate potential so as to leave the field undisturbed.   The portion of the field between the equipotential surfaces can then be discharged, leaving the remainder of the field unchanged.   The energy recovered in this way can be evaluated by calculating the energy between the two equipotential surfaces at the rate per unit volume given by Eqs. (8.23).

To illustrate numerically the order of magnitude of the energy density in an electrostatic field, consider a parallel-plate capacitor for which the plates are of area 100 cm^2, the separation is 1 mm, and the dielectric is air.   Let the voltage between the plates be 1,000 volts.   If the capacitance of the capacitor is calculated and substituted into the formula $\frac{1}{2}CV^2$, the total energy in the capacitor works out to 4.4 × 10^{-5} joule. Neglecting fringing, this is spread uniformly over a volume equal to 10^{-5} m^2.   Hence the energy per unit volume is 4.4 joules/m^3.

8.7. Density of Energy in a Dielectric.   At a point in a dielectric where the capacitivity is ϵ and the electric field strength is E, the energy per unit volume is $\frac{1}{2}\epsilon E^2$, and this can be written in the form

$$\frac{1}{2}\epsilon_v E^2 + \left(\frac{\epsilon}{\epsilon_v} - 1\right) \frac{1}{2}\epsilon_v E^2 \qquad (8.24)$$

The first term in this expression is the energy per unit volume that would exist in free space, and the second term is the energy per unit volume that arises from the fact that the dielectric constant ϵ/ϵ_v differs from unity. The second term is the energy per unit volume arising from electric polarization, that is, from displacement, of the charges constituting the atoms of the dielectric.   If the dielectric constant exceeds 2, a majority of the energy per unit volume is associated with distortion of the atoms. If the dielectric constant is large compared with unity, then most of the energy stored per unit volume is associated with presence of the atoms constituting the dielectric.

Filling the volume between the plates of a capacitor with a dielectric of high dielectric constant is one way of reducing fringing.   With a high dielectric constant, most of the stored energy is associated with presence of the atoms of the dielectric, and the energy associated with the field in free space plays a correspondingly reduced role.   For a given voltage between the plates of the capacitor the dielectric increases the charge on the surface of the plates facing each other in the ratio ϵ/ϵ_v to 1 while leaving the charge on the outer surfaces unchanged.   The charge associated with the fringing field is therefore a smaller fraction of the whole charge on a plate when a dielectric is placed between the plates.   The higher the dielectric constant used between the plates, the more is it possible to relax the restriction that the separation between plates should be small compared with the linear dimensions of the plates if fringing is to be negligible.   The extent to which fringing can be controlled in this way is limited by the fact that dielectric constants much larger than 100 are not available.

SUMMARIZING EXERCISES

8.1. Prove that the energy required to charge a capacitor to voltage V is $\frac{1}{2}VQ$, where Q and $-Q$ are the charges developed on the plates. Prove that alternative expressions for the potential energy stored in the capacitor are $\frac{1}{2}CV^2$ and $\frac{1}{2}Q^2/C$, where C is the capacitance of the capacitor. Give a physical explanation for the presence of the factor $\frac{1}{2}$.

8.2. Prove that the potential energy stored in a network of capacitors for which the voltages of the nodes are V_1, V_2, . . . and the charges associated with the nodes are Q_1, Q_2, . . . , respectively, is $\frac{1}{2}(V_1Q_1 + V_2Q_2 + \cdots)$. By making use of the coefficients of capacitance of the network, express the stored energy in terms of the voltages of the nodes and not in terms of the charges. By making use of the coefficients of elastance of the network express the stored energy in terms of the charges of the nodes and not in terms of the voltages.

8.3. A network of capacitors and sources has a pair of output terminals, and the Thévenin and Norton capacitance for the arrangement is C. A load capacitor of variable capacitance is connected across the output terminals, and its capacitance is varied until the energy stored in the load capacitor is a maximum. Prove that, when so adjusted, the capacitance of the load is equal to C.

8.4. Explain what is meant by a tube of electric flux. Show that tubes of electric flux and equipotential surfaces can be used to dissect any electrostatic field into "building blocks" in each of which the field is that of a parallel-plate capacitor with no fringing. Show that any electrostatic field may be regarded as a system of ideal parallel-plate capacitors connected appropriately in series and in parallel.

8.5. Explain what is meant by the statement that the electric energy stored in a parallel-plate capacitor (fringing avoided) may be regarded as distributed uniformly throughout the volume between the plates. Prove that the energy per unit volume is given by $\frac{1}{2}ED$, by $\frac{1}{2}\epsilon E^2$, and by $\frac{1}{2}D^2/\epsilon$, where E and D are, respectively, the electric field strength and the electric flux density in the capacitor and ϵ is the capacitivity of the dielectric.

8.6. By using "building-block" analysis, explain why the potential energy associated with an electrostatic field is distributed throughout the field and why, at a point in the field where the electric field strength is E and the electric flux density is D, the energy density is $\frac{1}{2}ED$ per unit volume.

CHAPTER 9

COEFFICIENTS OF CAPACITANCE AND ELASTANCE
FOR ANY SYSTEM OF CONDUCTORS

9.1. Introduction. We introduced the coefficients of capacitance and elastance in connection with networks of capacitors such as those shown in Figs. 6.1 and 6.2. A network of capacitors forms a system of metallic conductors of special shape. Each conductor consists of several capacitor plates joined together by metallic wires to a node. However, most of the ideas that we have developed in connection with these networks are in fact applicable to systems of conductors of any shape. In particular they are applicable to systems of conductors such as those found in multielectrode vacuum tubes.

9.2. The Principle of Superposition. Let us consider a system of metallic conductors numbered 1, 2, . . . , and let us suppose that these are enclosed in a conductor at zero potential which could be the conductor at infinity. In the networks shown in Figs. 6.1 and 6.2 it is the central node at zero potential which played the part of the conductor at infinity and it is nodes 1, 2, . . . that played the parts of conductors 1, 2, ... We now have to establish the fact that equations such as (6.4) to (6.6) can be applied to any system of conductors in electrostatics.

First of all we have to establish the principle of superposition in a form applicable to a system of conductors. For the given system of conductors let charges Q_1, Q_2, . . . be applied to conductors 1, 2, ... Let us suppose that the resulting electric field between the conductors is fully calculated. In particular we suppose that we know the electric potential ϕ at all points and that from it we have calculated the electric vector $\mathbf{E}$ and also the electric-flux-density vector $\mathbf{D}$ at all points. In particular we have then calculated the potentials V_1, V_2, . . . of the conductors. Using the same set of conductors, let us now charge them differently. Let us apply charges Q_1', Q_2', . . . to conductors 1, 2, . . . , and let us calculate the new electric field at all points in the space between the conductors. This means that we have calculated the new potential ϕ' at all points and from it have deduced the electric vector $\mathbf{E}'$ and also the electric-flux-density vector $\mathbf{D}'$ at all points. In particular we have deduced the voltages V_1', V_2', . . . of the conductors. It is now asserted that, if we place on the conductors charges $Q_1 + Q_1'$, $Q_2 + Q_2'$, . . . , then the potentials of the conductors will be $V_1 + V_1'$, $V_2 + V_2'$, ... This fact is known as the principle of superposition.

To prove the result we start by considering, in the region between the conductors, a distribution of electric potential equal to $\phi + \phi'$. From this potential function we can work out the corresponding electric vector at each point of space, and it will be $\mathbf{E} + \mathbf{E}'$. Furthermore we can work out the electric-flux-density vector at each point, and it will be $\mathbf{D} + \mathbf{D}'$. Now the gradient of ϕ and ϕ' along the surface of each conductor is zero because the conductor is an equipotential surface. It follows that the gradient of $\phi + \phi'$ along the surface of every conductor is zero. Consequently, in the assumed field corresponding to $\phi + \phi'$, there are no forces tending to redistribute charge on the conductors, and consequently the conductors are in electrostatic equilibrium. It follows that the electric field that we have constructed is a feasible electrostatic field between the conductors. This field is, however, the field for which the potentials of the conductors are $V_1 + V_1'$, $V_2 + V_2'$, ... Moreover it is the field for which the electric-flux-density vector at each point of space is $\mathbf{D} + \mathbf{D}'$, and this applies in particular at the surfaces of the conductors. Consequently the charge per unit area at each point of each conductor in the field corresponding to $\phi + \phi'$ is the sum of the charges per unit area in the fields corresponding to ϕ and to ϕ' separately. Thus the field corresponding to $\phi + \phi'$ is the one for which the charges on the conductors are $Q_1 + Q_1'$, $Q_2 + Q_2'$, ... It follows therefore that the superposition of two situations in one of which the charges on the conductors are Q_1, Q_2, . . . and the potentials are V_1, V_2, . . . and in the other the charges are Q_1', Q_2', . . . and the potentials are V_1', V_2', . . . creates a situation in which the charges on the conductors are $Q_1 + Q_1'$, $Q_2 + Q_2'$, . . . and the potentials are $V_1 + V_1'$, $V_2 + V_2'$, ...

With the principle of superposition established for a system of conductors we can now proceed to introduce the coefficients of capacitance in the following way. Consider a situation in which the potentials of the conductors are

$$1, 0, 0, \ldots \tag{9.1}$$

so that the potential of conductor 1 is unity and the potentials of all other conductors are zero. Under these circumstances let the charges on the conductors be

$$c_{11}, c_{21}, c_{31}, \ldots \tag{9.2}$$

Now consider a situation in which the potentials on the conductors are

$$0, 1, 0, \ldots \tag{9.3}$$

so that there is now a unit potential on conductor 2 but zero potential on all other conductors. Under these circumstances let the charges on the conductors be

$$c_{12}, c_{22}, c_{32}, \ldots \qquad (9.4)$$

Likewise when the potentials on the conductors are

$$0, 0, 1, \ldots \qquad (9.5)$$

let the charges on the conductors be

$$c_{13}, c_{23}, c_{33}, \ldots \qquad (9.6)$$

and so on. In this way we define the coefficients of capacitance for the system of conductors.

From the principle of superposition it follows that, if we multiply the potentials (9.1) by V_1, the charges (9.2) are also multiplied by V_1. Likewise if the potentials (9.3) are multiplied by V_2, then the charges (9.4) are also multiplied by V_2. In the same way if the potentials (9.5) are multiplied by V_3, the charges (9.6) are multiplied by V_3, and so on. If all these situations are then superposed in accordance with the principle of superposition, we obtain for the charges Q_1, Q_2, . . . on the conductors the equations

$$\begin{aligned}
Q_1 &= c_{11}V_1 + c_{12}V_2 + c_{13}V_3 + \cdots \\
Q_2 &= c_{21}V_1 + c_{22}V_2 + c_{23}V_3 + \cdots \\
Q_3 &= c_{31}V_1 + c_{32}V_2 + c_{33}V_3 + \cdots
\end{aligned} \qquad (9.7)$$

$$\cdot \ \cdot \ \cdot \ \cdot \ \cdot \ \cdot \ \cdot \ \cdot \ \cdot \ \cdot \ \cdot \ \cdot \ \cdot \ \cdot \ \cdot \ \cdot \ \cdot \ \cdot$$

These are of the same form as Eqs. (6.4) to (6.6) or Eqs. (6.19) to (6.23) or Eqs. (8.10).

In the same way we can introduce the coefficients of elastance for a system of conductors in the following way: When the charges on the conductors are

$$1, 0, 0, \ldots \qquad (9.8)$$

let the potentials of the conductors be

$$b_{11}, b_{21}, b_{31}, \ldots \qquad (9.9)$$

When the charges on the conductors are

$$0, 1, 0, \ldots \qquad (9.10)$$

let the potentials of the conductors be

$$b_{12}, b_{22}, b_{32}, \ldots \qquad (9.11)$$

When the charges on the conductors are

$$0, 0, 1, \ldots \qquad (9.12)$$

let the potentials of the conductors be

$$b_{13}, b_{23}, b_{33}, \ldots \tag{9.13}$$

and so on.   From the principle of superposition it follows that, when the charges on the conductors are Q_1, Q_2, Q_3, . . . , then the potentials of the conductors are

$$\begin{aligned}
V_1 &= b_{11}Q_1 + b_{12}Q_2 + b_{13}Q_3 + \cdots \\
V_2 &= b_{21}Q_1 + b_{22}Q_2 + b_{23}Q_3 + \cdots \\
V_3 &= b_{31}Q_1 + b_{32}Q_2 + b_{33}Q_3 + \cdots \\
& \cdots \cdots \cdots \cdots \cdots \cdots \cdots
\end{aligned} \tag{9.14}$$

These are in the same form as Eqs. (6.13) to (6.15) or Eqs. (6.26) to (6.30) or Eq. (8.12).

The energy of a system of charged conductors has already been calculated in Sec. 8.3 for the case when the conductors are the nodes of a network of capacitors.   The argument there given extends immediately to any system of charged conductors merely by replacing the word "node" by the word "conductor."   It follows that if charges $Q_1, Q_2, \ldots$ are given to any system of conductors and as a result they are raised to potentials $V_1, V_2, \ldots$ above the potential at infinity, then the potential energy of the system is given by Eq. (8.9).   Moreover, in terms of the coefficients of capacitance and elastance that we have now defined for systems of conductors, it further follows that Eq. (8.11) gives the potential energy of a system of conductors in terms of the potentials of the conductors and Eq. (8.13) gives the potential energy in terms of the charges of the conductors.

In deriving Eqs. (8.11) and (8.13) from Eq. (8.9) in Sec. 8.3 it was, however, assumed that

$$c_{rs} = c_{sr} \tag{9.15}$$

and that

$$b_{rs} = b_{sr} \tag{9.16}$$

For a network of capacitors Eq. (9.15) followed from the fact that both the left- and right-hand sides are simply the capacitance of the capacitor joining node number r to node number s, and then the truth of Eq. (9.16) followed by algebraic process.   For any system of conductors it may be argued from the building-block principle that any electrostatic field can be analyzed into parallel-plate capacitors connected in series and in parallel.   The truth of Eqs. (9.15) and (9.16) for a system of conductors then follows from the truth of the same equations for a network of capacitors.   This argument can be placed upon a more reliable basis by means of the following theorem.

9.3. Green's Reciprocal Theorem for Electrostatics.   To a given system of conductors numbered 1, 2, . . . , apply charges $Q_1, Q_2, \ldots$

and let the corresponding potentials of the conductors be V_1, V_2, ...
For the same system of conductors apply charges Q_1', Q_2', . . . and let
the corresponding potentials of the conductors be V_1', V_2', ... Then
Green's reciprocal theorem states that

$$V_1 Q_1' + V_2 Q_2' + \cdots = V_1' Q_1 + V_2' Q_2 + \cdots \qquad (9.17)$$

In writing down the result (9.17) it is convenient to list the charges and
potentials of the conductors according to the following scheme:

$$
\begin{array}{cccc}
V_1 & V_2 & \cdots \\
Q_1 & Q_2 & \cdots \\
\hline
V_1' & V_2' & \cdots \\
Q_1' & Q_2' & \cdots
\end{array}
$$

One side of Eq. (9.17) is then formed by multiplying line 1 by line 4 and
adding, while the other side of the equation is formed by multiplying
line 2 by line 3 and adding. It is also frequently convenient to abbreviate
Eq. (9.17) in the form

$$\Sigma V Q' = \Sigma V' Q \qquad (9.18)$$

where Σ denotes summation over the conductors.

Let us examine the implications of Green's reciprocal theorem before
actually proving the theorem.

First of all let us consider a situation in which the potential of conductor 1 is V and the potentials of all other conductors are zero; let the
charges on the conductors under these circumstances be Q_1, Q_2, Q_3, ...
Let us compare this with a situation in which the potential of conductor 2
is V and the potentials of all other conductors are zero; in this situation
let the charges on the conductors be Q_1', Q_2', Q_3', ... These potentials
and charges are summarized in the following table:

$$
\begin{array}{cccc}
V & 0 & 0 & \cdots \\
Q_1 & Q_2 & Q_3 & \cdots \\
\hline
0 & V & 0 & \cdots \\
Q_1' & Q_2' & Q_3' & \cdots
\end{array}
$$

To this pair of situations we now apply Green's reciprocal theorem. In
Eq. (9.17) there is only one nonvanishing term on each side of the equation, and we derive

$$V Q_1' = V Q_2$$
or
$$Q_1' = Q_2 \qquad (9.19)$$

This result states that the charge on conductor 1 due to potential V
on conductor 2 (the other conductors being grounded) is equal to the

charge on conductor 2 when the potential V is applied to conductor 1 (the other conductors being grounded).

In the result expressed by Eq. (9.19) let us now put $V = 1$. Q_1' is then the charge on conductor 1 when unit potential is applied to conductor 2 and zero potential to all other conductors. By definition of the coefficients of capacitance we therefore have

$$Q_1' = c_{12} \qquad (9.20)$$

In the same way we have

$$Q_2 = c_{21} \qquad (9.21)$$

Green's reciprocal theorem in this case therefore yields

$$c_{12} = c_{21} \qquad (9.22)$$

Since the numbers 1 and 2 could have been assigned to any pair of conductors of the system, the truth of Eq. (9.15) is established.

As another application of Green's reciprocal theorem let us put a charge Q on conductor 1 and leave all the other conductors uncharged; in these circumstances let the potentials of the conductors be V_1, V_2, V_3, ... Let us compare this with a situation in which the charge Q is placed on conductor 2 and all the other conductors are uncharged; in these circumstances let the potentials of the conductors be V_1', V_2', V_3', ... These potentials and charges are shown in the following table

V_1	V_2	V_3	$\cdots$
Q	0	0	$\cdots$
V_1'	V_2'	V_3'	$\cdots$
0	Q	0	$\cdots$

Applying Green's reciprocal theorem, Eq. (9.17) reduces to

$$V_2 Q = V_1' Q$$

and so to

$$V_2 = V_1' \qquad (9.23)$$

Hence the potential of conductor 2 when a charge Q is applied to conductor 1 (the other conductors being uncharged) is equal to the potential of conductor 1 when the charge Q is applied to conductor 2 (the other conductors being uncharged).

We now consider the special case of the result implied in Eq. (9.23) that occurs when $Q = 1$. From the definitions of the coefficients of elastance we then have

$$V_2 = b_{21} \qquad (9.24)$$

and

$$V_1' = b_{12} \qquad (9.25)$$

From Eq. (9.23) it follows that

$$b_{21} = b_{12} \qquad (9.26)$$

and this establishes Eq. (9.16).

To prove Green's reciprocal theorem [Eq. (9.17)], we proceed along lines somewhat similar to those used in establishing Eq. (8.9). Consider a situation in which the potentials of the conductors are

$$(1 - x)V_1 + xV_1' \qquad (1 - x)V_2 + xV_2' \qquad \cdots \qquad (9.27)$$

where x is a fraction less than unity. By the principle of superposition the charges on the conductors are then

$$(1 - x)Q_1 + xQ_1' \qquad (1 - x)Q_2 + xQ_2' \qquad \cdots \qquad (9.28)$$

These potentials and charges have been chosen so that, when $x = 0$, they are identical with the first set of potentials and charges contemplated in Green's reciprocal theorem; on the other hand, when $x = 1$, the potentials and charges (9.27) and (9.28) are identical with the second set of potentials and charges contemplated in Green's reciprocal theorem. We can thus pass from the first set of potentials and charges in the theorem to the second set by allowing x to go from zero to unity.

Let us calculate the work done in changing over from the first set of potentials and charges to the second set of potentials and charges. When x changes to $x + dx$, the charge on conductor 1 increases by

$$d[(1 - x)Q_1 + xQ_1'] \qquad (9.29)$$

and this is equal to

$$(Q_1' - Q_1)\, dx \qquad (9.30)$$

To effect this increment in charge, an amount of charge (9.30) has to be brought up from infinity, where it is at zero potential, to the potential of conductor 1, which is

$$(1 - x)V_1 + xV_1' \qquad (9.31)$$

The work done is therefore the product of the expressions (9.30) and (9.31) and is therefore

$$[(1 - x)V_1 + xV_1'](Q_1' - Q)\, dx \qquad (9.32)$$

This calculation must be made for all conductors and a summation performed. Hence the work done in increasing x to $x + dx$ is

$$\Sigma[(1 - x)V + xV'](Q' - Q)\, dx \qquad (9.33)$$

and this can be rearranged as

$$\Sigma[V(Q' - Q)\, dx + (V' - V)(Q' - Q)x\, dx] \qquad (9.34)$$

The total work done in changing over from the first system of potentials and charges to the second system of potentials and charges is obtained by integrating the expression (9.34) with respect to x from zero to unity. It is, therefore,

$$\sum V(Q' - Q) \int_0^1 dx + \sum (V' - V)(Q' - Q) \int_0^1 x \, dx \qquad (9.35)$$

On evaluating the integrals, expression (9.35) becomes

$$\Sigma[V(Q' - Q) + \tfrac{1}{2}(V' - V)(Q' - Q)]$$

and this can be rearranged as

$$(\tfrac{1}{2}\Sigma V'Q' - \tfrac{1}{2}\Sigma VQ) + \tfrac{1}{2}(\Sigma VQ' - \Sigma V'Q) \qquad (9.36)$$

Now the work done in changing over from the first system of potentials and charges to the second system of potentials and charges must be equal to the increase in the energy of the system. But, according to Eq. (8.9), the increase in energy of the system is the first expression in parentheses in expression (9.36). It follows therefore that the second expression in parentheses in expression (9.36) must vanish, and this establishes the truth of Eq. (9.18).

9.4. Calculation of the Coefficients of Capacitance for an Idealized Triode Vacuum Tube. Figure 9.1 shows an idealized triode vacuum tube consisting of three conductors, or electrodes, marked 1, 2, and 3, surrounded by a metal box at zero potential. Electrodes 1 and 3 are flat metal sheets of area S. Electrode 2 is a flat metal sheet of area S from which an area $S - S'$ has been removed, leaving an area S'. The area removed forms a number of holes in the plate, converting the plate into a "grid." The metal box is of cylindrical shape with flat ends parallel to the electrodes. The spacing between the box and electrode 1 is a, the spacing between electrodes 1 and 2 is b, the spacing between electrodes 2 and 3 is c, and the spacing between electrode 3 and the metal box is d. We need to calculate the coefficients of capacitance for the three electrodes. We shall make this calculation on the assumption that all fringing can be neglected, even at the edges of the holes in the grid, although this would not be an adequate approximation for a practical triode.

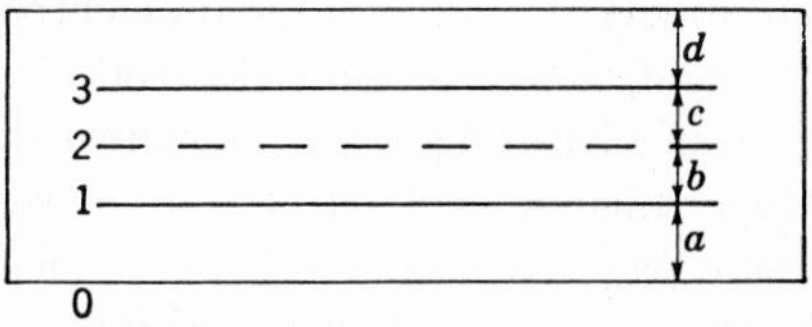

Fig. 9.1. Illustrating an idealized triode vacuum tube.

The undersurface of electrode 1 forms with the bottom of the box a parallel-plate capacitor whose capacitance, neglecting fringing, is

$$\frac{\epsilon_v S}{a} \qquad (9.37)$$

The upper surface of electrode 1 forms with the lower surface of electrode

2, whose area is S', a capacitor whose capacitance is

$$\frac{\epsilon_v S'}{b} \tag{9.38}$$

if fringing is neglected. The upper surface of electrode 2 forms with the lower surface of electrode 3 a capacitor whose capacitance, neglecting fringing, is

$$\frac{\epsilon_v S'}{c} \tag{9.39}$$

The upper surface of electrode 3 forms with the top of the metal box a capacitor whose capacitance, neglecting fringing, is

$$\frac{\epsilon_v S}{d} \tag{9.40}$$

Let us proceed to calculate the coefficients of capacitance c_{11}, c_{21}, and c_{31}. These are the charges on electrodes 1, 2, and 3 when unit potential is placed on electrode 1 and zero potential on electrodes 2 and 3. This means that electrodes 2 and 3 are short-circuited to the box at zero potential while electrode 1 is raised to unit potential. Under these circumstances the charge on electrode 1 is c_{11}, the charge on electrode 2 is c_{21}, and the charge on electrode 3 is c_{31}. Lines of force from the lower face of electrode 1 pass downward to the box. Lines of force from the upper face of electrode 1 go upward. Some terminate on electrode 2, and some pass through the holes in electrode 2 and terminate on electrode 3. Since we are neglecting fringing, all lines of force are normal to the electrodes. This arrangement involves three capacitors connected in parallel. One is the capacitor between the undersurface of electrode 1 and the bottom of the box and has a capacitance given by expression (9.37). The second capacitor is between the upper surface of electrode 1 and the lower surface of electrode 2 and has a capacitance given by expression (9.38). The third capacitor is between electrodes 1 and 3 and involves the lines of force that pass through the holes in electrode 2. Neglecting fringing, this is a parallel-plate capacitor whose area is the combined area $S - S'$ of the holes and whose separation is $b + c$. Its capacitance is therefore

$$\frac{\epsilon_v (S - S')}{b + c} \tag{9.41}$$

if fringing is neglected. It follows that, with unit potential on electrode 1 and zero potential on all other conductors, the charge on electrode 1 is

$$c_{11} = \frac{\epsilon_v S}{a} + \frac{\epsilon_v S'}{b} + \frac{\epsilon_v (S - S')}{b + c} \tag{9.42}$$

The charge on electrode 2 is the negative of expression (9.38) and so

$$c_{21} = -\frac{\epsilon_v S'}{b} \tag{9.43}$$

The charge on electrode 3 is the negative of expression (9.41) and so

$$c_{31} = -\frac{\epsilon_v (S - S')}{b + c} \tag{9.44}$$

Equations (9.42) to (9.44) give the coefficients of capacitance c_{11}, c_{21}, and c_{31} for the electrodes. By a similar procedure the remaining coefficients of capacitance of the system can be calculated.

For an actual triode vacuum tube, electrode 2 would consist of a grid of wires, and one of the other electrodes, say electrode 1, would be fitted with a heater so that it could emit electrons easily and would be called the cathode. Such an arrangement is used for amplifying changes of voltage, and in this application particular importance attaches to the ratio of the coefficient of capacitance c_{21} to the coefficient of capacitance c_{31}, this ratio being what is known as the amplification factor of the tube. From Eqs. (9.43) and (9.44) we see that

$$\frac{c_{21}}{c_{31}} = \frac{S'}{S - S'} \frac{b + c}{b} \tag{9.45}$$

From this equation it is possible to see that the amplification factor of a triode can be made fairly large. Values of the amplification factor lie in practice between about 10 and 100. Neglect of fringing in calculating the amplification factor of a practical triode vacuum tube is not, however, satisfactory. A more careful calculation is required using the method to be outlined in Sec. 11.5.

SUMMARIZING EXERCISES

9.1. Define the coefficients of self- and mutual capacitance of a system of conductors in electrostatics. By applying the principle of superposition, express the charges on each conductor in terms of the potentials of the conductors and the coefficients of self- and mutual capacitance. By means of the coefficients of self- and mutual elastance of the system of conductors, express the potentials of the conductors in terms of the charges of the conductors.

9.2. State and prove Green's reciprocal theorem for a system of conductors in electrostatics. Use the theorem to deduce that the coefficients of capacitance c_{rs} of the system of conductors and the coefficients of elastance b_{rs} of the system of conductors are such that $c_{rs} = c_{sr}$ and $b_{rs} = b_{sr}$.

9.3. Show that the potential energy stored by a system of conductors whose potentials are V_1, V_2, . . . and whose charges are Q_1, Q_2, . . . respectively is $\frac{1}{2}(V_1 Q_1 + V_2 Q_2 + \cdots)$. Explain why the expression is the same as that for the potential energy stored by a network of capacitors for which the potentials of the nodes are V_1, V_2, . . . and the charges associated with the nodes are Q_1, Q_2, . . . respectively.

9.4. An idealized triode vacuum tube consists of two parallel plates of area S with a parallel grid between them as shown in Fig. 9.1.   Conductor 1 is the cathode, conductor 2 is the grid, conductor 3 is the anode, and these electrodes are enclosed by a cylindrical metal can with flat ends parallel to the other conductors.   The separations between the conductors are a, b, c, d, as shown in Fig. 9.1.   The grid is formed by cutting holes in a plate of area S so that the remaining area is S', and all electric fields may be assumed to be strictly perpendicular to the cathode and anode.   Calculate the coefficients of mutual capacitance between (a) the cathode and the grid, (b) the cathode and the anode.

CHAPTER 10

FORCES EXERTED ON CHARGED CONDUCTORS

10.1. Introduction. The total force exerted upon a charged conductor can, in principle, be calculated from the law of inverse squares. The charges distributed over the surfaces of all the conductors of a system may be divided into elements of charge between which the law of inverse squares applies. For a particular conductor the total force exerted on each element of the charge on its surface can, in principle, be evaluated from the law of inverse squares, and the vector sum of these forces gives the total mechanical force exerted on the charged conductor. In practice it is nearly always more convenient to use another method.

In connection with Eq. (2.1) we discussed the fact that, if the point of application of a force F moves through a small distance dx, then the work done is $F\,dx$, and this is equal to the decrement $-dW$ of the energy of the system provided that the system was what was called conservative. This means that, during the displacement dx, there must be no loss of energy due to friction and no supply of energy from some source of energy connected to the system. Equation (2.1) led to Eq. (2.2), giving force as the negative space derivative of energy for a conservative system. When the energy of a system of charged conductors has been calculated, it is often convenient to calculate the force on a particular conductor from Eq. (2.2).

10.2. Force of Attraction between the Conductors of a Parallel-plate Capacitor. Let us apply this concept to calculate the force between the plates of a charged parallel-plate capacitor, neglecting fringing. Let us suppose that S is the area of the plates, s is their separation, and ϵ is the capacitivity of the medium between the plates. Let Q and $-Q$ be the charges on the plates. Let F be the force on each plate tending to increase s. It is obvious that the force between the plates is in the direction perpendicular to the plates and is one of attraction, so that F as defined is negative. Consider a small displacement in which the separation between the plates is increased from s to $s + ds$. From the principle of work expressed by Eq. (2.1) we deduce that

$$F\,ds = -dW \tag{10.1}$$

provided that the capacitor is not connected to any source of energy.

153

This condition would not be satisfied if the voltage between the plates of the capacitor were maintained constant during displacement because it would be necessary to connect to the capacitor a battery of given voltage in order to maintain the constant voltage. Energy would then be supplied to the capacitor or removed from the capacitor by the battery maintaining the constant voltage, and this would upset the validity of Eq. (10.1). To apply Eq. (10.1) it is therefore necessary to keep the charges on the plates constant during the displacement ds because this corresponds to the situation in which the plates are insulated and therefore unconnected to any supply of energy. To use Eq. (10.1) it is therefore essential (1) to express the energy W of the capacitor entirely in terms of the charge Q of the capacitor and not in terms of the voltage and (2) to keep Q constant during the displacement ds. We therefore write

$$W = \frac{1}{2}\frac{Q^2}{C} \tag{10.2}$$

where C is the capacitance of the capacitor given by Eq. (4.23). Substituting this value for C into Eq. (10.2) we derive

$$W = \frac{1}{2}\frac{s}{\epsilon S}Q^2 \tag{10.3}$$

From our discussion of Eq. (10.1) we have seen that the force tending to increase s is

$$F = -\frac{dW}{ds} \qquad \text{at constant } Q \tag{10.4}$$

and if we now substitute from Eq. (10.3) into Eq. (10.4) we derive

$$F = -\frac{1}{2}\frac{1}{\epsilon S}Q^2 \tag{10.5}$$

Let us rewrite Eq. (10.5) as

$$F = -\frac{1}{2}\frac{1}{\epsilon}\left(\frac{Q}{S}\right)^2 S \tag{10.6}$$

so that we can identify Q/S as the charge per unit area on the positive plate of the capacitor and therefore as the electric flux density D in the capacitor. We can then write Eq. (10.6) as

$$F = -\frac{1}{2}\frac{D^2}{\epsilon}S \tag{10.7}$$

or, since D/ϵ is equal to the electric field strength E in the capacitor, as

$$F = -(\tfrac{1}{2}ED)S \tag{10.8}$$

The negative sign tells us that the force is not in fact tending to increase s but to decrease it, or in other words that the force between the plates of the capacitor is attractive.   Since S in Eq. (10.8) is the area of the plates, the magnitude of the force is $\frac{1}{2}DE$ per unit area of a plate.   Thus there is a force of attraction between the plates of the capacitor which, measured per unit area of the plates, has any of the following equivalent values:

$$\frac{1}{2} ED = \frac{1}{2} \epsilon E^2 = \frac{1}{2\epsilon} D^2 \tag{10.9}$$

As a numerical example let us suppose that the plates of the capacitor are 1 mm apart in air and that the voltage of the capacitor is 1,000 volts. The electric field strength is 10^6 volts/m, and from the middle expression in Eqs. (10.9) the force of attraction per unit area of the plates evaluates to be 4.4 newtons/m^2.

The appearance of the factor $\frac{1}{2}$ in the expressions (10.9) is worthy of comment.   Since D is the charge per unit area on a plate and E is the force per unit charge just outside the plate, it might be asked why the force per unit area on the plate is not simply the product of E with D.   It should be noted, however, that while E is the force per unit charge just outside the plate, the force per unit area just within the conductor is zero. Expressions (10.9) show that, to obtain the force per unit area on a plate, the charge per unit area D has to be multiplied by the mean of the force per unit charge E just outside the metal plate and the zero force per unit charge inside the metal plate.

10.3. Tension in Tubes of Flux.   Expressions (10.9) have been shown to give the force per unit area on the plates of a parallel-plate capacitor for which fringing is neglected and for which the electric field strength is E and the electric flux density is D.   For any charged conductor in any system of conductors, there is at every point of the surface an outward force which is perpendicular to the surface of the conductor.   Moreover this force is calculated per unit area of the surface of the conductor from the electric flux density and electric field strength just outside the surface by the expressions (10.9).   This follows immediately from the building-block picture of the electric field illustrated in Fig. 8.3.   The field close to any conductor at a point of its surface is simply the field in the building block touching the conductor at that point, and this is the field of a parallel-plate capacitor with no fringing, to which expressions (10.9) apply.   Hence, if D and E are the electric flux density and electric field strength close to a point of the surface of a conductor, then the outward normal force on the conductor at that point, measured per unit area, is given by expressions (10.9).   By evaluating this force per unit area all over the surface of the conductor and summing the contributions vectorially, we arrive at the total force on the conductor.   This result is

frequently expressed by saying that the tubes of flux attached to a conductor are pulling the conductor and that the total force on the conductor
is the vector sum of the pulls exerted by all the tubes of flux attached to
the conductor.

The concept of tubes of flux pulling the conductors to which they are
attached may be extended by saying that tubes of flux are in tension.
Let us ask what is meant by the statement that a tube of flux is in tension.
Let us first remind ourselves what is meant by the statement that a
stretched string is in tension.   If a string is in tension and the tension is
T, we mean that, if we cut the string at any point, equal and opposite
forces T would have to be introduced at the break in order to maintain the
string in position.   Thus, to decide whether or not tubes of flux are in
tension, we must devise some means of cutting the tubes and examining

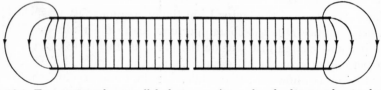

Fig. 10.1. Two rectangular parallel-plate capacitors placed edge to edge to demonstrate the sideways pressure of tubes of flux.

what forces would be required to hold the tubes in position.   Tubes of
flux can be cut by introducing along any equipotential surface a double
layer of metal foil whose potential coincides with that of the equipotential
surface.   At a point on the equipotential surface where the electric flux
density is D and the electric field strength is E, forces per unit area given
by expressions (10.9) act normally outward from the two layers of foil,
tending to pull them apart.   To keep the two layers of foil in position,
therefore, force will be required between them, and the force per unit area
required at each point is given by expressions (10.9).   We may therefore
say that the tubes of flux are in tension and that, at a point where the
electric flux density is D and the electric field strength is E, the tension per
unit cross section is given by expressions (10.9).   It is the tension of tubes
of flux at their points of attachment to a conductor that adds up vectorially to give the total force on the conductor.

10.4. Sideways Pressure of Tubes of Flux.   Tubes of flux, besides
being in tension, exert a sideways pressure on each other.   This sideways
pressure may be regarded as the cause of fringing in a parallel-plate
capacitor.   The tubes of flux between the plates of the capacitor are
pushing each other sideways, and at the edge of the capacitor there would
be nothing to support this outward pressure if fringing did not exist.
The existence of sideways pressure on tubes of flux can be demonstrated
by placing two rectangular parallel-plate capacitors edge to edge as shown

in Fig. 10.1. Forces are required to hold the two capacitors together against the sideways pressure of the tubes of flux in one capacitor on those in the other.

Pressure at a point is defined as the force per unit area at this point, and we shall show that, at a point in an electrostatic field where the electric flux density is D and the electric field strength is E, the sideways pressure of tubes of flux upon each other is given by the same expressions (10.9) previously encountered. To do this consider a short section of a tube of flux as illustrated in Fig. 10.2. There is no objection to regarding this short section of a tube of flux as forming a parallel-plate capacitor with no fringing. It will be convenient to take the plates of this capacitor as circles of radius a and perimeter $2\pi a$. Let s be the distance between the plates. We shall consider a situation in which the radius a of the plates undergoes a small expansion to $a + da$. In this process the work done by the pressure p of the field inside the capacitor is the product of p, of the

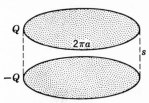

FIG. 10.2. Illustrating the calculation of the sideways pressure of tubes of flux.

area $2\pi as$ of the curved surface of the cylinder in Fig. 10.2, and of the displacement da. Provided that the charges Q and $-Q$ on the plates of the capacitor are kept constant, the work done by the pressure during the expansion is equal to the decrement of the energy of the capacitor. This relation is expressed by the equation

$$p(2\pi as)\, da = -dW \tag{10.10}$$

Hence the sideways pressure of tubes of flux is given by

$$p = -\frac{1}{2\pi as}\frac{dW}{da} \qquad \text{at constant } Q \tag{10.11}$$

It is essential in Eq. (10.11) to use an expression for the energy W of the capacitor expressed in terms of the charge of the capacitor and not in terms of its voltage. We therefore write

$$W = \frac{1}{2}\frac{Q^2}{C} \tag{10.12}$$

where the capacitance C of the capacitor is given in terms of the capacitivity ϵ of the medium and the dimensions of the capacitor by the formula

$$C = \epsilon\frac{\pi a^2}{s} \tag{10.13}$$

Substitution from Eq. (10.13) into Eq. (10.12) gives

$$W = \frac{s}{2\pi\epsilon a^2}Q^2 \tag{10.14}$$

Substitution from this equation into Eq. (10.11) gives

$$p = \frac{1}{2\pi as}\frac{s}{\pi \epsilon a^3} Q^2$$

and this can be rearranged as

$$p = \frac{1}{2\epsilon}\left(\frac{Q}{\pi a^2}\right)^2 \tag{10.15}$$

Now the expression $Q/\pi a^2$ is the charge per unit area on the positive plate of the capacitor and is therefore equal to the electric flux density D in the capacitor. Equation (10.15) can therefore be written

$$p = \frac{1}{2\epsilon} D^2 \tag{10.16}$$

Moreover, since the capacitivity ϵ of the medium is the ratio of the electric flux density D to the electric field strength E in the capacitor, Eq. (10.16) can also be written as

$$p = \tfrac{1}{2}ED \tag{10.17}$$

We therefore see that, in an electrostatic field at a point where the electric flux density is D and the electric field strength is E, the tubes of flux are to be thought of as exerting a sideways pressure on each other given by any of the equivalent expressions

$$\tfrac{1}{2}\,ED = \tfrac{1}{2}\,\epsilon E^2 = \frac{1}{2\epsilon}\,D^2 \tag{10.18}$$

We notice that expressions (10.18) for the sideways pressure of tubes of electric flux are not only identical with expressions (10.9) for the tension in tubes of flux per unit cross-sectional area but are also identical with the expressions (8.23) for the energy per unit volume. Dimensionally, energy per unit volume is identical with force per unit area because energy is force times distance.

10.5. Calculation of Force on a Conductor Using Displacements at Constant Voltage. In connection with Eqs. (10.1) and (10.4) for calculating force from energy by a displacement of the point of application of the force, we have emphasized the necessity of keeping the charges constant. If voltage were kept constant during the displacement, a battery would be required to maintain the constancy of the voltage, and this would introduce energy into or remove energy from the system that would upset Eqs. (10.1) and (10.4). It is, however, possible to derive a modification of Eqs. (10.1) and (10.4) that is applicable when the voltages are kept constant instead of the charges.

Consider a system of conductors on which the charges are denoted by $Q_1, Q_2, \ldots$ and the potentials by $V_1, V_2, \ldots$. In accordance with Eq. (8.9), the energy of the system is given by

$$W = \tfrac{1}{2}\Sigma VQ \qquad (10.19)$$

where Σ denotes summation over the conductors. In any situation involving increments in charges on the conductors of $dQ_1, dQ_2, \ldots$ and increments in the voltages of the conductors of $dV_1, dV_2, \ldots$, the corresponding increase in the potential energy of the system is, taking differentials in Eq. (10.19),

$$dW = \tfrac{1}{2}\Sigma(V\,dQ + Q\,dV) \qquad (10.20)$$

Now suppose that we are interested in calculating a certain force F. Consider a displacement of the system in which the point of application of this force moves through a distance dx. The work done by the force is $F\,dx$ and would be equal to the decrement $-dW$ in the energy of the system if the charges were kept constant. If, however, the charges on the conductors are subject to increments, a charge dQ_1 is brought up to potential V_1, a charge dQ_2 is brought up to potential V_2, and so on. Hence there is introduced into the system an amount of energy $\Sigma V\,dQ$. This introduced energy must be allowed for in relating the work done $F\,dx$ and the decrement $-dW$ in the potential energy of the system. We therefore arrive at the equation

$$F\,dx = -dW + \Sigma V\,dQ \qquad (10.21)$$

which reduces to the usual Eq. (10.1) when the charges are kept constant. By substituting for dW from Eq. (10.20) into Eq. (10.21) we obtain

$$F\,dx = \tfrac{1}{2}\Sigma(V\,dQ - Q\,dV) \qquad (10.22)$$

Now compare expression (10.22) for the work done $F\,dx$ and expression (10.20) for the change dW in the energy of the system. By making the increments of charge vanish, we arrive at the equation

$$F\,dx = -dW \qquad \text{at constant } Q \qquad (10.23)$$

and this is identical with Eq. (10.1). But by making the increments of voltage in Eqs. (10.20) and (10.22) vanish, we arrive at the equation

$$F\,dx = +dW \qquad \text{at constant } V \qquad (10.24)$$

We thus see that, whereas the work done in a displacement in which the charges are kept constant is the decrement in the energy of the system, the work done in a displacement in which the voltages are kept constant is the increment in the energy of the system, the difference in energy being that supplied by the batteries maintaining the constant voltages. We can therefore apply the energy method to calculate force using displacements at constant voltage provided that we use the positive sign in Eq. (10.24) instead of the negative sign in Eq. (10.23).

As an example, let us use the constant-voltage method to calculate the force of attraction between the plates of a parallel-plate capacitor. If s is the distance between the plates, the force tending to increase s is, in accordance with Eq. (10.24),

$$F = + \frac{dW}{ds} \qquad \text{at constant } V \qquad (10.25)$$

In using this equation we must express the energy W in the capacitor in terms of the voltage of the capacitor and not in terms of its charge. We therefore write

$$W = \tfrac{1}{2}CV^2 \qquad (10.26)$$

where C is the capacitance of the capacitor. This is given in terms of the capacitivity ϵ of the medium between the plates, the area S of the plates, and the separation s between the plates by Eq. (4.23). Substitution from Eq. (4.23) into Eq. (10.26) gives

$$W = \frac{1}{2} \frac{\epsilon S}{s} V^2 \qquad (10.27)$$

This is the expression for the energy in terms of the voltage of the capacitor to be substituted into Eq. (10.25). We obtain

$$F = - \frac{1}{2} \frac{\epsilon S}{s^2} V^2 \qquad (10.28)$$

or, since V/s is the electric field strength E in the capacitor,

$$F = -(\tfrac{1}{2}\epsilon E^2)S \qquad (10.29)$$

The negative sign indicates as before that the force is in fact one tending to decrease s, and the magnitude of the force per unit area of plate given by Eq. (10.29) leads to the same expressions (10.9) as before.

We thus see that force can be calculated from energy either by expressing the energy in terms of the charges and keeping the charges constant in a displacement or by expressing the energy in terms of the voltages and keeping the voltages constant in a displacement. In the former case we use Eq. (10.23) and in the latter Eq. (10.24). Use of the wrong equation leads to a force of the right magnitude pointing in the direction reverse to the true direction. The direction of the force is, however, frequently obvious. Thus for the parallel-plate capacitor it is clear that the force between the plates is one of attraction and it is only the magnitude that needs to be calculated.

SUMMARIZING EXERCISES

10.1. Explain how the principle of virtual work can be used for calculating the force on a conductor in electrostatics.   State why, when equating the virtual work of the forces to the decrement in potential energy of the system, it is necessary to ensure that the charges on the conductors remain constant.

10.2. A parallel-plate capacitor has plates of area S with a separation s.   The capacitivity of the medium between the plates is ϵ, and fringing can be neglected. Calculate an expression for the potential energy W stored in the capacitor in terms of the charges $\pm Q$ on the plates, and not involving the potential difference between the plates.   Prove that the force tending to increase s is $-dW/ds$, provided that Q is kept constant.   Evaluate this force, and show that it is equivalent to a force $\frac{1}{2}ED$ per unit area on each plate directed toward the opposite plate, where E is the electric field strength and D is the electric flux density in the capacitor.

10.3. Explain what is meant by the statement that the tubes of electric flux in an electrostatic field are in tension.   Show that, at a point in an electrostatic field where the electric field strength is E and the electric flux density is D, the tension in a tube of electric flux is $\frac{1}{2}ED$ per unit cross-sectional area.

10.4. Explain what is meant by the statement that the tubes of electric flux in an electrostatic field exert sideways pressure on each other.   Show that, at a point in an electrostatic field where the electric field strength is E and the electric flux density is D, the sideways pressure exerted by a tube of electric flux is $\frac{1}{2}ED$.

10.5. Explain a method whereby the force on a conductor in electrostatics can be calculated by means of a displacement in which the potentials of the conductors are kept constant instead of the charges.

CHAPTER 11

ELECTROSTATICS OF TRANSMISSION LINES

11.1. Introduction. The importance of using metallic wires to connect two points together has frequently come to our attention. In electrostatics the process of connecting two points together by a metallic wire is a means of ensuring that the two points are at the same potential. To ensure that the potential difference between two close points A and B is the same as the potential difference between two points A' and B', we can connect A to A' by means of a wire and B to B' by means of another wire. Such wire pairs are commonly used in electrical engineering and are known as transmission lines. Two important practical cases occur. One is the twin-wire transmission line in which the two wires forming the transmission line are parallel conducting wires of the same diameter. The other is the coaxial transmission line in which one conductor is a hollow circular cylinder and the other conductor is a wire running down the axis of this cylinder. A length of either of these transmission lines forms a capacitor the capacitance of which we are interested in calculating.

11.2. Electric Field of an Infinite Line Charge. Let us suppose that we have a straight wire whose diameter is extremely small and whose

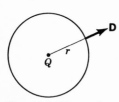

FIG. 11.1. Illustrating the calculation of the electric flux density for an infinite line charge.

length is extremely great. Let it be embedded in a medium of uniform capacitivity ϵ. Let us suppose that the wire carries a charge Q per unit length, the same at all points of the wire. It is clear from symmetry that the lines of force run radially outward from the wire and lie in planes perpendicular to the wire as indicated in Fig. 11.1. It is also clear from symmetry that the electric field strength at any point is a function only of the perpendicular distance r from the point to the wire. Thus, assuming that Q is positive, the electric vector $\mathbf{E}$ is radially outward from the wire, and its magnitude is a function of r only. The electric-flux-density vector $\mathbf{D}$ is also radially outward from the wire, and its magnitude is a function of r only. Moreover the electric potential ϕ is a function of r only, so that the equipotential surfaces are circular cylinders coaxial with the wire.

162

Let us first calculate the electric flux density D at distance r from the wire. If we think of a situation in which the charge Q existing between two geometrical planes perpendicular to the wire at unit distance apart is discharged along lines of force, we see that, at distance r from the wire, the charge Q is distributed uniformly over the curved surface of a cylinder of radius r and unit length. The area of this curved surface being $2\pi r$, it follows that

$$D(2\pi r) = Q \qquad (11.1)$$

The argument leading to this equation can also be stated as follows. Apply Gauss' theorem to the closed geometrical surface formed by a circular cylinder of radius r coaxial with the wire, cut off by two planes perpendicular to the wire at unit distance apart. There is no electric flux out of the flat ends of this closed surface because the normal component of the electric-flux-density vector is zero. However, the electric flux out of the curved surface of the cylinder is equal to the expression on the left-hand side of Eq. (11.1). By Gauss' theorem this is equal to the charge within the closed surface, and this is the charge Q on a unit length of the wire. We thus arrive at Eq. (11.1). From this equation we deduce that

$$D = \frac{Q}{2\pi r} \qquad (11.2)$$

Thus the electric flux density for an infinite line charge is inversely proportional to distance from the wire.

We derive the electric field strength E at distance r from the wire by dividing the electric flux density D by the uniform capacitivity ϵ of the medium. We thus derive from Eq. (11.2)

$$E = \frac{Q}{2\pi\epsilon}\frac{1}{r} \qquad (11.3)$$

We see that the electric field strength of an infinite line charge is also inversely proportional to distance from the wire. Equations (11.2) and (11.3) are to be compared and contrasted with Eqs. (4.24) and (4.26) giving the electric flux density and electric field strength for a point charge Q.

Since the electric vector is the downward gradient of the electric potential ϕ, Eq. (11.3) can be rewritten as

$$-\frac{d\phi}{dr} = \frac{Q}{2\pi\epsilon}\frac{1}{r} \qquad (11.4)$$

Integration of this equation with respect to r gives

$$\phi = -\frac{Q}{2\pi\epsilon}\ln r + \text{constant} \qquad (11.5)$$

The constant in this equation can be chosen to make the electric potential ϕ have any specified value at any specified distance from the wire. It cannot, however, be chosen to make the potential of the wire zero. Mathematically this is because ln r tends to minus infinity as r tends to zero. Physically it is because we have assumed so far that the wire has zero radius. What is more surprising is that the constant in Eq. (11.5) cannot be chosen so as to make the potential zero at infinity. Mathematically this is because ln r tends to infinity as r tends to infinity. Physically it is because we are dealing with a charged system which itself extends to infinity. In practice we would be dealing with a wire which, although long, had a finite length, and it would then be feasible to take the potential as zero at infinity if desired.

11.3. The Coaxial Transmission Line. Consider a coaxial transmission line consisting of two coaxial metal cylinders as shown in Fig. 11.2.

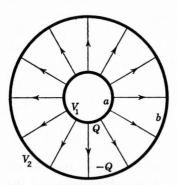

Let the space between the cylinders have an inner radius a and an outer radius b, and let it be filled with a medium of uniform capacitivity ϵ. The cylinders may be supposed to have infinite length, and we are interested in calculating the capacitance per unit length of the transmission line.

We arrive at the electric field of a coaxial transmission line by starting with the electric field of an infinite line charge carrying a charge Q per unit length. For this field the equipotential surfaces are circular cylinders coaxial with the line

FIG. 11.2. The electric field of a coaxial transmission line.

charge. The electric potential ϕ is given as a function of distance r from the line charge by Eq. 11.5. On the equipotential surface $r = a$ the potential is

$$V_1 = -\frac{Q}{2\pi\epsilon} \ln a + \text{constant} \tag{11.6}$$

and on the equipotential surface $r = b$ the potential is

$$V_2 = -\frac{Q}{2\pi\epsilon} \ln b + \text{constant} \tag{11.7}$$

Replace the equipotential surface $r = a$ by a conductor at the potential given by expression (11.6). Likewise replace the equipotential surface $r = b$ by a conductor at the potential given by expression (11.7). Now retain only the electric field between these two conductors. We then have the field in the coaxial transmission line shown in Fig. 11.2 under circumstances when the inner conductor carries a charge Q per unit length and the outer conductor carries a charge $-Q$ per unit length on its inner surface. By subtracting Eq. (11.7) from Eq. (11.6) we see that the excess of potential of the inner conductor over the outer conductor in these circumstances is

$$V_1 - V_2 = \frac{Q}{2\pi\epsilon} (\ln b - \ln a)$$

and this can be rewritten as

$$V_1 - V_2 = \frac{Q}{2\pi\epsilon} \ln \frac{b}{a} \qquad (11.8)$$

Now the capacitance per unit length of the transmission line is the ratio of the charge per unit length to the resulting difference of potential between the conductors. Hence the capacitance per unit length of the transmission line is

$$C = \frac{Q}{V_1 - V_2} \qquad (11.9)$$

and by substitution from Eq. (11.8) into Eq. (11.9) we derive

$$C = \frac{2\pi\epsilon}{\ln (b/a)} \qquad (11.10)$$

Thus the capacitance per unit length of a coaxial transmission line is directly proportional to the capacitivity of the medium between the conductors and inversely proportional to the natural logarithm of the ratio of the radii.

If b/a is about 2.7, which is not an unusual ratio of radii, the denominator in Eq. (11.10) is approximately unity, since the base e of natural logarithms is approximately 2.7. In these circumstances expression (11.10) reduces to $2\pi\epsilon$, and for free space this evaluates to about 56 $\mu\mu$f/m.

11.4. The Twin-wire Transmission Line. Consider a transmission line consisting of a pair of long straight wires, each of radius a, with their centers at a distance d apart. It is usually true in practice that d is large compared with a, and it will simplify the calculation to make this assumption. Let the medium surrounding the wires have a uniform capacitivity ϵ. We are interested in calculating the capacitance per unit length of the transmission line.

We start by considering a twin-wire transmission line for which the wires have zero radius and are at distance d apart, one wire having a charge Q per unit length and the other wire having a charge $-Q$ per unit length. Each wire then constitutes an infinite line charge of the type studied in Sec. 11.2. At a point whose perpendicular distance from the line charge Q per unit length is r_1 and whose perpendicular distance from the line charge $-Q$ per unit length is r_2, the electric potential, from Eq. (11.5), is

$$\phi = -\frac{Q}{2\pi\epsilon} \ln r_1 + \frac{Q}{2\pi\epsilon} \ln r_2 + \text{constant} \qquad (11.11)$$

and this can be rewritten as

$$\phi = \frac{Q}{2\pi\epsilon} \ln \frac{r_2}{r_1} + \text{constant} \qquad (11.12)$$

From this equation we see that the equipotential surfaces of the pair of equal and opposite line charges are the cylindrical surfaces whose equations are

$$\frac{r_2}{r_1} = \text{constant} \qquad (11.13)$$

and the lines of forces are the lines that intersect these surfaces at right angles. The lines of force and equipotential surfaces are shown in Fig. 11.3. The lines of force lie in planes perpendicular to the line charges,

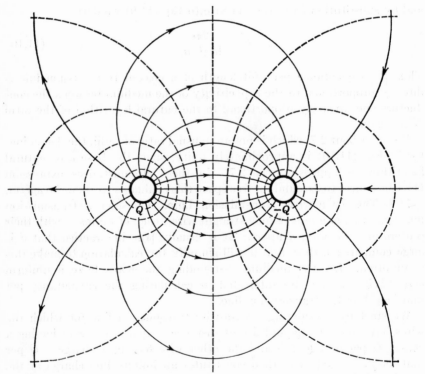

FIG. 11.3. The electric field of a twin-wire transmission line.

and each is an arc of a circle passing through the two line charges. The equipotential surfaces are circular cylinders with axes parallel to the line charges and enveloping either the line charge Q per unit length or the line charge $-Q$ per unit length. One of the equipotential surfaces is the symmetrical plane between the two line charges, and if the potential on this plane is taken as zero, the constant in Eq. (11.12) is zero.

Close to the line charges the equipotential surfaces become cylinders whose axes nearly coincide with the line charges. On such a small cylinder enveloping the charge Q per unit length the value of r_1 is practically the radius of the cylinder and the value of r_2 is practically the distance d between the line charges. On a small cylinder enveloping the charge $-Q$ per unit length the value of r_1 is practically the distance d between the line charges and the value of r_2 is practically the radius of the cylinder. Replace the small cylinder $r_1 = a$, which envelops the line charge Q per unit length, by a conductor at the potential

$$V_1 = \frac{Q}{2\pi\epsilon} \ln \frac{d}{a} + \text{constant} \tag{11.14}$$

This equation is obtained by putting $r_1 = a$ and $r_2 = d$ in Eq. (11.12). Replace the small cylinder $r_2 = a$, which envelops the line charge $-Q$ per unit length, by a conductor at potential

$$V_2 = \frac{Q}{2\pi\epsilon} \ln \frac{a}{d} + \text{constant} \tag{11.15}$$

This equation is obtained by putting $r_1 = d$ and $r_2 = a$ in Eq. (11.12). Now let us retain only the electric field existing between the two conductors. We then have the electric field of a twin-wire transmission line formed by two wires of small radius a at a distance d apart. The excess of the potential of the wire carrying charge Q per unit length over the wire carrying charge $-Q$ per unit length is obtained by subtracting Eq. (11.15) from Eq. (11.14) and is

$$V_1 - V_2 = \frac{Q}{2\pi\epsilon} \left(\ln \frac{d}{a} - \ln \frac{a}{d} \right)$$

which can be simplified to

$$V_1 - V_2 = \frac{Q}{\pi\epsilon} \ln \frac{d}{a} \tag{11.16}$$

The capacitance per unit length of the line is

$$C = \frac{Q}{V_1 - V_2} \tag{11.17}$$

and so, by substitution from Eq. (11.16) into Eq. (11.17), we derive

$$C = \frac{\pi\epsilon}{\ln{(d/a)}} \qquad (11.18)$$

The capacitance per unit length of a twin-wire transmission line is therefore proportional to the capacitivity of the medium and inversely proportional to the natural logarithm of the ratio of the separation between the wires to the radius of the wires.

A typical value for d/a is 10, and the natural logarithm of this ratio is 2.3. If the medium is air, we then derive for the capacitance per unit length of the line the value 12 $\mu\mu$f/m. We notice that the typical capacitance per unit length of a twin-wire transmission line is several times less than that for a coaxial transmission line.

For a twin-wire transmission line in which one wire carries a charge Q per unit length and the other wire carries a charge $-Q$ per unit length there is a force of attraction between the two wires. This force of attraction, measured per unit length, is easily calculated as follows: The electric field strength at one wire due to the other wire is, from Eq. (11.3),

$$\frac{Q}{2\pi\epsilon}\frac{1}{d} \qquad (11.19)$$

This is the force per unit charge on a wire carrying a charge Q per unit length. Hence the force of attraction between the wires per unit length is the product of Q with expression (11.19) and is therefore

$$\frac{1}{2\pi\epsilon}\frac{Q^2}{d} \qquad (11.20)$$

If Q equals 1 μcoulomb/m ($= 10^{-6}$ coulomb/m), d equals 10 cm ($= 10^{-1}$ m), and the medium is air, the attraction per unit length between the wires evaluates to about 0.2 newton/m.

11.5. Use of Complex Numbers. Problems involving only parallel wires and conductors in which the field is not dependent on the coordinate measured parallel to the wires can be solved with the aid of complex numbers. In a plane perpendicular to the length of the wires, let (x,y) be the cartesian coordinates of any point and let us introduce a complex number

$$z = x + jy \qquad (11.21)$$

to describe the position of the point. Now consider any function of z, denoted by $f(z)$. This can be any analytic function of z, such as log z, cos z, and so on. Let the real and imaginary parts of $f(z)$ be ϕ and ψ, so that

$$\phi + j\psi = f(z) \qquad (11.22)$$

ϕ and ψ are functions of x and y, and we can plot in the (x,y) plane families of curves given by the equations

$$\phi(x,y) = \text{constant} \tag{11.23}$$

and
$$\psi(x,y) = \text{constant} \tag{11.24}$$

using a series of values for the constants. In books concerned with tabulating and plotting functions (such as "Tables of Functions," by Jahnke and Emde), maps of the curves given by Eqs. (11.23) and (11.24) are given for many well-known functions. It is shown in books on functions of a complex variable that the properties of the curves corresponding to Eq. (11.23) are such that they represent the equipotential surfaces of an electrostatic field of which the curves corresponding to Eq. (11.24) are the lines of force. The particular electrostatic field represented depends on the function chosen for $f(z)$ in Eq. (11.22). By plotting the families of curves corresponding to Eqs. (11.23) and (11.24) for a series of well-known functions $f(z)$ in Eq. (11.22) we can build up a library of electrostatic fields available for use as required. In this way the solutions of a number of interesting problems can be recognized. For example, by taking $f(z)$ in Eq. (11.22) to be log z we arrive at the fields discussed in Secs. 11.2 and 11.3.

Using the method of complex numbers it is possible to give a much more satisfactory discussion of the electrostatic properties of a planar-triode vacuum tube than was given in Sec. 9.4. Suppose that the planar triode is constructed as shown in Fig. 11.4. The grid (electrode 2) is supposed to consist of parallel wires, each of radius a with their centers at a distance d apart large compared with a, the wires being all at the same potential. The center plane of the grid is supposed to be at a

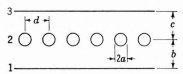

Fig. 11.4. A planar-triode vacuum tube.

distance b from the cathode (electrode 1) and at a distance c from the anode (electrode 3). We suppose that the area of electrodes 1 and 3 is S, and we neglect fringing at the edges of these electrodes. In the vicinity of the wires of the grid, however, full allowance is made for the fact that lines of force must intersect the surfaces of the wires at right angles. Using the method of complex numbers, the mutual capacitance between the cathode and the grid evaluates to

$$c_{12} = -\epsilon_v S \, \frac{c/\alpha}{b + c + bc/\alpha} \tag{11.25}$$

where
$$\alpha = \frac{d}{2\pi} \ln \frac{d}{2\pi a} \tag{11.26}$$

Likewise the mutual capacitance between the cathode and the anode evaluates to

$$c_{13} = -\epsilon_v S \frac{1}{b + c + bc/\alpha} \tag{11.27}$$

By dividing Eq. (11.25) by Eq. (11.27) we see that

$$\frac{c_{12}}{c_{13}} = \frac{c}{\alpha} \tag{11.28}$$

As described in Sec. 9.4 this ratio is the amplification factor μ of the tube. On substituting from Eq. (11.26) into Eq. (11.28) we derive

$$\mu = \frac{2\pi c}{d \ln (d/2\pi a)} \tag{11.29}$$

If $a = 0.1$ mm $(10^{-4}\,\mathrm{m})$, $d = 1$ mm $(10^{-3}\,\mathrm{m})$, and $c = 3$ mm $(3 \times 10^{-3}\,\mathrm{m})$, the amplification factor given by Eq. (11.29) evaluates to 35.

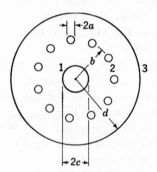

FIG. 11.5. A cylindrical-triode vacuum tube.

For the cylindrical triode illustrated in Fig. 11.5 the grid (electrode 2) consists of n equidistant wires of radius a, with their axes on a cylinder of radius b, the radii of the wires being small compared with their separations. The cathode (electrode 1) is the inner cylindrical conductor of radius c, and the anode (electrode 3) is the outer cylindrical conductor of radius d. The cylinders are supposed to have length l, and fringing at their ends is neglected. Using the method of complex numbers, the mutual capacitance between the cathode and the grid evaluates to

$$c_{12} = -\frac{2\pi\epsilon_v l \ln \dfrac{d}{b}}{\ln \dfrac{d}{b} \ln \dfrac{b}{c} + \dfrac{1}{n} \ln \dfrac{b}{na} \ln \dfrac{d}{c}} \tag{11.30}$$

and the mutual capacitance between the cathode and the anode evaluates to

$$c_{13} = - \cfrac{2\pi\epsilon_v l \dfrac{1}{n} \ln \dfrac{b}{na}}{\ln \dfrac{d}{b} \ln \dfrac{b}{c} + \dfrac{1}{n} \ln \dfrac{b}{na} \ln \dfrac{d}{c}} \tag{11.31}$$

By dividing Eq. (11.30) by Eq. (11.31) we deduce that the amplification factor of the tube is

$$\mu = n \frac{\ln (d/b)}{\ln (b/na)} \tag{11.32}$$

If $a = 0.1$ mm (10^{-4} m), $b = 1.5$ mm (1.5×10^{-3} m), $d = 6$ mm (6×10^{-3} m), and $n = 10$, the amplification factor given by Eq. (11.32) evaluates to 34.

SUMMARIZING EXERCISES

11.1. An indefinitely long, thin, straight conducting wire is embedded in a homogeneous dielectric of capacitivity ϵ. The wire carries a uniform charge Q per unit length. Calculate the electric flux density and the electric field strength at a point whose perpendicular distance from the axis of the wire is r.

11.2. For the same arrangement calculate the electric potential at a point whose perpendicular distance from the axis of the wire is r. Explain why the potential cannot be taken as zero at infinity.

11.3. The space between the inner and outer conductor of a coaxial transmission line has inner radius a and outer radius b and is filled with a homogeneous dielectric of capacitivity ϵ. Calculate the capacitance per unit length of the transmission line.

11.4. A twin-wire transmission line consists of a pair of long parallel wires, each of radius a, having a separation d between their axes, and d is large compared with a. The wires are embedded in a homogeneous dielectric of capacitivity ϵ. If the charge per unit length on one wire is Q and that on the other wire is $-Q$, calculate the electric potential at a point distant r_1 from the axis of one wire and r_2 from the axis of the other wire. Sketch the equipotential surfaces and lines of force, and deduce the capacitance per unit length of the transmission line.

PART 2

STEADY ELECTRIC CURRENTS AND VACUUM TUBES

CHAPTER 1

CONDUCTANCE AND RESISTANCE

1.1. Introduction. In electrostatics (Part 1) we studied distributions of electric charge that had reached an equilibrium state and were no longer in motion. We now proceed to consider some of the phenomena associated with electrical charge in motion. In electrical science, electrostatics plays the part that statics does in mechanical science, and we are now proceeding to what in electrical science corresponds to dynamics. In dynamics there are important differences between accelerated motion and unaccelerated motion. For similar reasons there are important differences in electrical science between electric currents that change with time and electric currents that are steady. It is steady electric currents that we are now to study.

Steady electric currents involve electric charges, usually electrons, in motion under electrostatic fields. Consider the electrostatic field of a charged capacitor. A charged capacitor carries equal and opposite amounts of electric charge on its plates, and as a result there is an electric field between the plates. This electric field is such that a positively charged particle between the plates is subject to a force attracting it toward the negative plate and a negatively charged particle between the plates is subject to a force attracting it toward the positive plate. If the capacitor holds its charge, the insulating medium between the plates of the capacitor must contain no charged particles (such as electrons) free of drift through the medium, for otherwise the electric field in the capacitor would cause these free charges to move and in the course of time the capacitor would be discharged. In actual fact, insulating materials between the plates of capacitors are never perfect, and in consequence capacitors do not hold their charge very long. The charge on the negative plate leaks through the insulator in the form of drifting electrons until it neutralizes the positive charge on the positive plate. While the charge is drifting through the medium between the plates, it is said to constitute an electric current. Now let us suppose that the capacitor is connected to a battery of given voltage. As the charges on the plates of the capacitor leak away through the medium, more charge is supplied by the battery. A situation is thus created in which there is a steady drift of charge through the medium between the plates of the capacitor, and this forms what is known as a steady electric current. In these circumstances the imperfect insulator between the plates of the capacitor is often referred to as a resistor, and the battery is said to be maintaining a steady electric current through the resistor. We are now going to study situations in which batteries maintain steady electric currents through resistors.

A steady electric current is often referred to as a direct current. Strictly speaking, a direct current involves a situation in which the direction of flow of charge is always the same and is to be contrasted to an alternating current, which involves a situation in which the current flows in opposite directions in alternate intervals of time. In practice, however, the expression "direct current" is generally used to describe a situation in which not only the direction of flow of charge remains the same but also the magnitude of the flow. Thus the expression direct current is used to describe a situation in which the flow of charge is steady both in magnitude and in direction. The standard abbreviation for direct current is d-c.

1.2. Voltaic Cell. Let us give some consideration to the way in which a battery maintains its voltage and supplies electric charge. A battery usually consists of a number of voltaic cells, each of which may be thought of as a capacitor having an unusual feature. A voltaic cell possesses two plates between which there is a medium that is frequently liquid. In some cases the liquid is made up in paste or jelly form so as to render it unspillable. The plates of a voltaic cell are usually known as its electrodes, and the liquid between the plates as the electrolyte. In order that this arrangement may function as a voltaic cell, the substances used for the electrodes and for the electrolyte must be specially chosen. Between the electrolyte and at least one of the electrodes there must be a chemical reaction such that electrons become attached to the electrode and the corresponding positively charged molecules remain in the electrolyte. When the substances are chosen in this way, the voltaic cell acts as a self-charging capacitor.

Let us simplify the behavior of a voltaic cell by supposing that there is a chemical reaction between the electrolyte and only one of the electrodes. Furthermore let us suppose that the electrodes and the electrolyte are good electrical conductors. The electrolyte does not constitute a short circuit between the two electrodes because of the chemical reaction in progress at the surface of the active electrode. When an uncharged molecule of electrolyte hits the active electrode, an electron becomes attached to the electrode, and the remainder of the molecule, which is positively charged, bounces back into the electrolyte. Thus the electrolyte close to the active electrode becomes positively charged,

and the active electrode itself becomes negatively charged. As this
process continues, an electric field builds up between the positive charge
in the electrolyte and the negative charge on the active electrode in the
same way as in a capacitor.   However, this electric field tends to pull the
positively charged molecules of electrolyte toward the negatively charged
active electrode.   A steady state is reached when the electric field is
returning positively charged molecules of electrolyte to the negatively
charged active electrode at the same rate as separation of these charges
is being produced by the chemical reaction.   This steady state is one
in which there is a layer of positively charged molecules of electrolyte
close to the negatively charged active electrode, the separation between
the layers of positive and negative charge being of the order of the radius

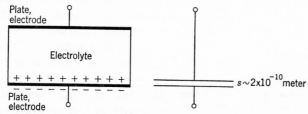

FIG. 1.1. Illustrating the operation of a voltaic cell with one active electrode.

of a molecule.   The surface where the electrolyte comes in "contact"
with the active electrode is therefore to be thought of as a parallel-plate
capacitor with positive charge on the electrolyte and negative charge
on the electrode, the distance between these layers of charge being of the
order of the radius of a molecule.   This distance is about 2×10^{-10} m.
Thus a voltaic cell constructed as shown on the left-hand side of Fig. 1.1
is to be thought of as a capacitor like that illustrated on the right-hand
side of Fig. 1.1.   This capacitor has an area S equal to the area of the
active electrode and a separation s equal to the molecular separation
between the positively charged surface of the electrolyte and the negatively charged surface of the active electrode.   The capacitor on the
right-hand side of Fig. 1.1 is to be thought of as maintained in a charged
condition as a result of the chemical process going on between the electrolyte and the active electrode.

   The voltage that develops between the electrolyte and the active
electrode in a steady state is that required to return positively charged
molecules of electrolyte to the active electrode at the same rate as the
chemical process is producing fresh positively charged molecules of electrolyte.   This voltage depends somewhat upon the substance used for
the active electrode and that used for the electrolyte, but is of the order
of a volt or two.   If there is a chemical reaction between the electrolyte
and both electrodes of the cell, then there is a voltage between the

electrolyte and each electrode. In these circumstances the voltage developed between the terminals of the cell is the algebraic sum of the voltages developed at the surfaces of the two electrodes. This voltage is usually of the order of 1.5 volts.

Because the separation between the positive and negative charge in a voltaic cell is of molecular dimensions, the capacitance of the capacitor so formed is high. From the formula for the capacitance of a parallel-plate capacitor in free space it is easily calculated that the capacitance involved in a voltaic cell is of the order of a few microfarads per square centimeter of active electrode and that the stored electrical energy is of the order of several joules per square centimeter of active electrode. If the cell is used to charge an external capacitor, the capacitor of high capacitance that constitutes the cell shares some of its charge with the external capacitor to which it is connected. This upsets the steady state within the cell, and the chemical reaction proceeds to restore this steady state and maintain the voltage of the cell.

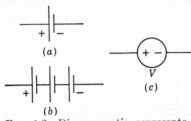

Fig. 1.2. Diagrammatic representation of (a) a single voltaic cell, (b) a battery, (c) a source of voltage V.

If a voltaic cell is connected across a resistor, then there is a steady drain of charge through the resistor, and the chemical process operates to make good this drain of charge and maintain the voltage of the cell.

We may say that a voltaic cell is a capacitor of high capacitance charged to a potential difference of about 1.5 volts; with the capacitor there is associated a chemical process that does its best to replace any charge removed from the plates and to maintain at a constant value the voltage between the terminals. If charge is to be removed externally from one terminal of a voltaic cell to the other at a rapid rate, the chemical process can maintain the flow only if large charges are stored in the cell. This means that the cell must have a high capacitance and therefore a large area of active electrode. This can be produced if desired by connecting together the positive terminals of a number of small cells and likewise connecting together the negative terminals, thereby producing from the group of cells a single cell with electrodes of large area. When it is necessary to produce voltages larger than about 1.5 volts, this can be done by connecting the positive terminal of one cell to the negative terminal of another, thereby making available a voltage of about 3 volts. More or less any voltage can be produced by connecting together a sufficient number of cells. Cells connected in this way are said to form a battery. Single cells and batteries are often represented diagrammatically as shown in Fig. 1.2a and b. When the precise form of the source of voltage is not of particular interest, but only the value of the voltage, the diagrammatic representation shown in Fig. 1.2c is frequently used.

1.3. Steady Electric Current (or Direct Current). Let us consider a situation in which a voltaic cell is employed to maintain a steady current in a resistor, and let us make the arrangements sufficiently simple so that we can see the process whereby the cell produces the current. Let us therefore consider an ideal voltaic cell of the type shown in Fig. 1.1. Let us suppose that the conducting electrodes of the cell are extended outside the cell in the form of conducting strips as shown in Fig. 1.3.

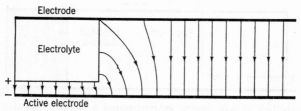

FIG. 1.3. Illustrating the process whereby a voltaic cell is used to produce an external electric field.

This arrangement then constitutes a charged capacitor for which one conductor is composed of the electrolyte, the inactive electrode, and the conducting strip connected to this electrode, while the other conductor is composed of the active electrode together with the conducting strip connected to this electrode. The lines of force and the equipotential surfaces are as indicated in Fig. 1.3 assuming that we neglect fringing at the edge of the conducting strips. Let us now take a piece of dielectric material in the form of a cylinder whose ends are normal cross sections. Let the length of the cylinder be equal to the separation between the conducting strips in Fig. 1.3. Let us fit this piece of dielectric between the conducting strips near the ends opposite those to which the cell is attached. We suppose that the dimensions are such that each flat end of the dielectric cylinder is at all points in contact with a conducting strip. If the dielectric is a perfect insulator, its insertion will have no effect upon the electric field between the strips, but the charge per unit area on the portions of the strips in contact with the dielectric will be increased in the ratio of the dielectric constant. Now let us suppose that the dielectric is not perfect but that some electrons exist in it that are not bound to atoms and that in consequence are free to drift through the dielectric under the influence of the electric field. This drift of electrons would discharge the capacitor if the charges of the conductors were not replenished as a result of the chemical reaction in the voltaic cell. As a result there is a current of electric charge round the system as indicated in Fig. 1.4.   The direction of the arrows in Fig. 1.4 illustrates the direction in which charges would flow round the circuit if they were positive.   In actual fact the free charges in the imperfect dielectric and in the conducting strips are electrons and are therefore negative.   These electrons consequently move in the direction opposite the arrows shown in Fig. 1.4. The direction of electric current is always specified by the direction of movement of the free charges assuming that these charges are positive. Since electric currents are most commonly produced by drifts of electrons, it has to be remembered that the direction of drift of the electrons is opposite the direction that we regard as the direction of the electric

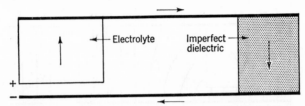

FIG. 1.4. Illustrating steady electric current round a circuit consisting of an ideal voltaic cell, a cylindrical piece of imperfect dielectric, and a pair of conducting strips joining them.

current.   It would have been more convenient if the convention concerning positive and negative charge had been chosen so as to make the charge on an electron positive, but the historical development of the subject was unfortunately such that the opposite convention came into use.

Let us consider more carefully the process whereby charge flows round the circuit illustrated in Fig. 1.4.   It is convenient to do this first of all in a rather oversimplified way.   Let us assume that electrons can drift so easily through the conducting strips that virtually no force is required to move an electron from one end to the other of either conducting strip. On the other hand, it will be assumed that substantial force is required to drive an electron through the imperfect dielectric.   This force is provided by the electric field of the battery brought to bear upon the dielectric by means of the conducting strips.   Let us examine the process whereby electrons drift through the imperfect dielectric under the influence of the electric field between the conducting strips.

It has to be realized that, while the free electrons in the imperfect dielectric acquire a mean drift velocity under the influence of the applied electric field, nevertheless no individual electron is moving through the dielectric with a steady velocity.   An electron starting from the lower edge of the imperfect dielectric in Fig. 1.4 is accelerated upward by the electric field between the conducting strips.   This is a uniform acceleration and continues until the electron collides with a molecule of the dielectric.   Its movement parallel to the lines of electric force is more or less stopped by this collision, and the electron is again accelerated from zero velocity by the electric field until it makes another collision with a molecule of the dielectric.   Thus an electron drifts through the imperfect dielectric as a result of successive accelerations from rest following collisions.   This leads to a mean drift of electrons through the dielectric in spite of the fact that each individual electron is either being accelerated by the electric field or being stopped by a collision.   The drift of free electrons through the imperfect dielectric can be compared with the movement of traffic across a busy city.   The total time of transit across the city might perhaps be evaluated on the basis of a mean speed of 15 mph.   This does not, however, mean that cars are moving through the city with a uniform speed of 15 mph.   On the contrary they are continually accelerating from rest to 30 mph and then having to stop again.   In the same way a steady electric current does not imply a situation in which electrons are drifting through a substance with uniform velocity, but a situation in which they are being uniformly accelerated by an electric field and the acceleration is being continually interrupted by collisions with molecules.

The process whereby electrons are driven through the conducting strips in Fig. 1.4 is in principle the same as that by which they are driven through the imperfect dielectric.   However, the forces called into play in the case of the conducting metal strips are far smaller than are required for the imperfect dielectric, and for the time being we neglect them.

The process whereby electric current moves through the electrolyte of the voltaic cell is somewhat different from that whereby it moves through the imperfect dielectric.   An electron made available at the surface of the inactive electrode does not pass through the electrolyte by itself.   Instead it becomes attached to a molecule of the liquid electrolyte, thereby forming a negatively charged molecule.   The current through the electrolyte is formed by a downward drift of negatively charged molecules of liquid electrolyte combined with upward drift of positively charged molecules of liquid electrolyte.   However, the forces required to create this drift in the electrolyte are smaller than are required to produce the drift of electrons through the imperfect dielectric, and for the time being we neglect them.   Thus the only part of the circuit shown in Fig. 1.4 for which significant force is required to drive the electric current is that formed by the imperfect dielectric.

We can thus describe the process whereby the voltaic cell drives electric current through the imperfect dielectric as follows: Each molecule of electrolyte separated by the chemical process into a positively charged molecule at the lower surface of the electrolyte and an electron on the active electrode increases the charge on the system thought of as a capacitor and thereby increases the electrostatic energy stored in the system. Each electron accelerated through the imperfect dielectric between one collision and the next converts some of the electrostatic energy of the system into kinetic energy. This is kinetic energy associated with motion of the electron round the circuit up to the moment when the electron makes a collision. At the collision the kinetic energy of the ordered motion of the electron round the circuit is converted into kinetic energy of disordered motion, and this is what is known as heat. Thus the process of charge separation at the active electrode of the voltaic cell is continually making increments in the electrostatic energy

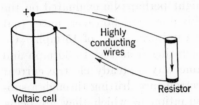

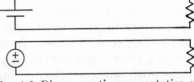

FIG. 1.5. Illustrating a circuit formed by a flashlight cell connected by conducting wires to a resistor.

FIG. 1.6. Diagrammatic representation of a voltaic cell connected to a resistor by highly conducting wires.

of the system, and the process of accelerating electrons between collisions in the dielectric is continually making decrements in the electrostatic energy of the system. The atomic energy originally stored in the molecules of electrolyte is converted first into electrostatic energy of the system thought of as a capacitor, then into kinetic energy of the ordered motion of the electrons in the imperfect dielectric, and then, by collisions, into the disordered motion of heat in the imperfect dielectric. As the imperfect dielectric becomes hotter, it loses heat to its surroundings by radiation, convection, and conduction, and in a steady state the rate of loss of heat is equal to the rate at which energy is being made available in the electrical form by the chemical process in the cell.

The special geometry illustrated in Fig. 1.4 has been chosen to facilitate understanding of the process whereby a voltaic cell can produce steady electric current through a resistor. This special geometry is not, however, essential to the argument. In practice the geometry of the arrangement might be more like that depicted in Fig. 1.5. For diagrammatic purposes such arrangements are usually represented in one or other of the ways shown in Fig. 1.6.

The electric current round a circuit is measured by the amount of charge that passes a particular cross section of the circuit in unit time and is therefore measured in coulombs per second. This unit is known as an ampere. A coulomb is thus the amount of charge that passes a cross section of a circuit in one second when the current flowing is one

ampere.   In describing the charge drifting through a resistor, such as the
imperfect dielectric considered in connection with Fig. 1.4, it is necessary
to specify at each point both the direction of drift and the amount of
charge crossing in unit time a unit area of a surface perpendicular to the
direction of flow.   A vector in the direction of mean flow at a point and
equal in magnitude to the charge crossing in unit time a unit area perpendicular to the direction of flow is known as the current-density vector
at the point.   Current density is measured in coulombs per second per
square meter or in other words in amperes per square meter.

1.4. Conductivity.   Let us consider a piece of imperfect dielectric and
suppose that a uniform electric field is applied to it.   The arrangement
might be as shown in Fig. 1.4.   At a point P in the imperfect dielectric
let the electric vector be $\mathbf{E}$.   Suppose that a steady current is flowing
through the imperfect dielectric, and at the point P where the electric
vector is $\mathbf{E}$, let the current-density vector be $\mathbf{J}$.   The direction of $\mathbf{J}$ is the
direction of the electric current at P, while the magnitude of $\mathbf{J}$ is the
current crossing unit area of a surface through P perpendicular to the
direction of flow.   Since the electric vector $\mathbf{E}$ is, in magnitude and direction, the force per unit charge creating the electric current and the current-density vector $\mathbf{J}$ measures, in magnitude and direction, the strength
of the current that results, one would expect the direction of $\mathbf{J}$ to be
identical with the direction of $\mathbf{E}$.   Moreover one would expect that, the
stronger the electric field, the stronger would be the flow of current
through the imperfect dielectric.   At all points in a simple material the
direction of the current-density vector $\mathbf{J}$ is identical with the direction of
the electric vector $\mathbf{E}$ and the magnitude of $\mathbf{J}$ is proportional to the magnitude of $\mathbf{E}$.   This relationship we write in the form

$$\mathbf{J} = \sigma\mathbf{E} \tag{1.1}$$

where σ is a constant of proportionality known as the conductivity of the
material concerned.

A perfect dielectric is one for which the conductivity is zero, so that,
no matter what the strength of the electric field, no current flows through
it.   The materials used as dielectrics in practice have extremely low
conductivities but not a zero conductivity.   A perfect conductor on
the other hand is a material for which the conductivity is infinite.   By
writing Eq. (1.1) in the form

$$\mathbf{E} = \frac{1}{\sigma}\mathbf{J} \tag{1.2}$$

we see that the electric field in a perfect conductor vanishes no matter
what current may be flowing through it.   A substance such as copper is
not a perfect conductor, but nevertheless it has a comparatively high

conductivity.   Consequently quite a small electric field in copper produces quite a large electric current.   Materials are available in practice
with an extraordinarily wide range of conductivities.   Thus the conductivity of copper is about 24 powers of 10 bigger than that of rubber.

1.5. Conductance.   Consider a cylindrical piece of material of conductivity σ.   Let s be the length of the cylinder and S the cross-sectional
area as shown in Fig. 1.7.   To the flat ends of the cylinder attach perfectly conducting plates of area S.   Now con-
nect between these plates a battery of voltage V,
and let us calculate the resulting current I that
flows through the material from one plate to the
other.

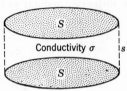

The two perfectly conducting plates in Fig.
1.7 constitute a parallel-plate capacitor which is
maintained in a charged condition by the battery
connected between the plates.   Let us assume
that the electric field in the material is the electric field of this parallel-
plate capacitor with fringing avoided.   Then the electric field in the
material is a uniform field perpendicular to the plates, and the electric
field strength is

FIG. 1.7. Illustrating the
calculation of conduct-
ance.

$$E = \frac{V}{s} \tag{1.3}$$

It follows from Eq. (1.1) that the current flowing from one plate to the
other per unit cross-sectional area is

$$J = \sigma \frac{V}{s} \tag{1.4}$$

The total current flowing from one plate to the other is obtained by
multiplying the current per unit cross-sectional area by the cross-sectional
area S.   It is therefore

$$I = JS \tag{1.5}$$

and by substituting for J from Eq. (1.4) into Eq. (1.5) we derive

$$I = \frac{\sigma S}{s} V \tag{1.6}$$

This equation states that the current flowing through the material from
one plate to the other is proportional to the voltage between the plates.
We write this relation in the form

$$I = GV \tag{1.7}$$

where
$$G = \frac{\sigma S}{s} \tag{1.8}$$

The quantity G is known as the conductance between the perfectly conducting plates caused by the presence of a cylindrical piece of material. We see from Eq. (1.8) that this conductance is proportional to the conductivity of the material between the plates. It is also directly proportional to the cross-sectional area of the cylinder and inversely proportional to its length.

1.6. Resistance. The reciprocal of conductance is known as resistance. Thus, if G is the conductance between the plates in Fig. 1.7, the resistance between the plates is

$$R = \frac{1}{G} \tag{1.9}$$

Substituting for G from Eq. (1.8) into Eq. (1.9) we derive

$$R = \frac{s}{\sigma S} \tag{1.10}$$

Thus the resistance between the plates is inversely proportional to the conductivity of the material. It is also inversely proportional to the cross-sectional area of the cylinder and directly proportional to its length.

In terms of conductance the relation connecting the voltage V maintained between the plates and the current I flowing from one plate to the other has been expressed by Eq. (1.7). We can reexpress this relation in terms of the resistance between the plates by substituting for G from Eq. (1.9) into Eq. (1.7). We thus obtain

$$V = RI \tag{1.11}$$

Equation (1.11) gives the voltage V that must be maintained between the plates in order to produce a given current I between the plates, while Eq. (1.7) gives the current I between the plates that is produced when a given voltage V is maintained between the plates. Equations (1.7) and (1.11) are alternative versions of the relation that exists between the voltage and current. Either equation expresses what is known as Ohm's law.

Since the voltage V in Eq. (1.11) is measured in volts and the current I is measured in amperes, the resistance R between the plates is measured in volts per ampere. This unit of resistance is known as an ohm. Conductance, being the reciprocal of resistance in accordance with Eq. (1.9), is measured in reciprocal ohms. This unit is also known as a "mho," which is ohm spelled backward.

1.7. The Unit of Conductivity. The relation between the concepts of conductivity and conductance can be illustrated in the following way: Take a unit cube of material of conductivity σ and attach to a pair of opposite faces perfectly conducting plates that completely cover the faces. For such a unit cube the cross-sectional area S is unity and the length s is unity. From Eq. (1.8) we therefore deduce that the conductance between the opposite faces of the unit cube is simply equal to the conductivity of the material. Thus the conductivity of a material can be described as the conductance between opposite faces of a unit cube of the material.

To appreciate the unit in terms of which conductivity is measured, it is convenient to consider a column of material as shown in Fig. 1.8.

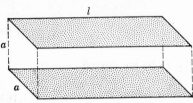

FIG. 1.8. Illustrating the relation between conductivity and conductance.

Figure 1.8 illustrates a column of material of conductivity σ, the length of the column being l and the normal cross section of the column being a square of edge a. To a pair of opposite faces of the column of area al are attached perfectly conducting plates that completely cover these faces. The conductance between these plates is calculated from Eq. (1.8) by substituting for the area S of a plate al and for the distance s between the plates a. The conductance between the plates in Fig. 1.8 is therefore

$$\frac{\sigma al}{a} \qquad (1.12)$$

Since a cancels from this expression, the conductance between the plates is independent of the dimension a. The expression (1.12) for the conductance between the plates in Fig. 1.8 reduces to

$$\sigma l \qquad (1.13)$$

and we see that the conductance is directly proportional to the length l of the column. For a unit length of the column the conductance is simply equal to the conductivity of the material. Thus the conductivity of the material can be described as the conductance between the plates in Fig. 1.8 measured per unit length of the column. Since the unit of conductance is the mho, it follows that the unit of conductivity is the mho per meter.

In terms of this unit of conductivity the conductivities of a number of well-known substances are listed in Table 1.1. Notice the tremendous range of conductivity that is available for use.

1.8. Relation between Capacitance and Conductance. In Fig. 1.7 the material between the plates has a capacitivity ϵ as well as a conductivity σ, and we can calculate the capacitance of the arrangement thought of as a capacitor. There is a close relationship between this capacitance and the conductance given by Eq. (1.8). Let V be the voltage between the

TABLE 1.1. CONDUCTIVITIES OF VARIOUS MATERIALS

Mhos/m

Imperfect conductors:
Silver................ 6.8×10^7
Copper............... 5.8×10^7
Aluminum............ 3.8×10^7
Brass............... $1.3\text{--}1.6 \times 10^7$
Iron................. 10^7
Lead................. 4.5×10^6
Nichrome........... 10^6
Carbon.............. 2.8×10^4
Substances of inter-
  mediate conductivity:
Sea water........... 4
Fresh water......... 10^{-3}
Damp soil........... 10^{-2}
Dry soil............ 10^{-5}
Imperfect insulators:
Wood............... $10^{-8}\text{--}10^{-11}$
Porcelain........... 10^{-13}
Mica................ 10^{-15}
Rubber............. 10^{-16}

perfectly conducting plates in Fig. 1.7, and let us assume that the electric field between the plates is perpendicular to the plates. Then this electric field is given by Eq. (1.3). We can exhibit the relationship between capacitance and conductance by arranging corresponding statements in two parallel columns as follows:

The relation between the electric flux density D and the electric field strength E is

$$D = \epsilon E \qquad (1.14a)$$

The relation between the current density J and the electric field strength E is

$$J = \sigma E \qquad (1.14b)$$

The relation between the charge Q and the electric flux density D is

$$Q = DS \qquad (1.15a)$$

The relation between the current I and the current density J is

$$I = JS \qquad (1.15b)$$

The relation between the charge Q and the voltage V is

$$Q = CV \qquad (1.16a)$$

The relation between the current I and the voltage V is

$$I = GV \qquad (1.16b)$$

The capacitance between the plates is

$$C = \frac{\epsilon S}{s} \qquad (1.17a)$$

The conductance between the plates is

$$G = \frac{\sigma S}{s} \qquad (1.17b)$$

We see the correspondence that exists (1) between the capacitivity ϵ of a medium and the conductivity σ of the medium, (2) between the electric flux density D and the current density J, (3) between the charge Q on the positive plate and the current I leaving the positive plate, and (4) between the capacitance C of the arrangement and the conductance G.

We can further note from Eqs. (1.17a) and (1.17b) that

$$\frac{C}{G} = \frac{\epsilon}{\sigma} \tag{1.18}$$

so that, for the arrangement shown in Fig. 1.7, the ratio of the capacitance between the plates to the conductance between the plates is simply the ratio of the capacitivity of the material to the conductivity of the material. Let us examine the dimensions of the ratio in Eq. (1.18). Capacitance is measured in farads, and this is the same thing as coulombs per volt. Conductance is measured in mhos, and this is the same thing as amperes per volt. Hence the ratio C/G in Eq. (1.18) has the dimensions of coulombs per ampere. But an ampere is a coulomb per second, and consequently the ratio given in Eq. (1.18) has the dimensions of time. We shall see later what significance is to be attached to the time given by Eq. (1.18); if the battery were disconnected from the arrangement, the charge on the capacitor would disappear as a result of the current through the material, and expression (1.18) is a measure of the time that it would take the capacitor to become discharged.

1.9. Resistance of Wires. The conductance and resistance of metallic wires are calculated from Eqs. (1.8) and (1.10) respectively. In these formulas σ is the conductivity of the metal, S is the normal cross-sectional area of the wire, and s is the length of the piece of wire under consideration. From Eq. (1.10) we see that the resistance of a piece of wire is directly proportional to the length of the wire and inversely proportional to its cross-sectional area.

In some countries the size of wire is specified in terms of its diameter. But in others wire size is specified in terms of gauge numbers 0, 1, 2, ... In the American wire gauge a number 0 wire has a diameter of 0.325 in. An increase of unity in the gauge number signifies that the diameter is decreased by a factor of 1.123. An increase of 3 in the gauge number therefore signifies that the cross-sectional area of the wire is decreased by a factor $[(1.123)^2]^3$, which is equal to 2.005. Thus an increase of 3 in the gauge number implies that the cross-sectional area of the wire is decreased by a factor of about 2. This implies a reduction of a factor of 2 in the conductance in accordance with Eq. (1.8) and an increase of a factor 2 in the resistance in accordance with Eq. (1.10). Some idea of the range of resistance conveniently available can be obtained from

Table 1.2. Notice that the range of resistance quoted in the table is nearly a million to one.

TABLE 1.2. RESISTANCE OF WIRES

Gauge number	Diameter, in.	Radius, mm	Area, mm^2	Resistance, ohms/km	
				Copper	Nichrome
0	0.325	4.13	53.5	0.322	18.7
10	0.1019	1.29	5.26	3.28	190
20	0.0320	4.06×10^{-1}	5.19×10^{-1}	33.2	1,930
30	0.01003	1.27×10^{-1}	5.10×10^{-2}	338	19,600
40	0.00314	3.99×10^{-2}	5.00×10^{-3}	3,450	200,000

1.10. The Occurrence of Electric Charge on the Surface of Wires Carrying Current. In discussing the conductance between the plates shown in Fig. 1.7 it is assumed that the electric field in the material is everywhere perpendicular to the plates and that there is no fringing. This state of affairs can be brought about by using plates whose area is much larger than the normal cross-sectional area of the resistive wire as illustrated in Fig. 1.9.

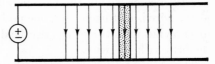

FIG. 1.9. Illustrating an arrangement for maintaining an electric field parallel to a resistive wire.

Let us now suppose, however, that the resistive wire running across from the upper perfectly conducting plate to the lower perfectly conducting plate is bent as shown in Fig. 1.10. Under these circumstances the electric field distorts in the manner shown, and surface charges develop on the wire as indicated by the + and − signs. At the moment when the

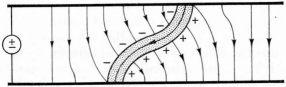

FIG. 1.10. Illustrating the occurrence of surface charge on a wire carrying current.

wire was first connected between the plates, the electric field would everywhere be perpendicular to the plates. This would cause a flow of current in the resistive wire that would not be simply along the wire but would have an important component transverse to the length of the wire. The component transverse to the wire would build up surface charge on the wire until the field became distorted to that indicated in Fig. 1.10. Equilibrium would be reached when the electric field inside the wire, and consequently the flow of current inside the wire, was strictly parallel to the length of the wire so that no further surface charge is built up. We thus see that, when a state of steady flow has been achieved in a resistive wire, the electric vector within the wire, and also the current-density vector within the wire, is strictly parallel to the length of the wire. The assumption made in connection with Fig. 1.7 that the electric field inside the conducting medium is perpendicular to the normal cross sections of the cylinder is therefore not an approximation. This configuration for the electric field inside a conducting wire is automatically brought into existence by the development of appropriate surface charges on the surface of the wire. Thus it follows that the conductance and resistance of even a bent wire can be calculated from Eqs. (1.8) and (1.10) respectively. If the resistive wire shown in Fig. 1.10 is distorted from one position to another, the electric field outside the wire changes and so also does the surface charge on the wire; this surface charge changes, however, in such a way as to keep the electric vector and the current-density vector within the wire parallel to the length of the wire. Thus, as the wire is distorted from one position to another, it may be thought of as carrying its internal electric field with it, although the external field distorts with the wire.

The ability to distort wires without having any significant influence on their resistance is of great importance in the design of compact resistors. For example, we see from Table 1.2 in the preceding section that to make a 10,000-ohm resistor with No. 30 Nichrome wire would require the use of more than $\frac{1}{2}$ km of wire. By winding this as a multilayer coil, however, it is possible to compress it into a cylindrical volume 10 cm long and less than 1 cm in diameter.

1.11. Power Delivered by a Battery. If a battery of voltage V is delivering a current I to an external resistor or resistors, the chemical process going on in the battery is doing work at a rate that we can calculate. For simplicity let us suppose that the battery has one active electrode, so that the difference of potential between the electrolyte and this electrode is V. When a molecule of electrolyte bounces off the electrode leaving an electron on the electrode and taking a charge e into the electrolyte, we have a situation in which a charge e has its electric potential raised by an amount V. Since electric potential is potential energy per unit charge, the work done by the chemical process in separating this electron from its molecule is eV. Suppose that, as a result of this process happening for a number of electrons, a total charge Q is transferred through the potential difference V by the chemical process. Then the work done is

$$VQ \tag{1.19}$$

If the charge transfer constitutes a steady electric current I, then I units of charge are transferred through the potential difference V in unit time. From expression (1.19) it follows that the rate at which the chemical process is doing work in supplying the current I at voltage V is

$$VI \tag{1.20}$$

Thus the power provided by the chemical process in a battery is the product of the voltage of the battery and the current delivered.

Potential is measured in volts, but since potential is potential energy per unit charge, it can also be measured in joules per coulomb. Current is measured in amperes, but since current is flow of charge per unit time, it can also be measured in coulombs per second. It follows that the product of the voltage and current can be measured in joules per second, and this is the unit known as the watt. Thus the power delivered by a battery in watts is the product of the potential difference of the battery in volts and the current it delivers in amperes.

A comparison should be made between the expression (1.19) for the work done by the chemical process in a battery when transferring a charge Q through the voltage V of the battery and the expression $\frac{1}{2}VQ$ for the work done in charging a capacitor to a voltage V by placing charges $\pm Q$ on its plates. In charging the capacitor the voltage rises from an initial value of zero to a final value V when the capacitor is fully charged. Consequently the charge Q is transferred through an average voltage of only $\frac{1}{2}V$. On the other hand, for the chemical process involved in a battery, the charge Q has to be transferred through the full voltage V of the battery, and consequently no factor $\frac{1}{2}$ appears.

1.12. Power Delivered to a Resistor. Suppose that power is being delivered to a resistor from a battery as shown in Fig. 1.9 or 1.10. Within the resistor, free electrons are accelerated under the electric field applied by the battery. The period of acceleration ends in a collision with an atom of the material. At the collision the ordered motion acquired by the electrons under the influence of the electric field of the battery is converted into random motion. The energy of this random motion is what is known as heat. Hence the passage of an electric current through a resistor heats the resistor. The temperature of the resistor would rise indefinitely if the resistor had no means of losing heat. The resistor loses heat partly by conduction to its cooler surroundings, partly by convection caused in the surrounding air, and partly by radiation. With a steady electric current through a resistor, the resistor reaches an equilibrium temperature such that it loses heat to its surroundings at the same rate as it gains heat from the electric current. A precise calculation of this equilibrium temperature is usually difficult. When equilibrium conditions have been reached, the rate at which heat is being lost by the resistor is not only equal to the rate at which the electric current is supplying heat to the resistor but is also equal to the rate at which the chemical process in the battery is supplying energy. It follows that, when a voltage V across a resistor results in a current I through the resistor, the rate at which the current produces heat energy in the resistor is given by

$$VI \qquad (1.21)$$

and this is also the rate at which heat energy is being lost by the resistor owing to conduction, convection, and radiation. By means of Eqs. (1.7) and (1.11) the power delivered to a resistor can be expressed entirely in terms of the voltage across the resistor or entirely in terms of the current through the resistor. Thus if there is a voltage V across a resistor whose conductance is G and whose resistance is R and as a result a current I flows through the resistor, the power delivered to the resistor is given by any of the following three equivalent expressions:

$$VI = GV^2 = RI^2 \qquad (1.22)$$

The power delivered to a resistor of given conductance and resistance is thus proportional to the square of voltage across the resistor and proportional to the square of the current through the resistor.

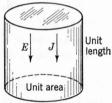

The energy absorbed from a current by a resistor and converted into heat is distributed throughout the volume of the resistor. This follows from the fact that the electronic collisions that create the conversion are themselves distributed throughout the volume of the resistor. Consider a unit volume in a resistor consisting of a cylinder of unit normal cross section and unit length parallel to the electric field as shown in Fig. 1.11. The voltage between the flat ends of the cylindrical unit volume is simply the electric field strength E, and the total current crossing a normal cross section of the cylindrical unit volume is simply the current density J. Moreover, in accordance with Eq. (1.8) the conductance between the flat ends of the unit volume is simply equal to the conductivity σ of the material, and in accordance with Eq. (1.9) the resistance between the flat ends is $1/\sigma$. It follows from Eq. (1.22) that the power absorbed from the current per

FIG. 1.11. Illustrating absorption of energy from an electric current by a unit volume of a resistor.

unit volume is given by any of the expressions

$$EJ = \sigma E^2 = \frac{1}{\sigma} J^2 \tag{1.23}$$

Thus the power absorbed in a resistive material per unit volume at any point is proportional to the square of the electric field strength at that point and is also proportional to the square of the electric current density at that point. The power absorbed by the entire resistor can be calculated at a rate per unit volume given by expressions (1.23). When contributions are added from the various units of volume, the total power absorbed by a resistor evaluates to the expressions (1.22).

A resistor carrying a current rises to a temperature that is controlled by the ability of the resistor to lose the heat that it acquires from the current. By increasing the surface area of the resistor one increases its ability to lose heat, and consequently the resistor operates at a lower temperature. Moreover by means of a blower it is possible to increase the rate at which air is moving over the surface of the resistor, and this increases the rate of loss of heat by convection. The temperature at which a resistor operates is of some practical importance. In the first place, if the resistor gets too hot, it may cause damage to itself or to its surroundings. Apart from this there is an important effect arising from the fact that the resistance of a resistor depends upon its temperature. When a resistor gets hotter, the increased random motion of the free electrons is transferred to other particles in the material, and as a result the atoms with which the free electrons have to collide become larger obstacles. The upshot is a rise of resistance with temperature. For copper, resistance increases by about 4 per cent for each 10°C rise in temperature. Thus for a resistor that runs hot, the resistance is substantially greater than it is when the resistor is cold. For a resistor used as an electric heater this effect is drastic. For a rise of temperature of 1,000°C the resistance is multiplied by about 4. For the filament of an electric lamp, for which the operating temperature might be 3,000°C, the resistance when hot is more than ten times that when cold.

1.13. Internal Resistance of a Battery. In discussing circuits such as those shown in Fig. 1.4 or 1.5 the assumption was made that the only resistance involved in the circuit is that in the resistor itself. Of course there is always some resistance involved in the leads. Moreover there is also resistance involved in the electrolyte of the battery, and it is sometimes important to take this into account. Thus a battery can be represented diagrammatically as shown in Fig. 1.12. The voltage V represents the discontinuity of voltage at the surface of the active electrode, or the algebraic sum of the discontinuities of voltage at the two electrodes. The resistance r is the resistance of the electrolyte between the electrodes. When the battery is on open circuit, so that no current is being delivered, the voltage between the terminals is simply V. But when the battery is delivering a current I, there is a drop of voltage rI

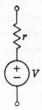

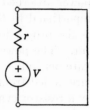

FIG. 1.12. Diagrammatic representation of a battery whose open-circuit voltage is V and whose internal resistance is r.

FIG. 1.13. Illustrating a battery of open-circuit voltage V and internal resistance r short-circuited by a wire of negligible resistance.

across the electrolyte in accordance with Ohm's law. Consequently the voltage between the terminals of the battery is

$$V - rI \qquad (1.24)$$

The internal resistance r of a battery is usually only a fraction of an ohm. If therefore the resistance connected externally across the battery is large compared with an ohm, the internal resistance of the battery is comparatively unimportant. If, however, the resistance connected externally between the terminals of the battery is comparable to the internal resistance of the battery, then it is essential to allow for this internal resistance in calculating the current. In particular, suppose that the terminals of the battery were short-circuited by a piece of wire of practically zero resistance as shown in Fig. 1.13. The internal resistance of the battery would then be the only resistance of importance in the circuit, and in accordance with Ohm's law, the current would be

$$I = \frac{V}{r} \qquad (1.25)$$

The rate at which the chemical process in the battery is delivering energy is then

$$VI = \frac{V^2}{r} \qquad (1.26)$$

and this energy is being used to heat the electrolyte. If the voltage of the battery is 1.5 volts and the internal resistance is 0.10 ohm, then Eq. (1.25) shows that the current delivered by the battery when on short circuit is 15 amp; from Eq. (1.26) the rate at which the chemical process is delivering energy is 22.5 watts. This is also the rate at which the current is supplying heat to the electrolyte and the rate at which the electrolyte is losing heat by conduction, convection, and radiation.

SUMMARIZING EXERCISES

1.1. Explain what is meant by an electric current, by electric current density, and by the current-density vector. Describe the relation between the current-density vector and the electric vector, explaining what is meant by the conductivity of a substance.

1.2. A cylindrical piece of material has a cross-sectional area S, a length s, and a conductivity σ. To the flat ends are attached perfectly conducting electrodes of area S, and the system is immersed in a nonconducting medium. Define the conductance between the electrodes and evaluate it in terms of σ, S, and s. Define the resistance between the electrodes and give an expression for it in terms of σ, S, and s.

1.3. Describe Ohm's law and explain what is meant by an ohm and a mho.

1.4. A column of material of conductivity σ has a length l and a square cross section of edge a. Perfectly conducting electrodes are applied to a pair of opposite faces of area al. Prove that the conductance between the electrodes per unit length of column is equal to the conductivity σ of the material. State the units in which conductivity is measured, and write down numerical values for the conductivity of (a) mica, (b) copper.

1.5. Calculate the resistance of 1 km of copper wire of radius (a) 1.3 mm (No. 10 gauge) and (b) 0.04 mm (No. 40 gauge).

1.6. If a voltage V applied to a resistor results in a current I through the resistor, show that the rate at which electrical energy is absorbed by the resistor is VI. Express this power in terms of V and the conductance G of the resistor. Express it also in terms of I and the resistance R of the resistor.

1.7. Show that the power absorbed by a resistor is distributed throughout the resistor at an amount per unit volume equal to the product of the electric field strength and the electric current density. Express this power per unit volume in terms of the electric field strength and the conductivity of the material. Express it also in terms of the electric current density and the conductivity.

1.8. Describe in outline the principle of operation of a voltaic cell (a) when on open circuit, (b) when a resistor is connected across the terminals. Explain what is meant by the internal resistance of the cell. Show that, when a cell possessing an internal resistance r and an open-circuit voltage V delivers a current I, the voltage developed between the terminals of the cell is $V - rI$.

1.9. Describe in what respects a parallel exists between the following pairs of quantities associated with static and with steady-current electricity:

Charge...................... Current
Electric potential.............. Electric potential
Capacitance.................. Conductance
Electric flux density.......... Electric current density
Electric field strength.......... Electric field strength
Capacitivity.................. Conductivity

CHAPTER 2

NETWORKS OF RESISTORS

2.1. Introduction. An enormous number of problems in electrical science are solved by joining together by short pieces of metallic wire individual electrical devices such as capacitors and resistors. Other devices that are commonly included in such systems are inductors, transformers, vacuum tubes, and transistors. An arrangement of elements of this type connected together by short pieces of conducting wire is known as an electrical network. The design of an electrical network to achieve a specific purpose corresponds to designing a machine in mechanics by suitably connecting together such elements as springs, shock absorbers, weights, cogs, pulleys, levers, and servomechanisms. Just as there is an endless variety of machines that can be designed by the mechanical engineer, so there is an endless variety of networks that can be designed by the electrical engineer. In the present chapter we are to discuss networks of resistors.

2.2. Resistors Connected in Parallel. Resistors connected by metal wires of negligible resistance as shown in Fig. 2.1 are said to be connected in parallel or in shunt. Let us suppose that a battery of voltage V is connected across the group of resistors shown in Fig. 2.1 and that we

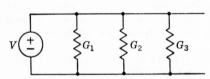

FIG. 2.1. Resistors connected in parallel.

are interested in calculating the total current delivered by the battery when this current has become steady. The connection between all the upper terminals of the resistors ensures that, in a state of steady flow, all these terminals are at the same potential, and the same applies to the lower terminals. Hence the voltage applied across each resistor is the same and is equal to the voltage V of the battery.

Let G_1, G_2, . . . be the conductances of the various resistors. Since the same voltage V is applied across all resistors, it follows from Eq. (1.7) that the currents through these resistors are G_1V, G_2V, ... Hence the currents through the resistors are in the ratio of their conductances.

In conformity with the principle of conservation of charge the total current flowing from the positive terminal of the battery divides between the various resistors and then recombines to give the total current flowing to the negative terminal of the battery. The total current supplied by the battery is consequently the sum of the currents through the various resistors and is therefore

$$(G_1 + G_2 + \cdots)V \qquad (2.1)$$

It follows that the total current supplied by the battery is the same as would be supplied if the battery were connected across a single resistor of conductance

$$G = G_1 + G_2 + \cdots \qquad (2.2)$$

This is known as the equivalent conductance of the group of resistors connected in parallel. Equation (2.2) states that, if a number of resistors are connected in parallel, they are equivalent to a single resistor whose conductance is the sum of the individual conductances.

Using Eq. (1.9) we can express Eq. (2.2) in terms of the resistances of the resistors instead of in terms of their conductances. Let R_1, R_2, $\ldots$ be the resistances of the various resistors, so that the reciprocals of these quantities are G_1, G_2, $\ldots$ respectively. Then we can say that the current delivered by the battery is the same as would be delivered if it were connected across a single resistor of resistance R where

$$\frac{1}{R} = \frac{1}{R_1} + \frac{1}{R_2} + \cdots \qquad (2.3)$$

This is merely a restatement of Eq. (2.2) in terms of resistances instead of conductances. Equation (2.3) states that, if a number of resistors are connected in parallel, they are equivalent to a single resistor the reciprocal of whose resistance is the sum of the reciprocals of the resistances of the individual resistors.

It should be noted that when a number of resistors are connected in parallel, the equivalent conductance of the group exceeds the conductance of the resistor of highest conductance in the group. This means that the equivalent resistance of a group of resistors connected in parallel is less than the resistance of the smallest resistor of the group.

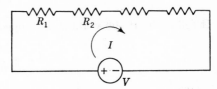

FIG. 2.2. Resistors connected in series.

2.3. Resistors Connected in Series. A group of resistors connected by metal wires of negligible resistance as shown in Fig. 2.2 is said to be connected in series. Let a battery of voltage V be connected to the resistors as shown in Fig. 2.2, and as a result let a steady current I flow round the circuit. Let the resistances of the various resistors be R_1, R_2, ... Since it is the same current I that flows through each resistor, it follows from Ohm's law that the voltages developed across the resistors are R_1I, R_2I, ... This implies that, when a number of resistors are connected in series, the voltage across them divides in the ratio of the resistances.

The total voltage across the group of resistors is obtained by adding up the voltages across the individual resistors. Hence the voltage of the battery is

$$V = (R_1 + R_2 + \cdots)I \tag{2.4}$$

The same voltage would be obtained if the battery were connected across a single resistor of resistance R such that

$$R = R_1 + R_2 + \cdots \tag{2.5}$$

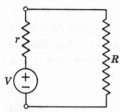

This implies that, if a number of resistors are connected in series, they are equivalent to a single resistor whose resistance is the sum of the resistances of the individual resistors.

2.4. Maximum Power from a Battery. As an example of resistors connected in series, let us consider a resistor of resistance R connected across the terminals of a battery of internal resistance r and open-circuit voltage V. This situation is

FIG. 2.3. A resistor connected across a battery possessing internal resistance.

illustrated in Fig. 2.3. The external resistance or load R is connected in series with the internal resistance r of the battery. The total resistance in the circuit is therefore $R + r$, and in accordance with Eq. (2.4), the current round the circuit is

$$I = \frac{1}{R + r} V \tag{2.6}$$

It follows that the voltage developed across the load is

$$RI = \frac{R}{R + r} V \tag{2.7}$$

and the power delivered to the load is

$$RI^2 = \frac{R}{(R + r)^2} V^2 \tag{2.8}$$

The total power provided by the chemical process in the battery is the product of the voltage V and the current given by Eq. (2.6), and is therefore

$$\frac{1}{R + r} V^2 \qquad (2.9)$$

The fraction of the power provided by the chemical process that is developed in the load R is obtained by dividing the expression (2.8) by expression (2.9) and is

$$\frac{R}{R + r} \qquad (2.10)$$

Let us suppose that the load resistance R is variable and let us plot the above expressions as functions of R. This is done in Fig. 2.4. Curve a

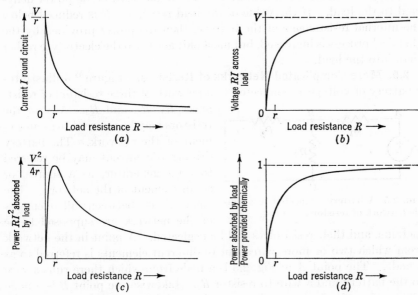

Fig. 2.4. Curves describing the phenomena occurring when a load of variable resistance R is connected across a battery of internal resistance r and open-circuit voltage V.

shows the variation with the load resistance R of the current round the circuit given by Eq. (2.6). Curve b shows the variation of the voltage across the load given by Eq. (2.7). Curve c shows the variation of the power absorbed by the load given by Eq. (2.8). Curve d shows, in accordance with expression (2.10), the variation of the fraction of the power provided by the chemical process that is developed in the load resistance R. From curve c we observe that the power developed in the load is maximum when

$$R = r \qquad (2.11)$$

that is, when the resistance of the load is adjusted to be equal to the internal resistance r of the battery. The power developed in the load is then

$$\frac{V^2}{4r} \tag{2.12}$$

and from curve d we see that this is one-half of the power provided by the chemical process. Thus, even when the resistance of the load is adjusted to maximize the power absorbed by the load, this power is only half of that provided by the chemical process in the battery, the other half being used to heat the electrolyte in the battery. If the load resistance R is increased above the internal resistance r of the battery, then the power provided by the chemical process is reduced and with it the power delivered to the load. If the value of the load resistance R is reduced below the internal resistance r of the battery, then the power provided by the chemical process is increased, but most of it goes into the electrolyte rather than into the load.

2.5. More Complicated Networks of Resistors. Figure 2.5 illustrates a battery of voltage V connected to a network of three resistors of resist-

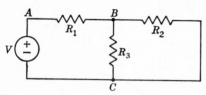

FIG. 2.5. A battery connected to a simple network of resistors.

ances R_1, R_2, and R_3. Any of the resistors may be referred to as an element of the network. The battery driving the current may be referred to as a generator, as a source, or as an element of the network. The connections between all elements of the network are supposed to be metallic, and their resistances will be neglected. A point in the network from which two or more wires run to different elements is referred to as a node. The point A in Fig. 2.5 is a node from which there runs a wire to the battery and a wire to resistor R_1. Likewise the point B is a node because from it there run wires to resistors R_1, R_2, and R_3. Point C is a node because from it there run wires to the battery, to resistor R_2, and to resistor R_3.

In an electrical network great importance attaches to closed geometrical circuits drawn so as to coincide as closely as possible with the metallic wires connecting the elements. In Fig. 2.5 we can start from node A, pass along the wire to resistor R_1, traverse this resistor, and then proceed along the wire connecting it to node B. We can then proceed down the wire connecting this node to resistor R_3, traverse this resistor, and then continue along the wire to the node C. We can then complete a closed geometrical circuit by passing along the wire to the battery, through the battery, and so back to the node A. Such a closed geometrical circuit is referred to as a mesh of the network. For the network shown in Fig.

2.5 another mesh is obtained by starting from node B, passing along the wire to resistor R_2, traversing this resistor, then passing around the wire to the lower terminal of the resistor R_3, traversing this resistor, and so returning by the wire to node B.

For a network such as that shown in Fig. 2.5 one is interested in calculating the currents through all elements and the potential differences across all elements. One may also be interested in calculating the power delivered to each resistor and the power provided by the battery.

2.6. Analysis of Networks into Parallel and Series Connections. A network as simple as that shown in Fig. 2.5 can be analyzed into parallel and series connections, and in this way all the information about the network can be calculated. Thus the resistor R_2 is in parallel with the resistor R_3, and in accordance with Eqs. (2.2) and (2.3), the two resistors are equivalent to a single resistor of conductance

$$\frac{1}{R_2} + \frac{1}{R_3} \tag{2.13}$$

It follows that the pair of resistors R_2 and R_3 are equivalent to a single resistor whose resistance is the reciprocal of expression (2.13), namely,

$$\frac{R_2 R_3}{R_2 + R_3} \tag{2.14}$$

In the network this resistor is connected in series with the resistor

$$R_1 \tag{2.15}$$

It follows from Eq. (2.5) that all three resistors are equivalent to a single resistor of resistance R connected across the battery where

$$R = R_1 + \frac{R_2 R_3}{R_2 + R_3} \tag{2.16}$$

This equation can be written as

$$R = \frac{R_2 R_3 + R_3 R_1 + R_1 R_2}{R_2 + R_3} \tag{2.17}$$

It follows from Ohm's law that the current delivered by the battery is

$$\frac{V}{R} = \frac{R_2 + R_3}{R_2 R_3 + R_3 R_1 + R_1 R_2} V \tag{2.18}$$

The current that is provided by the battery flows through the resistor R_1 and then divides between the resistors R_2 and R_3 in proportion to their conductances as described in Sec. 2.2. The currents through resistors R_2

and R_3 are therefore obtained by taking the fractions

$$\frac{1/R_2}{1/R_2 + 1/R_3} \quad \text{and} \quad \frac{1/R_3}{1/R_2 + 1/R_3}$$

of the current given by Eq. (2.18). These fractions can be written

$$\frac{R_3}{R_2 + R_3} \quad \text{and} \quad \frac{R_2}{R_2 + R_3} \tag{2.19}$$

respectively. The current through resistor R_2 is therefore

$$\frac{R_3}{R_2 + R_3} \frac{V}{R} = \frac{R_3}{R_2R_3 + R_3R_1 + R_1R_2} V \tag{2.20}$$

and the direction of the current is from left to right. In the same way the current through resistor R_3 is

$$\frac{R_2}{R_2 + R_3} \frac{V}{R} = \frac{R_2}{R_2R_3 + R_3R_1 + R_1R_2} V \tag{2.21}$$

and the direction of the flow is from top to bottom.

The voltages across the various resistors can be calculated by multiplying the currents through them by their respective resistances. From Eq. (2.18) we deduce that the voltage across resistor R_1 is

$$\frac{R_1(R_2 + R_3)}{R_2R_3 + R_3R_1 + R_1R_2} V \tag{2.22}$$

From Eqs. (2.20) and (2.21) we deduce that the common voltage drop across resistors R_2 and R_3 is

$$\frac{R_2R_3}{R_2R_3 + R_3R_1 + R_1R_2} V \tag{2.23}$$

We thus obtain all the information about the network by thinking of it as a resistor R_1 in series with a pair of resistors R_2 and R_3 that are connected in parallel. This procedure is frequently the simplest way of analyzing a network, provided that the network is not too complicated.

2.7. Analysis of a Network Using Kirchhoff's Laws. While a network can always be analyzed into parallel and series connections, this procedure is too unorganized to use in complicated networks. To arrive at a more systematic procedure for analyzing any network of resistors, it is convenient first to restate the principles upon which the analysis is carried out in the form of two laws known as Kirchhoff's laws.

2.8. Kirchhoff's Conservation Law. Suppose that electrons are approaching a node of a network on a particular wire or wires and are leaving the node on other wires. Each electron approaching the node on one wire leaves the node on another wire. From the principle of conservation of charge it follows that the total rate at which charge is arriving at the node is equal to the total rate at which charge is leaving the node. The rate at which charge is arriving at a node on a particular wire is the electric current flowing along this wire toward the node. We can thus say that the sum of the electric currents flowing into a node is equal to the sum of the electric currents flowing out of a node. If opposite algebraic signs are attached to currents flowing into and out from a node, we can say that the algebraic sum of the currents leaving a node is zero. Alternatively we can say that the algebraic sum of the currents entering a node is zero.

The statement that the algebraic sum of the currents leaving a node is zero is what is known as Kirchhoff's conservation law.

2.9. Kirchhoff's Circulation Law. Electric current is driven through a resistor by using conducting wires to bring to bear upon the resistor the electrostatic field of a battery. Thus it is an electrostatic field that drives steady current round an electric circuit. In an electrostatic field there is associated with each point in space a number known as the potential, which is the potential energy per unit charge of a test charge at the point. Associated with each point in space there is one and only one value of the electric potential. If we start out from a point P in an electrostatic field and follow a closed curve returning to P, the potential will in general change as we move round the curve but the final value of the potential will be the same as the initial value, this common value being the potential at the point P. For any closed curve in any electrostatic field the change in potential in passing round the curve and returning to the starting point is zero.

This principle, which applies to any closed curve in any electrostatic field, applies in particular to the geometrical circuits in a network of resistors that we have called meshes. In the left-hand mesh of the network shown in Fig. 2.5 let us start out from the point A and pass round the mesh in a clockwise sense, returning to the starting point. As we pass round the mesh from the left-hand terminal of resistor R_1 to the right-hand terminal, there is a drop of potential. As we continue round the left-hand mesh and pass from the upper terminal of resistor R_3 to the lower terminal, there is a further drop of potential. As we continue round the mesh past the point C and return to the starting point A, we pass through the battery, where there is a rise of potential V. The total change of potential in going round the mesh and returning to the starting point is zero. The drop in potential as we cross the resistors R_1 and R_3 is exactly balanced by the rise in potential as we pass through the battery.

For the right-hand mesh of the network shown in Fig. 2.5 there is no battery in the circuit. The excess of potential of the left-hand terminal of resistor R_2 over the right-hand terminal is the same as the excess of potential of the upper terminal of resistor R_3 over the lower terminal. This fact can also be described by making a circuit of the right-hand mesh, starting from the point B, passing round the mesh, and returning to the starting point. As we pass from the left-hand terminal of resistor R_2 to the right-hand terminal, there is a drop of potential. As we continue round the mesh and pass from the lower terminal of resistor R_3 to the upper terminal of resistor R_3, there is a rise of potential. The drop in potential as we pass through the resistor R_2 is exactly balanced by the rise in potential as we pass through the resistor R_3, so that there is no change of potential as we pass round the mesh and return to the starting point.

We thus arrive at Kirchhoff's circulation law. In going round a mesh of a network and returning to the starting point the algebraic sum of the drops in potential is zero.

In applying Kirchhoff's circulation law it is wise to adopt some convention concerning the direction in which one moves round the meshes. A common convention is to move round all meshes in a clockwise sense, but there are occasions when it is convenient to depart from the convention.

2.10. Application of Kirchhoff's Laws. In using Kirchhoff's laws to ascertain all the currents and potentials in a given network of resistors there are several ways of arranging the analysis. The broad outline of the method is, however, as follows. Mathematical unknown quantities are introduced for the unknown currents and potentials of the network. To each node of the network we apply Kirchhoff's conservation law. To each mesh of the network we apply Kirchhoff's circulation law. We then have enough equations to solve for the unknown currents and potentials. Since only linear algebraic equations are involved, the mathematical process of solution is straightforward. However, there are both neat and clumsy ways of arranging this calculation. Network analysis is in fact as much an exercise in good organization as it is an exercise in electrical science.

There are two broad methods of attack. One is to introduce mathematical unknowns to describe the unknown currents through the resistors. This is best done in such a way that Kirchhoff's conservation law is automatically satisfied. Equations for the unknowns are then obtained from Kirchhoff's circulation law. The other main method is to introduce mathematical unknowns to describe the potentials of the various nodes. Equations for the unknowns are then obtained by means of Kirchhoff's conservation law. One of these two methods of attack is usually simpler than the other in a particular case, and the simpler one is usually the one that involves the smaller number of mathematical unknowns.

2.11. The Current Method. The current method is the method in which the mathematical unknowns introduced are the currents through the various resistors. There are two versions of this method, the uncontracted current method and the contracted current method. The contracted current method is usually known as the mesh-current method and is the one to be recommended. We shall, however, first consider the uncontracted current method, also known as the branch-current method.

Let us apply the uncontracted current method to the network shown in Fig. 2.5. Let the currents through the resistors be I_1, I_2, and I_3, with the directions of the currents as shown in Fig. 2.6. Let us first apply Kirchhoff's conservation law to the various nodes. Application of the law to node A merely tells us that the current supplied from the positive terminal of the battery is I_1. Likewise application of Kirchhoff's conservation law to node C tells us

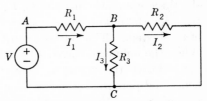

FIG. 2.6. Illustrating the uncontracted current method.

that the current flowing to the negative terminal of the battery is $I_2 + I_3$. Application of Kirchhoff's conservation law to node B gives us, however, the following relation between the unknowns:

$$-I_1 + I_2 + I_3 = 0 \qquad (2.24)$$

The three terms on the left-hand side of this equation are the currents leaving node B along resistors R_1, R_2, and R_3; the minus sign associated with the current I_1 arises from the fact that I_1 is defined in Fig. 2.6 as the current through resistor R_1 toward node B.

Kirchhoff's conservation law has now been applied to each node, and we turn to application of Kirchhoff's circulation law. To apply Kirchhoff's circulation law to the left-hand mesh in Fig. 2.6 we start from node A and proceed completely round the mesh in a clockwise sense. The drop in potential in passing through the resistor R_1 is $R_1 I_1$. The drop in potential in passing through the resistor R_3 is $R_3 I_3$. The rise in potential in going through the battery is V. Kirchhoff's circulation law for the left-hand mesh therefore gives

$$R_1 I_1 + R_3 I_3 - V = 0 \qquad (2.25)$$

For the right-hand mesh of Fig. 2.6 we start at node B and proceed in a clockwise sense. We first encounter the resistor R_2, and in passing through this resistor from left to right the drop in potential is $R_2 I_2$. Continuing round the mesh in a clockwise mesh we next encounter resistor R_3. In passing from the lower terminal to the upper terminal of resistor R_3 we are moving in a direction opposite the current I_3. Consequently there is a rise in potential as we cross through this resistor of amount R_3I_3. Thus in passing round the right-hand mesh of Fig. 2.6 in a clockwise sense the drop in potential in passing through the resistor R_3 is $-R_3I_3$. There is no battery in this mesh, and so, on equating the algebraic sum of the drops of potential in passing completely round the mesh to zero, we obtain the equation

$$R_2I_2 - R_3I_3 = 0 \qquad (2.26)$$

Equations (2.24) to (2.26) now constitute three equations to determine the three unknown currents I_1, I_2, and I_3. If we solve these three equations for the unknowns, we then know the currents through all resistors of the system. The voltages across the resistors are R_1I_1, R_2I_2, and R_3I_3. When the unknown currents have been calculated, therefore, we immediately derive the potential differences across the various resistors and hence the potential of every node in the system. The results obtained are, of course, the ones already deduced in Sec. 2.6 by analyzing the network into parallel and series connections.

2.12. The Mesh-current Method. Let us now turn to the contraction of the current method known as the mesh-current method. This is the

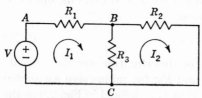

Fig. 2.7. Illustrating the mesh-current method.

recommended method when currents are used for the mathematical unknowns. In the mesh-current method for analyzing the network shown in Fig. 2.6 we introduce unknown mesh currents I_1 and I_2 flowing round the left- and right-hand meshes as indicated in Fig. 2.7. The mesh current I_1 is supposed to flow through the resistor R_1, through the resistor R_3, and through the battery. The mesh current I_2 is supposed to flow through the resistor R_2 and through the resistor R_3. It follows that, through the resistor R_3, there is a downward current I_1 arising from the current round the left-hand mesh and an upward current I_2 arising from the current round the right-hand mesh. The net current through resistor R_3 is therefore $I_1 - I_2$ in the downward direction, or alternatively $I_2 - I_1$ in the upward direction. Having taken the current round the left- and right-hand meshes to be in the same direction, namely, clockwise, the current through the resistor R_3 common to the two meshes is equal to the difference of the two mesh currents. On the other hand, for the resistor R_1, which is in the left-hand mesh only, the current through it is simply the mesh current I_1 in this mesh. Likewise for the resistor R_2, which is in the right-hand mesh only, the current through it is simply the mesh current I_2 in this mesh. The currents I_1 and I_2 in Fig. 2.7 are therefore the same currents that are represented by I_1 and I_2 in Fig. 2.6. However, the unknown current I_3 in Fig. 2.6 has not been introduced in Fig. 2.7, where it appears as $I_1 - I_2$. Thus in the mesh-current method illustrated in Fig. 2.7 fewer unknown currents are introduced. Moreover in the mesh-current method Kirchhoff's conservation law is automatically satisfied because the mesh currents entering any node, for example, node B in Fig. 2.7, are automatically balanced by the same mesh currents leaving that node. Thus, when mesh currents are used as the mathematical unknowns, fewer unknown currents have to be introduced and Kirchhoff's conservation law is automatically satisfied. The equations required to determine the unknown mesh currents are obtained by application of Kirchhoff's circulation law to the network.

Let us apply Kirchhoff's circulation law to the left-hand mesh in Fig. 2.7, starting from node A and passing round the mesh in a clockwise sense. The drop in potential in passing through resistor R_1 is R_1I_1. Continuing round the mesh in a clockwise sense, we next encounter resistor R_3, through which the current in a clockwise sense round the left-hand mesh is not I_1 but $I_1 - I_2$. Thus in going round the left-hand mesh in a clockwise sense the drop in potential in passing through resistor R_3 is $R_3(I_1 - I_2)$. We complete the circuit of the left-hand mesh by passing through the rise of potential V in the battery. Hence Kirchhoff's circulation law applied to the left-hand mesh of the network shown in Fig. 2.7 yields the equation

$$R_1I_1 + R_3(I_1 - I_2) - V = 0 \qquad (2.27)$$

In a similar way we apply Kirchhoff's circulation law to the right-hand mesh of the network shown in Fig. 2.7. We start from node B and proceed round the mesh in a clockwise sense. We first encounter resistor R_2. The drop in potential in passing through this resistor is R_2I_2. Continuing round the mesh in a clockwise sense we next encounter resistor R_3. The current through resistor R_3 in a clockwise sense round the right-hand mesh is not I_2 but $I_2 - I_1$. The drop in potential in passing through resistor R_3 in a clockwise sense round the right-hand mesh is therefore $R_3(I_2 - I_1)$. Kirchhoff's circulation law for the right-hand mesh of the network shown in Fig. 2.7 therefore gives

$$R_2I_2 + R_3(I_2 - I_1) = 0 \qquad (2.28)$$

Equations (2.27) and (2.28) are a pair of linear algebraic equations for the unknown mesh currents I_1 and I_2. When these have been determined, we can write down the currents through every element of the network in Fig. 2.7 and hence the voltages across every element.

It may be noted that Eqs. (2.27) and (2.28) can be obtained from Eqs. (2.25) and (2.26) by substituting for I_3 from Eq. (2.24) into Eqs. (2.25) and (2.26).   Thus the equations that we write down directly on the mesh-current method are the same as those obtained on the uncontracted current method after carrying out the first stage in the algebraic solution for the unknowns.   What the mesh-current method does is to take into account Eq. (2.24) by realizing that the current through the resistor R_3 common to the two meshes is the difference of the mesh currents, thereby leading directly to Eqs. (2.27) and (2.28) on applying Kirchhoff's circulation law.

In order to solve Eqs. (2.27) and (2.28) for I_1 and I_2, we can conveniently rearrange the equations in the following form:

$$(R_1 + R_3)I_1 - R_3I_2 = V \qquad (2.29)$$
$$-R_3I_1 + (R_2 + R_3)I_2 = 0 \qquad (2.30)$$

The algebraic solution of these equations for I_1 and I_2 then gives

$$I_1 = \frac{R_2 + R_3}{R_2R_3 + R_3R_1 + R_1R_2} V \qquad (2.31)$$

$$I_2 = \frac{R_3}{R_2R_3 + R_3R_1 + R_1R_2} V \qquad (2.32)$$

Equation (2.31) conveys the same information as Eq. (2.18), while Eq. (2.32) conveys the same information as Eq. (2.20).   Using Eqs. (2.31) and (2.32) we can deduce that the current through resistor R_3 is

$$I_1 - I_2 = \frac{R_2}{R_2R_3 + R_3R_1 + R_1R_2} V \qquad (2.33)$$

and this equation conveys the same information as Eq. (2.21).   The voltages across resistors R_1, R_2, and R_3 are respectively

$$R_1I_1 = \frac{R_1(R_2 + R_3)}{R_2R_3 + R_3R_1 + R_1R_2} V \qquad (2.34)$$

$$R_2I_2 = \frac{R_2R_3}{R_2R_3 + R_3R_2 + R_1R_2} V \qquad (2.35)$$

$$R_3(I_1 - I_2) = \frac{R_2R_3}{R_2R_3 + R_3R_1 + R_1R_2} V \qquad (2.36)$$

Equation (2.34) conveys the same information as Eq. (2.22), while Eqs. (2.35) and (2.36) convey the same information as Eq. (2.23).

The main feature of the approach used in the mesh-current method is to introduce the unknown currents in such a way that Kirchhoff's conservation law is already satisfied.   The equations to determine the currents are then obtained from Kirchhoff's circulation law applied to the various meshes.

It will be noticed that, for the network that we have used for illustrating the mesh-current method, this method is less convenient but more organized than that based on analyzing the network into parallel and series connections.   It is, however, easy to produce examples of networks in which the mesh-current method is considerably superior to any other method.

2.13. The Node-potential Method.   In any electrostatic field there is a unique electric potential associated with each point of the field, and this applies to the electrostatic fields that drive steady currents through resistive networks.   It follows that there is a unique potential associated with each node of a network of resistors carrying steady currents.   These potentials are known as the node potentials of the network.   In the node-potential method for calculating the various properties of a network of resistors it is the potentials of the nodes that are used as the mathematical unknowns.

It is usually convenient to select the potential of one of the nodes as zero.   If one of the nodes is connected to a metal chassis upon which the network is constructed or to a metal box within which the network is enclosed, it is usually convenient to make this node the one at zero potential.   Using the network shown in Fig. 2.7 as an example, we select node C as the one at zero potential.   Node A then has the potential V of the battery and is not an unknown potential. The only node whose potential requires calculation is node B.   Let the potential of this node be ϕ.   The potentials of the nodes are then as illustrated in Fig. 2.8.

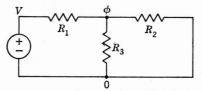

Fig. 2.8. Illustrating the node-potential method.

It will be noticed that, in using the node potentials as the mathematical unknowns in the network shown in Fig. 2.8, only one unknown is required, namely ϕ, whereas in the mesh-current method two unknown currents were involved.   Thus the number of mathematical unknowns involved in the two methods is not necessarily the same.

To calculate the unknown potential in Fig. 2.8 we have available Kirchhoff's laws.   Kirchhoff's circulation law states that, in a complete circuit of any mesh, we return to the initial potential.   The truth of this law has already been presumed in assigning unique potentials to the nodes. No matter what geometrical path we follow, whenever we return to the same node, we return to the same potential.   In the node-potential method, therefore, Kirchhoff's circulation law is automatically satisfied, and it is from Kirchhoff's conservation law that we obtain the equations necessary to determine the unknown node potentials.

To each node whose potential is unknown, we apply Kirchhoff's conservation law.   For the network shown in Fig. 2.8, ϕ is the only unknown potential, and so it is only to the node having this potential that we need apply Kirchhoff's conservation law. Kirchhoff's conservation law applied to this node states that the algebraic sum of the currents leaving the node is zero. For resistor R_1 the excess of potential of the right-hand terminal over the left-hand terminal is $\phi - V$, and therefore the current through it from right to left is $(\phi - V)/R_1$. For resistor R_2 the excess of potential of the left-hand terminal over the right-hand terminal is $\phi - 0$, and therefore the current through it from left to right is $(\phi - 0)/R_2$. For resistor R_3 the excess of potential of the upper terminal over the lower terminal is $\phi - 0$, and therefore the current through it from top to bottom is $(\phi - 0)/R_3$. Equating to zero the algebraic sum of the currents leaving the node of potential ϕ, we obtain

$$\frac{\phi - V}{R_1} + \frac{\phi - 0}{R_2} + \frac{\phi - 0}{R_3} = 0 \tag{2.37}$$

This is Kirchhoff's conservation law applied to the node of unknown potential ϕ, and it gives us an equation to determine this unknown potential. By solving Eq. (2.37) for ϕ we obtain

$$\phi = \frac{R_2 R_3}{R_2 R_3 + R_3 R_1 + R_1 R_2} V \tag{2.38}$$

With the potentials of all the nodes now known, we know the potential differences across all the resistors, and by dividing these by the resistances of the resistors we obtain the currents through the resistors. From Eq. (2.38) we can therefore derive all the information about the network shown in Fig. 2.8. For example, the current through the resistor R_2 is

$$\frac{\phi - 0}{R_2} = \frac{R_3}{R_2 R_3 + R_3 R_1 + R_1 R_2} V \tag{2.39}$$

This equation conveys the same information as Eq. (2.32) or (2.20).

It will be noticed that, in using Kirchhoff's conservation law to formulate Eq. (2.37), the procedure is to subtract from the potential of the node under consideration the potentials of each adjacent node and then divide the differences by the corresponding resistances. It is best to proceed in this orderly way even if it is obvious that the potential of the node under consideration is less than the potential of some adjacent node. Thus, for example, for the network shown in Fig. 2.8, it is reasonably obvious, and is in any case true, that the potential ϕ is less than the potential V, so that $\phi - V$ is negative. Thus the current through resistor R_1 from right to left is negative, and the term $(\phi - V)/R_1$ in Eq. (2.37) is numerically negative. It is not, however, necessary to bear this in mind in writing down Eq. (2.37), provided that in each term of this equation the first potential written down is the potential of the node to which Kirchhoff's conservation law is being applied.

It will be noticed that, for the network that we have used as an example, the node-potential method is superior to the mesh-current method. In the node-potential method only one mathematical unknown was required, and consequently only one linear equation was required to determine it. Whether the node-potential method of solving this particular network is superior to the method of analysis into parallel and series connections is debatable. The mathematical organization involved in the node-potential method is considerably superior, thought it might be argued that, by analysis into parallel and series connections, one obtains a better insight into the functioning of the network.

2.14. Choice of Method.   For any particular network a choice has to be made among the parallel-series method, the mesh-current method, and the node-potential method. This choice can be made from the following considerations: If the way in which the network analyzes into parallel and series connections is immediately obvious to the eye as soon as the network is drawn out, the parallel-series method may well be a good choice. If, on the other hand, any serious thought is required to see how the network analyzes into parallel and series connections, then it will probably be better to choose either the mesh-current or the node-potential method. To decide between the mesh-current and node-potential methods, draw out two diagrams of the network. On one, mark the unknowns required in the mesh-current method and on the other the unknowns required in the

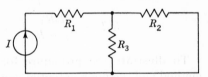

Fig. 2.9. Example of a network in which it is the current I delivered by the battery that is specified instead of the voltage of the battery.

node-potential method. The method to be preferred is the one that requires the smaller number of unknowns.

As an example, let us consider the problem illustrated in Fig. 2.9. This is the same network previously considered, but instead of the voltage of the battery being specified, it is the current I delivered by the battery that is specified. In terms of I and the resistances of the resistors it is required to calculate the currents through all resistors and the potential differences across them. It is immediately obvious that the resistors R_2 and R_3 are in parallel and that this parallel combination is in series with the resistor R_1. The parallel-series method would therefore be a good choice in this case. The current through resistor R_1 is the given current I delivered by the battery, and consequently the potential drop across

212   STEADY ELECTRIC CURRENTS AND VACUUM TUBES   [PART 2

this resistor is

$$R_1 I \qquad (2.40)$$

The current I through resistor R_1 divides between the resistors R_2 and R_3 in the inverse ratio of their resistances. Hence the current through resistor R_2 is

$$\frac{R_3}{R_2 + R_3} I \qquad (2.41)$$

and the current through resistor R_3 is

$$\frac{R_2}{R_2 + R_3} I \qquad (2.42)$$

The common potential across resistors R_2 and R_3 is obtained by either multiplying the current (2.41) by R_2 or multiplying the current (2.42) by R_3 and is therefore

$$\frac{R_2 R_3}{R_2 + R_3} I \qquad (2.43)$$

The voltage that the battery must have in order to deliver the given current I is the sum of the voltage (2.40) across resistor R_1 and the common voltage (2.42) across resistors R_2 and R_3. It is therefore

$$R_1 I + \frac{R_2 R_3}{R_2 + R_3} I = \frac{R_2 R_3 + R_3 R_1 + R_1 R_2}{R_2 + R_3} I \qquad (2.44)$$

To illustrate the procedure for choosing between the mesh-current method and the node-potential method, let us again consider the problem

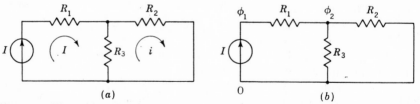

FIG. 2.10. Illustrating the choice between (a) the mesh-current method and (b) the node-potential method.

illustrated in Fig. 2.9. In Fig. 2.10 the network has been drawn out twice. In Fig. 2.10a have been marked the mesh currents. The current round the left-hand mesh is the given current I delivered by the battery and is consequently not an unknown. The current round the right-hand mesh has been labeled i and is the only mathematical unknown that has to be introduced in using the mesh-current method. In Fig. 2.10b are marked the potentials of the nodes. Choose the potential of the bottom terminal of the battery to be 0. Since it is the current I delivered by the battery that is prescribed, the potential of the upper terminal of the battery is an unknown potential ϕ_1. The potential of the remaining node is also unknown, and we denote it by ϕ_2. The potentials of all the nodes in Fig. 2.10b are now marked, and we see that there are two unknown node potentials, ϕ_1 and ϕ_2. Since one unknown i is required in the mesh-current method and two unknowns ϕ_1 and ϕ_2 are required in the node-potential method, it follows that the mesh-current method is to be preferred to the node-potential method in this case.

Using the mesh-current method, we obtain the equation necessary to determine the unknown current i from Kirchhoff's circulation law. Kirchhoff's circulation law when applied to the left-hand mesh in Fig. 2.10a determines the voltage of the battery if we need to calculate it. It is application of Kirchhoff's circulation law to the right-hand mesh in Fig. 2.10a that gives the equation required to determine the unknown current i associated with this mesh. Starting at the upper left-hand corner of the right-hand mesh and proceeding clockwise round the mesh in the usual way, we derive

$$R_2 i + R_3(i - I) = 0 \qquad (2.45)$$

Solution of this equation for i gives

$$i = \frac{R_3}{R_2 + R_3} I \qquad (2.46)$$

This is the current through resistor R_2. The current through resistor R_3 is

$$I - i = \frac{R_2}{R_2 + R_3} I \qquad (2.47)$$

The voltage that the battery must have in order to deliver the given current I can be obtained by applying Kirchhoff's circulation law to the left-hand mesh, or alternatively from the fact that it is the sum of the voltages across resistors R_1 and R_2. Using the second method, the voltage of the battery is

$$R_1 I + R_2 i \qquad (2.48)$$

and on substituting for i from Eq. (2.46) this becomes

$$\frac{R_2 R_3 + R_3 R_1 + R_1 R_2}{R_2 + R_3} I \qquad (2.49)$$

Equations (2.46), (2.47), and (2.49) convey the same information as Eqs. (2.41), (2.42), and (2.44).

In this problem the node-potential method is clearly inferior to the mesh-current method. The mesh-current method is mathematically more systematic than the parallel-series method, but the latter method perhaps gives better insight into the operation of the network.

2.15. Balanced Network. Networks frequently possess symmetry properties that permit a reduction in the number of mathematical unknowns that must be introduced to describe the network. Such a network is called a balanced network, and it is often convenient to take the potential on the plane of symmetry as zero. Figure 2.11 illus-

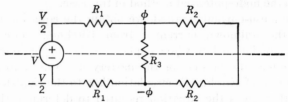

FIG. 2.11. Illustrating a network that is symmetrical with respect to the dashed line.

trates a balanced network, and the dashed line indicates the plane of symmetry. If we take the potential of this plane as zero, it follows that the potential of the node at the right-hand end of the network is zero. Moreover the potentials of the upper and lower terminals of the battery are $\frac{1}{2}V$ and $-\frac{1}{2}V$. There are now two nodes whose potentials have not yet been marked. From the symmetry of the network these potentials may be taken as ϕ and $-\phi$ so that only one unknown is necessary to describe both potentials. Thus by taking advantage of the symmetry properties of the network shown in Fig. 2.11 only one unknown potential need be introduced in analyzing it. The equation necessary to determine this unknown is obtained from Kirchhoff's conservation law applied to the node of potential ϕ. If the conservation law is applied to the node of potential $-\phi$, the same equation is obtained.

It is always desirable to use any symmetry that a network may possess to reduce the number of mathematical unknowns as far as possible.

2.16. Standard Procedure for Analyzing Networks of Resistors. From what has been said concerning the analysis of networks of resistors we see that the procedure is as follows: (1) Decide whether the network is sufficiently simple to use the parallel-series method. (2) If not, draw two diagrams of the network; mark the unknowns required in the mesh-current method on one diagram and the unknowns required in the node-potential method on the other diagram. Use the symmetry properties, if any, of the network to reduce the number of unknowns as far as possible. (3) If the mesh-current method involves the smaller number of unknowns, use it and derive equations for the unknowns by applying Kirchhoff's circulation law to the meshes. (4) If the node-potential method involves the fewer number of unknowns, use it and obtain equations for the unknowns by applying Kirchhoff's conservation law to the nodes. (5) Before solving the equations for the unknowns, decide which unknowns actually need to be determined in order to provide the information required.

Although it is not advisable to choose between the mesh-current and the node-potential methods by casual inspection of the network, it is worthwhile to realize what features of a network favor the mesh-current method and what features favor the node-potential method. The main consideration involved is the relative number of meshes and nodes in the network. Figure 2.1 is an example of a network with many meshes and yet only two nodes. Figure 2.2 is an example of a network with many nodes and yet only one mesh. Now in the mesh-current method there is a current associated with each mesh, while in the node-potential method there is a potential associated with each node. Hence a network with few meshes and many nodes is favorable to use of the mesh-current method, while a network with few nodes and many meshes is favorable to use of the node-potential method. However, another consideration affecting the relative number of mathematical unknowns involved in the mesh-current and the node-potential methods for a particular network is the way in which the information about the sources is specified. If the network is energized by sources having given voltages, these given voltages reduce the number of unknown node potentials and thus favor the node-potential method. On the other hand, if the network is energized by sources delivering specified currents, these specified currents reduce the number of unknown currents in the mesh-current method and so favor this method. To allow for all these considerations it is best, as previously stated, to draw two diagrams of the network, to mark on one diagram the unknowns required in the mesh-current method and on the other diagram the unknowns required in the node-potential method. In this way the method involving the smaller number of mathematical unknowns can be reliably recognized.

2.17. The Power Absorbed by a Network of Resistors. To calculate the rate at which energy is absorbed by a particular resistor of a network we first calculate either the voltage across the resistor or alternatively the current through it. We then use either the second or third of the expressions for the power absorbed by a resistor given in Eqs. (1.22).

To calculate the power delivered by a particular battery in a network we proceed as follows. If the voltage of the battery is specified, we calculate the current delivered by it. If the current delivered by the battery is specified, we calculate the voltage that the battery must have in order to deliver the specified current. When we have thus ascertained both the voltage of the battery and the current delivered by the battery, we calculate the rate at which energy is supplied by the battery from the first of the expressions in Eqs. (1.22).

It should be noted that, in a steady state, the total rate at which the batteries are supplying electrical energy to the network is necessarily equal to the total rate at which electrical energy is being absorbed by the resistors. This fact can frequently be used to save calculation. Thus suppose that we are discussing a network that contains a large number of resistors but only a few batteries, and suppose that we have to calculate the total power absorbed by the resistors. It would be possible to do this by calculating the power absorbed by each of the large number of resistors and adding the results. It is much easier, however, to take the alternative course of calculating the power supplied by the small number of batteries and to sum these. Suppose, for example, that we were required to calculate the total power absorbed by the resistors in the network shown in Fig. 2.5. We first argue that this is the same as the power delivered by the single battery of voltage V. We then calculate the equivalent resistance R connected across the battery by the argument leading to Eq. (2.16). The current delivered by the battery is then V/R, and the power delivered by the battery is V^2/R. This is therefore the total rate at which energy is absorbed by the resistors, and the value of R is given by Eq. (2.16).

SUMMARIZING EXERCISES

2.1. Prove that, if a number of resistors whose resistances are $R_1, R_2, \ldots, R_n$ are connected in series, the system can be used as a single resistor of resistance $R_1 + R_2 + \cdots + R_n$. Prove also that, if a number of resistors whose conductances are $G_1, G_2, \ldots, G_n$ are connected in parallel, the system can be used as a single resistor of conductance $G_1 + G_2 + \cdots + G_n$.

2.2. State and justify Kirchhoff's laws for networks of resistors carrying steady currents.

2.3. Explain how to calculate the voltages and currents in a network of resistors and batteries using (a) the method of analysis into parallel and series connections, (b) the mesh-current method, and (c) the node-potential method. Explain the advantages and disadvantages of the three methods.

2.4. Explain how the symmetry of a balanced network of resistors can be used to reduce the number of unknowns required to describe it.

2.5. If a network of resistors is energized by a single battery of given voltage, prove that the total rate at which energy is absorbed by all the resistors can be evaluated by calculating a single current.

2.6. A variable load resistor is connected across a battery having known internal resistance and known open-circuit voltage. Prove that the rate at which electrical energy is absorbed by the load resistor is greatest when this resistor is adjusted to be equal to the internal resistance of the battery.

CHAPTER 3

COEFFICIENTS OF CONDUCTANCE AND RESISTANCE
FOR NETWORKS OF RESISTORS

3.1. Introduction. Let us apply the principles that we have developed for analyzing networks of resistors to the network shown in Fig. 3.1. In this network the central node, marked 0, is a node taken to have zero potential. Steady currents I_1, I_2, and I_3 are led into the network through nodes 1, 2, and 3 respectively, and the combined current $I_1 + I_2 + I_3$ is led out through node 0. As a result let the potentials of nodes 1, 2, and 3 be V_1, V_2, and V_3 respectively. Applying Kirchhoff's conservation law to node 1 we obtain

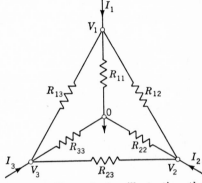

FIG. 3.1. Network for illustrating the coefficients of conductance and resistance.

$$I_1 = \frac{V_1 - 0}{R_{11}} + \frac{V_1 - V_2}{R_{12}} + \frac{V_1 - V_3}{R_{13}}$$

In the same way by applying Kirchhoff's conservation law to nodes 2 and 3 we obtain respectively

$$I_2 = \frac{V_2 - 0}{R_{22}} + \frac{V_2 - V_1}{R_{12}} + \frac{V_2 - V_3}{R_{23}}$$

$$I_3 = \frac{V_3 - 0}{R_{33}} + \frac{V_3 - V_1}{R_{13}} + \frac{V_3 - V_2}{R_{23}}$$

On collecting the terms in V_1, V_2, and V_3, these equations become

$$I_1 = \left(\frac{1}{R_{11}} + \frac{1}{R_{12}} + \frac{1}{R_{13}}\right) V_1 - \frac{1}{R_{12}} V_2 - \frac{1}{R_{13}} V_3 \qquad (3.1)$$

$$I_2 = - \frac{1}{R_{12}} V_1 + \left(\frac{1}{R_{22}} + \frac{1}{R_{23}} + \frac{1}{R_{12}}\right) V_2 - \frac{1}{R_{23}} V_3 \qquad (3.2)$$

$$I_3 = - \frac{1}{R_{13}} V_1 - \frac{1}{R_{23}} V_2 + \left(\frac{1}{R_{33}} + \frac{1}{R_{13}} + \frac{1}{R_{23}}\right) V_3 \qquad (3.3)$$

Equations (3.1) to (3.3) are the equations which determine the potentials V_1, V_2, and V_3 of nodes 1, 2, and 3 when given currents I_1, I_2, and I_3 are led in through them. Alternatively these equations give the currents I_1, I_2, and I_3 that must be led through nodes 1, 2, and 3 in order to raise these nodes to given potentials V_1, V_2, and V_3 above the potential of the central node.

Equations (3.1) to (3.3) relating the currents I_1, I_2, and I_3 to the potentials V_1, V_2, and V_3 are of the form

$$I_1 = g_{11}V_1 + g_{12}V_2 + g_{13}V_3 \qquad (3.4)$$
$$I_2 = g_{21}V_1 + g_{22}V_2 + g_{23}V_3 \qquad (3.5)$$
$$I_3 = g_{31}V_1 + g_{32}V_2 + g_{33}V_3 \qquad (3.6)$$

By comparing Eq. (3.4) with Eq. (3.1), Eq. (3.5) with Eq. (3.2), and Eq. (3.6) with Eq. (3.3) we see that the diagonal coefficients in Eqs. (3.4) to (3.6) are

$$g_{11} = \frac{1}{R_{11}} + \frac{1}{R_{12}} + \frac{1}{R_{13}} \qquad (3.7)$$

$$g_{22} = \frac{1}{R_{22}} + \frac{1}{R_{23}} + \frac{1}{R_{12}} \qquad (3.8)$$

$$g_{33} = \frac{1}{R_{33}} + \frac{1}{R_{13}} + \frac{1}{R_{23}} \qquad (3.9)$$

and the nondiagonal coefficients are

$$g_{12} = g_{21} = - \frac{1}{R_{12}} \qquad (3.10)$$

$$g_{23} = g_{32} = - \frac{1}{R_{23}} \qquad (3.11)$$

$$g_{31} = g_{13} = - \frac{1}{R_{13}} \qquad (3.12)$$

When the coefficients in Eqs. (3.4) to (3.6) have been calculated in terms of the resistances of the resistors forming the network in accordance with Eqs. (3.7) to (3.12), we can apply any potentials to nodes 1, 2, and 3 and deduce from Eqs. (3.4) to (3.6) the corresponding currents that must be supplied to these nodes. The coefficients in Eqs. (3.4) to (3.6) are known as the coefficients of conductance of the network.

Equations (3.4) to (3.6) are in a form convenient to use when the problem is to calculate the currents that must be supplied to nodes 1, 2, and 3 when the potentials of these nodes are specified. If, however, it is the currents to the nodes that are specified and the potentials of the nodes that have to be calculated, then Eqs. (3.4) to (3.6) must be solved for V_1, V_2, and V_3 in terms of I_1, I_2, and I_3. This solution is carried out by the ordinary process for solving linear algebraic equations and leads to equations of the form

$$V_1 = r_{11}I_1 + r_{12}I_2 + r_{13}I_3 \qquad (3.13)$$
$$V_2 = r_{21}I_1 + r_{22}I_2 + r_{23}I_3 \qquad (3.14)$$
$$V_3 = r_{31}I_1 + r_{32}I_2 + r_{33}I_3 \qquad (3.15)$$

When the process of solution is carried out in detail, the coefficients in Eqs. (3.13) to (3.15) can be expressed in terms of those in Eqs. (3.4) to (3.6) and hence in terms of the resistances of the resistors forming the network. In the process of solution it follows that

$$r_{12} = r_{21} \qquad (3.16)$$
$$r_{23} = r_{32} \qquad (3.17)$$
$$r_{31} = r_{13} \qquad (3.18)$$

Thus the symmetry of the nondiagonal coefficients of conductance expressed by Eqs. (3.10) to (3.12) leads to a corresponding symmetry of the nondiagonal coefficients in Eqs. (3.13) to (3.15). The coefficients in Eqs. (3.13) to (3.15) are known as the coefficients of resistance of the network. When the coefficients of resistance of a network have been calculated, we can supply any currents I_1, I_2, and I_3 to nodes 1, 2, and 3 and deduce the corresponding potentials V_1, V_2, and V_3 of the nodes from Eqs. (3.13) to (3.15).

The diagonal coefficients g_{11}, g_{22}, and g_{33} in Eqs. (3.4) to (3.6) are known as the coefficients of self-conductance of the network, while the remaining coefficients in these equations are known as the coefficients of mutual conductance. Likewise the diagonal coefficients r_{11}, r_{22}, and r_{33} in Eqs. (3.13) to (3.15) are known as the coefficients of self-resistance of the system while the remaining coefficients in these equations are known as the coefficients of mutual resistance. It should be noted that the reciprocal of a coefficient of conductance does not give the corresponding coefficient of resistance; the relation between the coefficients of conductance and the coefficients of resistance must be obtained either by solving Eqs. (3.4) to (3.6) for V_1, V_2, and V_3 so as to obtain equations of the form (3.13) to (3.15) or alternatively by solving Eqs. (3.13) to (3.15) for I_1, I_2, and I_3 so as to obtain equations of the form (3.4) to (3.6).

The procedure that we have outlined in connection with the network shown in Fig. 3.1 could equally well be applied to the network shown in Fig. 3.2. In this case there are five nodes in addition to the central node at zero potential. We thus have five linear equations expressing the currents supplied to nodes 1, 2, 3, 4, and 5 in terms of their potentials or

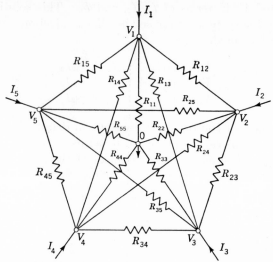

FIG. 3.2. More complicated network for illustrating the coefficients of conductance and resistance.

alternatively expressing the potentials in terms of the currents. Corresponding to Eqs. (3.4) to (3.6) we have

$$I_1 = g_{11}V_1 + g_{12}V_2 + g_{13}V_3 + g_{14}V_4 + g_{15}V_5 \qquad (3.19)$$
$$I_2 = g_{21}V_1 + g_{22}V_2 + g_{23}V_3 + g_{24}V_4 + g_{25}V_5 \qquad (3.20)$$
$$I_3 = g_{31}V_1 + g_{32}V_2 + g_{33}V_3 + g_{34}V_4 + g_{35}V_5 \qquad (3.21)$$
$$I_4 = g_{41}V_1 + g_{42}V_2 + g_{43}V_3 + g_{44}V_4 + g_{45}V_5 \qquad (3.22)$$
$$I_5 = g_{51}V_1 + g_{52}V_2 + g_{53}V_3 + g_{54}V_4 + g_{55}V_5 \qquad (3.23)$$

where
$$g_{11} = \frac{1}{R_{11}} + \frac{1}{R_{12}} + \frac{1}{R_{13}} + \frac{1}{R_{14}} + \frac{1}{R_{15}} \qquad (3.24)$$
$$. \ . \ . \ . \ . \ . \ . \ . \ . \ . \ . \ . \ . \ . \ . \ . \ . \ .$$

$$g_{12} = g_{21} = -\frac{1}{R_{12}} \qquad (3.25)$$
$$. \ . \ . \ . \ . \ . \ . \ . \ . \ .$$

Corresponding to Eqs. (3.13) to (3.15) we have

$$V_1 = r_{11}I_1 + r_{12}I_2 + r_{13}I_3 + r_{14}I_4 + r_{15}I_5 \qquad (3.26)$$
$$V_2 = r_{21}I_1 + r_{22}I_2 + r_{23}I_3 + r_{24}I_4 + r_{25}I_5 \qquad (3.27)$$
$$V_3 = r_{31}I_1 + r_{32}I_2 + r_{33}I_3 + r_{34}I_4 + r_{35}I_5 \qquad (3.28)$$
$$V_4 = r_{41}I_1 + r_{42}I_2 + r_{43}I_3 + r_{44}I_4 + r_{45}I_5 \qquad (3.29)$$
$$V_5 = r_{51}I_1 + r_{52}I_2 + r_{53}I_3 + r_{54}I_4 + r_{55}I_5 \qquad (3.30)$$

where
$$r_{12} = r_{21} \qquad \cdots \qquad (3.31)$$

Equations (3.26) to (3.30) are obtained by solving Eqs. (3.19) to (3.23) for V_1, V_2, V_3, V_4, and V_5.

3.2. An Interpretation of the Coefficients of Conductance and Resistance. Let us consider the network shown in Fig. 3.1. Let us suppose for the time being that node 1 is at unit potential while nodes 2 and 3 are at zero potential. In Eqs. (3.4) to (3.6) we then put

$$V_1 = 1 \qquad V_2 = 0 \qquad V_3 = 0 \qquad (3.32)$$

and obtain

$$I_1 = g_{11} \qquad I_2 = g_{21} \qquad I_3 = g_{31} \qquad (3.33)$$

We thus see that the coefficients g_{11}, g_{21}, and g_{31} are the currents that must be supplied to nodes 1, 2, and 3 when node 1 is at unit potential and all the other nodes are at zero potential. In the same way we can substitute into Eqs. (3.4) to (3.6) the potentials

$$V_1 = 0 \qquad V_2 = 1 \qquad V_3 = 0 \qquad (3.34)$$

and obtain the currents

$$I_1 = g_{12} \qquad I_2 = g_{22} \qquad I_3 = g_{32} \qquad (3.35)$$

Likewise if we substitute

$$V_1 = 0 \qquad V_2 = 0 \qquad V_3 = 1 \qquad (3.36)$$

we obtain

$$I_1 = g_{13} \qquad I_2 = g_{23} \qquad I_3 = g_{33} \qquad (3.37)$$

We can summarize the information contained in Eqs. (3.32) to (3.37) by saying that the coefficient of conductance g_{mn} is numerically equal to the current supplied to node m when unit potential is applied to node n and all other nodes are at zero potential.

In a similar way we can obtain an interpretation of the coefficients of resistance from Eqs. (3.13) to (3.15). By putting

$$I_1 = 1 \qquad I_2 = 0 \qquad I_3 = 0 \qquad (3.38)$$

we obtain

$$V_1 = r_{11} \qquad V_2 = r_{21} \qquad V_3 = r_{31} \qquad (3.39)$$

By putting

$$I_1 = 0 \qquad I_2 = 1 \qquad I_3 = 0 \qquad (3.40)$$

we obtain

$$V_1 = r_{12} \qquad V_2 = r_{22} \qquad V_3 = r_{32} \qquad (3.41)$$

and by putting

$$I_1 = 0 \qquad I_2 = 0 \qquad I_3 = 1 \qquad (3.42)$$

we obtain

$$V_1 = r_{13} \qquad V_2 = r_{23} \qquad V_3 = r_{33} \qquad (3.43)$$

We can summarize the information contained in Eqs. (3.38) to (3.43) by saying that the coefficient of resistance r_{mn} is numerically equal to the potential of node m when unit current is supplied to node n and no current is supplied to the other nodes; it is understood that the unit current led in at node n is led out at node 0.

Equations (3.10) to (3.12) can be summarized by the single equation

$$g_{mn} = g_{nm} \tag{3.44}$$

the left- and right-hand sides of this equation both being equal to the reciprocal of the resistance of the resistor in the network for which one terminal is attached to node m and the other to node n. Likewise Eqs. (3.16) to (3.18) can be summarized by the single equation

$$r_{mn} = r_{nm} \tag{3.45}$$

Equation (3.44) can be interpreted by saying that the current that must be led in at node m when node n is at unit potential, all other nodes being at zero potential, is the same as the current that must be led in at node n when node m is at unit potential, all other nodes being at zero potential. Likewise Eq. (3.45) can be interpreted by saying that the potential of node m when unit current is supplied to node n is the same as the potential of node n when unit current is supplied to node m; it is understood in each case that no current is supplied to any other node but that the unit current led in at node m or n is led out at node 0. These results constitute what is known as Green's reciprocal theorem for networks of resistors.

3.3. The Principle of Superposition. The equations that we have developed relating the currents supplied to the nodes of a network of resistors and the potentials of the nodes are what are known mathematically as linear equations. No squares of the currents or voltages and no product terms in the currents and voltages are involved. The linearity of the equations relating the currents and voltages is the mathematical expression of a physical fact known as the principle of superposition.

Let us consider the network shown in Fig. 3.1 and make a study of the linear equations expressing the currents supplied to the nodes in terms of the potentials of the nodes. These are Eqs. (3.4) to (3.6). Let us consider the following three circumstances:

1. Let the potential of node 1 be V_1 and the potentials of nodes 2 and 3 be zero. In these circumstances the currents supplied to nodes 1, 2, and 3 are given by the first column on the right-hand side of Eqs. (3.4) to (3.6).

2. Let the potential of node 2 be V_2, and let the potentials of nodes 1 and 3 be zero. In these circumstances the currents supplied to nodes 1, 2, and 3 are given by the second column on the right-hand side of Eqs. (3.4) to (3.6).

3. Let the potential of node 3 be V_3, and let the potentials of nodes 1 and 2 be zero.   In these circumstances the currents supplied to nodes 1, 2, and 3 are given by the third column on the right-hand side of Eqs. (3.4) to (3.6).

Now let us consider a situation in which a potential V_1 is applied to node 1, a potential V_2 is applied to node 2, and a potential V_3 to node 3. In these circumstances the currents supplied to nodes 1, 2, and 3 are given by Eqs. (3.4) to (3.6).   These currents are, however, the sums of the currents obtained in the three situations 1, 2, and 3 discussed above. It follows therefore that the currents supplied when the potentials of the nodes are (V_1, V_2, V_3) are obtained by superposing the currents supplied in the cases when the potentials are $(V_1,0,0)$, $(0,V_2,0)$, and $(0,0,V_3)$. This is known as the principle of superposition and arises from the linearity of the equations relating currents and potentials.

The principle of superposition also includes the following more obvious point.   If a potential V_1 is applied to node 1 and zero potential to nodes 2 and 3, then the currents supplied to nodes 1, 2, and 3 are given by the first column on the right-hand side of Eqs. (3.4) to (3.6); these currents are V_1 times the currents given in Eqs. (3.33) appropriate to the situation in which unit potential is applied to node 1 and zero potentials to nodes 2 and 3.   It thus follows that the currents supplied to the nodes when the potentials are $(V_1,0,0)$ can be obtained by superposition of V_1 situations in each of which the potentials of the nodes are $(1,0,0)$.   In the same way the currents supplied to the nodes when the potentials are $(0,V_2,0)$ can be obtained by superposition of V_2 situations in each of which the potentials are $(0,1,0)$.   Likewise the currents supplied to the nodes when the potentials are $(0,0,V_3)$ can be obtained by superposition of V_3 situations in each of which the potentials of the nodes are $(0,0,1)$.

We thus see that the currents supplied to the nodes when the potentials are (V_1,V_2,V_3) can be obtained by superposition of V_1 situations in which the potentials are $(1,0,0)$, V_2 situations in which the potentials are $(0,1,0)$, and V_3 situations in which the potentials are $(0,0,1)$.   In the same way it follows from Eqs. (3.13) to (3.15) that the potentials on nodes 1, 2, and 3 when the currents supplied are (I_1,I_2,I_3) can be obtained by superposition of I_1 situations in which the currents supplied to nodes 1, 2, and 3 are $(1,0,0)$, I_2 situations in which the currents supplied are $(0,1,0)$, and I_3 situations in which the currents are $(0,0,1)$.

3.4. Networks of Resistors with a Limited Number of Accessible Nodes.   It frequently happens that networks are constructed in such a way that only a few of the nodes are easily accessible.   In Fig. 3.3 the dashed rectangular line represents a metal box whose potential we take to be the zero of potential.   The network contains six nodes marked

0, 1, 2, 3, 4, and 5. Node 0 is connected to the enclosing metal box and therefore is at zero potential. Nodes 1 and 2 are connected through holes in the metal box to terminals that are accessible exterior to the box. Nodes 3, 4, and 5 are interior to the box and inaccessible from the outside except by opening the box. We contemplate a situation in which a voltage is applied between terminals 1 and 0 or between terminals 2 and 0 or both, and we are interested in calculating the currents supplied to these terminals.

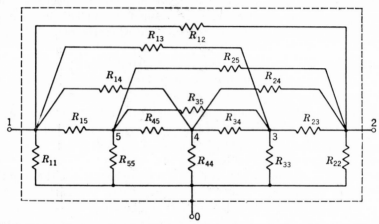

FIG. 3.3. Illustrating a network with accessible nodes (0, 1, 2) and inaccessible nodes (3, 4, 5).

An arrangement such as that shown in Fig. 3.3 might be used in the following way: A resistor of resistance R_L might be connected exterior to the box between nodes 2 and 0. A battery of given voltage might be connected between nodes 1 and 0, and it might be required to calculate the resulting steady current through the resistor of resistance R_L. In these circumstances the battery connected between nodes 1 and 0 is called a "source," and the resistor connected externally between nodes 2 and 0 is called the "load." Node 1 would be called the "input terminal" of the network, and node 2 the "output terminal." Networks containing no batteries but to which batteries can be connected through a pair of accessible nodes in addition to the node at zero potential have special properties that we shall now study.

For a network such as that shown in Fig. 3.3 there are coefficients of conductance and coefficients of resistance that can be calculated in terms of the resistances of the individual resistors of the network in the manner already studied. In fact the network shown in Fig. 3.3 is identical with the network shown in Fig. 3.2. In Fig. 3.2 the network was drawn so as to exhibit symmetry among nodes 1, 2, 3, 4, and 5. In Fig. 3.3 the same network has been drawn in such a way as to exhibit a distinction between nodes 0, 1, and 2, now to be regarded as external nodes, and nodes 3, 4, and 5, now to be regarded as internal nodes to which no current is supplied. The equations expressing the potentials of the nodes in terms of the currents supplied to them are therefore Eqs. (3.26) to (3.30). If these equations are solved to express the currents supplied to the nodes in terms of their potentials, we obtain Eqs. (3.19) to (3.23).

The special feature of which we now have to take account is that nodes 3, 4, and 5 are internal nodes to which no current is supplied from without. This is expressed by the equations

$$I_3 = I_4 = I_5 = 0 \tag{3.46}$$

These equations make the left-hand sides of Eqs. (3.21) to (3.23) zero. These three equations can therefore be solved for the potentials V_3, V_4, and V_5 of the internal nodes in terms of the potentials V_1 and V_2 of the exterior terminals. The expressions for V_3, V_4, and V_5 thereby obtained can then be substituted into Eqs. (3.19) and (3.20). On collecting the terms involving V_1 and V_2 we obtain equations of the form

$$I_1 = s_{11}V_1 + s_{12}V_2 \tag{3.47}$$
$$I_2 = s_{21}V_1 + s_{22}V_2 \tag{3.48}$$

These equations determine the currents I_1 and I_2 that must be led in at the exterior terminals 1 and 2 and led out at terminal 0, in order to raise terminals 1 and 2 to potentials V_1 and V_2 respectively. In the course of carrying out the algebraic processes described, the coefficients s_{11}, s_{22}, s_{12}, s_{21} would be determined in terms of the resistances of the resistors of the given network. It would follow from Eqs. (3.25) that

$$s_{12} = s_{21} \tag{3.49}$$

Instead of discussing the network shown in Fig. 3.3 in terms of Eqs. (3.19) to (3.23), we can discuss it in terms of Eqs. (3.26) to (3.30). Substituting into these equations from Eqs. (3.46) we see that the third, fourth, and fifth columns on the right-hand sides disappear. Equations (3.28) to (3.30) then give the potentials V_3, V_4, and V_5 of the internal nodes in terms of the currents I_1, I_2 applied to the exterior terminals. Equations (3.26) and (3.27) give the potentials V_1 and V_2 of the exterior terminals in terms of the currents I_1 and I_2 supplied to these terminals. Because of Eqs. (3.46) these two equations become

$$V_1 = r_{11}I_1 + r_{12}I_2 \tag{3.50}$$
$$V_2 = r_{21}I_1 + r_{22}I_2 \tag{3.51}$$

and, of course, Eq. (3.31) is still valid.

Equations (3.47) and (3.48) give the currents entering the exterior terminals 1 and 2 and leaving via terminal 0 in terms of the potentials of terminals 1 and 2. Equations (3.50) and (3.51) give the potentials of the exterior terminals 1 and 2 in terms of the currents entering them and leaving via terminal 0. Either pair of equations can be obtained from the other by algebraic solution. In converting Eqs. (3.19) to (3.23) into Eqs. (3.47) and (3.48), and Eqs. (3.26) to (3.30) into Eqs. (3.50) and (3.51), we have eliminated the potentials of the internal nodes and obtained relations between the potentials of the exterior terminals and the currents entering them and leaving via terminal 0.

Calculation of the coefficients in Eqs. (3.47) and (3.48), or alternatively in Eqs. (3.50) and (3.51), is likely to be rather tiresome if the network is complicated. In some cases it is helpful to use the following properties of the coefficients. Consider the situation that exists when terminal 2 is connected metallically to the box at zero potential. This situation is described as one in which terminal 2 is "short-circuited" to terminal 0. It is represented mathematically by the equation $V_2 = 0$. If terminal 2 is short-circuited to terminal 0, and terminal 1 is raised to unit potential, then Eqs. (3.47) and (3.48) show that the currents supplied to terminals 1 and 2 are s_{11} and s_{21}. Likewise, if terminal 1 is short-circuited to terminal 0, and terminal 2 is raised to unit potential, then Eqs. (3.47) and (3.48) show that the currents supplied to terminals 1 and 2 are s_{12} and s_{22} respectively. We thus see that s_{11} is numerically equal to the current supplied to terminal 1 when this terminal is raised to unit potential and terminal 2 is short-circuited to terminal 0. The coefficient s_{22} is numerically equal to the current supplied to terminal 2 when this terminal is raised to unit potential and terminal 1 is short-circuited to terminal 0. The common value of the coefficients s_{12} and s_{21} is numerically equal to both (1) the current flowing in at terminal 1 when terminal 2 is raised to unit potential and terminal 1 is short-circuited to terminal 0 and (2) the current flowing in at terminal 2 when terminal 1 is raised to unit potential and terminal 2 is short-circuited to terminal 0.

To study the significance of the coefficients in Eqs. (3.50) and (3.51) it is convenient to consider a situation in which one or another of the terminals is not supplied with current. A terminal to which no current is supplied is often said to be "open-circuited." Let us suppose that terminal 2 is open-circuited and that a unit current is led in at terminal 1 and out at terminal 0. Then Eqs. (3.50) and (3.51) show that in these circumstances the potentials of terminals 1 and 2 are r_{11} and r_{21} respectively. In the same way, if terminal 1 is open-circuited and terminal 2 is supplied with a unit current that is led out from terminal 0, then Eqs. (3.50) and (3.51) show that the potentials of terminals 1 and 2 are r_{12} and r_{22} respectively. We thus see that r_{11} is numerically equal to the potential of terminal 1 when this terminal is supplied with a unit current that is led out from terminal 0 and terminal 2 is open-circuited. The coefficient r_{22} is numerically equal to the potential of terminal 2 when this terminal is supplied with a unit current that is led out from terminal 0 and terminal 1 is open-circuited. The common value of the coefficients r_{12} and r_{21} is numerically equal to both (1) the voltage of terminal 2 when this terminal is open-circuited and a unit current is led in at terminal 1 and out at terminal 0 and (2) the voltage of terminal 1 when this terminal is open-circuited and a unit current is led in at terminal 2 and out at terminal 0.

As an example, let us consider the network shown in Fig. 3.4. To calculate the coefficients r_{11} and r_{21} let us leave terminal 2 on open circuit and lead a unit current in at terminal 1 and out at terminal 0. The network then consists of two resistors of resistances R_1 and R_3 connected in series, and the potential of the node where these two resistors are joined is the potential of terminal 2. The two resistors R_1 and R_3 connected in series are equivalent to a single resistor of resistance $R_1 + R_3$. Hence, with unit current led in at terminal 1 and out at terminal 0, the potential of terminal 1 is $R_1 + R_3$.

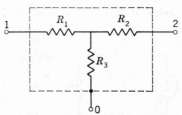

FIG. 3.4. An example of a network with one inaccessible node.

But the potential of terminal 1 when terminal 2 is open-circuited and a unit current is led in at terminal 1 and out at terminal 0 is the coefficient r_{11}. Hence,

$$r_{11} = R_1 + R_3 \qquad (3.52)$$

With terminal 2 on open circuit, a unit current led in at terminal 1 and out at terminal 0 results in a unit current through resistor R_3 and hence a potential R_3 on terminal 2. But the potential of terminal 2 when this terminal is open-circuited and a unit current is led in at terminal 1 and out at terminal 0 is the coefficient r_{21}. Hence,

$$r_{21} = R_3 \qquad (3.53)$$

By leaving terminal 1 on open circuit and leading a unit current in at terminal 2 and out at terminal 0 we can derive in the same way the expressions

$$r_{22} = R_2 + R_3 \qquad (3.54)$$
$$r_{12} = R_3 \qquad (3.55)$$

To derive Eqs. (3.54) and (3.55) it is not in fact necessary to repeat the argument involved in deriving Eqs. (3.52) and (3.53). From the symmetry of the network we notice that the process of interchanging terminals 1 and 2 is equivalent to the process of interchanging resistors R_1

and R_2.   Hence Eqs. (3.54) and (3.55) are obtained from Eqs. (3.52) and (3.53) by interchanging subscripts 1 and 2.   We notice that this leads to the equality of the coefficients r_{12} and r_{21}, as it should.   By substituting from Eqs. (3.52) to (3.55) into Eqs. (3.50) and (3.51) we see that the expressions for the potentials of terminals 1 and 2 in the network shown in Fig. 3.4 in terms of the currents led in at terminals 1 and 2 and out at terminal 0 are

$$V_1 = (R_1 + R_3)I_1 + R_3I_2 \qquad (3.56)$$
$$V_2 = R_3I_1 + (R_2 + R_3)I_2 \qquad (3.57)$$

Of course with a network as simple as that shown in Fig. 3.4 we can arrive at Eqs. (3.56) and (3.57) more directly by a simple application of Kirchhoff's circulation law.   As shown in Fig. 3.5 the mesh currents are I_1 and I_2, and the current through the resistor R_3 common to the two meshes is $I_1 + I_2$.   Applying Kirchhoff's circulation law to the left-hand mesh we obtain

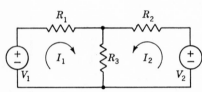

FIG. 3.5. Illustrating calculation of the coefficients of resistance of a network.

$$V_1 = R_1I_1 + R_3(I_1 + I_2) \qquad (3.58)$$

Applying Kirchhoff's circulation law to the right-hand mesh (operating in a counterclockwise direction) we obtain

$$V_2 = R_2I_2 + R_3(I_2 + I_1) \qquad (3.59)$$

Equations (3.58) and (3.59) can be rearranged to give Eqs. (3.56) and (3.57), and this establishes the truth of Eqs. (3.52) to (3.55) for the coefficients of resistance of the network shown in Fig. 3.4.

If, for the network shown in Fig. 3.4, it is desired to express the currents led in at terminals 1 and 2 and out at terminal 0 in terms of the potentials of terminals 1 and 2, we can achieve this by solving Eqs. (3.56) and (3.57) for I_1 and I_2, thereby obtaining

$$I_1 = \frac{1}{R_2R_3 + R_3R_1 + R_1R_2}[(R_2 + R_3)V_1 - R_3V_2] \qquad (3.60)$$

$$I_2 = \frac{1}{R_2R_3 + R_3R_1 + R_1R_2}[-R_3V_1 + (R_1 + R_3)V_2] \qquad (3.61)$$

These are the Eqs. (3.47) and (3.48) for the network shown in Fig. 3.4. Alternatively we can arrive at Eqs. (3.60) and (3.61) by direct calculation of the coefficients appearing in Eqs. (3.47) and (3.48) as follows: To calculate the coefficients s_{11} and s_{21} we short-circuit terminal 2 to terminal 0 in Fig. 3.4 and apply a unit potential to terminal 1.   The current through resistor R_1 from left to right is then the coefficient s_{11}, and the current through resistor R_2 from right to left is the coefficient s_{21}.   With terminals 2 and 0 short-circuited, resistor R_2 is in parallel with resistor R_3, and this combination is in series with resistor R_1. The equivalent resistance between terminals 1 and 0 in these circumstances is

$$R_1 + \frac{1}{1/R_2 + 1/R_3} \tag{3.62}$$

and this can be rewritten as

$$\frac{R_2R_3 + R_3R_1 + R_1R_2}{R_2 + R_3} \tag{3.63}$$

With unit potential applied to terminal 1, the current entering terminal 1 is the reciprocal of expression (3.63), and hence

$$s_{11} = \frac{R_2 + R_3}{R_2R_3 + R_3R_1 + R_1R_2} \tag{3.64}$$

With terminal 2 short-circuited to terminal 0 and unit potential applied to terminal 1, the sum of the currents through resistors R_2 and R_3 is given by expression (3.62) or expression (3.63).   The fraction of this combined current that flows through resistor R_2 is $R_3/(R_2 + R_3)$.   Hence the current flowing through resistor R_2 from left to right is

$$\frac{R_3}{R_2 + R_3} \frac{R_2 + R_3}{R_2R_3 + R_3R_1 + R_1R_2}$$

and this can be rewritten as

$$\frac{R_3}{R_2R_3 + R_3R_1 + R_1R_2} \tag{3.65}$$

The coefficient s_{21} is the current entering terminal 2 in these circumstances.   Hence

$$s_{21} = - \frac{R_3}{R_2R_3 + R_3R_1 + R_1R_2} \tag{3.66}$$

To obtain the coefficients s_{22} and s_{12} we can interchange terminals 1 and 2 in the above argument, and from Fig. 3.4 we see that this is equivalent to interchanging resistors R_1 and R_2. By interchanging subscripts 1 and 2 and Eqs. (3.64) and (3.66) we derive

$$s_{22} = \frac{R_1 + R_3}{R_2R_3 + R_3R_1 + R_1R_2} \tag{3.67}$$

$$s_{12} = - \frac{R_3}{R_2R_3 + R_3R_1 + R_1R_2} \tag{3.68}$$

We notice that s_{12} is equal to s_{21} and that the common value is negative.

By substituting from Eqs. (3.64) and (3.66) to (3.68) into Eqs. (3.47) and (3.48) we derive Eqs. (3.60) and (3.61).

3.5. Power Absorbed by a Network of Resistors.   Consider a network such as that shown in Fig. 3.2.   Let the central node be taken to be at zero potential.   Let batteries be connected between the central node and the peripheral nodes.   Let the potentials of these nodes be V_1, V_2, . . . , and let the currents supplied to these nodes be I_1, I_2, . . . respectively. Then the power delivered by the battery connected to node 1 is $V_1 I_1$. The power delivered by the battery connected to node 2 is $V_2 I_2$, and so on. Hence the total rate at which energy is being supplied to the network is

$$P = V_1 I_1 + V_2 I_2 + \cdots \tag{3.69}$$

This is also the total rate at which power is being absorbed by the resistors of the network.

Let us suppose that we are dealing with a network of resistors for which the coefficients of conductance g_{mn} and the coefficients of resistance r_{mn} have been calculated.   In terms of them it is possible to express the power (3.69) delivered by the batteries to the resistors entirely in terms of the potentials of nodes 1, 2, . . . or entirely in terms of the currents that are supplied to the nodes 1, 2, . . . and drawn off from node 0.   The currents led in at nodes 1, 2, . . . and out at node 0 are expressed in terms of the potentials of the nodes by means of the equations

$$\begin{aligned} I_1 &= g_{11}V_1 + g_{12}V_2 + \cdots \\ I_2 &= g_{21}V_1 + g_{22}V_2 + \cdots \\ &\cdots \cdots \cdots \cdots \cdots \cdots \cdots \end{aligned} \tag{3.70}$$

Substituting for the currents in terms of the potentials from Eqs. (3.70) into Eq. (3.69) and remembering that $g_{mn} = g_{nm}$, we obtain

$$\begin{aligned} P = g_{11}V_1{}^2 &+ g_{22}V_2{}^2 + \cdots \\ &+ 2g_{12}V_1 V_2 + \cdots \end{aligned} \tag{3.71}$$

This expresses the power delivered to the network in terms of the potentials of the nodes and the coefficients of conductance of the network. Alternatively we can use the coefficients of resistance to express the potentials of nodes 1, 2, . . . in terms of the currents that are led in at nodes 1, 2, . . . and out at node 0.   These equations are

$$\begin{aligned} V_1 &= r_{11}I_1 + r_{12}I_2 + \cdots \\ V_2 &= r_{21}I_1 + r_{22}I_2 + \cdots \\ &\cdots \cdots \cdots \cdots \cdots \cdots \cdots \end{aligned} \tag{3.72}$$

Substituting for the potentials in terms of the currents from Eqs. (3.72) into Eq. (3.69) and remembering that $r_{mn} = r_{nm}$, we obtain

$$P = r_{11}I_1{}^2 + r_{22}I_2{}^2 + \cdots$$
$$+ 2r_{12}I_1I_2 + \cdots \tag{3.73}$$

This expresses the power delivered to the system in terms of the coefficients of resistance of the system and the currents led in at nodes 1, 2, . . . and out at node 0. Equations (3.69), (3.71), and (3.73) for a network of resistors correspond to Eq. (1.22) for a single resistor.

A considerable simplification takes place in the calculation of the power delivered to a network of resistors if there are a number of nodes to which no current is supplied. Consider networks such as those shown in Figs. 3.3 and 3.4, in which the only accessible nodes are 0, 1, and 2. The currents supplied to all internal nodes are zero, and Eq. (3.69) reduces to

$$P = V_1I_1 + V_2I_2 \tag{3.74}$$

Thus the total power supplied to the network within the box is obtained by multiplying the voltages applied to the exterior terminals by their corresponding currents and adding. By using the s and r coefficients of the network defined by Eqs. (3.47), (3.48), (3.50), and (3.51), the expression (3.74) for the power supplied to the network within the box can be expressed entirely in terms of the potentials of the exterior terminals or entirely in terms of the currents supplied to them. By substituting from Eqs. (3.47) and (3.48) into Eq. (3.74) we derive

$$P = s_{11}V_1{}^2 + 2s_{12}V_1V_2 + s_{22}V_2{}^2 \tag{3.75}$$

Likewise by substituting from Eqs. (3.50) and (3.51) into Eq. (3.74) we derive

$$P = r_{11}I_1{}^2 + 2r_{12}I_1I_2 + r_{22}I_2{}^2 \tag{3.76}$$

Equation (3.75) expresses the power delivered to the network in terms of the potentials of the exterior terminals, while Eq. (3.76) expresses the power delivered to the network in the box in terms of the currents led in at the exterior terminals 1 and 2 and out at terminal 0.

As an example, consider the network shown in Fig. 3.4. Suppose that a current I_1 is led in at terminal 1 and out at terminal 0 while a current I_2 is led in at terminal 2 and out at terminal 0. We wish to calculate the total power absorbed by the network. The r coefficients for this network have already been calculated and are given by Eqs. (3.52) to (3.55). It follows from Eq. (3.76) that the power delivered to the network is

$$P = (R_1 + R_3)I_1{}^2 + 2R_3I_1I_2 + (R_2 + R_3)I_2{}^2 \tag{3.77}$$

Of course with a network as simple as that shown in Fig. 3.4 it is not necessary to refer to the coefficients of resistance in order to arrive at the expression (3.77) for the total power absorbed by the network. After using Kirchhoff's circulation law in Fig. 3.5 to obtain Eqs. (3.58) and (3.59), we can rearrange them in the forms (3.56) and (3.57). Substitution for V_1 and V_2 from these equations into Eq. (3.74) then gives Eq. (3.77).

SUMMARIZING EXERCISES

3.1. Steady currents enter a network of resistors via certain nodes and leave at a node whose potential is taken to be zero. Show that the relations between the currents entering the network and the potentials of the nodes by which they enter are linear algebraic equations. Explain what is meant by the coefficients of conductance g_{mn} and the coefficients of resistance r_{mn} (a) when $m = n$ and (b) when $m \neq n$. Explain why $g_{mn} = g_{nm}$ and why $r_{mn} = r_{nm}$.

3.2. Give an interpretation of the coefficients of conductance of a network of resistors by considering a situation in which all the nodes are at zero potential except one. Give a similar interpretation of the coefficients of resistance of a network of resistors.

3.3. Explain the physical significance of Green's reciprocal theorem for networks of resistors.

3.4. For a network of resistors, explain what is meant by the principle of superposition.

3.5. Explain what is meant by a network of resistors that has input and output terminals. If V_1 and I_1 are the voltage and current at the input terminals and V_2 and I_2 are the voltage and current at the output terminals, describe the relations between V_1, V_2, I_1, and I_2 in terms of certain coefficients.

3.6. Prove that the rate of absorption of electric energy in a network of resistors for which the voltages of the nodes are V_1, V_2, . . . and the currents entering these nodes are I_1, I_2, . . . respectively is $V_1I_1 + V_2I_2 + \cdot \cdot \cdot \cdot$. By making use of the coefficients of conductance of the network express the power absorbed in terms of the voltages of the nodes and not in terms of the currents. By making use of the coefficients of resistance of the network express the power absorbed in terms of the currents entering the nodes and not in terms of the voltages.

CHAPTER 4

USE OF EQUIVALENT NETWORKS

4.1. Introduction. We have seen that evaluation of the coefficients s_{11}, s_{22}, and s_{12} in Eqs. (3.47) and (3.48), or alternatively of the coefficients r_{11}, r_{22}, and r_{12} in Eqs. (3.50) and (3.51), involves a substantial calculation for a comparatively complicated network such as that shown in Fig. 3.3. There is, however, a substantial advantage accruing from the performance of this calculation. Suppose that, for the network shown in Fig. 3.3, terminal 0 is maintained at zero potential and given potentials are applied to terminals 1 and 2. Suppose that we require to calculate the corresponding currents that enter at terminals 1 and 2 and leave at terminal 0. One way of doing this would be to apply Kirchhoff's laws to the network, to eliminate the mathematical variables in which we are not interested, and so deduce the quantities required. When a new pair of potentials was applied to terminals 1 and 2, we could repeat the whole process from the beginning. After this process of repetition had been performed a number of times, it would become apparent that, although each new pair of potentials presented a new problem, nevertheless there was a close connection between successive calculations. We would then search for a mathematical procedure that avoided starting the problem from the beginning on each occasion that the potentials of terminals 1 and 2 were changed. This would lead us to the procedure of calculating for the network the coefficients s_{11}, s_{22}, and s_{12} in Eqs. (3.47) and (3.48). We would then be able to alter the potentials V_1 and V_2 of terminals 1 and 2 in any way and immediately calculate the corresponding currents I_1 and I_2. Likewise, if it is the currents led in at terminals 1 and 2 and out at terminal 0 that are specified and the potentials at terminals 1 and 2 that have to be calculated, then this calculation can easily be repeated for any numbers of pairs of currents as soon as the coefficients r_{11}, r_{22}, and r_{12} in Eqs. (3.50) and (3.51) have been calculated. Thus the coefficients s_{11}, s_{22}, and s_{12}, or alternatively the coefficients r_{11}, r_{22}, and r_{12}, completely describe the network no matter what currents or potentials are applied to the external terminals. These coefficients change if the network changes, but they do not alter with changes in the currents and potentials applied externally.

By electrical measurements made externally to the network it is possible to deduce the coefficients s_{11}, s_{22}, and s_{12}, or alternatively the corresponding coefficients r_{11}, r_{22}, and r_{12}. For example, by putting unit potential on terminal 1 and zero potential on terminals 2 and 0 we see from Eqs. (3.47) and (3.48) that the currents entering terminals 1 and 2 under these circumstances are s_{11} and s_{21}, which is equal to s_{12}. Hence, by putting unit potential on terminal 1 and zero potential on terminals 2 and 0, and then measuring the currents entering terminals 1 and 2, we derive the two coefficients s_{11} and s_{12}. In the same way, by putting unit potential on terminal 2 and zero potential on terminals 1 and 0, we can measure the current entering terminal 2 and derive the coefficient s_{22}. By measuring at the same time the current entering terminal 1 we can verify the fact that s_{12} is equal to s_{21}. By leading unit and zero currents in at terminals 1 and 2 and out at terminal 0 instead of applying unit and zero potentials, we can determine the coefficients r_{11}, r_{22}, and r_{12} in accordance with Eqs. (3.50) and (3.51). It is important to notice, however, that when we have determined the three coefficients s_{11}, s_{22}, and s_{12}, or alternatively the three corresponding coefficients r_{11}, r_{22}, and r_{12}, there is nothing more that we can determine about the network purely from measurements made externally to the enclosing metal box using steady voltages and currents. There are in fact numerous networks that lead to the same s and r coefficients, and these cannot be distinguished from one another by d-c measurements made external to the box.

The fact that there are in general a number of networks having the same r and s coefficients leads to the important concept of equivalent networks. All networks of resistors enclosed in a metal box equipped with external terminals 0, 1, and 2 are said to be equivalent if they lead to the same r and s coefficients. Equivalent networks cannot be distinguished from one another by means of measurements made external to the box.

The concept of equivalent networks is important for the following reason: Suppose that two networks are known to be equivalent in the sense described. Then they have the same r and s coefficients, so that the relations between the potentials and currents of the exterior terminals are the same for both networks. Let us suppose further that one of the networks is complicated and the other network is simple. It follows that, in any discussion of the exterior behavior of the complicated network, we can use the simple network.

4.2. The Equivalent T and π Networks. Let us suppose that a complicated network is to be replaced by a simple equivalent network, and let us ask how simple the simple network can be. The complicated network is specified by the three coefficients s_{11}, s_{22}, and s_{12}, or alternatively by the three corresponding coefficients r_{11}, r_{22}, and r_{12}. Three quantities are thus involved in specifying the exterior behavior of the complicated network. The simple network must therefore possess at least three parameters that can be adjusted to produce the right r and s coefficients. It should therefore be possible, for the complicated network of resistors, to devise an equivalent simple network involving only three resistors. Suitable equivalent networks involving three adjustable resistors are shown in Fig. 4.1. By suitable choice of the resistances of the resistors in either of the networks shown in Fig. 4.1 it is possible to produce a network that, as far as external behavior is concerned, is identical with that of a much more complicated network such as that shown in Fig. 3.3. The networks shown in Fig. 4.1 can be redrawn in the form shown in Fig. 4.2. In these forms the geometrical con-figurations of the networks suggest

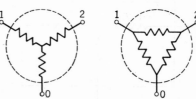

FIG. 4.1. Simple equivalent networks involving three resistors.

the letter T and the letter π. If for a given complicated network an equivalent network is formed as shown on the left in Fig. 4.2, this is called the equivalent T network for the given network. If on the other hand the equivalent network is formed as shown on the right in Fig. 4.2, this is called the equivalent π network for the given network.

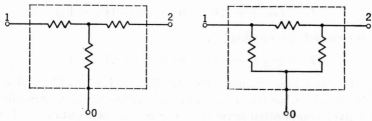

FIG. 4.2. T and π networks of resistors.

Let us calculate the equivalent T network for a given complicated network. For the complicated network we suppose that the coefficients r_{11}, r_{22}, and r_{12} have been calculated. Now these coefficients, for a net-work of the type shown on the left-hand side of Fig. 4.2, have already been calculated in connection with Fig. 3.4 and are given by Eqs. (3.52), (3.54), and (3.55). These equations therefore tell us how the resistances R_1, R_2, and R_3 for the network shown in Fig. 3.4 must be related to the coefficients r_{11}, r_{22}, and r_{12} of the complicated network if the networks are to be equivalent. By solving Eqs. (3.52), (3.54), and (3.55) for R_1, R_2, and R_3 we obtain

$$R_1 = r_{11} - r_{12} \tag{4.1}$$
$$R_2 = r_{22} - r_{12} \tag{4.2}$$
$$R_3 = r_{12} \tag{4.3}$$

It follows that the network shown in Fig. 4.3 is the equivalent T network of any network of resistors whose r coefficients are r_{11}, r_{22}, and r_{12}. Application of Kirchhoff's laws to the network shown in Fig. 4.3 leads to Eqs. (3.50) and (3.51).

In the same way it is possible to derive the equivalent π network of a given network of resistors. This is shown in Fig. 4.4. We suppose that,

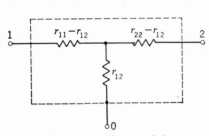

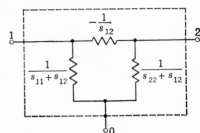

FIG. 4.3. Equivalent T network for a network of resistors.

FIG. 4.4. Equivalent π network for a network of resistors.

for the given complicated network of resistors, the coefficients s_{11}, s_{22}, and s_{12} have been calculated. In terms of these coefficients the resistances involved in the equivalent π network are as shown in Fig. 4.4. This is proved by applying Kirchhoff's conservation law to terminal 1, obtaining

$$I_1 = (s_{11} + s_{12})(V_1 - 0) + (-s_{12})(V_1 - V_2) \tag{4.4}$$

and to terminal 2, obtaining

$$I_2 = (s_{22} + s_{12})(V_2 - 0) + (-s_{12})(V_2 - V_1) \tag{4.5}$$

These two equations immediately simplify to Eqs. (3.47) and (3.48) thereby showing that the network in Fig. 4.4 has the same s coefficients as the given complicated network. The resistor of resistance $-1/s_{12}$ in Fig. 4.4 in fact has a positive resistance, since s_{12} is numerically negative.

For any network whose s coefficients have been calculated, the currents entering terminals 1 and 2 and leaving terminal 0 are related to the excesses of potential of terminals 1 and 2 over terminal 0 in the manner described by Eqs. (3.47) and (3.48), and these are also the equations appropriate to the π network shown in Fig. 4.4. Likewise for any network whose r coefficients have been calculated, the currents entering terminals 1 and 2 and leaving terminal 0 are related to the excesses of potential of terminals 1 and 2 over terminal 0 in the manner described by Eqs. (3.50) and (3.51), and these are also the equations appropriate to the T network shown in Fig. 4.3. In studying the external properties of the given network we can use either Eqs. (3.47) and (3.48) or Eqs. (3.50) and (3.51) or use the equivalent network shown in Fig. 4.3 or use the equivalent network shown in Fig. 4.4. In each case the same relation is implied between the potentials V_1 and V_2 of terminals 1 and 2 and the currents I_1 and I_2 entering terminals 1 and 2 and leaving terminal 0.

4.3. The Thévenin and Norton Equivalent Circuits for Networks of Resistors. Let us consider a network of resistors enclosed in a metal box at zero potential with a pair of exterior terminals 1 and 2. Let us suppose that the r and s coefficients of the network have been calculated. The relations between the currents supplied to the exterior terminals and the potentials of the exterior terminals are then given by Eqs. (3.47) and (3.48) or by Eqs. (3.50) and (3.51). These relations can be expressed as networks equivalent to the original network as shown in either Fig. 4.3 or Fig. 4.4. With these equivalent networks any changes can be made in the potentials of terminals 1 and 2, and the corresponding

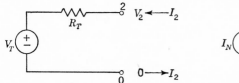
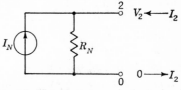

FIG. 4.5. The Thévenin equivalent circuit.   FIG. 4.6. The Norton equivalent circuit.

changes in the currents supplied to terminals 1 and 2 are identical with those for the original network. Let us now suppose, however, that we are faced with a simpler problem in which either the potential of terminal 1 is held fixed or alternatively a fixed current is led in at terminal 1 and out at terminal 0. Let us suppose that we wish to study under these circumstances what the relation is between the potential of terminal 2 and the current led in at terminal 2 and out at terminal 0. To do this we could replace the given network by the equivalent T network shown in Fig. 4.3 or by the equivalent π network shown in Fig. 4.4. This simpler problem can, however, be solved with the aid of a simpler equivalent network. There are in fact two simpler equivalent networks available to describe the relation between the potential of terminal 2 and the current entering terminal 2 when either the potential of terminal 1 has a fixed value or the current led in at terminal 1 has a fixed value. One of these is shown in Fig. 4.5 and is known as the Thévenin equivalent circuit. The other is shown in Fig. 4.6 and is known as the Norton equivalent circuit.

In each of these equivalent networks the upper terminal on the right-hand side corresponds to terminal 2 of the original network and the lower terminal on the right-hand side corresponds to terminal 0 of the original network. In the Thévenin equivalent circuit there is a resistor of resistance R_T, known as the Thévenin resistor, whose value is to be calculated in terms of the properties of the original network. In the Norton equivalent circuit there is a resistor of resistance R_N, known as the Norton resistor, whose value likewise is to be determined in terms of the properties of the original network. In the Thévenin equivalent circuit there is a battery of voltage V_T, known as the Thévenin voltage, whose value is to be calculated in terms of the properties of the original network and in terms of the constant voltage or current maintained at terminal 1. In the Norton equivalent circuit there is a battery that delivers a current I_N, known as the Norton current, which is to be calculated in terms of the properties of the original network and the constant voltage or current maintained at terminal 1.

Let us now suppose that, with the given voltage or current maintained at terminal 1 of the original network, a voltage V_2 is applied between terminals 2 and 0 and that as a result a current I_2 enters terminal 2 and leaves terminal 0. We require to calculate for the original network the way in which I_2 varies with V_2. It is a fact that this calculation for the original network can equally well be made for the network shown in Fig. 4.5 or for the network shown in Fig. 4.6 provided that the elements in these equivalent networks have been properly evaluated. We now have to verify the truth of this statement and find out how to evaluate V_T and R_T in the Thévenin equivalent circuit and likewise how to evaluate I_N and R_N in the Norton equivalent circuit.

To begin with let us write down the relation between V_2 and I_2 appropriate to the Thévenin equivalent circuit. From Fig. 4.5 we see that the current I_2 entering terminal 2 is a current through the resistor R_T from right to left. We also see that the excess of voltage of the right-hand terminal of resistor R_T over the left-hand terminal is $V_2 - V_T$. From Ohm's law we therefore have

$$V_2 - V_T = R_T I_2 \qquad (4.6)$$

This is the relation between V_2 and I_2 indicated by the Thévenin equivalent circuit. Let us also write down the relation between V_2 and I_2 corresponding to the Norton equivalent circuit. In Fig. 4.6 the excess of potential of the upper terminal of resistor R_N over the lower terminal is V_2. The current through this resistor in the downward direction is $I_2 + I_N$. It follows from Ohm's law that

$$I_2 + I_N = \frac{1}{R_N} V_2 \qquad (4.7)$$

This is the relation between V_2 and I_2 appropriate to the Norton equivalent circuit.

Now let us inquire what the relation between V_2 and I_2 is for the original network. Two cases arise according as it is the current I_1 entering terminal 1 and leaving terminal 0 that is kept constant or the voltage V_1 of terminal 1 that is kept constant. Let us first consider the case in which I_1 is kept constant. Assuming that the r coefficients of the network have been calculated, the relation between V_2 and I_2 for the specified constant value of I_1 is given by Eq. (3.51). This equation can be rewritten in either of the forms

$$V_2 - r_{21}I_1 = r_{22}I_2 \tag{4.8}$$

$$I_2 + \frac{r_{21}}{r_{22}} I_1 = \frac{1}{r_{22}} V_2 \tag{4.9}$$

These rearrangements of Eq. (3.51) have been chosen so as to put this equation as nearly as possible in the forms (4.6) and (4.7) respectively. By comparing Eq. (4.6) with Eq. (4.8) we see that they are identical provided that

$$V_T = r_{21}I_1 \tag{4.10}$$
$$R_T = r_{22} \tag{4.11}$$

By comparing Eq. (4.7) with Eq. (4.9) we see that the two equations are identical provided that

$$I_N = \frac{r_{21}}{r_{22}} I_1 \tag{4.12}$$

$$R_N = r_{22} \tag{4.13}$$

It follows that, for a given current I_1 entering terminal 1 of the original network and leaving terminal 0, the relation (3.51) between V_2 and I_2 is the same as the relation (4.6) for the Thévenin equivalent circuit provided that the Thévenin voltage V_T is given by Eq. (4.10) and the Thévenin resistance R_T is given by Eq. (4.11). It likewise follows that the relation (3.51) between V_2 and I_2 is identical with the relation (4.7) for the Norton equivalent circuit provided that the Norton current I_N is given by Eq. (4.12) and the Norton resistance R_N is given by Eq. (4.13). We have thus proved the validity of the Thévenin and Norton equivalent circuits for the case when we hold constant the current I_1 entering terminal 1 of the original network and leaving terminal 0. Moreover we have established formulas for the elements in these equivalent circuits in terms of the r coefficient of the original network and the constant current I_1.

Let us now consider the case in which it is the potential V_1 of terminal 1 of the original network that is held constant. Assuming that the s coefficients of the original network have been calculated, the relation between V_2 and I_2 when V_1 is held constant is given by Eq. (3.48). This equation can be rearranged in either of the forms

$$V_2 - \left(-\frac{s_{21}}{s_{22}} V_1\right) = \frac{1}{s_{22}} I_2 \tag{4.14}$$

$$I_2 + (-s_{21}V_1) = s_{22}V_2 \tag{4.15}$$

These two rearrangements were chosen so as to bring Eq. (3.48) into the forms of Eqs. (4.6) and (4.7) respectively. By comparing Eq. (4.6) with Eq. (4.14) we see that they are identical provided that

$$V_T = -\frac{s_{21}}{s_{22}} V_1 \qquad (4.16)$$

$$R_T = \frac{1}{s_{22}} \qquad (4.17)$$

Likewise by comparing Eq. (4.7) with Eq. (4.15) we see that they are identical provided that

$$I_N = -s_{21}V_1 \qquad (4.18)$$

$$R_N = \frac{1}{s_{22}} \qquad (4.19)$$

Thus, if the voltage V_1 of terminal 1 of the original network is held constant, the relation (3.48) between V_2 and I_2 is identical with the relation (4.6) for the Thévenin equivalent circuit provided that the Thévenin voltage V_T is given by Eq. (4.16) and the Thévenin resistance R_T is given by Eq. (4.17). Likewise the relation (3.48) between V_2 and I_2 is identical with the relation (4.7) for the Norton equivalent circuit provided that the Norton current I_N is given by Eq. (4.18) and the Norton resistance R_N is given by Eq. (4.19). We have thus established the validity of the Thévenin and Norton equivalent circuits for the case when the voltage V_1 of terminal 1 of the original network is held constant. Moreover we have obtained expressions for the elements in the Thévenin and Norton equivalent circuits in terms of the s coefficients of the original network and the constant voltage V_1.

By comparing Fig. 4.5 with Fig. 1.12 we see that the Thévenin voltage V_T and the Thévenin resistance R_T in the Thévenin equivalent circuit can be thought of as forming a single battery whose open-circuit voltage is V_T and whose internal resistance is R_T. The Thévenin equivalent circuit therefore states that the original network, together with its constant voltage or current applied to terminal 1, is equivalent to a single battery of open-circuit voltage V_T and internal resistance R_T.

4.4. Evaluation of the Elements in Thévenin and Norton Equivalent Circuits. If the r coefficients of the original network have been calculated, then the values of V_T, R_T, I_N, and R_N in the Thévenin and Norton equivalent circuits are given by Eqs. (4.10) to (4.13) in the case when it is the current I_1 supplied to terminal 1 of the original network that is kept constant. Likewise if the s coefficients of the original network have been calculated, then the values of V_T, R_T, I_N, and R_N in the Thévenin and Norton equivalent circuits are given by Eqs. (4.16) to (4.19) in the case when it is the voltage V_1 on terminal 1 of the original network that is kept constant.   If, however, the r and s coefficients of the original network have not been calculated, then there is another method for evaluating V_T, R_T, I_N, and R_N that is likely to be more convenient.

For the original network let us apply to terminal 1 the given current I_1 or alternatively the given voltage V_1, and let us leave terminal 2 on open circuit.   Let us calculate the voltage V_2 on terminal 2 in these circumstances.   To do this we use the Thévenin equivalent circuit illustrated in Fig. 4.5.   With terminal 2 on open circuit no current enters terminal 2, and consequently no current flows through the Thévenin resistor R_T. In these circumstances the voltage of terminal 2 is simply the Thévenin voltage V_T.   We thus have shown that the Thévenin voltage V_T is the potential of terminal 2 when this terminal is left on open circuit.   We therefore arrive at the following procedure for calculating the Thévenin voltage V_T.   Using the original network, leave terminal 2 on open circuit and apply between terminals 1 and 0 either the given current I_1 or alternatively the given voltage V_1.   For these circumstances calculate the excess of the voltage of terminal 2 over that of terminal 0.   This is then the Thévenin voltage V_T to be used in the Thévenin equivalent circuit of Fig. 4.5.

A similar procedure can be devised for calculating the Norton current I_N appropriate to the Norton equivalent circuit illustrated in Fig. 4.6. For the original network let us apply to terminal 1 the given current I_1 or alternatively the given voltage V_1, and let us short-circuit terminal 2 to terminal 0.   In these circumstances current flows out of terminal 2 and passes into terminal 0.   Let us calculate this current using the Norton equivalent circuit shown in Fig. 4.6.   With terminal 2 short-circuited to terminal 0 in Fig. 4.6 the Norton resistor R_N is short-circuited and the current through the short circuit is therefore I_N.   The current that leaves terminal 2 when this terminal is short-circuited to terminal 0 is therefore the Norton current I_N.   We therefore arrive at the following procedure for calculating the Norton current I_N: Using the original network, short-circuit terminal 2 to terminal 0 and then apply between terminal 1 and terminal 0 either the given current I_1 or alternatively the given voltage V_1.   Calculate the resulting steady current leaving terminal 2 and passing through the short circuit to terminal 0.   This current is the Norton current I_N to be used in the Norton equivalent circuit illustrated in Fig. 4.6.

Let us now turn our attention to evaluation of R_T and R_N.   From Eqs. (4.10) and (4.16) we observe that, if the current I_1, or alternatively the voltage V_1, applied to terminal 1 is reduced to zero, then so also is the Thévenin voltage V_T.   In other words, if no source is applied between terminals 1 and 0 of the original network, then the Thévenin voltage V_T in Fig. 4.5 is to be short-circuited.   Under these circumstances the

Thévenin resistance R_T is connected directly between terminals 2 and 0. It follows that the Thévenin resistance R_T is the equivalent resistance between terminals 2 and 0 when no source is applied to terminal 1 of the original network. Thus, instead of using either Eq. (4.11) or (4.17) to calculate the Thévenin resistance R_T, we can use the following procedure: With no source applied between terminals 1 and 0, calculate the equivalent resistance between terminals 2 and 0. This resistance is then the Thévenin resistance R_T to be used in the Thévenin equivalent circuit illustrated in Fig. 4.5.

In the procedure just described for calculating the Thévenin resistance R_T, it is important to understand what is implied by the statement that no source is applied between terminals 1 and 0 of the original network. If we are studying the relation between V_2 and I_2 under circumstances when it is the current I_1 applied between terminals 1 and 0 of the original network that is kept constant, then no source implies that I_1 is zero. This means that terminal 1 is left on open circuit. On the other hand if we are studying the relation between V_2 and I_2 under circumstances when it is the voltage V_1 applied between terminals 1 and 0 of the original network that is kept constant, then no source implies that V_1 is zero. This means that terminal 1 is short-circuited to terminal 0. Thus if the Thévenin equivalent circuit illustrated in Fig. 4.5 is to describe the relation between V_2 and I_2 under circumstances when I_1 is kept constant, then the Thévenin resistance R_T is the equivalent resistance between terminals 2 and 0 under circumstances when terminal 1 is left on open circuit. But if the Thévenin equivalent circuit of Fig. 4.5 is to describe the relation between V_2 and I_2 under circumstances when V_1 is kept constant, then the Thévenin resistance R_T is the equivalent resistance between terminals 2 and 0 when terminal 1 is short-circuited to terminal 0. These two different values for the Thévenin resistance R_T can, of course, also be calculated from the two different formulas (4.11) and (4.17).

Again, we observe from Eqs. (4.12) and (4.18) that, if the fixed current I_1 or alternatively the fixed voltage V_1 applied to terminal 1 of the original network is reduced to zero, so also is the Norton current I_N to be used in the Norton equivalent circuit illustrated in Fig. 4.6. If I_N in Fig. 4.6 is zero, the Norton equivalent circuit simply consists of a resistor of resistance R_N connected between terminals 2 and 0. It follows that the Norton resistance R_N is the equivalent resistance between terminals 2 and 0 when no source is applied between terminals 1 and 0 of the original network. Thus, instead of using either Eq. (4.13) or (4.19) to calculate the Norton resistance R_N, we can use the following procedure: When no source is applied at terminal 1 we calculate the equivalent resistance between terminals 2 and 0. This resistance is then the Norton resistance R_N to be used in the Norton equivalent circuit illustrated in Fig. 4.6.

It should be noted that the procedure just described for calculating R_N is in fact identical with the corresponding procedure previously described for calculating R_T. It follows that the Thévenin and Norton resistances are identical in value. This can be verified by comparing Eq. (4.11) with Eq. (4.13) or Eq. (4.17) with Eq. (4.19).

4.5. Relations between the Thévenin and Norton Equivalent Circuits. We have just drawn attention to the fact that the Thévenin resistance R_T is in fact identical with the Norton resistance R_N. This is not the only simple relation that exists between the Thévenin and Norton equivalent circuits. A more complete statement is made by the equations

$$R_T = R_N = \frac{V_T}{I_N} \tag{4.20}$$

the validity of which we shall now investigate. If desired, the truth of Eqs. (4.20) can be established from Eqs. (4.10) to (4.13) or alternatively Eqs. (4.16) to (4.19). It is merely a matter of substituting into Eqs. (4.20) the appropriate expressions for V_T, R_T, I_N, and R_N. The truth of Eqs. (4.20) can, however, be derived without explicit reference to the r and s coefficients of the original network.

We have seen that removal of the source at terminal 1 of the original network makes V_T zero in Fig. 4.5 and I_N zero in Fig. 4.6. In these circumstances R_T is the equivalent resistance between terminals 2 and 0 in Fig. 4.5, and R_N is the same thing in Fig. 4.6, and this establishes the equality of the two resistances.

To establish the second equality in Eqs. (4.20) we remember that the Thévenin voltage V_T is the voltage of terminal 2 when left on open circuit. Let us use the Norton equivalent circuit to calculate the voltage of terminal 2 when left on open circuit. If terminal 2 in Fig. 4.6 is left on open circuit, the current I_N must flow entirely through the resistor R_N, so that the voltage of terminal 2 is $R_N I_N$. This is the voltage of terminal 2 when on open circuit and is therefore the Thévenin voltage V_T by definition. Hence $R_N I_N$ is equal to V_T, and this is the statement made in the second equality in Eqs. (4.20). Thus both the Thévenin and Norton resistances are the ratio of the Thévenin voltage to the Norton current.

Equations (4.20) imply that, between the four quantities V_T, R_T, I_N, and R_N, there are two relations. It follows therefore that, in calculating the elements in the Thévenin and Norton equivalent circuits, it is only necessary to make an initial calculation of either R_T or R_N and either V_T or I_N. The other two quantities can then be derived from Eqs. (4.20).

The significance of the relations (4.20) and also of the Eqs. (4.6) and (4.7) relating I_2 to V_2 for the Thévenin and Norton equivalent circuits is summarized in Fig. 4.7. In this diagram, the sloping straight line is a plot of the way in which the current I_2 entering terminal 2 varies with the

voltage of terminal 2 when the source of given voltage or current is applied
at terminal 1.   The intercepts on the voltage and current axes in Fig. 4.7
are marked as V_T and I_N, while the slope of the line has the common value
of $1/R_T$ and $1/R_N$.   If the equation of the sloping straight line in Fig. 4.7
is written down in accordance with standard formulas in analytical geometry, we arrive at either Eq. (4.6) or (4.7).   Thus the sloping straight line
in Fig. 4.7 describes the relation between V_2 and I_2 involved in either the

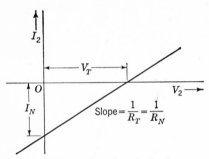

Thévenin or Norton equivalent
circuit.   In particular, we verify
from Fig. 4.7 that V_T is the value
of V_2 when $I_2 = 0$, that is, when
terminal 2 is on open circuit.   Likewise, we verify from Fig. 4.7 that
I_N is the negative of the value of I_2
for which $V_2 = 0$, and this means
that I_N is the current that leaves
terminal 2 when this terminal is

FIG. 4.7. Illustrating the relation between
the current and the voltage at a pair of
output terminals.

short-circuited to terminal 0.   In
Fig. 4.7 the relations (4.20) simply
express an obvious geometrical
property of the triangle formed by the sloping straight line with the axes
of coordinates.

**4.6. Thévenin and Norton Equivalent Circuits for Networks of Resis-
tors Having Many Sources.**   In discussing the Thévenin and Norton
equivalent circuits we have considered a network of resistors to which is
applied only one source, namely, that between terminals 1 and 0.   The
Thévenin and Norton equivalent circuits are, however, applicable when
many sources are connected into the network, some of them having constant voltage and some constant current.   Let us therefore consider a
network such as that shown in Fig. 3.2.   Let terminal 0 be at zero potential.   To some of the other nodes apply fixed currents which leave the
network at terminal 0 and to other nodes apply fixed potentials.   Let us
suppose that one particular node, which we shall take as node 2, is singled
out for special treatment.   To this node we shall apply a variable voltage
V_2 and calculate the corresponding variable current I_2 led into this node,
the potentials or currents of the other nodes being maintained constant.
In discussing this situation it is necessary to write down equations for the
network from Kirchhoff's laws and to eliminate mathematical variables
from them until we arrive at a linear equation relating V_2, I_2, and the fixed
voltages or currents of the sources.   This linear relation between V_2 and
I_2 can be represented graphically as shown in Fig. 4.7, or by means of
equivalent circuits as shown in Figs. 4.5 and 4.6, and this establishes the

applicability of the Thévenin and Norton equivalent circuits to this more complicated situation.

We still deduce from Fig. 4.5 that the Thévenin voltage V_T is the voltage of terminal 2 when on open circuit. Likewise we still deduce from Fig. 4.6 that the Norton current I_N is the current that leaves terminal 2 when this terminal is short-circuited to terminal 0. Furthermore it still remains true from Figs. 4.5 and 4.6 that R_T and R_N are each equal to the equivalent resistance between terminals 2 and 0 when all sources are removed. Removal of the sources necessitates short-circuiting the constant-voltage sources and open-circuiting the constant-current sources. Relations (4.20) are still true, so that, from the values of V_T and R_T, the values of I_N and R_N could immediately be derived, or vice versa. In this way we are able to apply the Thévenin

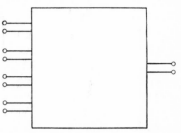

Fig. 4.8. Illustrating a network in which many nodes are accessible through exterior terminals.

and Norton equivalent circuits shown in Figs. 4.5 and 4.6 to a situation that we shall illustrate with the aid of Fig. 4.8.

Suppose that we have a network of resistors and that some, but not necessarily all, nodes are accessible through terminals as shown in Fig. 4.8. Let it be supposed that the terminals are arranged in pairs so as to be convenient for connecting sources or loads. One pair of terminals is to be treated in a special way, and this has been drawn on the right in Fig. 4.8. We are interested in applying a voltage V_2 between this pair of terminals and calculating the corresponding current I_2 that enters the positive terminal and leaves the negative terminal. Moreover we are interested in having V_2 take a series of values and in calculating the corresponding series of values for I_2. In other words we are interested in calculating the voltage-current relationship for the right-hand pair of terminals in Fig. 4.8. This calculation is to be made for certain specified conditions at the left-hand pairs of terminals. At each pair of terminals on the left we shall maintain constant either the voltage between the pair of terminals or alternatively the current entering the positive terminal and leaving the negative terminal. From what has been said, it follows that the relation between the voltage V_2 and the current I_2 at the right-hand terminals in Fig. 4.8 can be calculated by replacing the entire network, together with the sources applied to the left-hand terminals in Fig. 4.8, by a Thévenin equivalent circuit as shown in Fig. 4.5 or by a Norton equivalent circuit as shown in Fig. 4.6. Moreover the Thévenin voltage V_T required in Fig. 4.5 is the voltage appearing at the right-hand terminals in Fig. 4.8 when these terminals are left on open circuit. Likewise the Norton current I_N required in Fig. 4.6 is the current that leaves the positive terminal on the right-hand side of Fig. 4.8 and enters the negative terminal when these terminals are short-circuited. The ratio of the Norton voltage V_T to the Norton current I_N is the Thévenin resistance R_T and the Norton resistance R_N in accordance with Eqs. (4.20). Alternatively the common value of R_T and R_N can be derived by calculating the equivalent resistance across the terminals on the right-hand side of Fig. 4.8 when the sources applied to the left-hand terminals in Fig. 4.8 are removed; removal of the sources on the left-hand side of Fig. 4.8 implies short-circuiting each pair of terminals to which a constant-voltage source is applied and open-circuiting each pair of terminals to which a constant-current source is applied.

It is not necessary for one of a pair of terminals in Fig. 4.8 to be at zero potential. Suppose that the network is enclosed in a metal box through which the terminals project via insulators. Let the potential of the metal box be taken as the zero of potential, and let the box be labeled terminal 0. Then to connect a source between a pair of terminals labeled + and − we could use a pair of sources, one connected between the positive terminal and terminal 0 and the other connected between the negative terminal and terminal 0. The whole arrangement can thus be reduced to a situation in which all sources are connected between terminal 0 and one of the other terminals.

We have thus derived the ability to apply the Thévenin and Norton equivalent circuits to any network of resistors in which are connected any number of constant-voltage or constant-current sources. The statements concerning the Thévenin and Norton equivalent circuits that we have now made incorporate all special cases previously considered.

4.7. Application of the Thévenin and Norton Equivalent Circuits. The most straightforward application of a Thévenin or Norton equivalent

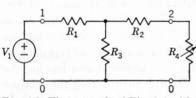

circuit occurs when a network such as that shown in Fig. 3.4 has a battery of a voltage V connected between terminals 1 and 0 and a load resistor of resistance R_4 between terminals 2 and 0 as shown in Fig. 4.9. Suppose that the load resistor has a variable resistance and that we are interested in calculating how the voltage and current for the load resistor vary with its

FIG. 4.9. The network of Fig. 3.4 with a constant voltage V_1 applied between terminals 1 and 0 and with a load of variable resistance R_4 applied between terminals 2 and 0.

resistance. Then it is convenient to replace the network to the left of terminal 2 in Fig. 4.9, including the source applied between terminals 1 and 0, with a Thévenin or Norton equivalent circuit, as shown in Fig. 4.10 or 4.11 respectively. Instead of applying the load resistor of variable resistance R_4 to the original network and source, we apply it to the equivalent Thévenin circuit as shown in Fig. 4.10 or alternatively to the equivalent Norton circuit as shown in Fig. 4.11. From the network shown in Fig. 4.10 it is easy to calculate the voltage and current for the resistor R_4 provided that the Thévenin voltage V_T and the Thévenin resistance R_T can be evaluated. It is equally simple to calculate the voltage and current for the resistor R_4 from the network shown in Fig. 4.11 provided that the Norton current I_N and the Norton resistance R_N have previously been

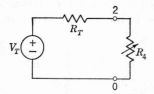

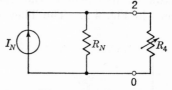

FIG. 4.10. Thévenin circuit equivalent to network of Fig. 4.9.

FIG. 4.11. Norton circuit equivalent to network of Fig. 4.9.

evaluated. For the network shown in Fig. 3.4 we have already calculated the r and s coefficients; the r coefficients are given by Eqs. (3.52), (3.54), and (3.55) while the s coefficients are given by Eqs. (3.64), (3.67), and (3.68). We could therefore calculate the elements in the equivalent Thévenin circuit in Fig. 4.10 and in the equivalent Norton circuit shown in Fig. 4.11 by substituting these r and s coefficients into the expressions for V_T, R_T, I_N, and R_N given in Sec. 4.3. It is more common, however, to meet a situation in which we require to calculate the elements either in the equivalent Thévenin circuit or in the equivalent Norton circuit under circumstances when the r and s coefficients of a given network have not been calculated and are not specifically required. We can then use the alternative procedure described in Sec. 4.4 in the way now to be described.

To calculate V_T and R_T or alternatively I_N and R_N, it is necessary to be clear whether it is the voltage of terminal 1 that is to be kept constant as the load resistor is varied or the current supplied to terminal 1 that is kept constant as the load resistor is varied. For the network shown in Fig. 4.9 it is the voltage V_1 on terminal 1 that is kept constant as the load resistor R_4 is varied, and we wish to calculate the elements of the Thévenin equivalent circuit shown in Fig. 4.10 or alternatively of the Norton equivalent circuit shown in Fig. 4.11.

Let us now calculate the common value of R_T and R_N in Figs. 4.10 and 4.11. Since it is the voltage of terminal 1 that is to be kept constant as the load R_4 varies, we short-circuit terminals 1 to 0, thereby forming the network shown in Fig. 4.12. The common value of R_T and R_N is the equivalent resistance between terminals 2 and 0 for the network shown in Fig. 4.12.   Since the resistor R_1 is in parallel with the resistor R_3 and this combination is in series with the resistor R_2, we derive

$$R_T = R_N = R_2 + \frac{1}{1/R_1 + 1/R_3} \tag{4.21}$$

and this may be rewritten as

$$R_T = R_N = \frac{R_2R_3 + R_3R_1 + R_1R_2}{R_1 + R_3} \tag{4.22}$$

Now let us calculate the Thévenin voltage V_T for the arrangement shown in Fig. 4.9.   The Thévenin voltage is the voltage of terminal 2

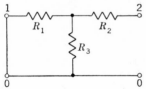

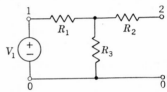

FIG. 4.12. Network for calculating the Thévenin and Norton resistance for the arrangement shown in Fig. 4.9.

FIG. 4.13. Network for calculating the Thévenin voltage for the arrangement shown in Fig. 4.9.

when left on open circuit.   It is therefore the voltage of terminal 2 in the network shown in Fig. 4.13.   For the network shown in Fig. 4.13 terminal 2 is insulated.   Consequently there is no current through resistor R_2 and no difference of potential across resistor R_2.   The network therefore simply consists of resistor R_1 in series with resistor R_3, and the required Thévenin voltage is the voltage of the node joining resistor R_1 to resistor R_3.   Now the voltage V_1 divides between the two resistors R_1 and R_3 connected in series proportionally to their resistances.   Hence the voltage across the resistor R_3 is the fraction $R_3/(R_1 + R_3)$ of the voltage across the pair of resistors.   It follows that the required Thévenin voltage is

$$V_T = \frac{R_3}{R_1 + R_3} V_1 \tag{4.23}$$

We can therefore calculate the voltage and current associated with the variable load resistor R_4 in Fig. 4.9 by using the circuit shown in Fig. 4.10 with the value (4.23) for V_T and the value (4.22) for R_T.

If alternatively it is desired to use the Norton equivalent circuit in Fig. 4.11, then it is necessary to calculate I_N.   Since we have already calculated the Thévenin voltage V_T and the Thévenin resistance R_T, the Norton current I_N can be calculated in accordance with Eqs. (4.20) by dividing expression (4.23) by expression (4.22).   However, if we had decided initially to use the Norton equivalent circuit rather than the Thévenin equivalent circuit, we would be interested in making a direct calculation of the Norton current I_N. This we would do as follows: The Norton current is the current that leaves terminal 2 when this terminal is short-circuited to terminal 0. It is therefore the current flowing from terminal 2 to terminal 0 in Fig. 4.14. The network in Fig. 4.14 involves two resistors of resistances R_2 and R_3 connected in parallel, and this pair is connected in series with the resistor of resistance R_1.

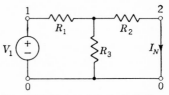

FIG. 4.14. Network for calculating the Norton current for the arrangement shown in Fig. 4.9.

The equivalent resistance between terminals 1 and 0 is therefore

$$R_1 + \frac{1}{1/R_2 + 1/R_3} \qquad (4.24)$$

and this may be rewritten as

$$\frac{R_2R_3 + R_3R_1 + R_1R_2}{R_2 + R_3} \qquad (4.25)$$

The current through resistor R_1 is therefore

$$\frac{R_2 + R_3}{R_2R_3 + R_3R_1 + R_1R_2} V_1 \qquad (4.26)$$

and this divides between resistor R_2 and resistor R_3 in the ratio R_3 to R_2. The current through resistor R_2 is therefore

$$\frac{R_3}{R_2 + R_3} \frac{R_2 + R_3}{R_2R_3 + R_3R_1 + R_1R_2} V_1 \qquad (4.27)$$

and this flows from left to right in Fig. 4.14. We therefore deduce that the required Norton current is

$$I_N = \frac{R_3}{R_2R_3 + R_3R_1 + R_1R_2} V_1 \qquad (4.28)$$

We notice that this is in fact the quotient of expression (4.23) by expression (4.22), as it should be in accordance with Eqs. (4.20). We can therefore calculate the voltage and current for the variable load resistor of resistance R_4 in the arrangement shown in Fig. 4.9 by using the Norton equivalent circuit shown in Fig. 4.11 with the value (4.28) for I_N and the value (4.22) for R_N.

In handling the arrangement shown in Fig. 4.9 it is a matter of choice whether we use the Thévenin equivalent circuit shown in Fig. 4.10 or the

Norton equivalent circuit shown in Fig. 4.11. In this particular case rather less calculation was involved in evaluating the elements for the Thévenin equivalent circuit.

In the application of the Thévenin and Norton equivalent circuits considered above we commenced with the network shown in Fig. 3.4. This was a network already enclosed in a metal box at zero potential, and we connected a battery between terminals 1 and 0 and a load resistor between

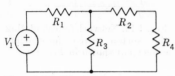

FIG. 4.15. Illustrating a network for which Thévenin and Norton equivalent circuits are derived.

terminals 2 and 0. Thévenin and Norton equivalent circuits can, however, be applied in other circumstances. Suppose, for example, that we were given the network shown in Fig. 4.15 and asked to calculate the voltage and current for the resistor R_4 for a series of values of its resistance, with a fixed voltage V_1 applied at the left. We could immediately reduce this problem to the one already solved, regarding the resistors R_1, R_2, and R_3 as enclosed in a box, with the resistor R_4 as a load resistor. This illustrates the fact that it is possible to apply the Thévenin and Norton equivalent circuits in the following way: Suppose that we have any network of resistors energized by sources of constant voltage or constant current connected to the network in specified ways. Now select any resistor of the network. Suppose that we are interested in calculating the voltage and current for this resistor for various values of its resistance. This selected resistor can then be regarded as a load resistor, and the rest of the network, together with the sources, can be replaced by a Thévenin or Norton equivalent circuit.

As an example, let us suppose that the network of resistors is that shown in Fig. 4.15 and that to it is applied a fixed voltage V_1 as indicated. Let us further suppose that the selected resistor is R_3 and that we are inter-

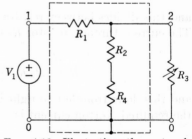

FIG. 4.16. Illustrating the network shown in Fig. 4.15, redrawn so as to make resistor R_3 a load resistor.

ested in calculating the voltage and current for this resistor for various values of the resistance R_3, the voltage V_1 remaining constant. By redrawing the network as shown in Fig. 4.16 we see that the resistors R_1, R_2, and R_4 can be regarded as in a box at zero potential (terminal 0) with two external terminals 1 and 2. Between terminals 1 and 0 is applied a constant voltage V_1, and between terminals 2 and 0 is connected a variable load resistor R_3. The network shown in Fig. 4.16 can therefore be reduced to the Thévenin form shown in Fig. 4.17 or to the Norton form shown in Fig. 4.18 according to preference.   The resistances R_T and R_N

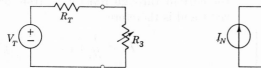

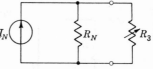

FIG. 4.17. The Thévenin equivalent circuit for the arrangement shown in Fig. 4.16.

FIG. 4.18. The Norton equivalent circuit for the arrangement shown in Fig. 4.16.

are the equivalent resistances across the right-hand terminals in the network shown in Fig. 4.19.   It follows that

$$R_T = R_N = \frac{1}{1/R_1 + 1/(R_2 + R_4)} \tag{4.29}$$

which can be rewritten as

$$R_T = R_N = \frac{R_1(R_2 + R_4)}{R_1 + R_2 + R_4} \tag{4.30}$$

The Thévenin voltage V_T to be used in Fig. 4.17 is calculated from the network shown in Fig. 4.20.   The Thévenin voltage is the excess of the

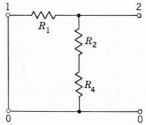

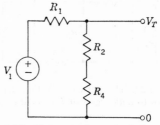

FIG. 4.19. Network for calculating the Thévenin and Norton resistances for the arrangement shown in Fig. 4.16.

FIG. 4.20. Network for calculating the Thévenin voltage for the arrangement shown in Fig. 4.16.

voltage of the upper right-hand terminal over that of the lower right-hand terminal in Fig. 4.20 and is therefore

$$V_T = \frac{R_2 + R_4}{R_1 + R_2 + R_4} V_1 \tag{4.31}$$

The network shown in Fig. 4.16 is therefore equivalent to that shown in Fig. 4.17 provided that the value of V_T is given by Eq. (4.31) and the value of R_T by Eq. (4.30).   If alternatively we wish to use the Norton equivalent circuit shown in Fig. 4.18, then we have to calculate the Norton current I_N.   This is the current flowing vertically downward from terminal 2 to terminal 0 at the right-hand side of Fig. 4.21 when the fixed voltage V_1 is applied at the left.   The Norton current is therefore simply the current through resistor R_1 from left to right and is therefore

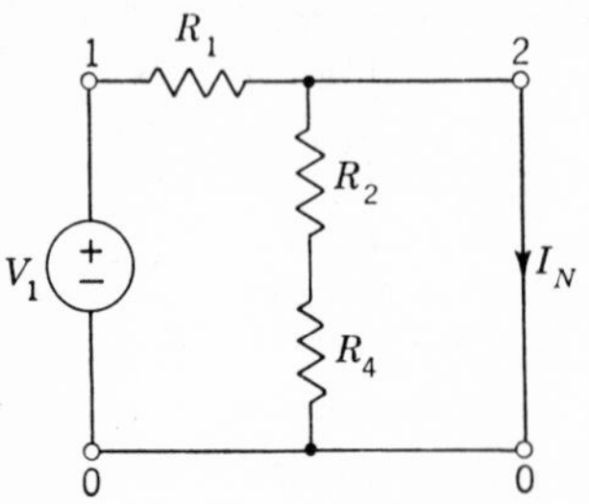

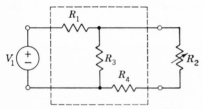

$$I_N = \frac{1}{R_1} V_1 \qquad (4.32)$$

The arrangement shown in Fig. 4.16 is therefore equivalent to the circuit shown in Fig. 4.18 provided that I_N has the value given by Eq. (4.32) and R_N the value given by Eq. (4.30).

FIG. 4.21. Network for calculating the Norton current for the arrangement shown in Fig. 4.16.

Let us now return to the network shown in Fig. 4.15 and select resistor R_2 instead of resistor R_3; we desire to know the voltage and current for resistor R_2 for a series of values of its resistance and for a fixed voltage V_1 applied at the left of the network.   In this case we can use the Thévenin and Norton equivalent circuits by redrawing the network of Fig. 4.15 as shown in Fig. 4.22.   We can now replace the network shown in Fig. 4.22 by the Thévenin equivalent circuit shown in

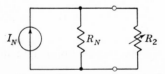

FIG. 4.22. The network of Fig. 4.15 redrawn to make resistor R_2 a load resistor.

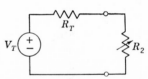

FIG. 4.23. The Thévenin equivalent circuit for the arrangement shown in Fig. 4.22.

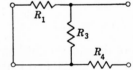

FIG. 4.24. The Norton equivalent circuit for the arrangement shown in Fig. 4.22.

FIG. 4.25. Network for deriving the Thévenin and Norton resistances for the arrangement shown in Fig. 4.22.

Fig. 4.23 or by the Norton equivalent circuit shown in Fig. 4.24 according to preference.   To calculate R_T and R_N we use the network shown in Fig. 4.25 and derive

$$R_T = R_N = R_4 + \frac{1}{1/R_1 + 1/R_3} \qquad (4.33)$$

or, on simplification,

$$R_T = R_N = \frac{R_1 R_3 + R_3 R_4 + R_4 R_1}{R_1 + R_3} \qquad (4.34)$$

To derive the Thévenin voltage V_T we use the network shown in Fig. 4.26 and calculate the voltage across the right-hand terminals when on open circuit. We derive

$$V_T = \frac{R_3}{R_1 + R_3} V_1 \qquad (4.35)$$

The arrangement shown in Fig. 4.22 is therefore equivalent to that shown in Fig. 4.23 provided that V_T has the value given by Eq. (4.35) and R_T has the value given by Eq. (4.34).   If we are using the Norton equivalent

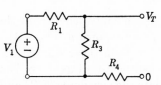

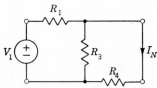

FIG. 4.26. Network for calculating the Thévenin voltage for the arrangement shown in Fig. 4.22.

FIG. 4.27. Network for calculating the Norton current for the arrangement shown in Fig. 4.22.

circuit shown in Fig. 4.24, we calculate the Norton current I_N using the network shown in Fig. 4.27.   We require the current flowing vertically downward at the extreme right of the network shown in Fig. 4.27 when the voltage V_1 is applied at the left-hand side.   By thinking of the network as a resistor R_3 in parallel with the resistor R_4, this pair being in series with the resistor R_1, we derive for the current through resistor R_4 from right to left

$$\frac{R_3}{R_3 + R_4} \frac{1}{R_1 + 1/(1/R_3 + 1/R_4)} V_1 \qquad (4.36)$$

On simplification we derive

$$I_N = \frac{R_3}{R_1 R_3 + R_3 R_4 + R_4 R_1} V_1 \qquad (4.37)$$

Hence the arrangement shown in Fig. 4.22 is equivalent to that shown in Fig. 4.24 provided that I_N has the value given by Eq. (4.37) and R_N has the value given by Eq. (4.34).

In all the above applications of the Thévenin and Norton equivalent circuits it is the voltage V_1 of the source that has been kept constant. Let us now consider an example in which it is the current I_1 of the source that is kept constant.   Let us suppose that a source delivering a fixed current I_1 is applied at the left-hand side of the network shown in Fig. 4.28.   Let us select resistor R_2 and ask what the voltage and the current for this resistor are for various values of its resistance and for a fixed value of I_1.   As before, we rearrange the network as shown in Fig. 4.29.   This

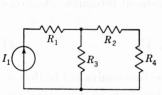

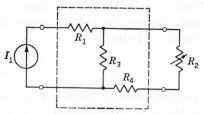

FIG. 4.28. An example of a network with a constant-current source.

FIG. 4.29. The network shown in Fig. 4.28 redrawn to make resistor R_2 a load resistor.

network can again be replaced by the Thévenin equivalent circuit shown in Fig. 4.23 or by the Norton equivalent circuit shown in Fig. 4.24, but new values must be calculated for the elements in these equivalent circuits, since it is the current I_1 that is now kept constant as the resistance of the load resistor R_2 is varied.   To calculate the new value of R_T and R_N we use the network shown in Fig. 4.30 in which the terminals on the left

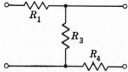

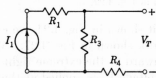

FIG. 4.30. Network for calculating the Thévenin and Norton resistances for the arrangement shown in Fig. 4.29.

FIG. 4.31. Network for calculating the Thévenin voltage for the arrangement shown in Fig. 4.29.

are now open-circuited instead of short-circuited.   The required resistance is the equivalent resistance across the right-hand terminals in Fig. 4.30 and is therefore

$$R_T = R_N = R_3 + R_4 \qquad (4.38)$$

The new value of the Thévenin voltage V_T to be used in Fig. 4.23 is the excess of voltage of the upper right-hand terminal over the lower right-hand terminal in Fig. 4.31.   Since there is no voltage across resistor R_4 and the current through resistor R_3 is I_1, the required voltage is

$$V_T = R_3 I_1 \qquad (4.39)$$

The arrangement shown in Fig. 4.29 is therefore equivalent to that shown in Fig. 4.23 provided that V_T has the value given by Eq. (4.39) and R_T the value given by Eq. (4.38).   If we use the Norton equivalent circuit shown in Fig. 4.24, the new value for the Norton current I_N is calculated

from the network shown in Fig. 4.32.   The required current is the current
from right to left through resistor R_4 in Fig. 4.32 and hence

$$I_N = \frac{R_3}{R_3 + R_4} I_1 \qquad (4.40)$$

The arrangement shown in Fig. 4.29 is therefore equivalent to that shown
in Fig. 4.24 provided that I_N has the value given by Eq. (4.40) and R_N
has the value given by Eq. (4.38).

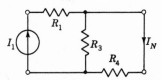

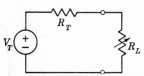

FIG. 4.32. Network for calculating the
Norton current for the arrangement
shown in Fig. 4.29.

FIG. 4.33. Illustrating the variation of a
load resistance to maximize the power
absorbed by it.

**4.8. Maximizing the Power Absorbed by a Selected Resistor of a
Network.** Let us suppose that we have a given network of resistors
energized by sources of fixed voltage or fixed current. Let us suppose
that the resistance of one of the resistors of the network is variable and
that we are interested in adjusting its value so as to maximize the power
absorbed by this resistor. As described in the previous section we regard
the selected resistor as a load resistor and replace the remainder of the
system by a Thévenin equivalent circuit or by a Norton equivalent circuit. It is then a simple matter to vary the resistance of the selected
resistor in the Thévenin or Norton equivalent circuit so as to ascertain
what value the load resistance must have in order to maximize the power
absorbed by it.

Let us suppose that we elect to use a Thévenin equivalent circuit as
shown in Fig. 4.33. R_L is the variable resistance of the selected resistor,
thought of as a load resistor. The Thévenin voltage V_T and the Thévenin
resistance R_T are supposed to have been calculated from the remainder of
the network and the sources connected to it as described in the previous
section. Let us now calculate what value R_L in Fig. 4.33 must have in
order to maximize the power absorbed by the load resistor. This calculation has already been done in connection with Fig. 2.3. The Thévenin
equivalent circuit implies that the whole of the network other than the
load resistor is equivalent to a battery of open-circuit voltage V_T and
of internal resistance R_T. It follows that the variations with R_L of the
current through the load, the voltage across the load, and the power
absorbed by the load are given by Fig. 2.4a, b, and c on replacing V by
V_T, r by R_T, and R by R_L. We thus arrive at Fig. 4.34. From Fig. 4.34

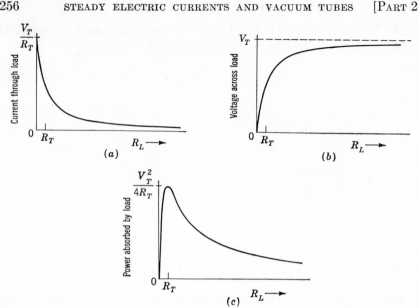

FIG. 4.34. Illustrating the variation with the load resistance R_L of (a) the current through the load, (b) the voltage across the load, and (c) the power absorbed by the load.

we see that the power absorbed by the load is maximum when the load resistance is equal to the Thévenin resistance R_T. The value of the power absorbed by the load is then

$$\frac{1}{4}\frac{V_T{}^2}{R_T} \tag{4.41}$$

This result could also have been obtained by using the Norton equivalent circuit shown in Fig. 4.35. A simple calculation on this circuit yields the curves shown in Fig. 4.36. The curves in Fig. 4.36 are in fact identical with those in Fig. 4.34, but they are labeled differently. In particular it should be noted that the abscissa is the conductance $1/R_L$ of the load resistor, and not its resistance. We again see from Fig. 4.36 that the power absorbed by the load is maximum when the resistance R_L of the load is adjusted to be equal to the

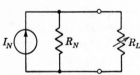

FIG. 4.35. Illustrating the variation of a load resistance to maximize the power absorbed by it.

Norton resistance R_N. This is, of course, the same value as the Thévenin resistance R_T. From Fig. 4.36c the maximum power absorbed by the load is

$$\tfrac{1}{4}R_N I_N{}^2 \tag{4.42}$$

We thus see that the resistance that the load must have in order to maxi-

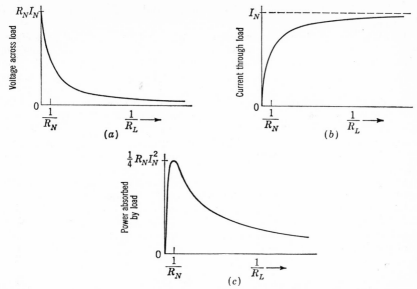

Fɪɢ. 4.36. Illustrating the variation with the conductance $1/R_L$ of the load resistor of (a) the voltage across the load, (b) the current through the load, and (c) the power absorbed by the load.

mize the power absorbed by it is equal to the common value of the Thévenin resistance R_T and the Norton resistance R_N. For example, to maximize the power absorbed by resistor R_2 in Fig. 4.15 for a constant value of the voltage V_1, we must adjust R_2 to have the value given by Eq. (4.34). To maximize the power absorbed by resistor R_2 in the network shown in Fig. 4.28 for a constant value of the current I_1, the resistance R_2 must be adjusted to have the value given by Eq. (4.38).

Using Eqs. (4.20) we see that the power (4.41) or (4.42) absorbed by the load resistor when adjusted to maximize this power can be written in any of the following equivalent forms:

$$\frac{1}{4}\frac{V_T^2}{R_T} = \frac{1}{4}R_N I_N^2 = \frac{1}{4}V_T I_N \qquad (4.43)$$

SUMMARIZING EXERCISES

4.1. Explain what is meant by the statement that one network of resistors possessing input and output terminals is equivalent to a second network of resistors possessing input and output terminals. Describe circumstances in which it is convenient to make use of the concept of equivalent networks.

4.2. Explain what is meant by the equivalent T and π networks for a given network of resistors possessing input and output terminals.

4.3. A network of resistors possesses a pair of output terminals. It is energized either by a source of given voltage or by a source delivering a given current or both.

Explain what is meant by the Thévenin and Norton equivalent circuits for the arrangement.

4.4. A network of resistors is contained in a box from which protrude pairs of terminals connected to nodes of the network. One pair of terminals is used as a pair of output terminals. The other pairs of terminals are used to energize the network. For some of these pairs of terminals this is achieved by connecting a source having prescribed voltage, while for other pairs of terminals it is achieved by connecting a source delivering a prescribed current. It is required to evaluate the elements of the Thévenin and Norton equivalent circuits for the arrangement. Explain how this can be achieved by measurement without opening the box to examine the contents. Explain how to use the same method for calculating theoretically the elements in the Thévenin and Norton equivalent circuits in terms of the elements of the given network and the given energizing sources.

4.5. Describe circumstances under which it is convenient to replace a network of resistors and energizing sources by a Thévenin and Norton equivalent circuit.

4.6. A network of given resistors and sources has a pair of output terminals, and the Thévenin and Norton resistance for the arrangement is R. A load resistor of variable resistance is connected across the output terminals, and its resistance is varied until the power in the load resistor is a maximum. Prove that, when so adjusted, the resistance of the load is equal to R.

CHAPTER 5

RESISTANCE BETWEEN ELECTRODES EMBEDDED IN RESISTIVE MATERIAL

5.1. Introduction. In Chap. 1 we saw that steady electric currents are driven through resistive material by means of electrostatic fields provided from batteries. In Sec. 1.5 we calculated the conductance between the flat ends of a cylindrical piece of resistive material of conductivity σ, cross-sectional area S, and length s. It was assumed that the flat ends of the cylindrical piece of resistive material were provided with perfectly conducting sheets each of area S between which a battery could be connected. The conductance G between these sheets was evaluated in Eq. (1.8), and the result was

$$G = \frac{\sigma S}{s} \tag{5.1}$$

This result was compared in Sec. 1.8 with the capacitance C between the plates given by the equation

$$C = \frac{\epsilon S}{s} \tag{5.2}$$

where ϵ is the capacitivity of the medium between the plates and fringing is neglected. Many resistors may be considered to have the form of cylindrical pieces of resistive material to which Eq. (5.1) can be applied. However, circumstances arise in which it is necessary to calculate the resistance between a pair of terminals under quite different conditions. Suppose, for example, that a pair of metal stakes are driven into the ground some distance apart, or suppose that they are immersed in water some distance apart, and that it is required to calculate the resistance between the stakes in terms of the conductivity of the ground or water. In such cases it is necessary to examine the way in which an electrostatic field produces steady current through resistive material under conditions other than those considered in connection with Fig. 1.7.

5.2. Conductance between Parallel Plates. It is convenient to give some further attention to the conductance between parallel plates already discussed in Sec. 1.5. Figure 5.1 represents a pair of parallel perfectly conducting plates of area S with a separation s. Between the plates there is a medium whose capacitivity is ϵ and whose conductivity is σ. It is supposed that this material occupies only the volume between the two perfectly conducting plates. With a voltage V connected between the plates as shown, current flows uniformly through the material from the upper plate to the lower plate. The electric field within the resistive material is uniform and is perpendicular to the plates; there is also an electric field outside the volume between the plates. The conductance between the plates is given by Eq. (5.1). The capacitance between the

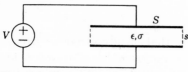

plates is given by Eq. (5.2) provided that all charge not on the lower surface of the upper plate or the upper surface of the lower plate is disregarded. Let us examine the relation between the steady current I flowing from the upper plate to the lower

Fig. 5.1. Illustrating the relation between conductance and capacitance.

plate and the equal and opposite charges Q and $-Q$ that exist on the lower surface of the upper plate and the upper surface of the lower plate.

In terms of the voltage V between the plates, the charge Q is given by

$$Q = CV \qquad (5.3)$$

and by substitution from Eq. (5.2) this becomes

$$Q = \frac{\epsilon S}{s} V \qquad (5.4)$$

In terms of the voltage V between the plates, the steady current I flowing from the upper plate to the lower plate is given by

$$I = GV \qquad (5.5)$$

and by substitution from Eq. (5.1) this becomes

$$I = \frac{\sigma S}{s} V \qquad (5.6)$$

If we now substitute for V from Eq. (5.6) into Eq. (5.4), we deduce that

$$Q = \frac{\epsilon}{\sigma} I \qquad (5.7)$$

This equation shows that, in order to produce a steady current I through the resistive material from the upper plate to the lower plate in Fig. 5.1, it is necessary for the lower surface of the upper plate to carry a charge Q given by Eq. (5.7) and for the upper surface of the lower plate to carry an equal and opposite charge $-Q$. These are the charges that produce the electrostatic field that drives the electric current through the resistive material.

When the battery is initially connected across the plates, the initial current from the battery is used more to build up the charges on the plates than to produce a current through the resistive material. A steady state is ultimately reached, however, in which the rate at which charge is supplied to the plates is exactly balanced by the leakage current between the plates through the resistive material. Attention has already been drawn in Sec. 1.8 to the fact that the ratio

$$\frac{\epsilon}{\sigma} \qquad (5.8)$$

has the dimensions of time. Equation (5.7) shows that the charge crossing any normal cross section of the resistive material in time ϵ/σ is equal to the positive charge on the lower surface of the upper plate and the negative charge on the upper surface of the lower plate. As charge leaks across from the one plate to the other, it is steadily replaced from the battery. The charge on the negative plate at any instant leaks across to the positive plate in an ensuing time given by expression (5.8).

5.3. Point Source of Steady Current in Resistive Material. Let us suppose that a large metal tank is filled with a resistive material such as water. Let us further suppose that, somewhere near the middle of the tank, there is a small metal sphere to which electrical contact can be made from outside the tank via an insulated metal wire. By connecting a battery between the wire and the tank it is possible to maintain a difference of potential between the small metal sphere in the middle of the tank and the metal surface of the tank. A steady current then flows through the water from the sphere to the walls of the tank, and we are interested in calculating the resistance between the sphere and the walls.

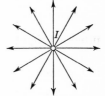

Fig. 5.2. The lines of flow for a point source of steady current I in a homogeneous medium.

Let us idealize this problem by replacing the walls of the tank by a perfectly conducting sphere of infinite radius. This sphere is the conductor at infinity in electrostatics. Let us suppose that the metal sphere within the tank is also perfectly conducting. For the time being let us also take its size to be indefinitely small. The space between this conductor and the conductor at infinity we take to be a homogeneous medium of capacitivity ϵ and conductivity σ. If a potential difference is maintained between the small sphere and the conductor at infinity, a steady current flows radially outward from the small sphere to the conductor at infinity. Let this current be I. If the size of the small sphere is allowed to tend to zero, we then have what is known as a point source of steady current I. The lines of flow are sketched in Fig. 5.2.

To maintain the flow of current I between the small sphere and the surrounding conductor at infinity there must be an excess of potential of the small sphere over that of the conductor at infinity. There is consequently a radial electric field from the point source to the conductor at infinity. The small sphere therefore carries a point charge Q and the conductor at infinity a total charge $-Q$ distributed uniformly over its inner surface. Thus a point source of steady current I implies the coexistence of a point charge Q, and we are interested in examining the relationship between Q and I.

The electric flux density D at distance r from the center of the small sphere is

$$D = \frac{Q}{4\pi r^2} \tag{5.9}$$

The direction of the electric flux density is radially outward from the point charge. The electric vector $\mathbf{E}$ is given in terms of the electric-flux-density vector $\mathbf{D}$ by the equation

$$\mathbf{E} = \frac{1}{\epsilon}\mathbf{D} \tag{5.10}$$

By substituting from Eq. (5.9) into Eq. (5.10) we see that the electric field strength at distance r from the point charge is

$$E = \frac{1}{4\pi\epsilon}\frac{Q}{r^2} \tag{5.11}$$

The corresponding electric potential is

$$\phi = \frac{1}{4\pi\epsilon}\frac{Q}{r} \tag{5.12}$$

provided that the potential of the conductor at infinity is taken as zero.

The steady current I leaving the source produces a current density J at distance r from the source given by

$$J = \frac{I}{4\pi r^2} \tag{5.13}$$

since the current I is spread uniformly over a sphere of radius r and area $4\pi r^2$. In terms of the current-density vector $\mathbf{J}$ the electric vector is

$$\mathbf{E} = \frac{1}{\sigma}\mathbf{J} \tag{5.14}$$

this equation being identical with Eq. (1.2). By substituting from Eq. (5.13) into Eq. (5.14) we deduce that

$$E = \frac{1}{4\pi\sigma}\frac{I}{r^2} \tag{5.15}$$

Let us now compare Eq. (5.11) with Eq. (5.15). Equation (5.11) expresses the electric field strength at distance r in terms of the charge Q at the source and the capacitivity ϵ of the medium. Equation (5.15) expresses the electric field strength at distance r in terms of the steady electric current I leaving the source and the conductivity σ of the medium. By comparing these two expressions for the electric field strength we see that

$$Q = \frac{\epsilon}{\sigma} I \qquad (5.16)$$

This equation tells us the strength of the point charge Q that must exist on the small sphere in order to produce the necessary radial electric field to drive the current I from the small sphere to the sphere at infinity. By substituting for Q from Eq. (5.16) into Eq. (5.12) we see that the electric potential at distance r may be expressed in terms of the current I leaving the source and the conductivity σ of the medium by the equation

$$\phi = \frac{1}{4\pi\sigma} \frac{I}{r} \qquad (5.17)$$

Equations (5.9) to (5.17) can be conveniently rearranged in the following way:

$$D = \frac{Q}{4\pi r^2} \quad (5.18a) \qquad\qquad J = \frac{I}{4\pi r^2} \quad (5.18b)$$

$$\mathbf{D} = \epsilon\mathbf{E} \quad (5.19a) \qquad\qquad \mathbf{J} = \sigma\mathbf{E} \quad (5.19b)$$

$$E = \frac{1}{4\pi\epsilon} \frac{Q}{r^2} = \frac{1}{4\pi\sigma} \frac{I}{r^2} \qquad (5.20)$$

$$\phi = \frac{1}{4\pi\epsilon} \frac{Q}{r} = \frac{1}{4\pi\sigma} \frac{I}{r} \qquad (5.21)$$

$$Q = \frac{\epsilon}{\sigma} I \qquad (5.22)$$

From Eqs. (5.20) and (5.21) we see that the electric field strength and the electric potential can be expressed either in terms of the conductivity σ of the medium and the current I delivered by the source or alternatively in terms of the capacitivity ϵ of the medium and the point charge Q that must exist at the source in order to provide the electric field required to drive the current. We also notice that Eq. (5.22) is identical with Eq. (5.7). Equation (5.22) states that the current flowing radially outward from the source would discharge the source in time ϵ/σ if the battery maintaining the current did not also maintain the charge.

The lines of force and equipotential surfaces of the system are, of course, simply those of the point charge Q. The lines of flow of electric current coincide with the lines of force.

5.4. Conductance between Concentric Spheres. Let us suppose that a perfectly conducting sphere of radius a is surrounded by a homogeneous medium of capacitivity ϵ and conductance σ extending to infinity. Let us suppose that the system is surrounded by a perfectly conducting concentric spherical conductor of infinite radius. We wish to calculate the conductance between the sphere of radius a and the conductor at infinity.

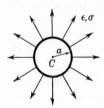

In Fig. 5.3 let C be the center of the spherical conductor of radius a. Remove the sphere and place a point charge Q at C, allowing the medium of capacitivity ϵ and conductivity σ to extend inward as far as C. The point charge Q results in a steady current I flowing outward from C to the conductor at infinity. The relation between Q and I is given by Eq. (5.22), and the electric potential at distances r from C is given by Eqs. (5.21). In the electrostatic field of the point charge Q we can replace any equipotential surface by a thin perfectly conducting shell at the same potential.

Fig. 5.3. Radially outward flow of current from a sphere of radius a into a homogeneous medium of conductivity σ.

The equipotential surfaces are spheres concentric with C, and the potential on the sphere $r = a$ is

$$V = \frac{1}{4\pi\epsilon} \frac{Q}{a} = \frac{1}{4\pi\sigma} \frac{I}{a} \qquad (5.23)$$

In the electrostatic field of the point charge we can replace the equipotential surface $r = a$ by a thin spherical perfectly conducting shell at the potential given by Eqs. (5.23) without affecting the field anywhere, either inside the sphere $r = a$ or outside the sphere $r = a$. There is now, in addition to the point charge at C, a charge $-Q$ distributed uniformly over the interior of the sphere $r = a$, a charge Q distributed uniformly over the exterior of the sphere $r = a$, and a charge $-Q$ on the sphere at infinity. Moreover the steady current I leaving C terminates on the interior surface of the sphere $r = a$, but an equal current I starts from the exterior surface of the sphere $r = a$ and flows radially outward to the sphere at infinity. In accordance with the principles described in Part 1, Sec. 3.7, we can abolish the field inside the sphere $r = a$ while retaining the field exterior to the sphere $r = a$. We then have a situation in which a perfectly conducting sphere of radius a is embedded in a homogeneous medium of capacitivity ϵ and conductivity σ, surrounded by the sphere at infinity. The sphere of radius a carries a charge Q uniformly distributed over it, and from its surface there flows a total current I distributed uniformly over its surface and proceeding radially to the conductor at infinity. We require to calculate the conductance between this sphere and the conductor at infinity.

Since the potential of the sphere $r = a$ is given by Eq.s (5.23) and the potential of the conductor at infinity has been taken as zero, Eqs. (5.23) also give the excess of potential of the sphere $r = a$ over the potential of the conductor at infinity. Since the current flowing is I, the conductance is

$$G = \frac{I}{V} \tag{5.24}$$

where the ratio of I to V is given by one of the Eqs. (5.23). By substituting from the appropriate Eq. (5.23) into Eq. (5.24) we deduce that the conductance between the sphere $r = a$ and the conductor at infinity is

$$G = 4\pi\sigma a \tag{5.25}$$

This conductance is therefore proportional to the conductivity σ of the medium and to the radius a of the sphere.

In the same way we can calculate the capacitance between the sphere $r = a$ and the conductor at infinity. It is given by

$$C = \frac{Q}{V} \tag{5.26}$$

and on substituting for the ratio Q/V from the appropriate Eq. (5.23) into Eq. (5.26), we deduce that the capacitance between the sphere of radius a and the conductor at infinity is

$$C = 4\pi\epsilon a \tag{5.27}$$

The result (5.27) has been previously derived in Part 1, Sec. 4.3.

Now suppose that we have two concentric perfectly conducting spherical shells of radii a and b, with a homogeneous medium of capacitivity ϵ and conductivity σ between them as shown in Fig. 5.4. We require to calculate the conductance between the spheres. Let the inner sphere of radius a be maintained at a potential above that of the outer sphere of radius b. As a result let there be a charge Q uniformly distributed over the sphere of radius a and a corresponding charge $-Q$ distributed uniformly over the inner surface of the sphere of radius b. Furthermore let the resulting steady current flowing radially and uniformly from the sphere of radius a to the sphere of radius b be I. The electric field between the spheres is the same as that for a point charge Q at the common center in the absence of the spheres, with the medium of capacitivity ϵ and conductivity σ filling all space. The potential at any point between the spheres $r = a$ and $r = b$ at dis-

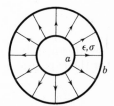

Fig. 5.4. Radial flow of current through a resistive medium between two concentric perfectly conducting spheres.

tance r from the common center is therefore given by Eqs. (5.21). The potential of the sphere of radius a is

$$V_1 = \frac{1}{4\pi\epsilon}\frac{Q}{a} = \frac{1}{4\pi\sigma}\frac{I}{a} \tag{5.28}$$

and that of the sphere of radius b is

$$V_2 = \frac{1}{4\pi\epsilon}\frac{Q}{b} = \frac{1}{4\pi\sigma}\frac{I}{b} \tag{5.29}$$

The excess of the potential of the sphere of radius a over the sphere of radius b is therefore

$$V_1 - V_2 = \frac{Q}{4\pi\epsilon}\left(\frac{1}{a} - \frac{1}{b}\right) = \frac{I}{4\pi\sigma}\left(\frac{1}{a} - \frac{1}{b}\right) \tag{5.30}$$

The conductance between the spheres is

$$G = \frac{I}{V_1 - V_2} \tag{5.31}$$

and this may be evaluated from the appropriate Eq. (5.30). We deduce for the conductance between a sphere of radius a and a larger concentric sphere of radius b with a medium of uniform conductivity σ between them

$$G = \frac{4\pi\sigma}{1/a - 1/b} \tag{5.32}$$

In the same way we can write down the capacitance between the spheres as

$$C = \frac{Q}{V_1 - V_2} \tag{5.33}$$

and this may be evaluated from the appropriate Eq. (5.30). We deduce for the capacitance of the arrangement, regarded as a spherical capacitor,

$$C = \frac{4\pi}{1/a - 1/b} \tag{5.34}$$

This is the usual expression for the capacitance of a spherical capacitor deduced in Part 1, Sec. 4.4.

5.5. Line Source of Current Embedded in a Resistive Medium. Let us suppose that we have a straight perfectly conducting wire whose diameter is indefinitely small and whose length is extremely great. Let it be embedded in a medium of uniform capacitivity ϵ and uniform conductivity σ. Let the wire be surrounded by a perfectly conducting coaxial cylinder whose radius is assumed to be large. Let us suppose that a potential difference is maintained between the wire and the cylinder as a result of which current flows radially from the wire to the cylinder. Let I be the current leaving the wire per unit length.   It is clear from the cylindrical symmetry of the arrangement that the lines of flow run radially outward from the wire and lie in planes perpendicular to the wire as indicated in Fig. 5.5. The electric field required to drive this current must also run radially outward from the wire to the indefinitely large cylinder and is produced by a charge Q per unit length on the wires combined with an equal negative charge $-Q$ per unit length on the large cylinder.   This electric field has already been discussed in Part 1, Sec. 11.2.   The electric flux density at distance r from the wire is

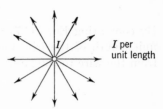

FIG. 5.5. The lines of flow from an infinite line source of current.

$$D = \frac{Q}{2\pi r} \tag{5.35}$$

From this we derive the electric vector in accordance with the relation

$$\mathbf{E} = \frac{1}{\epsilon}\,\mathbf{D} \tag{5.36}$$

thereby obtaining for the electric field strength at distance r from the wire

$$E = \frac{1}{2\pi\epsilon}\,\frac{Q}{r} \tag{5.37}$$

From the electric field strength we derive by integration the electric potential ϕ at distance r from the wire in the form

$$\phi = -\frac{Q}{2\pi\epsilon}\ln r + \text{constant} \tag{5.38}$$

The current density at distance r from the wire is

$$J = \frac{I}{2\pi r} \tag{5.39}$$

since the current I leaving unit length of the wire is, at distance r from the wire, spread uniformly over the surface of a cylinder of radius r and unit length.   The electric vector is deduced from the current-density vector in accordance with the equation

$$\mathbf{E} = \frac{1}{\sigma}\,\mathbf{J} \tag{5.40}$$

from which it follows that the electric field strength at distance r from the wire is

$$E = \frac{1}{2\pi\sigma}\frac{I}{r}$$ (5.41)

By comparing Eq. (5.37) with Eq. (5.41) we see that the charge Q per unit length of the wire required to drive the current I per unit length from the wire to the large cylinder is given by the equation

$$Q = \frac{\epsilon}{\sigma}I$$ (5.42)

Substituting from Eq. (5.42) into Eq. (5.38) we see that the electric potential at distance r from the wire can be expressed in terms of the current I leaving unit length of the wire by means of the equation

$$\phi = -\frac{I}{2\pi\sigma}\ln r + \text{constant}$$ (5.43)

The constant in Eqs. (5.38) and (5.43) may be chosen to make the potential zero at any distance from the wire other than zero or infinity.

Equations (5.35) to (5.43) can be conveniently arranged in the following way:

$$D = \frac{Q}{2\pi r} \quad (5.44a) \qquad\qquad J = \frac{I}{2\pi r} \quad (5.44b)$$

$$\mathbf{D} = \epsilon\mathbf{E} \quad (5.45a) \qquad\qquad \mathbf{J} = \sigma\mathbf{E} \quad (5.45b)$$

$$E = \frac{1}{2\pi\epsilon}\frac{Q}{r} = \frac{1}{4\pi\sigma}\frac{I}{r}$$ (5.46)

$$\phi = -\frac{Q}{2\pi\epsilon}\ln r + \text{constant} = -\frac{I}{2\pi\sigma}\ln r + \text{constant}$$ (5.47)

$$Q = \frac{\epsilon}{\sigma}I$$ (5.48)

5.6. Leakage in a Coaxial Transmission Line.

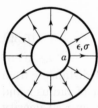

FIG. 5.6. The leakage current for a coaxial transmission line.

Consider a coaxial transmission line consisting of two perfectly conducting coaxial metal cylinders as shown in Fig. 5.6. Let the space between the cylinders have an inner radius a and an outer radius b, and let it be filled with a medium of uniform capacitivity ϵ and uniform conductivity σ. The cylinders may be supposed to have infinite length, and we are interested in calculating the conductance between the inner and outer conductors per unit length of the transmission line.

We arrive at the electric field of a coaxial transmission line by starting with the electric field of an infinite line charge carrying a charge Q per unit length. For this field the equipotential surfaces are circular cylinders coaxial with the line charge. The electric potential ϕ is given as a function of distance r from the line charge by Eqs. (5.47). On the equipotential surface $r = a$ the potential is

$$V_1 = -\frac{Q}{2\pi\epsilon}\ln a + \text{constant} = -\frac{I}{2\pi\sigma}\ln a + \text{constant} \qquad (5.49)$$

and on the equipotential surface $r = b$ the potential is

$$V_2 = -\frac{Q}{2\pi\epsilon}\ln b + \text{constant} = -\frac{I}{2\pi\sigma}\ln b + \text{constant} \qquad (5.50)$$

We replace the equipotential surface $r = a$ by a perfectly conducting cylinder at the potential (5.49) and the equipotential surface $r = b$ by a perfectly conducting cylinder at the potential (5.50); retain only the field between these two conductors. We then have the field in the coaxial transmission line shown in Fig. 5.6 under circumstances when the inner conductor carries a charge Q per unit length and the outer conductor carries a charge $-Q$ per unit length on its inner surface, while there is a current I per unit length flowing radially from the inner conductor to the outer conductor. By subtracting Eqs. (5.50) from Eqs. (5.49) we see that the excess of potential of the inner conductor over the outer conductor in these circumstances is

$$V_1 - V_2 = \frac{Q}{2\pi\epsilon}\ln\frac{b}{a} = \frac{I}{2\pi\sigma}\ln\frac{b}{a} \qquad (5.51)$$

The conductance between the inner and outer conductors per unit length of the transmission line is the ratio of the current per unit length between the conductors to the corresponding difference of potential between the conductors. Hence the conductance per unit length of the transmission line is

$$G = \frac{I}{V_1 - V_2} \qquad (5.52)$$

and by substitution from the appropriate Eq. (5.51) into Eq. (5.52) we derive

$$G = \frac{2\pi\sigma}{\ln (b/a)} \qquad (5.53)$$

Thus the conductance per unit length of a coaxial transmission line is directly proportional to the conductivity of the medium between the conductors and inversely proportional to the natural logarithm of the ratio of the radii.

In the same way we can derive the capacitance per unit length of the transmission line.   This is given by

$$C = \frac{Q}{V_1 - V_2} \tag{5.54}$$

and by substitution from the appropriate Eq. (5.51) into Eq. (5.54) we deduce that

$$C = \frac{2\pi\epsilon}{\ln (b/a)} \tag{5.55}$$

a result already obtained in Part 1, Sec. 11.3.

If b/a is about 2.7, which is not an unusual ratio of radii, the denominator in Eq. (5.53) is approximately unity since the base e of natural logarithms is approximately 2.7.   In these circumstances expression (5.53) reduces to $2\pi\sigma$, and from the values of σ given in Table 1.1 we can read off values for the conductance per unit length in mhos per meter for coaxial transmission lines filled with various materials.

5.7. Leakage in a Twin-wire Transmission Line.   Consider a transmission line consisting of a pair of long straight perfectly conducting wires, each of radius a, with their centers at a distance d apart.   It is usually true that d is large compared with a, and it will simplify the calculations to make this assumption.   Let the medium surrounding the wires have uniform capacitivity ϵ and uniform conductivity σ.   We are interested in calculating the conductance between the wires per unit length of the transmission line.

We start by considering a twin-wire transmission line for which the wires have zero radius and are at distance d apart.   We suppose that there is a current I per unit length of the line flowing through the resistive medium from one wire to the other.   This current is driven by an electric field that arises from a charge Q per unit length on the wire from which the current emanates and a charge $-Q$ per unit length on the wire to which the current flows.   This situation is illustrated in Fig. 5.7.   The left-hand wire in Fig. 5.7 then constitutes a line source of current of the type studied in connection with Fig. 5.5, while the right-hand wire represents the same thing except that the current is arriving instead of leaving.   Now the electric field for the arrangement shown in Fig. 5.7 has already been studied in Part 1, Sec. 11.4.   At the point whose perpendicular distance from the line charge Q per unit length is r_1 and whose perpendicular distance from the line charge $-Q$ per unit length is r_2 the electric potential is, from Eqs. (5.47),

$$\phi = -\frac{Q}{2\pi\epsilon} \ln r_1 + \frac{Q}{2\pi\epsilon} \ln r_2 + \text{constant}$$

$$= -\frac{I}{2\pi\sigma} \ln r_1 + \frac{I}{2\pi\sigma} \ln r_2 + \text{constant} \tag{5.56}$$

and this can be rewritten as

$$\phi = \frac{Q}{2\pi\epsilon} \ln \frac{r_2}{r_1} = \frac{I}{2\pi\sigma} \ln \frac{r_2}{r_1} \tag{5.57}$$

if the zero of potential is taken on the symmetrical plane $r_1 = r_2$. From this equation we see that the equipotential surfaces of the pair of equal

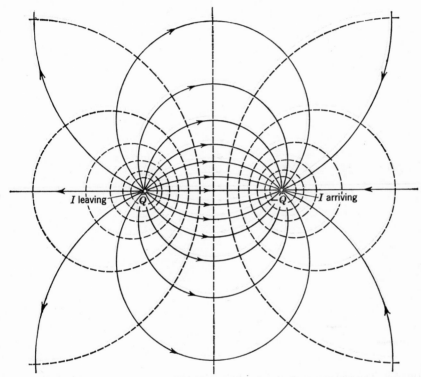

FIG. 5.7. The leakage current for a twin-wire transmission line for which the wires are indefinitely thin.

and opposite line charges are the cylindrical surfaces whose equations are

$$\frac{r_2}{r_1} = \text{constant} \tag{5.58}$$

The lines of force and lines of flow are the curves intersecting these surfaces at right angles. The lines of flow and equipotential surfaces are shown in Fig. 5.7. The lines of flow lie in planes perpendicular to the wires, and each is an arc of a circle passing through the two wires. The equipotential surfaces are circular cylinders with axes parallel to the wires and enveloping either the wire carrying charge Q per unit length or the wire carrying charge $-Q$ per unit length. One of the equipotential surfaces is the symmetrical plane between the two line charges upon which the potential has been taken as zero.

Close to the thin wires the equipotential surfaces become cylinders whose axes nearly coincide with the thin wires. On each such small cylinder enveloping the line charge Q per unit length the value of r_1 is practically the radius of the cylinder and the value of r_2 is practically

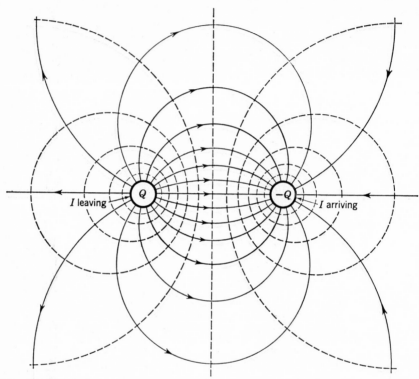

FIG. 5.8. The leakage current for a twin-wire transmission line for which the wires have a nonvanishing radius. (Compare Part 1, Fig. 11.3.)

the distance d between the wires. On a small cylinder enveloping the line charge $-Q$ per unit length the value of r_1 is practically the distance d between the line charges and the value of r_2 is practically the radius of the cylinder. Replace the small cylinder $r_1 = a$, which envelops the line charge Q per unit length, by a perfectly conducting cylinder at the potential

$$V_1 = \frac{Q}{2\pi\epsilon} \ln \frac{d}{a} = \frac{I}{2\pi\sigma} \ln \frac{d}{a} \qquad (5.59)$$

These equations follow by putting $r_1 = a$ and $r_2 = d$ in Eqs. (5.57). Replace the small cylinder $r_2 = a$, which envelops the line charge $-Q$

per unit length, by a perfectly conducting cylinder at potential

$$V_2 = \frac{Q}{2\pi\epsilon} \ln \frac{a}{d} = \frac{I}{2\pi\sigma} \log \frac{a}{d} \qquad (5.60)$$

These equations follow by putting $r_1 = d$ and $r_2 = a$ in Eqs. (5.57). After replacing these equipotential surfaces by conductors at the potentials (5.59) and (5.60), retain only the field between the conductors as shown in Fig. 5.8. This field represents a leakage current I per unit length between the conductors of a twin-wire transmission line embedded in a resistive medium, the radii of the wires being a, the distance between their centers being approximately d, and the conductivity of the medium being σ. The excess of potential of the wire from which the current emanates over the wire to which the current flows is obtained by subtracting Eq. (5.60) from Eq. (5.59) and is

$$\begin{aligned} V_1 - V_2 &= \frac{Q}{2\pi\epsilon} \left(\ln \frac{d}{a} - \ln \frac{a}{d} \right) \\ &= \frac{I}{2\pi\sigma} \left(\ln \frac{d}{a} - \ln \frac{a}{d} \right) \end{aligned} \qquad (5.61)$$

which can be simplified to

$$V_1 - V_2 = \frac{Q}{\pi\epsilon} \ln \frac{d}{a} = \frac{I}{\pi\sigma} \ln \frac{d}{a} \qquad (5.62)$$

The conductance per unit length of the line is

$$G = \frac{I}{V_1 - V_2} \qquad (5.63)$$

and on substituting from the appropriate Eq. (5.62) into Eq. (5.63) we derive

$$G = \frac{\pi\sigma}{\ln (d/a)} \qquad (5.64)$$

The conductance per unit length of a twin-wire transmission line embedded in a resistive medium is therefore proportional to the conductivity of the medium and inversely proportional to the natural logarithm of the ratio of the separation between the wires to the radius of the wires.

We can at the same time calculate the capacitance per unit length of the twin-wire transmission line previously derived in Part 1, Sec. 11.4. The capacitance per unit length of the line is

$$C = \frac{Q}{V_1 - V_2} \qquad (5.65)$$

and on substituting from the appropriate Eq. (5.62) into Eq. (5.65) we derive

$$C = \frac{\pi\epsilon}{\ln (d/a)} \qquad (5.66)$$

A typical value for d/a is about 10, and the natural logarithm of this is 2.3. The conductance per unit length of such a twin-wire transmission line is therefore $\pi/2.3$, or 1.4, times the conductivity of the material in which the line is embedded. Typical values for this conductivity can be read from Table 1.1. We may notice that the typical leakage conductance per unit length of a twin-wire line is several times less than that for a coaxial line using the same insulating medium.

5.8. Relation between Conductance and Capacitance. That there is a close relation between conductance and capacitance can be seen by comparing Eq. (5.1) with Eq. (5.2), Eq. (5.25) with Eq. (5.27), Eq. (5.32) with Eq. (5.34), Eq. (5.53) with Eq. (5.55), and Eq. (5.64) with Eq. (5.66). Consider any capacitor between whose plates there exists a medium of uniform capacitivity ϵ and zero conductivity. If the capacitor is charged, we can in principle calculate from the charges on the plates the electric field between the plates and hence the capacitance of the capacitor. Now suppose that the medium acquires a uniform nonvanishing conductivity σ. A battery is then required to maintain the charges on the plates, and a current flows through the medium from one plate to the other. The electrostatic effects are precisely the same as before, but the capacitor is now also a resistor for which we can calculate the conductance. The formula for conductance is obtained from the formula for capacitance by replacing the capacitivity ϵ of the medium by its conductivity σ.

The situation is in fact simply one in which the discharge process along lines of force used in defining electric flux density is continually taking place. Just as the building-block method was used in electrostatics (Part 1, Sec. 8.5) to represent any electric field as a system of parallel-plate capacitors connected in parallel round the equipotential surfaces and in series along the lines of flux, so the building-block method can be used when the medium has conductivity to represent the field as a system of parallel-plate resistors connected in parallel along the equipotential surfaces and in series along the tubes of flow.

5.9. Coefficients of Conductance and Resistance for a System of Perfect Conductors Embedded in Resistive Material. Suppose that a system of perfect conductors is embedded in a resistive material and that the whole is surrounded by a perfectly conducting envelope. This envelope can be the conductor at infinity, and its potential will be taken as zero. If potential differences are maintained between the various conductors, an electric field exists in the medium between them and charges exist on their surfaces. The relation between the charges and the potentials of the conductors can be expressed by means of the coefficients of capacitance and elastance of the system discussed in electrostatics (Part 1, Sec. 9.2). Since the medium is now supposed to be resistive, current flows through it, this current being supplied by the various batteries maintaining the potentials of the conductors. Current leaves the conductor of highest potential in the system and arrives at the conductor of lowest potential. For a conductor of intermediate potential, current arrives over some part of its surface and leaves over another part; the net current leaving the conductor is supplied by the battery maintaining the potential of that conductor. Each conductor therefore has a potential, and from it there flows through the resistive medium a certain current which is positive for some conductors and negative for others. The relation between the potentials of the conductors and the currents leaving them can be described by means of a system of coefficients of conductance and resistance for the system.

Let the conductors be numbered 1, 2, ... Let the potentials of these conductors be V_1, V_2, . . . respectively, and let the currents that flow from them through the resistive medium be I_1, I_2, . . . respectively. Then the currents leaving the conductors can be expressed in terms of the potentials of the conductors by means of equations of the form

$$I_1 = g_{11}V_1 + g_{12}V_2 + g_{13}V_3 + \cdots$$
$$I_2 = g_{21}V_1 + g_{22}V_2 + g_{23}V_3 + \cdots \qquad (5.67)$$
$$I_3 = g_{31}V_1 + g_{32}V_2 + g_{33}V_3 + \cdots$$
$$. \ . \ . \ . \ . \ . \ . \ . \ . \ . \ . \ . \ . \ . \ . \ . \ . \ .$$

where $$g_{mn} = g_{nm} \qquad (5.68)$$

Likewise the potentials of the conductors can be expressed in terms of the currents leaving them by means of equations of the form

$$V_1 = r_{11}I_1 + r_{12}I_2 + r_{13}I_3 + \cdots$$
$$V_2 = r_{21}I_1 + r_{22}I_2 + r_{23}I_3 + \cdots \qquad (5.69)$$
$$V_3 = r_{31}I_1 + r_{32}I_2 + r_{33}I_3 + \cdots$$
$$. \ . \ . \ . \ . \ . \ . \ . \ . \ . \ . \ . \ . \ . \ . \ . \ . \ .$$

where $$r_{mn} = r_{nm} \qquad (5.70)$$

Equations (5.67) and (5.69) convey identical information in different forms. Equations (5.69) can be obtained by solving Eqs. (5.67) for V_1, V_2, . . . in terms of I_1, I_2, ... Likewise Eqs. (5.67) can be obtained from Eqs. (5.69) by solving the latter for I_1, I_2, . . . in terms of V_1, V_2, ... The g coefficients in Eqs. (5.67) are known as the coefficients of conductance of the system. The coefficients g_{11}, g_{22}, . . . in the main diagonal are known as the coefficients of self-conductance, while the remainder are known as the coefficients of mutual conductance. Equation (5.68) expresses the fact that the coefficients of mutual conductance are symmetrical with respect to the main diagonal. The r coefficients in Eq. (5.69) are known as the coefficients of resistance of the system. The coefficients r_{11}, r_{22}, . . . in the main diagonal are known as the coefficients of self-resistance and the remaining coefficients are known as the coefficients of mutual resistance. Equation (5.70) expresses the fact that the coefficients of mutual resistance are symmetrical with respect to the main diagonal.

Equations (5.67) are to be compared with Eqs. (3.4) to (3.6). Equations (5.69) are to be compared with Eqs. (3.13) to (3.15). The equations appearing in Chap. 3 are in fact simply the version of Eqs. (5.67) and (5.69) appropriate when the resistive material is restricted to a number of limited regions known as resistors. Alternatively one can divide up the region between the conductors contemplated in connection with Eqs. (5.67) and (5.69) by means of equipotential surfaces and tubes of flow into individual resistors connected in parallel and in series. The entire system of conductors together with the resistive material between them can thus be thought of as a network of resistors for which the conductors are the accessible terminals. Equations (5.67) to (5.70) for a system of conductors embedded in a resistive medium thus require no special proof but follow from what has already been said in Chap. 3 about networks of resistors.

From Eqs. (5.67) we see that the coefficient g_{mn} is numerically equal to the current supplied to conductor m when conductor n is at unit potential and all other conductors are at zero potential. Likewise from Eqs. (5.69) we see that the coefficient r_{mn} is numerically equal to the voltage of conductor m when unit current flows from conductor n to the conductor at infinity and no net current leaves or arrives at any other conductor.

Equation (5.68) states that the current supplied by conductor m when conductor n is at unit potential and all other conductors are at zero potential is the same as the current supplied by conductor n when conductor m is at unit potential and all other conductors are at zero potential. Likewise Eq. (5.70) states that the voltage on conductor m when unit current flows from conductor n to the conductor at infinity, no net currents being supplied by any other conductor, is the same as the voltage of conductor n when unit current flows from conductor m to the conductor at infinity, no net current being supplied by any other conductor. These statements constitute Green's reciprocal theorem for steady electric currents. This theorem can also be stated in the following form: For a given system of conductors embedded in resistive material let voltages V_1, V_2, . . . be applied to the conductors, and let the corresponding currents leaving the conductors be I_1, I_2, ... For the same system of conductors embedded in the same resistive material let potentials V'_1, V'_2, . . . be applied to the conductors, and let the corresponding currents provided by the conductors now be I'_1, I'_2, . . . respectively. Then Green's reciprocal theorem states that

$$V_1 I'_1 + V_2 I'_2 + \cdots = V'_1 I_1 + V'_2 I_2 + \cdots \qquad (5.71)$$

This equation can be established by substituting from Eqs. (5.67) into Eq. (5.71) for the currents in terms of the voltages and using Eq. (5.68). Alternatively it can be established by substituting from Eqs. (5.69) into Eq. (5.71) for the voltages in terms of the currents and using Eq. (5.70).

When the potentials of the conductors are V_1, V_2, . . . and the corresponding currents supplied by the conductors are I_1, I_2, . . . respectively, the power supplied to the resistive medium from the batteries maintaining the potentials of the conductors is

$$P = V_1 I_1 + V_2 I_2 + \cdots \qquad (5.72)$$

By substituting from Eqs. (5.67) into Eq. (5.72) for the currents in terms of the potentials, the power supplied to the resistive material can be expressed entirely in terms of the potentials of the conductors by means of the equation

$$\begin{aligned} P = g_{11} V_1{}^2 + g_{22} V_2{}^2 + \cdots \\ + 2g_{12} V_1 V_2 + \cdots \end{aligned} \qquad (5.73)$$

Likewise by substituting from Eqs. (5.69) into Eq. (5.72) for the voltages in terms of currents, the power supplied to the resistive material can be expressed entirely in terms of the currents leaving the conductors by means of the equation

$$\begin{aligned} P = r_{11} I_1{}^2 + r_{22} I_2{}^2 + \cdots \\ + 2r_{12} I_1 I_2 + \cdots \end{aligned} \qquad (5.74)$$

Equations (5.72) to (5.74) are simply a restatement of Eqs. (3.69), (3.71), and (3.73) for any system of perfect conductors embedded in resistive material.

5.10. The Electrolytic Tank. Let us suppose that a system of perfect conductors is embedded in a resistive medium of uniform conductivity σ, the whole being enclosed in a large enveloping conductor. In order that it may be convenient to move from point to point in the resistive medium let us suppose that this medium is a fluid, or electrolyte. We further suppose that the conductivity of the electrolyte is not too high, so that it is quite practicable to simulate "perfect" conductors by means of conductors made of metal. With an arrangement of this type it is feasible to explore the electric field in the electrolyte between the conductors in the following way: Use a small conductor, or "probe," that can be located anywhere within the electrolyte. By means of an insulated wire, connect this probe to the enveloping tank through a battery whose voltage V is adjustable. Now suppose that the various conductors of the system are maintained at known voltages, so that an electric field is produced in the electrolyte and current flows through the electrolyte. With the aid of the probe we can explore this field. The battery connected to the probe maintains the probe at potential V. Now move the probe about the electrolyte until no current is delivered by the battery maintaining the potential of the probe. The probe is then located at a point of that equipotential surface in the electrolyte for which the potential is V. If we now move the probe around in the electrolyte in such a way that the battery maintaining the potential of the probe continues to deliver no current, the probe then traces out the equipotential surface of potential V in the electrolyte. By allowing V to take in succession a series of values such as 1 volt, 2 volts, . . . the various equipotential surfaces in the electrolyte can be traced out. By drawing curves perpendicular to these equipotential surfaces we can then obtain the lines of force and the lines of flow. Such an arrangement is known as an electrolytic tank.

An electrolytic tank can be used to explore the electrostatic field of a system of conductors even when the medium between them is a pure dielectric. Consider a situation in which the medium surrounding a system of conductors is a dielectric of uniform capacitivity ϵ. We replace the dielectric by an electrolyte of uniform conductivity σ, placing the whole arrangement inside a large conducting tank that represents the conductor at infinity. If we now apply to the conductors in the tank the same potentials in which we were originally interested when the medium was a dielectric, the electrostatic field between the conductors is the same, and this can be explored by the probe.

Let us suppose in particular that the system of conductors under investigation is simply a pair of conductors forming a capacitor and that we are interested in ascertaining the capacitance of the capacitor when the medium between the conductors is a dielectric of uniform capacitivity ϵ. We can then proceed as follows: Make a model of the arrangement in the electrolytic tank, and let σ be the conductivity of the electrolyte. Instead of measuring the capacitance between the conductors, measure instead the conductance between the conductors. By dividing this conductance by σ and multiplying by ϵ we obtain the required capacitance of the capacitor. This is because the ratio of the capacitance between the conductors to the conductance between the conductors is simply equal to the ratio of the capacitivity of the medium to the conductivity of the medium.

It is possible in the same way to use an electrolytic tank to arrive at the coefficients of capacitance for a system of conductors, such as a multielectrode vacuum tube. We set up a model of the conductors in the electrolytic tank and measure the coefficients of conductance for the system of conductors. This we do by putting unit potential on one conductor and zero potential on the remaining conductors and then measuring the currents supplied to the various conductors. When this experiment has been repeated with the unit potential on each conductor in succession, all the coefficients of conductance for the system have been measured. We now divide these coefficients of conductance by the conductivity of the electrolyte and multiply by the capacitivity of the medium in which we were originally interested. We then have the coefficients of capacitance for the system of conductors.

An electrolytic tank is a particularly convenient arrangement for investigating the properties of transmission lines and vacuum tubes or any arrangement of long parallel conductors of uniform cross section. In this case we can use an insulating tank with an open top. The tank can be arranged horizontally and filled with electrolyte to a depth τ. Let us suppose that we are interested in studying the electric field of the twin-wire transmission line illustrated in Fig. 5.8. Two metal cylinders each of radius a and of length greater than τ are placed on the bottom of the tank with their axes vertical and at distance d apart. If a potential difference is maintained between the cylinders, an electric field is produced in the electrolyte that produces current from one cylinder to the other. This is the electric field that we wish to investigate, and the investigation can be carried out by the probe and battery technique. However, the probe can now be conveniently dipped into the surface of the electrolyte from above and moved about horizontally while tracing equipotential surfaces. It is frequently convenient to make the vertical walls of the tank, but not the base, conducting and to use the potential of this conductor as the zero of potential. The conductance of the twin-wire transmission line per unit length can be directly measured by measuring the conductance between the two cylinders and dividing by the depth τ of the electrolyte. If we are interested in the conductance per unit length of the twin-wire transmission line when embedded in a medium of conductivity other than that of the electrolyte, it is merely a matter of dividing by the conductivity of the electrolyte and multiplying by that of the desired medium in accordance with Eq. (5.64). Moreover, having measured the conductance per unit length of the transmission line in the electrolyte, we can deduce the capacitance per unit length of the transmission line by dividing by the conductivity of the electrolyte and multiplying by the capacitivity of the desired medium surrounding the transmission line in accordance with Eqs. (5.64) and (5.66).

The electrolytic tank for investigating transmission-line and vacuum-tube problems can, if desired, be replaced by a flat resistive sheet of conductivity σ and thickness τ. The cylinders representing the conductors are then put on the sheets with the flat ends of the cylinders making good metallic contact with the sheet. It is necessary for the conductivity of the material of which the sheet is constructed to be small compared with that of the cylinders representing the conductors. Alternatively the thickness τ of the sheet can be made extremely small. In either case it is necessary for the cylinders representing the conductors to function effectively as perfect conductors.

SUMMARIZING EXERCISES

5.1. A cylindrical piece of material of conductivity σ and capacitivity ϵ has cross-sectional area S and length s. Perfectly conducting electrodes of area S are attached to the flat ends, and a voltage is maintained between the electrodes. Prove that, if a steady current I flows from one electrode to the other, then the charges on the electrodes are equal to $\pm (\epsilon/\sigma)I$.

5.2. A perfectly conducting sphere of radius a is immersed in a fluid of uniform conductivity σ that fills a large perfectly conducting tank. The tank may be idealized as an infinite sphere. A voltage is maintained between the sphere of radius a and the tank at infinity, so that there is produced a steady radial current I from the sphere to the tank. At a distance r ($>a$) from the center of the sphere calculate in terms of σ, I, and r (a) the electric current density, (b) the electric field strength, and (c) the electric potential, taking the potential of the tank as zero.

5.3. The space between two concentric perfectly conducting spheres has internal radius a and external radius b and is filled with a homogeneous medium of conductivity σ. Calculate the conductance between the two spheres.

5.4. A long straight perfectly conducting wire of radius a is immersed in fluid of uniform conductivity σ that fills a large perfectly conducting tank. The wire may be taken as infinitely long and the tank may be idealized as a circular cylinder of infinite radius coaxial with the wire. A current I per unit length flows radially and symmetrically from the wire to the tank. At a perpendicular distance r ($>a$) from the axis of the wire, calculate the electric current density, the electric field strength, and the electric potential. Explain why the potential cannot be taken to be zero at infinity.

5.5. A coaxial transmission line has perfectly conducting inner and outer conductors. The space between these conductors has inner radius a and outer radius b and is filled with a homogeneous medium of conductivity σ. Calculate the leakage conductance per unit length between the inner and outer conductors.

5.6. The space between two perfectly conducting surfaces is filled with a homogeneous medium of capacitivity ϵ and conductivity σ. Explain why the ratio of the capacitance between the surfaces to the conductance between the surfaces is equal to ϵ/σ. A twin-wire transmission line is embedded in a homogeneous medium of capacitivity ϵ and conductivity σ. From the expression for the capacitance per unit length of the transmission line deduce an expression for the leakage conductance per unit length of the transmission line.

5.7. Explain what is meant by an electrolytic tank and outline its principles of operation.

CHAPTER 6

THE DIODE VACUUM TUBE

6.1. Introduction. In our study of electrostatics we saw that the relation between the voltages on the nodes of a network of capacitors and the charges on these nodes is expressed by means of what mathematicians call linear equations. Likewise in our study of steady electric currents we have seen that the relation between the voltages of the nodes of a network of resistors and the currents supplied to these nodes is also expressed by means of linear equations. The linear equations in electrostatics were a development from the fact that the charges on the plates of a capacitor are proportional to the voltage between the plates. Likewise the linear equations encountered in the study of resistive networks arose from the fact that the current through a resistor is proportional to the voltage across it. The fact that many of the fundamental laws of electricity are expressible mathematically by means of linear equations greatly simplifies the subject and has a dominant influence on the mathematical procedures employed. However, not all devices used in electrical science behave in a linear manner. Devices that do not behave in a linear manner are more difficult to understand and analyze. However, tremendous advantages accrue from understanding devices that behave in a nonlinear manner, because such devices permit the attainment of objectives that are beyond reach with devices that behave in a purely linear manner. For example, with a nonlinear device it is possible to convert alternating current into direct current.

In discussing the linear equations involved in networks of capacitors and networks of resistors it was pointed out that the linearity of the equations was the mathematical expression of a physical fact known as the principle of superposition. It follows that, for nonlinear devices, the principle of superposition does not apply. Consider a nonlinear device in which the application of a voltage V results in a current I given by the equation

$$I = \alpha V^2 \tag{6.1}$$

If to this device we apply a voltage V_1, the resulting current is

$$I_1 = \alpha V_1^2 \tag{6.2}$$

If on the other hand we apply to the device a voltage V_2, then the resulting current is

$$I_2 = \alpha V_2{}^2 \qquad (6.3)$$

Now let us apply to the device a voltage

$$V_1 + V_2 \qquad (6.4)$$

From Eq. (6.1) the resulting current is

$$I = \alpha(V_1 + V_2)^2 \qquad (6.5)$$

This equation can be rewritten as

$$I = \alpha(V_1{}^2 + 2V_1V_2 + V_2{}^2) \qquad (6.6)$$

and on substitution from Eqs. (6.2) and (6.3) we obtain

$$I = I_1 + I_2 + 2\alpha V_1 V_2 \qquad (6.7)$$

We thus see that, when the voltage applied to the nonlinear device is equal to expression (6.4), the current through the device is given by Eq. (6.7). The addition of voltages across the device does not therefore result simply in the addition of the corresponding currents through the device. There is an extra current equal to $2\alpha V_1 V_2$. The presence of this term in Eq. (6.7) implies what is described as mixing between the two applied voltages V_1 and V_2.

There are certain semiconducting materials that possess the nonlinear properties under discussion. If such a semiconductor is provided with two electrodes so as to form a nonlinear resistor, the device is known as a rectifier. The current through the device is not proportional to the voltage across it, so that Ohm's law does not apply. This is sometimes described by saying that the resistance or conductance appearing in Ohm's law varies with the voltage applied to the device. A rectifier is normally such that reversal of the sign of the voltage across it alters drastically the magnitude of the current through it. A rectifier is sometimes idealized by saying that it passes current in one direction but not in the other. It is easy to see that an alternating voltage applied across the terminals of such a rectifier results in unidirectional current through the rectifier.

A transistor is a device in which semiconducting material that behaves in a nonlinear manner is used as the medium between three or more conducting electrodes. Let the electrodes be numbered 0, 1, and 2, and let electrode 0 be maintained at zero potential. If the semiconducting material behaved in a linear way, the relation between the potentials of the electrodes and the currents supplied to them would be described by a system of coefficients of conductance and resistance as explained in Sec. 5.9.

When the device acts as a transistor, however, the semiconducting material behaves in a nonlinear manner, and this can be described by saying that the coefficients of conductance and resistance of the system depend upon the voltages applied to the electrodes.

Another well-known example of a nonlinear electrical device is the thermionic vacuum tube. It is this nonlinear device that we shall study in this chapter and the next.

6.2. Thermionic Emission of Electrons. Suppose that we have an evacuated space contained within a glass or metal envelope. Let there exist within the evacuated space a parallel-plate capacitor from whose plates there run insulated metal wires to the region outside. By means of these wires let the capacitor be charged. Let us suppose that the plates are supported within the evacuated space by means of ideal insulators. One might then suppose that there could be no leakage of electrons from the negative plate to the positive plate and that the capacitor would hold its charge indefinitely. Actually this is not true.

The free electrons within the metal plates forming the capacitor have a random motion known as their thermic motion. The mean speed involved in this motion is measured by the temperature of the plates. The potential energy of free electrons within the metal is less than the potential energy of an electron outside the metal. Thus, as a free electron approaches the boundary of the metal from within, it encounters a steep rise of potential energy amounting to a cliff. Most free electrons within the metal do not possess sufficient energy to climb the cliff and escape from the metal. They consequently bounce back from the boundary of the metal and execute a random motion within the confines of the metal. However, a few free electrons within the metal do acquire sufficient energy to surmount the cliff of potential energy at the boundary of the metal. These electrons are thus able to emerge from the metal, although they do so with a greatly reduced velocity. Let us consider what happens to electrons that emerge from the positive plate of a capacitor mounted in a vacuum tube. These electrons find themselves in an electric field directed toward the negative plate of the capacitor. The electrons, being negatively charged, are thus subject to a force which returns them to the positive plate. Now let us consider what happens to electrons that manage to emerge from the negative plate of the capacitor. These electrons are subject to a force which pulls them across to the positive plate. Thus there are always a few electrons that manage to emerge from the negative plate of the capacitor and are attracted across to the positive plate through the intervening vacuum. In time these electrons will discharge the capacitor unless the voltage between the plates is maintained by a battery. In the latter case a small current flows from one plate of the capacitor to the other in spite of the intervening vacuum.

The process whereby the free electrons within a metal can escape from the metal is known as thermionic emission of electrons from the metal. The resulting current between the plates of a charged capacitor in a vacuum is known as a thermionic current.

Let us inquire how thermionic emission and thermionic current can be increased in importance. To increase the number of electrons escaping from the metal it is necessary to increase the speed with which free electrons within the metal execute random motions. This corresponds to increasing the temperature of the metal. Thermionic emission from a metal is quite small at room temperatures but becomes large if the metal is made red hot. Thus to increase the thermionic current between the plates of a capacitor in a vacuum tube, the procedure is to provide the negative plate with a heater, as indicated in Fig. 6.1. The heater increases the thermic velocity of free electrons within the negative plate so that they escape from the negative plate in substantial numbers and

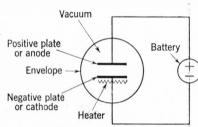

FIG. 6.1. A diode vacuum tube.

are attracted across to the positive plate through the intervening vacuum.

A capacitor constructed in an evacuated space and having one plate fitted with a heater is known as a diode vacuum tube. The plate to which the heat is applied is capable of substantial thermionic emission of electrons and is known as the cathode. The other plate is known as the anode, or simply as "the plate." The heater built into the cathode takes the form of an electrical heater. In some cases the heater current is passed directly through the cathode in order to heat it. The cathode is usually coated with a substance that improves its thermionic emission and permits operation of the cathode at a lower temperature. In the diode shown in Fig. 6.1 a parallel-plate capacitor has been indicated, and this is a convenient arrangement in studying the behavior of a vacuum tube. In practice, however, it is more common to use a cylindrical capacitor in which the anode surrounds the cathode.

A diode vacuum tube can be converted into a capacitor simply by switching off the heater. It is true that, even with the heater switched off, there is some thermionic emission from the cathode. However, for many practical purposes the thermionic emission from a cold cathode may be considered negligible.

Because the convention concerning the sign of electric charge has been chosen so as to make the charge of the electron negative, an electric current in one direction round an electric circuit implies an electronic current in the reverse direction. A vacuum tube is no exception to this. The

electronic current from the cathode to the anode has to be described as an
electric current from the anode to the cathode.   While this is an unnecessary inconvenience associated with the historical development of electrical science, it is an inconvenience that must in practice be tolerated.   In
recognition of this fact it will now be convenient to denote the charge on
an electron by $-e$ so that the numerical value of e is positive.   The magnitude of the negative charge on an electron is

$$e = 1.60 \times 10^{-19} \text{ coulomb} \qquad (6.8)$$

and the mass of an electron is

$$m = 9.1 \times 10^{-31} \text{ kg} \qquad (6.9)$$

The ratio of the magnitude of the negative charge on an electron to the
mass of an electron is

$$\frac{e}{m} = 1.76 \times 10^{11} \text{ coulombs/kg} \qquad (6.10)$$

6.3. An Electron Gun.   Suppose that a diode vacuum tube is mounted
as shown in Fig. 6.2 and that a hole is cut in the anode.   Taking the
potential of the cathode as zero, let the anode be maintained at a positive
potential V.   Electrons leaving the cathode are accelerated in the electric
field of the capacitor formed by the
cathode and the anode.   Let u_a be
the velocity with which electrons
arrive at the anode.   Some of these
electrons pass through the hole in
the anode and form a beam of electrons moving with uniform velocity
u_a.   The electrons in the beam tend

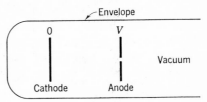

FIG. 6.2. An electron gun.

to repel each other, and so the beam of electrons would diverge.   This
effect can, however, be counteracted by means of focusing devices that
will not be described.

Let us calculate the velocity of the electrons in the beam.   This is the
same as the velocity u_a with which electrons arrive at the anode from the
cathode.   Electrons are emitted from the cathode with a small velocity
that may be taken as zero in simple calculations.   An electron is therefore
to be thought of as leaving the cathode with negligible kinetic energy, but
by the time it arrives at the anode it has acquired a kinetic energy $\frac{1}{2}mu_a^2$.
This gain in kinetic energy has taken place at the expense of potential
energy.   Since electric potential is potential energy per unit charge, a
charge Q going from the cathode to the anode would gain potential energy
of amount QV.   For an electron of charge $-e$ there is a loss of potential
energy in going from the cathode to the anode of amount eV.   It is this

loss of potential energy that appears as a gain $\frac{1}{2}mu_a{}^2$ in kinetic energy. Thus the velocity u_a with which an electron reaches the anode is given by the energy equation

$$\frac{1}{2}mu_a{}^2 = eV \qquad (6.11)$$

By solving this equation for u_a we derive for the velocity of the electrons in the beam

$$u_a = \left(\frac{2eV}{m}\right)^{\frac{1}{2}} \qquad (6.12)$$

and on substituting the numerical value of e/m from Eq. (6.10), this becomes

$$u_a = 5.9 \times 10^5 V^{\frac{1}{2}} \qquad (6.13)$$

If into this equation we substitute the anode potential V in volts, we derive the beam velocity u_a in meters per second.

The relations among (1) the anode voltage V, (2) the beam velocity u_a given by Eq. (6.12), and (3) the kinetic energy $\frac{1}{2}mu_a{}^2$ of an electron in the beam given by Eq. (6.11) are shown in Table 6.1. From the

TABLE 6.1. SPEED AND ENERGY OF ELECTRONS

Anode potential V, volts	Beam velocity u_a, m/sec	Electron energy, $\frac{1}{2}mu_a{}^2$, joules
1	5.9×10^5	1.6×10^{-19}
10	1.9×10^6	1.6×10^{-18}
10^2	5.9×10^6	1.6×10^{-17}
10^3	1.9×10^7	1.6×10^{-16}
10^4	5.9×10^7	1.6×10^{-15}

middle column in the table we see that an electron that has been accelerated through 10,000 volts has a velocity that is an appreciable fraction of the velocity of light (3×10^8 m/sec). For accelerating potentials in excess of 10,000 volts it is necessary to allow for the variation of the mass of an electron with its velocity in accordance with the theory of relativity. For accelerating potentials less than 10,000 volts, however, the simple calculation that we have made is usually adequate.

It is common practice to specify the velocities and energies of electrons in terms of the voltage through which they would have to be accelerated from rest in order to acquire the given velocity or energy. Thus instead of saying that an electron has a velocity of 1.9×10^7 m/sec or that it has a kinetic energy of 1.6×10^{-16} joule, it is more usual to say that it is a 1,000-volt electron. Indeed, the energies of particles are frequently expressed in terms of a unit known as the electron-volt. This is the kinetic energy acquired by an electron in being accelerated from rest through a

potential difference of one volt.   From Table 6.1 we see that an electron-
volt is an energy of 1.6×10^{-19} joule.

6.4. The Cathode-ray Oscilloscope.   A cathode-ray oscilloscope consists of an evacuated envelope in which an electron gun shoots a beam of
electrons at a fluorescent screen as shown in Fig. 6.3.   At the point where
the beam of electrons hits the fluorescent screen, a spot of light is produced that is visible from outside the envelope.   On its way from the gun
to the screen the beam passes between the plates of a parallel-plate capacitor as shown in Fig. 6.3.   The plates of this capacitor are known as the
deflecting plates.   By applying a voltage between the two deflecting

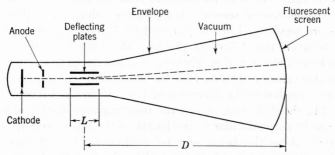

FIG. 6.3. Cathode-ray oscilloscope with electrostatic deflection.

plates, an electric field is produced that accelerates electrons approximately perpendicular to their direction of motion in the beam.   This
deflects the beam and moves the spot of light away from the center of the
fluorescent screen.   The spot of light on the screen can be moved up and
down by altering the voltage applied between the deflecting plates.
When the beam is passed through two pairs of deflecting plates, one pair
arranged horizontally and the other pair arranged vertically, the spot of
light on the screen can be deflected both vertically and horizontally.

The cathode-ray oscilloscope is widely known as a result of its use in
television receivers.   In this application voltages are applied to the
deflecting plates so as to make the spot scan the screen in much the same
way as the eye scans type on a printed page.   As the spot scans, the number of electrons hitting the screen per unit time is varied in such a way as
to produce the picture.   However, the scientific importance of the
cathode-ray oscilloscope rests rather upon its use as a measuring instrument.   Imagine that we have two quantities that vary with time, and
suppose that we wish to plot one quantity as ordinate against the other as
abscissa.   We convert the two functions of time into voltages that we
apply to the two pairs of perpendicularly situated deflecting plates, and
the spot on the screen then traces the required curve.   Moreover, the
mass of the electron beam is so small that it will respond in a microsecond

just as easily as it will in a second.   If the curve is traced on the screen extremely quickly, it is impossible for the eye to follow the curve.   This difficulty can be overcome by arranging for the curve to be continuously repeated.   Persistence of vision then results in the complete curve appearing on the screen.   The cathode-ray oscilloscope is one of the most widely used indicating devices in circumstances where quick response is essential.

The behavior of a cathode-ray oscilloscope can be analyzed in the following way: Let s be the distance between the deflecting plates illustrated in Fig. 6.3.   Let L be the length of the deflecting plates measured along the beam.   Let D be the distance from the center of the deflecting plates to the fluorescent screen.   Let V be the voltage through which the electrons are accelerated in the gun, and let V_d be the deflection voltage applied between the deflecting plates.   The velocity with which the electrons leave the gun is then given by Eq. (6.12).   The electrons would maintain this velocity until they hit the fluorescent screen if no deflection voltage were applied to the deflecting plates.   Even if a deflection voltage is applied to the deflecting plates, the resulting acceleration of the electrons is nearly perpendicular to the length of the beam, and acceleration of electrons along the beam can be neglected.   It will therefore be assumed that the velocity of electrons along the beam is always given by Eq. (6.12).

Let us now consider the sideways acceleration given to electrons by the deflecting plates.   Neglecting fringing, the electric field strength between the deflecting plates is V_d/s, and consequently the force acting on an electron in a direction perpendicular to the deflecting plates is eV_d/s.   The deflecting acceleration of an electron is therefore

$$\frac{eV_d}{ms} \tag{6.14}$$

An electron in the beam is subject to the deflecting acceleration given by expression (6.14) while it is passing through the electric field between the deflecting plates.   The electron passes between the deflecting plates at a speed u_a and is in the field over a length L, provided that fringing is neglected.   The time during which the electron in the beam is subject to the deflecting acceleration given by expression (6.14) is therefore

$$\frac{L}{u_a} \tag{6.15}$$

The deflection velocity acquired by an electron when it emerges from the deflecting field is the product of the rate of increase of velocity given by expression (6.14) with the time given by expression (6.15).   The deflection velocity on leaving the space between the deflecting plates is therefore

$$v = \frac{eV_d}{ms} \frac{L}{u_a} \qquad (6.16)$$

On emerging from the region between the deflecting plates an electron in the beam therefore has a velocity u_a toward the screen given by Eq. (6.12) and a velocity in the perpendicular direction given by Eq. (6.16).

In unit time the ratio of the distance by which the electron has been deflected to the distance it has moved from the deflecting plates toward the screen is v/u_a, and consequently the total deflection of the electron when it has traversed the distance D to the screen is approximately $(v/u_a)D$. Using the expression (6.16) for v, the deflection of the spot on the screen is

$$\frac{v}{u_a}D = \frac{eV_d}{ms} \frac{LD}{u_a{}^2} \qquad (6.17)$$

On substituting for u_a from Eq. (6.12), this expression becomes

$$\frac{eV_dLD}{ms} \frac{m}{2eV} \qquad (6.18)$$

We notice that the ratio e/m cancels out and that the deflection of the spot on the screen evaluates to

$$\frac{LD}{2s} \frac{V_d}{V} \qquad (6.19)$$

We see that the deflection of the spot on the screen is directly proportional to the deflection voltage V_d applied between the deflecting plates.

The various approximations used in deriving expression (6.19) for the deflection of the spot on the screen are satisfactory provided that the separation s between the deflecting plates is small compared with their linear dimensions and provided that the deflection of the spot is small compared with the distance D of the screen from the deflecting plates. The distance D should be measured from the center of the deflecting plates, where the straight lines coinciding with the rectilinear sections of the deflected beam intersect.

Suppose that the deflecting voltage V_d is 1 volt, the voltage of the gun is 1,000 volts, the length L of the deflecting plates is 3 cm (3×10^{-2} m), the separation s between the deflecting plates is 1 cm (10^{-2} m), and the distance D from the deflecting plates to the screen is 30 cm (3×10^{-1} m). By substituting these values into the expression (6.19) we deduce that the deflection of the spot is 4.5×10^{-4} m or 0.45 mm. Since the deflection of the spot is proportional to the deflection voltage V_d, we can say that the deflection of the spot per unit deflection voltage is 0.45 mm/volt.   If the deflection voltage were 100 volts, the deflection of the spot on the screen would be 4.5 cm.

6.5. The Diode Vacuum Tube.   For the diode vacuum tube illustrated in Fig. 6.1 let us take the potential of the cathode as zero, and let us suppose that the anode is maintained at a fixed potential V.   As a result a steady current I flows through the tube.   We are interested in calculating the relation between the voltage V applied between the anode and the cathode and the resulting steady current I through the tube.

The calculation is extremely easy if the potential of the anode is negative.   In this case the potential of the anode is less than that of the cathode, and it is the anode that is the negatively charged electrode.   Electrons made available at the heated cathode are therefore repelled back into the cathode by the negative charge on the anode, and there is no current through the tube.   We thus have

$$I = 0 \qquad \text{if } V < 0 \qquad\qquad (6.20)$$

If the voltage V of the anode is positive with respect to the cathode, then current does flow through the tube and a calculation is required. The electronic current leaving the cathode is composed of those free electrons within the cathode that have a thermic velocity sufficient for them to mount the cliff of potential energy existing at the surface of the cathode.   The higher the temperature of the cathode, the more free electrons there are with sufficient thermic velocity to escape from the cathode.   It might be supposed therefore that the electronic current leaving the cathode is a function of the temperature of the cathode.   The correct statement is that the maximum electronic current that can leave the cathode is controlled by the temperature T of the cathode.   Let this current be I_T.   In any particular case the electronic current leaving the cathode will be less than I_T.   A simple example of this occurs when the potential of the anode is negative with respect to the cathode.   We have already seen that in this case no electronic current flows from the cathode to the anode.   Electrons emitted by the cathode are repelled back to the cathode by the negative charge on the anode.   Even when the potential of the anode is positive with respect to the cathode, so that there is a current flowing through the tube, this current is less than I_T.   The reason for this is that an electron made available at the cathode is not simply subject to a force of attraction from the positive charge on the anode; it is also subject to a force of repulsion from the electrons in flight from the cathode to the anode.   Both of these forces have to be taken into account in assessing the ease with which electrons can leave the cathode. This results in the current I through the tube being less than I_T, although in extreme cases I may be very nearly equal to I_T.

The electrons in flight from the cathode to the anode form what is known as a space charge between the cathode and the anode. Consider a unit of volume at a point between the cathode and the anode at distance x from the cathode. Electrons are continually entering this unit volume from the cathode and departing to the anode. Suppose that, on the average, there are N electrons in the unit volume. Then N is what is known as the electron density at distance x from the cathode. Each electron within the unit volume at a particular instant carries the charge $-e$, and consequently the electric charge within the unit volume on the average is $-Ne$. This is known as the space-charge density at distance x from the cathode. Thus, if $-\rho$ is the space charge per unit volume at distance x from the cathode, then

$$\rho = Ne \qquad (6.21)$$

The velocity with which electrons are emitted from the cathode is small compared with that attained before reaching the anode, and it will simplify our calculations to assume that the velocity of electrons at the cathode is zero. Electrons are therefore pictured as leaving the cathode with zero velocity and as being accelerated until they reach the anode. This results in an electron density N and a density ρ of negative space charge that is high at the surface of the cathode and decreases as we move across to the anode. Electrons close to the cathode are moving slowly and are bunched together, but by the time they approach the anode they are moving fast and are well separated. Thus both N and ρ in Eq. (6.21) depend upon the distance x from the cathode and decrease as x increases from zero to the separation s between cathode and anode.

We thus have a situation in which the velocity of electrons increases as we move from the cathode to the anode while the density of negative space charge decreases. However, the product of these two quantities is in fact independent of the distance x from the cathode and is a measure of the current through the tube. The charge arriving at the anode between a time t and a slightly later time $t + dt$ is the charge which, at time t, is within a distance $u_a\,dt$ of the anode, where u_a is the velocity with which electrons arrive at the anode. Hence, the negative charge arriving at unit area of the anode between t and $t + dt$ is $\rho_a u_a\,dt$, where ρ_a is the density of negative space charge close to the anode. Negative charge is therefore arriving at the anode at the rate $\rho_a u_a$ per unit area per unit time. If S is the area of the anode, the current through the tube is $\rho_a u_a S$. This argument can be applied at any plane between the cathode and the anode at distance x from the cathode. If at this distance from the cathode the negative space-charge density is ρ and the velocity of electrons toward the anode is u, then negative charge is crossing unit area of this plane at the rate ρu per unit time. Since the current is distributed over an area S of this plane, the current through the tube is

$$I = \rho u S \qquad (6.22)$$

As we move across the tube from the cathode to the anode, the velocity u of electrons increases and the density ρ of negative space charge decreases; but the product ρu remains constant in accordance with Eq. (6.22) and is a measure of the current through the tube.

This situation may be compared with one in which automobiles arrive at a stop sign in a steady procession and then accelerate from rest along a

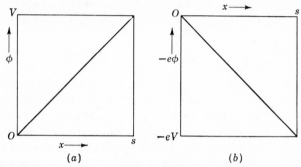

FIG. 6.4. Illustrating for no space charge (a) the variation of electric potential ϕ between the cathode and the anode and (b) the variation of the potential energy $-e\phi$ of an electron between the cathode and the anode.

highway. Let us suppose that each car is accelerated in the same way and that no speed limit is involved. Then the car density on the highway is large near the stop sign and decreases as we move away from the stop sign. As we move down the highway from the stop sign, the velocities of cars increase but the number per unit length of highway decreases. The product of the car density and the velocity is, however, the same at all points of the highway and is equal to the number of cars leaving the stop sign per unit time.

If there were no space charge between the cathode and the anode, the electric field would be uniform, provided that fringing is neglected. The electric potential ϕ would therefore rise from zero at the cathode to V at the anode as shown in Fig. 6.4a. The corresponding variation of the potential energy of an electron between the cathode and the anode is shown in Fig. 6.4b. In going from the cathode to the anode the potential energy of an electron drops by an amount eV. If the electron leaves the cathode with negligible velocity, the velocity u_a with which it arrives at the anode is given by the energy equation

$$\tfrac{1}{2}mu_a{}^2 = eV \qquad (6.23)$$

When the electron has reached a distance x from the cathode where the electric potential is ϕ, the velocity u of the electron toward the anode is given in the same way by the equation

$$\tfrac{1}{2}mu^2 = e\phi \tag{6.24}$$

We can describe this situation by saying that a single electron made available at the cathode with negligible velocity runs down the uniform potential-energy slope illustrated in Fig. 6.4b, acquiring a velocity u given by Eq. (6.24) at a point where the electric potential is ϕ and the velocity u_a given by Eq. (6.23) when it arrives at the anode.

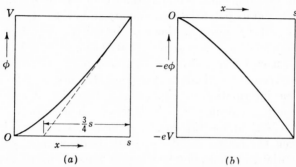

(a)   (b)

FIG. 6.5. Illustrating in the presence of space charge (a) the variation of electric potential between the cathode and anode and (b) the variation of the potential energy of an electron between the cathode and the anode. (Compare Fig. 6.4.)

When there is a continuous stream of electrons leaving the cathode, a negative space charge is formed between the cathode and the anode as already described. The distribution of electric potential ϕ between the cathode and the anode shown in Fig. 6.4a is then modified as shown in Fig. 6.5a. Likewise the distribution of the potential energy of an electron between the cathode and the anode shown in Fig. 6.4b is modified as shown in Fig. 6.5b. Electric field strength being the downward gradient of electric potential, a comparison of Figs. 6.4a and 6.5a shows that the effect of space charge is to reduce the magnitude of the electric field strength near the cathode. This is because the attraction toward the positive charge on the anode experienced by an electron near the cathode is partially balanced by the repulsion it experiences from the negative space charge. Figure 6.5a is drawn so as to show no gradient of potential at the cathode, and this implies a zero electric field strength at the cathode. When the anode potential is first applied to the tube, there is no space charge and the distribution of potential across the tube is as shown in Fig. 6.4a. As electrons leave the cathode, the negative space charge is built up, and consequently the electric field at the cathode is reduced. The space charge continues to build up until the electric field at the cathode has been reduced to zero. If the space charge were to build up beyond this point, the electric field at the surface of the cathode would be reversed in direction. This would cut off the electronic current leaving the cathode, reduce the space charge, and restore the electric field at the surface of the cathode to zero. Thus a steady state is reached in which the space charge between the cathode and the anode is so arranged that the gradient of potential at the surface of the cathode is zero as shown in Fig. 6.5a. In these circumstances the variation of the potential energy of an electron between the cathode and the anode is as shown in Fig. 6.5b. An electron made available at the cathode with negligible velocity finds itself in unstable equilibrium at the top of a potential hill. It runs down this hill, and its potential drops an amount eV by the time it arrives at the anode. Its velocity is then u_a given by Eq. (6.23). Thus the velocity with which the electron arrives at the anode is unaffected by the presence of space charge, being determined only by the difference in potential between the cathode and anode. Equation (6.23) conveys in fact the same information as Eq. (6.11). Likewise, when an electron reaches a distance x from the cathode where the electric potential is ϕ, its velocity u is given by Eq. (6.24). The velocity of an electron at a point between the cathode and the anode is determined solely by the electric potential ϕ at that point as in the absence of space charge. However, comparison of Fig. 6.4a with Fig. 6.5a shows that, in the presence of space charge, a given potential occurs at a greater distance from the cathode in the presence of space charge than it does in the absence of space charge.

We are faced with the problem of determining the shape of the curves shown in Fig. 6.5. Since in the presence of space charge the electric field

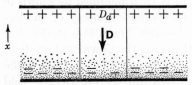

FIG. 6.6. Illustrating the fact that a diode vacuum tube carrying a steady current limited by space charge is a capacitor in which the negative charge associated with the cathode is in the form of space charge.

strength at the surface of the cathode is zero, it follows that the electric flux density at the surface of the cathode is zero and consequently that the cathode carries no surface charge. Thus a diode vacuum tube carrying a steady electric current is a capacitor with a positive charge on the surface of the anode and a negative charge which consists entirely of the space charge. The negative charge that is located on the surface of the cathode when the heater is switched off becomes distributed in front of the cathode in the form of space charge when the heater is switched on as indicated in Fig. 6.6. A capacitor of this type was not studied in electrostatics. We must now make a study of it if we are to arrive at the relation between the voltage across a diode vacuum tube and the current through it.

6.6. The Relation between Electric Potential and Density of Space Charge. Consider a parallel-plate capacitor, such as that shown in Fig. 6.6, in which there is space charge between the plates. Let ρ be the space charge per unit volume at distance x from the lower plate. Consider a tube of electric flux of unit cross-sectional area as indicated in Fig. 6.6. Let us suppose that, close to the upper plate of the capacitor, the electric flux density is D_a. Then the charge per unit area on the upper plate is D_a, and this is also the charge at the upper end of the tube of flux of unit cross section. Inside the metal of the upper plate the electric field is small and would vanish if this plate were a perfect conductor. Thus, as we cross the surface of the upper plate from within the conductor to the space between the conductors, the electric flux density changes discontinuously, and the net change is equal to the charge per unit area on the surface of the top plate. The tube of electric flux of unit cross section that starts on a charge D_a at the upper plate terminates on a charge $-D_a$. We are supposing, however, that this charge $-D_a$ is not concentrated on the lower plate but is distributed through the column as space charge. Thus, although there is a discontinuous rise of electric flux density as we enter the tube of flux at the top, there is no corresponding discontinuous decrease of electric flux density as we leave the tube at the bottom; instead there is a gradual decrease of electric flux density as we move down the tube through the space charge. Let us calculate the way in which this gradual decrease of electric flux density takes place in terms of the density of space charge. At distance x from the lower plate let the electric flux density be D and the density of space charge be ρ. Between the planes distant x and $x + dx$ from the lower plate there is within the tube of unit cross section a small volume dx and consequently a small amount of charge

$$\rho \, dx \qquad (6.25)$$

In crossing this amount of charge, the electric flux density in the tube decreases, and the decrease is equal to the amount of charge crossed. If the change in electric flux density as we move from the plane $x + dx$ to the plane x is denoted by dD, it follows that

$$dD = \rho \, dx \qquad (6.26)$$

In this equation either we can take the space charge density to be positive and the electric flux density to be measured in the direction x increasing, or we can consider ρ to be the negative space charge per unit volume and D to be the electric flux density directed toward the lower plate. It is the latter view that is appropriate if Fig. 6.6 represents a diode vacuum tube in which the lower plate is the cathode and the upper plate is the anode.   By dividing Eq. (6.26) by dx we arrive at the equation

$$\frac{dD}{dx} = \rho \qquad (6.27)$$

This equation shows that the rate at which the electric flux density changes as we move along the tube at any point is equal to the space charge per unit volume at that point.   If we know the way in which D varies with x, we can substitute this function into Eq. (6.27) and derive the corresponding variation with x in the space-charge density ρ.   Conversely, if we know the variation with x of the space-charge density ρ, we can substitute into Eq. (6.27) and, by means of an integration with respect to x, derive the variation with x of the electric flux density D.

As a special example of Eq. (6.27) we could consider a parallel-plate capacitor consisting of a diode vacuum tube with a cold cathode.   In these circumstances the space charge between the plates is negligible and ρ in Eq. (6.27) is zero.   The equation then states that there is no variation of the electric flux density D as we go across from one plate to the other.   We simply have the uniform field appropriate to a parallel-plate capacitor.

Equation (6.27) may be expressed in terms of the electric field strength E instead of in terms of the electric flux density D.   If ϵ_v is the vacuum capacitivity then

$$D = \epsilon_v E \qquad (6.28)$$

and substitution from this equation into Eq. (6.27) gives

$$\frac{dE}{dx} = \frac{1}{\epsilon_v} \rho \qquad (6.29)$$

If the variation with x of either E or ρ is known, the variation of the other quantity with x can be deduced from Eq. (6.29).

Equation (6.29) may, if desired, be expressed in terms of the electric potential ϕ.   Since the electric field strength is the downward gradient of the potential, we have

$$E = -\frac{d\phi}{dx} \qquad (6.30)$$

and substitution from this equation into Eq. (6.29) gives

$$\frac{d^2\phi}{dx^2} = -\frac{1}{\epsilon_v} \rho \qquad (6.31)$$

By integration of this equation we can calculate the variation with x of the electric potential ϕ if we know the variation with x of the space-charge density ρ.   Alternatively we can deduce from Eq. (6.31) the variation with x of the space-charge density ρ if we know the variation with x of the electric potential ϕ.

There are more elaborate versions of Eqs. (6.27), (6.29), and (6.31) appropriate to situations when the quantities ρ, D, E, and ϕ are not simply functions of one cartesian coordinate x. Equation (6.27) is the one-dimensional version of an equation known as Maxwell's electric divergence equation, while Eq. (6.31) is the one-dimensional version of an equation known as Poisson's equation.

6.7. The Current through a Diode When Limited by Space Charge. We are now in a position to calculate the relation between the voltage across a diode vacuum tube and the current through the tube. We are supposing that this current is limited by the fact that, as space charge builds up, the electric field at the surface of the cathode is reduced to zero, and a steady state then ensues.

Let the potential of the cathode be taken as zero, and let the potential of the anode be V. Let x denote the distance from the cathode. Let S be the area of the electrodes and s be the separation between them. At a point distant x from the cathode let the electric potential be ϕ. At the cathode, where $x = 0$, we have $\phi = 0$. At the anode, where $x = s$, we have $\phi = V$. At distance x from the cathode let the space-charge density be ρ. Both ϕ and ρ vary with x, and the relation between them is given by Eq. (6.31). At present, however, we know the variation with x of neither ϕ nor ρ. Hence Eq. (6.31) is a relation between two functions both of which are as yet unknown.

We have already discussed the fact that, as electrons leave the cathode, their speed increases and their number per unit volume decreases. At distance x from the cathode let u be the velocity of an electron. Then the product ρu remains constant as we move from the cathode to the anode. This fact is expressed in terms of the current I through the tube by means of Eq. (6.22). However, we do not yet know the variation with x of either the space-charge density ρ or the electronic velocity u. Hence Eq. (6.22) is another relation between functions of x neither of which we yet know.

The kinetic energy of an electron at distance x from the cathode is expressed in terms of the electric potential at distance x from the cathode by Eq. (6.24). This equation expresses the electronic velocity u at distance x from the cathode in terms of the electric potential ϕ at distance x from the cathode. This is yet another relation between two functions of x neither of which we yet know.

Taken together, Eqs. (6.31), (6.22), and (6.24) constitute three equations for the three functions of x that we do not know, namely, the electric potential ϕ, the space-charge density ρ, and the electronic velocity u. These three unknown functions can therefore be obtained by solving the following three equations relating them:

$$\frac{d^2\phi}{dx^2} = -\frac{1}{\epsilon_v}\rho \qquad (6.32)$$

$$I = \rho u S \qquad (6.33)$$

$$\tfrac{1}{2}mu^2 = e\phi \qquad (6.34)$$

By eliminating ρ and u from these three equations and solving for the electric potential ϕ as a function of x we shall ascertain, for a given current I through the tube, the distribution of electric potential between the cathode and the anode. In particular we shall ascertain, for a given current through the tube, the difference of potential between the anode and the cathode, and it is the relation between these two quantities that we seek. In making this calculation we shall need to use the fact that at the cathode

$$x = 0 \qquad \phi = 0 \qquad \frac{d\phi}{dx} = 0 \qquad (6.35)$$

The third of these equations expresses the fact that the steady state is reached in the tube when the space charge has built up to the point where the electric field at the surface of the cathode is zero.

Substitute for u from Eq. (6.34) into Eq. (6.33) and then for ρ from Eq. (6.33) into Eq. (6.32). In performing this calculation it is convenient to introduce a constant k defined by the equation

$$k^2 = \frac{1}{\epsilon_v}\left(\frac{m}{2e}\right)^{\frac{1}{2}}\frac{I}{S} \qquad (6.36)$$

The elimination of u and ρ from Eqs. (6.32) to (6.34) gives

$$\frac{d^2\phi}{dx^2} = k^2\phi^{-\frac{1}{2}} \qquad (6.37)$$

This equation can be solved for the electric potential ϕ as a function of distance x from the cathode. To do so we multiply Eq. (6.37) by $2d\phi/dx$, thereby obtaining

$$2\frac{d\phi}{dx}\frac{d^2\phi}{dx^2} = 2k^2\phi^{-\frac{1}{2}}\frac{d\phi}{dx}$$

By integrating this equation with respect to x we obtain

$$\left(\frac{d\phi}{dx}\right)^2 = 2k^2\frac{\phi^{\frac{1}{2}}}{\frac{1}{2}} + \text{constant} \qquad (6.38)$$

By putting $x = 0$ in this equation and using Eqs. (6.35) we find that the constant of integration is zero. Equation (6.38) can therefore be rewritten as

$$\phi^{-\frac{1}{4}} \frac{d\phi}{dx} = 2k \tag{6.39}$$

This equation can again be integrated with respect to x, giving

$$\frac{\phi^{\frac{3}{4}}}{\frac{3}{4}} = 2kx + \text{constant} \tag{6.40}$$

By putting $x = 0$ in this equation and using Eqs. (6.35) we again find that the constant of integration is zero. Hence Eq. (6.40) can be rewritten as

$$\phi = (\tfrac{3}{2})^{\frac{4}{3}} k^{\frac{4}{3}} x^{\frac{4}{3}} \tag{6.41}$$

By substituting for the constant k from Eq. (6.36) into Eq. (6.41) we obtain

$$\phi = \left(\frac{3}{2}\right)^{\frac{4}{3}} \left[\frac{1}{\epsilon_v} \left(\frac{m}{2e}\right)^{\frac{1}{2}} \frac{I}{S}\right]^{\frac{2}{3}} x^{\frac{4}{3}} \tag{6.42}$$

This equation gives the relation between the electric potential ϕ and the distance x from the cathode in terms of the current I through the tube, the area S of the electrodes, the charge and mass of an electron, and the vacuum capacitivity ϵ_v. It is Eq. (6.42) that leads to the curve shown in Fig. 6.5a.

From Eq. (6.42) we can derive the relation that we are seeking between the voltage across the diode and the current through it. At the anode we have

$$x = s \qquad \phi = V \tag{6.43}$$

Substituting these values of x and ϕ into Eq. (6.42) we derive

$$V = \left(\frac{3}{2}\right)^{\frac{4}{3}} \left[\frac{1}{\epsilon_v} \left(\frac{m}{2e}\right)^{\frac{1}{2}} \frac{I}{S}\right]^{\frac{2}{3}} s^{\frac{4}{3}} \tag{6.44}$$

This can be rewritten as

$$I = \alpha V^{\frac{3}{2}} \tag{6.45}$$

where

$$\alpha = \frac{4\sqrt{2}}{9} \epsilon_v \left(\frac{e}{m}\right)^{\frac{1}{2}} \frac{S}{s^2} \tag{6.46}$$

Thus, when the current through a diode vacuum tube is limited by space charge, the current is proportional to the $\frac{3}{2}$ power of the excess of the potential of the anode over that of the cathode. This is known as Child's law. The constant α in Eq. (6.45) is given by Eq. (6.46). It is proportional to the area of the electrodes and inversely proportional to the square of the distance s between them.

If we substitute into Eq. (6.46) the value for the ratio of the charge to the mass of an electron given by Eq. (6.10) and also the value

$$\epsilon_v = 8.854 \times 10^{-12} \text{ farad/m} \qquad (6.47)$$

for the vacuum capacitivity, we derive

$$\alpha = 2.33 \times 10^{-6} \frac{S}{s^2} \qquad (6.48)$$

In this equation it is supposed that the area S of the electrode is measured

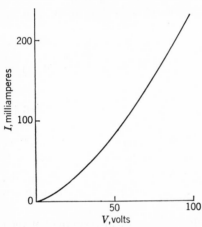

FIG. 6.7. Relation between the space-charge-limited current through a diode vacuum tube and the excess of anode potential over cathode potential, the electrodes having an area of 1 cm² with a separation of 1 mm.

in square meters and that the separation s between the electrodes is measured in meters. Furthermore, it is supposed that, when the value for α derived from Eq. (6.48) is substituted into Eq. (6.45), the potential difference V across the diode is measured in volts and the current I through the diode is measured in amperes. If S equals 1 cm² (10^{-4} m²) and s equals 1 mm (10^{-3} m), then the expression (6.48) for α evaluates to 2.33 × 10⁻⁴. If this numerical value for α is substituted into Eq. (6.45) and the current I through the diode is expressed in milliamperes, we obtain

$$I = 0.233 V^{3/2} \qquad (6.49)$$

provided that the anode potential V is still measured in volts. This relation between the current through a diode and the excess of the anode potential over the cathode potential is shown in Fig. 6.7.

The calculation that we have just made illustrates the power of mathematics to steer our process of thought in a difficult situation. Each of the Eqs. (6.32) to (6.34) describes a physical fact that is not too difficult to understand. As applied to the diode vacuum tube, however, it is somewhat disconcerting to find that each equation relates a pair of functions of x neither of which we know. Yet the three equations relate the three functions $\phi(x)$, $\rho(x)$, and $u(x)$ in such a way that all three functions can be determined. The process of thought necessary to determine them, however, is brought within the ability of the human mind to comprehend by application of the theory of differential equations.

6.8. The Electric Field and Space-charge Density in a Diode Whose Current Is Limited by Space Charge. To plot the variation of the electric potential ϕ with distance x from the cathode it is convenient to divide Eq. (6.42) by Eq. (6.44), thereby obtaining

$$\frac{\phi}{V} = \left(\frac{x}{s}\right)^{4\!/\!3} \tag{6.50}$$

It is this relation between ϕ and x that was plotted in Fig. 6.5a. The electric field at points between the cathode and the anode is obtained by taking the downward gradient of the potential ϕ. If E is the electric field strength toward the cathode at distance x from the cathode, then E is the derivative of ϕ with respect to x, and this can be calculated from Eq. (6.50). We obtain

$$E = \frac{d\phi}{dx} = \frac{4}{3}\frac{V}{s}\left(\frac{x}{s}\right)^{1\!/\!3} \tag{6.51}$$

By putting x equal to s in this equation we obtain the electric field strength at the anode, namely,

$$E_a = \frac{4}{3}\frac{V}{s} \tag{6.52}$$

In the absence of space charge the electric field strength between the cathode and the anode would be V/s. Equation (6.52) shows that the effect of space charge is to increase the electric field strength at the anode by a factor of $4\!/\!3$ (see Fig. 6.5a). By dividing Eq. (6.51) by Eq. (6.52) we obtain the

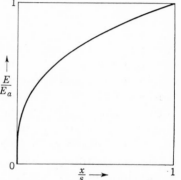

FIG. 6.8. Distribution of electric field strength E in a space-charge-limited diode vacuum tube with distance x from the cathode.

ratio of the electric field strength E at distance x from the cathode to the electric field strength at the anode. We obtain

$$\frac{E}{E_a} = \left(\frac{x}{s}\right)^{1\!/\!3} \tag{6.53}$$

and the resulting variation of electric field strength from the cathode to the anode is illustrated in Fig. 6.8. In the absence of space charge the electric field strength between the cathode and the anode would be uniform.

The electric flux density at the anode is obtained by multiplying the electric field strength E_a by the capacitivity ϵ_v. Since this electric flux density at the anode is the charge per unit area on the anode, the total charge on the anode is

$$Q = S\epsilon_v E_a \tag{6.54}$$

Substituting for E_a from Eq. (6.52) into Eq. (6.54) we derive

$$Q = \frac{4}{3} \frac{\epsilon_v S}{s} V \tag{6.55}$$

This charge is not only the total surface charge on the anode, but also equal and opposite to the negative charge, which takes the form of space charge between the cathode and the anode. Equation (6.55) shows that the ratio of the positive charge on the surface of the anode, or the total negative space charge between the cathode and the anode, to the excess of voltage of the anode over the cathode is

$$\frac{4}{3} \frac{\epsilon_v S}{s} \tag{6.56}$$

Now $\epsilon_v S/s$ is the capacitance between the cathode and the anode in the absence of space charge. Expression (6.56) therefore shows that the effect of space charge is to increase the positive charge on the surface of the anode by a factor $\frac{4}{3}$ as compared with the situation when the cathode is cold. This arises from the fact that, when the cathode is cold, the negative charge is on the surface of the anode, but when the cathode is hot, the negative charge associated with the cathode takes the form of space charge between the cathode and the anode. Consequently the distance by which the negative charge is separated from the positive charge on the surface of the anode is reduced and the capacitance correspondingly increased. We can write Eq. (6.55) in the form

$$Q = \frac{\epsilon_v S}{s'} V \tag{6.57}$$

where
$$s' = \tfrac{3}{4}s \tag{6.58}$$

Equations (6.57) and (6.58) show that the positive charge on the surface of the anode when the cathode is hot is the same as it would be if the cathode were cold and the distance of the cathode from the anode were reduced to $\frac{3}{4}s$. Thus, if a space-charge-limited diode vacuum tube is thought of as a capacitor, the distance between the positive and the negative charge is to be regarded as three-quarters of the distance between the anode and the cathode (see Fig. 6.5a).

Let us now calculate the way in which the density of space charge is distributed between the cathode and the anode. Since we have now calculated the way in which the electric potential ϕ depends upon distance x from the cathode, we can obtain the dependence of the space charge density ρ upon distance x from the cathode from Poisson's equation (6.32). The space-charge density is given by

$$\rho = -\epsilon_v \frac{d^2\phi}{dx^2} \tag{6.59}$$

where ϕ is given by Eq. (6.50) and $d\phi/dx$ is given by Eq. (6.51). By differentiating Eq. (6.51) with respect to x and substituting into Eq. (6.59) we obtain

$$\rho = -\frac{4}{9}\,\epsilon_v\,\frac{V}{s^2}\left(\frac{x}{s}\right)^{-\frac{2}{3}} \tag{6.60}$$

The total negative space charge between the cathode and the anode is $-Q$, where Q is given by Eq. (6.55). If this were distributed uniformly over the volume Ss between the cathode and the anode, the mean density of space charge would be

$$\bar{\rho} = -\frac{Q}{Ss} \tag{6.61}$$

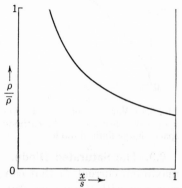

The ratio of the space-charge density at distance x from the cathode to the mean space-charge density is therefore obtained by dividing Eq. (6.60) by Eq. (6.61). We obtain, after using the expression (6.55) for Q,

$$\frac{\rho}{\bar{\rho}} = \frac{1}{3}\left(\frac{x}{s}\right)^{-\frac{2}{3}} \tag{6.62}$$

FIG. 6.9. The distribution with distance x from the cathode of the ratio of the space-charge density ρ to the mean space-charge density $\bar{\rho}$ in a space-charge-limited diode.

The distribution of the space-charge density with distance x from the cathode is therefore as shown in Fig. 6.9. The space-charge density is indefinitely large close to the cathode and decreases rapidly as we move toward the anode, where it has decreased to one-third of the mean value.

The ratio of the velocity u of electrons at distance x from the cathode to the velocity u_a with which they arrive at the anode is obtained by dividing Eq. (6.24) by (Eq. (6.23) and taking the square root. We obtain

$$\frac{u}{u_a} = \left(\frac{\phi}{V}\right)^{\frac{1}{2}} \tag{6.63}$$

where ϕ/V has already been calculated in Eq. (6.50). Substitution from Eq. (6.50) into Eq. (6.63) gives for the ratio of the velocity u of electrons at distance x from the cathode to the velocity u_a with which they arrive at the anode

$$\frac{u}{u_a} = \left(\frac{x}{s}\right)^{\frac{2}{3}} \tag{6.64}$$

The variation of electronic velocity with distance from the cathode is therefore as shown in Fig. 6.10. In the absence of space charge the curve would be a parabola. We verify from Eqs. (6.62) and (6.64) that the product of the electronic velocity u and the space-charge density ρ is independent of distance x from the cathode, as it should be in accordance with Eq. (6.33).

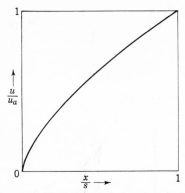

FIG. 6.10. Variation of electronic velocity u with distance s from the cathode in a space-charge-limited diode.

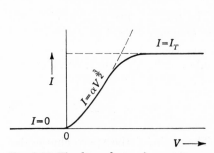

FIG. 6.11. The dependence of current upon voltage for a diode vacuum tube, illustrating the effect of saturation.

6.9. The Saturated Diode. It was stated in Sec. 6.5 that there is a maximum current I_T that can be delivered by a cathode. This current increases with the temperature T of the cathode. It depends upon the area of the cathode, the metal of which it is made, and the way in which its surface has been treated. The calculation made in the preceding section applies only if the current given by Eq. (6.45) (Child's law) is appreciably less than the current I_T. As the current I through the diode increases to the saturation current I_T, the variation of I with the voltage V applied between the anode and the cathode behaves as shown in Fig. 6.11. If the voltage V of the anode is negative with respect to the cathode, the current through the diode is negligible. When the voltage V of the anode becomes positive with respect to the cathode, the current I is at first limited by the fact that space charge builds up in the tube to the point where the electric field at the surface of the cathode is reduced practically to zero. Under these circumstances the relation between I and V is given by Eq. (6.45). As the voltage of the cathode is increased the current I given by Eq. (6.45) increases to the saturation current I_T, and the curve relating I to V flattens out as shown in Fig. 6.11. The point at which the curve departs appreciably from Child's law and levels off can be altered by altering the temperature T of the cathode and consequently the saturation current I_T. Values of I_T can vary from less than 10 to more than 100 ma.

A curve, such as that shown in Fig. 6.11, giving the relation between current and voltage for a vacuum tube is known as a characteristic curve of the tube, or simply as a "characteristic."

6.10. Linear Behavior of a Diode Vacuum Tube. The transition shown in Fig. 6.11 between the condition in which the current through the diode is limited by space charge ($I = \alpha V^{3/2}$) and that in which the current is limited by the temperature of the cathode ($I = I_T$) leads to a point of inflection on the curve relating current to voltage. In the neighborhood of this point of inflection the relation between current and voltage is approximately linear as shown by the sloping dashed line in Fig. 6.12. Let the tangent to the curve at the point of inflection intersect the voltage axis at $V = V_0$, and let the slope of this tangent be G. Then the relation between I and V represented by the tangent at the point of inflection is

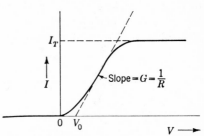

FIG. 6.12. Illustrating the approximately linear relation between current and voltage near the point of inflection on a diode characteristic curve.

$$I = G(V - V_0) \qquad (6.65)$$

There is an interval of voltage and an interval of current near the values appropriate to the point of inflection where the relation between the current I through the diode and the voltage V across it is given approximately by the linear relation (6.65). Equation (6.65) expresses the current I through the tube in terms of the voltage V across it over the linear sloping portion of the characteristic curve. By solving Eq. (6.65) for V in terms of I we can write this same relationship in the form

$$V = V_0 + RI \qquad (6.66)$$

where

$$R = \frac{1}{G} \qquad (6.67)$$

Over the limited ranges of voltage and current where Eqs. (6.65) and (6.66) apply, a diode vacuum tube can be represented by a Thévenin equivalent circuit as shown in Fig. 6.13 or by a Norton equivalent circuit as shown in Fig. 6.14. In Figs. 6.13 and 6.14 the point A denotes the anode terminal of the diode and the point C the cathode terminal. In Fig. 6.13 we have a generator of voltage V_0, which is the intercept on the voltage axis for the linear sloping portion of the characteristic curve of the diode as shown in Fig. 6.12. The generator of voltage V_0 in Fig. 6.13 is connected in series with a resistor whose resistance, in accordance with Eq. (6.67), is the reciprocal of the slope of the linear portion of the characteristic curve in Fig. 6.12. This same resistance is involved in the equivalent circuit shown in Fig. 6.14, where it is labeled by its conductance G. In Fig. 6.14 this resistor is connected in parallel with a generator that delivers a current GV_0. This is the negative of the value of I given by the intercept with the current axis in Fig. 6.12 of the dashed line that fits the sloping linear portion of the characteristic curve. If in either Fig. 6.13 or 6.14 a voltage V is applied between the anode terminal and the cathode terminal, the current I entering the anode terminal and

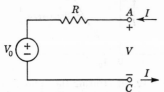

FIG. 6.13. The Thévenin equivalent circuit for a diode vacuum tube operating over the linear portion of its characteristic curve.

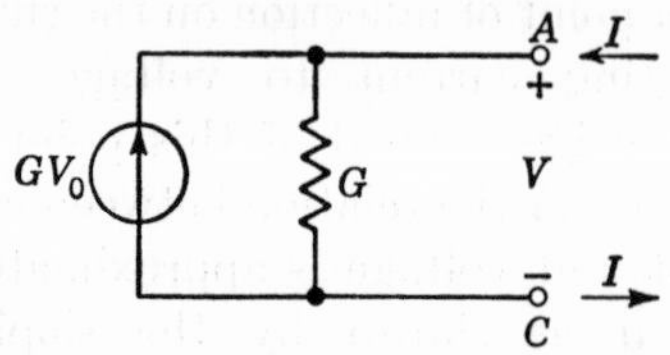

FIG. 6.14. The Norton equivalent circuit for a diode vacuum tube operating over the linear portion of its characteristic curve.

leaving the cathode terminal can easily be calculated and is given by Eqs. (6.66) and (6.65) respectively. This demonstrates that either of the equivalent circuits shown in Figs. 6.13 and 6.14 describes the behavior of the diode vacuum tube over the sloping linear portion of its characteristic curve. The sloping dashed line in Fig. 6.12 is related to the equivalent circuits shown in Figs. 6.13 and 6.14 in the same way that the sloping line in Fig. 4.7 is related to the Thévenin and Norton equivalent circuits shown in Figs. 4.5 and 4.6.

The numerical value of V_0 in Fig. 6.13 is usually a few volts. The numerical value of R is usually between 200 and 2,000 ohms. From Eq. (6.67) the corresponding numerical value for G in Fig. 6.14 is between 500 and 5,000 μmhos. Hence the current GV_0 is of the order of a few milliamperes. These values are determined for a particular diode by fitting a tangent to the characteristic curve at the point of inflection as shown in Fig. 6.12. These values are therefore determined by the saturation current I_T and by the value of the constant α appearing in Eq. (6.45) and given for a planar diode by Eq. (6.46). The values of V_0, R, and G are therefore determined by the geometry of the electrode structure, by the properties of the material of which the cathode is constructed, and by the temperature at which the cathode is operated.

It is particularly to be noticed that the equivalent circuits of a diode vacuum tube shown in Figs. 6.13 and 6.14 apply only when the voltage across the tube and the current through the tube are such as to correspond to the sloping linear portion of the characteristic of the tube shown in Fig. 6.12. The equivalent circuits shown in Figs. 6.13 and 6.14 do not describe the fact that, if the voltage V across the tube is increased sufficiently, the current I through the tube approaches the saturation value I_T. The equivalent circuits shown in Figs. 6.13 and 6.14 do not describe the fact that, if the voltage V of the anode is made negative with respect to the cathode, the current through the tube is negligible.

6.11. Use of Diode Vacuum Tubes. The most striking property of a diode vacuum tube is that, if a voltage is connected across the tube in such a way that the potential of the anode exceeds that of the cathode, there is a current through the tube, but if the voltage is connected across the tube in such a way that the potential of the cathode exceeds that of the anode, there is no current through the tube. This is illustrated in Fig. 6.15, where it is supposed that the current I is appreciably less than the saturation current I_T. This situation is fre-

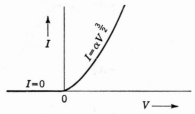

FIG. 6.15. The characteristic curve of a diode vacuum tube when the current is appreciably less than the saturation current.

quently described by saying that the tube conducts when the anode potential exceeds the cathode potential but does not conduct when the anode potential is less than the cathode potential.

Any device in which the relation between voltage and current is non-linear is capable of converting alternating current into direct current. Let us apply across the diode whose characteristic curve is as shown in Fig. 6.15 a voltage V which varies with time t in accordance with the equation

$$V = A \sin \frac{2\pi t}{T} \tag{6.68}$$

This is what is known as a sinusoidal, or alternating, voltage. A is known as the amplitude of the oscillation, and T is the periodic time. V oscillates between the extreme values A and $-A$ and back again in time T as shown in Fig. 6.16a. In the odd half periods the voltage of the anode is positive with respect to the cathode, while in the even half periods the voltage of the anode is negative with respect to the cathode. Using this voltage in relation to the characteristic curve shown in Fig. 6.15 we see that in the even half periods no current flows through the tube. In the odd half periods current flows through the tube as shown in Fig. 6.16b. Thus application to the diode of the alternating voltage shown in Fig. 6.16a yields the unidirectional current shown in Fig. 6.16b. If means are available to smooth out the unidirectional current shown in Fig. 6.16b, we would then obtain the steady current indicated by the dashed line.

A diode vacuum tube can also be used as a switch. Suppose that a voltage V is applied to the anode large enough to make the current through the tube substantially equal to the saturation current I_T. If the voltage on the anode is reversed in sign, the current through the tube becomes zero. Thus the current through the tube can be switched between 0 and I_T by reversing the sign of the anode voltage provided

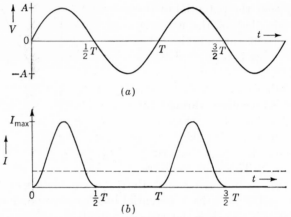

(a)

(b)

Fig. 6.16. (a) Alternating voltage applied across a diode vacuum tube, and (b) the corresponding current through the tube, for the characteristic curve shown in Fig. 6.15.

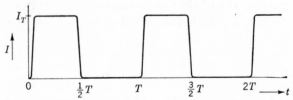

Fig. 6.17. Current through a diode vacuum tube produced by the applied voltage shown in Fig. 6.16a when the amplitude of the voltage is sufficiently large to saturate the tube.

that the magnitude of this voltage is sufficiently large. If the alternating voltage given by Eq. (6.68) is applied across the tube and the amplitude A of this voltage is large compared with that required to produce through the tube the saturation current I_T, the resulting current through the tube is that shown in Fig. 6.17. During odd half periods the voltage of the anode is sufficiently positive to make the current through the tube practically equal to the saturation value I_T, while during the even half periods the tube is nonconducting. Thus rectangular pulses of current are produced through a diode by applying across it an alternating voltage of sufficiently large amplitude.

It will be noticed that our discussion of the relation between the current through a diode vacuum tube and the voltage across it has been based upon the assumption that the current and voltage are steady, whereas in Figs. 6.16 and 6.17 we have contemplated situations in which the current and voltage vary with time. There is no objection to the voltage across the tube varying with time as long as there is no appreciable variation of voltage during the time taken by an electron to move from the cathode to the anode. Let us therefore calculate how long it takes an electron to move from the cathode to the anode. In the absence of space charge, an electron accelerates uniformly from rest at the cathode to a velocity u_a at the anode given by Eq. (6.23). The electron is traveling with a mean velocity $\frac{1}{2}u_a$ through the distance s from the cathode to the anode. Its time of flight is therefore $2s/u_a$. By using Eq. (6.64) allowance can be made for the effect of space charge. The transit time then evaluates to

$$3\,\frac{s}{u_a} \qquad\qquad (6.69)$$

Putting $s = 1$ mm (10^{-3} m) and $V = 100$ volts we deduce either from Eq. (6.13) or from Table 6.1 that $u_a = 5.9 \times 10^6$ m/sec, and we then deduce from expression (6.69) that the time of flight of an electron from the cathode to the anode is 5×10^{-10} sec. It follows that, for the variation of voltage with time given by Eq. (6.68), the potential difference between the anode and the cathode scarcely changes during the time of flight of an electron from the cathode to the anode provided that T is large compared with $2\pi(5 \times 10^{-10})$ sec, or about 3×10^{-9} sec. The steady-state characteristic curve of a diode can therefore be used for alternating currents with periodic times down to about 10^{-8} sec, and this corresponds to frequencies of oscillation up to about 10^8 cycles/sec, or 100 Mc/sec.

SUMMARIZING EXERCISES

6.1. Describe what is meant by thermionic emission and thermionic current. Explain these ideas with reference to a diode vacuum tube.

6.2. Explain what is meant by an electron gun. An electron (charge $-e$ and mass m) is emitted from a cathode with negligible velocity and is accelerated toward an anode whose potential exceeds that of the cathode by V. Calculate the velocity with which the electron arrives at the anode. Define an electron-volt and calculate its numerical equivalent in joules.

6.3. Describe the principal features of a cathode-ray tube having electrostatic deflection. If V is the accelerating potential, s is the separation between the deflecting plates, L is the length of the deflecting plates parallel to the electron beam, and D is the distance from the center of the deflecting plates to the fluorescent screen, calculate the deflection of the spot on the screen per unit voltage applied across the deflecting plates. Describe any approximations used. Write down typical numerical values for the parameters of the tube and evaluate the corresponding deflection of the spot per unit deflecting voltage.

6.4. Explain what is meant by space charge in a diode vacuum tube. A planar diode has electrodes of area S, and fringing can be neglected. A steady current I flows through the tube from one electrode to the other. Show that the variations across the tube from the cathode to the anode of (a) the negative space-charge density ρ and (b) the electronic velocity u are such that

$$I = \rho u S$$

6.5. The cathode and anode of a diode vacuum tube are parallel metal plates, and fringing can be neglected. The anode is maintained at a positive potential with respect to the cathode, and there is a space charge of density $\rho(x)$ per unit volume at distance x from the cathode. Explain why the electric flux density D is a function of x, and prove that

$$\frac{dD}{dx} = \rho$$

where the positive direction of $\mathbf{D}$ is the direction in which x increases. Deduce that the electric potential ϕ is a function of x such that

$$\frac{d^2\phi}{dx^2} = -\frac{1}{\epsilon_v}\rho$$

where ϵ_v is the vacuum capacitivity.

6.6. Electrons (charge $-e$ and mass m) leave the cathode of a diode vacuum tube with negligible velocity. When they reach a point where the potential exceeds the potential of the cathode by ϕ, show that their velocity u is given by

$$\tfrac{1}{2}mu^2 = e\phi$$

6.7. Explain the circumstances under which the electric field at the surface of a diode vacuum tube may be taken as zero.

6.8. For a planar diode vacuum tube subject to the condition mentioned in Exercise 6.7, describe a method for solving the equations given in Exercises 6.4 to 6.6 to obtain the electric potential ϕ, the space-charge density ρ, and the electronic velocity u as functions of distance x from the cathode. Deduce the electric field strength as a function of x. Sketch curves to show the variations of these quantities with x.

6.9. From the previous exercise derive Charles' law for a planar diode. Taking suitable numerical values for the area of the electrodes and the separation between them, sketch a curve showing the way in which the current through a diode varies with the voltage across it in accordance with Child's law.

6.10. Describe the phenomenon of saturation in a diode vacuum tube. Explain how this phenomenon leads to a nearly linear relation between voltage and current over a restricted range of these variables.

6.11. Explain what is meant by the Thévenin and Norton equivalent circuits for a diode vacuum tube. Describe how to evaluate the elements in these circuits from the characteristic curve of the tube relating voltage to current. Mention typical numerical values for these elements. Explain the circumstances under which the Thévenin and Norton equivalent circuits can be used to represent the behavior of the tube.

6.12. Explain how a diode vacuum tube can be used for converting alternating current into direct current.

CHAPTER 7

MULTIELECTRODE VACUUM TUBES

7.1. Introduction. Over the linear portion of the characteristic curve of a diode vacuum tube, the tube operates as described by the equivalent circuits illustrated in Figs. 6.13 and 6.14. The immense importance of the linear portion of the characteristic curve comes to light only when a third electrode, known as a grid, is interposed between the cathode and the anode, thereby converting the diode vacuum tube into a triode vacuum tube.

7.2. The Triode Vacuum Tube. A triode vacuum tube is a diode vacuum tube in which an additional electrode, in the form of a grid of wires, is interposed between the cathode and the anode. This additional electrode is known as the grid. The grid frequently takes the form of a cage of wires enclosing the cathode, while the anode takes the form of a metal cylinder enclosing the grid. For simplicity, however, it will be convenient to consider a planar triode in which the cathode, the grid, and the anode occupy parallel planes as indicated in Fig. 7.1. Conductor number 1 represents the cathode, conductor 2 the grid, and conductor 3 the anode. The electrodes are contained in an evacuated glass or metal envelope. If the envelope is metallic, it is usually convenient to take its potential as zero. Otherwise we take the

Fig. 7.1. Illustrating a triode vacuum tube in which conductor 1 is the cathode, conductor 2 the grid, and conductor 3 the anode.

"conductor at infinity" to have zero potential; in practice this conductor might be the metal chassis upon which the equipment is constructed.

The cathode, grid, and anode possess coefficients of capacitance c_{rs} that can be calculated from the geometry of the tube in a manner that has been discussed in electrostatics (Part 1, Secs. 9.4 and 11.5). We shall be particularly interested in the coefficient of mutual capacitance c_{12} between the cathode and the grid and the coefficient of mutual capacitance c_{13} between the cathode and the anode. Let potentials V_1, V_2, and V_3 be applied to the cathode, grid, and anode respectively, and let the corresponding charges on these electrodes be Q_1, Q_2, and Q_3. In terms of the coefficients of self- and mutual capacitance of the electrodes the

311

charges can be expressed in terms of the potentials by means of the equations

$$Q_1 = c_{11}V_1 + c_{12}V_2 + c_{13}V_3 \qquad (7.1)$$

$$Q_2 = c_{21}V_1 + c_{22}V_2 + c_{23}V_3 \qquad (7.2)$$

$$Q_3 = c_{31}V_1 + c_{32}V_2 + c_{33}V_3 \qquad (7.3)$$

where $\qquad c_{12} = c_{21} \qquad c_{23} = c_{32} \qquad c_{31} = c_{13} \qquad (7.4)$

If the cathode is cold, the coefficients of capacitance appearing in Eqs. (7.1) to (7.4) are to be calculated by the methods described in electrostatics. If the cathode is hot, the charge on the surface of the cathode is replaced by space charge close to the cathode, as in the case of a diode. This modifies the calculation of the coefficients of capacitance of the system to some extent. What matters is not the location of the cathode but the location of the charge associated with the cathode. Under normal operating conditions the distribution of space charge between the cathode and the grid of a triode is similar to that between the cathode and the anode of a diode. Thus the coefficients of capacitance of a triode when the cathode is hot are substantially the same as the coefficients of capacitance when the cathode is cold provided that the distance of the cathode from the grid is reduced by a factor of approximately $\frac{3}{4}$ [compare Eq. (6.58)]. In what follows it is supposed that the cathode is hot and that the coefficients of capacitance have been calculated for this condition.

A triode vacuum tube is normally operated with the potential of the cathode not very different from that of the surrounding envelope. It will simplify our initial consideration to suppose that the cathode is at the same potential as the surrounding envelope and to take this potential as zero. We can thus put

$$V_1 = 0 \qquad (7.5)$$

in Eqs. (7.1) to (7.3). We are particularly interested in Eq. (7.1), which becomes

$$Q_1 = c_{12}V_2 + c_{13}V_3 \qquad (7.6)$$

This equation expresses the charge associated with the cathode in terms of the potential of the grid and the potential of the anode on the assumption that the potential of the cathode is zero. When the cathode is hot, the charge associated with the cathode is the space charge. Hence Eq. (7.6) expresses the space charge close to the cathode in terms of the potential of the grid and the potential of the anode.

Before considering the full potentialities of the tube as a triode, let us see how it can be operated as a diode. In principle, one way of doing this is to connect the anode of the triode to the envelope and use the grid of the triode as the anode of a diode. In these circumstances the space between the grid and the cathode is being used as a diode.   Let V be the potential of the grid, so that the potentials of the various electrodes are

$$V_1 = 0 \qquad V_2 = V \qquad V_3 = 0 \tag{7.7}$$

The current I between the grid and the cathode under these circumstances is related to V by means of a characteristic curve of the type shown in Fig. 6.11.   When the current is limited by space charge, the relation between I and V is given by Eqs. (6.45) and (6.46), where s is now the separation between the grid and the cathode.   Substituting from Eqs. (7.7) into Eq. (7.1) or (7.6) we obtain

$$Q_1 = c_{12}V \tag{7.8}$$

This equation expresses the space charge close to the cathode in terms of the potential of the grid when both the cathode and the anode are at zero potential.

The arrangement just described for using a triode vacuum tube as a diode will be of considerable theoretical interest to us.   If, however, we require in practice to use a triode vacuum tube as a diode, a slightly different arrangement is used.   The construction of the grid is not normally sufficiently rugged to withstand the bombardment of the electrons constituting the current.   The practical procedure therefore is to connect the grid and anode of the triode together and use this common conductor as the anode in diode operation.   In these circumstances the potentials of the electrodes are

$$V_1 = 0 \qquad V_2 = V \qquad V_3 = V \tag{7.9}$$

and Eq. (7.6) becomes

$$Q_1 = (c_{12} + c_{13})V \tag{7.10}$$

Since the magnitude of c_{13} is normally small compared with that of c_{12}, there is little numerical difference between Eqs. (7.10) and (7.8).

Let us now consider the operation of the tube as a triode.   With the cathode maintained at zero potential, let V_g be the potential of the grid and V_a be the potential of the anode.   Then the potentials of the electrodes are

$$V_1 = 0 \qquad V_2 = V_g \qquad V_3 = V_a \tag{7.11}$$

and Eq. (7.6) can be rewritten as

$$Q_1 = c_{12}V_g + c_{13}V_a \tag{7.12}$$

This equation expresses the space charge close to the cathode in terms of the potential V_g of the grid and the potential V_a of the anode.   Let us compare this situation with the one in which the space between the cathode and the grid is used as a diode.   This is the situation in which the potentials of the electrodes are given by Eq. (7.7) and the corresponding space charge close to the cathode is given by Eq. (7.8). By comparing Eq. (7.8) with Eq. (7.12) we see that the space charge close to the cathode is the same in both situations if

$$c_{12}V = c_{12}V_g + c_{13}V_a \tag{7.13}$$

that is, if

$$V = V_g + \frac{1}{\mu}V_a \tag{7.14}$$

where

$$\mu = \frac{c_{12}}{c_{13}} \tag{7.15}$$

Thus, if the tube is used as a triode with the cathode at zero potential, the grid at potential V_g, and the anode at potential V_a, the space charge close to the cathode is the same as if the tube is used as a diode with the cathode and anode at zero potential and the grid at potential V given by Eq. (7.14).

In practice the magnitude of the mutual capacitance c_{12} between the cathode and the grid is considerably greater than the magnitude of the mutual capacitance c_{13} between the cathode and the anode. Indeed the ratio μ given by Eq. (7.15) usually has a value between 10 and 100. Thus Eq. (7.14) shows that, when the potential of the anode is of the same order of magnitude as the potential of the grid, the space charge close to the cathode is controlled almost entirely by the potential of the grid. However, it is quite possible to make the potential of the anode between 10 and 100 times the potential of the grid, and then the potential of the anode is as important as the potential of the grid in controlling the amount of space charge close to the cathode.

The space charge close to the cathode consists of the electrons leaving the cathode and forming the current through the tube in the space between the cathode and the grid. It follows that Eq. (7.14) can be interpreted in the following way: If the tube is operated as a triode with zero potential on the cathode, potential V_g on the grid, and potential V_a on the anode, then the current between the grid and the cathode is the same as if the tube is operated as a diode with zero potential on the cathode and the anode, and a potential V on the grid given by Eq. (7.14). Now the diode has already been studied in Chap. 6, and its behavior is summarized by the characteristic curve shown in Fig. 6.11. From this behavior we can now deduce the behavior of a triode by using Eq. (7.14). In Fig. 6.11 we replace V by $V_g + (1/\mu)V_a$ in accordance with Eq. (7.14) and thereby obtain Fig. 7.2. This diagram tells us how to calculate the current I in the space between the cathode and the grid of a triode vacuum tube in terms of the voltage V_g of the grid and the voltage V_a of the anode when the voltage of the cathode is taken as zero.

Of all the electrons leaving the cathode, some in general go to the grid while some pass through the holes in the grid and go to the anode. The case of greatest practical importance, however, is the one in which none of the electrons go to the grid and they all pass through the holes in the grid on their way to the anode. This occurs if the potential V_g of the grid is negative with respect to the cathode. In these circumstances the potential energy of an electron at the grid exceeds the potential energy of an electron at the cathode because the electron is negatively charged. Thus the electrons leaving the cath-

ode are unable to arrive at the grid. If, however, the anode has a sufficiently high positive potential V_a with respect to the cathode, the electrons pass through the holes in the grid and go to the anode. In these circumstances the current between the anode and the grid is the same as the current between the grid and the cathode. Thus, provided that the potential V_g of the grid is negative with respect to the cathode, the current I in Fig.

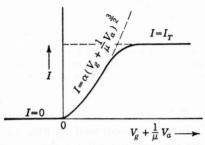

FIG. 7.2. The relation connecting the current I between the grid and the cathode in a triode vacuum tube and the voltages V_g and V_a of the grid and anode, respectively.

7.2 can be interpreted as the current not only in the space between the cathode and the grid but also in the space between the grid and the anode. This is the normal operating condition of a triode. A voltage is connected between the grid and the cathode so as to maintain the grid at a negative potential V_g with respect to the cathode; no current is supplied by the battery maintaining this potential difference. The voltage V_a is now applied between the anode and the cathode. The battery maintaining this potential then produces current through the tube as shown in Fig. 7.2.

The shape of the characteristic curve of a triode vacuum tube shown in Fig. 7.2 depends upon the geometry of the tube, on the substance of which the cathode is constructed, on the way in which its surface is treated, and on the temperature of the cathode in the manner described in connection with diode vacuum tubes. The constant μ appearing in Fig. 7.2 is given by Eq. (7.15) and depends mainly upon the geometry of the tube.

A characteristic curve for a triode such as that shown in Fig. 7.2 is frequently replotted in various ways. Thus the anode current I can be plotted as a function of the grid voltage V_g for a series of fixed values of the anode potential V_a. Suppose, for example, that we use Eq. (7.14) to convert the characteristic curve of the diode illustrated in Fig. 6.15 into the characteristic curve for a triode shown in Fig. 7.3. If we plot the anode current I as a function of the grid voltage V_g for a series of values of the anode potential V_a, we obtain the family of curves shown in Fig. 7.4.

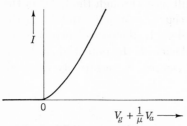

In this diagram only negative values of grid potential are shown, since for positive potentials the current I would not be simply the anode current but the sum of the anode and grid currents. The curves shown in Fig. 7.4 are simply displacements of the curve shown in Fig. 7.3 by amounts V_a/μ to the left in accordance with Eq. (7.14). Again it is sometimes convenient to plot the anode current I as a function of the anode potential

FIG. 7.3. Characteristic curve for a planar triode when the anode current is appreciably less than the saturation current.

V_a for a series of negative values of the grid potential V_g. In Fig. 7.5 the information contained in Fig. 7.3 is replotted in this way. The curve for zero grid potential is the same as the curve shown in Fig. 7.3 except for the fact that the scale on the abscissa is changed by a factor μ in

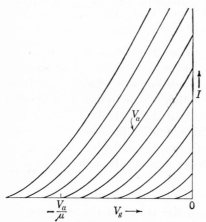

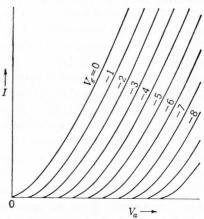

FIG. 7.4. Illustrating the relation between the anode current and the grid potential of a triode vacuum tube for a series of fixed values of anode potential.

FIG. 7.5. The relation between the anode current I of a triode vacuum tube and the anode potential V_a for a series of fixed negative values of the grid potential V_g.

accordance with Eq. (7.14). The other curves in Fig. 7.5 are displacements of the curve for $V_g = 0$ through distances $-\mu V_g$ to the right.

7.3. Effect of a Nonzero Cathode Potential. In the preceding section the potential of the cathode was taken as zero, that is, the same as the potential of the surrounding envelope. In practice it is not always convenient to operate the cathode at the same potential as the envelope, and neither is it necessary to do so. Moreover, in practice the electrodes usually take a cylindrical form in which the cathode is enclosed by the grid and the grid by the anode as indicated in Fig. 7.6. This represents a situation in which the cathode (conductor 1) is surrounded by the grid (conductor 2) except at the open ends of the cylinder. In the same way the anode (conductor 3) surrounds the grid except at the open ends of the cylinder. The whole arrangement of electrodes is enclosed in an envelope (conductor 0), the potential of which we take to be zero.

Let us suppose that the grid and anode are connected to the envelope and that a unit potential is maintained at the cathode. The potentials of the conductors are then

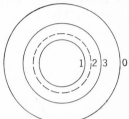

FIG. 7.6. Cylindrical triode vacuum tube in which the cathode (conductor 1) is surrounded by the grid (conductor 2), the grid is surrounded by the anode (conductor 3), the whole being enclosed in an envelope (conductor 0).

$$V_1 = 1 \qquad V_2 = 0 \qquad V_3 = 0 \qquad (7.16)$$

In terms of the coefficients of capacitance of the tube, we can derive the charges on the conductors from Eqs. (7.1) to (7.3). By substituting from Eqs. (7.16) into Eqs. (7.1) to (7.3) we derive

$$Q_1 = c_{11} \qquad Q_2 = c_{21} \qquad Q_3 = c_{31} \qquad (7.17)$$

Thus, with unit potential on the cathode and zero potential on the grid, the anode, and the envelope, the positive charge on the cathode is c_{11}, the negative charge on the grid is c_{21}, and the negative charge on the anode is c_{31}. Neglecting fringing at the edges of the electrodes, all lines of force leaving the cathode terminate on either the grid or the anode. Hence the positive charge c_{11} on the cathode is equal and opposite to the algebraic sum of the charges c_{21} and c_{31} on the grid and anode. This result is expressed by the equation

$$c_{11} = -(c_{21} + c_{31}) \qquad (7.18)$$

and can be rewritten as

$$c_{11} = -(c_{12} + c_{13}) \qquad (7.19)$$

by use of Eqs. (7.4). Substituting the expression (7.19) for c_{11} into Eq. (7.1) we derive

$$Q_1 = c_{12}(V_2 - V_1) + c_{13}(V_3 - V_1) \qquad (7.20)$$

This equation is of the same form as Eq. (7.6) except that V_2 and V_3 are replaced by $V_2 - V_1$ and $V_3 - V_1$ respectively.

The discussion of the triode vacuum tube that took place in the previous section on the basis of Eq. (7.6), assuming that the potential of the cathode was zero, could equally well take place on the basis of Eq. (7.20), assuming that the potential of the cathode is V_1. It follows that there is no necessity in the previous section for the potential of the cathode to be zero. It is merely necessary to interpret the grid potential V_g as the excess of the potential of the grid over the potential of the cathode and the anode potential V_a as the excess of the potential of the anode over the potential of the cathode.

7.4. Linear Behavior of a Triode Vacuum Tube. One of the most important applications of the triode vacuum tube is as an amplifier, and for this purpose it is the sloping linear portion of the characteristic curve shown in Fig. 7.2 that is important. This corresponds to the sloping

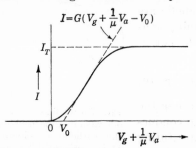

$$I = G\left(V_g + \frac{1}{\mu}V_a - V_0\right)$$

FIG. 7.7. Illustrating the linear behavior of the characteristic curve of a triode vacuum tube near the point of inflection.

linear portion of the diode characteristic shown in Fig. 6.12. Over this portion of the diode characteristic, the relation between anode current I and anode voltage V is given by Eq. (6.65) or alternatively Eq. (6.66). Let us suppose that the triode vacuum tube under consideration is such that, if its cathode-grid space is used as a diode, its characteristic curve is as shown in Fig. 6.12, and the sloping linear portion of this characteristic is represented by either Eq. (6.65) or (6.66). The numerical value of the conductance G is likely to lie between 500 and 5,000 μmhos, while the corresponding resistance R is likely to lie between 200 and 2,000 ohms. When operating the tube as a triode with the grid at potential V_g above that of the cathode and the anode at potential V_a above that of the cathode, we replace V in Fig. 6.12 by $V_g + (1/\mu)V_a$ in accordance with Eq. (7.14) and so obtain the characteristic curve of the triode shown in Fig. 7.7. Over the linear sloping portion of this characteristic curve we replace V by $V_g + (1/\mu)V_a$ in Eq. (6.65), thereby obtaining

$$I = G\left(V_g + \frac{1}{\mu}V_a - V_0\right) \tag{7.21}$$

This equation describes the linear sloping portion of the characteristic curve of the triode as shown in Fig. 7.7. The quantity G is the slope of the tangent to the characteristic curve at the point of inflection, and V_0 is the abscissa of the point where this tangent intersects the voltage axis. Provided that the voltage V_g of the grid with respect to the cathode is maintained negative, all the electrons leaving the cathode pass through the holes in the grid and go to the anode. Under these circumstances the current I is the anode current, and Eq. (7.21) shows how the anode current depends upon the grid voltage and the anode voltage over the sloping linear portion of the characteristic curve. The quantities G and V_0 appearing in Eq. (7.21) are the same as those appearing in Eq. (6.65) for the situation in which the grid-cathode space is used as a diode. Thus V_0 is usually a few volts, while G is usually in the range from 500 to 5,000 μmhos. As applied to a triode vacuum tube, the quantity G is usually called the transconductance.

Instead of representing the sloping linear portion of the diode characteristic curve for the grid-cathode space by means of Eq. (6.65), we can alternatively use Eq. (6.66). On substituting for V from Eq. (7.14) into Eq. (6.66), we obtain

$$V_g + \frac{1}{\mu} V_a = V_0 + RI \tag{7.22}$$

Equation (7.22) is what Eq. (7.21) becomes when G is replaced by $1/R$ in accordance with Eq. (6.67). Equation (7.22) expresses the relation between the grid voltage V_g, the anode voltage V_a, and the anode current I over the sloping linear portion of the characteristic curve, it being understood that the grid voltage is negative and that all voltages are measured relative to the cathode. The value of V_0 is usually a few volts, while the value of R is usually between 200 and 2,000 ohms.

Over the portion of the characteristic curve of a triode where Eqs. (7.21) and (7.22) apply, a triode vacuum tube can be represented by a Thévenin equivalent circuit as shown in Fig. 7.8 or by a Norton equivalent

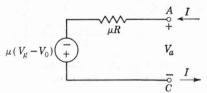

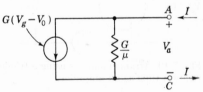

FIG. 7.8. The Thévenin equivalent circuit for a triode vacuum tube over the sloping linear portion of its characteristic curve when the grid voltage is negative with respect to the cathode.

FIG. 7.9. The Norton equivalent circuit for a triode vacuum tube over the sloping linear portion of its characteristic curve when the grid voltage is negative with respect to the cathode.

circuit as shown in Fig. 7.9. In Figs. 7.8 and 7.9, the point A denotes the anode terminal of the triode and the point C the cathode terminal. In the Thévenin equivalent circuit shown in Fig. 7.8, we have a source of voltage $\mu(V_g - V_0)$ in series with a resistor of resistance μR. This resistance is known as the anode resistance, or plate resistance, of the tube. The same resistance is involved in the Norton equivalent circuit shown in Fig. 7.9, where it is labeled with its conductance G/μ. In the Norton equivalent circuit, this resistor is connected in parallel with a source delivering a current $G(V_g - V_0)$. Application of Kirchhoff's circulation law to the circuit shown in Fig. 7.8 gives

$$V_a + \mu(V_g - V_0) = (\mu R)I \tag{7.23}$$

and this is equivalent to Eq. (7.22). Application of Kirchhoff's conservation law to the circuit shown in Fig. 7.9 gives

$$I = \frac{G}{\mu} V_a + G(V_g - V_0) \tag{7.24}$$

and this is equivalent to Eq. (7.21). Thus, either of the equivalent circuits shown in Figs. 7.8 and 7.9 describes the behavior of the triode vacuum tube over the sloping linear portion of its characteristic curve.

We see from the equivalent circuit shown in Fig. 7.8 that a variation in the grid voltage V_g leads to a variation μ times as large in the voltage appearing in the equivalent circuit. It is for this reason that the quantity μ defined by Eq. (7.15) is known as the amplification factor of the tube. For a triode, values of μ usually lie between 10 and 100 and values of the anode resistance μR usually lie between 10,000 and 100,000 ohms.

7.5. The Triode Vacuum Tube as an Amplifier. To use a triode vacuum tube as an amplifier we use an arrangement such as that shown in Fig. 7.10. The anode circuit of the tube contains a battery of fixed voltage V known as the anode battery. Variations in the grid voltage

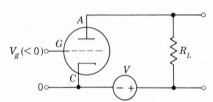

FIG. 7.10. Arrangement for using a triode vacuum tube as an amplifier.

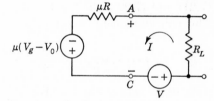

FIG. 7.11. Equivalent circuit for the arrangement shown in Fig. 7.10.

V_g of the tube produce variations in the anode current and consequently in the voltage developed across the load resistor R_L. Thus variations in the voltage applied between the terminals at the left lead to variations in the voltage developed between the terminals at the right. If the vacuum tube is appropriately operated, the variations in voltage between the terminals on the right are a more or less faithful reproduction of variations in voltage between the terminals on the left, and the former voltage is large compared with the latter. Appropriate operation of the vacuum tube means operating it over the linear portion of its characteristic curve and keeping the grid voltage negative with respect to the cathode. Under these circumstances the tube can be replaced by its Thévenin equivalent circuit shown in Fig. 7.8, thereby producing the equivalent circuit shown in Fig. 7.11.

In the circuit shown in Fig. 7.11 the total voltage acting in the direction shown by the arrow is

$$V + \mu(V_g - V_0) \tag{7.25}$$

and the total resistance in the circuit is

$$R_L + \mu R \tag{7.26}$$

Consequently the anode current I is given by the equation

$$I = \frac{V + \mu(V_g - V_0)}{R_L + \mu R} \tag{7.27}$$

The voltage developed across the load resistor R_L is therefore

$$\frac{R_L}{R_L + \mu R} [V + \mu(V_g - V_0)] \tag{7.28}$$

It follows from this expression that a variation δV_g in the grid voltage produces a variation in the voltage developed across the load resistor R_L of

$$\frac{R_L}{R_L + \mu R} \mu \, \delta V_g \tag{7.29}$$

Hence the ratio of the change in voltage developed at the right-hand terminals in Fig. 7.11 to the change in voltage applied between the left-hand terminals is

$$\frac{R_L}{R_L + \mu R} \mu \tag{7.30}$$

This is the amplification in voltage produced by the tube and is known as the voltage gain of the amplifier shown in Fig. 7.10. If the value of the load resistance R_L is large compared with the anode resistance μR of the tube, expression (7.30) is practically the amplification factor μ of the tube. In practice, however, it is usually inconvenient to make the load resistance R_L too large. If the resistance R_L is large, then a large voltage V must be used for the anode battery in order to produce a given difference of potential between the anode and cathode of the tube. It is quite common therefore for the load resistance R_L to be of the same order of magnitude as the anode resistance μR of the tube, and the voltage gain of the arrangement shown in Fig. 7.10 is then somewhat less than the amplification factor of the tube.

7.6. Vacuum Tubes Possessing a Screen Grid. In order to increase the amplification factor of a triode vacuum tube it is necessary to reduce the mutual capacitance between the anode and the cathode in accordance with Eq. (7.15). This can be done by introducing an additional grid, known as a screen grid. In addition to the cathode, the control grid, and the anode possessed by a triode vacuum tube, we then have a screen grid between the control grid and the anode. Introduction of a screen grid, besides increasing the amplification factor of the tube, also has other advantages, particularly in radio applications. Such four-electrode tubes are known as tetrodes.

In many tubes possessing a screen grid the rate at which electrons are hitting the anode leads to a phenomenon of secondary emission of electrons from the anode. In these circumstances the anode is to some extent acting as a cathode, and this upsets the behavior of the tube. Devices are frequently incorporated in screen-grid tubes to minimize the effect of secondary emission from the anode. One such device leads to what is known as the beam-power tetrode, and another device leads to what is known as the pentode. In each case, however, the feature of primary importance is the introduction of a screen grid between the control grid and the anode.

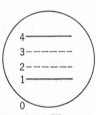

FIG. 7.12. Illustrating a vacuum tube possessing a screen grid (conductor 3) in addition to a control grid (conductor 2), a cathode (conductor 1), and an anode (conductor 4).

Figure 7.12 illustrates a vacuum tube in which conductor 1 is the cathode, conductor 2 is the control grid, conductor 3 is the screen grid, and conductor 4 is the anode. The electrodes are supposed to be enclosed in an envelope (conductor 0) whose potential will be taken as zero. Coefficients of self- and mutual capacitance c_{rs} can be defined for the system of electrodes as described in electrostatics (Part 1, Sec. 9.2). We shall be particularly interested in the coefficient of mutual capacitance c_{12} between the cathode and the control grid, the coefficient of mutual capacitance c_{13} between the cathode and the screen grid, and the coefficient of mutual capacitance c_{14} between the cathode and the anode. The coefficient of self-capacitance of the cathode c_{11} will also appear. The control grid and the screen grid are so constructed that the magnitude of c_{12} is large compared with the magnitude of c_{13}, while this in turn is large compared with the magnitude of c_{14}. We shall be particularly interested in the following ratios:

$$\mu = \frac{c_{12}}{c_{14}} \tag{7.31}$$

$$\mu' = \frac{c_{12}}{c_{13}} \tag{7.32}$$

A typical value for μ is 1,000, and a typical value for μ' is 20.

In terms of the coefficients of capacitance of the electrodes, the equation giving the space charge Q_1 adjacent to the cathode in terms of the potential V_1 of the cathode, the potential V_2 of the control grid, the potential V_3 of the screen grid, and the potential V_4 of the anode is

$$Q_1 = c_{11}V_1 + c_{12}V_2 + c_{13}V_3 + c_{14}V_4 \qquad (7.33)$$

Let us suppose that the potential of the control grid is V_g, the potential of the screen grid is V_s, and the potential of the anode is V_a. If we further suppose that the cathode is connected to the envelope, the potentials of the electrodes are

$$V_1 = 0 \qquad V_2 = V_g \qquad V_3 = V_s \qquad V_4 = V_a \qquad (7.34)$$

In these circumstances Eq. (7.33) becomes

$$Q_1 = c_{12}V_g + c_{13}V_s + c_{14}V_a \qquad (7.35)$$

As in the case of a triode, Eq. (7.35) is true even if the potential of the cathode is not identical with that of the envelope provided that V_g is interpreted as the excess of potential of the control grid over that of the cathode, V_s is interpreted as the excess of potential of the screen grid over that of the cathode, and V_a is interpreted as the excess of potential of the anode over that of the cathode (see Sec. 7.3).

It is possible for a vacuum tube with a screen grid to be used as a triode or even as a diode. Let us consider first of all operation of a tetrode as a triode. In theory this can be achieved by connecting the anode to the envelope and using the screen grid as the anode for triode operation. In these circumstances the value of V_a in Eq. (7.35) is zero and V_s is the anode potential for triode operation. Equation (7.35) then takes the same form as Eq. (7.12), and we see that the amplification factor of the tube used as a triode is μ', given by Eq. (7.32). In practice, operation of a tetrode as a triode would be achieved by connecting the anode to the screen grid. In these circumstances V_s would be equal to V_a in Eq. (7.35) and the equation would become

$$Q_1 = c_{12}V_g + (c_{13} + c_{14})V_a \qquad (7.36)$$

The amplification factor would then be $c_{12}/(c_{13} + c_{14})$, but the numerical value of this is not substantially different from μ' given by Eq. (7.32).

Diode operation of a tetrode can in theory be achieved by connecting the screen grid and the anode to the envelope and using the control grid as the anode for diode operation. In this way diode behavior is obtained between the control grid and the cathode. If V is the potential of the grid for diode operation, then the potentials of the electrodes are

$$V_1 = 0 \qquad V_2 = V \qquad V_3 = 0 \qquad V_4 = 0 \qquad (7.37)$$

and Eq. (7.33) becomes

$$Q_1 = c_{12}V \qquad (7.38)$$

This equation gives the space charge Q_1 adjacent to the cathode when the grid-cathode space is used as a diode and the potential of the grid exceeds that of the cathode by V. In practice, if a tetrode were to be used as a diode, the screen grid and the anode would be connected to the control grid to form the anode for diode operation. In these circumstances V_g, V_s, and V_a in Eq. (7.35) would all be set equal to V. As a result c_{12} in Eq. (7.38) would be replaced by $c_{12} + c_{13} + c_{14}$, but the numerical modification would be minor.

Let us now consider a situation in which the tube is operated as a tetrode with the potential of the control grid exceeding that of the cathode by V_g, the potential of the screen grid exceeding that of the cathode by V_s, and the potential of the anode exceeding that of the cathode by V_a. Let us compare this with a situation in which the space between the control grid and the cathode is used as a diode with the potential of the grid exceeding that of the cathode by V. In diode operation let us adjust the potential V of the grid so as to produce the same space charge adjacent to the cathode as that obtained in tetrode operation. The required value of V is obtained by equating the expression for Q_1 given in Eq. (7.38) to the expression for Q_1 given in Eq. (7.35). We thus obtain

$$c_{12}V = c_{12}V_g + c_{13}V_s + c_{14}V_a \qquad (7.39)$$

and this can be written as

$$V = V_g + \frac{1}{\mu'} V_s + \frac{1}{\mu} V_a \qquad (7.40)$$

where μ and μ' are given by Eqs. (7.31) and (7.32). We see that, when the tube is operated as a tetrode with the control grid at a potential V_g, the screen grid at a potential V_s, and the anode at a potential V_a with respect to the cathode, the same space charge adjacent to the cathode is obtained as when the region between the control grid and the cathode is used as a diode with the control grid at a voltage V with respect to the cathode provided that V is given by Eq. (7.40).

As in the case of the triode, identity of the space charge adjacent to the cathode implies identity of the electric current in the grid-cathode space. It follows therefore that, if the characteristic curve of the tube for diode operation is given by Fig. 6.12, then the characteristic curve for tetrode operation is obtained by replacing V by the expression on the right-hand side of Eq. (7.40) as shown in Fig. 7.13. This diagram shows how the current in the space between the control grid and the cathode of a tetrode vacuum tube depends upon the potentials V_g of the control grid, V_s of the screen grid, and V_a of the anode, each being measured relative to the potential of the cathode.

Provided that the potential V_g of the control grid is maintained negative with respect to the cathode, electrons are not captured by the control grid, and the current between the control grid and the screen grid is the same as that between the cathode and the control grid. This is the normal operating condition of a vacuum tube possessing a screen grid. The potential of the screen grid is not, however, maintained negative with respect to the cathode, and consequently some electrons from the cathode are bound to be captured by the screen grid. If, however, the potential V_a of the anode is appreciably greater than the potential V_s of the screen grid, then most of the electrons are not captured by the screen grid but pass through its holes and go to the anode. In these circumstances the current

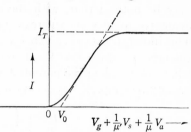

Fig. 7.13. The relation connecting the current I between the grid and the cathode of a tetrode vacuum tube and the potentials V_g of the control grid, V_s of the screen grid, and V_a of the anode.

between the anode and the screen grid is not a great deal less than that in the rest of the tube. The normal operating condition of a tetrode is therefore

$$V_g < 0 \qquad V_s > 0 \qquad V_a > V_s \qquad (7.41)$$

and in these circumstances the current I in Fig. 7.13 is substantially the anode current. A typical potential for the screen grid is between 100 and 300 volts, while a typical potential for the anode is roughly twice that for the screen grid.

7.7. The Tetrode Vacuum Tube as an Amplifier. A tube with a screen grid is normally used as an amplifier using the linear portion of its characteristic curve. Let us suppose that, when the space between the control grid and the cathode of a tetrode is used as a diode, the linear portion of its characteristic curve is given by Eq. (6.65). By substituting for V from Eq. (7.40) into Eq. (6.65) we see that the sloping linear portion of the tetrode characteristic curve in Fig. 7.13 is given by the equation

$$I = G\left(V_g + \frac{1}{\mu'} V_s + \frac{1}{\mu} V_a - V_0\right) \qquad (7.42)$$

This equation gives, over the sloping linear portion of the characteristic curve, the anode current I of a tetrode as a function of the voltages of the control grid, the screen grid, and the anode, provided that the potential of the control grid is maintained negative with respect to the cathode and the voltage of the anode is maintained sufficiently positive with respect to the screen grid.

Typical values of the parameters in Eq. (7.42) are $G = 1,500$ μmhos, $\mu' = 20$, $\mu = 1,000$, and $V_0 = 2$ volts. A typical potential for the screen grid is $V_s = 200$ volts and for the anode $V_a = 400$ volts. If the control grid is maintained at a potential of -3 volts with respect to the cathode, then the anode current given by Eq. (7.42) evaluates to about 8 ma. It may be noticed that, with these figures, the term V_s/μ' in Eq. (7.42) evaluates to 10 volts whereas the term V_a/μ evaluates to only 0.4 volt. This illustrates the fact that the anode current is not influenced much by the precise value of the anode potential as long as this potential is somewhat greater than the potential of the screen grid. Thus Eq. (7.42) can usually be simplified under normal operating conditions to

$$I = G \left(V_g + \frac{1}{\mu'} V_s - V_0 \right) \tag{7.43}$$

To this degree of approximation, the anode current I is determined by the voltage of the control grid and the voltage of the screen grid but is independent of the voltage of the anode. Of course it is necessary that the

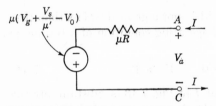

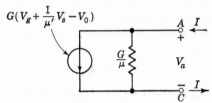

FIG. 7.14. The Thévenin equivalent circuit for calculating the anode current of a tetrode vacuum tube over the sloping linear portion of the characteristic curve under circumstances when most of the electrons leaving the cathode go through to the anode.

FIG. 7.15. The Norton equivalent circuit for calculating the anode current of a tetrode vacuum tube over the sloping linear portion of the characteristic curve under circumstances when most of the electrons leaving the cathode go through to the anode.

anode potential exceed the screen potential so that most of the electrons passing through the tube go to the anode. It is also necessary that the anode potential be not enormously large, for otherwise the current through the tube would be limited by the temperature of the cathode and the tube would not be working in the linear portion of its characteristic curve. However, provided that the anode potential is kept within these limits, it has little influence upon the anode current, and Eq. (7.43) is a useful approximate equation for calculating the anode current.

As in the case of the triode, Eq. (7.42) can be represented by a Thévenin equivalent circuit as shown in Fig. 7.14. In this diagram, R is the reciprocal of G and has a value of the order of 700 ohms. If μ is of the order of 1,000, the anode resistance μR has a high value of the order of 700,000 ohms. Alternatively, Eq. (7.42) can be represented by a Norton equivalent circuit as shown in Fig. 7.15. For a tube possessing a screen grid, it is the Norton equivalent circuit that it is usually convenient to

use. The resistor of conductance G/μ in Fig. 7.15 has a high resistance
of the order of 700,000 ohms and so can usually be omitted from the circuit because of a much lower load resistance connected in the anode
circuit between terminals A and C.

Let us consider a situation in which a vacuum tube possessing a
screen grid is used as an amplifier
in conjunction with a load resistor
of conductance G_L and an anode
battery of voltage V as shown in
Fig. 7.16. Replacing the tube by
its Norton equivalent circuit, we
derive the equivalent circuit shown
in Fig. 7.17. If in this diagram
we neglect the conductance G/μ in
comparison with the load conduct-

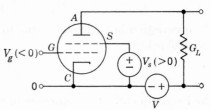

FIG. 7.16. Arrangement for using a vacuum tube possessing a screen grid as an
amplifier.

ance G_L, the anode current I is simply the current delivered by the
generator on the left; the voltage V of the anode battery is irrelevant
except for ensuring that the tube is operated over the part of its characteristic curve that is described by Eq. (7.42). In these circumstances
the equivalent circuit shown in Fig. 7.17 simplifies to that shown in Fig.

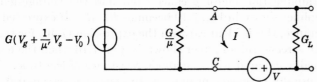

FIG. 7.17. Equivalent circuit for the arrangement shown in Fig. 7.16.

7.18.   Figure 7.18 is, in fact, the equivalent circuit that would be obtained
by using, not Eq. (7.42), but Eq. (7.43), which is derived from Eq. (7.42)
by neglecting the effect of anode potential upon anode current. According to this simplified picture, the tube delivers a current given by Eq.
(7.43) into the load in the anode circuit, and this situation is represented

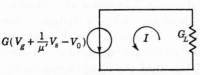

FIG. 7.18. Simplified equivalent circuit
for the arrangement shown in Fig. 7.16.

by the equivalent circuit shown in
Fig. 7.18. Use of the equivalent
circuit shown in Fig. 7.18 implies
operation of the tube over the linear
portion of its characteristic curve
under circumstances when conditions (7.41) are satisfied and under

circumstances when the term V_a/μ in Eq. (7.42) can be neglected. These
are, however, the conditions under which a vacuum tube possessing a
screen grid is normally operated.

To calculate the voltage gain of the amplifier shown in Fig. 7.16, let us neglect the conductance G/μ in the equivalent circuit shown in Fig. 7.17 and use Eq. (7.43) for the current I through the load of conductance G_L in accordance with Fig. 7.18. The voltage developed across the load is then

$$\frac{G}{G_L}\left(V_g + \frac{1}{\mu'}V_s - V_0\right)$$ (7.44)

The variation in this voltage due to a variation δV_g in the voltage of the control grid is

$$\frac{G}{G_L}\delta V_g$$ (7.45)

and consequently the voltage gain of the amplifier is

$$\frac{G}{G_L}$$ (7.46)

It will be noticed that this expression for the gain of the screen-grid amplifier shown in Fig. 7.16 does not involve the amplification factor μ of the tube.   The same is true for a triode when its anode resistance μR is large compared with the load resistance R_L in the anode circuit; if, in expression (7.30), we neglect R_L in the denominator in comparison with μR, the amplification factor μ cancels out and the voltage gain of the triode amplifier shown in Fig. 7.10 becomes R_L/R.   If expressed in terms of conductance, this is identical with the expression (7.46) for the voltage gain of the screen-grid amplifier shown in Fig. 7.16 when the load resistance is small compared with the anode resistance of the tube.   The fact that it is usually necessary in practice to operate a screen-grid amplifier in this way restricts, of course, the voltage gain obtained.   Nevertheless, the voltage gain is substantial, since there is no difficulty in practice in making the conductance G_L of the load small compared with the transconductance G of the tube.

In many applications the real advantage of a screen-grid tube arises from the fact that, if it is properly used, the tube is a good approximation to a constant-current source as indicated in Fig. 7.18 and as described by Eq. (7.43).   Within the range of validity of Eq. (7.43), variation of the voltage of the anode does not vary the anode current.   In the arrangement shown in Fig. 7.16, let us suppose that the potentials of the control grid and screen grid are kept constant but that the conductance of the load resistor is variable.   Variation of the load resistance varies the anode potential.   This does not, however, vary the anode current within the range of validity of Eq. (7.43).   Thus, variation of the load resistance in Fig. 7.16 varies the voltage across the load rather than the current through it.   This is the reverse of what happens when a load resistor is connected across a battery of negligible internal resistance; in this case variation of the load resistance varies the current through the load rather than the voltage across it.   Thus, a vacuum tube possessing a screen grid, particularly in the pentode form, is a good approximation to a constant-current source in the same way that a battery is a good approximation to a constant-voltage source.   With the vacuum tube, the constant current that is delivered more or less regardless of the value of the load resistance can be adjusted by adjusting the grid potentials.

7.8. Vacuum-tube Manuals.   There are hundreds of different types of tubes sold by manufacturers of vacuum tubes.   The characteristics of these tubes are listed in vacuum-tube manuals.   Among the parameters frequently listed are the amplification factor of the tube and its interelectrode capacitances.   Suppose that we select a particular triode vacuum tube listed in a tube manual and look up the values for its amplification factor μ, for its grid-cathode capacitance, and for its anode-cathode capacitance.   It might be supposed that these three quantities would fit together in the manner given by Eq. (7.15).   In actual fact it will be found that this is not true.   The reason is that the interelectrode capacitances quoted in tube manuals differ in an important respect from the magnitudes of the coefficients of mutual capacitance for the electrodes that we have been using.   In a practical vacuum tube metal wires have to be led from the various electrodes through the envelope so that electrical contact can be made with them.   The coefficients of capacitance that we have been using are those for the electrodes excluding the wires by which connection is made to them, and these are the appropriate coefficients of capacitance to use in discussing the electronic behavior of the tube.   The interelectrode capacitances quoted in tube manuals are the interelectrode capacitances of the electrodes including the wires by which connection is made to them.   These values are quoted because they are frequently required in radio applications of the tubes.   For discussing the electronic behavior of the tube, however, it is the interelectrode capacitances excluding the capacitances of the leads that are required, and these are not usually quoted in vacuum-tube manuals.   The manuals do, however, contain the necessary ratios of interelectrode capacitances excluding the leads, and these are quoted as amplification factors.

SUMMARIZING EXERCISES

7.1. Explain what is meant by a triode vacuum tube.   A triode vacuum tube is operated in such a way that the space charge may be regarded as a surface charge on the cathode.   Taking the potential of the cathode as zero, a potential V_g is maintained on the grid and V_a on the anode.   Prove that the charge on the cathode is the same as would exist if the anode were at the same potential as the cathode and the grid were maintained at a potential $V_g + (1/\mu)V_a$, where μ is the ratio of the coefficient of mutual capacitance between cathode and grid to that between cathode and anode.

7.2. For a triode vacuum tube, sketch curves to illustrate the relation between the anode current and the grid voltage for a series of values of anode voltage, taking the anode voltage as positive and the grid voltage as negative with respect to the cathode. For the same arrangement, sketch curves to illustrate the relation between the anode current and the anode voltage for a series of negative values of the grid voltage.

7.3. Explain what is meant by the linear behavior of a triode vacuum tube. Describe the Thévenin and Norton equivalent circuits for the tube and explain how to evaluate the elements in these circuits from the characteristic curve of the tube. Explain what is meant by transconductance and anode resistance.

7.4. Describe a simple triode amplifying circuit and evaluate its voltage gain. Explain why the voltage gain is less than the amplification factor of the tube. Write down typical numerical values of the parameters involved.

7.5. Explain what is meant by a vacuum tube possessing a screen grid. Describe the behavior of such a tube as a linear amplifier, and explain why the tube is an approximation to a constant-current source.

PART 3

MAGNETIC FIELDS AND CIRCUITS

CHAPTER 1

THE EFFECT OF ELECTRIC CHARGE ON INERTIA

1.1. Introduction. In dynamics we are familiar with the fact that a particle of mass m moving with velocity v possesses momentum p given by

$$p = mv \tag{1.1}$$

A particle upon which no net force acts either is in equilibrium or is moving with constant momentum. If the particle is acted upon by a resultant force F, the momentum p of the particle in the direction of the force increases with time. The relation between the force F applied to the particle and the rate at which its momentum p increases is given by the equation

$$F = \frac{dp}{dt} \tag{1.2}$$

Substitution for p from Eq. (1.1) into Eq. (1.2) gives

$$F = \frac{d}{dt}(mv) \tag{1.3}$$

and, provided that the mass of the particle does not vary with time, this can be rewritten as

$$F = m\frac{dv}{dt} \tag{1.4}$$

This equation shows that the acceleration experienced by a particle of constant mass is proportional to the applied force and that the constant of proportionality is the mass of the particle.

In electricity we are frequently concerned with particles that possess not only mass but also electric charge. Moreover we know that, between particles that possess electric charge, forces act that can be much stronger than those arising from the mass of the particles. It is therefore appropriate to ask the question whether a particle that possesses both charge and mass is endowed not only with inertia on account of its mass but also with inertia on account of its charge.

1.2. Rotation of a Charged Flywheel. That charged particles do possess inertia on account of their charge can be seen by consideration of

333

the following idealized experiment.   Suppose that a flywheel has a heavy metal rim supported by light insulating spokes.   Suppose that the rim has a total mass M.   To speed up or slow down the wheel a torque must be applied the magnitude of which can be calculated in terms of the angular acceleration produced, the mass M of the rim, and the size of the wheel. Let us now suppose that the rim is given an electric charge Q per unit length, and let us inquire whether this affects the torque that must be applied to produce a given acceleration or deceleration of the wheel.

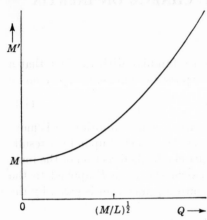

The answer is that the wheel possesses more inertia when it is charged than when it is uncharged. When the rim is charged, it in fact behaves like an uncharged rim whose mass is

$$M' = M + LQ^2 \quad (1.5)$$

where L is a parameter that depends upon the geometrical dimensions of the rim and is known as its inductance.   Equation (1.5)

Fig. 1.1. Variation of the equivalent mass of a charged flywheel with the charge per unit length on the rim.

shows that the equivalent mass M' of the charged wheel varies with the charge Q per unit length of the rim as shown in Fig. 1.1.

We see that, if the charge on the rim is zero, or if the magnitude of the charge per unit length is small compared with

$$\left(\frac{M}{L}\right)^{1/2} \qquad (1.6)$$

then the equivalent mass M' of the rim is substantially the same as its actual mass M.   On the other hand, if the charge Q per unit length on the rim is large compared with expression (1.6), the term M in Eq. (1.5) is relatively unimportant.   The inertia properties of the wheel are then controlled by its charge instead of by its mass.

For wheels used in mechanics the mass is so large and the charge so small that the charge on the wheel has no influence upon its inertia.   Let us, however, consider an "electronic wheel" consisting of a circle of fixed conducting wire through which a current of electrons is flowing.   Here the moving rim consists only of the electrons that constitute the current. This is an extremely light rim whose charge per unit length is enormous compared with the value given by expression (1.6).   Consequently the inertia of an electronic wheel consisting of an electric current flowing round a circuit is controlled by the electric charge of the electrons rather than by their mass. The inertia effects of electric currents are therefore much greater than would be calculated purely from the mass of the moving electrons that constitute the current, although they are still small compared with the inertia effects usually encountered in mechanics.

1.3. The Concept of Momentum in Electrical Science. From what has been said in the preceding section it follows that, if an electric current I flowing round an electric circuit is to increase or decrease with time t, it is necessary that force be applied to the electrons. Moreover the ratio of the force applied to the resulting rate of change of current is associated with the charge of the electrons rather than with their mass. The most convenient way in which to apply to electrons the forces necessary to accelerate or decelerate them is with the aid of an electric field. A convenient way of applying an electric field to the free electrons in an electric circuit is to connect in the circuit a battery. Figure 1.2 represents a pair of metal wires to the left-hand ends of which is connected a battery of voltage V. The right-hand ends of the wires can be connected metallically together by means of

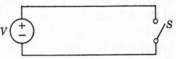

FIG. 1.2. An electric circuit for which the current may be allowed to start from zero and increase with time.

a switch S. Let us suppose that, initially, the switch is open as shown in the diagram. The two wires then form a capacitor connected across the battery. The upper wire is positively charged, the lower wire is negatively charged, and lines of electric force run from the upper wire to the lower wire in substantially the manner appropriate to a twin-wire transmission line. Within the metal wires the electric field is zero, and there is no current. Let us now suppose that, at time zero, the switch S is closed, thereby connecting the right-hand ends of the two wires metallically. Shortly after the switch has been closed, there is an electric field within the wire tending to accelerate electrons round the circuit. This produces round the circuit a current I that starts from zero at time zero and increases with time. The rate at which the current begins to increase after the switch is closed is proportional to the voltage V of the battery, and we can write

$$V = L \frac{dI}{dt} \tag{1.7}$$

where L is a constant of proportionality that depends upon the geometry of the circuit and is known as its inductance. Equation (1.7) describes the way in which the charged electrons in the circuit are accelerated from rest in the same way that Eq. (1.4) describes the way in which a body possessing mass is accelerated from rest by a force. Equation (1.7), however, is based upon the inertia of the electrons arising from their charge rather than upon the comparatively negligible inertia of the electrons arising from their mass.

When a body such as an automobile is accelerated from rest, friction comes into play, and acceleration of the body then depends upon the extent by which the driving force exceeds the frictional force. The body ultimately reaches a steady velocity when the driving force is only sufficient to overcome the frictional force. A similar process happens with an electric circuit. When the switch S in Fig. 1.2 is closed, the electrons are accelerated round the circuit and the current I increases with time at a rate given by Eq. (1.7). But the electrons begin to make collisions with the fixed metallic atoms in the wire, and this converts some of the ordered motion acquired by acceleration along the wire into random motion of heat. The retarding impulses associated with the collisions of the drifting electrons with the fixed atoms add up to a frictional retarding force that gets bigger as the current increases. Thus, while the initial rate of increase of the current is given by Eq. (1.7), increase of the current subsequently depends upon the amount by which the voltage of the battery exceeds the voltage required to overcome the resistance of the circuit. A steady current is ultimately reached when the voltage of the battery no longer exceeds the potential difference required to maintain the current against the resistance of the circuit. Thereafter the current round the circuit is steady and has the value given by Ohm's law. The time taken to achieve this steady current depends upon the geometry of the circuit, but it is usually less than 1 sec, and frequently a great deal less.

In studies of steady current using Ohm's law it is assumed that the transient process whereby the currents build up from zero to a steady value has been completed. Considerable interest attaches, however, to the process whereby the current builds up. Moreover many of the most important situations encountered in electrical science are ones in which the currents never become steady but are continually either increasing or decreasing with time. To study these situations we have to extend the fundamental equations of mechanics so as to allow for the tremendous inertia phenomena arising from the fact that electrons have not only mass but also charge. This implies developing electrical versions of Eqs. (1.1) to (1.4) that result in Eq. (1.4) being replaced by Eq. (1.7).

The process of developing electrical counterparts of Eqs. (1.1) to (1.4) depends very largely upon developing the electrical counterpart of Eq. (1.1). The concept of momentum in electrical science is, however, by no means so easy to understand as it is in mechanical science. Equation (1.1) does little more than state in a precise form what most people know intuitively even before studying mechanics. The concept of momentum in electrical science involves, however, ideas that are not met with in mechanical science until one studies the dynamics of fluids. It will therefore be necessary for us to make an extended study of a phenomenon known as magnetic flux, which is the electrical counterpart of momentum in mechanics.

1.4. Use of Vector Algebra. In discussing the phenomenon of magnetic flux it is convenient to make use of vector concepts. In Parts 1 and 2 we have already encountered the electric-flux-density vector **D**, the electric vector **E**, and the current-density vector **J**. In employing vectors, use has been made of the fact that a vector has magnitude and direction and that it resolves according to the cosine law. Use has also been made of the parallelogram law of vector addition. No use has yet been made, however, of a product of two vectors. Occasions have occurred when use could have been made of what is known as the scalar product of two vectors. Moreover in the coming discussion of the phenomenon of magnetic flux we shall frequently have to make certain statements concerning the relation among three vectors. These relations are most conveniently stated in terms of what is known as the vector product of two vectors. It is convenient therefore, before commencing study of magnetic flux, to introduce the concepts of scalar and vector products of two vectors.

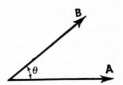

FIG. 1.3. Diagram for illustrating the scalar and vector products of two vectors.

1.5. The Scalar Product of Two Vectors. Let **A** and **B** be two vectors and let θ be the angle between them as illustrated in Fig. 1.3. The scalar product of the two vectors **A** and **B** is a number, or "scalar quantity," whose value is equal to the product of the magnitude of the vector **A**, the magnitude of the vector **B**, and the cosine of the angle θ between them. The scalar product is denoted by **A** · **B**, so that we write

$$\mathbf{A} \cdot \mathbf{B} = AB \cos \theta \tag{1.8}$$

The scalar product of the vector **B** with the vector **A** is

$$\mathbf{B} \cdot \mathbf{A} = BA \cos \theta \tag{1.9}$$

It follows from Eqs. (1.8) and (1.9) that

$$\mathbf{A} \cdot \mathbf{B} = \mathbf{B} \cdot \mathbf{A} \tag{1.10}$$

so that, as in ordinary multiplication of numbers, it does not matter whether we take the scalar product of the vector **A** with the vector **B** or the scalar product of the vector **B** with the vector **A**. Equation (1.8) can be interpreted by saying that the scalar product of the vector **A** with the vector **B** is the magnitude of the vector **A** multiplied by the component

$B \cos \theta$ of the vector **B** in the direction of the vector **A**.   Alternatively we can say that the scalar product of the vector **A** with the vector **B** is the product of the magnitude of the vector **B** with the component $A \cos \theta$ of the vector **A** in the direction of the vector **B**.

An example of the application of the concept of scalar product occurs in calculating the work done when the point of application of a force F receives a displacement s.   The force and the dis-placement can be represented by vectors as shown in Fig. 1.4, and the direction of the displacement vector **s** is not necessarily the same as that of the force vector **F**.   The work done during the displacement can be expressed either by the product of the magni-tude of the force F and the component in the direc-tion of the force of the displacement **s**, or alternatively by the product of the magnitude of the displacement **s** and the component of the force **F** in the direction of the displacement.   From either point of view the work done is the scalar product **F** · **s**.

Fig. 1.4. Illustrat-ing a force **F** whose point of application receives a displace-ment **s**.

1.6. The Vector Product of Two Vectors.   The vector product of two vectors is a vector.   The vector product of the two vectors **A** and **B** shown in Fig. 1.3 is a vector perpendicular to the plane of the paper.   The direction upward from the paper in Fig. 1.3 is the direction of advance of a right-hand screw that turns from the direction of the vector **A** to the direction of the vector **B** through the angle θ.   It is the direction of advance of this right-hand screw that is taken as the direction of the vector that constitutes the vector product of the vectors **A** and **B**.   The magnitude of the vector that constitutes the vector product of **A** with **B** is defined as the product of the magnitude of the vector **A**, the magnitude of the vector **B**, and the sine of the angle θ between the vectors, that is,

$$AB \sin \theta \qquad (1.11)$$

The vector product of two vectors **A** and **B** is therefore a vector whose magnitude is given by the expression (1.11) and whose direction is related by the right-hand-screw rule to rotation from the direction of **A** and to the direction of **B** through the angle θ.

We see from expression (1.11) that the magnitude of the vector product of two vectors **A** and **B** is the area of the parallelogram for which the vectors **A** and **B** are two adjacent sides.   We can also say that the magni-tude of the vector product of two vectors **A** and **B** is the product of the magnitude of the vector **A** with the component $B \sin \theta$ of the vector **B** in a direction that is perpendicular to the vector **A** and is in the plane of the two vectors.   Again we can say that the magnitude of the vector product of two vectors **A** and **B** is the product of the magnitude of the vector **B** and the component $A \sin \theta$ of the vector $\mathbf{A}$ in a direction that is perpendicular to the vector $\mathbf{B}$ and is in the plane of the two vectors.

The vector product of two vectors has unusual properties not possessed by the scalar product of two vectors and not possessed by the product of two numbers. Thus, suppose that the two vectors $\mathbf{A}$ and $\mathbf{B}$ are in the same direction. Then the angle θ in Fig. 1.3 is zero, and expression (1.11) for the magnitude of the vector product of the two vectors is zero. Thus the vector product of two vectors that point in the same direction is zero. In particular, if the vector $\mathbf{B}$ is identical with the vector $\mathbf{A}$, we have the result

$$\mathbf{A} \times \mathbf{A} = 0 \qquad (1.12)$$

Thus the vector product of any vector with itself is zero. Moreover the concept of vector product is not such that the vector product of $\mathbf{A}$ with $\mathbf{B}$ is identical with the vector product of $\mathbf{B}$ with $\mathbf{A}$. In taking the vector product of $\mathbf{B}$ with $\mathbf{A}$ in Fig. 1.3 the right-hand-screw rule leads to a vector that is downward through the paper, whereas the vector product of $\mathbf{A}$ with $\mathbf{B}$ is a vector that is upward from the paper. Thus the vector product of $\mathbf{B}$ with $\mathbf{A}$ is identical in magnitude with the vector product of $\mathbf{A}$ with $\mathbf{B}$ but points in the opposite direction. In other words

$$\mathbf{B} \times \mathbf{A} = -\mathbf{A} \times \mathbf{B} \qquad (1.13)$$

Thus reversal of the order of a vector product also reverses the sign.

An example of the use of the concept of vector product in mechanics occurs in connection with the calculation of torque. Suppose that a force $\mathbf{F}$ has a point of application whose position vector relative to an origin O is $\mathbf{r}$ as shown in Fig. 1.5. The magnitude of the torque of the force $\mathbf{F}$ about the point O is the product of the magnitude of $\mathbf{F}$ and the perpendicular from O onto the line of action of $\mathbf{F}$. The latter is the component of the position vector $\mathbf{r}$ in a direction which is perpendicular to that of the force $\mathbf{F}$ and which lies in the plane of the two vectors. Hence the magnitude of the torque of $\mathbf{F}$ about O is the magnitude of the vector product $\mathbf{r} \times \mathbf{F}$. The direction of the vector $\mathbf{r} \times \mathbf{F}$ is the axis about which the

Fig. 1.5. Illustrating use of a vector product to calculate torque.

torque acts, the direction of the torque being related by the right-hand-screw rule to the direction of the vector $\mathbf{r} \times \mathbf{F}$.

1.7. Line Integrals Involving Scalar Products. In discussing magnetic phenomena it will be convenient to make use of a line integral involving the scalar product of two vectors. A similar application of a line integral involving the scalar product of two vectors can also be made in electrostatics. It is convenient at this point to illustrate the use of such line integrals by considering their application in electrostatics.

Consider a specified electrostatic field. There is at each point an electric potential ϕ and an electric vector **E**. Let a curve be drawn in the field from a point A to a point B, and let us calculate the work done by the field in taking a unit test charge from the point A to the point B. Let ds be an element of length of the curve. Introduce a vector element of length ds of the curve whose magnitude is equal to ds and whose direction is along the curve at P from A to B, as shown in Fig. 1.6. If **E** is the electric vector at the point P, the work done by the field in taking a unit test charge along the element of length ds in the direction from A to B is

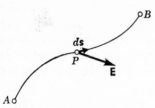

FIG. 1.6. Illustrating a line integral of a scalar product of two vectors.

$$\mathbf{E} \cdot d\mathbf{s} \qquad (1.14)$$

By adding up such contributions for all the elements of length of the curve we obtain the work done by the field in taking the unit test charge from A to B, and we write this work done in the form

$$\int_A^B \mathbf{E} \cdot d\mathbf{s} \qquad (1.15)$$

An integral such as this, taken along a curve from a point A to a point B, is known as a line integral. The line integral (1.15) involves the integration of the scalar product of a vector element of length at a point of the curve and the electric vector at this point.

The work done by an electrostatic field upon a unit charge in going from a point A to a point B is the amount by which the electric potential falls as we go from A to B. Hence, if ϕ_A is the potential at A and ϕ_B is the potential at B, it follows from expression (1.15) that

$$\phi_A - \phi_B = \int_A^B \mathbf{E} \cdot d\mathbf{s} \qquad (1.16)$$

where the line integral is taken along a curve joining the point A to the point B. In particular, if the curve is a closed curve C, so that the points A and B are identical and the potentials ϕ_A and ϕ_B are equal, the integral of expression (1.14) round the closed curve C is zero. This result can be written

$$\int_C \mathbf{E} \cdot d\mathbf{s} = 0 \qquad (1.17)$$

and expresses the fact that the work done in taking a unit test charge round any closed curve in an electrostatic field and returning to the starting point is zero.   It is Eq. (1.17) applied to the closed curves that form the meshes of networks of capacitors or resistors that leads to Kirchhoff's circulation law.

1.8. Surface Integrals Involving Scalar Products.   In our discussion of magnetic flux we shall be interested in evaluating integrals that involve a scalar product and that are taken over a surface.   Such integrals can also be used in discussing the flow of electric currents and in discussing electric flux in electrostatics.   Let us use these phenomena as examples to illustrate surface integrals that involve scalar products.

Suppose that we are interested in the flow of electric current in a conducting medium.   At each point P of the conducting medium electric current is flowing in a particular direction, and charge is crossing a surface drawn through P perpendicular to this direction at a certain rate per unit area per unit time.   The magnitude of this flow of charge per unit area per unit time at P is what is called the current density J at P. A vector of this magnitude drawn at P in the direction of current flow is what is known as the current-density vector $\mathbf{J}$ at P.   Now let us draw in the conducting medium a geometrical surface S bounded by a closed curve C as

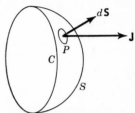

FIG. 1.7.   Illustrating distributed current crossing a surface S bounded by a rim C.

shown in Fig. 1.7.   Let us inquire how much current is threading the closed curve C and therefore crossing the surface S from one side to the other.

Let dS be an element of area at a point P of the surface S.   Introduce a vector $d\mathbf{S}$ whose magnitude is dS and whose direction is along the normal to S at P.   The normal to S at P can point in one or another of two directions, and we use the direction corresponding to the direction of the flow across S that we wish to calculate.   We call $d\mathbf{S}$ a vector element of area of the surface S at P.   Let $\mathbf{J}$ be the current-density vector at the point P.   Then the total electric current crossing the element of area dS is obtained by taking the component of the current-density vector $\mathbf{J}$ in the direction of the vector element of area $d\mathbf{S}$ and multiplying by the magnitude of the vector $d\mathbf{S}$.   This is the scalar product of the current-density vector $\mathbf{J}$ and the vector element of area $d\mathbf{S}$ and is written

$$\mathbf{J} \cdot d\mathbf{S} \tag{1.18}$$

Alternatively we can say that the total current crossing the element of area dS is obtained by multiplying the magnitude of the current-density vector $\mathbf{J}$ by the projection of the element of area upon a surface through P normal to the direction of the current.   This projected area is, however, the component of the vector element of area $d\mathbf{S}$ in the direction of the current-density vector **J**. Hence the total current crossing the element of area is the product of the magnitude of the current-density vector **J** with the component of the vector element of area $d\mathbf{S}$ in the direction of **J**. This is again the scalar product of **J** with $d\mathbf{S}$ exhibited in expression (1.18). The total current threading the rim C, and therefore crossing the surface S from one side to the other, is the sum of contributions such as that given by expression (1.18) from all the elements of area of the surface S. We write this summation as

$$\int_S \mathbf{J} \cdot d\mathbf{S} \qquad (1.19)$$

We can then say that the total current crossing the surface S from one side to the other is

$$I = \int_S \mathbf{J} \cdot d\mathbf{S} \qquad (1.20)$$

Thus to express the total current threading a closed curve C in a conducting medium we require a surface integral taken over a surface of which the closed curve C is the rim. The quantity to be integrated over the surface S is the scalar product of a vector element of area $d\mathbf{S}$ at a point of S and the current-density vector **J** at this point of S.

Let us suppose that the surface S is a closed surface so that the rim C has shrunk to a point. The surface S might be an egg-shaped surface in which there is a pinhole, the rim of which is the closed curve C. If the vector elements $d\mathbf{S}$ of the surface S point outward from the closed surface, the integral (1.19) gives the total electric current leaving the closed surface S. For a steady flow of electric current, however, the principle of conservation of charge requires that, if current is leaving a closed surface S over one portion of the surface, an equal amount of current must be entering the closed surface S over another portion of S. Hence for a closed surface S drawn in a flow of steady electric current the integral (1.19) must vanish. We write this result as

$$\oint \mathbf{J} \cdot d\mathbf{S} = 0 \qquad (1.21)$$

for any closed surface S drawn in any flow of steady electric current. If this result is applied to a small closed surface enclosing a node of a network of resistors, the flow across the closed surface is zero except where wires cross the surface, and Eq. (1.21) then becomes Kirchhoff's conservation law for networks of resistors.

Similar statements can be made with regard to the electric-flux-density vector **D**. At a point P in an electrostatic field let **D** be the electric-flux-density vector. If the system were discharged along lines of force, the charge passing the point P would move in the direction of the vector **D**, and the magnitude of **D** gives the charge per unit area that would cross a surface drawn through P perpendicular to the direction of **D**. Now suppose that we draw in the electrostatic field a surface S having a rim C. Let us inquire how much charge would thread through the closed curve C when the sytem is discharged along lines of force. This is known as the total electric flux threading C. It is equal to the total charge that crosses the surface S from one side to the other. Let $d\mathbf{S}$ be a vector element of area of the surface S at a point where the electric-flux-density vector is **D**. Then the charge crossing this element of area is

$$\mathbf{D} \cdot d\mathbf{S} \tag{1.22}$$

and the total electric flux across the surface S is

$$\int_S \mathbf{D} \cdot d\mathbf{S} \tag{1.23}$$

This is the charge that would thread the rim C of the surface S if the system were discharged along lines of force. The integral (1.23) evaluates the electric flux crossing the surface S from one side to the other in the direction determined by the directions of the vector elements of area $d\mathbf{S}$ of the surface S.

Let us suppose that the surface S is a closed surface, so that the rim C has shrunk to a point. If the vector elements $d\mathbf{S}$ of the surface S point outward from the closed surface, the integral (1.23) gives the total electric flux out of S. This is the total charge that would leave the closed surface S if the system were discharged along lines of force and is therefore the total charge Q that is inside the closed surface S before the system is discharged. Hence, for a closed surface S enclosing a total electric charge Q in an electrostatic field, we have

$$\int_S \mathbf{D} \cdot d\mathbf{S} = Q \tag{1.24}$$

This is Gauss' theorem and was expressed in Part 1, Eq. (3.20), without the use of vector algebra.

Surface integrals of the types (1.19) and (1.23) are required to explain what is meant by magnetic flux.

1.9. The Concept of Solid Angle. In evaluation of integrals of the types (1.19) and (1.23), the concept of solid angle is frequently useful.

A plane angle between two lines is defined by drawing in the plane of the lines a circle of unit radius with center at the point of intersection of the lines, as shown in Fig. 1.8. The two lines cut off on the unit circle an arc of a certain length. It is the length of this arc that we use to measure the angle between the two lines. If the angle between the two radial straight lines opens out until the portion of the plane between the lines becomes the whole of the plane, the angle contained by the lines is numerically equal to the perimeter of a circle of unit radius and is therefore 2π.

Now suppose that we have a cone and that we wish to define the solid angle within the cone. Draw a sphere of unit radius with center at the apex of the cone as shown in Fig. 1.9. The cone intercepts upon the unit sphere a certain area. This area measures the solid angle contained

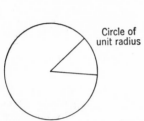

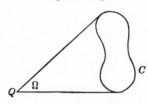

FIG. 1.8. Illustrating the definition of a plane angle between two intersecting straight lines.

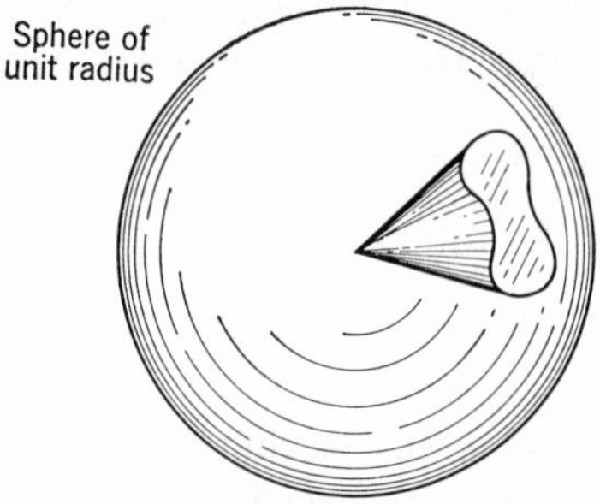

FIG. 1.9. Illustrating the definition of the solid angle contained within a cone.

within the cone. Thus the solid angle within a cone is the area intercepted by the cone upon a unit sphere with center at the apex of the cone. If the cone shown in Fig. 1.9 opens out so that the volume contained within it becomes the whole of space, the solid angle contained by the cone is the complete area of a sphere of unit radius, and this is 4π. Thus the solid angle subtended at any point by the whole of space is 4π.

As an example of the use of solid angle, let us suppose that there exists in free space a point charge of strength Q. In the electric field of the point charge let us draw a closed curve C as shown in Fig. 1.10. Join the position of the point charge to the points of the closed curve C thereby forming a cone as shown in Fig. 1.10, and let the solid angle of this cone be Ω. To calculate the total electric flux threading the closed curve C it is not necessary to draw a surface S spanning the curve C and to evaluate for this surface the integral (1.23). Instead we can argue as follows: The total electric flux leaving the point charge is Q, and this is spread uniformly over a total solid angle 4π. The fraction that goes into the solid angle Ω illustrated in Fig. 1.10 is therefore

FIG. 1.10. Illustrating the use of the concept of solid angle in calculating the electric flux from a point charge Q through a closed curve C.

$$\frac{\Omega}{4\pi} Q \qquad\qquad (1.25)$$

and this is the required flux threading the closed curve C. We now complete the calculation of the electric flux threading the closed curve C by evaluating the solid angle Ω appearing in expression (1.25). In Figure 1.10 this involves finding the area intercepted by the cone on a sphere of unit radius with center at the point charge. If the cone is a circular cone of semivertical angle θ, the solid angle evaluates to

$$\Omega = 4\pi \, \sin^2 \frac{\theta}{2} \tag{1.26}$$

and the electric flux given by expression (1.25) becomes

$$Q \, \sin^2 \frac{\theta}{2} \tag{1.27}$$

With the aid of the preliminary concepts developed in this chapter we are now in a position to approach the study of magnetic flux.

SUMMARIZING EXERCISES

1.1. Explain what is meant by the scalar and vector products of two vectors. Give an example of the use of each of these products. Show that reversal in the order of a vector product involves a change of sign.

1.2. Explain what is meant by a vector element of length of a curve. In an electrostatic field A and B are two points joined by a geometrical curve. A vector element of length of the curve is denoted by $d\mathbf{s}$ and is directed along the curve from A to B. At this element the electric vector is $\mathbf{E}$. Show that the electric potential at A exceeds the electric potential at B by an amount

$$\int_A^B \mathbf{E} \cdot d\mathbf{s}$$

1.3. For any closed curve C in any electrostatic field, $d\mathbf{s}$ denotes a vector element of length and $\mathbf{E}$ is the electric vector at the element. Prove that the integral round C of the scalar product of $\mathbf{E}$ with $d\mathbf{s}$ vanishes.

1.4. Explain what is meant by a vector element of area, describing the two alternative directions in which the vector can point. Steady electric current is flowing through conducting material, and in the material is drawn a closed geometrical curve C spanned by a geometrical surface S. A vector element of area of S is denoted by $d\mathbf{S}$, and $\mathbf{J}$ is the current-density vector at this element. Prove that the total current threading the closed curve C is

$$\int_S \mathbf{J} \cdot d\mathbf{S}$$

Explain how the direction in which this current threads C is specified by the direction of the vector element of area $d\mathbf{S}$.

1.5. A closed geometrical surface S is drawn in an electrostatic field and encloses a total charge Q. A vector element of area of S is denoted by $d\mathbf{S}$ and is directed along the outward normal to the surface.   Show that Gauss' theorem can be expressed in the form

$$\int_S \mathbf{D} \cdot d\mathbf{S} = Q$$

1.6. Explain what is meant by a solid angle.   Calculate the solid angle contained within a circular cone of semivertical angle θ.

1.7. Show that the total solid angle subtended by the whole of space at any point is 4π.   For a point charge Q located in free space at the vertex of a geometrical cone of solid angle Ω, show that the total electric flux within the solid is $Q\Omega/4\pi$.

CHAPTER 2

MAGNETIC FLUX

2.1. Introduction. In building up our concepts of electric fields in Part 1 we started with the electric field of a single point charge. By combining the electric fields of many point charges we were ultimately able to ascertain the electric fields for comparatively complicated distributions of electric charge. In commencing our study of magnetic fields we shall likewise start with the fields appropriate to simple situations. The simple situations that we shall choose are those appropriate to transmission lines. Using the magnetic fields of transmission lines it is possible to illustrate practically all the fundamental properties possessed by magnetic fields. It will be convenient to list the properties possessed by magnetic fields after these properties have been encountered and analyzed for transmission lines and other simple situations.

2.2. The Field of Magnetic Flux of a Coaxial Transmission Line. Consider a coaxial transmission line consisting of a pair of hollow conducting circular cylinders having a common axis as shown in Fig. 2.1. We suppose that the conductors are indefinitely long. Let a steady current I flow along the inner conductor and back along the outer conductor. In Fig. 2.1 it is supposed that the current along the inner conductor is flowing upward out of the paper and that along the outer conductor is flowing downward. It is further supposed that the current is uniformly distributed round the perimeter of each of the hollow conductors, so that the

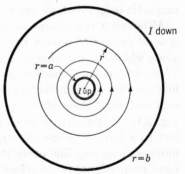

FIG. 2.1. The field of magnetic flux of a coaxial transmission line.

arrangement has cylindrical symmetry around the common axis of the two conductors. To overcome resistance in the conductors an electric field is necessary in the direction of current flow. This can be provided by connecting the inner conductor to the outer conductor at one end of the long piece of coaxial transmission line and then applying a battery between the inner and outer conductors at the other end. The better

347

the conductivity of the conductors, the smaller is the electric field strength required to drive a given current through them. In order to separate electric and magnetic phenomena it is convenient to consider the ideal case of a coaxial transmission line made of perfectly conducting cylinders. In this case the electric field required to drive the current I along the inner conductor and back along the outer conductor is negligible. In these circumstances we have a current I flowing along the inner conductor and back along the outer conductor with essentially no electric field present. This permits us to allow those phenomena that depend upon the electric field to recede into the background so that we can focus our attention upon the phenomena that depend on the magnetic field.

If the inner and outer conductors of the coaxial transmission line are perfectly conducting so that no electric field is required to drive the current through them, a test charge placed at any point in space should be subject to no force. This statement is, however, true only if the test charge is stationary relative to the coaxial transmission line. If a test charge between the inner and outer conductors moves relative to the transmission line, force is exerted upon it. This force is proportional to the velocity v with which the test charge moves. The force changes sign with v and vanishes for a stationary test charge. Forces exerted upon a test charge by virtue of its motion are called forces of magnetic origin, while forces exerted upon a stationary test charge are called forces of electric origin. Both forces of electric origin and forces of magnetic origin arise, however, from the existence of electric charge. It is force of magnetic origin that we are now to study.

Although a test charge in motion relative to an electric current is in general subject to a force by virtue of its motion, there are certain lines along which the test charge can move without being subject to this force. These are known as lines of magnetic flux. For the coaxial transmission line the lines of magnetic flux are circles with their centers on the common axis and with their planes perpendicular to this axis as illustrated in Fig. 2.1. A test charge which moves round one of these circles is not subject to a force of magnetic origin in spite of its motion. A test charge moving along any line other than a line of magnetic flux is subject to a force proportional to its velocity.

Let us consider the force of magnetic origin acting upon a test charge moving in a radial plane through the common axis of the coaxial transmission line shown in Fig. 2.1. An axial cross section of Fig. 2.1 is shown in Fig. 2.2. The current I on the inner conductor is flowing to the right in Fig. 2.2 and the current on the outer conductor to the left. Motion of a test charge between the conductors in an axial plane is necessarily perpendicular to the lines of magnetic flux shown in Fig. 2.1. Consequently there is a force of magnetic origin upon the test charge proportional to its velocity v. The force upon the test charge is also proportional to the strength e of the test charge and changes sign with e. The force of magnetic origin upon the test charge is also proportional to the current I flowing along the inner conductor and back along the outer, and the force changes sign with I.

The force of magnetic origin on the moving test charge is stronger near the inner conductor than it is near the outer conductor. It vanishes inside the hollow inner conductor and outside the outer conductor. Between the conductors the force is inversely proportional to the distance r from the common axis. This can also be stated by saying that, as the test charge moves through a fixed point P between the conductors, the force of magnetic origin upon it is inversely proportional to the length $2\pi r$ of the line of magnetic flux through P. Thus, for motion of a test charge between the conductors in an axial plane, the magnitude F of the force of magnetic origin exerted upon it depends upon the strength

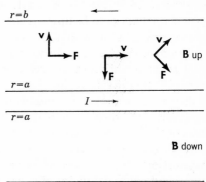

Fig. 2.2. Illustrating the direction of the force **F** acting upon a positive test charge moving with velocity **v** in an axial plane between the inner and outer conductors of a coaxial transmission line.

e of the charge, the velocity v with which it is moving, the strength I of the current, and the distance r from the common axis according to the relation

$$F \propto ev \frac{I}{2\pi r} \qquad (2.1)$$

We now have to consider the direction in which this force acts.

In describing the direction of the force whose magnitude is discussed in relation (2.1) it is convenient to assume that the test charge is positive. If the charge moves radially outward from the inner conductor to the outer conductor, the force of magnetic origin on it has the same direction as the current on the inner conductor, as shown in Fig. 2.2. If the direction of motion of the charge is the same as the direction of the current on the inner conductor, the force of magnetic origin upon the charge is radially inward toward the inner conductor. For other directions of motion of the test charge in an axial plane through the common axis of the conductors, the direction of the force of magnetic origin on a positive test charge is as shown at the right in Fig. 2.2. The direction of the force is perpendicular to the direction of motion of the test charge and also perpendicular to the line of magnetic flux through the position of the charge. However, there are two opposite directions both of which are perpendicular to the direction of motion of the test charge and to the line of magnetic flux through its position. The correct direction to choose is the one illustrated in Fig. 2.2 and can be defined as follows: On the lines of magnetic flux place arrows in a direction related by the right-hand-screw rule to the direction of the current on the inner conductor. These arrows are illustrated in Fig. 2.1. In Fig. 2.2 the arrows on the lines of magnetic flux would be upward out of the paper above the inner conductor and downward through the paper below the inner conductor. At the position of the test charge we now have two directions specified. The first is the direction of the velocity of the test charge, and the second is the direction that we have marked along the line of magnetic flux. Application of the right-hand-screw rule to rotation from the direction of the velocity to the direction along the line of magnetic flux gives the direction of the force of magnetic origin acting on the test charge. This statement, together with the relation (2.1), specifies, except for a constant of proportionality, the force acting upon a test charge moving between the inner and outer conductor of a coaxial transmission line in an axial plane.

Let us suppose now that the test charge is not moving in an axial plane through the common axis of the conductors. This means that the direction of motion is not perpendicular to the lines of magnetic flux illustrated in Fig. 2.1. We can therefore resolve the velocity of the test charge into two components, one of which is along the line of magnetic flux through its position and the other of which is perpendicular to the line of magnetic flux through its position. The component of velocity along the line of magnetic flux leads to no force on the test charge, as previously described. The component of velocity perpendicular to the line of magnetic flux leads to a force or the test charge as described in connection with relation (2.1). Thus it is only the component of the velocity of a test charge perpendicular to the lines of magnetic flux that is involved in calculating the force on the moving test charge.

The above description of the force acting upon a moving test charge can be greatly simplified by use of the vector product of two vectors. The first of these vectors is the velocity **v** of the test charge. The second is a vector **B** known as the magnetic-flux-density vector; its magnitude B is known as the magnetic flux density. At each point P between the inner and outer conductors the magnetic-flux-density vector **B** is directed along the line of magnetic flux passing through P in the direction of the arrow already attached to the line of magnetic flux and illustrated in Fig. 2.1. The magnitude B of the magnetic-flux-density vector **B** at any point P is defined for a coaxial transmission line as follows: Inside the hollow inner conductor, B is zero. Outside the outer conductor, B is also zero.

Between the two conductors B is directly proportional to the current I flowing along one conductor and back along the other, and is inversely proportional to the distance r from the common axis. The latter statement can also be made by saying that the magnitude of the magnetic flux density B at a point P distant r from the common axis is inversely proportional to the length $2\pi r$ of the line of magnetic flux through P. We thus have for the magnitude of the magnetic-flux-density vector $\mathbf{B}$ at a point P between the two conductors at distance r from the common axis

$$B \propto \frac{I}{2\pi r} \tag{2.2}$$

and the direction of $\mathbf{B}$ is along the line of magnetic flux through P in the direction related by the right-hand-screw rule to the direction of the electric current on the inner conductor.

In terms of the magnetic-flux-density vector $\mathbf{B}$ at the point P and the velocity $\mathbf{v}$ of a test charge of strength e passing through the point P, we can summarize what we have said about the force $\mathbf{F}$ of magnetic origin exerted upon the test charge at P by means of the vector equation

$$\mathbf{F} = e\mathbf{v} \times \mathbf{B} \tag{2.3}$$

This equation implies that the magnitude of the force exerted on the test charge is proportional to the strength e of the charge. It also implies that the magnitude of the force on the test charge is proportional to the magnitude of the velocity $\mathbf{v}$ of the test charge. More particularly the vector product in Eq. (2.3) implies that the magnitude of the force on the test charge is proportional to the component of the velocity $\mathbf{v}$ of the test charge in a direction perpendicular to the magnetic-flux-density vector $\mathbf{B}$ at P. Furthermore Eq. (2.3) implies that the magnitude of the force on the test charge is proportional to the magnitude B of the magnetic-flux-density vector $\mathbf{B}$ at P, and B satisfies relation (2.2). Finally Eq. (2.3) implies that the direction of the force $\mathbf{F}$ on the test charge is perpendicular to the vectors $\mathbf{v}$ and $\mathbf{B}$ and is related by the right-hand-screw rule to rotation from $\mathbf{v}$ to $\mathbf{B}$. All this simply constitutes the description that we have given of the force of magnetic origin exerted on a moving test charge in the space between the inner and outer conductors of a coaxial transmission line. Thus the force of magnetic origin acting on a test charge moving between the inner and outer conductors of a coaxial transmission line is summarized by Eq. (2.3), where the direction of $\mathbf{B}$ is indicated in Fig. 2.1 and the magnitude of $\mathbf{B}$ satisfies relation (2.2).

So far we have described how to calculate the magnetic-flux-density vector $\mathbf{B}$ at a point of space only for a coaxial transmission line with a current I along the hollow inner conductor and back along the outer conductor. In due course we shall see how to calculate the magnetic-flux-density vector **B** at any point of space due to any electric circuit. We shall see that, through each point P of space, there is in general a line of magnetic flux, and directed along this line of magnetic flux at P there is a magnetic-flux-density vector **B**. If a test charge of strength e moves through P with velocity represented by the vector **v**, then there is a force of magnetic origin acting upon the test charge given by Eq. (2.3). This force acts in a direction perpendicular to the velocity vector **v** and the magnetic-flux-density vector **B**. The direction is related by the right-hand-screw rule to rotation from **v** to **B**. The magnitude of the force is proportional to the strength e of the charge, to the magnitude v of the velocity of the test charge, to the magnitude B of the magnetic-flux-density vector at P, and to the sine of the angle between the directions of the vectors **v** and **B**. If at the point P there is in addition an electric field whose magnitude and direction are represented by the electric vector **E**, then the total force acting upon the test charge is given by

$$\mathbf{F} = e(\mathbf{E} + \mathbf{v} \times \mathbf{B}) \tag{2.4}$$

The first term $e\mathbf{E}$ on the right-hand side of Eq. (2.4) is the force on the test charge of electric origin, and the second term $e\mathbf{v} \times \mathbf{B}$ is the force of magnetic origin.

2.3. Inductivity. The relation (2.2) expressing the magnetic flux density between the conductors of a coaxial transmission line in terms of the current flowing along one conductor and back along the other involves a constant of proportionality. If the space between the conductors is a vacuum, this constant of proportionality is denoted by μ_v and is called the vacuum inductivity. Inserting this constant of proportionality, Eq. (2.2) becomes

$$B = \mu_v \frac{I}{2\pi r} \tag{2.5}$$

The constant 2π in the denominator of this equation could, in principle, be absorbed into the constant of proportionality μ_v, but it is not convenient or customary to do so. A complete statement concerning the magnetic flux density for the coaxial transmission line illustrated in Fig. 2.1 is therefore

$$B = \begin{cases} 0 & 0 \le r < a \tag{2.6} \\ \mu_v \dfrac{I}{2\pi r} & a < r < b \tag{2.7} \\ 0 & r > b \tag{2.8} \end{cases}$$

Expression (2.6) describes the zero magnetic flux density existing inside the hollow inner conductor; expression (2.8) describes the zero magnetic flux density existing outside the outer conductor; expression (2.7) is a restatement of Eq. (2.5). The force of magnetic origin acting upon a test charge moving in the presence of a coaxial transmission line carrying a current I along the hollow inner conductor and back along the outer conductor is obtained by substituting from Eqs. (2.6) to (2.8) into Eq. (2.3), taking the direction of the vector **B** to be as shown in Fig. 2.1.

We need to know the numerical value of the vacuum inductivity μ_v. Let us measure the force **F** in Eq. (2.3) in newtons, the charge e in coulombs, and the velocity **v** in meters per second. Let us measure the current I in Eq. (2.5) in amperes and the distance r in meters. Then the numerical value for the vacuum inductivity is

$$\mu_v = \frac{2\pi}{5} \times 10^{-6} \tag{2.9}$$

If this value for μ_v is substituted into Eq. (2.5) and the resulting value for the magnetic-flux-density vector is substituted into Eq. (2.3), we obtain the force of magnetic origin acting on a test charge moving between the conductors of a coaxial transmission line.

It is comparatively unusual for the space between the conductors of a coaxial transmission line to be a vacuum. Usually it is filled with some nonconducting material, of which air is an example. In principle this modifies the numerical value of the constant of proportionality in relation (2.2) so that Eq. (2.5) becomes

$$B = \mu \frac{I}{2\pi r} \tag{2.10}$$

and Eqs. (2.6) to (2.8) become

$$B = \begin{cases} 0 & 0 \leq r < a \tag{2.11} \\ \mu \dfrac{I}{2\pi r} & a < r < b \tag{2.12} \\ 0 & r > b \tag{2.13} \end{cases}$$

The quantity μ is known as the inductivity of the medium between the conductors. For practically all materials used between the conductors of a transmission line the numerical value of the inductivity μ does not differ significantly from the vacuum inductivity μ_v given by Eq. (2.9). A major exception to this statement would occur, however, if use were made between the conductors of so-called ferromagnetic material to be discussed in Chap. 8.

The inductivity of a material performs for forces of magnetic origin a function similar to that performed for forces of electric origin by the capacitivity. For a vacuum the numerical value of the capacitivity is

$$\epsilon_v = 8.854 \times 10^{-12} \tag{2.14}$$

It will be noticed that there is an interesting difference between the numerical values for the vacuum inductivity and vacuum capacitivity.

Whereas the vacuum capacitivity is quoted to four significant figures, the vacuum inductivity is an exact number. The choice made historically for the magnitude of the unit of charge known as the coulomb could have been arranged so as to make either the vacuum capacitivity or the vacuum inductivity an exact number. Today it would seem more logical to have arranged the choice so as to make the vacuum capacitivity an exact and simple number. However, the historical development of the subject was such that the coulomb was so chosen to make the vacuum inductivity an exact number. It may be asked why, in choosing the magnitude of the unit of charge so as to make the vacuum inductivity have a prescribed number, a simpler number than that given in Eq. (2.9) was not chosen. The original choice was in fact made so as to give the vacuum inductivity the numerical value 10^{-7}. However, this choice was made at a time when an inconvenient system of units known as unrationalized units was in general use. When a change was subsequently made to the so-called rationalized system of units used nowadays, the numerical value of the vacuum inductivity had to be changed to $4\pi \times 10^{-7}$, and this is the value quoted in Eq. (2.9).

2.4. Field of Magnetic Flux of a Long, Straight, Hollow Wire Carrying a Steady Current. Suppose that we have an infinitely long, perfectly conducting hollow cylinder of radius a embedded in a homogeneous medium of inductivity μ. Let a steady current I flow along the wire parallel to the axis and uniformly distributed round the circumference. The field of magnetic flux produced by this current can be obtained from that appropriate to the coaxial transmission line shown in Fig. 2.1 by making the radius b of the outer cylinder infinite. The magnetic flux density inside the hollow wire is zero. Outside the wire the lines of magnetic flux are in circles whose centers are on the axis of the wire and whose planes

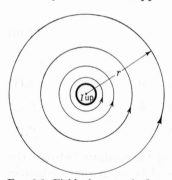

FIG. 2.3. Field of magnetic flux of a hollow wire carrying a steady current I.

are perpendicular to the wire. The magnetic-flux-density vector **B** at each point outside the wire is directed round the line of magnetic flux through the point in the direction related by the right-hand-screw rule to the direction of the current along the wire as shown in Fig. 2.3. The magnitude of the magnetic flux density at a point outside the wire distant r from the axis is given by Eq. (2.10). We thus have

$$B = \begin{cases} 0 & r < a \qquad (2.15) \\ \mu \dfrac{I}{2\pi r} & r > a \qquad (2.16) \end{cases}$$

and the direction of the vector **B** is as shown in Fig. 2.3. From the field
of magnetic flux density **B** at any point we can calculate the force of
magnetic origin on a test charge moving through the point in accordance
with Eq. (2.3).

Suppose that a point charge of strength e is moving with velocity v
parallel to the wire in the same direction as the electric current I along
the wire. Let the point charge be outside the wire and at a distance r
from the axis of the wire. Then Eq. (2.3) shows that the charge is subject
to a force that is directed radially inward toward the wire and is given in
magnitude by

$$F = evB \tag{2.17}$$

Substituting from Eq. (2.16) into Eq. (2.17) we see that the magnitude
of this force is

$$F = \mu \frac{evI}{2\pi r} \tag{2.18}$$

If $e = 1$ μcoulomb (10^{-6} coulomb), $v = 100$ m/sec, $I = 100$ amp, $r = 1$
cm (10^{-2} m), and $\mu = \mu_v$ given by Eq. (2.9), the force given by Eq. (2.18)
evaluates to 0.2 μnewton.

It will be observed from Eq. (2.16) that the field of magnetic flux outside the wire is independent of the radius a of the wire. This field is
therefore the same as if the cylinder of radius a were removed and the
current I were concentrated in an indefinitely thin wire at the axis of the
cylinder.

While the wire illustrated in Fig. 2.3 is supposed to be straight, the
field of magnetic flux close to it would not be substantially different if it
were bent. A closed loop of wire carrying a steady current I has a
field of magnetic flux which we shall ultimately be able to calculate and
which is illustrated in Fig. 6.15 for a circular loop. Close to the wire this
field of magnetic flux behaves substantially as shown in Fig. 2.3.

2.5. Superposition of Magnetic Fields. Any closed circuit of electric
current has closed lines of magnetic flux that thread through the circuit
in the direction related by the right-hand-screw rule to the direction of
the current round the circuit. A test charge moving round one of these
lines of magnetic flux is not subject to any force of magnetic origin. If
the test charge moves at an angle to the lines of magnetic flux, then it is
subject to a force of magnetic origin. If the strength of the test charge is
e and its velocity is **v**, the force **F** acting on it is given by Eq. (2.3), where
B is the magnetic-flux-density vector at the position of the test charge.

Now suppose that there are several electric circuits that are simultaneously carrying current. Then the force on a test charge at a point P
is the vector sum of the forces arising from the individual electric currents. Thus, if there are several electric circuits numbered 1, 2, . . . ,

and if the electric currents round these circuits exert on the test charge at P forces F_1, F_2, . . . , the total force F exerted upon the test charge in the presence of all the electric circuits is given by

$$F = F_1 + F_2 + \cdots \tag{2.19}$$

If the magnetic-flux-density vectors at P due to the individual electric circuits are B_1, B_2, . . . , the forces exerted by the individual electric circuits upon a test charge of strength e moving through the point P with velocity v are respectively

$$F_1 = ev \times B_1 \qquad F_2 = ev \times B_2 \qquad \cdots \tag{2.20}$$

Substitution from Eqs. (2.20) into Eq. (2.19) shows that the force exerted upon the moving test charge in the presence of all the electric currents is

$$F = ev \times B_1 + ev \times B_2 + \cdots \tag{2.21}$$

and this can be written as

$$F = ev \times (B_1 + B_2 + \cdots) \tag{2.22}$$

From this equation we see that the force exerted upon the moving test charge in the presence of all the electric currents can be written in the form of Eq. (2.3), where

$$B = B_1 + B_2 + \cdots \tag{2.23}$$

We therefore see that the procedure for calculating the force on a moving test charge due to a number of electric circuits is as follows: Calculate at the position of the test charge the magnetic-flux-density vectors B_1, B_2, . . . due to the individual electric circuits. Take the vector sum of these magnetic-flux-density vectors to form the resultant magnetic-flux-density vector B due to all the circuits. From this resultant magnetic-flux-density vector calculate the force on the moving test charge in accordance with Eq. (2.3). Calculation of the forces on a moving test charge due to a number of electric currents thus reduces to calculating the field of magnetic-flux-density vector B by vector addition of the contributions from each of the electric currents present.

2.6. The Field of Magnetic Flux of a Long, Straight, Solid Wire Carrying Current Uniformly Distributed throughout the Wire. Consider an infinite, straight, solid, circular wire of radius a carrying a steady current I uniformly distributed over each cross section. The solid wire may be thought of as a series of hollow cylindrical wires of successively increasing radius, each one fitting inside the next and the largest being of radius a. The entire current I along the solid wire can thus be divided up into a series of currents in hollow wires. In accordance with what has been said in the preceding section, the field of magnetic flux for the current in the solid wire can be calculated by superposition of the fields of magnetic flux for the currents along the hollow cylinders.

Let us first calculate the field of magnetic flux outside the solid wire. In accordance with Eq. (2.16), the field outside a hollow wire carrying current is the same as if the current were concentrated along the axis of the wire. This is true for each hollow wire into which the solid wire can be subdivided. Hence the field outside the solid wire is the same as if the solid wire were removed and the entire current I were concentrated along the axis. The lines of magnetic flux therefore lie in planes perpendicular to the wire and are circles with center on the axis of the wire. The magnetic-flux-density vector **B** is directed round the lines of magnetic flux in the direction related by the right-hand-screw rule to the direction of the current along the wire. At a point outside the wire distant r from the axis, the magnitude of the magnetic-flux-density vector is

$$B = \mu \frac{I}{2\pi r} \qquad r > a \qquad (2.24)$$

The field of magnetic flux outside a wire carrying a steady current I does not depend upon whether the wire is solid or hollow.

Now let us calculate the magnetic flux density at a point P inside the solid wire at distance r from its axis. We think of the current uniformly distributed over the cross section of the solid wire as divided up into currents along hollow wires fitting inside one another. For the hollow wires of radius less than r, the point P is outside the cylinders, but for hollow wires of radius greater than r, the point P is inside the cylinders. Now, in accordance with Eq. (2.15), the magnetic flux density at a point inside a hollow wire carrying a steady electric current is zero, and hence the portion of the current in the solid wire flowing at a distance from the axis greater than r makes no contribution to the magnetic flux density at P. For the current at distances from the axis less than r, the magnetic flux density at P is the same as if this current were concentrated along the axis of the wire. Thus the magnetic flux density at the point P inside the solid wire at distance r from the axis is the same as if all the current in the solid wire at distance less than r from the axis were concentrated along the axis. The fraction of the total current I flowing along the solid conductor at distances less than r from the axis is the ratio of the area of a circle of radius r to the area of a circle of radius a. Hence, for calculating the magnetic flux density at a point inside the solid wire at distance r from the axis, the amount of current to be thought of as concentrated along the axis of the wire is

$$\frac{r^2}{a^2} I \qquad (2.25)$$

Replacing I in Eq. (2.10) by expression (2.25), we obtain

$$B = \mu \frac{1}{2\pi r} \frac{r^2}{a^2} I \qquad r < a \qquad (2.26)$$

and this can be written as

$$B = \mu \frac{I}{2\pi a^2} r \qquad r < a \qquad (2.27)$$

This gives the magnitude of magnetic-flux-density vector inside the wire at distance r from the axis; its direction points round a circle of radius r whose plane is perpendicular to the length of the wire and whose center is on the axis of the wire.

We thus see that, for a solid wire, the magnetic flux density increases from zero at the center of the wire to the value

$$\mu \frac{I}{2\pi a} \qquad (2.28)$$

at the surface of the wire in accordance with Eq. (2.27) and then decreases again outside the wire in accordance with Eq. (2.24). This behavior is

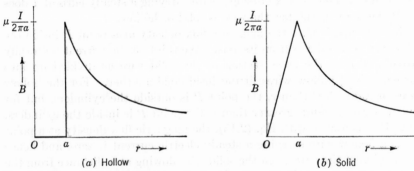

(a) Hollow   (b) Solid

FIG. 2.4. The variation of the magnetic flux density with distance from the axis on a long straight wire carrying steady current (a) when the wire is hollow, (b) when the wire is solid.

illustrated in Fig. 2.4b, and the corresponding behavior for a hollow wire is shown in Fig. 2.4a. At all distances from the axis, the magnetic-flux-density vector points round a circular line of magnetic flux in the direction related by the right-hand-screw rule to the direction of the current along the wire. Each line of magnetic flux is a circle whose center lies on the axis of the wire and whose plane is perpendicular to the length of the wire.

2.7. Relation between the Electric and Magnetic Fields of a Coaxial Transmission Line. The electric field of a coaxial transmission line carrying a charge Q per unit length on the inner conductor and $-Q$ per unit length on the inner surface of the outer conductor has been investigated in Part 1, Sec. 11.3. The lines of electric force are radial as shown in Fig. 2.5, and the equipotential surfaces are cylinders coaxial with the conductors. If ϵ is the capacitivity of the homogeneous medium between the conductors, the electric field strength at a point between the conductors at distance r from the common axis is

$$E = \frac{1}{\epsilon} \frac{Q}{2\pi r} \qquad (2.29)$$

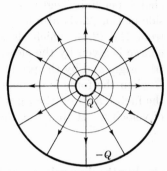

Comparison of Fig. 2.5 with Fig. 2.1 and of Eq. (2.29) with Eq. (2.10) shows an interesting relation between the electric field of the coaxial transmission line and the field of magnetic flux density of the coaxial transmission line. From Eqs. (2.29) and (2.10) we see that both the electric field strength E and the magnetic flux density B

FIG. 2.5. The electric field of a coaxial transmission line.

between the conductors vary inversely as the distance r from the common axis. In fact the ratio of the electric field strength E at a point P between the conductors to the magnetic flux density B at P is independent of the position of the point P and is given by

$$\frac{E}{B} = \frac{1}{\mu\epsilon} \frac{Q}{I} \qquad (2.30)$$

However, the directions of the electric vector $\mathbf{E}$ at the point P and of the magnetic-flux-density vector $\mathbf{B}$ at P are mutually perpendicular. The electric vector is directed radially from the positive charge on one conductor to the negative charge on the other, while the magnetic-flux-density vector points round the circular lines of magnetic flux in the direction related by the right-hand-screw rule to the direction of the current along the inner conductor. The lines of magnetic flux for the magnetic field lie on the equipotential surfaces for the electric field. In fact the lines of magnetic flux are the curves in which the equipotential surfaces for the electric field are intercepted by planes perpendicular to the axis of the transmission line. The magnetic-flux-density vector at any point P between the conductors shown in Fig. 2.1 could be calculated by first evaluating the electric vector at the same point P in Fig. 2.5. To obtain the direction of $\mathbf{B}$ from that of $\mathbf{E}$ it would be necessary to rotate the vector through a right angle in the direction related by the right-hand-screw rule to the direction of the current on the inner conductor. To obtain the magnitude of $\mathbf{B}$ from the magnitude of $\mathbf{E}$ it would be necessary to apply the ratio given by Eq. (2.30).

Equation (2.30) can be written in the form

$$\frac{1}{\mu\epsilon} = \frac{I}{Q} \frac{E}{B} \qquad (2.31)$$

The factor I/Q on the right-hand side of this equation has the dimensions of velocity because I represents charge per unit time and Q represents charge per unit length. Furthermore the factor E/B on the right-hand side of Eq. (2.31) also has the dimensions of velocity. This can be seen from Eq. (2.4), which shows that the force per unit charge on a test charge is given by the electric field strength E when the force is of electric origin and by the product of a velocity and the magnetic flux density B when the force is of magnetic origin. Thus both the factor I/Q and the factor E/B on the right-hand side of Eq. (2.31) have the dimensions of velocity. It therefore follows that the expression

$$\frac{1}{(\mu\epsilon)^{\frac{1}{2}}} \tag{2.32}$$

also has the dimensions of velocity. Thus the reciprocal of the geometric mean of the inductivity and capacitivity of a material is a velocity characteristic of the material. It will ultimately transpire that this velocity is the velocity of propagation of electromagnetic waves in the material, and this is identical with the velocity of light in the material.

For a vacuum, the inductivity is given by Eq. (2.9) and the capacitivity by Eq. (2.14). Substitution of these values into expression (2.32) gives

$$\frac{1}{(\mu_v\epsilon_v)^{\frac{1}{2}}} = 2.998 \times 10^8 \text{ m/sec} \tag{2.33}$$

and we recognize this velocity as the measured value of the velocity of light in a vacuum. In actual fact it is from Eq. (2.33) that the numerical value of the vacuum capacitivity is deduced. The procedure is as follows: First the unit of charge known as the coulomb is chosen to make the vacuum inductivity have the value given by Eq. (2.9). This value of μ_v is then substituted into Eq. (2.33) in order to derive the value for ϵ_v given by Eq. (2.14). Thus the numerical value of the vacuum capacitivity depends on the measured value for the velocity of light. A new determination of the velocity of light would lead to a modification in the numerical value of the vacuum capacitivity. This would not alter the vacuum inductivity, however, because the coulomb has been so defined that the vacuum inductivity has the precise value given by Eq. (2.9). It would have been equally reasonable, indeed perhaps more reasonable, to have chosen the coulomb to make the vacuum capacitivity have an exact numerical value and then to have deduced the vacuum inductivity from Eq. (2.33), but historically this is not what happened.

2.8. The Field of Magnetic Flux of a Twin-wire Transmission Line. Consider a twin-wire transmission line consisting of a pair of parallel wires that are indefinitely thin and indefinitely long. Let them be embedded in a homogeneous medium whose inductivity is μ and whose capacitivity is ϵ. Let a steady electric current I flow along one wire and

back along the other as shown in Fig. 2.6.   Consider a point P whose
perpendicular distance from one wire is r_1 and from the other wire is r_2 as
shown in Fig. 2.6.   Then the magnetic-flux-density vector $\mathbf{B}_1$ at the point
P due to the left-hand wire has
magnitude

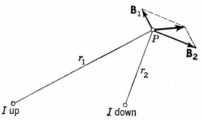

$$B_1 = \mu \frac{I}{2\pi r_1} \qquad (2.34)$$

and it points in the direction indicated in Fig. 2.6.   Likewise the
magnetic-flux-density vector $\mathbf{B}_2$ at
the point P due to the right-hand
wire has magnitude

FIG. 2.6. Illustrating the calculation of
the field of magnetic flux of a twin-
wire transmission line.

$$B_2 = \mu \frac{I}{2\pi r_2} \qquad (2.35)$$

and it is directed as indicated in Fig. 2.6.   To obtain the magnetic-flux-
density vector at P due to the two wires we combine the vectors due to
the separate wires by a vector addition as shown in Fig. 2.6 in accordance

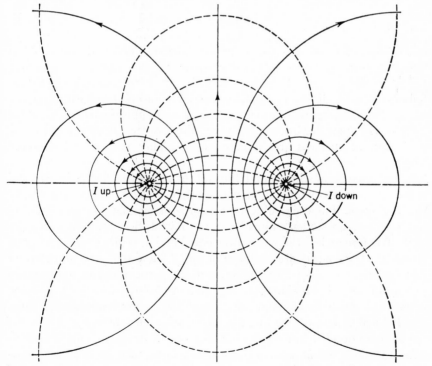

FIG. 2.7. Lines of magnetic flux for a twin-wire transmission line (unbroken curves).

with Eq. (2.23). In this way we may calculate the magnetic-flux-density vector at all points in the region surrounding the wires and hence draw the lines of magnetic flux as shown by the unbroken curves in Fig. 2.7. The lines of magnetic flux are closed lines threading between the wires carrying the current.

As in the case of a coaxial transmission line, so also for a twin-wire transmission line there is a close relation between the magnetic field produced by equal and opposite currents on the wires and the electric field produced by equal and opposite charges per unit length on the wires. To calculate the electric field at the point P due to charges Q and $-Q$ per unit length on the wires we apply Eq. (2.29) to each wire as shown in Fig. 2.8. The vector diagram shown in Fig. 2.8 is the same as the vector diagram shown in Fig. 2.6 except for a rotation through a right angle.

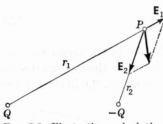

FIG. 2.8. Illustrating calculation of the electric field of a twin-wire transmission line due to equal and opposite charges per unit length on the wires.

Thus the magnetic-flux-density vector at the point P can be obtained by first calculating the electric vector at P due to charges Q and $-Q$ per unit length on the wires. We then rotate the vector through a right angle, apply to the magnitude of the vector the ratio given by Eq. (2.30), and so obtain the magnetic-flux-density vector at the point P due to equal and opposite currents I on the wires. As in the case of a coaxial transmission line, so also for a twin-wire transmission line it follows that the lines of magnetic flux for equal and opposite currents lie on the equipotential surfaces for equal and opposite charges per unit length. In fact the lines of magnetic flux are the curves in which the equipotential surfaces are intersected by planes perpendicular to the wires.

A test charge moving round the unbroken curves shown in Fig. 2.7 is not subject to any force of magnetic origin, but if it moves at an angle to these lines, it is then subject to a force of magnetic origin given by Eq. (2.3). Now we have already seen in Part 1, Sec. 11.4, that the lines of electric force when the wires carry equal and opposite charges per unit length are the dashed circles shown in Fig. 2.7 and that the equipotential surfaces are cylinders intersecting a plane perpendicular to the wires in the full-line circles shown in Fig. 2.7. It follows that these full-line circles are the lines of magnetic flux of the transmission line when a steady current flows along one wire and back along the other wire.

For more detailed calculations of the field of magnetic flux of a twin-wire transmission line we can proceed as follows: Take an origin O midway between the wires, and let the z axis be parallel to the wires. Let the

x and y axes be as shown in Fig. 2.9, so that the plane of the wires is the plane $y = 0$ and the symmetrical plane between the wires is the plane $x = 0$. Let d be the distance between the wires. Let us suppose first of all that we are interested in calcu-
lating the magnetic flux density at points in the plane of the two wires. Let us calculate the magnetic flux density at the point $(x,0,0)$. It is clear from Fig. 2.7 that the mag-netic-flux-density vector at this point is directed parallel to the positive y axis if $-\frac{1}{2}d < x < \frac{1}{2}d$. On the other hand, if x is greater than $\frac{1}{2}d$ or is more negative than $-\frac{1}{2}d$, then the magnetic-flux-density vector is parallel to the negative y axis. At the point $(x,0,0)$ the magnetic flux

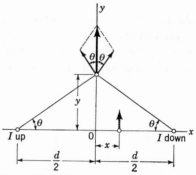

FIG. 2.9. Illustrating calculation of magnetic flux density for a twin-wire transmission line.

density in the y direction due to the left-hand wire in Fig. 2.9 is, from Eq. (2.34),

$$\frac{\mu I}{2\pi(\frac{1}{2}d + x)} \tag{2.36}$$

At the same point the magnetic flux density in the y direction due to the right-hand wire is

$$\frac{\mu I}{2\pi(\frac{1}{2}d - x)} \tag{2.37}$$

The total magnetic flux density in the y direction at the point $(x,0,0)$ is therefore

$$B = \frac{\mu I}{2\pi}\left(\frac{1}{\frac{1}{2}d + x} + \frac{1}{\frac{1}{2}d - x}\right) \tag{2.38}$$

The variation of the magnetic flux density B in the y direction with the distance x from the center line between the two wires is shown in Fig. 2.10. The positive values plotted for the region $-\frac{1}{2}d < x < \frac{1}{2}d$ indicate the fact that the direction of the magnetic-flux-density vector between the wires is that of the positive y axis in Fig. 2.9 as illustrated in Fig. 2.7. Outside the region between the wires the direction of the magnetic-flux-density vector is parallel to the negative y axis in Fig. 2.9 as shown in Fig. 2.7, and this is indicated in Fig. 2.10 by the negative ordinates when x is greater than $\frac{1}{2}d$ and when x is more negative than $-\frac{1}{2}d$. The magnetic flux density is large near the wires and falls to zero at a large distance from the wires. Halfway between the wires the magnetic flux density has the value

$$\frac{2\mu I}{\pi d} \tag{2.39}$$

obtained by putting $x = 0$ in Eq. (2.38).

To calculate the magnetic flux density in the symmetrical plane between the wires let us consider the point whose coordinates are $(0,y,0)$. The distance of this point from each of the wires is $(\frac{1}{4}d^2 + y^2)^{\frac{1}{2}}$, and

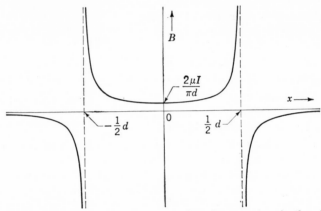

FIG. 2.10. The magnetic flux density in the y direction at points in the plane of the wires of a twin-wire transmission line as a function of the distance x from the center line between the wires.

consequently the magnitude of the magnetic flux density produced at this point by the separate currents is

$$\frac{\mu I}{2\pi} \frac{1}{(\frac{1}{4}d^2 + y^2)^{\frac{1}{2}}} \tag{2.40}$$

The components of the magnetic-flux-density vectors from the two currents cancel in the x direction and add in the y direction as shown in Fig. 2.9. Hence the resultant magnetic-flux-density vector is in the direction of the positive y axis. The cosine of the angle θ shown in Fig. 2.9 is

$$\frac{\frac{1}{2}d}{(\frac{1}{4}d^2 + y^2)^{\frac{1}{2}}} \tag{2.41}$$

The magnitude of the resultant magnetic-flux-density vector at the point $(0,y,0)$ is obtained by multiplying the magnetic flux density of an individual current given by expression (2.40) by the cosine of the angle θ given by expression (2.41) and doubling to allow for both currents. Hence the magnitude of the magnetic-flux-density vector at the point

(0,y,0) is

$$B = \frac{\mu I}{2\pi} \frac{d}{\frac{1}{4}d^2 + y^2}$$ (2.42)

and the direction is that of the positive y axis. The variation with y of the expression (2.42) is illustrated in Fig. 2.11. We see that in the symmetrical plane between the two wires the magnetic flux density is greatest in the plane of the wires, where it has the value given by expression (2.39), and decreases symmetrically as we move away from the plane of the wires in either direction.

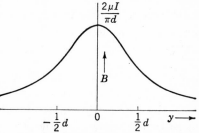

FIG. 2.11. The magnetic flux density of a twin-wire transmission line in the plane of symmetry as a function of the distance y from the plane of the wires.

2.9. Tubes of Magnetic Flux. The lines of magnetic flux drawn through any small closed curve form what is known as a tube of magnetic flux. Any field of magnetic flux can be dissected into tubes of magnetic flux, and the tubes are closed tubes. For the field of magnetic flux of a coaxial transmission line shown in Fig. 2.1 the tubes of magnetic flux are circular rings of uniform cross section. A typical tube of rectangular cross section would be bounded by a pair of geometrical circular cylinders whose axes coincide with the common axis of the conductors and by a pair of planes perpendicular to the common axis. The entire field of magnetic flux between the inner and outer conductors can be divided up into tubes of magnetic flux of this type.

While tubes of magnetic flux always take the form of closed tubes, their cross-sectional area is in general different at different points of the tube. This is illustrated in the field of magnetic flux of a twin-wire transmission line shown in Fig. 2.7. Through a pair of closely spaced lines of magnetic flux as shown in Fig. 2.12 draw cylinders with axes parallel to the wires. Intersect these two cylinders by a pair of planes at unit distance apart perpendicular to the wires. The space thereby enclosed forms a tube of magnetic flux. At a

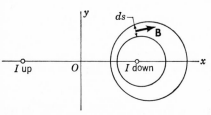

FIG. 2.12. Illustrating the fact that, as we move round a tube of magnetic flux, the product of the magnetic flux density and the normal cross-sectional area remains constant.

point of the tube where the cylinders have a separation ds, the normal cross section of the tube has dimensions ds in the plane of Fig. 2.12 and unity perpendicular to this plane, so that the cross-sectional area is

$$dS = ds \qquad (2.43)$$

From Eq. (2.43) and Fig. 2.12 we can see the way in which the normal cross-sectional area of a tube changes as we move round the tube.

The magnetic flux density B also varies as we move round the tube, and it varies in such a way that the product of the magnetic flux density and the normal cross-sectional area is the same at all points of the tube. For a tube of magnetic flux of a twin-wire transmission line this can be demonstrated in the following way: If equal and opposite charges per unit length were placed upon the wires of the transmission line, the two cylinders illustrated in Fig. 2.12 would be equipotential surfaces. If E is the field strength at the place where the separation between the equipotential surfaces is ds, the difference of potential between the two surfaces is $E\,ds$, since electric field strength is the downward gradient of electric potential. At different places between the two equipotential surfaces the separation ds has different values and the electric field strength E has different values. Since the potential difference between the surfaces is the same everywhere, it follows that, as we move round between the two equipotential surfaces, we must have

$$E\,ds = \text{constant} \qquad (2.44)$$

the constant on the right-hand side being the potential difference between the two surfaces. Now we have seen that the variation from place to place in the electric field strength E when the wires carry equal and opposite charges Q and $-Q$ per unit length is the same as the variation from place to place in the magnetic flux density B when the wires carry equal and opposite currents I and $-I$. In fact the ratio of E to B is given by Eq. (2.30). It therefore follows from Eq. (2.44) that, if B is the magnetic flux density at the place where the separation between the cylinders in Fig. 2.12 is ds, then as we move round the tube of magnetic flux,

$$B\,ds = \text{constant} \qquad (2.45)$$

Moreover, since the normal cross-sectional area of the tube is given by Eq. (2.43), Eq. (2.45) can be written as

$$B\,dS = \text{constant} \qquad (2.46)$$

We thus see that, as we move round the tube, the product of the magnetic flux density B at any point and the normal cross-sectional area dS at that point remains constant. Where the tube is thin, the magnetic flux density is high, and vice versa. The product $B\,dS$ is therefore a property of the tube as a whole and is known as the magnetic flux associated with the tube.

The magnetic flux associated with any tube of magnetic flux is the product of the magnetic flux density at any point of the tube and the normal cross-sectional area of the tube at that point. Alternatively we can say that the magnetic flux density at any point of the tube is the magnetic flux associated with the tube divided by the normal cross-sectional area of the tube at that point. Magnetic flux density is thus magnetic flux per unit area, and this explains the use of the terminology magnetic flux density.

If desired, the magnetic flux associated with a tube of magnetic flux can be expressed in terms of a cross-sectional area of the tube for other than a normal cross section. To do this it is convenient to use a scalar product of two vectors. In a field of magnetic flux let $d\mathbf{S}$ be a vector element of area at a point where the magnetic-flux-density vector is $\mathbf{B}$. Consider the tube of magnetic flux formed by lines of magnetic flux drawn through the rim of the vector element of area $d\mathbf{S}$. This element of area is not in general a normal cross section of the tube, and consequently the vector $d\mathbf{S}$ makes an angle with the vector $\mathbf{B}$ at this point of the tube as shown in Fig. 2.13. The normal cross-sectional area of the tube at the point is therefore the component of the vector element of area $d\mathbf{S}$ in the direction of the magnetic-flux-density vector $\mathbf{B}$. Hence the product of the magnetic flux density and the normal cross-sectional area of the tube is the product

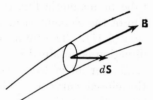

Fig. 2.13. Illustrating the fact that the magnetic flux associated with a tube is the scalar product of the magnetic-flux-density vector $\mathbf{B}$ and the vector $d\mathbf{S}$ representing the area of any cross section of the tube at the point.

of the magnitude of the vector $\mathbf{B}$ and the component of the vector $d\mathbf{S}$ in the direction of $\mathbf{B}$, and this is the scalar product of the vector $\mathbf{B}$ with the vector $d\mathbf{S}$. Hence the magnetic flux in the tube is

$$\mathbf{B} \cdot d\mathbf{S} \qquad\qquad (2.47)$$

We can thus say that, if $d\mathbf{S}$ is the vector representing any cross section of a tube, normal or otherwise, and if $\mathbf{B}$ is the magnetic-flux-density vector at this point of the tube, the scalar product given by expression (2.47) is constant for all cross sections of the tube at all points of the tube. Expression (2.47) is thus a property of the tube and is known as the magnetic flux associated with the tube.

2.10. The Magnetic Flux Threading a Closed Geometrical Curve. Let C be a closed geometrical curve drawn in a magnetic field. Through the closed curve C there pass tubes of magnetic flux for each of which the magnetic flux can be evaluated in accordance with expression (2.47). The algebraic sum of the magnetic fluxes of the tubes threading the closed curve C constitutes what is known as the magnetic flux threading the closed curve. This statement can be made more precisely as follows.

Let S be any surface spanning the closed curve C, so that C is the rim of the surface S. Let a tube of magnetic flux intersect the surface S in an element of area dS. Let $d\mathbf{S}$ be a vector whose magnitude is equal to the area of the element dS and whose direction is along the normal to the element. Of the two normal directions available, select one. To this selected normal direction there is related by the right-hand-screw rule a direction round the closed curve C. Denote this direction round C by an arrow drawn on C. We shall calculate the magnetic flux threading the closed curve C in the direction related by the right-hand-screw rule to the specified direction round C. At the vector element of area $d\mathbf{S}$ of the surface S let the magnetic-flux-density vector be $\mathbf{B}$. Then the tube of magnetic flux consisting of lines of magnetic flux through the rim of the element of area $d\mathbf{S}$ possesses a magnetic flux given by expression (2.47). The total flux threading the closed curve C in the specified direction is obtained by adding up the contributions given by expression (2.47) for all of the vector elements of area of the surface S spanning the closed curve C. This statement is expressed by saying that the magnetic flux threading the closed curve is

$$\Phi = \int_S \mathbf{B} \cdot d\mathbf{S} \qquad (2.48)$$

As a simple example, let us suppose that, in the region of space with which we are concerned, the field of magnetic flux is uniform. This means that the magnetic-flux-density vector is pointing in the same direction at all points with which we are concerned, and the magnitude of the vector is likewise the same at all points. In Fig. 2.14 it is supposed that the direction of the uniform magnetic-flux-density vector is vertically upward from the paper. Let us also suppose that the closed curve C with which we are concerned lies in the plane of the paper and encloses a total area A. Let the specified direction round the closed curve C be as shown in Fig. 2.14, so that we are interested in evaluating the magnetic flux threading the closed curve C in the direction normally upward from the paper, that is, in the direction of the uniform field of magnetic flux. In this case we can take as the surface S spanning the closed curve C the portion of the plane of paper enclosed by C. Each element of area $d\mathbf{S}$ is therefore represented by a vector normally upward from the paper, so that the cosine on the angle between the direction of $d\mathbf{S}$ and of the

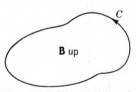

FIG. 2.14. Illustrating calculation of the magnetic flux threading a closed geometrical curve C in a plane at right angles to a uniform field of magnetic flux.

magnetic-flux-density vector **B** is unity. Equation (2.48) therefore reduces to

$$\Phi = \int_S B \, dS \tag{2.49}$$

in which the scalar product has now become an ordinary algebraic product. For the uniform field of magnetic flux with which we are concerned the value of B is the same at all points of the surface. Equation (2.49) can therefore be written as

$$\Phi = B \int_S dS \tag{2.50}$$

The integral is now simply the area A enclosed by the curve C, and we deduce that

$$\Phi = BA \tag{2.51}$$

This equation states that, when a uniform magnetic field of flux density B crosses an area A normal to the field, the total magnetic flux threading the rim of the area is the product of the magnetic flux density B and the area A. Equation (2.51) demonstrates in its simplest form the fact that magnetic flux density B is magnetic flux per unit area. Had the specified direction round the closed curve C in Fig. 2.14 been in the opposite direction, we would have been required to calculate the magnetic flux threading C in the downward direction through the paper, and this is the direction opposite to that of the magnetic-flux-density vector **B**. In this case the magnetic flux threading C would be given by Eq. (2.51) but with the opposite algebraic sign.

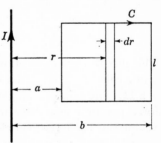

FIG. 2.15. Illustrating calculation of the magnetic flux threading a rectangle due to a current I flowing along an infinite straight coplanar wire parallel to a pair of edges of the rectangle.

As a further example of the calculation of the total magnetic flux threading a closed geometrical curve C, let us consider the field of magnetic flux of a long straight wire carrying a steady current I. Let the closed geometrical curve C have the form of a rectangle lying in an axial plane through the wire as shown in Fig. 2.15. Let two edges of the rectangle be of length l and be parallel to the wire. Let the other two edges of the rectangle be at distances a and b from the wire, b being larger than a. Let the specified direction round the rectangle be as shown in Fig. 2.15, and let μ be the inductivity of the uniform medium surrounding the wire. Consider a narrow strip of the rectangle of width dr at distance r from the wire as shown in Fig. 2.15. Along this strip the magnetic flux density B has the same value and is given by Eq. (2.10). The area of the strip is

$$dS = l\, dr \tag{2.52}$$

Hence the magnetic flux crossing this strip is

$$B\, dS = \frac{\mu}{2\pi}\, Il \frac{dr}{r} \tag{2.53}$$

and there is no need to use the scalar product because the tubes of magnetic flux cross the rectangle at right angles. Integration of Eq. (2.53) over the rectangle gives

$$\int_S B\, dS = \frac{\mu}{2\pi}\, Il \int_a^b \frac{dr}{r} \tag{2.54}$$

By evaluation of the integral on the right-hand side of Eq. (2.54), we deduce that the magnetic flux threading the rectangle is

$$\Phi = \frac{\mu}{2\pi}\, Il \ln \frac{b}{a} \tag{2.55}$$

This flux threads the rectangle in the direction related by the right-hand-screw rule to the direction of the current I along the wire.

2.11. The Unit of Magnetic Flux. From Eq. (2.4) we see that the force per unit charge acting on a test charge is given by the electric vector **E** if the force is of electric origin and by the vector product of the velocity **v** of the test charge and the magnetic-flux-density vector **B** if the force is of magnetic origin. It follows that the product of the velocity v and magnetic flux density B is measured in the same units as electric field strength E. Hence

$$\begin{aligned} \text{Unit of } B &= \frac{\text{unit of } E}{\text{unit of } v} \\ &= \frac{\text{volt/m}}{\text{m/sec}} \\ &= \frac{\text{volt-sec}}{\text{m}^2} \end{aligned}$$

Thus magnetic flux density is measured in volt-seconds per unit area. Since magnetic flux density is magnetic flux per unit area, it follows that the unit of magnetic flux is the volt-second. This unit of magnetic flux is also known as the weber. In terms of the weber, magnetic flux density is measured in webers per square meter.

A magnetic flux density of 1 weber/m^2 is quite a large magnetic flux density in practice. Consequently a smaller unit of magnetic flux density is frequently required. This is the gauss, which is 10^{-4} weber/m^2. The Earth has a magnetic field which, measured at its surface, varies from about 0.3 gauss at the equator to about 0.6 gauss at a pole. For extremely small magnetic fields, such as the small variations that occur in the Earth's magnetic field, an even smaller unit of magnetic flux density is sometimes used. This is the gamma, which is 10^{-5} gauss, or 10^{-9} weber/m^2.

From Eq. (2.10) we can evaluate the magnetic flux density at a distance of 1 cm from the axis of a current of 1 amp flowing along a thin wire in free space. Putting $I = 1$ amp, $r = 10^{-2}$ m, and $\mu = \mu_v$ from Eq. (2.9), we obtain a magnetic flux density of 2.2×10^{-5} weber/m^2 or 0.22 gauss. For the rectangle shown in Fig. 2.15 we can evaluate the magnetic flux threading it on the assumption that $I = 1$ amp, $l = 10$ cm (10^{-1} m), $b/a = 2.7$, and $\mu = \mu_v$, given by Eq. (2.9). For these numerical values the magnetic flux threading the rectangle evaluates to 2×10^{-8} weber.

The fact that the weber is an alternative name for the volt-second can also be stated by saying that the time rate of change of magnetic flux is measured in volts. The rate of change of the magnetic flux threading a closed curve C will be of great interest to us, especially in cases where the closed curve C coincides with an electric circuit. For an electric circuit the magnetic flux threading it will be a measure of the momentum of the electric current round the circuit arising from the fact that electrons have charge. The time rate of change of the magnetic flux threading the circuit will thus be a measure of the force required to drive the electrons round the circuit and hence of the voltage of the source required to produce the current. Thus the time rate of change of the magnetic flux threading an electric circuit is related to the voltage driving the current round the circuit in the same way that the time rate of change of momentum in mechanics is related to force, as shown by Eq. (1.2). It is no accident therefore that the time rate of change of magnetic flux is measured in volts.

SUMMARIZING EXERCISES

2.1. A transmission line consists of a pair of coaxial circular conducting cylinders with thin walls. A steady, uniformly distributed current flows along one cylinder and back along the other, parallel to the axes. Describe the resulting field of magnetic flux density (a) between the conductors, (b) inside the inner conductor, and (c) outside the outer conductor.

2.2. Explain how to calculate in magnitude and direction the force exerted on a test charge moving in a magnetic field.

2.3. Explain what is meant by the inductivity of a substance, and write down the numerical value for the inductivity of free space. Show that the reciprocal of the geometric mean of the vacuum inductivity and the vacuum capacitivity is a velocity. Evaluate the numerical magnitude of the velocity and state its physical significance.

2.4. If the fields of magnetic flux density of two steady currents have been calculated separately, explain how to calculate the field of magnetic flux density produced when both currents exist simultaneously.

2.5. A long straight wire of radius a embedded in a homogeneous medium of inductivity μ carries a steady current I uniformly distributed over its cross section. Calculate the field of magnetic flux density at distance r from the axis of the wire (a) when $r > a$ and (b) when $r < a$.

2.6. The medium between the conductors of a coaxial transmission line has inductivity μ and capacitivity ϵ. A steady current I flows along the inner conductor and back along the outer conductor. A charge per unit length Q exists on the inner conductor and $-Q$ on the outer conductor. Describe the relation between the electric and magnetic fields produced.

2.7. A steady current I flows along one conductor of a twin-wire transmission line and back along the other. Explain how to calculate the resulting magnetic field, and sketch the lines of magnetic flux.

2.8. Explain what is meant by a tube of magnetic flux. Describe the variation along a tube of the product of (a) the normal cross-sectional area of the tube and (b) the magnetic flux density at that cross section. Define the magnetic flux associated with the tube. Show that if any cross section of the tube, normal or otherwise, has an area represented vectorially by $d\mathbf{S}$, and if at this cross section the magnetic flux density vector is $\mathbf{B}$, then the magnetic flux associated with the tube is the scalar product of $\mathbf{B}$ with $d\mathbf{S}$.

2.9. A geometrical closed curve C is drawn in a magnetic field. Explain what is meant by the magnetic flux threading the closed curve C in terms of an integral over a surface S spanning C. State what determines the direction in which the calculated magnetic flux threads the closed curve C.

2.10. Write down the units in which magnetic flux and magnetic flux density are measured. Explain how the unit of magnetic flux is related to the volt.

CHAPTER 3

MAGNETIC FIELD STRENGTH

3.1. Introduction. Equation (2.4) demonstrates that the magnetic-flux-density vector **B** plays for forces of magnetic origin the part that the electric vector **E** plays for forces of electric origin. The vectors **E** and **B** are the vector fields that describe at each point of space the way in which force is exerted on a test charge. The ways in which these two vectors must be used in order to derive the force on a test charge are, of course, different and are described by Eq. (2.4). In discussion of electrostatic fields it was found convenient to introduce, in addition to the electric vector **E**, the electric-flux-density vector **D**. The electric flux density gives the charge per unit area on the conductors of the system and also upon any conductor that could be introduced into the system without upsetting the field. Thus, whereas the electric vector **E** describes the way in which force is exerted in an electrostatic field, the electric-flux-density vector **D** describes what we need to know about charge geometry. A similar problem arises in connection with magnetic fields. The magnetic-flux-density vector **B** describes the way in which force is exerted in a magnetic field, but it is desirable to introduce another vector field to describe what we need to know about current geometry. This vector is known as the magnetic vector **H**, and its magnitude is known as the magnetic field strength.

From what has been said, it will be seen that the function performed by the electric vector **E** in an electric field corresponds to the function performed by the magnetic-flux-density vector **B** in a magnetic field, while the function performed by the electric-flux-density vector **D** in an electric field corresponds to the function performed by the magnetic vector **H** in a magnetic field. It may legitimately be wondered why the terminology has not been chosen so that the function performed by the electric vector corresponds to the function performed by the magnetic vector and the function performed by the electric flux density corresponds to the function performed by the magnetic flux density. The reason for using a similar terminology for the vectors **B** and **D** can be seen by comparing expression (2.48) with expression (1.23). In both cases a surface integral is involved, and this illustrates the fact that the vector **B**

373

handles mathematically like the vector **D** even though the physical connotation of the vector **B** is more akin to that of the vector **E** as shown by Eq. (2.4). In the same way we shall find that the magnetic vector **H** handles mathematically like the electric vector **E**, even though the physical information conveyed by the magnetic vector **H** is more akin to that conveyed by the electric-flux-density vector **D**.

Our handling of the electrostatic field in Part 1 was appreciably simplified by the ability to dissect the field by means of conducting sheets introduced along equipotential surfaces. Indeed the magnitude of the electric flux density at any point P in an electrostatic field measures the charge per unit area induced upon a conducting sheet coinciding with the equipotential surface through P. In a similar way it is possible to dissect magnetic fields by means of conducting surfaces suitably introduced into the field, and it is the current per unit width induced upon such a

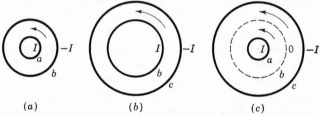

(a)   (b)   (c)

Fig. 3.1. Illustrating dissection of the magnetic field of a coaxial transmission line by means of a coaxial cylindrical surface between the conductors.

surface at a point P that is measured by the magnetic field strength H at P.

3.2. Dissection of Magnetic Fields by Conducting Surfaces. Consider a coaxial transmission line consisting of a pair of thin, hollow cylindrical conductors as shown in Fig. 3.1a. Let μ be the inductivity of the medium between the conductors. Let the radius of the inner conductor be a and the radius of the outer conductor be b. Let a steady electric current I, uniformly distributed round the perimeter, flow up along the inner conductor and back along the outer conductor. This produces between the conductors a field of magnetic flux in which the magnetic flux density at distance r from the common axis is given by Eq. (2.10). Now consider a similar coaxial transmission line in which the inner conductor has radius b and the outer conductor radius c as shown in Fig. 3.1b. On this transmission line let there be a steady current I flowing upward along the hollow inner conductor of radius b and back along the outer conductor, the magnitude of this current being the same as in the transmission line shown in Fig. 3.1a. The radius of the thin outer conductor in the transmission line shown in Fig. 3.1a has been deliberately chosen so as to be the same as the radius of the thin inner conductor for the transmission

line shown in Fig. 3.1b.   This has been done so that the transmission line
shown in Fig. 3.1a can be inserted inside the transmission line shown in
Fig. 3.1b thereby producing the situation illustrated in Fig. 3.1c.   In
Fig. 3.1c the circle of radius b indicated by a broken line represents both
the outer conductor of the transmission line shown in Fig. 3.1a and inner
conductor of the transmission line shown in Fig. 3.1b.   On this conductor
there is a downward current I associated with the transmission line illustrated in Fig. 3.1a and an upward current I associated with the transmission line shown in Fig. 3.1b.   Hence the net current on the conductor of
intermediate radius b in Fig. 3.1c is zero.   Thus Fig. 3.1c in fact represents a coaxial transmission line in which the inner conductor is of radius
a and the outer conductor is of radius c, with an upward current I on the
inner conductor and an equal downward current on the outer conductor.
Equation (2.10) gives the magnetic flux density in the region $a < r < b$
in accordance with Fig. 3.1a and also in the region $b < r < c$ in accordance with Fig. 3.1b.   Hence in Fig. 3.1c there is no discontinuity of the
magnetic flux density at the intermediate conductor of radius b, and the
magnetic flux density is given by Eq. (2.10) throughout the entire region
$a < r < c$.   Thus Fig. 3.1c represents the field of a coaxial transmission
line in which the inner conductor has radius a and the outer conductor has
radius c, and the conductor of intermediate radius b plays no part.

Figure 3.1c demonstrates the fact that it is possible to insert into the
magnetic field of a coaxial transmission line a thin conducting circular
cylinder coaxial with the transmission line without affecting the magnetic
field.   The characteristic feature of a conductor inserted into a magnetic
field without upsetting the field is that the conductor must not intersect
any tube of magnetic flux.   The surface must therefore be composed
entirely of lines of magnetic flux.   Any surface in any magnetic field
composed entirely of lines of magnetic flux can be replaced by a thin
conducting sheet without upsetting the magnetic field.   For a coaxial
transmission line, a circular cylinder between the conductors and coaxial
with them is composed entirely of lines of magnetic flux and can therefore
be replaced by a thin conducting cylinder without affecting the magnetic
field as shown in Fig. 3.1c.

After dissecting a magnetic field into two parts by means of a surface
composed entirely of lines of magnetic flux, it is possible to consider the
magnetic field on the two sides of the dissecting surface separately.
Thus, for the coaxial transmission line shown in Fig. 3.1c, we can introduce a dissecting surface composed of a coaxial circular cylinder of radius
b and then consider the magnetic field interior to the dissecting surface
separately from the magnetic field exterior to the dissecting surface as
shown in Fig. 3.1a and b.   It is convenient to imagine the dissecting surface to be composed of a double sheet of perfectly conducting material.

The two parts of the field can then have separate physical existence as shown in Fig. 3.1a and b.

For a coaxial transmission line there are many surfaces that may be drawn composed entirely of lines of magnetic flux. As an example, consider a plane drawn perpendicular to the axis of the transmission line. The portion of the plane between the conductors is composed entirely of circular lines of magnetic flux. Hence any plane perpendicular to the axis of the transmission line can be replaced by a pair of contiguous, perfectly conducting sheets without affecting the magnetic field. The two halves into which the transmission line is thereby divided can then be separated as shown in Fig. 3.2. In the left-hand half of the transmis-

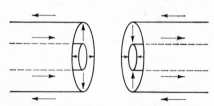

sion line shown in Fig. 3.2 current I flows along the surface of the inner conductor, then radially outward over the flat end and back along the outer conductor. For the right-hand half of the transmission line shown in Fig. 3.2 current I flows to the left along the outer conductor, then radially inward over the flat end and to the right along the surface of the inner

FIG. 3.2. Illustrating dissection of the magnetic field of a coaxial transmission line into two parts by means of a plane surface normal to the axis of the transmission line.

conductor. The magnetic fields in the two halves of the lines are the same as for an infinite coaxial transmission line carrying a current I to the right on the inner conductor and to the left on the outer conductor.

3.3. The Magnetic Vector H. Let us give further study to the magnetic field of the coaxial transmission line illustrated in Fig. 3.1a. The inner conductor is supposed to be hollow, and the steady current I on it is supposed to be uniformly distributed round its perimeter, the length of which is $2\pi a$. Hence the current flowing along the surface of the inner conductor, measured per unit width perpendicular to the direction of flow, is

$$\frac{I}{2\pi a} \tag{3.1}$$

Now the magnetic flux density between the conductors is given by Eq. (2.10), and consequently the magnetic flux density close to the inner conductor is

$$B = \mu \frac{I}{2\pi a} \tag{3.2}$$

Comparison of expression (3.1) with Eq. (3.2) shows that there is a close relation between the current per unit width flowing along the inner conductor and the magnetic flux density close to the inner conductor.

To describe the relation between the magnetic flux density close to a bounding conductor of a magnetic field and the current per unit width flowing on the bounding conductor it is convenient to introduce a vector **H** related to the magnetic-flux-density vector **B** by the equation

$$\mathbf{H} = \frac{1}{\mu}\,\mathbf{B} \tag{3.3}$$

By means of this equation a vector **H** is defined for each point in the magnetic field.   The vector **H** at a point is known as the magnetic vector at the point, and its magnitude is known as the magnetic field strength at the point.   From Eq. (3.3) it follows that, at each point of a magnetic field, the magnetic vector **H** is directed along the line of magnetic flux passing through the point, and points in the same direction as the magnetic-flux-density vector **B**.   From the vector equation (3.3) it also follows that the relation between the magnetic field strength H and the magnetic flux density B is

$$H = \frac{1}{\mu}\,B \tag{3.4}$$

Thus the magnetic field strength at any point in a magnetic field is obtained by dividing the magnetic flux density at that point by the inductivity μ of the medium.   Except for ferromagnetic materials, the numerical value of μ is practically that of μ_v given by Eq. (2.9).

By substituting from Eq. (2.10) into Eq. (3.4) we see that the magnetic field strength at a point between the conductors of a coaxial transmission line at distance r from the axis is

$$H = \frac{I}{2\pi r} \tag{3.5}$$

As in the case of the magnetic flux density, the magnetic field strength of a coaxial transmission line is zero outside the outer conductor.   It is also zero inside the inner conductor if the inner conductor is hollow.

From Eq. (3.5) we see that the magnetic field strength close to the inner conductor of the coaxial transmission line is given by expression (3.1), and this is the current per unit width flowing on the hollow inner conductor.   This illustrates an important property possessed by the magnetic field strength H.   If a magnetic field is bounded by a conducting surface carrying current, there being no magnetic field on the opposite side of the surface, then the current per unit width flowing on the bounding conductor is equal in magnitude to the magnetic field strength close to the conductor.   Moreover, the direction of the flow of current on the bounding conductor can be derived from the direction of the magnetic vector close to the conductor as follows.   Consider a point

P on the surface of the inner conductor of the coaxial transmission line shown in Fig. 3.1a. At the point P draw a vector **n** of unit length normal to the inner conductor. This normal is to be drawn from the point P into the magnetic field between the conductors. The relation among this unit normal vector **n**, the direction of the magnetic vector **H** just outside the conductor, and the direction of flow of the current on the conductor is then as shown in Fig. 3.3. By employing the concept of vector product we can say that the direction of the electric current on the bounding conductor is the direction of the vector

$$\mathbf{n} \times \mathbf{H} \qquad (3.6)$$

Moreover the magnitude of this vector is the product of (1) the unit length of **n**, (2) the magnetic field strength H, and (3) the sine of the angle $\frac{1}{2}\pi$ between the two vectors. The magnitude of the vector (3.6) is therefore simply the magnetic field strength H just outside the conductor and is therefore also the magnitude of the current per unit width flowing on the conductor. We can therefore say that, if a magnetic field is bounded by a conducting surface carrying current, the current per unit width flowing on the bounding surface at a point P is represented in magnitude and direction by the vector (3.6), where **n** is the unit vector drawn normal to the bounding surface at P pointing into the magnetic field and **H** is the magnetic vector close to the bounding surface at P.

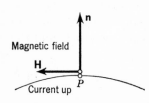

Magnetic field

No magnetic field

FIG. 3.3. Illustrating the relation between the direction of the current on a conductor bounding a magnetic field and the direction of the magnetic vector close to the conductor.

Let us apply the expression (3.6) for the current per unit width on a bounding surface of a magnetic field to the outer conductor of the coaxial transmission line illustrated in Fig. 3.1a. From Eq. (3.5) it follows that the magnetic field strength close to the outer conductor is

$$\frac{I}{2\pi b} \qquad (3.7)$$

and consequently this must be the current per unit width flowing on the outer conductor. This agrees with the fact that we have on the outer conductor a total current I distributed uniformly round a conductor of perimeter $2\pi b$. At a point on the outer conductor draw a normal to the outer conductor directed into the magnetic field between the conductors. This normal is drawn radially inward. Since the direction of the magnetic vector **H** in Fig. 3.1a is right-handed about the current on the inner conductor, it follows that the direction of the vector product (3.6) is downward through the paper in Fig. 3.1a. We deduce that the current per unit width flowing on the outer conductor is given in magnitude by expression (3.7), and its direction is downward through the paper in Fig. 3.1a. Thus the expression (3.6) correctly relates, in both magnitude and direction, the current per unit width flowing on the outer conductor with the magnetic vector **H** measured close to the outer conductor.

We can further illustrate the application of expression (3.6) for the current per unit width flowing on the bounding surface of a magnetic field as follows: Consider the left-hand half of the dissected coaxial transmission line shown in Fig. 3.2. Over the flat end of the transmission line, current is flowing radially outward from the inner conductor to the outer conductor as shown in Fig. 3.4. On the flat end of the transmission line we have a total current I flowing radially and symmetrically outward from the inner edge to the outer edge. At distance r from the axis of the transmission line the current per unit width flowing over the flat end is obtained by dividing the total current flowing by the perimeter $2\pi r$ of a circle of radius r. Hence the current per unit width flowing radially outward across the flat end at a point distant r from the axis of the transmission line is

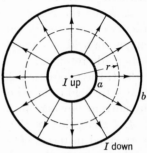

Fig. 3.4. Illustrating the current flowing over the flat end of the dissected transmission line shown on the left of Fig. 3.2.

$$\frac{I}{2\pi r} \qquad (3.8)$$

The magnetic field strength between the conductors of the transmission line is given by Eq. (3.5), and this applies in particular close to the flat end. Comparison of expression (3.8) with Eq. (3.5) shows that the current per unit width flowing over the flat end at a point P is equal to the magnetic field strength in the transmission line close to the point P. At the point P of the flat end draw a normal into the magnetic field. In Fig. 3.4 this is drawn downward through the paper. Since the magnetic vector **H** close to P is directed right-handed about the current along the inner conductor, it follows that the direction of the vector product (3.6) is radially outward and therefore in the direction of the current flowing over the flat end. Thus consideration of the flat end of the transmission line on the left-hand side in Fig. 3.2 again verifies that the current per unit width flowing over the bounding surface of a magnetic field at a point P is represented in magnitude and direction by the vector (3.6), where **n** is the unit vector drawn normal to the bounding surface at P pointing into the magnetic field and **H** is the magnetic vector close to the bounding surface at P.

3.4. Rules for Dissecting Magnetic Fields. We are now in a position to exploit the idea of dissecting magnetic fields by means of conducting surfaces in the same way that we exploited the idea of dissecting electrostatic fields by means of conductors introduced along equipotential surfaces. The principles involved are:

1. Any surface composed of lines of magnetic flux, and therefore not intersecting tubes of magnetic flux, can be replaced by a conducting sheet without upsetting the magnetic field.

2. After the conducting surface is introduced, the magnetic field on the two sides of it can be considered separately. In particular the magnetic field on one side of the surface can be abolished and that on the other side retained.

3. If the magnetic field on one side of the surface is abolished, then the magnetic field retained on the other side of the surface must be supported by current flowing on the introduced conductor.

4. Calculation of the current flowing on the introduced conductor is performed in terms of the magnetic vector $\mathbf{H}$, which is defined in terms of the magnetic-flux-density vector $\mathbf{B}$ by the equation

$$\mathbf{H} = \frac{1}{\mu} \mathbf{B} \tag{3.9}$$

where μ is the inductivity of the medium.

5. To calculate the current flowing along the introduced conductor per unit width when the magnetic field on one side has been abolished, we draw at a point P of the conductor a vector $\mathbf{n}$ of unit length normal to the conductor and pointing into the magnetic field. If $\mathbf{H}$ is the magnetic vector close to the point P, the current per unit width flowing along the conductor at P is given in magnitude and direction by the vector

$$\mathbf{n} \times \mathbf{H} \tag{3.10}$$

Let us use these principles to discuss some examples of what are known as inductors. An inductor is a device for conveniently packaging a magnetic field in much the same way that a capacitor is a device for conveniently packaging an electric field.

3.5. The Coaxial Inductor. Let us start with the magnetic field produced when a steady current I flows along a straight wire that is indefinitely thin and indefinitely long. In this magnetic field replace the following surfaces by conducting sheets:

1. A circular cylinder of radius a coaxial with the wire
2. A circular cylinder of radius b $(>a)$ coaxial with the wire
3. A plane perpendicular to the wire
4. A parallel plane separated from the previous plane by a perpendicular distance l

Introduction of these conducting surfaces does not alter the magnetic field of the original infinite straight current I because none of the surfaces cuts tubes of magnetic flux. Now abolish all the magnetic field that does not lie within the toroidal space enclosed by the four introduced conductors. We then have a magnetic field enclosed between a pair of coaxial circular cylinders and a pair of planes perpendicular to the axis as shown in Fig. 3.5.

Having abolished the magnetic field outside the enclosed toroidal space, and with it the current along the infinite wire, it is necessary to introduce appropriate electric currents on the bounding conductors. Within the toroidal space, the magnetic field is simply that of the original current I along the infinite wire. Hence at a point within the toroidal space distant r from the axis, the magnetic flux density is given by Eq. (2.10) and the magnetic field strength by Eq. (3.5), the lines of magnetic flux being circles coaxial with the original current I. From the magnetic field within the toroidal space we can calculate the magnetic vector at the surfaces of the toroidal space and hence the current per unit width on the bounding conductors in accordance with expression (3.10).

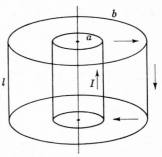

FIG. 3.5. A coaxial inductor.

From Eq. (3.5) the magnetic field strength at the surface of the inner cylinder is $I/2\pi a$, and this is consequently the current per unit width flowing on the inner cylinder. From expression (3.10) it follows that this current is flowing up the inner cylinder parallel to the current on the original straight wire. Since the perimeter of the inner cylinder is $2\pi a$, the total current flowing down the inner cylinder is I, the same as the current flowing along the original wire. In the same way the magnetic field strength at the surface of the outer cylinder is $I/2\pi b$, and this is therefore the current per unit width flowing on the outer cylinder. From expression (3.10) the direction of this current is downward in Fig. 3.5. Since the perimeter of the outer cylinder is $2\pi b$, the total current flowing downward on the outer cylinder is I.

Let us now calculate the current over the flat ends of the toroidal inductor using Eq. (3.5). At a point on a flat end distant r from the axis, the magnetic field strength is $I/2\pi r$, and this is therefore the current per unit width over a flat end at distance r from the axis. From expression (3.10) the direction of flow is radially outward on the upper flat end in Fig. 3.5 and radially inward on the lower flat end. On a flat end draw a concentric circle of radius r and perimeter $2\pi r$. The total current crossing such a circle is obtained by multiplying the current per unit width by the perimeter $2\pi r$ and is therefore I. Hence the current required on the surface of the toroidal inductor in Fig. 3.5 in order to maintain the magnetic field within the toroidal space, with no magnetic field outside, is a current I flowing up the inner cylinder, radially outward across the top flat end, down the outer cylinder, and radially inward across the bottom flat end.

A coaxial inductor is simply a portion of a coaxial transmission line obtained by inserting a pair of conducting planes at a pair of normal cross sections by the method illustrated in Fig. 3.2. The coaxial inductor does a perfect job of packaging the magnetic field.

3.6. The Toroidal Inductor. The coaxial inductor has the form of a toroid of rectangular cross section, but it is not necessary for the cross section of a toroidal inductor to be rectangular.

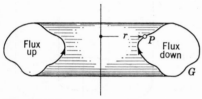

FIG. 3.6. Illustrating an axial cross section of a toroidal inductor.

Consider again the magnetic field of a long straight wire carrying a steady current I. Consider an axial plane drawn through the wire, and in this plane draw a closed curve G that does not intersect the wire. Now rotate the closed curve G round the wire to form a toroidal surface as indicated in Fig. 3.6. The curve G is known as a generating curve of the toroid and may be of any shape as long as it does not intersect the wire. The toroidal surface thus generated does not intersect any of the tubes of magnetic flux of the current I flowing along the straight wire. Hence the toroidal surface generated by the closed curve G can be replaced by a conducting surface without upsetting the magnetic field of the wire. Now retain the magnetic field within the toroidal surface and abolish the magnetic field exterior to the toroidal surface. In doing this we remove the current I on the straight wire and support the magnetic field inside the toroid by currents on the surface of the toroid. From expression (3.10) these currents flow round the generating curves G of the toroid in the direction related by the right-hand-screw rule to the magnetic flux through the toroid. Let P be a point of the toroidal surface at distance r from the axis. Close to the point P the magnetic field strength, being the same as that due to the original current I on the straight wire, is

$$H = \frac{I}{2\pi r} \qquad (3.11)$$

This is therefore the current per unit width flowing over the conducting toroidal surface round the generating curves G.

As a generating curve G traces out the toroidal surface, the point

P of G generates a circle C of radius r with axis coinciding with the original straight wire. Let us calculate the total current crossing this circle C lying round the toroidal conducting surface. Let ds be an element of length of the circle C. The current crossing C per unit length is equal to the magnetic field strength H within the toroidal surface close to the curve C. It follows that the current crossing the element of length ds of the circle C is $H\,ds$. The total current crossing the circle C is obtained by adding up the contributions from the various elements of length of the circle and is therefore equal to

$$\int_C H\,ds \tag{3.12}$$

where the integral is to be taken right around the circle C. Since r in Eq. (3.11) is the radius of the circle C, it follows that the magnetic field strength H along the circle C has the same value at all points. Hence the integrand H in expression (3.12) is constant. The integral therefore evaluates to $H(2\pi r)$, and this, from Eq. (3.11), is I. Thus for the circle C generated on the toroidal conductor by the point P of the generating curve G we have

$$\int_C H\,ds = I \tag{3.13}$$

This applies to the circle generated by any point P of the generating curve G. Equation (3.13) therefore shows the total current crossing any of these circles is identical with the current I originally on the straight wire. Thus the portion of the original magnetic field that is contained within the toroidal surface can be maintained by itself by causing the current I to flow uniformly round the generating curves of the toroid instead of along the original straight wire.

3.7. The Individuality of Tubes of Magnetic Flux. In the discussion of a toroidal inductor in the previous section let us suppose that the generating curve G is the perimeter of an element of area. The toroid then becomes a tube of magnetic flux. We thus see that a tube of magnetic flux can exist by itself provided that a suitable current flows over the surface of the tube. The required current must flow round the generating curves, that is, round the perimeters of the normal cross sections of the tube. The direction of current flow round the perimeters of the normal cross sections of the tube must be related by the right-hand-screw rule to the direction of the magnetic flux through the tube. The current per unit length required at any point of the tube is equal to the magnetic field strength H in the tube close to this point. Thus, if at a particular cross section of the tube the magnetic field strength is H, then H is the current per unit length that must flow round the tube at this cross section to maintain the tube in existence by itself.

This provides a convenient way of visualizing the significance of the magnetic vector **H** at any point P in a magnetic field.   Consider a tube of magnetic flux containing the point P as shown in Fig. 3.7.   The magnetic field existing in the neighborhood of the point P can be specified by means of current that would have to flow round the curved surface of the tube if this tube existed by itself.   The magnitude of the magnetic vector **H** at P gives the magnitude of the current per unit length that must flow round the curved surface of the tube at P.   The direction of the magnetic vector **H** specifies by the right-hand-screw rule the direction in which the current must flow round the curved surface of the tube.

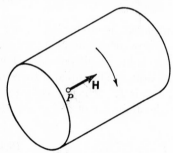

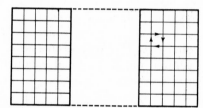

FIG. 3.7. Illustrating the physical significance of the magnetic vector **H** in terms of current per unit length round the curved surface of a tube of magnetic flux.

FIG. 3.8. Illustrating a coaxial inductor regarded as an aggregate of individually created tubes of magnetic flux.

Thus the magnetic vector **H** at a point P in a magnetic field specifies the local current system that would produce the magnetic field at P.   In particular the magnetic field strength H at the point P is the local current per unit length that must flow round the curved surface of a tube of magnetic flux containing the point P in order to keep this tube in existence by itself.   The unit in which magnetic field strength is measured is therefore that of the current per unit length, that is, amperes per meter.

Any magnetic field can be regarded as an aggregate of individually created tubes of magnetic flux packed side by side.   Figure 3.8 illustrates how the magnetic field of a coaxial inductor can be subdivided into tubes of magnetic flux.   Each individual tube of magnetic flux could exist by itself as a thin coaxial inductor if a suitable current flowed round the perimeters of the normal cross sections of the tube.   Equation (3.13) shows that, since the field was originally that of a steady current I along the axis, the current appropriate to each of the tubes is I.   Hence the total current required round each tube of magnetic flux to keep this tube in existence by itself is equal to the current I originally flowing along the axis.   When the tubes are packed together as shown in Fig. 3.8, the currents over adjacent surfaces cancel, leaving a current I flowing round

the outer surface of the large coaxial inductor.   The magnetic field of the
large coaxial inductor can thus be regarded as an aggregate of individually
created tubes of magnetic flux packed side by side.

3.8. The Circulation Law for the Magnetic Vector.   In connection
with Fig. 3.6 consideration was given to a circle C generated by the rotation of the point P around an axis.   This circle C is a line of magnetic flux
in the magnetic field of a current I along the axis.   For a line of magnetic
flux C the integral (3.12) taken right around the line is known as the circulation of the magnetic field strength around the line of magnetic flux.
Equation (3.13) shows that, in the magnetic field of a long straight wire
carrying a steady current I, the circulation of the magnetic field strength
round any line of magnetic flux is equal to the current I producing the
field.   This can be stated by saying that the circulation of the magnetic
field strength round any line of magnetic flux is equal to the current
threading the line of magnetic flux.

A more general statement can be made as follows: In the magnetic
field of a long straight wire carrying a steady current I let C be any closed
curve encircling the current, not necessarily coinciding with a line of
magnetic flux.   Let $d\mathbf{s}$ be a vector element of length of the curve C
pointing round C in a specified direction, and at this element of length
of C let $\mathbf{H}$ be the magnetic vector due to the current on the wire.   Evaluate the scalar product of the magnetic vector $\mathbf{H}$ with the vector element of
length $d\mathbf{s}$, and add the results for all the elements of length of the closed
curve C, thereby forming the integral

$$\int_C \mathbf{H} \cdot d\mathbf{s} \tag{3.14}$$

taken round the closed curve C.   The integral (3.14) is then known as the
circulation of the magnetic vector taken round the closed curve C in the
direction specified by the vector elements of length $d\mathbf{s}$.   We can show
that, if the specified direction round C is related by the right-hand-screw
rule to the direction of the current I threading C, then

$$\int_C \mathbf{H} \cdot d\mathbf{s} = I \tag{3.15}$$

If the closed curve C is drawn in such a way that no current threads it,
then

$$\int_C \mathbf{H} \cdot d\mathbf{s} = 0 \tag{3.16}$$

In other words we can show that the circulation of the magnetic vector
round any closed curve C in a specified direction is equal to whatever
current happens to be threading the closed curve C in the direction
related by the right-hand-screw rule to the specified direction round C.

Equation (3.13) is simply the special case of Eq. (3.15) when the closed curve C is a line of magnetic flux and the specified direction round the line of magnetic flux is related by the right-hand-screw rule to the direction of the current I threading it.   In this case the directions of the magnetic vector $\mathbf{H}$ and of the vector element of length $d\mathbf{s}$ round C are identical and the scalar product in Eq. (3.15) becomes an ordinary algebraic product in Eq. (3.13).

To demonstrate the truth of Eq. (3.15) for the magnetic field of a steady current I flowing along an infinite straight wire, draw through the closed curve C all the lines of magnetic flux that intersect the curve.   These form a toroidal surface of the type indicated in Fig. 3.6, and the curve C is a closed curve drawn on the surface of this toroid.   Two cases arise.

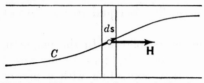

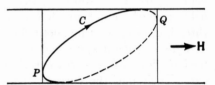

Fig. 3.9. Illustrating the circulation law for the magnetic vector round a closed curve threaded by a current.

Fig. 3.10. Illustrating the circulation law for the magnetic vector round a closed curve not threaded by current.

In the first case the closed curve C drawn on the surface of the toroid encircles the axis of the toroid.   In these circumstances the closed curve C is a distorted form of the circle C generated by rotation of a point such as P in Fig. 3.6 around the axis.   In this case the equation to be established is Eq. (3.15).   The second case is that in which the closed curve C does not encircle the axis but instead encircles the magnetic flux passing through the toroid.   In these circumstances the closed curve C is a distorted form of a generating curve G in Fig. 3.6.   In this case the appropriate equation to be established is Eq. (3.16).

Let us consider the first case, in which the closed curve C encircles the axis.   Figure 3.9 represents a portion of the closed curve C together with a portion of the toroidal surface formed by lines of magnetic flux intersecting C.   Let $d\mathbf{s}$ be a vector element of length of C pointing round C in the direction related by the right-hand-screw rule to the direction of the current I threading C.   Through the two extremities of the vector element of length $d\mathbf{s}$ draw normal cross sections of the toroid as indicated in Fig. 3.9.   The width of toroidal surface between these normal cross sections is the component of the vector element of length $d\mathbf{s}$ in the direction of the magnetic vector $\mathbf{H}$.   Thus, when the toroidal surface is used as a toroidal inductor, the current flowing round this strip of toroidal surface is the scalar product

$$\mathbf{H} \cdot d\mathbf{s} \qquad\qquad (3.17)$$

The total current flowing round the surface of the toroid and crossing the closed curve C is obtained by adding up the contributions (3.17) for all the elements of length of C and is therefore given by the integral (3.14). But it was shown in Sec. 3.6 that this current is equal to the current I originally flowing along the axis, and from this the truth of Eq. (3.15) follows.

Now consider the case in which the closed curve C does not encircle the axis. As before, draw the lines of magnetic flux through the closed curve C, thereby forming a toroidal surface. The closed curve C now, however, encircles the magnetic flux passing through the toroidal surface as indicated in Fig. 3.10. Suppose that the toroidal surface is used as a toroidal inductor, so that the current I originally flowing along the axis is now flowing round the toroidal surface. Let P and Q be the points where the closed curve C touches extreme normal cross sections of the toroid as shown in Fig. 3.10. For the same reasons as before

$$\int_P^Q \mathbf{H} \cdot d\mathbf{s} \tag{3.18}$$

taken along C from the point P to the point Q represents the current flowing round the toroidal surface between the normal cross sections defined by the points P and Q; the direction is related by the right-hand-screw rule to the specified direction round the closed curve C. In the same way

$$\int_Q^P \mathbf{H} \cdot d\mathbf{s} \tag{3.19}$$

taken round the remainder of the closed curve C also represents the current round the toroidal surface between the extreme normal sections defined by the points P and Q, but this time in the opposite direction. It follows therefore that the sum of the integrals (3.18) and (3.19) taken round the two parts of the closed curve C is zero, and this establishes the validity of Eq. (3.16).

We thus see that, for any closed curve C drawn in the magnetic field of a long straight wire carrying a steady current I, the circulation of the magnetic vector, defined by the integral (3.14), is equal to the current threading the closed curve C in the direction related by the right-hand-screw rule to the direction round C defined by the vector elements of length $d\mathbf{s}$ of C. This statement is in fact true for the magnetic field arising from any system of steady electric currents.

SUMMARIZING EXERCISES

3.1. Describe the circumstances under which a perfectly conducting sheet can be introduced into a magnetic field in free space without upsetting the field. If the magnetic field on one side of the sheet is abolished, explain the relation that exists between the current flowing in the introduced sheet at any point and the magnetic-flux-density vector close to the sheet at that point.

3.2. Using the technique of dissection, derive from the magnetic field of a long straight wire carrying a steady current the magnetic fields of (a) a coaxial transmission line, (b) a coaxial inductor, and (c) a toroidal inductor of any cross-sectional shape.

3.3. By suitably introducing perfectly conducting surfaces in a magnetic field, show that every tube of magnetic flux can be regarded as existing independently. Show that, at a point of a tube where the magnetic flux density is B, the current per unit length that would flow round the tube if it existed independently is B/μ, where μ is the inductivity of the medium.

3.4. Explain how to analyze the magnetic field of a toroidal inductor into independently existing tubes of magnetic flux.

3.5. Explain what is meant by magnetic field strength and by the magnetic vector **H**. Describe the circulation law for the magnetic vector (a) using a line of magnetic flux and (b) using any closed curve drawn in the magnetic field.

CHAPTER 4

FUNDAMENTAL PROPERTIES OF MAGNETIC FIELDS

4.1. Introduction. In the preceding two chapters we have discussed in some detail the magnetic fields of coaxial and twin-wire transmission lines and of toroidal inductors. All these magnetic fields can in fact be derived from the magnetic field of a long straight wire carrying steady current by the process of replacing appropriate surfaces by conducting sheets. In this way it has been possible for us to encounter practically all the main features possessed by all magnetic fields. We have now reached a stage, therefore, at which it is feasible to list the general laws pertaining to magnetic fields.

4.2. General Laws Pertaining to Magnetic Fields. 1. Through every point in a magnetic field there may be drawn a line of magnetic flux. Lines of magnetic flux are closed curves, but they are not in general circles or even plane curves. A test charge moving along a line of magnetic flux is subject to no force of magnetic origin.

2. At each point of a magnetic field there is a magnetic-flux-density vector **B** directed along the line of magnetic flux through the point. Lines of magnetic flux passing through a small closed curve form a tube of magnetic flux. Since lines of magnetic flux are closed curves, tubes of magnetic flux are closed tubes. As one moves round a tube of magnetic flux, the product of the magnetic flux density B and the normal cross-sectional areas dS of the tube remains constant and is equal to the magnetic flux in the tube. If $d\mathbf{S}$ is a vector representing a cross section of the tube, not necessarily a normal cross section, and if at this cross section the magnetic-flux-density vector is **B**, then the scalar product $\mathbf{B} \cdot d\mathbf{S}$ has the same value at all points of the tube and for all cross sections of the tube. This scalar product $\mathbf{B} \cdot d\mathbf{S}$ is the magnetic flux in the tube. The total magnetic flux threading a closed curve C spanned by a surface S is

$$\Phi = \int_S \mathbf{B} \cdot d\mathbf{S} \tag{4.1}$$

where $d\mathbf{S}$ is a vector element of area of S at a point where the magnetic-flux-density vector is **B**.

3. A test charge of strength e moving with velocity **v** through a magnetic field for which the flux-density vector is **B** is subject to a force **F** of

magnetic origin given by the equation

$$\mathbf{F} = e\mathbf{v} \times \mathbf{B} \qquad (4.2)$$

4. A perfectly conducting surface can be introduced into a magnetic field without affecting the field, provided that it weaves its way between the tubes of flux without intersecting them. If the magnetic field is divided into two parts in this way, the magnetic field on one side of the introduced conductor can be abolished without affecting the magnetic field on the other side, provided that a suitable distribution of electric current flows on the introduced surface. This current is conveniently defined in terms of the magnetic vector $\mathbf{H}$ defined by the equation

$$\mathbf{H} = \frac{1}{\mu}\,\mathbf{B} \qquad (4.3)$$

where μ is the inductivity of the medium. Unless the medium has ferromagnetic properties, the inductivity is very close to the value for a vacuum, namely,

$$\mu_v = \frac{2\pi}{5} \times 10^{-6} \qquad (4.4)$$

In terms of the magnetic vector $\mathbf{H}$ the current that must flow on the bounding conductor of a magnetic field is defined as follows: At a point P of the bounding surface, let $\mathbf{n}$ be a unit vector drawn normally into the magnetic field and let $\mathbf{H}$ be the magnetic vector close to the point P. The current per unit width on the bounding surface is then given in magnitude and direction by the vector

$$\mathbf{n} \times \mathbf{H} \qquad (4.5)$$

Each tube of magnetic flux can exist by itself provided that there flows round its toroidal surface a current given by expression (4.5). The required current per unit length round the tube at any point P is equal to the magnitude of the magnetic vector $\mathbf{H}$ at P, and it must flow in the direction related by the right-hand-screw rule to the direction of the magnetic vector $\mathbf{H}$ at P.

5. For any closed geometrical curve C drawn in the magnetic field of any system of steady electric currents, the circulation of the magnetic vector $\mathbf{H}$ round C in a specified direction is equal to the total electric current I threading C in the direction related by the right-hand-screw rule to the specified direction round C. As an equation this is written

$$\int_C \mathbf{H} \cdot d\mathbf{s} = I \qquad (4.6)$$

where $d\mathbf{s}$ is a vector element of length of C pointing round C in the specified direction.

The circulation law for the magnetic vector expressed by Eq. (4.6) can be used to verify that the current per unit width on the bounding conductor of a magnetic field is given in magnitude and direction by expression (4.5). In Fig. 4.1 it is supposed that there is no magnetic field below the bounding conductor, while above the bounding conductor there is a magnetic field such that the magnetic vector close to the point P of the bounding surface is H. The direction of H is necessarily parallel to the bounding surface, since this surface cannot intersect a tube of magnetic flux. Consider an elongated rectangular curve surrounding the point P as shown in Fig. 4.1. The length of the rectangle parallel to the surface can be regarded as unity, and the width of

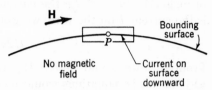

FIG. 4.1. Illustrating calculation of the current per unit width on the bounding surface of a magnetic field from the circulation law.

the rectangle perpendicular to the bounding surface is supposed to be small compared with unity. The plane of the rectangle is perpendicular to the bounding surface and contains the direction of the magnetic vector H close to the point P. The circulation round the rectangle in the clockwise sense in Fig. 4.1 is simply H. This is the contribution from the long side of the rectangle in the magnetic field. The other long side is not in a magnetic field, while the two short sides are perpendicular to the magnetic field and so do not contribute to the scalar product involved in the integral of Eq. (4.6). The circulation of the magnetic vector round the rectangle shown in Fig. 4.1 is equal to the current threading the rectangle, and this is the current on unit width of the bounding surface. Since the circulation round the rectangle is H, it follows that the current per unit width on the bounding surface is equal to the magnetic field strength close to the point P. This is the magnitude of the vector (4.5), and it can be verified that the direction of the current per unit width on the bounding surface is the direction of the vector (4.5).

4.3. Application of the Laws Pertaining to Magnetic Fields. In principle, the above laws governing the behavior of magnetic fields could have been stated at the outset of our study of magnetic fields, but there would have been some difficulty in comprehending their significance. Had we done so, however, it would then have been possible from them to derive all the results concerning transmission lines and inductors described in Chaps. 2 and 3. This would have been done as follows.

First we would have considered the magnetic field of a long, thin, straight wire carrying a steady current I. From symmetry we would have deduced that the lines of magnetic flux are in circles coaxial with the wire and that the magnetic flux density B and the magnetic field strength

H are functions only of the distance r from the wire. We would then have applied the circulation law for the magnetic vector to a line of magnetic flux of radius r. Since the magnetic field strength H does not vary along such a line, the circulation of the magnetic field strength round the line of magnetic flux is simply the product of the constant magnetic field strength H at distance r from the wire and the perimeter $2\pi r$ of the line of magnetic flux. Since the current threading the line of magnetic flux is the current I on the wire, we would deduce from Eq. (4.6) that

$$H2\pi r = I \tag{4.7}$$

From this we would derive Eq. (3.5) and hence Eq. (2.10). In this way our initial equations would be established, and the remainder of the discussion on transmission lines and inductors would then follow. The magnetic field of a coaxial transmission line would be obtained from that of a steady current I on a thin, infinite, straight wire by replacing circular cylindrical surfaces of radii a and b coaxial with the wire by conducting surfaces and retaining only the magnetic field between the conductors.

The circulation law for the magnetic vector can be used to verify the fact that there is no magnetic field inside the hollow inner conductor of a coaxial transmission line, because any closed curve drawn inside the hollow inner conductor cannot encircle any current. Likewise the circulation law for the magnetic vector can be used to verify the fact that there is no magnetic field outside the outer conductor of a coaxial transmission line carrying equal and opposite currents on the two conductors, for any closed curve encircling the outer conductor necessarily encircles a net electric current of zero.

4.4. The Magnetic Field of a Long, Thin Solenoidal Inductor. While the coaxial and toroidal inductors illustrated in Figs. 3.5 and 3.6 do a

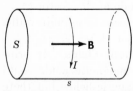

FIG. 4.2. A solenoidal inductor.

perfect job of packaging a magnetic field, there are many occasions on which these inductors are too clumsy. The inductor commonly used in such circumstances is the solenoidal inductor, which is more compact although it does an imperfect job of packaging the magnetic field. A solenoidal inductor takes the form of a cylindrical conductor of length s and normal cross-sectional area S with open ends as shown in Fig. 4.2. Round the curved surface of the cylinder there flows a current I uniformly distributed along the length of the cylinder.

It will be convenient to study initially a solenoidal inductor for which the length is large compared with the linear dimensions of a normal cross section. Such a solenoid behaves to an important extent like a portion of a toroidal inductor of small curvature.   Outside the toroidal inductor there is no magnetic field, while inside the toroid there is a magnetic field that is nearly the same at all points.   For the solenoidal inductor the tubes of magnetic flux thread through from one end to the other substantially as for the toroidal inductor, but these tubes must then form into closed tubes of magnetic flux outside the cylinder as indicated in Fig. 4.3.   Inside the solenoid the magnetic field is almost uniform and is strong.   It becomes stronger as the linear dimensions of a normal cross section of the cylinder become smaller in comparison with its length.   Compared with the magnetic field inside the solenoidal inductor, the magnetic field outside the solenoid is weak except near the open ends, and this becomes truer as the cross-sectional area of the cylinder becomes smaller.   Thus, for an indefinitely thin solenoid, the magnetic field inside the solenoid can be regarded as bounded by the current on the curved surface in the same way as for a toroid.   Hence the uniform magnetic field strength H inside a long, thin solenoidal inductor is practically equal to the

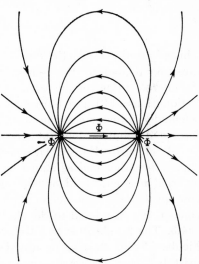

FIG. 4.3.   Magnetic flux threading through a long, thin solenoid.

current per unit length flowing round the curved surface.   It is upon this basis that the simple calculations concerning the magnetic field of a long, thin solenoid are carried out.

Since the total current flowing round the curved surface of the cylinder is I and the length of the cylinder is s, the current per unit length flowing round the cylinder is I/s.   Hence the magnetic field strength inside the solenoid is

$$H = \frac{I}{s} \qquad (4.8)$$

It follows that the magnetic flux density inside the solenoid is

$$B = \mu \frac{I}{s} \qquad (4.9)$$

where μ is the inductivity of the medium inside the solenoidal inductor. Since we are assuming that the magnetic flux density is uniform inside the solenoidal inductor, it follows that the total magnetic flux through every normal cross section of the inductor is the same and is obtained by multiplying the uniform magnetic flux density B by the cross-sectional area S. Hence the magnetic flux Φ entering one end of the solenoidal inductor and leaving the other is

$$\Phi = BS \qquad (4.10)$$

Substitution from Eq. (4.9) into Eq. (4.10) gives

$$\Phi = \frac{\mu S}{s} I \qquad (4.11)$$

This gives the magnetic flux threading through the solenoid in the direction related by the right-hand-screw rule to the current I round the curved surface of the solenoid.

Equations (4.8) and (4.9) give the magnetic field inside a long, thin solenoidal inductor carrying a current I round the curved surface, uniformly distributed along its length. In these circumstances a magnetic flux Φ, given by Eq. (4.11), emerges from one end of the solenoid and enters the other end as shown in Fig. 4.3. To calculate the resulting external magnetic field of the solenoid it is convenient to introduce a concept known as a magnetic pole. A magnetic pole is a magnetic concept that is related to the electric concept of a point charge.

4.5. The Similarities and Differences between Electric and Magnetic Fields. From what has been said so far it is clear that certain similarities exist between electric and magnetic fields, and it is now desirable to compare and contrast the properties of electric and magnetic fields.

Similarity exists between the physical significance of the electric vector **E** and that of the magnetic-flux-density vector **B**. In an electric field it is the function of the electric vector **E** to describe the way in which the electric field exerts force. The force **F** exerted on a test charge of strength e in an electric field in which the electric vector is **E** is given by

$$\mathbf{F} = e\mathbf{E} \qquad (4.12)$$

It is the function of the magnetic-flux-density vector **B** to describe the way in which force is exerted by a magnetic field. The force **F** exerted upon a test charge of strength e moving with velocity **v** in a magnetic field for which the flux-density vector is **B** is given by

$$\mathbf{F} = e\mathbf{v} \times \mathbf{B} \qquad (4.13)$$

We see that the electric vector **E** and the magnetic-flux-density vector **B** are both introduced to describe the way in which the fields exert force. We can say therefore that there is similarity between the electric vector **E** and the magnetic-flux-density vector **B** as far as physical significance is concerned, but we must remember that the formula (4.12), whereby the electric vector **E** describes the force exerted on a test charge, is different from the formula (4.13), whereby the magnetic-flux-density vector **B** describes the force exerted on a test charge.

We can also say that there is a similarity in physical significance between the electric-flux-density vector **D** in an electric field and the magnetic vector **H** in a magnetic field. If an electric field terminates at the surface of a conductor, the charge per unit area of the conductor is given by the component of the electric-flux-density vector **D** along the normal to the surface drawn into the field. If a magnetic field terminates at a conducting surface, the magnetic vector **H** close to the surface gives the current per unit width flowing on the surface in accordance with expression (4.5). The electric-flux-density vector **D** describes the distribution of the charge per unit area over all conductors associated with the electric field, including conductors used for dissecting the field. The magnetic vector **H** describes, in magnitude and direction, the current per unit width flowing on all conductors associated with the magnetic field, including conductors used for dissecting the field. Thus the electric-flux-density vector **D** makes a complete statement concerning charge geometry in an electric field, while the magnetic vector **H** makes a complete statement concerning current geometry in a magnetic field. Hence the electric-flux-density vector **D** in an electric field is similar to the magnetic vector **H** in a magnetic field as far as physical significance is concerned. It must be remembered, however, that the charge per unit area on a bounding conductor of an electric field is obtained by taking at the surface of the conductor the component of **D** along the normal drawn into the field, whereas the current per unit width on a bounding conductor of a magnetic field is obtained by using expression (4.5) at the surface of the conductor. Thus although the **D** and **H** fields perform similar functions for electric and magnetic fields, they have to be used in association with different formulas.

In spite of the fact that, from the viewpoint of physical significance, it is **E** that corresponds to **B** and **D** to **H**, a different situation presents itself if we examine the way in which these vectors handle mathematically. In an electrostatic field the work done in taking a unit test charge round a closed geometrical curve C and returning to the starting point is zero. This fact can be expressed by the equation

$$\int_C \mathbf{E} \cdot d\mathbf{s} = 0 \tag{4.14}$$

where $d\mathbf{s}$ is a vector element of length pointing round the closed curve C. It is this fact that makes it possible in electrostatics to associate with each point in the field a number known as the electric potential and to express the electric vector as the downward gradient of the potential.

Thus in handling the electric vector **E** in an electrostatic field we are involved in circulation integrals of the type indicated in Eq. (4.14). In discussing the magnetic field of steady currents we are also involved in circulation integrals, and these are integrals involving the magnetic vector **H**. For any closed geometrical curve C drawn in the magnetic field of a system of steady currents we have

$$\int_C \mathbf{H} \cdot d\mathbf{s} = I \tag{4.15}$$

where I is the total current threading the closed curve C in the direction related by the right-hand-screw rule to the direction round C in which the vector element of length $d\mathbf{s}$ points. Comparison of Eq. (4.14) with Eq. (4.15) shows that in handling both the **E** and **H** fields we are involved in line integrals of the scalar product of the vector with a vector element of length $d\mathbf{s}$. It is for this reason that it can be said that the electric vector **E** handles mathematically like the magnetic vector **H**. It must be noticed, however, that, whereas the circulation of the electric vector **E** round any closed curve C in an electrostatic field is zero, the circulation of the magnetic vector **H** round any closed curve C in the magnetic field of a system of steady currents is not in general zero but is equal to the total current threading the closed curve C. Thus, although the electric vector **E** handles mathematically like the magnetic vector **H**, they do not satisfy identical laws.

Whereas in handling the electric vector **E** in an electric field one is concerned with line integrals such as that in Eq. (4.14), in handling the electric-flux-density vector **D** one is concerned with surface integrals. Suppose that S is a closed geometrical surface in an electric field. Let $d\mathbf{S}$ be a vector element of area of S pointing normally outward. At the element of area $d\mathbf{S}$ of S let the electric-flux-density vector be **D**. Then, in accordance with Eq. (1.24),

$$\int_S \mathbf{D} \cdot d\mathbf{S} = Q \tag{4.16}$$

where Q is the total charge within the closed surface S. This is Gauss' theorem and involves an integral of the electric-flux-density vector **D** over a closed surface.

Again, whereas in handling the magnetic vector **H** one is concerned with line integrals such as that in Eq. (4.15), in handling the magnetic-flux-density vector **B** one is concerned with surface integrals. Suppose that S is a geometrical surface in a magnetic field. Let $d\mathbf{S}$ be a vector element of area of S at a point in the field where the magnetic-flux-density vector is **B**. The magnetic flux crossing the element $d\mathbf{S}$ is therefore $\mathbf{B} \cdot d\mathbf{S}$, and the total magnetic flux crossing the surface S is given by

Eq. (4.1). Now suppose that S is a closed surface. It then follows that

$$\int_S \mathbf{B} \cdot d\mathbf{S} = 0 \qquad (4.17)$$

This arises from the fact that tubes of magnetic flux are closed tubes and the scalar product of the magnetic-flux-density vector $\mathbf{B}$ at any point of the tube with the vector $d\mathbf{S}$ representing a cross section of the tube at the point does not vary as we move along the tube. Hence the contribution to the integral on the left-hand side of Eq. (4.17) from any particular closed tube of magnetic flux occurs in equal and opposite amounts where the tube enters and leaves the closed surface S. Equation (4.17), involving an integral of the magnetic-flux-density vector $\mathbf{B}$ over a closed surface, is, in fact, simply a mathematical statement of the fact that tubes of magnetic flux are closed tubes and carry the same magnetic flux at all points.

Comparison of Eq. (4.16) with Eq. (4.17) illustrates the fact that surface integrals are involved in the handling of both the electric-flux-density vector $\mathbf{D}$ and the magnetic-flux-density vector $\mathbf{B}$. This is what is meant by saying that the electric-flux-density $\mathbf{D}$ handles mathematically like the magnetic-flux-density vector $\mathbf{B}$. It must be noticed, however, that, whereas the integral of the electric-flux-density vector $\mathbf{D}$ over a closed surface is equal to the enclosed electric charge Q in accordance with Eq. (4.16), the integral of the magnetic-flux-density vector $\mathbf{B}$ over a closed surface is zero in accordance with Eq. (4.17). Thus while the electric and magnetic flux densities handle mathematically in a similar way, they do not satisfy identical laws.

The nonzero values appearing on the right-hand sides of Eqs. (4.16) and (4.15) involving $\mathbf{D}$ and $\mathbf{H}$ arise from the electric charges and currents producing the fields. The fact that zeros appear on the right-hand sides of Eqs. (4.14) and (4.17) involving $\mathbf{E}$ and $\mathbf{B}$ is sometimes expressed by saying that there is no phenomenon of magnetic charge or current. Both electric and magnetic fields arise from electric charge either at rest or in motion.

We thus see that, while there is considerable similarity between electric and magnetic fields, there is no single simple over-all statement to describe this similarity. From the point of view of physical significance, the electric vector $\mathbf{E}$ corresponds to the magnetic-flux-density vector $\mathbf{B}$, and the electric-flux-density vector $\mathbf{D}$ corresponds to the magnetic vector $\mathbf{H}$. On the other hand, it is the electric vector $\mathbf{E}$ that handles mathematically like the magnetic vector $\mathbf{H}$ and the electric-flux-density vector $\mathbf{D}$ that handles mathematically like the magnetic-flux-density vector $\mathbf{B}$. Even so, however, there are significant differences in corresponding equations arising from the fact that there is no phenomenon of magnetic charge.

Both electric and magnetic fields arise from electric charge either at rest or in motion.

4.6. Magnetic Poles. Since there is no phenomenon of magnetic charge, there can be no magnetic field corresponding precisely to the electric field of an electric point charge.   There is, however, a magnetic field of some importance that has many of the properties corresponding to the electric field of an electric point charge, but not all of them.   Let us contemplate for a moment the possibility of a magnetic field corresponding precisely to the electric field of an electric point charge, in order that we can see in what respects this field fails to satisfy the fundamental properties of magnetic fields.   In this way we shall be able to recognize the modifications required in the field and so arrive at what is known as a magnetic pole.

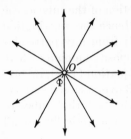

FIG. 4.4. An impossible magnetic field consisting of radial lines of magnetic flux associated with a point source of magnetic flux at the point O.

In a homogeneous medium of inductivity μ consider the possibility of a magnetic field in which the lines of magnetic flux run radially outward from a point O as shown in Fig. 4.4.

Let the total magnetic flux originating at O be Φ.   At distance r from O this magnetic flux is spread uniformly over a sphere of radius r and area $4\pi r^2$.   Hence the magnetic flux density at distance r from O is

$$B = \frac{\Phi}{4\pi r^2} \tag{4.18}$$

The corresponding magnetic field strength is

$$H = \frac{1}{4\pi\mu}\frac{\Phi}{r^2} \tag{4.19}$$

The tubes of magnetic flux are cones with apex at O.   Consider a tube of magnetic flux having a small solid angle $d\Omega$ (see Sec. 1.9).   The normal cross-sectional area of the tube at unit distance from O is $d\Omega$ and at distance r from O is $r^2\,d\Omega$.   It follows from Eq. (4.18) that the product of the magnetic flux density at distance r and the normal cross section of a tube of magnetic flux at distance r is independent of r.   This is one of the properties that the field must satisfy in order to comply with the laws enunciated in Sec. 4.2.   Likewise from Eq. (4.19) it can be shown that the circulation of the magnetic vector **H** taken round any closed geometrical curve in the field is zero.   This is obvious from the corresponding property of the electric field of an electric point charge given by Eq. (4.14).   Again, since no electric current exists, it follows that Eq. (4.6) is satisfied for the field shown in Fig. 4.4.   We can in fact verify that the magnetic field illustrated in Fig. 4.4 satisfies all the fundamental laws of a magnetic field except one.   The field is an impossible one because it does not consist of closed tubes.   As drawn in Fig. 4.4 the tubes of magnetic flux originate at the point O and terminate on the sphere at infinity.   According to Sec. 4.2, item 1, all tubes of magnetic flux must be closed tubes, and consequently the magnetic field illustrated in Fig. 4.4 is, as it stands, an impossible one.

However, there is now no difficulty in seeing how to modify the field illustrated in Fig. 4.4 so as to avoid the difficulty that magnetic flux cannot originate at a point.   It will be remembered that, in Part 2, Sec. 5.3, we studied a point source of steady current in a conducting medium and that the point source of current was produced by piping the current into the point by means of an insulated wire.   In the same way a situation in which magnetic flux emerges from the point O in Fig. 4.4 can be produced by piping the flux into the point O.   This may be done by means of a long, thin solenoid as illustrated in Fig. 4.5.   This diagram illustrates a long, thin solenoid extending from infinity at the left to the point O and carrying a total magnetic flux Φ.   The solenoid is supposed to be indefinitely thin and yet to carry a nonzero magnetic flux Φ.   This flux piped in by the sole-noid to the point O can then diverge

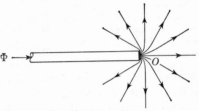

Fig. 4.5. The magnetic field of a magnetic pole.

radially from O, thereby producing at distance r from O a magnetic flux density given by Eq. (4.18) and a magnetic field strength given by Eq. (4.19).   It should be noted, however, that Eqs. (4.18) and (4.19) do not apply inside the thin solenoid that pipes the flux Φ into the point O.

We can now see how to calculate the magnetic field of the long, thin solenoid depicted in Fig. 4.3 at an external point P.   The magnetic flux Φ entering the left-hand end of the solenoid and emerging from the right-hand end is given by Eq. (4.11).   For the magnetic flux Φ emerging from the right-hand end of the solenoid, we apply Eqs. (4.18) and (4.19), using for r the distance from the right-hand end of the solenoid to the external point P at which the magnetic field is being evaluated.   For the magnetic flux entering the left-hand end of the solenoid, we apply Eqs. (4.18) and (4.19), replacing Φ by $-\Phi$ and using for r the distance from the left-hand end of the solenoid to the point P.   The complete magnetic field at P is now obtained by vector addition of the contributions from the two ends of the solenoid.   The external magnetic field of a long, thin solenoid is thus calculated in the same way as the electric field of a pair of equal and opposite charges is calculated.   The lines of magnetic flux external to the solenoid in Fig. 4.3 are in fact identical with the lines of force shown in Part 1, Fig. 1.12, for a pair of equal and opposite point charges. For the solenoid, however, it is vital to realize that the flux arriving at the left-hand end of the solenoid does not terminate there but is piped through the solenoid to the right-hand end. In this way is produced the strong internal magnetic field of the solenoid that is described by Eqs. (4.8) and (4.9).

If in Fig. 4.3 we fix the right-hand end of the solenoid at a point O and allow the length of the solenoid to become indefinitely large, the magnetic field becomes that shown in Fig. 4.5. The magnetic field illustrated in Fig. 4.5 is known as the field of a magnetic pole, while that

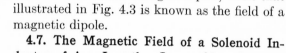
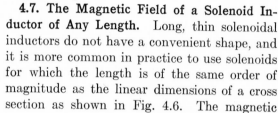

illustrated in Fig. 4.3 is known as the field of a magnetic dipole.

4.7. The Magnetic Field of a Solenoid Inductor of Any Length. Long, thin solenoidal inductors do not have a convenient shape, and it is more common in practice to use solenoids for which the length is of the same order of magnitude as the linear dimensions of a cross section as shown in Fig. 4.6. The magnetic

FIG. 4.6. Illustrating dissection of a solenoid of any length into long, thin solenoids.

field of a solenoidal inductor of any length can be deduced from that of a long, thin solenoid already investigated.

Consider a solenoid such as that illustrated in Fig. 4.6, and suppose that a current I flows round the curved surface, uniformly distributed along its length. Such a solenoid may be thought of as made up of a large number of long, thin solenoids, one of which is indicated in Fig. 4.6. Each of these long, thin solenoids has the same length as the original solenoid but has an indefinitely small cross-sectional area. The same current I is supposed to flow round the curved surface of the long, thin solenoid, uniformly distributed along its length. Suppose that a large number of such long, thin solenoids are packed closely together side by side so as to fill the entire volume within the large solenoid. Then the currents flowing round the curved surfaces of the long, thin solenoids cancel each other over contiguous surfaces, leaving a current I flowing round the outer curved surface of the stack of long, thin solenoids. This is simply the current I flowing round the curved surface of the original solenoid. We thus see that the original solenoid, for which the linear dimensions of the cross section are not small compared with the length, can be dissected into a large number of long, thin solenoids, each carrying the same current I round the curved surface. For each of the long, thin solenoids the complete magnetic field can be calculated as described in connection with Fig. 4.3. In this way we can calculate the complete magnetic field of a solenoid for which the linear dimensions of a normal cross section bear any relation to the length of the solenoid. For a solenoid of circular cross section the result is of the form shown in Fig. 4.7.

From Fig. 4.7 we see that the magnetic field inside a solenoidal inductor for which the length is comparable to the diameter is still roughly uniform. For some purposes it is still adequate to use Eq. (4.8) for the magnetic field strength within the solenoid and Eq. (4.9) for the magnetic flux density within the solenoid. To this degree of approximation we then have a flux Φ entering the left-hand end of the solenoid in Fig. 4.7 and leaving the right-hand end, and this flux is given by Eq. (4.11). In actual fact, however, we can see from Fig. 4.7 that there is a fraction of the total flux near the curved surface of the solenoid that encircles only a portion of the current flowing round the curved surface. This phenomenon is referred to as "leakage," and use of formula (4.11) for the magnetic flux threading the solenoid implies neglect of leakage. Leakage

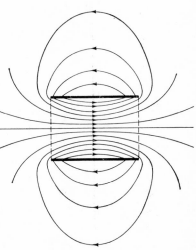

FIG. 4.7. The lines of magnetic flux of a solenoid for which the linear dimensions of a normal cross section are comparable to the length.

is small for a long, thin solenoidal inductor and nonexistent for the toroidal inductor.

4.8. Magnets. In connection with Fig. 4.6 we have seen that a solenoid may be regarded as assembled from a large number of long, thin solenoids packed side by side. Moreover each long, thin solenoid may be regarded as made up from a number of shorter solenoids packed end to end. A complete solenoid may therefore be regarded as made up from small solenoids packed end to end and side to side in building-block fashion, and the current per unit length flowing round the curved surface of each building block is the same. A situation equivalent to this occurs in the case of a magnet.

A magnet is a piece of ferromagnetic material for which the atoms or molecules themselves constitute the building blocks. An atom containing a spinning electron is equivalent to a small solenoid. If the spinning electrons in the various atoms constituting the ferromagnetic material are perfectly aligned, they fit together in lines to form the equivalent of long, thin solenoids, and these lines fit together side by side to form the equivalent of a large solenoid. This cylindrical bar magnet is one in which the spinning electrons are aligned parallel to the length of the cylinder, and it is equivalent to a solenoid of the same shape as the bar magnet with current flowing round the curved surface. The current per unit length for the equivalent solenoid is called the intensity of magnetization M of the magnet. The direction of magnetization of the magnet is the direction related by the right-hand-screw rule to the direction of the current round the equivalent solenoid. Thus a cylindrical bar magnet magnetized parallel to its length to an intensity M produces a field of magnetic flux identical with that which would be produced in free space by a solenoid of the same shape as the bar magnet with a current M per unit length flowing round the curved surface. The field of magnetic flux of a cylindrical bar magnet is therefore as indicated in Fig. 4.7.

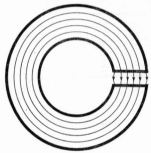

A long, thin bar magnet is known as a magnetic needle. It is equivalent to a long, thin solenoid and consequently produces a field of magnetic flux as indicated in Fig. 4.3. The total flux Φ leaving one end of a magnetic needle and arriving at the other end is known as the pole strength of the needle. The product of the pole strength of the needle and its length is known as the moment of the magnet.

FIG. 4.8. A magnet used to produce a nearly uniform magnetic field between the pole faces.

In an actual magnet the spinning electrons are not in fact so perfectly aligned as has been suggested above. However, a sufficient degree of alignment exists to make a cylindrical bar magnet equivalent to a solenoid in the manner stated. The behavior of ferromagnetic material will be discussed in greater detail in Chap. 8.

Magnets are frequently used to produce nearly uniform magnetic fields by bending them into nearly closed loops so that their flat ends face each other at a short distance apart as shown in Fig. 4.8. The field of magnetic flux is then substantially that of a toroidal inductor with a small amount of fringing at the edge of the gap between the pole faces. This is a convenient way of producing a nearly uniform magnetic field when it is desired to have access to the field from the edge. When it is desired to produce a nearly uniform magnetic field and to have access to it from the ends, a solenoid is the convenient arrangement.

SUMMARIZING EXERCISES

4.1. Describe and explain carefully laws of the magnetic-flux-density vector **B** and the magnetic vector **H** that are true for all magnetic fields in free space. Describe any additional law that is true for all magnetic fields that arise from steady electric currents.

4.2. A long straight circular wire of radius a carries a steady electric current I, uniformly distributed over the cross section. Using the symmetry properties of the field, show how to apply the circulation law to derive the magnetic field strength at all points outside and inside the wire.

4.3. Discuss the similarities and differences between electric and magnetic fields. Explain in what respects the electric vector corresponds to the magnetic vector and in what respects it corresponds to the magnetic-flux-density vector. Explain also in what respects the electric-flux-density vector corresponds to the magnetic-flux-density vector and in what respects it corresponds to the magnetic vector.

4.4. A long, thin solenoid of length l, with open ends at A and B, carries a magnetic flux Φ internally from B to A. Explain how to calculate the external magnetic field of the solenoid, describing what is meant by a magnetic pole.

4.5. A cylindrical solenoid carries round its curved surfaces a steady current uniformly distributed along the length. Explain how the solenoid can be dissected into long, thin solenoids. Sketch the lines of magnetic flux of a cylindrical solenoid whose length is comparable to the linear dimensions of a normal cross section.

4.6. Explain what is meant by (a) a cylindrical bar magnet having intensity of magnetization M, and (b) a magnetic needle having pole strength Φ. In each case sketch the lines of magnetic flux.

CHAPTER 5

INDUCTANCE OF ELECTRIC CIRCUITS

5.1. Introduction. The magnetic flux Φ threading an inductor is a measure of the momentum of the electrons round the inductor arising from their charge, and so considerable importance attaches to the calculation of Φ in terms of the current I round the inductor. Doubling the current round the inductor doubles the current per unit length round the inductor and hence the magnetic intensity H within and around the inductor. In a vacuum this doubles the magnetic flux density at all points in accordance with Eq. (4.3). Consequently the magnetic flux threading the inductor is also doubled. It follows that, in a vacuum, the ratio of the magnetic flux threading an inductor to the current round the inductor depends only upon the geometry of the inductor. The same is true if the region around the inductor is filled with any homogeneous material other than a ferromagnetic substance. For materials that are not ferromagnetic, the inductivity differs by a small amount from the vacuum inductivity. This does not upset proportionality of the magnetic flux threading an inductor to the current round the inductor, although it affects the magnitude of this ratio by a small amount. Even if the region surrounding an inductor contains ferromagnetic material, it is a common practice to take the necessary precautions to ensure that no serious departure takes place in the proportionality of magnetic flux to current. The ratio of the magnetic flux threading an inductor to the current round the inductor is called the inductance of the inductor. Thus, if I is the current flowing round an inductor and Φ is the magnetic flux threading the inductor in the direction related by the right-hand-screw rule to the direction of current flow, then the inductance of the inductor is defined as

$$L = \frac{\Phi}{I} \qquad (5.1)$$

The inductance of an inductor is the quantity by which the current flowing round the inductor must be multiplied in order to obtain the magnetic flux threading the inductor in the direction related by the right-hand-screw rule to the direction of current flow. We proceed to consider how to calculate the inductance of an inductor in terms of its geometrical dimensions and the inductivity of the medium in which it exists.

5.2. Inductance of a Thin Toroidal Inductor.   Consider the inductance of the toroidal inductor illustrated in Fig. 3.6.   Let S be the area of a normal cross section of the toroid existing in an axial plane.   Let μ be the inductivity of the material within the toroid.   If I is the total current round the curved surface of the toroid, the magnetic field strength within the toroid is given by Eq. (3.11) and there is no magnetic field outside the toroid.   Over the cross section of the toroid, therefore, the magnetic field strength varies inversely proportional to distance from the axis of the toroid.   It will simplify calculations to suppose that the toroid is sufficiently thin so that the variation of the magnetic field strength over a normal cross section can be neglected.   If r is the mean distance from the axis of the toroid to the various points of a normal cross section, we may take the magnetic field strength within the toroid as uniform over a cross section and given by Eq. (3.11).   Hence the magnetic field strength in the thin toroid can be written

$$H = \frac{I}{s} \tag{5.2}$$

where s is the perimeter of the toroid given by

$$s = 2\pi r \tag{5.3}$$

It follows that the magnetic flux density in the toroid is

$$B = \mu \frac{I}{s} \tag{5.4}$$

Since S is the cross-sectional area of the toroid, the total magnetic flux threading the toroid is

$$\Phi = BS \tag{5.5}$$

and substitution into this equation from Eq. (5.4) gives

$$\Phi = \frac{\mu S}{s} I \tag{5.6}$$

This equation illustrates the fact that the magnetic flux Φ threading the inductor is proportional to the current I round it.   By substituting from Eq. (5.6) into Eq. (5.1) we deduce that the inductance of the toroid is

$$L = \frac{\mu S}{s} \tag{5.7}$$

Thus the inductance of a toroid is directly proportional to the inductivity of the medium within the toroid.   It is also directly proportional to the cross-sectional area of the toroid and inversely proportional to its length.

5.3. The Inductance of a Solenoidal Inductor. Consider a long, thin solenoidal inductor such as that illustrated in Fig. 4.3. Let S be the area of a normal cross section of the inductor and s the length. Let μ be the inductivity of the medium within the solenoid. Let there be a total current I flowing round the curved surface of the inductor uniformly distributed over its length, and let the resulting magnetic flux threading the solenoid be Φ. To a first approximation we can regard the current round the curved surface of the inductor as the bounding current of the magnetic field within the solenoid. This assumes that the magnetic field close to the surface of the inductor outside the solenoid is small compared with that inside the solenoid. On this assumption the magnetic field strength H inside the solenoid is equal to the current per unit length flowing round the curved surface of the solenoid. Since there is a total current I uniformly distributed along a length s of the curved surface, the current per unit length is I/s. It follows that the magnetic field strength inside the solenoid is

$$H = \frac{I}{s} \tag{5.8}$$

The magnetic flux density inside the solenoid is therefore

$$B = \mu \frac{I}{s} \tag{5.9}$$

The total magnetic flux threading through the solenoid is

$$\Phi = BS \tag{5.10}$$

and substitution from Eq. (5.9) into Eq. (5.10) gives

$$\Phi = \frac{\mu S}{s} I \tag{5.11}$$

It follows from Eq. (5.1) that the inductance of the solenoid is

$$L = \frac{\mu S}{s} \tag{5.12}$$

Thus the inductance of a long, thin solenoid is proportional to the inductivity μ of the medium within the solenoid. It is also proportional to the cross-sectional area S of the solenoid and inversely proportional to the length s of the solenoid.

The above calculation is satisfactory if the length of the solenoid is large compared with the linear dimensions of a normal cross section. In practice it is frequently convenient to use a solenoid for which the length is comparable to the linear dimensions of a normal cross section, and a significant correction must then be applied to the inductance calculated from the formula (5.12). The field of magnetic flux is that shown in Fig. 4.7, and the magnetic flux crossing a normal cross section of the solenoid is different for different cross sections. It is necessary to calculate the average of the magnetic fluxes through the various normal cross sections, and this leads to a more complicated formula for the inductance of the solenoid. However, there is some difficulty in using any formula to design a solenoidal inductor to have given inductance. It is usually convenient to use a simple formula to arrive at an approximate design and then to complete the design experimentally.

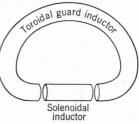

The nonuniformity of the magnetic field of a solenoid illustrated in Fig. 4.7 can be avoided by regarding the solenoid as part of a toroidal inductor, as shown in Fig. 5.1. The magnetic flux emanating from one end of the solenoid is conveyed to the other end through the toroidal guard inductor. In place of the toroidal guard inductor it is also

Fig. 5.1. Illustrating the use of a toroidal guard inductor to avoid nonuniformity of the magnetic field in a solenoidal inductor.

possible to use ferromagnetic material in a manner to be discussed in Chap. 8.

5.4. Unit of Inductance. Inductance, being the ratio of magnetic flux to electric current, is measured in volt-seconds per ampere, or webers per ampere. This unit of inductance is known as the henry. Consider a solenoid for which s equals 10 cm (10^{-1} m) and $S = 1$ cm² (10^{-4} m²). If the medium within the solenoid is not ferromagnetic, its inductivity is given approximately by Eq. (4.4). In accordance with Eq. (5.12), the inductance of the solenoid evaluates to 1.26×10^{-9} henry, or 1,260 $\mu\mu$h. A toroidal inductor having a cross-sectional area of 1 cm² and a perimeter of 10 cm would, in accordance with Eq. (5.7), have the same inductance, provided that the medium within the toroid is not ferromagnetic.

5.5. Interpretation of the Inductivity of a Medium. Consider a unit cube of material of inductivity μ. Cover four faces of the cube with perfectly conducting sheets of unit area in such a way as to leave a pair of opposite faces uncovered. By connecting the conducting faces together along their contiguous edges, we can form a solenoidal inductor of unit dimensions as shown in Fig. 5.2. Let us suppose that current flows round the solenoid uniformly distributed along its length and that the solenoid is fitted with a toroidal guard inductor so that the magnetic field inside the cube may be taken as uniform. The inductance associated with the unit cube is then obtained by putting S and s each equal to unity in Eq. (5.12). We thus see that the inductance of a unit cube used as illustrated in Fig. 5.2 is simply equal to the inductivity of the medium.

The inductivity of a material may thus be thought of as the inductance associated with a unit cube of the material when used in the manner illustrated in Fig. 5.2 and nonuniformity of the magnetic field in the solenoid is avoided. If the medium is a vacuum, then Eq. (4.4) shows that the inductance associated with a unit cube is $\frac{2}{5}\pi$ μh. For the reasons described in Sec. 2.3, it is the choice of this numerical value for the inductance of a unit cube in free space that controls the value of the

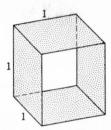

FIG. 5.2. A unit cube used as a solenoidal   FIG. 5.3. A column of square cross section
inductor.   used as a solenoidal inductor.

coulomb. To realize in what units the inductivity of a material is measured it is convenient to take a column of the material of length l and with square cross section of edge a. Round four contiguous faces of this column of areas al, a^2, al, and a^2 as shown in Fig. 5.3, wrap a perfectly conducting sheet so as to form a solenoid of cross-sectional areas al and length a. If nonuniformity of the magnetic field in the solenoid is avoided, the inductance, from Eq. (5.12), is

$$\mu l \tag{5.13}$$

Thus the inductance per unit length of the column is equal to the inductivity of the medium. This brings out the fact that the inductivity of a medium is to be measured in units of inductance per unit length. The unit of inductivity is therefore the henry per meter. The inductivity of a vacuum is

$$\mu_v = \frac{2\pi}{5} \times 10^{-6} \text{ henry/m} \tag{5.14}$$

which can also be written as

$$\mu_v = \frac{2\pi}{5} \mu\text{h/m} \tag{5.15}$$

The ratio of the inductivity of a substance to the vacuum inductivity is known as the permeability of the substance. Except for ferromagnetic substances, permeabilities are so close to unity that they can be taken as unity for many practical purposes. In Chap. 8 we shall see that, for ferromagnetic substances, the magnetic flux density B is only approximately proportional to the magnetic field strength H and then only if certain precautions are taken.   However, provided that these precautions are taken, an inductivity and a permeability can be assigned to ferromagnetic materials.   The permeabilities of ferromagnetic materials are extremely high and are of the order of 1,000.   Thus the inductance of almost any inductor can be increased by a factor of the order of 1,000 by filling its interior with ferromagnetic material.   For other than ferromagnetic materials, however, the permeability is practically unity.

5.6. Comparison among Inductance, Capacitance, and Conductance.   Consider a cylindrical sample of a material having normal cross-sectional area S and length s.   Let μ be the inductivity of the material, ϵ its capacitivity, and σ its conductivity.   Round the curved surface of the sample we may wrap a perfectly conducting sheet of width s forming an inductor as shown in Fig. 5.4a.   If nonuniformity of the magnetic field within the inductor is avoided, the inductance of the inductor is

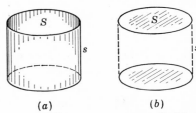

(a)   (b)

FIG. 5.4. Illustrating use of a cylindrical sample of material (a) as an inductor and (b) as a capacitor and resistor.

$$L = \frac{\mu S}{s} \qquad (5.16)$$

The same cylindrical piece of material can, however, be used as a capacitor by attaching perfectly conducting plates of area S to the flat ends as shown in Fig. 5.4b.   If nonuniformity of the electric field in the capacitor is avoided by means of guard plates, the capacitance of the capacitor is

$$C = \frac{\epsilon S}{s} \qquad (5.17)$$

If the cylindrical piece of material is not a perfect insulator, the arrangement shown in Fig. 5.4b can also be used as a resistor.   The conductance between the plates is given by

$$G = \frac{\sigma S}{s} \qquad (5.18)$$

Equations (5.16) to (5.18) demonstrate the similarity that exists among the formulas for inductance, capacitance, and conductance.   They also illustrate the way in which the inductivity, capacitivity, and conductivity of a material correspond to the concepts of inductance, capacitance, and conductance respectively.

The inductance L given by Eq. (5.16) relates the magnetic flux Φ threading the inductor with the current I round the inductor in accordance with the equation

$$\Phi = LI \tag{5.19}$$

while the capacitance C given by Eq. (5.17) relates the equal and opposite charges $\pm Q$ on the plates with the difference of potential V between the plates in accordance with the equation

$$Q = CV \tag{5.20}$$

Equations (5.19) and (5.20) illustrate the fact that the quantities Φ, I, and L associated with an inductor handle mathematically as the quantities Q, V, and C handle for a capacitor. It has to be noticed, however, that, as far as physical significance is concerned, the correspondence between the electrical and magnetic quantities must be viewed differently. Thus the phenomena associated with a capacitor arise from the existence of electric charge Q, while the phenomena associated with an inductor arise from motion of charge in the form of an electric current I. In this sense it is I in Eq. (5.19) that corresponds to Q in Eq. (5.20) even though Q handles mathematically like Φ. Again magnetic flux Φ has the property that its time rate of change is measured in volts as described in Sec. 2.11, and in this sense magnetic flux Φ in Eq. (5.19) corresponds to the voltage V in Eq. (5.20).

5.7. Inductance per Unit Length of a Coaxial Transmission Line. Consider a coaxial transmission line for which the space between the conductors has an inner radius a and an outer radius b, the inductivity of the medium being μ. By inserting a pair of conducting planes perpendicular to the axis of the line at distance l apart we obtain a coaxial inductor as shown in Fig. 3.5. When l is unity, the inductance of this coaxial inductor is known as the inductance per unit length of the coaxial transmission line.

To calculate the inductance of the coaxial inductor shown in Fig. 3.5 we must calculate the total magnetic flux crossing an axial plane. This is the magnetic flux through a rectangle in an axial plane with length l parallel to the axis, with inner edge distant a from the axis and outer edge distant b from the axis. This calculation has already been made in connection with Fig. 2.15, since the field in a coaxial transmission line with a current I flowing along the inner conductor and back along the outer conductor is identical with that of a current I flowing along the axis in the absence of the conductors. It follows that the magnetic flux threading through the coaxial inductor is given by Eq. (2.55). Substituting from Eq. (2.55) into Eq. (5.1), we see that the inductance of the coaxial inductor shown in Fig. 3.5 is

$$\frac{\mu}{2\pi} l \ln \frac{b}{a} \tag{5.21}$$

Putting l equal to unity in this equation, we deduce that the inductance per unit length of a coaxial transmission line for which the space between the conductors has an inner radius a and an outer radius b and is filled with a material of inductivity μ is

$$L = \frac{\mu}{2\pi} \ln \frac{b}{a} \tag{5.22}$$

If μ is given by Eq. (5.15) and $b = 2.7a$, then the natural logarithm appearing in Eq. (5.22) is practically unity, and the inductance per unit length of the coaxial line is $0.2\ \mu h/m$.

5.8. Inductance per Unit Length of a Twin-wire Transmission Line.
Consider a twin-wire transmission line consisting of a pair of circular

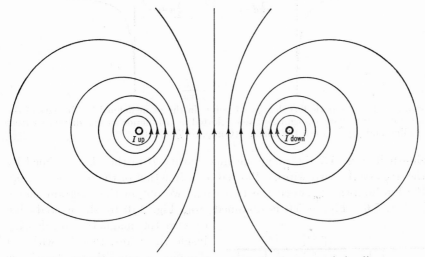

FIG. 5.5. The field of magnetic flux of a twin-wire transmission line.

wires, each of radius a, with their centers at distance d apart. Let μ be the inductivity of the medium surrounding the wires. It will simplify our consideration somewhat to take the wires as hollow and to let their radius be small compared with their distance d apart. If a current I flows along one wire and back along the other, a field of magnetic flux is produced threading between the wires as shown in Fig. 2.7. Figure 2.7 refers to a transmission line whose wires are indefinitely thin. However, the lines of magnetic flux close to either wire are circular, and cylinders of radius a can be drawn enclosing the line currents in Fig. 2.7 and composed entirely of lines of magnetic flux. These cylinders can then be replaced by conducting cylinders, and the field inside the cylinders can be abolished. In this way we arrive at Fig. 5.5 for the field of magnetic flux of a twin-wire transmission line having wires of finite radius a. For the magnetic field shown in Fig. 2.7 the magnetic flux density in the plane of the wires was calculated as a function of the distance x from the line midway between the wires.   The result is given by expression (2.38) and is plotted in Fig. 2.10.   In the same way we can plot for the magnetic field

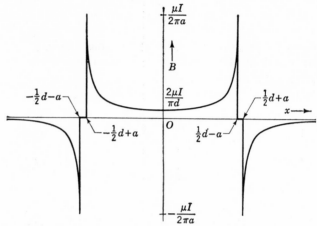

FIG. 5.6. The magnetic flux density at points in the plane defined by the axes of the wires of a twin-wire transmission line, plotted as a function of the distance x from the line midway between the wires.   (Compare Fig. 2.10.)

shown in Fig. 5.5 the magnetic flux density B in the plane defined by the axes of the two wires.   Plotted as a function of the distance x from the line midway between the two wires, we obtain the diagram shown in Fig. 5.6.   Figure 5.6 is obtained from Fig. 2.10 by simply reducing to zero the magnetic flux density inside the wires, that is, within a distance a on either side of the positions $x = \pm \frac{1}{2}d$.

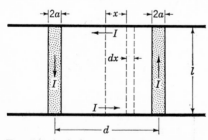

FIG. 5.7. An inductor formed by a length l of twin-wire transmission lines together with a pair of perpendicular conducting planes at distance l apart.

Draw a pair of geometrical planes perpendicular to the wires at distance l apart.   These planes consist entirely of lines of magnetic flux and so can be replaced by conducting sheets without upsetting the magnetic field.   If we consider only the magnetic field between the conducting planes, we see that this is produced by the arrangement illustrated in Fig. 5.7. A current I flows down the left-hand wire, through the lower sheet, up the right-hand wire, and back through the upper sheet in the direction indicated.   As a result, magnetic flux threads through the rectangle formed by the wires and the conducting planes in the direction outward from the paper in Fig. 5.7.   Half of this magnetic flux passes downward through the paper to the left of the left-hand wire and the other half to the right of the right-hand wire.   The arrangement shown in Fig. 5.7 thus constitutes an inductor of which we can calculate the inductance.   When l is equal to unity, this inductance is known as the inductance per unit length of the twin-wire transmission line.

The magnetic flux density B upward from the paper in Fig. 5.7 at a point distance x from the line midway between the wires is plotted in Fig. 5.6.   From this curve we have to calculate the total flux threading between the wires in Fig. 5.7.   Consider the rectangular area in the plane of the paper in Fig. 5.7 lying between the wires and between the con-ducting planes.   This is a rectangle of length l parallel to the wires and of width $d - 2a$ parallel to the conducting planes.   In Fig. 5.6 the rectangle extends from $x = -\frac{1}{2}d + a$ to $x = \frac{1}{2}d - a$.   Consider a strip of this rectangle of width dx at distance x from the line midway between the wires as shown in Fig. 5.7.   The area of this strip is $l\,dx$ and the uniform magnetic flux density over it is the ordinate in Fig. 5.6 at the point x.   The magnetic flux threading through the rectangular strip is $Bl\,dx$, and consequently the total magnetic flux threading between the wires and the conducting planes in Fig. 5.7 is

$$\Phi = l \int_{-d/2+a}^{d/2-a} B \, dx \tag{5.23}$$

The integral involved in this equation is the area under the curve plotted in Fig. 5.6 between the ordinates $x = -\frac{1}{2}d + a$ and $x = \frac{1}{2}d - a$. In this integral the expression for B is given by Eq. (2.38).   Substitut-ing this expression into Eq. (5.23), we obtain for the magnetic flux threading the inductor

$$\Phi = \frac{\mu I}{2\pi} l \int_{-d/2+a}^{d/2-a} \left(\frac{1}{\frac{1}{2}d + x} + \frac{1}{\frac{1}{2}d - x} \right) dx \tag{5.24}$$

Each of the terms of the integrand in Eq. (5.24) can be integrated in terms of a logarithm, and after some algebraic reduction we obtain

$$\Phi = \frac{\mu I}{\pi} l \ln \frac{d - a}{a} \tag{5.25}$$

Since we are assuming that a is small compared with d, Eq. (5.25) becomes

$$\Phi = \frac{\mu I}{\pi} l \ln \frac{d}{a} \tag{5.26}$$

Substituting from Eq. (5.26) into Eq. (5.1) we see that the inductance of the inductor illustrated in Fig. 5.7 is

$$\frac{\mu}{\pi} l \ln \frac{d}{a} \tag{5.27}$$

Putting l equal to unity, we obtain for the inductance per unit length

$$L = \frac{\mu}{\pi} \ln \frac{d}{a} \tag{5.28}$$

This is the inductance per unit length of a transmission line consisting of two wires of radius a, small compared with the distance d between their axes, the inductivity of the medium in which the wires are embedded being μ.

If $d = 10a$, the logarithm in Eq. (5.28) is about 2.3. Taking μ to have the value given by Eq. (5.15), we obtain for the inductance per unit length of the twin-wire transmission line about 0.92 μh/m. The inductance per unit length of a twin-wire transmission line is usually several times that for a coaxial transmission line.

Consider an inductor of the type shown in Fig. 5.7, and let us now suppose that the length l of the section of twin-wire transmission line involved is large compared with the distance d between the wires. In these circumstances only a minor modification in the entire magnetic field would take place if the short-circuiting planes at the two ends of the section of the transmission line were replaced by wires. We then have a rectangle of wire of length l and width d, the radius of the wire being a, and its inductance is given approximately by expression (5.27). Use of the expression (5.27) for the inductance of a rectangle of wire assumes that the length l of the rectangle is large compared with the width d and that the width d is large compared with the radius a of the wire. For a rectangle of wire of length 10 cm and width 1 cm constructed in free space from wire of radius 1 mm, the inductance evaluates to about 0.1 μh.

5.9. Relation between the Inductance per Unit Length and the Capacitance per Unit Length of a Transmission Line. The inductances L per unit length of the coaxial and the twin-wire transmission lines calculated in the preceding two sections can be compared with the capacitances C per unit length of these transmission lines calculated in Part 1, Chap. 11. For the coaxial transmission line we have

$$L = \frac{\mu}{2\pi} \ln \frac{b}{a} \tag{5.29}$$

$$C = \frac{2\pi\epsilon}{\ln (b/a)} \tag{5.30}$$

and for the twin-wire transmission line we have

$$L = \frac{\mu}{\pi} \ln \frac{d}{a} \qquad (5.31)$$

$$C = \frac{\pi\epsilon}{\ln (d/a)} \qquad (5.32)$$

μ and ϵ being the inductivity and capacitivity of the medium between the conductors. In both cases we see that there is a close relation between the inductance per unit length and the capacitance per unit length, and indeed this is true of all transmission lines. If we multiply Eq. (5.29) by Eq. (5.30), or alternatively Eq. (5.31) by Eq. (5.32), we obtain

$$LC = \mu\epsilon \qquad (5.33)$$

This illustrates the fact that the product of the inductance per unit length and the capacitance per unit length of a transmission line does not depend upon the geometry of the transmission line. It does, however, depend upon the medium in which the conductors are embedded.

Let us write Eq. (5.33) in the form

$$\frac{1}{(LC)^{\frac{1}{2}}} = \frac{1}{(\mu\epsilon)^{\frac{1}{2}}} \qquad (5.34)$$

The right-hand side of this equation is identical with expression (2.32). We recall that this expression has the dimensions of a velocity and is in fact the velocity of light and of radio waves in the medium. We thus see that the reciprocal of the geometric mean of the inductance per unit length and the capacitance per unit length for a transmission line is a velocity. It ultimately transpires that the velocity (5.34) is the velocity of transmission of electromagnetic waves along the transmission line.

5.10. Necessity for a Wide Range of Inductance Values. The inductors that we have considered so far are of the type frequently used in microwave radio equipment. In some cases the inductors take the form of short sections of coaxial transmission line. In the microwave vacuum tube known as the klystron, the inductor is a metal toroid. The toroid is usually split along its inner rim and is connected to a parallel-plate capacitor; Fig. 5.8 shows an axial cross section of the arrangement. In

Fig. 5.8. Axial cross section of a toroidal inductor and connected parallel-plate capacitor used in a klystron vacuum tube.

the microwave vacuum tube known as the magnetron, inductors frequently take the form of holes drilled in a metal block as shown in Fig. 5.9. Current flows round the inner surface of the hole, thereby forming a solenoidal inductor.   The solenoidal inductor is usually connected to a parallel-plate capacitor as shown in Fig. 5.9.   In microwave equipment the numerical values of inductance required are usually only a tiny fraction of a microhenry, and inductors of the type that we have described are satisfactory.

In equipment used for radio broadcast transmission and reception considerably higher numerical values of inductance are required.   While inductors of the type that we have considered could in principle be used, their size would be inconveniently large. Still higher numerical values of inductance are required in equipment used for sound reproduction and in the distribution of electric power.   In these applications inductors of the type we have described would not only be inconveniently large; they would be utterly absurd.   Methods are therefore required for adapting the simple inductors that we have so far investigated in order to obtain large numerical values of inductance without the use of inconveniently large physical dimensions.   For achieving this objective two methods are available:

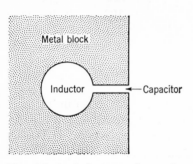

FIG. 5.9. An inductor and capacitor frequently used in a magnetron vacuum tube.

1. Use of a multiturn inductor in the form of a helix of wire, the successive turns of which are insulated from each other.   In this way it is possible, for the same over-all geometrical dimensions, to increase the inductance by roughly the square of the number of turns on the helix.

2. The use of ferromagnetic material in place of air in the region within the inductor and to an appropriate extent outside this region.   If suitable precautions are taken to ensure that the magnetic flux density in the ferromagnetic material remains approximately proportional to the magnetic field strength, then replacement of air by ferromagnetic material multiplies the numerical value of the inductance by the permeability of the material.   The permeability of ferromagnetic material is usually of the order of 1,000, and so by use of ferromagnetic material the inductance of an inductor can be increased by a factor of the order of 1,000 for roughly the same geometrical dimensions.

For inductors of extremely high inductance it is necessary to use both of the above methods simultaneously.   For inductors of medium inductance, however, it is frequently convenient to use method 1 only.   For inductors of small inductance the arrangements previously described can be used.

5.11. Multiturn Inductors.   Let us now consider a multiturn inductor consisting of a conducting wire wound as a helix on a form of length s and normal cross-sectional area S.   The form on which the inductor is wound can have the shape of a toroid of perimeter s as shown in Fig. 5.10 or alternatively the shape of a cylinder of length s as shown in Fig. 5.11.   In either case we shall neglect the variation in the magnitude and direction of the magnetic field over a normal cross section.   We assume that there are n turns of wire, that successive turns are closely wound, and that they are insulated from each other. The wire thus constitutes a helix of small pitch, and at all points the wire makes only a small angle with a normal cross section of the form. Let the helical wire be joined to a source delivering a steady current I as indicated in Figs. 5.10 and 5.11.

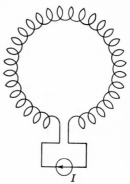

FIG. 5.10. A multiturn toroidal inductor.

The wire forming the inductor, together with the connections to the current generator, forms a closed geometrical curve that we shall denote by C. This closed curve C will be referred to as the electric circuit associated with the inductor. For any electric circuit C the inductance L is defined as the ratio of the magnetic flux Φ threading C to the current I flowing round C in the direction related by the right-hand-screw rule to the direction of the magnetic flux. For an inductor such as that shown in Fig. 5.11, therefore, we have to calculate the magnetic flux threading the closed curve C formed by the wire. In calculating the magnetic flux threading any closed curve C the procedure is to draw a surface S spanning the closed curve C and to calculate the magnetic flux crossing S in accordance with Eq. (2.48). Let us consider therefore how to draw a surface spanning the closed

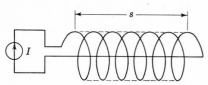

FIG. 5.11. A multiturn solenoidal inductor.

curve C formed by the wire in Fig. 5.11. We can do this by dropping perpendiculars from each point of the wire onto the axis of the helix, thereby forming a corkscrew surface known geometrically as a helicoid. It is the magnetic flux crossing this helicoid that has to be calculated and divided by the current I in the wire in order to evaluate the inductance of the electric circuit formed by the inductor. In doing this it is convenient to modify the arrangement to that shown in Fig. 5.12. The inductor now consists of a series of parallel plane loops of wire connected in series.   The surface spanning the electric circuit consists of n plane areas, each of area S, connected together by a narrow strip running along the bottom of the coil to the generator.   We assume that the area of the narrow strip is unimportant compared with the total area of the remainder of the surface spanning the electric circuit.   The total area of the surface spanning the electric circuit is therefore nS.   If B is the magnetic flux density within the inductor, and if this is assumed to be uniform, then the total magnetic flux traversing the surface spanning the electric circuit is

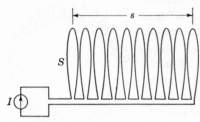

FIG. 5.12. A multiturn solenoidal inductor arranged so as to consist of a series of parallel plane loops of wire connected in series.

$$\Phi = BnS \qquad (5.35)$$

With a current I flowing round each of the n turns constituting the inductor, the total current flowing round the curved surface of the inductor is nI.   The magnetic field of the inductor is therefore substantially the same as if the form had a conducting curved surface with a current nI flowing round the curved surface uniformly distributed along the length.   The current per unit length is therefore nI/s.   Neglecting nonuniformity of the magnetic field within the solenoid, the magnetic field strength inside the solenoid is therefore

$$H = \frac{nI}{s} \qquad (5.36)$$

Taking the inductivity of the medium to be μ, the magnetic flux density inside the solenoid is

$$B = \mu \frac{nI}{s} \qquad (5.37)$$

Substituting for B from Eq. (5.37) into Eq. (5.35), we see that the magnetic flux threading the electric circuit is

$$\Phi = n^2 \frac{\mu S}{s} I \qquad (5.38)$$

Substituting this value of magnetic flux into Eq. (5.1), we see that the inductance of the electric circuit formed by the multiturn inductor is

$$L = n^2 \frac{\mu S}{s} \qquad (5.39)$$

If we had used a solenoid constructed by wrapping a metal strip of width s round the form of normal cross-sectional area S, the inductance of the one-turn inductor thus formed would be, in accordance with Eq. (5.12), $\mu S/s$. We thus see from Eq. (5.39) that the effect of constructing the inductor so as to have n turns on a form of the same size and shape is to multiply the inductance of the electric circuit by the square of the number of turns used. One of the factors n in Eq. (5.39) arises from the fact that the area of the surface spanning the electric circuit is n times the cross-sectional area of the form. The other factor n in Eq. (5.39) arises from the fact that the current flowing round the curved surface of the form is n times the current flowing round the wire constituting the electric circuit.

The argument by which we arrive at Eq. (5.35) is that the area of the surface spanning the electric circuit is nS and the magnetic flux per unit area over this surface is B. There is an alternative way of stating this argument that it is sometimes convenient to use. The area of a normal cross section of the form is S, and within the solenoidal inductor the magnetic flux density, assumed uniform, is B. Hence the magnetic flux crossing a normal cross section of the form is

$$\Phi_1 = BS \qquad (5.40)$$

This is the magnetic flux entering one end of the solenoid and leaving the other end, assuming that the magnetic field in the solenoid is uniform. To calculate the inductance of the electric circuit we require, not the magnetic flux Φ_1 crossing a single normal cross section of the form, but the magnetic flux crossing a surface spanning the electric circuit. As shown in Fig. 5.12 this surface consists of n normal cross sections of the form. Hence the flux Φ_1 given by Eq. (5.40) threads the electric circuit n times, and consequently the magnetic flux Φ threading the electric circuit is related to the magnetic flux Φ_1 crossing a single normal cross section of the form by the equation

$$\Phi = n\Phi_1 \qquad (5.41)$$

This equation, combined with Eq. (5.40), then gives Eq. (5.35) and so Eq. (5.39). In this method of arriving at Eq. (5.35) two magnetic fluxes are involved, Φ_1 and Φ. The magnetic flux Φ_1 is the magnetic flux threading a closed curve consisting of the rim of a normal cross section of the form. Assuming that the magnetic field in the inductor is uniform, this is the magnetic field entering one end of the solenoid and leaving the other. On the other hand the magnetic flux Φ is the magnetic flux crossing a surface of which the wire is the rim, and this is a surface consisting of n normal cross sections of the form as shown in Fig. 5.12. It is the magnetic flux Φ threading the electric circuit that is involved in the definition of the inductance of the electric circuit. The magnetic flux Φ_1 may be described as the magnetic flux threading one turn, and the magnetic flux Φ as the magnetic flux threading n turns, the relation between them being given by Eq. (5.41).

As a numerical example of Eq. (5.39), consider a solenoid for which $S = 1$ cm² $(10^{-4}$ m²$)$, $s = 1$ cm $(10^{-2}$ m$)$, and $n = 100$. Let the medium be air, for which the inductivity μ is given by Eq. (5.14). Substituting these numerical values into Eq. (5.39), we find that the inductance L of the solenoid evaluates to 1.26×10^{-4} henry, or 126 μh. Again, if $S = 100$ cm² $(10^{-2}$ m²$)$, $s = 10$ cm $(10^{-1}$ m$)$, $n = 1,000$, and $\mu = \mu_v$, then L evaluates to 0.126 henry. These inductances are substantially greater than those obtained without the use of multiple turns. Still greater inductances can be obtained by winding the coils on ferromagnetic material. If $S = 1$ cm² $(10^{-4}$ m²$)$, $s = 1$ cm $(10^{-2}$ m$)$, $n = 1,000$, and $\mu/\mu_v = 1,000$, then L evaluates to 12.6 henrys.

If convenient, the turns of an inductor can be wound, not in a single layer, but in a number of superimposed layers. In these circumstances the magnetic flux produced by the outer layers does not all thread the inner layers, and a loss of inductance is thereby involved. The loss of inductance is not, however, serious in comparison with the convenience of multilayer winding when the number of turns is large.

5.12. Use of Multiturn Inductors to Produce Magnetic Flux Density. We have seen that, if an inductor of given dimensions is wound as a multiturn inductor, its inductance is greatly increased. Multiturn inductors are also used in situations where the objective is to produce a magnetic field of given flux density, but the reasons for using a multiturn construction in this case are somewhat different. Consider a solenoid consisting of n closely wound turns on a form of length s, the inductivity of the medium being μ. Let us assume that nonuniformity of the magnetic field within the inductor can be neglected. If I is the current through the wire, then the magnetic flux density B within the inductor is given by Eq. (5.37). This equation shows that, for a given current I through the wire, the magnetic flux density within the inductor is increased by a factor n as a result of using the multiturn construction.

Now let us suppose, however, that the inductor is wound with wire of given diameter having a given resistance r per unit length. If l is the length of a single turn, the over-all length of the wire required for the inductor is nl, and its resistance is nlr. Hence the voltage required to drive the current I through the inductor is

$$V = nlrI \qquad (5.42)$$

Thus, although the use of more turns increases the magnetic flux density for a given current through the wire in accordance with Eq. (5.37), the voltage V required to drive the current also increases proportionally to the number of turns in accordance with Eq. (5.42). If we substitute for

I from Eq. (5.42) into Eq. (5.37), we derive

$$B = \frac{\mu V}{slr} \tag{5.43}$$

This equation is independent of the number of turns. It shows that the magnetic flux density within the inductor is determined by the inductivity μ of the medium, the voltage V driving the current, the dimensions s and l of the inductor, and the resistance r per unit length of the wire. For a given voltage V applied to the inductor, doubling the number of turns does not double the magnetic flux density in the inductor, because the resistance is doubled, and this halves the current. Thus, for given coil geometry and wire size, the magnetic flux density in the inductor is proportional to the applied voltage and is independent of the number of turns.

There is, however, another feature entering into the number of turns that it is desirable to use when designing an inductor to produce a specified magnetic flux density. The over-all resistance of the wire being nlr, the power dissipated in the wire as heat is

$$\frac{V^2}{nlr} \tag{5.44}$$

We see that, if the wire has a given length l per turn and a given resistance r per unit length, the power dissipated by the wire for a given applied voltage V is inversely proportional to the number n of turns. Thus, by using a large number of turns, the power dissipated as heat can be reduced. If in a particular situation it is undesirable for the power dissipated as heat to exceed P, then it is necessary for expression (5.44) to be less than P. This requires that

$$n > \frac{V^2}{lrP} \tag{5.45}$$

Thus, although the number n of turns does not appear in the Eq. (5.43) giving the magnetic flux density in the inductor in terms of the voltage V applied to the inductor, a lower limit to the number of turns to be used is often set by the inequality (5.45) in order to prevent the inductor operating at too high a temperature.

As an example suppose that the inductor is wound on ferromagnetic material of permeability 1,000, that the length of the form is $s = 10$ cm (10^{-1} m), and that the perimeter of the form is $l = 10$ cm (10^{-1} m). Suppose that it is required to produce a magnetic flux density $B = 3,000$ gauss (0.3 weber/m^2), and the power dissipated as heat P must not exceed 1 watt. If No. 40 copper wire is used, let us find what voltage must be applied to the inductor and how many turns are required. From Part 2,

Table 1.2, the resistance per unit length of the wire is 3.45 ohms/m. In Eq. (5.43) we therefore substitute r = 3.45 ohms/m, μ = 1,000μ_v, s = 10^{-1} m, l = 10^{-1} m, and so deduce that V = 7.6 volts. In the right-hand side of inequality (5.45) we now substitute this value of V together with the values of r and l. Putting in addition P = 1 watt, the right-hand side of inequality (5.45) evaluates to 168. We deduce therefore that, to keep the rate of dissipation of heat below 1 watt, we must use more than 168 turns and that the voltage that must be applied to the inductor to produce the required magnetic flux density is 7.6 volts.

SUMMARIZING EXERCISES

5.1. Explain what is meant by inductance, and define the unit of inductance. Show that the inductance of a thin conducting toroid of cross-sectional area S and perimeter s is $\mu S/s$, where μ is the inductivity of the medium within the toroid. Show that the same expression applies to a conducting solenoid of cross-sectional area S and length s provided that nonuniformity of the magnetic field is avoided.

5.2. A column of material having length l and square cross section of edge a has conducting plates of area a^2 attached to the ends. Conducting plates of area al are also attached to two of the remaining faces so as to leave a pair of opposite faces uncovered. The four conductors are joined at adjacent edges to form a continuous conducting solenoid, and nonuniformity of the magnetic field in the inductor may be neglected. Calculate the inductance of the inductor and show that the inductance per unit length of the column is equal to the inductivity of the material. State the units in which inductivity is measured and define permeability.

5.3. A cylindrical sample of material has normal cross-sectional area S and length s. The inductivity of the material is μ, the capacitivity is ϵ, and the conductivity is σ. By suitably applying metal surfaces to the material, illustrate how the properties of inductivity, capacitivity, and conductivity correspond respectively to the phenomena of inductance, capacitance, and conductance.

5.4. The space between the inner and outer conductors of a coaxial transmission line has inner radius a and outer radius b, and the inductivity of the medium is μ. Explain what is meant by the inductance per unit length of the transmission line and calculate its value.

5.5. A twin-wire transmission line consists of a pair of long, parallel, perfectly conducting wires, each of radius a, having a separation d between their axes, and d is large compared with a. The medium surrounding the wires is homogeneous and has inductivity μ. Explain what is meant by the inductance per unit length of the transmission line, and calculate its value.

5.6. Show that, both for a coaxial transmission line and for a twin-wire transmission line, the reciprocal of the geometric mean of the inductance per unit length and the capacitance per unit length is a velocity. State what velocity is involved.

5.7. A solenoidal inductor is formed by winding wire on a cylindrical form made of material of given inductivity. The wire is wound closely and uniformly along the whole length of the form so that each turn is nearly in a plane perpendicular to the axis of the solenoid. There are n turns of wire, and the terminals of the inductor are connected together through a source of steady electric current. Explain what is meant by (a) the magnetic flux entering one end of the solenoid and leaving the other and (b) the magnetic flux threading the electric circuit formed by the wire.

5.8. For calculating the magnetic flux threading the electric circuit formed by the wire in the previous exercise, describe how to span the electric circuit with a suitable geometrical surface. Describe the circumstances under which this surface may be regarded as equivalent to n normal cross sections of the form. Explain what further approximation is necessary in order to equate the magnetic flux threading the electric circuit to n times the magnetic flux entering one end of the solenoid and leaving the other end.

5.9. A toroidal inductor is formed by winding wire on a toroidal form made of material of given inductivity. The wire is wound closely and uniformly along the whole length of the form so that each turn is nearly in a plane through the axis of symmetry of the toroid. There are n turns of wire altogether. Define the inductance of the inductor and prove that its value is n^2 times that of a toroid constructed by wrapping the form tightly with a conducting surface and passing current toroidally round this surface uniformly distributed along the perimeter. Prove that the same is true of a solenoidal inductor provided that nonuniformity of the magnetic field is avoided.

5.10. A multiturn solenoid of length s is wound with wire of resistance r per unit length, and a battery of voltage V is connected across the terminals. The inductivity of the medium within the inductor is μ and nonuniformity of the magnetic field can be neglected. If l is the mean length of a single turn, calculate the magnetic flux density within the solenoid. Explain why the expression for the magnetic flux density is independent of the number of turns. Calculate the power dissipated in the wire, and deduce the minimum number of turns that must be used in order to keep the power dissipated less than a prescribed amount P.

CHAPTER 6

FORCES OF MAGNETIC ORIGIN

6.1. Introduction. Electric motors can be designed to operate using either forces of electric origin or forces of magnetic origin. At first sight it might appear that a design based upon forces of electric origin is more promising. Equation (2.4) shows that an electric charge moving with velocity v perpendicularly across a magnetic field of flux density B is subject to a force vB per unit charge, whereas the same charge in the presence of an electric field of field strength E is subject to a force E per unit charge. Now the largest electric field strength that can be conveniently produced in air, measured in volts per meter, is about a million times the largest magnetic flux density, measured in webers per square meter, that can be conveniently produced. For the magnetic field to produce on the charge a force comparable to the electric field it would be necessary for the charge to move across the magnetic field with a velocity of about a million meters per second. While velocities of this magnitude can be communicated to electrons by means of an electron gun, it is not feasible to produce such large velocities with rotating machinery. It would appear therefore at first sight that an electric motor could be made to work more conveniently by using forces of electric origin rather than by using forces of magnetic origin. However, other factors come into play. While it is true that force is more easily brought to bear upon an individual electron by means of an electric field rather than by means of a magnetic field, it is necessary to compound the forces on an enormous number of electrons in order to create a powerful electric motor. For this purpose large numbers of electrons can be assembled in the form of charges on the plates of capacitors or in the form of currents through inductors. To increase the driving forces available we can also exploit the concepts of multiplate capacitors and multiturn inductors. Furthermore, to enhance the phenomena, we have available materials of high dielectric constant and high permeability. When all these factors are taken into consideration, it turns out to be more convenient for most practical purposes to design electric motors by exploiting forces of magnetic origin. These are the forces that operate in accordance with Eq. (2.3).

Forces of magnetic origin are of importance not only in the design of rotating electrical machinery but also in the design of instruments for measuring current and voltage. Furthermore, forces of magnetic origin are of importance in controlling beams of electrons of the type involved in a cathode-ray tube.

6.2. Magnetic Deflection in a Cathode-ray Tube. In the cathode-ray tube described in Part 2, Sec. 6.4, it is possible to replace the electrostatic deflection plates within the tube by a pair of magnetic deflecting coils exterior to the tube as shown in Fig. 6.1. By means of a pair of coils

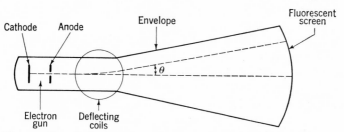

Fig. 6.1. A cathode-ray tube using magnetic deflection of the beam.

placed on either side of the tube it is possible to create within roughly the circular region indicated in Fig. 6.1 a magnetic field approximately perpendicular to the plane of the paper. The region indicated by the circle in Fig. 6.1 is the region within a circular cylinder whose axis intersects the axis of the undeflected beam at right angles. It will be assumed that the diameter of this cylinder is L, that the magnetic field has uniform flux density B within the cylinder parallel to its axis, and that, exterior to the cylinder, there is no magnetic field.

Let $-e$ and m be the charge and mass of an electron, and let electrons accelerate through a potential difference V in the gun. In accordance with Part 2, Eq. (6.12), electrons leave the gun with a velocity u given by

$$u = \left(\frac{2eV}{m}\right)^{1/2} \tag{6.1}$$

When an electron enters the magnetic field of flux density B produced by the deflecting coils, it is subject to a force given by Eq. (2.3). Since the direction of motion of an electron is perpendicular to the direction of the magnetic field, the strength of the force is euB and its direction is perpendicular to the direction of motion. The magnetic field does not therefore increase or decrease the velocity of an electron in the beam. It does, however, deflect the direction of motion of the electron. As a result the spot produced by the electron beam on the fluorescent screen of the tube is shifted away from the center of the screen.

While moving perpendicularly across the magnetic field, an electron is subject to a uniform force euB at right angles to its direction of motion.

Now a particle that moves under a force of constant magnitude directed perpendicular to the direction of motion describes a circle. Thus the portion of the beam within the magnetic field of the deflecting coils is circular. Let the radius of this circle be r. A particle moving with steady velocity u round a circle of radius r is subject to a centripetal acceleration u^2/r, and this is the acceleration produced by the constant force perpendicular to the direction of motion. Hence the equation of motion of an electron while in the magnetic field of the deflecting coils is

$$m \frac{u^2}{r} = euB \qquad (6.2)$$

This is the equation that determines the radius r of the circular path followed by an electron while passing through the magnetic field of the deflecting coils.

Equation (6.2) can be rewritten as

$$\frac{u}{r} = \frac{eB}{m} \qquad (6.3)$$

The left-hand side of this equation is the angular velocity of the electron round its circular path in the magnetic field of the deflecting coils. Equation (6.3) therefore states that, if an electron is projected perpendicular to a magnetic field of flux density B, then it executes a circular orbit in a plane perpendicular to the magnetic field with angular velocity

$$\frac{eB}{m} \qquad (6.4)$$

Apart from the charge and mass of an electron, this angular velocity is determined solely by the strength of the magnetic field. The angular velocity given by expression (6.4) is known as the angular gyrofrequency associated with the magnetic field. For an electron describing a circular orbit in a plane perpendicular to the magnetic field, the angular gyrofrequency gives the number of radians executed in unit time. It should be noticed that the angular velocity with which an electron describes a circular orbit in a magnetic field is independent of the speed of the electron. Equation (6.3) shows that, if the speed u of the electron is large, then the radius r of the circular orbit that it describes is also large, and the ratio of u to r is equal to the angular gyrofrequency associated with the magnetic field and given by expression (6.4).

In a cathode-ray tube an electron is only in the magnetic field of the deflecting coils long enough to describe a small fraction of a complete circular path. The angular velocity given by expression (6.4) is the angle turned through in unit time by an electron as it moves through the magnetic field of the deflecting coils. Now the distance advanced by the electron in unit time is u. Hence the angle turned through by the direction of motion of the beam as it proceeds a unit distance through the magnetic field of the deflecting coils is obtained by dividing the angular velocity (6.4) by the linear velocity u. In other words the angular deflection of the beam per unit distance of travel through the magnetic field of the deflecting coils is

$$\frac{eB}{mu} \tag{6.5}$$

If L is the length of the beam in the magnetic field of the deflecting coils, the total deflection produced is obtained by multiplying L by the rate of deflection given by expression (6.5). The total deflection produced in the beam by the deflecting coils is therefore

$$\theta = L\,\frac{eB}{mu} \tag{6.6}$$

If D is the distance from the axis of the deflecting coils to the fluorescent screen, the deflection of the spot on the screen is

$$D\theta = DL\,\frac{e}{mu}\,B \tag{6.7}$$

Substituting for the beam velocity u from Eq. (6.1) into Eq. (6.7) we obtain for the deflection of the spot on the screen caused by a magnetic field of flux density B in the deflecting coils

$$\frac{1}{\sqrt{2}}\left(\frac{e}{m}\right)^{\frac{1}{2}}\frac{LD}{V^{\frac{1}{2}}}\,B \tag{6.8}$$

We thus see that the deflection of the spot on the screen is proportional to the magnetic field produced by the deflecting coils and therefore to the current in the deflecting coils. By using two pairs of deflecting coils with their axes perpendicular to each other and to the line of the unde-flected beam, deflection of the spot on the screen from the center of the screen can be produced independently in perpendicular directions.

The cathode-ray tube using magnetic deflection was originally used to measure the ratio of the charge of an electron to the mass of an electron. In expression (6.8) for the deflection of the spot, the dimension L is known, being substantially the diameter of the deflecting coils, and the distance D is known, being the distance from the axis of the deflecting coils to the fluorescent screen. Moreover the voltage V through which electrons are accelerated in the gun can be measured, and so also can the magnetic flux density B in the deflecting coils. Hence a measurement of the deflection of the spot on the screen is a measurement of the numerical value of expression (6.8), and this leads to a numerical value for e/m. If the experiment is carried out with care and various corrections are applied, the numerical value obtained for the ratio of the charge to the mass of an electron is

$$\frac{e}{m} = 1.76 \times 10^{11} \text{ coulombs/kg} \tag{6.9}$$

Nowadays the numerical value for the ratio of the charge to the mass of an electron given by Eq. (6.9) is taken for granted, and expression (6.8) is used to relate the magnetic flux density B in the deflecting coils to the resulting deflection of the spot on the screen. Suppose that $L = 3$ cm (3×10^{-2} m), $D = 30$ cm (3×10^{-1} m), $V = 1,000$ volts, and that we wish to calculate the magnetic flux density in the deflecting coils required to produce a deflection on the screen of 5 cm (5×10^{-2} m). By substitution of these numerical values into expression (6.8) we derive for the magnetic flux density B in the deflecting coils the value 6×10^{-4} weber/m², or 6 gauss.

6.3. Force per Unit Length on a Wire Carrying a Current in a Magnetic Field. Suppose that by means of an arrangement of inductors or magnets we produce a magnetic field of flux density **B** and apply it to a metal wire carrying a current I. The current I is composed of electrons, each of charge e, drifting along the wire with velocity **v**. Each electron therefore constitutes a charge of strength e moving with velocity **v** through the applied magnetic field of flux density **B**. Each electron is therefore acted upon by a force given by Eq. (2.3). All the electrons constituting the current I are acted upon by a similar force, and the vector sum of all these forces constitutes a force acting upon the electric current I.

The force exerted by the applied magnetic field upon the electrons moving through the wire is in fact transferred to the wire in the following way: The force on the electrons given by Eq. (2.3), being perpendicular to the direction of drift, is perpendicular to the wire. This force therefore tends to displace the electrons sideways in the wire. As soon as this displacement takes place, however, strong electrostatic forces between the electrons and the positively charged atoms in the metal come into play. Hence the force exerted by the magnetic field on the moving electrons is transferred to the positively charged atoms in the crystal lattice of the metal and so acts upon the wire as a whole. In practice therefore we may say that the forces exerted by the applied magnetic field upon the electrons forming the electric current I are in fact forces acting upon the wire.

Let there be N drifting particles per unit length of the wire. Let each particle have a charge e and be drifting along the wire with velocity v. The number of particles that pass a particular normal cross section of the wire in unit time is the number of particles in a length v of the wire, and this is Nv. Each particle carries a charge e past this normal cross section, and consequently the amount of charge passing the cross section per unit time is Nev. Since the charge passing a particular normal cross section of the wire per unit time is the electric current I, it follows that

$$I = Nev \qquad (6.10)$$

It is convenient to introduce a vector $\mathbf{I}$ whose magnitude is the magnitude of the current I along the wire and whose direction is the direction of flow of the current along the wire. For positively charged particles the direction of the vector $\mathbf{I}$ is the same as the direction of the vector $\mathbf{v}$ representing the velocity of drift of the particles. Hence Eq. (6.10) can be written vectorially as

$$\mathbf{I} = N e \mathbf{v} \qquad (6.11)$$

Since the particles carrying the charge forming the current are normally electrons and are negatively charged, the direction of their velocity of drift is in reality opposite to the direction of the vector $\mathbf{I}$. This is allowed for in Eq. (6.11), however, by taking e numerically negative for electrons.

Let us now calculate the force $\mathbf{F}$ per unit length acting upon the wire in the presence of the applied magnetic field of flux density $\mathbf{B}$. In a unit length of the wire there are N electrons, each of which is acted upon by a force given by Eq. (2.3). Hence the total force acting on a unit length of the wire is

$$\mathbf{F} = N e \mathbf{v} \times \mathbf{B} \qquad (6.12)$$

We can express this force on the wire per unit length in terms of the current along the wire by means of Eq. (6.11). Substituting from Eq. (6.11) into Eq. (6.12) we obtain

$$\mathbf{F} = \mathbf{I} \times \mathbf{B} \qquad (6.13)$$

This equation states that, if a magnetic field of flux density $\mathbf{B}$ is applied to a wire carrying a current, and if at a particular point P of the wire the current is represented in magnitude and direction by the vector $\mathbf{I}$, then the force per unit length acting upon the wire at P is represented in magnitude and direction by the vector product of the current vector $\mathbf{I}$ and the magnetic-flux-density vector $\mathbf{B}$. The direction of the force per unit length of the wire is thus perpendicular both to the wire at the point P and to the line of magnetic flux through P due to the inductors or magnets used for applying the magnetic field to the wire. The magnitude of the force is proportional to the strength of the current along the wire, to the strength of the applied magnetic field, and to the sine of the angle between their directions.

As an example of the application of Eq. (6.13) consider a twin-wire transmission line consisting of two thin wires at a distance d apart. Suppose that a steady current I flows along one wire and back along the other and that it is required to calculate the force of magnetic origin between the two wires. In Fig. 6.2 the current through the left-hand wire applies to the right-hand wire a magnetic flux density **B** that is in the direction indicated and is of magnitude

$$B = \mu \frac{I}{2\pi d} \qquad (6.14)$$

μ being the inductivity of the medium around the wires. The current through the right-hand wire in Fig. 6.2 is represented vectorially by a

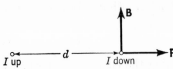

vector **I** downward into the paper. This current, flowing in the presence of the field of magnetic flux density **B** produced by the left-hand wire, causes a force per unit length **F** on the right-hand wire to be calculated from Eq. (6.13). The direction of this force is to the right in Fig. 6.2, and consequently the force of magnetic origin between the two wires is a force of repulsion. The magnitude of

FIG. 6.2. Illustrating the force of repulsion per unit length between the wires of a twin-wire transmission line carrying a steady current I along one wire and back along the other.

the force per unit length is the magnitude of the vector (6.13) and in this case is IB. It follows therefore from Eqs. (6.13) and (6.14) that the force of repulsion per unit length between the two wires is

$$F = \mu \frac{I^2}{2\pi d} \qquad (6.15)$$

There is, of course, an equal and opposite force exerted by the right-hand wire on the left-hand wire in Fig. 6.2, and this can be calculated in the same way. Figure 6.2 illustrates in a particular case the general tendency of electric circuits to expand unless prevented from doing so by the mechanical strength of the conductor and its supporting arrangements. This corresponds to the tendency of the rim of a rotating flywheel to expand unless prevented from doing so by the mechanical strength of the wheel.

If the current flowing in Fig. 6.2 is 1 amp, the distance between the wires is 1 cm (10^{-2} m), and the inductivity of the medium is given by Eq. (5.14), then the force of repulsion between the wires per unit length evaluates to 20 μnewtons/m.

6.4. A Simple Electric Motor. Suppose that by means of a magnet we produce in a certain region of space a uniform magnetic field of flux density B (see Fig. 4.8). In this magnetic field let a loop of metal wire be arranged so that it can rotate about an axis perpendicular to the direction of the magnetic field. For simplicity let the loop be rectangular in shape with sides of length a parallel to the axis of rotation and sides of length b perpendicular to the axis of rotation. The area of the loop is therefore

$$S = ab \tag{6.16}$$

Let the axis of rotation A lie halfway between the sides of length a as shown in Fig. 6.3. Let there be a steady current I round the loop. It is convenient to introduce the vector area $\mathbf{S}$ of the loop whose magnitude is equal to expression (6.16) and whose direction is normal to the loop and related by the right-hand-screw rule to the direction of the current I round the loop. Let the direction of the vector area $\mathbf{S}$ of the loop make an angle θ with the direction of the magnetic-flux-density vector $\mathbf{B}$ due to the magnet as shown in Fig. 6.3.

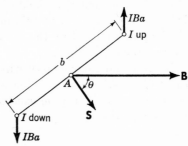

The magnetic field of the magnet exerts force upon the current flowing round the loop that can be calculated in accordance with Eq. (6.13). Consider first the forces exerted upon the sides of the loop of length b. In accordance with Eq. (6.13) the directions of these forces are parallel to the axis of rotation. The forces on the sides of length b can therefore have no torque about the axis of rotation. They do not even tend to slide the

Fig. 6.3. Illustrating the operation of an elementary electric motor consisting of a rectangular loop of wire able to rotate about an axis A in a uniform magnetic field of flux density B.

loop along the axis of rotation because the forces on these two sides of the loop cancel. It is the forces exerted upon the sides of the loop parallel to the axis of rotation that are of interest. In accordance with Eq. (6.13) the forces upon the sides of length a are in the directions shown in Fig. 6.3. The magnitudes are IB per unit length. The forces upon the sides of the loop of length a are therefore of magnitude IBa, and their lines of action are separated by a distance $b \sin \theta$. These forces therefore produce a torque tending to turn the loop round its axis, and the magnitude of the torque is

$$T = IBab \sin \theta \tag{6.17}$$

In terms of the area of the loop given by Eq. (6.16), the torque expressed by Eq. (6.17) can be written as

$$T = IBS \sin \theta \tag{6.18}$$

The direction of the torque is such as to turn the direction of the vector area $\mathbf{S}$ of the loop toward the direction of the magnetic-flux-density vector $\mathbf{B}$. Let the torque be represented by a vector $\mathbf{T}$ along the axis of rotation with a direction related by the right-hand-screw rule to the direction in which the torque acts. Then the torque is given in magnitude and direction by the equation

$$\mathbf{T} = I\mathbf{S} \times \mathbf{B} \tag{6.19}$$

This equation gives the direction about which the torque acts and also the magnitude of the torque in accordance with Eq. (6.18), θ being the angle between the directions of the vectors $\mathbf{S}$ and $\mathbf{B}$. We thus see that the torque tending to turn the loop about the axis is proportional to the strength of the current round the loop, to the area of the loop, to the strength of the magnetic field of the magnet, and to the sine of the angle between the direction of this magnetic field and a direction normal to the loop and related by the right-hand-screw rule to the direction of the current round the loop.

If the rectangular loop of wire is replaced by a rectangular coil of the same dimensions and carrying n turns of wire, identical forces act upon each turn and the torque exerted upon the coil is represented vectorially by the equation

$$\mathbf{T} = nI\mathbf{S} \times \mathbf{B} \tag{6.20}$$

and in magnitude by the equation

$$T = nISB \sin \theta \tag{6.21}$$

If the loop is not rectangular in shape, it can be subdivided into elements of area dS, each of which may be taken as rectangular in shape, and Eqs. (6.18) to (6.21) are not affected. Even if the loop is nonplanar, it can be divided into vector elements of area $d\mathbf{S}$ and the vector area of the loop can be calculated from the equation

$$\mathbf{S} = \int d\mathbf{S} \tag{6.22}$$

where the integral on the right is taken over a surface spanning the loop. Equation (6.22) then gives the appropriate vector area of the loop to be substituted into Eq. (6.19) or (6.20).

Let us now suppose that the loop in Fig. 6.3, instead of being held at a particular angle θ, is free to rotate on the axis. In accordance with Eq. (6.21) the torque on the loop vanishes when $\theta = 0$. Alternatively we may say that, in accordance with Eq. (6.20), the torque vanishes when the direction of the vector area $\mathbf{S}$ of the loop coincides with the direction of the flux-density vector $\mathbf{B}$ due to the magnet. The position $\theta = 0$ is therefore a position of equilibrium. In the same way the position $\theta = \pi$ is also a position of equilibrium. Since the torque on the coil tends to decrease θ, the position $\theta = 0$ is a position of stable equilibrium while the position $\theta = \pi$ is a position of unstable equilibrium.

Suppose now that the loop is released from rest at some position other than a position of equilibrium. If the loop has inertia and its bearings are smooth, the loop will oscillate about the position of stable equilibrium at $\theta = 0$. Now let us suppose, however, that each time that the plane of the loop becomes perpendicular to the direction of the magnetic

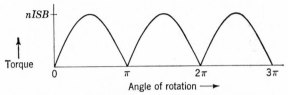

FIG. 6.4. Variation of torque with angle of rotation for an elementary electric motor consisting of a coil rotating in a uniform magnetic field.

field, the direction of the current I round the loop is reversed. This can be done by attaching to the axis a rotary switch known as a commutator. As the loop swings through a position of stable equilibrium, the current reverses and interchanges the positions of stable and unstable equilibrium. The coil therefore swings on through a further angle of π toward the new position of stable equilibrium. As it crosses this new position of equilibrium, the positions of stable and unstable equilibrium again interchange, and the coil once more swings on toward the new position of stable equilibrium. In this way continuous rotation of the coil is maintained. The variation of torque on the coil with angle of rotation is shown in Fig. 6.4. The sections of the curve in Fig. 6.4 are sinusoids arising from the sine of the angle θ between the directions of the vector $\mathbf{S}$ and the vector $\mathbf{B}$ in Eqs. (6.20) and (6.21).

In practice it is desirable to arrange for the torque to vary with the angle of rotation to a substantially smaller extent than is shown in Fig. 6.4. To do this, it is necessary to avoid as far as possible the

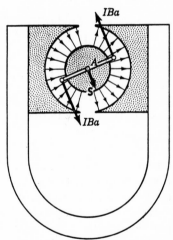

FIG. 6.5. A simple electric motor.

factor $\sin \theta$ in Eq. (6.21), and this requires that the forces of magnitude IBa in Fig. 6.3 be perpendicular to the plane of the loop instead of parallel to a fixed direction. To achieve this, it is necessary to arrange that the portion of the magnetic field swept out by the sides of the loop of length a involves a direction of magnetic field that is nearly radially outward from the axis of rotation or radially inward to the axis of rotation. This can be achieved by an arrangement such as that shown in Fig. 6.5. This diagram shows a magnetic field produced by a magnet having specially shaped pole pieces designed to produce a magnetic field that is radially inward toward the axis of rotation A on the left and radially outward from the axis of rotation on the right. To assist in shaping the magnetic field properly, a ferromagnetic armature is placed between the pole pieces in the shape of a circular cylinder whose axis coincides with the axis of rotation. In accordance with Eq. (6.13) the directions of the forces on the sides of the loop of length a are as shown in Fig. 6.5. The magnitude of the torque on the loop is therefore

$$T = IBab \tag{6.23}$$

and using Eq. (6.16) this can be written as

$$T = IBS \tag{6.24}$$

If the loop is replaced by a coil possessing n turns, the torque is given by

$$T = nIBS \tag{6.25}$$

As the sides of length a pass from one pole piece to the other in Fig. 6.5, the direction of the torque given by Eq. (6.25) reverses. This reversal

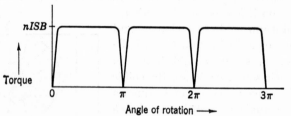

FIG. 6.6. Variation of torque with angle of rotation for an electric motor of the type shown in Fig. 6.5.

can, however, be avoided if the current I in the coil is reversed by a commutator at the same time. The variation of torque with angle of rotation is then as shown in Fig. 6.6. The torque is now nearly constant at the value given by Eq. (6.25).

If the coil turns through an angle θ, the work done is obtained by multiplying θ by the torque given by Eq. (6.25). If the coil rotates at a uniform angular velocity ω, the work done per unit time is

$$T\omega = nIBS\omega \tag{6.26}$$

If I is measured in amperes, B in webers per square meter, S in square meters, and ω in radians per second, then expression (6.26) gives the power of the motor in watts. This would have to be divided by 746 to convert the power into horsepower.

Suppose that the coil of the electric motor has 1,000 turns, each of area 100 cm² (10^{-2} m²), and operates in a magnetic field of flux density

10,000 gauss (1 weber/m^2). If the current through the winding is 10 amp, Eq. (6.25) shows that the torque exerted is 100 newton-m. If the motor operates at a speed of 1,000 rpm, the angular velocity is about 2.6 radians/sec. Equation (6.26) then shows that the motor is working at a rate of about 260 watts, or 0.35 horsepower.

6.5. Moving-coil Measuring Instruments. Instruments are frequently required for measuring electric current and voltage. The commonest arrangement for measuring electric current takes the form already described in connection with Fig. 6.5. When used as an instrument for measuring current the arrangement shown in Fig. 6.5 usually has a much lighter construction, and the rectangular coil does not make complete revolutions on the axis A. Instead each edge of length a of the rectangular coil remains in proximity with one of the pole pieces. A pointer is attached to the rectangular coil to indicate the position of the coil on an appropriate scale. The coil is fitted with a mechanical spring which, in the absence of other forces, keeps the coil in equilibrium in a position marked zero on the scale. The spring is such that, if the coil is rotated from the zero position through an angle θ about the axis A, the spring exerts upon the coil a restoring torque proportional to angle of rotation. When the coil is rotated through an angle θ from the zero position, let the restoring torque exerted by the spring be $k\theta$.

Now suppose that a current I flows through the coil. Then the coil is subject to a torque proportional to I and given by Eq. (6.25). The coil, together with the needle attached to it, turns under the influence of this torque and comes to rest after a rotation through an angle θ such that the restoring torque

$$k\theta \tag{6.27}$$

due to the spring balances the torque due to the current given by Eq. (6.25). In these circumstances it follows that

$$nIBS = k\theta \tag{6.28}$$

We see therefore that the current I through the coil is proportional to the angular displacement θ of the needle, and we can write

$$I = \frac{k}{nBS}\,\theta \tag{6.29}$$

It is possible therefore to mark the scale over which the needle moves in units of current. By suitable design, the numerical value of the coefficient of θ on the right-hand side of Eq. (6.29) can be adjusted so that the instrument is able to measure currents of the order of amperes, milliamperes, or microamperes. Such instruments are known as ammeters, milliammeters, or microammeters.

An instrument for measuring current can also be used for measuring voltage. We apply the voltage to a suitable resistor, measure the current through the resistor, and then apply Ohm's law. If desired, the resistor can be built into the instrument and the scale calibrated directly in voltage. Such an instrument is known as a voltmeter.

Both in the measurement of current and in the measurement of voltage it is essential to make sure that the arrangements are such that incorporation of the measuring instrument into the circuit does not modify seriously the quantity to be measured. In the measurement of current this means that the resistance of the coil of the instrument must be small compared with the resistance in series with it. In the measurement of voltage it is likewise essential to ensure that the resistance across which the voltage is developed for measuring purposes is large compared with the resistance in parallel with it.

6.6. Forces on Magnetic Poles. Consider a long, thin solenoid in the form of a closely wound helix having n turns, each carrying a steady current I. Let s be the length of the solenoid and S the area of a normal cross section, so that the linear dimensions of S are small compared with s. Let μ be the inductivity of the medium inside and outside the solenoid. The magnetic field strength inside the solenoid is then given by Eq. (5.36), and the corresponding magnetic flux density by Eq. (5.37). In accordance with Eq. (5.40) the magnetic flux entering one end of the solenoid and leaving the other is

$$\Phi = \frac{\mu S}{s} nI \tag{6.30}$$

The magnetic field outside the solenoid is that of a pair of magnetic poles of strengths Φ and $-\Phi$ at opposite ends of the thin solenoid.

Now suppose that to the thin solenoid is applied a uniform magnetic field of flux density B. This magnetic field could be produced by another solenoid or by means of a magnet. Let the direction of the applied field of magnetic flux density B make an angle θ with the length of the thin solenoid as shown in Fig. 6.7. Let us calculate the torque on the thin solenoid exerted by the applied magnetic field. The torque exerted upon each turn of the solenoid is given by Eq. (6.18). The torque exerted upon all n turns of the solenoid is therefore

$$T = nIBS \sin \theta \tag{6.31}$$

This equation can be rearranged in the form

$$T = \left(\frac{\mu S}{s} nI\right)\left(\frac{B}{\mu}\right)(s \sin \theta) \tag{6.32}$$

The first parenthesis on the right-hand side of Eq. (6.32) is the magnetic pole strength of the long, thin solenoid given by Eq. (6.30). The second parenthesis on the right-hand side of Eq. (6.32) is the magnetic field strength applied to the long, thin solenoid. If this is denoted by H, Eq. (6.32) can be rewritten as

$$T = \Phi H s \sin \theta \qquad (6.33)$$

Thus the torque on the long, thin solenoid is proportional to the pole strength Φ of the solenoid, the length s of the solenoid, the magnetic field strength H of the applied magnetic field, and the sine of the angle between the direction of the applied field and the axis of the solenoid.

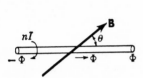

Fig. 6.7. Illustrating application of a magnetic field of flux density B to a long, thin solenoid carrying a magnetic flux Φ.

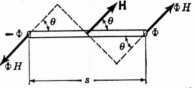

Fig. 6.8. Illustrating the use of magnetic poles in the calculation of force.

There is an interesting interpretation of Eq. (6.33) that it is frequently convenient to employ. This interpretation is illustrated in Fig. 6.8. In this diagram a magnetic flux Φ enters the left-hand end of the long, thin solenoid and emerges from the right-hand end. The magnetic field applied to the solenoid has a magnetic vector $\mathbf{H}$ that makes an angle θ with the length of the axis of the solenoid. Imagine that a force $\Phi\mathbf{H}$ is applied at the right-hand end of the solenoid and a force $-\Phi\mathbf{H}$ at the left-hand end. The perpendicular distance between the lines of action of these two forces is $s \sin \theta$. The two forces shown in Fig. 6.8 as acting on the ends of the solenoid would exert upon the solenoid the torque given by Eq. (6.33). Thus we could imagine that the magnetic vector $\mathbf{H}$ of the applied magnetic field is the force acting on an end of the long, thin solenoid per unit magnetic flux emerging from that end. This would give forces $\Phi\mathbf{H}$ and $-\Phi\mathbf{H}$ at the two ends of the solenoid as shown in Fig. 6.8 and would reproduce the torque exerted on the solenoid by the applied magnetic field and given by Eq. (6.33).

We thus see that the concept of magnetic poles has two applications. In the first place the concept of magnetic poles provides a convenient way of calculating the exterior field of a long, thin solenoid as illustrated in Figs. 4.5 and 4.3. In the second place the concept of magnetic poles provides a convenient method for evaluating the torque exerted upon a long, thin solenoid by an applied magnetic field as illustrated in Fig. 6.8. It is important to notice, however, that there is no implication in these statements of the existence of magnetic charge. Figure 4.3 shows that the exterior magnetic field of a long, thin solenoid can be calculated as though there were equal and opposite magnetic charges at the ends of the solenoid.   But magnetic flux does not originate at one end of the solenoid and terminate at the other.   The magnetic flux arriving at one end of the sylenoid threads through the solenoid and constitutes the magnetic flux leaving the other end.   Likewise, while the torque exerted upon a long, thin solenoid by an applied magnetic field can be calculated as shown in Fig. 6.8, the forces exerted by the magnetic field upon the solenoid do not in fact consist of a pair of forces ΦH and $-\Phi H$ acting at the ends of the solenoid.   The applied magnetic field in reality exerts force upon the electrons moving along the wire of the solenoid and constituting the electric current.   The force per unit length acting on the wire is given by Eq. (6.13).   The vector sum of the forces acting on all the elements of length of the wire constitutes a torque given by Eq. (6.20).   It is the magnitude of this torque which is expressed by Eq. (6.31) and which leads to Eq. (6.33).   Thus the applied magnetic field exerts force on the electrons moving through the wire, but these forces add up to a torque that can be conveniently written down as shown in Fig. 6.8.

Equation (6.33) and Fig. 6.8 apply equally well to a magnetic needle of pole strength Φ to which is applied a uniform magnetic field for which the magnetic vector is H.   Again it must be said that, while the magnetic vector H may be thought of as giving the force per unit magnetic flux on magnetic poles at the ends of the needle, the forces exerted by the applied magnetic field on the magnetic needle are in reality applied to the spinning electrons distributed throughout the magnet.

The fact that the magnetic vector H may be thought of as the force per unit magnetic flux on a magnetic pole suggests that a magnetic pole could be used to explore a magnetic field in much the same way as an electric point charge is used to explore an electric field.   In principle, this can be achieved in the following way: Take a large number of short magnetic needles of unit pole strength.   Link them together to form a chain of magnetic needles for which the positive pole of one needle is attached to the negative pole of the next needle.   We thereby form a long magnetic chain with a magnetic pole of strength 1 at one end and a magnetic pole of strength -1 at the other end.   Let us suppose that this magnetic chain is weightless and that no friction is involved in its use. Place the negative end of the chain outside the magnetic field to be investigated.   This situation may be idealized by supposing that the magnetic chain is indefinitely long and that the negative end is attached to a point at infinity.   Now use the positive end of the magnetic chain to explore the given magnetic field.   Such a flexible magnetic chain with a pole strength -1 at infinity and 1 at the exploring point may be described as a unit magnetic chain.   Suppose that the positive pole of the unit magnetic chain is placed in the given magnetic field at a point P where the magnetic vector is **H**. Then the force exerted on the unit magnetic chain is equivalent to a force **H** on the positive pole at P and a zero force on the negative pole at infinity. The total force on the unit magnetic chain is thus equal to the magnetic vector **H** at the positive pole. We can therefore evaluate the magnetic vector at all points in a given magnetic field by moving the positive pole of the unit magnetic chain from point to point in the field and evaluating for each point the total force of the unit magnetic chain. While use of a flexible unit magnetic chain with the negative pole attached to a point at infinity is scarcely a convenient method for measuring the magnetic vector at a point in a magnetic field, it is sometimes convenient for theoretical purposes to use this concept to visualize the effect of a magnetic field at a particular point.

6.7. The Law of Inverse Squares between Magnetic Poles.

Suppose that a magnetic chain having pole strength Φ_1 has the end from which the magnetic flux Φ_1 emerges located at a point P and the other end located at infinity. Suppose that a second magnetic chain of pole strength Φ_2 has the end from which the magnetic flux Φ_2 emerges located at a point Q and the other end located at infinity as shown in Fig. 6.9. Let the medium between the chains have a uniform inductivity μ, and let us ask what the forces are that

FIG. 6.9. Illustrating the law of inverse squares between magnetic poles.

act between the two magnetic chains. This force can be expressed in terms of the distance r between the points P and Q where magnetic flux emerges from the chains.

In accordance with Eqs. (4.18) and (4.19) the magnetic flux density produced by the chain of pole strength Φ_1 at distance r from the point P is radially outward from P and has the value

$$B = \frac{\Phi_1}{4\pi r^2} \tag{6.34}$$

and the corresponding magnetic field strength is

$$H = \frac{1}{4\pi\mu}\frac{\Phi_1}{r^2} \tag{6.35}$$

The force exerted upon the chain of pole strength Φ_2 is

$$F = \Phi_2 H \tag{6.36}$$

and substitution for H from Eq. (6.35) into Eq. (6.36) gives

$$F = \frac{1}{4\pi\mu}\frac{\Phi_1\Phi_2}{r^2} \tag{6.37}$$

We thus see that the total force exerted by the spinning electrons in the magnetic chain of pole strength Φ_1 upon the spinning electrons in the magnetic chain of pole strength Φ_2 is equivalent to a force acting at the point Q in Fig. 6.9 in the direction from P to Q and of strength given by Eq. (6.37). In the same way the total force exerted by the spinning electrons in the magnetic chain of pole strength Φ_2 upon the spinning electrons in the magnetic chain of pole strength Φ_1 is equivalent to a force acting at the point P in Fig. 6.9 in the direction from Q to P and of strength given by Eq. (6.37). These statements are conveniently abbreviated by saying that, between the magnetic pole of strength Φ_1 at

FIG. 6.10. Illustrating the calculation of force between a pair of magnetic needles.

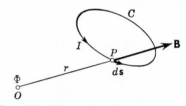

FIG. 6.11. Illustrating the calculation of the force between a magnetic chain of pole strength Φ and a loop of steady electric current I.

the point P in Fig. 6.9 and the magnetic pole of strength Φ_2 at the point Q, there is a force of repulsion given by Eq. (6.37). This force of repulsion is proportional to the strengths Φ_1 and Φ_2 of the magnetic poles and is inversely proportional to the square of the distance r between them. The constant of proportionality is the reciprocal of 4π times the inductivity of the homogeneous medium in which the magnetic chains are located.

Use of the law of inverse squares between magnetic poles usually provides the simplest method for calculating the forces between magnetic needles. Suppose that two magnetic needles of pole strengths Φ_1 and Φ_2 exist in a uniform medium of inductivity μ as shown in Fig. 6.10. The forces acting on the right-hand needle in Fig. 6.10 may be regarded as a pair of forces acting upon the magnetic poles Φ_2 and $-\Phi_2$. The force on each of these poles can be calculated from the magnetic poles associated with the left-hand magnetic needle in accordance with the law of inverse squares expressed by Eq. (6.37). The vector sum of the forces associated with the magnetic poles Φ_2 and $-\Phi_2$ then gives the total force on the right-hand magnetic needle in Fig. 6.10. The same method could be used if either or both of the magnetic needles in Fig. 6.10 were replaced by long, thin solenoids.

The same method can be adapted to solenoids and bar magnets for which the linear dimensions of the cross-sectional area are comparable to the length.   The procedure is to analyze the solenoid into long, thin solenoids as shown in Fig. 4.6.

6.8. Force between a Magnetic Pole and a Loop of Current.   Let us suppose that, in a homogeneous medium, a magnetic chain of pole strength Φ extends from infinity to a point O, so that outside the chain the magnetic field is that of a magnetic pole of strength Φ at O.   In the presence of this magnetic field let there be a steady current I flowing round a closed loop of wire C as shown in Fig. 6.11.   Let us calculate the force between the magnetic chain and the loop of steady current.

Let ds be an element of length at the point P of the closed curve C round which the current flows.   Let the distance of P from the location O of the magnetic pole be r.   Then the magnitude of the magnetic flux density at P due to the magnetic pole of strength Φ at O is given by Eq. (4.18).   The direction of this magnetic flux density is radially outward from O to P.   Let $\mathbf{u}_r$ be a unit vector directed from the point O toward P. Then the magnetic-flux-density vector $\mathbf{B}$ at P due to the magnetic pole at O is represented vectorially by the equation

$$\mathbf{B} = \frac{\Phi}{4\pi r^2}\,\mathbf{u}_r \tag{6.38}$$

Now the force per unit length exerted by the magnetic pole on the wire C carrying the steady current I is calculated from Eq. (6.13).   The force on the element of length ds and P is therefore

$$(\mathbf{I} \times \mathbf{B})\,ds \tag{6.39}$$

where the magnetic-flux-density vector $\mathbf{B}$ is given by Eq. (6.38) and $\mathbf{I}$ represents the current at P vectorially.

It is convenient to introduce a vector element of length $d\mathbf{s}$ of the closed curve C at the point P.   The magnitude of $d\mathbf{s}$ is equal to ds, and its direction is that of the current I at P.   Since the vectors $d\mathbf{s}$ and $\mathbf{I}$ have the same direction, the vector $\mathbf{I}\,ds$ appearing in expression (6.39) can be replaced by $I\,d\mathbf{s}$.   Hence the force exerted by the magnetic pole at O upon the element of length ds of the wire at P can be written as

$$I(d\mathbf{s} \times \mathbf{B}) \tag{6.40}$$

Substitution for the magnetic-flux-density vector $\mathbf{B}$ from Eq. (6.38) into expression (6.40) gives for the force exerted by the magnetic pole on the element of length ds of the wire at P

$$\frac{I\Phi}{4\pi}\frac{d\mathbf{s} \times \mathbf{u}_r}{r^2} \tag{6.41}$$

If we now add up the contributions given by expression (6.41) for all the elements of length of the wire, we obtain for the total force exerted by the magnetic pole of strength Φ at O upon the steady current I flowing round the loop C

$$\mathbf{F} = \frac{I\Phi}{4\pi} \int_C \frac{d\mathbf{s} \times \mathbf{u}_r}{r^2} \tag{6.42}$$

The magnitude of the force is thus proportional to the strength of the current and to the strength of the magnetic pole. The dependence of the force upon the geometry of the arrangement is described by the integral round the closed curve C appearing in Eq. (6.42).

The force exerted by the current loop shown in Fig. 6.11 upon the magnetic pole at O is equal and opposite to the force given by Eq. (6.42). In accordance with Eq. (1.13) the sign on the right-hand side of Eq. (6.42) can be reversed by interchanging the order of the vector product in the integrand. It follows that the force exerted by the steady current I flowing round the loop C in Fig. 6.11 upon the magnetic pole of strength Φ at O is

$$\frac{I\Phi}{4\pi} \int_C \frac{\mathbf{u}_r \times d\mathbf{s}}{r^2} \tag{6.43}$$

Evaluation of this force depends upon whether the geometry of the arrangement is sufficiently simple to permit evaluation of the integral round the closed curve C appearing in expression (6.43).

6.9. The Magnetic Field of a Loop of Steady Current. Let us suppose that a steady electric current I flows round a closed curve C as shown in Fig. 6.11 and that we wish to calculate the resulting magnetic vector $\mathbf{H}$ at a point such as O. In Sec. 6.6 we saw that the magnetic vector at a point in a magnetic field may be thought of as the force on a unit magnetic chain extending from infinity to the point. To calculate the magnetic vector $\mathbf{H}$ at the point O in Fig. 6.11 due to the steady current I round C it is merely necessary to calculate the force on a unit magnetic pole located at O. This is obtained by putting Φ equal to unity in expression (6.43). Hence the magnetic vector at the point O in Fig. 6.11 due to the steady current I round the closed curve C is

$$\mathbf{H} = \frac{I}{4\pi} \int_C \frac{\mathbf{u}_r \times d\mathbf{s}}{r^2} \tag{6.44}$$

This equation is known as Biot's formula and can be used to calculate the magnetic field at any point due to a steady current flowing round any circuit.

Biot's formula is sometimes expressed by saying that the element of length $d\mathbf{s}$ of the electric circuit C in Fig. 6.11 carrying the steady current I produces at the point O a magnetic vector

$$\frac{I}{4\pi} \frac{\mathbf{u}_r \times d\mathbf{s}}{r^2} \tag{6.45}$$

and the total magnetic vector at O due to the entire circuit is obtained by adding up the contributions (6.45) from the various elements of length of the circuit, thereby arriving at Eq. (6.44). Expression (6.45) is frequently described as the magnetic vector at the point O in Fig. 6.11 due to the current element $I\,ds$ at the point P. While this statement is often a convenient one to make in applying Biot's formula to a circuit of steady current, the statement is in fact inaccurate. It is possible to calculate the magnetic vector at the point O due to the motion of only those electrons associated with the current I that exists at a particular instant in the element of length ds of C. This calculation leads to expression (6.45) with, however, a correction. When the contributions to the magnetic vector at O due to all the elements of length in a complete closed circuit of steady current are totaled, the corrections to expression (6.45) add up to zero. Thus Eq. (6.44) is an accurate statement of the magnetic vector due to a complete closed circuit of steady current, whereas expression (6.45) is only an approximate expression for the magnetic vector due to a single element ds of the circuit.

6.10. Application of Biot's Formula. In applying Biot's formula to calculate the magnetic vector at a point O due to a steady current I flowing round a closed curve C it is convenient first to calculate the contribution to the magnetic vector at O from an element of length ds of the circuit at a point P in accordance with expression (6.45) and then combine the contributions from the various elements of length of the circuit in accordance with Eq. (6.44). In applying expression (6.45) it is convenient to use a diagram of the type shown in Fig. 6.12. In this diagram $I\,ds$ represents a current element of the circuit at the point P, and r is the distance to this element from the point O at which the magnetic vector is to be evaluated. The vector $\mathbf{u}_r$ is a unit vector pointing in the direction from O to P, and θ is the angle between the direction of $\mathbf{u}_r$ and the direction of $d\mathbf{s}$.

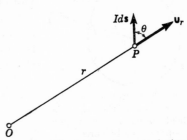

FIG. 6.12. Illustrating the calculation of the magnetic vector at a point O due to a current element $I\,ds$ at a point P.

It will be convenient to suppose that the plane of the paper in Fig. 6.12 is the plane of the vectors $\mathbf{u}_r$ and $d\mathbf{s}$.

Expression (6.45) shows that the direction of the magnetic vector at the point O due to the current element at the point P is the direction of the vector $\mathbf{u}_r \times d\mathbf{s}$. This direction is upward out of the paper. Expression (6.45), interpreted in accordance with expression (1.11), also shows that the magnitude of the magnetic vector at O due to the current element at P is

$$\frac{I \, ds \, \sin \theta}{4\pi r^2} \tag{6.46}$$

Thus the magnetic field strength at O due to the current element at P is proportional to the magnitude of the current element $I \, ds$ and to the sine of the angle θ in Fig. 6.12, while it is inversely proportional to the square of the distance from the current element to the point at which the magnetic field strength is evaluated. To apply Biot's formula (6.44) to calculate the magnetic vector at the point O due to the entire circuit of steady current we must evaluate the field strength at O due to each element of the circuit in accordance with expression (6.46), assign to this magnetic field strength its appropriate direction, and then take the vector sum of the contributions from all elements of the circuit.

Biot's formula can be used to evaluate the magnetic field of any wire carrying steady current. In particular Biot's formula can be used to evaluate the magnetic field of any of the electric circuits previously considered. For the coaxial transmission line, for example, Biot's formula can be used to arrive at Eq. (3.5), but this procedure is clumsy. It is much easier in such a case to recognize the axial symmetry of the problem and thus to arrive at Eq. (3.5) by an application of the circulation law for the magnetic vector as described in Sec. 4.3. There are other cases, however, in which use of Biot's formula provides the most convenient means of calculation.

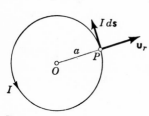

Suppose that a steady current I is flowing round a thin circular wire of radius a and that it is required to calculate the magnetic vector at the center of the circle. Figure 6.13 shows that, in this case, the radius vector from the center O of the circle to any point P of the wire has length a. Moreover this radius vector is perpendicular to the direction of the current round the wire at all points, so that the angle θ in expression (6.46) is $\frac{1}{2}\pi$. The magnetic field strength at O due to an element of length ds of the wire at the point P is therefore, in this case,

FIG. 6.13. Illustrating the calculation of the magnetic field strength of a circular loop of steady current at the center of the circle.

$$\frac{I}{4\pi a^2} \, ds \tag{6.47}$$

Moreover the direction of the vectors $\mathbf{u}_r \times d\mathbf{s}$ is, for all elements of the wire, parallel to the axis of the circle and in the direction related by the right-hand-screw rule to the direction of the current round the circle. In this case, therefore, the direction of the magnetic vector at the point O is along the axis of the wire, and the resultant magnetic field strength is obtained by algebraic addition of the contributions from the various elements of length of the wire given by expression (6.47).   Since the coefficient of ds in expression (6.47) is the same for all points P of the wire, algebraic addition of the contributions given by expression (6.47) simply involves algebraic addition of the lengths ds of the elements of the circuit, and this is equal to the perimeter $2\pi a$ of the circuit.   Hence the magnetic field strength at the center of the circle is

$$H = \frac{I}{4\pi a^2} 2\pi a$$

or
$$H = \frac{I}{2a} \tag{6.48}$$

Thus the magnetic field strength at the center of a circular loop of wire carrying a steady current I is proportional to the current and inversely proportional to the radius of the circle. The direction of the field is along the axis in the direction related by the right-hand-screw rule to the direction of the current.

If the circular loop of wire were replaced by a thin coil possessing n turns, each carrying a current I, the total current round the circle would be nI, and Eq. (6.48) would be replaced by

$$H = \frac{nI}{2a} \tag{6.49}$$

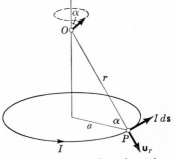

FIG. 6.14. Illustrating the calculation of the magnetic field of a circular loop of steady current at a point on the axis of the loop.

If $n = 100$, $I = 1$ amp, and $a = 10$ cm $(10^{-1}$ m), the magnetic field strength at the center of the circular coil evaluates to 500 amp/m.   In a medium whose inductivity is that of a vacuum the corresponding magnetic flux density is 6.3×10^{-4} weber/m^2, or 6.3 gauss.

Let us now use Biot's formula to calculate, for a circular loop of wire carrying a steady current I, the magnetic field at a point O on the axis of the wire other than the center of the circle.   This situation is illustrated in Fig. 6.14.   The point O on the axis of the wire at which the magnetic field is to be evaluated is equidistant from all points P on the wire.   Let this distance be r and let the radius of the wire be a.   The angle between the vectors $\mathbf{u}_r$ and $d\mathbf{s}$ in expression (6.45) is again $\tfrac{1}{2}\pi$.   Hence the angle θ in expression (6.46) is $\tfrac{1}{2}\pi$, and the magnitude of expression (6.46) is

$$\frac{I}{4\pi r^2} ds \tag{6.50}$$

This is the magnitude of the magnetic vector at the point O in Fig. 6.14 due to the current element $I\,ds$ at the point P of the wire. The direction of this contribution to the magnetic vector at the point O is the direction of the vector $\mathbf{u}_r \times d\mathbf{s}$. It therefore makes an angle α with the axis of the wire as indicated in Fig. 6.14, and α is given by the equation

$$\cos\alpha = \frac{a}{r} \tag{6.51}$$

The vector contributions to the magnetic vector at O from the various elements of the wire therefore lie round a cone with vertex at O and semi-vertical angle α as indicated in Fig. 6.14. Since all these vectors have the same magnitude given by expression (6.50), the resultant vector is directed along the axis of the wire in the direction related by the right-hand-screw rule to the direction of the current I round the wire. To calculate the magnitude of the magnetic vector at O we take the component along the axis at O of the contribution from the current element $I\,ds$ and then add up these components for the various elements of the wire. Hence the contribution of the element ds of the wire to the axial magnetic vector at O is obtained by multiplying expression (6.50) by $\cos\alpha$, given by Eq. (6.51), thereby obtaining

$$\frac{Ia}{4\pi r^3}\,ds \tag{6.52}$$

The coefficient of ds in this equation is the same for all points P of the wire, and hence an integration of expression (6.52) round the wire simply replaces ds by the perimeter $2\pi a$ of the wire. The magnitude of the magnetic vector at O is therefore

$$H = \frac{Ia}{4\pi r^3}\,2\pi a$$

or

$$H = \frac{Ia^2}{2r^3} \tag{6.53}$$

If the loop of wire is replaced by a thin coil possessing n turns, each carrying a current I, the total current flowing round the circle is nI, and Eq. (6.53) is replaced by

$$H = \frac{nIa^2}{2r^3} \tag{6.54}$$

This equation reduces to Eq. (6.49) when $r = a$. We see that, for a steady current I flowing round a circular wire, the axial magnetic field decreases as we move along the axis away from the center of the circle. The decrease is inversely proportional to the cube of the distance r from the wire.

Biot's formula can, in principle, be used to calculate the magnetic field of a circular loop of steady current at points not on the axis of the circle, but the calculation is difficult. An axial cross section of the lines of

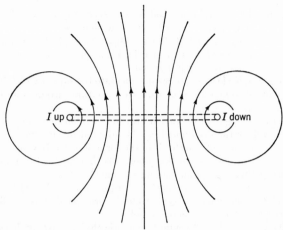

Fig. 6.15. An axial cross section of the lines of magnetic flux of a circular wire carrying a steady current.

magnetic flux of a circular loop of wire carrying a steady current is shown in Fig. 6.15.

SUMMARIZING EXERCISES

6.1. Describe the force exerted on an electron (charge $-e$ and mass m) moving with velocity u at right angles to a uniform magnetic field of flux density B. Show that, in the absence of other constraints, the electron describes a circular orbit with angular velocity eB/m. Explain why this angular velocity is independent of u, and calculate the radius of the orbit.

6.2. Describe the operation of a cathode-ray tube incorporating magnetic deflection. The deflecting magnetic field may be assumed to have a uniform magnetic flux density B and to occupy a circular cylinder whose axis intersects the line of the unde-flected beam. The distance from this axis to the screen is D, and the length of beam in the deflecting magnetic field is L. If V is the accelerating potential of the gun, calculate the deflection of the spot on the screen. Describe any approximations used.

6.3. An electric current represented vectorially by $\mathbf{I}$ flows through a wire, and to the wire is applied a magnetic field for which the magnetic-flux-density vector is $\mathbf{B}$. Show that the force acting on the wire per unit length is given in magnitude and direction by the vector product of $\mathbf{I}$ with $\mathbf{B}$.

6.4. A twin-wire transmission line consists of a pair of thin wires whose axes are at a distance d apart in a medium of inductivity μ. A current I flows along one wire and back along the other. Calculate in magnitude and direction the resulting force per unit length between the wires.

6.5. A rectangular coil is mounted so that it is free to turn about an axis running through the mid-point of a pair of opposite sides. There are n turns of wire on the coil; each is of area S and carries a steady current I.   A uniform magnetic field of flux density B is applied perpendicular to the axis of rotation.   If the normal to the coil makes an angle θ with the direction of the magnetic field, show that the field exerts on the coil a torque $nIBS \sin \theta$.   Describe the direction in which the torque tends to turn the coil.

6.6. If in the previous exercise the coil is not necessarily rectangular and the area of each turn is represented vectorially by **S**, show that the torque acting on the coil is represented vectorially by nI**S** ✕ **B**, where **B** is the applied magnetic-flux-density vector.   Describe the relation that must exist between the direction of the vector **S** and the direction of the current I in the coil.

6.7. Describe a simple electric motor and calculate the rate at which it does work in terms of the rate of rotation of the armature, the armature current, and the parameters of the machine.

6.8. Explain the principle of operation of a moving-coil instrument for measuring current.   Describe how the instrument can be adapted for measurement of voltage.

6.9. A long, thin solenoid of length s is in the form of a closely wound helix carrying a magnetic flux Φ from one end to the other.   To it is applied a uniform magnetic field of flux density B in a direction making an angle θ with the direction in which the flux Φ threads the solenoid.   Show that the torque on the solenoid has a magnitude $\Phi Hs \sin \theta$, where H is the magnetic field strength corresponding to the flux density B. Interpret this result in terms of magnetic poles.

6.10. Describe what is meant by a unit magnetic chain.   Explain how the magnetic vector at a point P in a magnetic field can be interpreted as the resultant force acting on a unit magnetic chain extending from infinity to P.

6.11. Derive the law of inverse squares between magnetic poles.   Explain how it can be used to calculate the forces acting between (*a*) a pair of magnetic needles, (*b*) a pair of long, thin solenoids, and (*c*) a magnetic needle and a long, thin solenoid.

6.12. Derive Biot's formula for the magnetic vector at any point in the magnetic field of a closed electric circuit carrying steady current.

6.13. Explain how to apply Biot's formula for calculating the magnetic field produced by a steady electric current.   Calculate the magnetic field strength at any point on the axis of a circular wire of radius a carrying a steady current I.

CHAPTER 7

MAGNETIC SCALAR POTENTIAL

7.1. Introduction. In the magnetic field of a steady current or system of steady currents the magnetic vector **H** at a point P describes the current per unit length that would have to flow round a tube of magnetic flux at P if that tube were maintained in existence by itself. We have also seen, however, that the magnetic vector **H** at P may be thought of as the resultant force acting upon a unit magnetic chain extending from infinity to the point P. From the latter point of view the magnetic vector **H** may be compared with the electric vector **E** in electrostatics, which is the force acting upon a unit test charge. In electrostatics it was found convenient to associate with each point in an electric field a scalar quantity ϕ known as the electric potential, and the electric vector at a point in the field was the downward gradient of the electric potential. One is led to ask whether it is feasible, in the case of a magnetic field produced by steady currents, to associate with each point of the field a scalar quantity ψ the downward gradient of which gives the magnetic vector **H**. It is in fact feasible to do this but only in parts of space where no current flows. The quantity ψ is known as the magnetic scalar potential.

Suppose that a solid metal wire carries a steady electric current. In the space surrounding the wire it is not only feasible but also convenient to associate with each point of the field a magnetic scalar potential ψ; the magnetic vector **H** at each point outside the wire is then given by the downward gradient at that point of the magnetic scalar potential. However, inside the metal wire, where the current is flowing, it is not even feasible to express the magnetic vector as the downward gradient of a magnetic scalar potential. The concept of magnetic scalar potential is thus applicable for discussing the magnetic field of steady currents only in parts of space where no current is flowing. The concept of magnetic scalar potential is therefore more restricted than the concept of electric potential. The concept of magnetic scalar potential is ultimately supplemented by a more widely applicable concept known as magnetic vector potential to be discussed in Chap. 10.

7.2. The Relation between Magnetic Scalar Potential and Potential Energy. Consider a magnetic field arising from steady electric current, and let us first think of the magnetic vector **H** at a point in the field as giving the resultant force upon a unit magnetic chain extending from infinity to the point. Let us now move the end of the unit chain from a point P to a point Q along a curve in the field as shown in Fig. 7.1. Let ds be a vector element of length of the curve pointing from P to Q. At the position of this vector element of length let the magnetic vector be **H**.

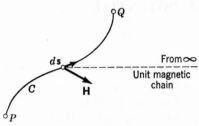

FIG. 7.1. Illustrating the work done on a unit magnetic chain as its end is moved from a point P to a point Q in a magnetic field.

Then **H** is the resultant force acting on the unit magnetic chain when its end is at the position of the vector element of length ds of the curve. If the end of the chain receives a vector displacement ds, the work done by the field on the chain is

$$\mathbf{H} \cdot d\mathbf{s} \qquad (7.1)$$

The work done by the field when the end of the unit chain moves from P to Q is obtained by adding up the contributions given by expression (7.1) for each element of length of the curve C, and this we write as

$$\int_P^Q \mathbf{H} \cdot d\mathbf{s} \qquad (7.2)$$

If the end of the unit chain is taken round a closed curve C and returned to the starting point, then the work done by the field upon the chain is obtained by adding up the contributions given by expression (7.1) for all elements of the closed curve C, and we write this as

$$\int_C \mathbf{H} \cdot d\mathbf{s} \qquad (7.3)$$

In studying electrostatic fields we saw that, in order to equate work done by a system to its loss of potential energy, it is necessary that there should be no frictional or other nonconservative forces acting. This means that the net work done in any process in which the system finally returns to its initial configuration must be zero. In the case of an electrostatic field this means that the work done in taking a test charge round any closed curve and returning it to the starting point is zero. This is the circulation law for the electric vector in electrostatics, and it is expressed by means of Eq. (1.17). A corresponding statement can be made for a magnetic field arising from steady currents as follows. Expression (7.2) gives the work done by the field upon a unit magnetic chain as its end moves from P to Q. This can only be equated to the loss of potential energy of the system provided that the net work done in any process in which the system finally returns to its initial configuration is zero. This means that the work done in taking the end of a magnetic chain round any closed curve and returning it to the starting point must be zero. From expression (7.3), this requires that

$$\int_C \mathbf{H} \cdot d\mathbf{s} = 0 \qquad (7.4)$$

for any closed curve C drawn in the magnetic field.

The circulation law for the magnetic vector, given by Eq. (4.6), states that the integral (7.3) does not in general vanish but instead is equal to the current threading the closed curve C. Hence, in general, the work done in taking the end of a magnetic chain round any closed curve and returning it to the starting point is not zero, and Eq. (7.4) is not satisfied. However, although the circulation of the magnetic vector round any closed curve in a magnetic field produced by steady currents does not in general vanish, there are restricted circumstances under which the circulation does vanish. Consider, for example, the volume inside a solenoidal inductor carrying a steady electric current. Any closed curve drawn inside this volume is not threaded by current. Hence the circulation law for the magnetic vector given by Eq. (4.6) establishes the truth of Eq. (7.4) for any closed curve drawn entirely inside the volume lying within the solenoidal inductor. This means that no net work is done in taking the end of a magnetic chain round a closed curve within the solenoid and returning it to the starting point. Within this volume therefore the system is what is called conservative. This means that, if the end of a unit magnetic chain is allowed to move from a point P within the solenoid to another point Q within the solenoid along a curve lying within the solenoid, the work done by the field upon the chain, given by expression (7.2), can be equated to the drop in potential energy of the system.

Let us therefore consider a magnetic field arising from steady electric currents, and let us consider a volume V of space in which no electric current is flowing and in which closed curves do not encircle electric current. For any closed curve C in this volume, Eq. (7.4) is satisfied. In the volume V select a reference point O, which might be at infinity in a particular case. Consider a unit magnetic chain extending from infinity to the point O. Within the volume V the work done in taking the end of the unit magnetic chain from O to P is defined as the magnetic scalar potential at P. The magnetic scalar potential at P is therefore also the work that can be recovered from the field by allowing the end of the unit magnetic chain to return from P to O. From Eq. (7.2) it therefore follows that the magnetic scalar potential at P is

$$\psi = \int_P^O \mathbf{H} \cdot d\mathbf{s} \qquad (7.5)$$

The volume V may be marked out with surfaces of constant magnetic scalar potential ψ in a manner analogous to the equipotential surfaces of electrostatics. As illustrated in Fig. 7.2, lines drawn so as to intersect at right angles the surfaces of constant magnetic scalar potential are lines giving at each point the direction of the magnetic vector **H**. Let P and Q be two points on a line of magnetic flux distance ds apart and let the

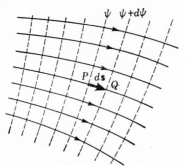

magnetic scalar potentials at P and Q be ψ and $\psi + d\psi$. If H is the magnetic field strength acting from P to Q, the work done by the field on a unit magnetic chain as its end moves from P to Q is $H\,ds$. Since the drop in potential energy of the system is $-d\psi$, it follows that

$$H\,ds = -d\psi \qquad (7.6)$$

and hence that $\quad H = -\dfrac{d\psi}{ds} \qquad (7.7)$

FIG. 7.2. Illustrating surfaces of constant magnetic scalar potential (broken lines) and lines of magnetic flux (full lines).

The magnitude of the magnetic vector is therefore the downward gradient of the magnetic scalar potential, and the direction of the magnetic vector is the direction of steepest descent of ψ. This relation between the magnetic vector **H** at any point of the volume V and the magnetic scalar potential ψ in V is written as

$$\mathbf{H} = -\operatorname{grad} \psi \qquad (7.8)$$

It must be remembered, however, that the magnetic vector can be expressed as the downward gradient of a magnetic scalar potential only in a region of space where Eq. (7.4) is satisfied, and this means, in accordance with Eq. (4.6), a region of space free from electric current.

7.3. Magnetic Scalar Potential of a Long, Straight, Steady Current. Consider a long, straight, solid circular wire of radius a, embedded in a homogeneous medium of inductivity μ. Let the wire carry a steady current I, uniformly distributed over the cross section. Both outside and inside the wire the lines of magnetic flux are circles whose centers lie on the axis of the wire and whose planes are perpendicular to the wire. At a point distant r from the axis of the wire the magnetic flux density outside the wire is given by Eq. (2.24) and that inside the wire by Eq. (2.27). Hence the magnetic field strength outside the wire is

$$H = \frac{I}{2\pi r} \qquad (7.9)$$

and that inside the wire is

$$H = \frac{I}{2\pi a^2}\, r \qquad (7.10)$$

Outside the wire it is possible to represent the magnetic vector at all points as the downward gradient of a magnetic scalar potential ψ. Surfaces drawn so as to intersect the circular lines of magnetic flux at right angles are planes through the axis of the wire. Outside the wire these planes are therefore the planes of constant magnetic scalar potential. Select one of these planes to be the one upon which the magnetic scalar potential is taken as zero, as shown in Fig. 7.3. Let θ be an azimuthal angle measured round the axis of the wire as shown in Fig. 7.3. Let θ vanish on the plane on which the magnetic scalar potential is chosen to be zero, and let θ increase in the direction related by the right-hand-screw rule to the direction of the current along the wire. The axial planes are therefore the planes for which θ = constant. These are also

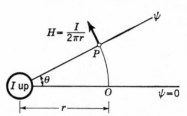

FIG. 7.3. Illustrating the calculation of the magnetic scalar potential at points outside a long straight wire carrying steady current.

the equipotential surfaces outside the wire, being the surfaces perpendicular to the circular lines of magnetic flux. We have to calculate the way in which the magnetic scalar potential ψ depends upon θ.

Consider a line of magnetic flux of radius r, greater than the radius a of the wire. Let this line of magnetic flux intersect the reference plane in the point O and the axial plane at angle θ in the point P as shown in Fig. 7.3. Let a unit magnetic chain extend from infinity to the point P, and let us calculate the work done on it by the field as the end of the chain moves from P to O. In accordance with Eq. (7.5) this is the magnetic scalar potential at P. An element of length of the circle OP subtending an angle $d\theta$ at the axis has length $r\, d\theta$. The work done in moving the end of the unit chain along this element of the circle is therefore $Hr\, d\theta$. It follows from Eq. (7.5) that the magnetic scalar potential at P is

$$\psi = \int_{\theta}^{0} Hr\, d\theta \qquad (7.11)$$

Substitution for H from Eq. (7.9) into Eq. (7.11) gives

$$\psi = \frac{I}{2\pi} \int_{\theta}^{0} d\theta \qquad (7.12)$$

and on performing the integration this becomes

$$\psi = -\frac{I}{2\pi}\, \theta \qquad (7.13)$$

This equation verifies the fact that the planes θ = constant are the equipotential surfaces and describes the way in which the magnetic scalar potential varies with θ.

By taking the downward gradient of the magnetic scalar potential given in Eq. (7.13), we can recover the magnetic vector at points outside the wire. Equation (7.13) shows that the magnetic scalar potential does not vary with r, and this implies that there is no component of the magnetic vector along a radius from the wire. We verify therefore that the magnetic vector is directed in circles round the axis of the wire. To verify expression (7.9) for the magnetic field strength outside the wire, we must take the downward gradient of ψ at distance r from the axis in the direction in which θ increases.

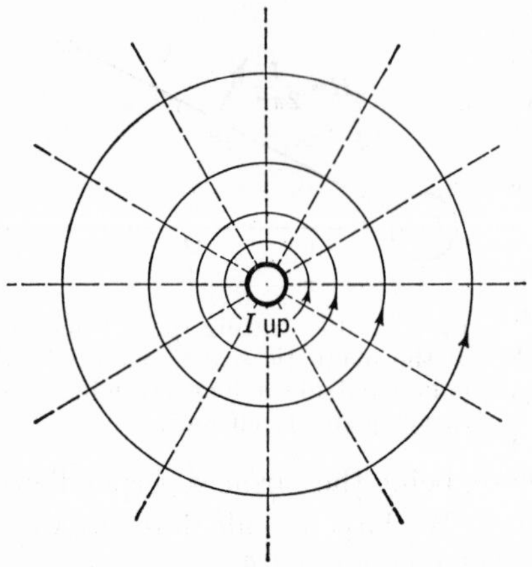

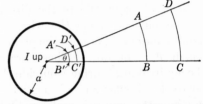

FIG. 7.4. Illustrating the planes of constant magnetic scalar potential (broken lines) and the lines of magnetic flux (full lines) at points outside a long straight wire carrying steady current.

FIG. 7.5. Illustrating the application of the circulation law for the magnetic field outside and inside a wire carrying steady current.

Since an increment $d\theta$ in θ corresponds to a displacement $r\, d\theta$, the downward gradient of ψ in the direction θ increasing is

$$H = -\frac{\partial \psi}{r\, \partial \theta} \tag{7.14}$$

On substituting the expression (7.13) for the magnetic scalar potential into Eq. (7.14) we verify Eq. (7.9). The equipotential surfaces outside a long straight wire carrying steady current are shown in Fig. 7.4 in relation to the lines of magnetic flux.

It is to be noticed that, in substituting for H from Eq. (7.9) into Eq. (7.11), the radial distance r cancels out, so that the magnetic scalar potential given by Eq. (7.13) is independent of r. This means that the work done on the end of a unit magnetic chain as it moves from A to B in Fig. 7.5 is the same as when it moves from D to C. Hence the work done when it moves from A to B is equal and opposite to that done when it moves from C to D. The work done in going along a side DA or BC of the closed curve $ABCDA$ in Fig. 7.5 is zero because there is no radial component of the magnetic vector. Hence the work done when the end of a unit magnetic chain moves round the closed curve $ABCDA$ in Fig.

7.5 is zero.   This is the condition that is expressed in Eq. (7.4) and that must be satisfied in a region of space in order that the magnetic vector can be expressed as the downward gradient of a magnetic scalar potential.

7.4. Nonapplicability of Magnetic Scalar Potential inside a Wire Carrying Current. The concept of magnetic scalar potential is not applicable in a region of space where current flows.   In consequence the magnetic vector inside the solid wire in Fig. 7.5 cannot be expressed as the downward gradient of a magnetic scalar potential.   Let us illustrate this fact by calculating the work done in taking the end of a unit magnetic chain round a closed curve inside the wire carrying the current.

It should perhaps be remarked that the experiment of taking the end of a unit magnetic chain round a closed curve inside a solid wire might seem impracticable.   However, it may also be remarked that, in order to have a steady current I flowing along a circular cylinder of radius a, it is not necessary for a wire to be present; the current could take the form of a beam of electrons ejected from an electronic gun.

Let us evaluate the work done in taking the end of a unit magnetic chain round the closed curve $A'B'C'D'A'$ illustrated in Fig. 7.5.   Equation (7.11) still gives the work done in taking the end of a unit magnetic chain from the point A' to the point B', but now it is necessary to substitute for H into this equation from Eq. (7.10) instead of Eq. (7.9).   The radial distance r does not now cancel out, and we arrive at the expression

$$-\frac{I}{2\pi a^2}\, r_1{}^2\theta \qquad\qquad (7.15)$$

for the work done in taking the end of the unit magnetic chain from A' to B', where r_1 is the radius of the circle $A'B'$.   In the same way if r_2 is the radius of the circle $C'D'$, the work done in taking the end of a unit magnetic chain from C' to D' is

$$\frac{I}{2\pi a^2}\, r_2{}^2\theta \qquad\qquad (7.16)$$

It follows that the work done in taking the end of a unit magnetic chain round the closed curve $A'B'C'D'A'$ is

$$\frac{I}{2\pi a^2}\, (r_2{}^2 - r_1{}^2)\theta \qquad\qquad (7.17)$$

This work done is simply the circulation of the magnetic vector round the closed curve and is therefore, in accordance with the circulation law of the magnetic field, equal to the current threading through the closed curve $A'B'C'D'A'$.   It is easily verified that expression (7.17) is in fact the portion of the total current I that threads the closed curve $A'B'C'D'A'$. Thus, in taking the end of a unit magnetic chain round a closed curve inside the wire and returning to the starting point the work done does not vanish. This means that, in a process in which the system finally returns to its initial configuration, net work is done, and so the system is not conservative. It is not therefore possible to speak of the potential energy of the magnetic chain in a particular configuration when its end is located inside the wire carrying the current and so it is impossible to describe the magnetic field within the wire in terms of a magnetic scalar potential. This illustrates the fact that the concept of magnetic scalar potential is applicable for description of the magnetic field of steady currents only in those regions of space where no current flows.

7.5. The Multivalued Character of Magnetic Scalar Potential. Even in a region of space where no current flows, care is necessary in application of the concept of magnetic scalar potential. It is true that the circulation of the magnetic vector round the closed curve $ABCDA$ in Fig. 7.5 is zero. Moreover this is true for any closed curve drawn in the space outside the wire provided that it does not enclose the wire. If a closed curve is drawn in the space surrounding the wire in such a way as to enclose the wire, the circulation of the magnetic vector round it is not zero. In accordance with the circulation law for the magnetic vector the circulation is equal to the current threading the closed curve and is consequently equal to the current I along the wire. This can be verified from Eq. (7.13). In one complete circuit of the wire in the direction related by the right-hand-screw rule to the direction of the current along the wire the angle θ increases by 2π. Hence the magnetic scalar potential given by Eq. (7.13) decreases by I. Thus the work done in taking the end of a unit magnetic chain round a closed curve encircling the wire is not zero but is equal to the current flowing along the wire.

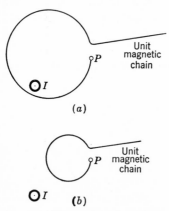

FIG. 7.6. Illustrating the process of moving the end of a unit magnetic chain round a closed curve (a) encircling a wire carrying a steady current I, and (b) not encircling the wire.

Figure 7.6 illustrates a unit magnetic chain extending from a point at infinity to a point P in the neighborhood of a wire carrying a steady current I. In each part of the diagram the end of the magnetic chain has been taken round a closed curve and returned to the point P. In Fig. 7.6a the closed curve encircles the current so that the potential energy of the unit magnetic chain drops by I during the process. In Fig. 7.6b the closed curve does not encircle the current, and so the potential energy of the unit magnetic chain returns to its original value.   Thus even in the space outside the wire carrying the current the magnetic scalar potential is not unique.   Each time the end of the unit magnetic chain is taken round the current I in the direction related by the right-hand-screw rule to the direction of the current, the magnetic scalar potential drops by I. This point is illustrated by Eq. (7.13).   Each time θ increases by 2π in this equation, the magnetic scalar potential drops by I.   Thus the magnetic scalar potential at each point is what mathematicians call multivalued.   Associated with each point there is a series of values of the magnetic scalar potential, each differing from the next by I; the various values depend upon how many times the unit magnetic chain has been wound round the wire carrying the current.   However, it does not matter how many times the magnetic chain has been wound round the current when considering the work done in a small displacement of the end of the chain in the space outside the wire.   The multivalued character of the magnetic scalar potential does not therefore affect the validity of Eqs. (7.6) to (7.8).

7.6. The Relation between Magnetic Scalar Potential and Amperage.

It is not the main objective of the magnetic vector $\mathbf{H}$ at a point P in a magnetic field to give the resultant force on a unit magnetic chain extending from infinity to P.   The primary significance of the magnetic field strength H at a point P is to give the current per unit length that would have to flow round a tube of magnetic flux at P if this tube were maintained in existence by itself.   The direction of the magnetic vector $\mathbf{H}$ at P is related by the right-hand-screw rule to the direction of the current that would flow round the tube.   Since the primary interpretation of the mag-

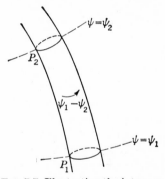

FIG. 7.7. Illustrating the interpretation of difference of magnetic scalar potential as amperage.

netic vector $\mathbf{H}$ is in terms of current per unit distance, it is to be expected that the magnetic scalar potential ψ can be interpreted in terms of current.

Suppose that steady electric currents are producing a magnetic field, and consider the part of the magnetic field outside the wires.   In this region of space the magnetic vector $\mathbf{H}$ may be regarded as the downward gradient of a magnetic scalar potential ψ.   In Fig. 7.7 the broken curves represent the equipotential surfaces $\psi = \psi_1$ and $\psi = \psi_2$. P_1P_2 is a line of magnetic flux lying on a tube of magnetic flux intersecting the equipotential surfaces at right angles.   It is supposed that the magnetic vector is directed from P_1 to P_2 so that ψ_1 exceeds ψ_2. According to the definition of magnetic scalar potential given in Eq. (7.5),

$$\psi_1 - \psi_2 = \int_{P_1}^{P_2} H \, ds \qquad (7.18)$$

Since it is supposed that the integral in this equation is taken along the line of magnetic flux P_1P_2, a scalar product is not required. Equation (7.18) can in fact be obtained by integrating Eq. (7.6) along the line of magnetic flux from P_1 to P_2. Now suppose that the tube of magnetic flux indicated in Fig. 7.7 is permitted to exist by itself. To achieve this, a current would have to flow toroidally round the tube, and the current per unit length of the tube at any point would be equal to the magnetic field strength H in the tube at this point. Hence the current flowing round the tube over the length ds is $H \, ds$, and the total current flowing round the tube between the normal cross sections at P_1 and P_2 is given by the right-hand side of Eq. (7.18). Equation (7.18) therefore shows that the total current flowing round the tube between any two normal cross sections is the drop in magnetic scalar potential as we move along the tube in the direction related by the right-hand-screw rule to the direction of the current round the tube. The amount of current that must flow toroidally round a tube of magnetic flux between any two normal cross sections when the tube exists by itself may be called the amperage round the tube between the two cross sections. Equation (7.18) states that the drop in magnetic scalar potential between any two normal cross sections of a tube of magnetic flux is equal to the amperage round the tube between these cross sections.

It is clear that amperage, and therefore magnetic scalar potential, is measured in amperes. The difference in magnetic scalar potential between any two equipotential surfaces is equal to the amperage that would be required round the intervening section of any tube of magnetic flux intersecting the equipotential surfaces if that tube were to exist by itself. The direction round the tube of this amperage is related by the right-hand-screw rule to the direction of fall of magnetic scalar potential along the tube.

7.7. The Magnetic Scalar Potential in a Toroidal Inductor. Consider the magnetic field outside a long straight wire carrying a steady current I. If θ is an azimuthal angle measured round the wire in the direction related by the right-hand-screw rule to the direction of current flow, the magnetic scalar potential outside the wire is given by Eq. (7.13). The equipotential surfaces are axial planes as shown in Fig. 7.4, and the lines of magnetic flux are the circles intersecting these planes at right angles. Consider a particular tube of flux as shown in Fig. 7.8. Suppose now that this tube of magnetic flux exists by itself and that all the other tubes are abolished.   To do this, current must flow over the surface of the tube in the form appropriate to a toroidal inductor.   As described in Sec. 3.6, the total current flowing round the toroidal inductor is I.   The fraction of this current between two axial planes containing an angle θ as shown in Fig. 7.8 is the fraction $\theta/2\pi$ of the total current I flowing round the toroidal inductor.   The amperage round the inductor over a section between two axial planes containing an angle θ is therefore

$$\frac{\theta}{2\pi} I \tag{7.19}$$

The magnetic scalar potential inside the toroidal inductor is the same as that for the original straight current and is therefore given by Eq. (7.13).

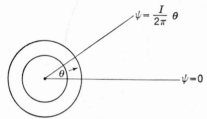

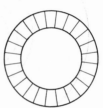

FIG. 7.8. Illustrating the calculation of the magnetic scalar potential for a toroidal inductor.

FIG. 7.9. The surfaces of constant magnetic scalar potential for a toroidal inductor.

We therefore see that, if we move an angular distance θ through the inductor in the direction related by the right-hand-screw rule to the direction of current flow round the inductor, the magnetic scalar potential falls by an amount

$$\frac{I}{2\pi} \theta \tag{7.20}$$

The equality of expressions (7.19) and (7.20) verifies that the amperage round the inductor between any two normal cross sections is equal to the difference in magnetic scalar potential between these normal cross sections.

The surfaces of constant magnetic scalar potential for a toroidal inductor are the normal cross sections of the toroid as shown in Fig. 7.9.   The variation in the magnetic scalar potential with angular distance θ measured round the toroid is given by Eq. (7.13).   Suppose that we start from a particular normal cross section of the toroidal inductor and proceed through the toroid in the direction related by the right-hand-screw rule to the direction of current round the toroid.   The drop in the magnetic scalar potential between any two normal cross sections of the toroid is the amperage round the toroid between these normal cross sections.

Let us make a complete loop through the toroid so that θ increases by 2π. During such a complete loop the magnetic scalar potential falls by I in accordance with Eq. (7.13). This registers the fact that the total current flowing round the toroid is I. Suppose now that we continue on round the toroid and make another complete loop in the same direction, returning to the initial normal cross section. Then the magnetic scalar potential again falls by I in accordance with Eq. (7.13), and we can repeat this process any number of times. This illustrates the multivalued nature of magnetic scalar potential previously described in Sec. 7.5.

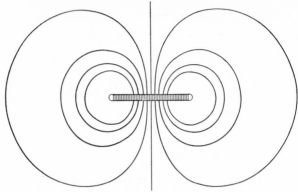

Fig. 7.10. The surfaces of constant magnetic scalar potential for a long, thin solenoid.

When interpreting magnetic scalar potential in terms of amperage, we see that the multivalued nature of the magnetic scalar potential is of no special interest. Starting from a particular normal cross section and moving through the toroid, the magnetic scalar potential records the inductor amperage traversed. After one complete loop inside the toroid all the current flowing round the inductor has been registered. If we continue on through the toroid beyond a complete loop, we are counting the same current twice, and this there is no point in doing.

7.8. The Magnetic Scalar Potential of a Solenoidal Inductor. Consider a long, thin solenoidal inductor of length s and cross-sectional area S in a medium of inductivity μ. Let a total current I flow round the curved surface of the inductor, uniformly distributed along the length. As a result let a total magnetic flux Φ thread through the solenoid from one end to the other. On the assumption that the linear dimensions of a normal cross section of the solenoid are small compared with the length, the inductance of the solenoid is given by Eq. (5.12). The flux threading through the solenoid is therefore expressed in terms of the current flowing round the solenoid by the equation

$$\Phi = \frac{\mu S}{s} I \qquad (7.21)$$

The strong part of the field of a solenoid is inside the solenoid.   Here the magnetic field is substantially the same as for a section of toroid of indefinitely large radius.   The surfaces of constant magnetic scalar potential inside the solenoid are therefore the normal cross sections of the solenoid as shown in Fig. 7.10.   The difference in magnetic scalar potential between any two normal cross sections of the solenoid is equal to the amperage round the solenoid between these normal cross sections.

Near the ends of the solenoid the surfaces of constant magnetic scalar potential become distorted from normal cross sections, as shown in Fig. 7.10.   Outside the solenoid and well away from the ends, the magnetic field is that of a pair of magnetic poles of strengths Φ and $-\Phi$ at the ends of the solenoid as described in connection with Figs. 4.3 and 4.5.   The surfaces of constant magnetic scalar potential outside the solenoid can therefore be calculated in substantially the same way as the equipotential surfaces of a pair of equal and opposite charges in electrostatics.   As in electrostatics it follows that the magnetic scalar potential at distance r from a magnetic pole of strength Φ in a homogeneous medium of inductivity μ is

$$\psi = \frac{1}{4\pi\mu}\frac{\Phi}{r} \tag{7.22}$$

provided that the potential is taken as zero at infinity.   Let P be a point outside the solenoid at distance r_1 from the end of the solenoid where the flux Φ emerges and at distance r_2 from the end of the solenoid where the flux Φ enters, as shown in Fig. 7.11. From Eq. (7.22) it follows that the magnetic scalar potential at the point P due to the solenoid is

$$\psi = \frac{1}{4\pi\mu}\frac{\Phi}{r_1} - \frac{1}{4\pi\mu}\frac{\Phi}{r_2} \tag{7.23}$$

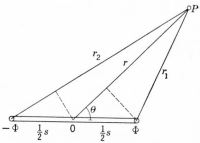

From this equation the equipotential surfaces outside the solenoid can be plotted in the same way as for a pair of equal and opposite point charges in electrostatics.   The resulting equipotential surfaces outside the

FIG. 7.11. Illustrating the calculation of the magnetic scalar potential at a point outside a long, thin solenoid.

solenoid are shown in Fig. 7.10, and we can see how these surfaces fit with the interior equipotential surfaces at the ends of the solenoid.

7.9. The Distant Magnetic Field of a Solenoid.   Compared with the magnetic field inside a solenoidal inductor, the magnetic field outside the inductor is weak.   At distances from the solenoid large compared with the linear dimensions of the solenoid, the magnetic field is particularly weak.   Nevertheless interest attaches to a calculation of the field of a solenoid at distances from it large compared with the linear dimensions.

Let us consider a long, thin solenoid as shown in Fig. 7.11.   The magnetic scalar potential at a point P distant r_1 from the end of the solenoid where the magnetic flux Φ emerges and distant r_2 from the end of the solenoid where the magnetic flux Φ enters the solenoid is given by Eq. (7.23).   Let O be the center point of the solenoid, and let the distance of the point P from O be r.   Let the radius vector from O to P make an angle θ with the direction in which magnetic flux threads through the solenoid, as shown in Fig. 7.11.   If r is large compared with the length s of the solenoid, the lines drawn to P from the center and the two ends of the solenoid are practically parallel.   In these circumstances the distance r_1 is less than the distance r by approximately the projection of half the length of the solenoid upon the radius vector from O to P.   In the same way the distance r_2 exceeds the distance r by practically the same amount. We therefore have approximately

$$r_1 = r - \tfrac{1}{2}s \cos \theta \qquad (7.24)$$

and
$$r_2 = r + \tfrac{1}{2}s \cos \theta \qquad (7.25)$$

Substituting these expressions for r_1 and r_2 into Eq. (7.23) and taking a common denominator we derive

$$\psi = \frac{\Phi}{4\pi\mu} \frac{s \cos \theta}{r^2 - (\tfrac{1}{2}s \cos \theta)^2} \qquad (7.26)$$

Since we are assuming that r is large compared with s, the second term in the denominator of Eq. (7.26) can be neglected.   Hence the magnetic scalar potential of a long, thin solenoid of length s and pole strength Φ at a large distance r in the direction θ shown in Fig. 7.11 is

$$\psi = \frac{\Phi s}{4\pi\mu} \frac{\cos \theta}{r^2} \qquad (7.27)$$

The property of the solenoid upon which the distant field principally depends is therefore the product of its pole strength Φ and its length s. This product is known as the dipole moment of the long, thin solenoid. This property can also be expressed in terms of the product of the current I round the curved surface of the solenoid and the cross-sectional area S of the solenoid.   This is done by writing Eq. (7.21) in the form

$$\Phi s = \mu I S \qquad (7.28)$$

If we substitute from Eq. (7.28) into Eq. (7.27), we derive

$$\psi = \frac{IS}{4\pi} \frac{\cos \theta}{r^2} \qquad (7.29)$$

This equation shows that the magnetic scalar potential at distances from a solenoid large compared with its linear dimensions, in addition to being proportional to the cross-sectional area S of the solenoid and the current I round the solenoid, is proportional to the cosine of the angle θ shown in Fig. 7.11 and inversely proportional to the square of the distance r from the center of the solenoid.

To derive the magnetic vector **H** at a large distance from the solenoid we have to take the downward gradient of the magnetic scalar potential ψ given by Eq. (7.29) in accordance with Eq. (7.8). It is convenient to calculate the magnetic vector at a distant point P in two components H_r and H_θ as shown in Fig. 7.12. The radial component H_r of the magnetic vector at P is the rate at which

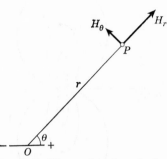

FIG. 7.12. Illustrating the calculation of the magnetic vector at a large distance r from a solenoid.

the magnetic scalar potential ψ is decreasing with radial distance r at P. Hence

$$H_r = - \frac{\partial \psi}{\partial r} \tag{7.30}$$

The transverse component H_θ of the magnetic vector at P is the rate at which the magnetic scalar potential ψ decreases with distance as we move from P perpendicular to the radius vector in the direction in which θ increases. Since an increment $d\theta$ in the angle θ in Fig. 7.12 involves a linear displacement $r\,d\theta$ at P, it follows that

$$H_\theta = - \frac{\partial \psi}{r\,\partial \theta} \tag{7.31}$$

We obtain the radial and transverse components of the magnetic vector at P by substituting into Eqs. (7.30) and (7.31) the expression for ψ given in Eq. (7.29). In Eq. (7.30) we regard θ as constant while differentiating expression (7.29) with regard to r, while in Eq. (7.31) we regard r as a constant while differentiating expression (7.29) with regard to θ. We thus derive

$$H_r = \frac{IS}{4\pi} \frac{2\cos\theta}{r^3} \tag{7.32}$$

$$H_\theta = \frac{IS}{4\pi} \frac{\sin\theta}{r^3} \tag{7.33}$$

These equations show that the distant magnetic field of a solenoidal inductor carrying steady current decreases with distance inversely pro-

portional to the cube of the distance.   From Eqs. (7.32) and (7.33) the
lines of magnetic flux of the solenoid at large distances can be plotted and
are as shown in Fig. 7.13.

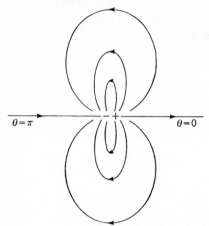

The Earth has a magnetic field
which, outside the Earth, is of the
type shown in Fig. 7.13 and described by Eqs. (7.32) and (7.33).
For the Earth the direction $\theta = 0$
corresponds to the southern geomagnetic pole and the direction
$\theta = \pi$ to the northern geomagnetic
pole.   These poles do not coincide
precisely with the geographic poles.
At the surface of the Earth the distance r in Eqs. (7.32) and (7.33) is
the radius of the Earth.   At the
equator, where $\theta = \frac{1}{2}\pi$, we see
from Eq. (7.32) that the radial
component of the Earth's field vanishes.   Thus the Earth's magnetic

FIG. 7.13. The distant lines of magnetic
flux of a solenoid carrying steady current.

field is horizontal at the equator, as may also be seen from Fig. 7.13.   The
magnetic field strength at the equator is obtained by putting $\theta = \frac{1}{2}\pi$ in
Eq. (7.33) and is

$$\frac{IS}{4\pi r^3} \tag{7.34}$$

where r is the radius of the Earth.   The value of the Earth's magnetic
flux density at the equator is measured to be about 0.3 gauss (3×10^{-5}
weber/m²).   Dividing this by the vacuum inductivity, we deduce for
the magnetic field strength at the equator about 24 amp/m.   Equating
this to expression (7.34) and using for the radius r of the Earth the value
6,370 km (6.37×10^6 m) we deduce that

$$IS = 8 \times 10^{22} \text{ amp-m}^2 \tag{7.35}$$

Thus the external magnetic field of the Earth is substantially the same as
that of a centrally located solenoid for which the product of the normal
cross-sectional area and the current round the curved surface is given by
Eq. (7.35).   The magnetic flux is to be thought of as threading through
this solenoid in the direction from north to south.   The actual currents
flowing in the liquid-metal core of the Earth are not, of course, those of a
solenoid, and their origin is not understood.

7.10. Distant Magnetic Scalar Potential of a Short Solenoidal Inductor.
Consider a solenoidal inductor whose length is not necessarily large com-

pared with the linear dimensions of its normal cross section as shown in Fig. 7.14.   Let us calculate the magnetic scalar potential ψ at a point P whose distance from the solenoid is large compared with the length of the solenoid.   It will not be necessary for the distance of the point P from the solenoid to be large compared with the linear dimensions of a normal cross section of the solenoid.

Let a steady current I flow round the curved surface of the solenoid uniformly distributed along its length.   Let dS be an element of area of the central normal cross section of the solenoid shown dashed in Fig. 7.14. Let the point P be at distance r from this element of area, and let the radius vector from the element of area to P make an angle θ with the axis on the solenoid, the direction $\theta = 0$ being that in which the magnetic flux threads the solenoid. The solenoid can be subdivided into a large number of long, thin solenoids in the manner already discussed in connection with Fig. 4.6.   Each long, thin solenoid carries the same steady current I round its curved surface as the large solenoid, and when all these

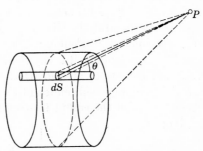

FIG. 7.14. Illustrating the calculation of the distant magnetic scalar potential of a short solenoid.

currents are combined, they constitute the current I flowing round the large solenoid.   Consider the thin solenoid defined by the element of area dS of the central normal cross section of the large solenoid as shown in Fig. 7.14.   The magnetic scalar potential produced by this thin solenoid at the point P is given by Eq. (7.29) if the area S is replaced by the element of area dS.   The contribution to the magnetic scalar potential at the distant point P due to the thin solenoid defined by the element of area dS is therefore

$$\frac{I}{4\pi} \frac{dS \cos \theta}{r^2} \tag{7.36}$$

This is conveniently expressed in terms of the solid angle $d\Omega$ subtended by the element of area dS at the point P.   The normal cross-sectional area of this solid angle at the position of the element of area dS is $dS \cos \theta$. Since this is the normal cross section of the solid angle at distance r from P, the normal cross section at unit distance from P is obtained by dividing $dS \cos \theta$ by r^2.   Hence

$$d\Omega = \frac{dS \cos \theta}{r^2} \tag{7.37}$$

It follows from Eq. (7.37) that the second term in expression (7.36) is simply the solid angle $d\Omega$ subtended by the element of area dS at the distant point P. It follows therefore that the contribution to the magnetic scalar potential at the distant point P due to the thin solenoid defined by the element of area dS of the central normal cross section of the large solenoid is

$$\frac{I}{4\pi}\,d\Omega \qquad (7.38)$$

where $d\Omega$ is the solid angle subtended by dS at P. To obtain the complete magnetic scalar potential ψ at P due to the large solenoid we have to add up the contributions given by expression (7.38) for all the thin solenoids corresponding to all the elements of area dS of the central normal cross section of the solenoid. Since it is the same current I flowing round all the thin solenoids, it is the elements of solid angle $d\Omega$ subtended by the various elements of area dS that must be summed. It follows that, if Ω is the solid angle subtended at the distant point P by the central normal cross section of the complete solenoid, the magnetic scalar potential at P is given by

$$\psi = \frac{I\Omega}{4\pi} \qquad (7.39)$$

It should be noted that Eq. (7.29), being derived for the situation depicted in Fig. 7.11, is based on the assumption that the distance r to the point P is large compared with the length of the thin solenoid. In applying Eq. (7.29) to derive Eq. (7.36) we have therefore assumed that the distance r to the point P is large compared with the length of the solenoid. It follows that Eq. (7.39) applies when the point P is outside the cylinder formed by the solenoid at a distance large compared with the length of the solenoid. For application of Eq. (7.39) it is not necessary that the point P be at a distance from the solenoid large compared with the linear dimensions of a normal cross section of the solenoid.

Let us suppose now that the point P is at a distance from the solenoid large compared not only with the length of the solenoid but also with the linear dimensions of a normal cross section. Then, for the same reasons that led to Eq. (7.37), we can write

$$\Omega = \frac{S\cos\theta}{r^2} \qquad (7.40)$$

where S is the normal cross-sectional area of the solenoid. Substitution of the expression (7.40) for Ω into Eq. (7.39) reproduces Eq. (7.29). It follows therefore that Eq. (7.29) gives the magnetic scalar potential of a solenoid at a distant point P even if the length of the solenoid is not large compared with the linear dimensions of a normal cross section. All that is required for application of Eq. (7.29) is that the distance of the point P from the solenoid be large compared with both the length of the solenoid and the linear dimensions of a normal cross section; the shape of the solenoid is not important.

If the length of the solenoid is small compared with the linear dimensions of a normal cross section, Eq. (7.39) has an advantage over Eq. (7.29). For application of Eq. (7.39) it is only necessary that the point P be outside the cylinder formed by the solenoid by an amount large compared with the length of the solenoid, and it does not matter how large the cross-sectional area of the solenoid may be. Thus, as we move away from a short solenoid, Eq. (7.39) becomes a satisfactory approximation to the magnetic scalar potential more quickly than Eq. (7.29).

7.11. Magnetic Scalar Potential of Any Loop of Wire Carrying Steady Current. Consider a solenoid for which the normal cross section is not necessarily circular and for which the linear dimensions of the normal cross section are large compared with the length of the solenoid. These are the circumstances in which Eq. (7.39) is particularly useful. Let us suppose that the length of the solenoid becomes indefinitely small, while the steady current flowing round its curved surface retains a constant value I. In these circumstances the solenoid becomes a loop of wire carrying a steady current I as shown in Fig. 7.15, and the point P may now be practically anywhere in the surrounding space. It follows there-

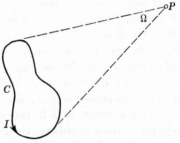

FIG. 7.15. Illustrating the calculation of the magnetic scalar potential of any loop of wire carrying a steady current.

fore that, if a steady current I flows round a closed circuit C, then the magnetic scalar potential at any point P is given by Eq. (7.39), where Ω is the solid angle subtended by the circuit C at the point P.

For application of Eq. (7.39) to calculation of the magnetic scalar potential due to a steady current I flowing round a closed circuit C, it is not even necessary that the circuit C lie in a plane. It can be a twisted circuit in three dimensions. In this case let S be a surface spanning the twisted closed curve C. The surface S can be divided up into elements of area each of which is substantially plane. If a steady current I flows round the perimeter of each of the elements of area in the same direction, the currents associated with adjacent elements of area cancel and we are left with the current I flowing round the twisted closed curve C. In this way the steady current I flowing round the twisted closed curve C can be analyzed into steady currents I flowing round plane circuits to which Eq. (7.39) is applicable. Since the current I is the same for all these plane circuits, addition of the magnetic scalar potential due to them simply involves addition of the solid angles that they subtend at the point P, and this gives the solid angle Ω subtended at P by the curve C. As a result Eq. (7.39) applies even to a nonplanar circuit of any shape whatever.

Some care is necessary in defining the solid angle Ω subtended by the closed circuit C at the point P in Fig. 7.15. The cone formed by joining the point P to the circuit C by means of straight lines has both an internal and an external solid angle. Moreover, as the point P threads through the circuit C, the internal solid angle converts into the external solid angle and vice versa. It is necessary to decide which of these two solid angles it is appropriate to use in Eq. (7.39). The solid angle to be chosen is the one that makes the magnetic scalar potential decrease as we thread through the circuit C in the direction of the magnetic flux.

It may be noticed that, if the point P threads through the closed circuit C in Fig. 7.15 and makes a complete trip round a closed line of magnetic flux, the solid angle Ω turns completely inside out. The magnitude of Ω thus changes by the complete area of a unit sphere, namely 4π. A complete trip round a line of magnetic flux in the direction of the flux therefore results in a decrease of 4π in the value of Ω in Eq. (7.39). It follows that a complete circuit round a line of magnetic flux in the direction of the flux causes a decrease of I in the magnetic scalar potential. This, of course, simply verifies in this particular case the circulation law for the magnetic vector given by Eq. (4.6).

7.12. Magnetic Scalar Potential on the Axis of a Circular Wire Carrying Steady Current. As an example of the application of Eq. (7.39) let us calculate the magnetic scalar potential ψ at a point P on the axis of a circular loop of wire of radius a carrying a steady current I as shown in Fig. 7.16. Let z be the distance of the point P from the center of the loop, and let it be arranged that, as z increases, the point P moves in the direction of the magnetic flux. Let Ω be the solid angle subtended at P by the wire, and let θ be the semivertical angle of the circular cone involved. The relation between Ω and θ is given by Eq. (1.26), and this can be written as

$$\Omega = 2\pi(1 - \cos \theta) \tag{7.41}$$

Substitution from Eq. (7.41) into Eq. (7.39) gives for the magnetic scalar potential at P

$$\psi = \tfrac{1}{2}I(1 - \cos \theta) \tag{7.42}$$

To express this in terms of z we use the geometry of Fig. 7.16 to deduce that

$$\cos \theta = \frac{z}{(a^2 + z^2)^{\frac{1}{2}}} \tag{7.43}$$

Substitution from this equation into Eq. (7.42) gives

$$\psi = \tfrac{1}{2}I \left[1 - \frac{z}{(a^2 + z^2)^{\frac{1}{2}}} \right] \tag{7.44}$$

This equation gives the variation of the magnetic scalar potential ψ with distance z along the axis of the circular wire measured from the center. This variation is illustrated in Fig. 7.17. Moving along the axis from

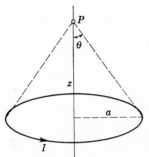

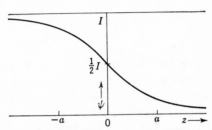

FIG. 7.16. Illustrating the calculation of the magnetic scalar potential at a point on the axis of a circular loop of wire carrying a steady current.

FIG. 7.17. Illustrating the variation of the magnetic scalar potential along the axis of a circular loop of wire carrying steady current.

$z = -\infty$ to $z = +\infty$ is equivalent to making a complete circuit through the loop in the direction related by the right-hand-screw rule to the direction of the current round the loop, and we notice from Fig. 7.17 that, in this process, the magnetic scalar potential falls by I, as it should in accordance with the circulation law for the magnetic vector.

7.13. Relation between the Magnetic Vector and the Magnetic Scalar Potential. Outside a wire carrying steady current the magnetic vector **H** is the downward gradient of the magnetic scalar potential ψ in accordance with Eq. (7.8). Now for a steady current I flowing round any closed circuit C the magnetic vector **H** is given by Biot's formula (6.44), and the magnetic scalar potential ψ is given by Eq. (7.39). It follows that the vector on the right-hand side of Eq. (6.44) is the downward gradient of the scalar quantity on the right-hand side of Eq. (7.39). It is possible to establish the truth of this statement by direct mathematical analysis if desired.

As an example of the relation between the magnetic vector and the magnetic scalar potential let us consider the magnetic field on the axis of a circular loop of wire of radius a carrying a steady current I. The magnetic scalar potential at a point P on the axis of the wire at distance z from the center in the direction of the magnetic flux is given by Eq. (7.44) and is plotted in Fig. 7.17. It follows from symmetry that the magnetic vector at P is in the direction in which z increases. From Eq. (7.8) we therefore deduce that the magnetic field strength at P is given by

$$H = -\frac{\partial \psi}{\partial z} \qquad (7.45)$$

The magnetic field strength on the axis of the circular current is therefore given by the downward slope of the curve shown in Fig. 7.17. Substitution for ψ from Eq. (7.44) into Eq. (7.45) leads to

$$H = \tfrac{1}{2}I \, \frac{a^2}{(a^2 + z^2)^{3/2}} \qquad (7.46)$$

Now the magnetic field strength at any point on the axis of a circular loop of wire carrying a steady current has already been calculated from Biot's formula (6.44) and is given in Eq. (6.53). That Eq. (7.46) conveys the same information as Eq. (6.53) follows from the fact that r in Fig. 6.14 is equal to $(a^2 + z^2)^{1/2}$ in Fig. 7.16.

7.14. Magnetic Scalar Potential for a Twin-wire Transmission Line. Consider a twin-wire transmission line for which the wires are thin and a

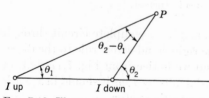

FIG. 7.18. Illustrating the calculation of the magnetic scalar potential for a twin-wire transmission line.

steady current I flows along one wire and back along the other. Let us calculate the magnetic scalar potential at any point P in the magnetic field outside the wires. Through each wire draw a plane passing through the point P. Let these planes make angles θ_1 and θ_2 with the plane containing both wires as shown in Fig. 7.18. The two planes passing through the point P then intersect at an angle $\theta_2 - \theta_1$.

Let us calculate the magnetic scalar potential at P using Eq. (7.39). To do this we regard the two wires as forming an elongated closed circuit. The solid angle subtended by this circuit at the point P is therefore the solid angle between the two planes intersecting at P. To calculate this solid angle we draw a sphere of unit radius with center at P and calculate the area of the sphere contained between the two planes. This is the fraction $(\theta_2 - \theta_1)/2\pi$ of the complete area 4π of the unit sphere. Hence the solid angle subtended by the twin-wire transmission line at the point P is

$$\Omega = 2(\theta_2 - \theta_1) \qquad (7.47)$$

Substitution from this equation into Eq. (7.39) gives for the magnetic scalar potential at P

$$\psi = \frac{I}{2\pi}(\theta_2 - \theta_1) \qquad (7.48)$$

Alternatively Eq. (7.48) can be derived by application of Eq. (7.13). The second term in Eq. (7.48) is obtained by applying Eq. (7.13) to the left-hand wire in Fig. 7.18. The first term in Eq. (7.48) is obtained by applying Eq. (7.13) to the right-hand wire in Fig. 7.18. For the pair of wires carrying equal and opposite currents I therefore the complete magnetic scalar potential at the point P is given by Eq. (7.48).

It follows from Eq. (7.48) that the surfaces of constant magnetic scalar potential are the surfaces for which $\theta_2 - \theta_1$ is constant. If the point P in Fig. 7.18 moves so as to maintain the angle $\theta_2 - \theta_1$ constant, it describes a circle passing through the points corresponding to the two wires. The equipotential surfaces of a twin-wire transmission line are therefore circular cylinders passing through the two wires. These are represented by the broken curves in Fig. 2.7 and intersect the lines of magnetic flux at right angles.

SUMMARIZING EXERCISES

7.1. Explain what is meant by magnetic scalar potential. Interpret the difference of magnetic scalar potential between two equipotential surfaces in terms of the intercepted solenoidal current associated with the tubes of magnetic flux.

7.2. A thin, infinite, straight wire embedded in a nonconducting medium carries a steady current I. Calculate the magnetic scalar potential at all points outside the wire. Deduce the magnetic scalar potential inside a toroidal inductor carrying a steady current I uniformly distributed round its perimeter.

7.3. Explain what is meant by the statement that the magnetic scalar potential calculated in the previous exercise is multivalued. Give a physical interpretation of the phenomenon.

7.4. Explain why the concept of magnetic scalar potential is applicable only in regions where the electric current density vanishes.

7.5. A thin solenoid of length s carries a magnetic flux Φ. A radial line is drawn from the center of the solenoid in a direction making an angle θ with the direction of the flux. Prove that, at a distance r large compared with s in the direction θ, the magnetic scalar potential is $(\Phi s \cos \theta)/4\pi\mu r^2$, where μ is the inductivity of the medium. Prove further that, if the solenoid has a cross-sectional area S and carries a total solenoidal current I round its curved surface, then the above magnetic scalar potential can also be written as $(IS \cos \theta)/4\pi r^2$.

7.6. Give a simple description of the magnetic field of the Earth exterior to the Earth's surface.

7.7. Show that the magnetic scalar potential at a point P due to a loop of wire carrying a steady current I is $I\Omega/4\pi$, where Ω is the solid angle subtended at P by the loop.

Explain why there are two such solid angles the sum of which is 4π, and describe how to make the appropriate choice between them.

7.8. A circular loop of wire of radius a carries a steady current I. Calculate the magnetic scalar potential at a point on the axis of the wire distant z from the center of the circle. Deduce the magnetic field strength at all points on the axis of the wire, and verify that the result is equivalent to that derived in Exercise 6.13.

7.9. A twin-wire transmission line consists of a pair of long, thin, parallel wires, and a steady current I flows along one wire and back along the other. Through a point P in the magnetic field two planes are drawn, each containing one of the wires, and the angle between the planes is θ. Show that the magnetic scalar potential at P may be taken as $I\theta/2\pi$. Deduce that the equipotential surfaces lie along circular cylinders containing the wires. Explain why the two parts into which such a cylinder is divided by the wires are at different potentials.

CHAPTER 8

FERROMAGNETIC CIRCUITS

8.1. Introduction. In our study of the toroidal inductor we saw how to relate the magnetic flux threading through the inductor with the current flowing round its curved surface. Suppose that the toroid is thin, so that the magnetic flux density B has substantially the same value at all points within the inductor. Let H be the corresponding magnetic field strength, so that H is the current per unit length flowing round the curved surface. If the region within the inductor is a vacuum, then

$$B = \mu_v H \qquad (8.1)$$

where μ_v is the vacuum inductivity given numerically by Eq. (5.14). If the region within the inductor is filled with some other substance, such as air, the numerical value of the inductivity is changed, but for most substances the numerical extent of the change is negligible. An exception, however, occurs if the region within the inductor is filled with ferromagnetic material. In this case the relation between the magnetic flux density B in the inductor and the current per unit length H round the inductor is not given even approximately by Eq. (8.1).

The magnetic field inside the toroidal inductor can be subdivided into tubes of magnetic flux, and each of these tubes can be subdivided into solenoids connected end to end. In this way the entire toroidal inductor can be subdivided into solenoidal building blocks in the manner already described in Sec. 4.8. Furthermore, as described in Sec. 4.8, it is possible to use as building blocks atoms or molecules containing spinning electrons. Such material is called ferromagnetic material, and if the spinning electrons are aligned in a more or less systematic way, the material constitutes a magnet. Consider a thin ring of ferromagnetic material of the same shape as the toroidal inductor discussed in the previous paragraph. Let the ferromagnetic material be magnetized to intensity M in the direction round the ring. We may think of the atoms containing the spinning electrons as fitting together like building blocks to form a toroidal inductor of the same shape as the magnet. The magnet thus has the same field of magnetic flux as a toroidal inductor whose surface coincides with the surface of the magnet and which carries a current per

473

unit length M uniformly distributed along the length.   Thus, in thinking of the field of magnetic flux produced by the spinning electrons in the magnet we may think instead of the field of magnetic flux of a toroidal inductor of the same shape carrying a current per unit length M round the curved surface.   Since the effect of the atoms of ferromagnetic material has now been replaced by the current per unit length M, this current is to be thought of as existing in free space.   In accordance with Eq. (8.1) the magnetic flux density inside the magnet is therefore

$$B = \mu_v M \qquad (8.2)$$

Thus if we wish to produce a field of magnetic flux threading through a toroidal space, we have the alternative of applying a current per unit length H round the curved surface of the toroid or of filling the toroidal space with ferromagnetic material magnetized to intensity M in the direction round the toroid.   In the one case the current takes the form of electrons drifting through a conductor coinciding with the surface of the toroidal space; in the other case the current takes the form of spinning electrons in the atoms of ferromagnetic material within the toroidal space.

Let us now suppose that both of these methods of producing a field of magnetic flux threading through the toroidal space are used simultaneously.   Let the toroidal space be filled with ferromagnetic material magnetized to intensity M in the direction round the toroid.   At the same time let the surface of the toroidal space carry a current per unit length H flowing round the curved surface in the direction related by the right-hand-screw rule to the direction of magnetization of the ferromagnetic material within the space.   The current round the surface of the toroid then contributes to the field of magnetic flux density within the toroidal space an amount given by Eq. (8.1), while the ferromagnetic material within the space contributes to the magnetic flux density threading through the toroid an amount given by Eq. (8.2).   The total magnetic flux density is the sum of these two contributions and is therefore

$$B = \mu_v(H + M) \qquad (8.3)$$

The first term on the right-hand side of this equation is the contribution to the magnetic flux density round the toroid due to the current per unit length H round the surface of the toroid, while the second term is the contribution from the spinning electrons in the atoms of ferromagnetic material within the toroid.

While the contribution to the magnetic flux density in the toroid from the current per unit length H round the curved surface simply adds to the equivalent current per unit length M associated with the spinning electrons in the ferromagnetic core, a major complication arises from the fact that the intensity of magnetization M of the ferromagnetic material is affected by the current H per unit length applied to it.   In other words M in Eq. (8.3) is a function of H.   When this functional dependence has been determined, it can be substituted into Eq. (8.3).   Equation (8.3) then gives, for a toroidal inductor with a ferromagnetic core, the dependence of the magnetic flux density B within the inductor upon the current per unit length H applied round the surface of the inductor.   The relation thus obtained between the magnetic flux density B in a thin toroidal inductor possessing a ferromagnetic core and the current per unit length H applied round the inductor describes the magnetization properties of the ferromagnetic material concerned.

8.2. The Magnetization Properties of Ferromagnetic Materials. Although the substances with which we are concerned are alloys of iron and other metals, it is convenient to begin by considering a gas, the molecules of which possess electron spin.   Let us therefore consider a thin toroidal inductor, the interior of which is filled with a gas whose molecules possess electron spin.   If no current is applied round the inductor, the collisions between the molecules maintain the axes of electron spin of the molecules in random directions.   Now suppose that a current per unit length H is applied to the inductor.   This produces a magnetic flux density within the toroid that, in the absence of the gas, would be given by Eq. (8.1).   Under the influence of the field of magnetic flux in the inductor the spinning electrons in the molecules are subject to a torque given by Eq. (6.19).   This tends to turn the vectors representing the electron spins of the molecules into the direction of the field of magnetic flux within the toroid.   However, the collisions between the molecules tend to randomize the directions of the vectors representing the electron spins.   Under these two influences the directions of the vectors representing the electron spins of the molecules, while maintaining some degree of randomness, show a preference for directions near that of the magnetic field within the toroid.   If the current per unit length H applied round the toroid is increased sufficiently, the directions of all the vectors representing electron spins of the molecules become nearly coincident with that of the magnetic field within the toroid.   At this stage the electron spins of the gas molecules are making their maximum contribution to the field of magnetic flux within the toroid.

Figure 8.1 illustrates what happens as the current per unit length H applied round the toroid is varied.   When H is zero, the electron spins of the molecules have random orientation.   While they produce local variations in magnetic field over distances comparable to the separation between molecules, they make no contribution to the net magnetic flux threading the toroid, and the intensity of magnetization M of the gas is zero.   As the current per unit length H round the toroid is increased, however, the tendency of the electron spins to turn toward the direction of the magnetic field in the toroid results in the gas having an intensity of magnetization M in this direction. As H increases from zero, M increases from zero in a linear manner as shown in Fig. 8.1. As H increases indefinitely, however, M increases to a saturation value M_s corresponding to the situation when all electronic spins are aligned along the length of the toroid. The variation in the intensity of magnetization M of the gas with the applied current H per unit length is therefore as shown in Fig. 8.1.

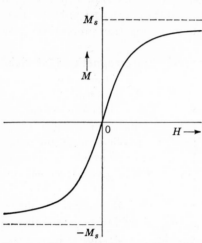

The complete magnetic flux density within the toroid consists of the two contributions shown in Eq. (8.3), the first from the current per unit length round the toroid and the second from the electron spins of the molecules within the toroid. This second contribution is, however, related to the first by means of the curve shown in Fig. 8.1. The complete magnetic flux density B within the toroid corresponding to a given current per unit length H round the toroid is therefore obtained by substituting into Eq. (8.3) M as a function of H from Fig. 8.1. With a gas within the inductor, however, the contribution to the magnetic flux through the inductor from the electron spins of the molecules is small compared with that from the current round the curved surface, and Eq. (8.3) does not differ from Eq. (8.1) to any important numerical extent.

FIG. 8.1. Illustrating the variation of intensity of magnetization M with applied current H per unit length.

Now let us consider a thin toroidal inductor the interior of which is filled with a solid ferromagnetic substance. A substantially similar situation occurs to that described in connection with Fig. 8.1. Let us start with a situation in which there is no current round the inductor and in which the electron spins in the ferromagnetic material are more or less randomly oriented. There is then no net magnetic flux threading the inductor. If the current per unit length H applied to the inductor is increased from zero, the intensity of magnetization M of the ferromagnetic material increases from zero in the manner shown in Fig. 8.1. If the current is increased sufficiently, the intensity of magnetization M approaches a saturation value M_s, when the electron spins of the ferromagnetic material are aligned as far as possible along the length of the toroid.

With solid ferromagnetic material as the core of the inductor, the situation differs from the gaseous situation previously contemplated in two important respects.   In the first place the intensity of magnetization M that can be produced in the solid ferromagnetic material is so great that M in Eq. (8.3) is normally large compared with H.   Thus, with an inductor having a ferromagnetic core, hardly any of the magnetic flux threading through it is produced directly by the current applied to the inductor.

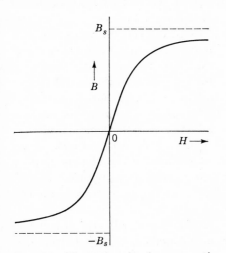

FIG. 8.2. Illustrating for ferromagnetic material the variation of magnetic flux density B with applied current H per unit length.

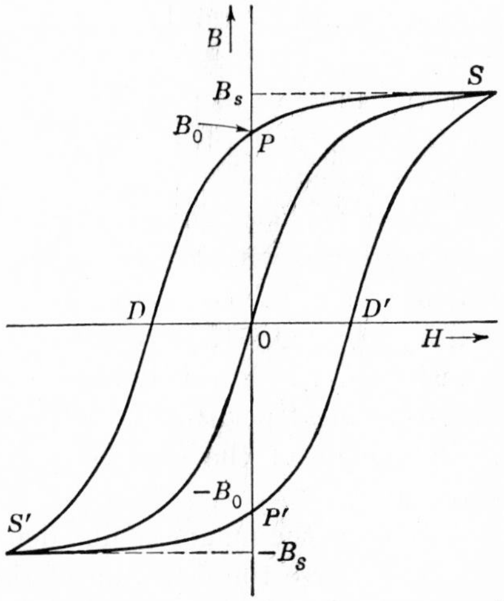

FIG. 8.3. Illustrating the phenomenon of magnetic hysteresis.

The principal function of the current applied to the inductor is to produce partial alignment of the electron spins contained in the ferromagnetic material.   It is these spins that then produce the majority of the magnetic flux threading the inductor.   In these circumstances H in Eq. (8.3) can be neglected, and Fig. 8.1 can be replotted as shown in Fig. 8.2, where

$$B_S = \mu_v M_S \qquad (8.4)$$

Figure 8.2 shows that, as the current per unit length H applied to the inductor increases from zero, the magnetic flux density B through the inductor increases linearly with H.   If the current per unit length H applied to the inductor becomes sufficiently large, however, the magnetic flux density B in the inductor approaches a saturation value B_S given by Eq. (8.4).

The second important respect in which a solid ferromagnetic material differs from the gaseous situation previously contemplated lies in the phenomenon of magnetic hysteresis illustrated in Fig. 8.3.   Let us again consider a thin toroidal inductor filled with ferromagnetic material, and let us start from a situation in which the current per unit length H round the toroid is zero. At the same time let the electron spins associated with magnetic material be more or less randomly oriented so that the intensity of magnetization of the ferromagnetic material is zero. There is then no magnetic flux threading through the inductor, and this situation is represented by the origin O in Fig. 8.3. If we now increase the current per unit length round the inductor, the magnetic flux density B in the inductor increases in accordance with the curve OS as already described in connection with Fig. 8.2. Having increased the current per unit length H round the inductor sufficiently to increase the magnetic flux density B to a value close to the saturation value B_S let us now decrease the current round the inductor. The magnetic flux density B in the inductor then decreases, but not in accordance with the curve SO. Instead it decreases in accordance with a curve such as SP. At the point P the current per unit length H applied to the solenoid is zero, but the magnetic flux density through the inductor has a nonzero value B_0. In these circumstances the ferromagnetic material within the toroidal inductor is said to form a "permanent" magnet. Magnetic flux is produced through it by means of the electron spins in it without any current applied externally.

To reduce the magnetic flux density in the inductor to zero, it is necessary to reverse the direction of the current per unit length H round it. The variation of the magnetic flux density B in the inductor is then given by the curve PD in Fig. 8.3. This is known as the demagnetization curve of the ferromagnetic material. At the point D the magnetic flux density B in the inductor has been reduced to zero, and the ferromagnetic material is said to be demagnetized. If we continue to vary the current round the inductor so as to make H in Fig. 8.3 more negative than the value corresponding to the point D, the magnetic flux density in the inductor is given by the curve DS'.

Let us suppose that the current per unit length H round the toroid is made sufficiently negative to produce in the inductor a saturation magnetic flux density $-B_S$. If we now decrease the magnitude of the current round the inductor, the magnetic flux density in the inductor varies in accordance with the curve $S'P'$ in Fig. 8.3. At the point P' the ferromagnetic material is again a permanent magnet because there is a magnetic flux density through it with no current applied round it. If we now make the value of H positive once more, the magnetic flux density B in the inductor varies in accordance with the curve $P'D'S$. If the current per unit length H round the toroid is successively varied between large positive values and large negative values, the magnetic flux density B in the inductor varies in accordance with the curve $SPDS'P'D'S$. This curve is known as the hysteresis loop of the ferromagnetic material under consideration.

The characteristic feature of the phenomenon of hysteresis is that, if the current round the inductor is increased from one value to another and then decreased again to the former value, the magnetic flux density through the inductor does not in general return to its original value. Suppose, for example, that, after H in Fig. 8.3 is increased to a large positive value, it is decreased to the value corresponding to the point D, so that the magnetic flux density B in the inductor varies in accordance with the curve SPD. At this stage let us suppose that H is now increased again. Then the increase in the magnetic flux density B within the inductor is not given by the curve DP, but instead by a curve of smaller slope. By appropriately chosen increases and decreases of the current round the inductor, it is possible to bring B and H to values corresponding to any point lying within the hystersis loop $SPDS'P'D'S$. The magnetic flux density B in the ferromagnetic material in Fig. 8.3 and the current H per unit length round the inductor can have values corresponding to any point whatever within the magnetic hysteresis loop depending upon the previous magnetic history of the ferromagnetic material.

Out of this complicated situation let us extract two features of particular importance. Suppose that we start again with no current round the surface of the thin toroid and with the ferromagnetic core unmagnetized. There is then no magnetic flux density B through the inductor, and this situation is represented by the point O in Fig. 8.3. Let us now increase the current per unit length H round the inductor so that the magnetic flux density B within the inductor increases in accordance with the curve OS. But let us now cease increasing H while the magnetic flux density B in the inductor is still small compared with the saturation value B_S. The increase of B with H is then represented by the rectilinear section of the curve OS near the origin. Before the curve OS departs from the rectilinear behavior, let us cease increasing H and start decreasing it again. Then the magnetic flux density B in the inductor decreases again quite closely in accordance with the rectilinear portion of the curve OS. A similar statement applies if H is negative. Thus, provided the current per unit length H round the inductor remains sufficiently small to avoid all saturation effects, the relation between B and H is represented fairly closely by the rectilinear section of the curve $S'OS$ near the origin. In these circumstances the relation between B and H is

$$B = \mu H \tag{8.5}$$

where μ is the slope of the curve $S'OS$ at the origin. When using ferromagnetic material as the core of the inductor, it is quite common to restrict the current round the inductor so as to avoid all saturation effects.

The relation between the magnetic flux density B through the inductor and the current per unit length round the inductor is then given approximately by Eq. (8.5). With these restrictions, the ferromagnetic material may be said to have an inductivity μ and a permeability μ/μ_v as described in Sec. 5.10.

For an inductor with a ferromagnetic core, the bulk of the magnetic flux threading through it is produced by the spinning electrons associated with the ferromagnetic material, and the main function of the current round the inductor is to make these spinning electrons available for producing magnetic flux through the inductor. The inductivity of ferromagnetic material is therefore large compared with that for a vacuum. The permeability μ/μ_v for ferromagnetic material is therefore large. Depending upon the alloy used in producing the ferromagnetic material, values between 100 and 10,000 are possible, with a value of the order of 1,000 being typical. For an inductor with a ferromagnetic core of permeability 1,000, only 0.1 per cent of the current required to produce the flux actually flows round the inductor. The remaining 99.9 per cent of the current is in the form of spinning electrons made available by the 0.1 per cent actually applied to the inductor.

The saturation magnetic flux density B_S for ferromagnetic material is usually of the order of a few webers per square meter, and to preserve the linear relation between B and H represented by Eq. (8.5) the magnetic flux density in the inductor must be kept small compared with this. For ferromagnetic material of permeability 1,000 this requires that the current per unit length H round the inductor be kept small compared with about 1,000 amp/m. There are an enormous number of practical situations in which this restriction can be tolerated, and in all these cases ferromagnetic material may be thought of simply as a material possessing a high permeability. The use of ferromagnetic material as the core of inductors in this way is of great practical importance for constructing inductors of high inductance. As described in Sec. 5.10, the inductance of an inductor of given geometrical construction is proportional to the permeability of the core. Replacing an air core by a ferromagnetic core therefore increases the inductance of the inductor by a factor equal to the permeability of the ferromagnetic material used.

Another feature that it is useful to pick out from the phenomenon of hysteresis is associated with the point P (or P') in Fig. 8.3. For a thin toroidal inductor, the point P represents the situation in which the ferromagnetic material is magnetized in spite of the fact that no current is applied to the inductor. In connection with permanent magnets the point P is of particular importance and so also is the demagnetization curve PD. For small departures from the point P, the curve through P in Fig. 8.3 may be represented by means of a straight line of slope μ', and the relation between B and H near P is then given by

$$B = B_0 + \mu'H \tag{8.6}$$

If no current per unit length H is applied round the thin toroid, then the magnetic flux density through the core has the value B_0, and the ferromagnetic material within the toroid is a permanent magnet. Equation (8.6) shows how the magnetic flux density B through the inductor begins to depart from B_0 as the current per unit length H round the inductor departs from zero. For large departures from the point P, however, the curvature of the demagnetization curve PD in Fig. 8.3 must be taken into account.

The magnetic flux density B_0 in Eq. (8.6) usually has the order of magnitude of 1 weber/m². The slope μ' at P of the curve through P in Fig. 8.3 is of the order of a power of 10 less than the slope μ of the curve passing through the origin. Hence the value of μ' in Eq. (8.6) is less than that of μ in Eq. (8.5).

From what has been said, it will be seen that the behavior of ferromagnetic material is complicated. However, if for a toroidal inductor with a ferromagnetic core we start from a situation in which the ferromagnetic material is not magnetized and there is no current round the inductor, and if all saturation effects are avoided, then the relation between the magnetic flux density B in the inductor and the current per unit length H applied round the inductor is given approximately by Eq. (8.5), and the value of μ is large compared with the inductivity μ_v for a vacuum. On the other hand if we start from a situation in which the ferromagnetic material within the toroid is permanently magnetized to flux density B_0, then the application of a small current per unit length H to the inductor gives a magnetic flux density B in the inductor described by Eq. (8.6). For situations not falling into these two categories a study must be made of the complete hysteresis behavior of the ferromagnetic material under discussion. Ferromagnetic material behaving in accordance with Eq. (8.5) will be described as soft iron of inductivity μ. Ferromagnetic material behaving in accordance with Eq. (8.6) will be described as a magnet of permanent flux density B_0 and inductivity μ'.

8.3. The Significance of Magnetic Field Strength in Ferromagnetic Material. We have seen that both a magnet and a solenoid can be thought of as constructed from a large number of building blocks each of which consists of a small solenoid. In the case of the magnet, however, the elementary solenoids take the form of spinning electrons. Now in moving through a magnet it is not feasible to thread the current formed by a spinning electron. If a hole were bored in a magnet, the path taken would necessarily go between the atoms constituting the magnet and consequently would pass between the spinning electrons that constitute the building-block solenoids. We normally picture a path through a magnet that does not thread any of the current formed by the spinning electrons. Thus for a closed curve C passing wholly or partly through ferromagnetic material the spinning electrons make no contribution to the current threading the curve if it passes between the atoms. The circulation of the magnetic vector round such a closed curve C is therefore equal to the electric current threading C on the conductors only, and there is no contribution from the spinning electrons. Thus, in a thin toroid with a ferromagnetic core, the magnetic field strength within the core is simply equal to the current per unit length applied round the curved surface of the toroid.

8.4. Electrical Conductivity of Ferromagnetic Material. Ferromagnetic material, being an alloy of iron and other metals, has a substantial degree of electrical conductivity. In this chapter we shall not be concerned with this conductivity. In some applications the fact that ferromagnetic material is electrically conducting is inconvenient, and steps are taken to reduce the conductivity. The most drastic procedure is to manufacture the ferromagnetic material in powder form and to embed the powder in an electrically insulating material.

8.5. Magnetic Circuits of Soft Iron. If a toroidal inductor is filled with soft iron, the iron forms what is known as a magnetic circuit. We have seen that, if such a magnetic circuit threads an inductor, the flux through the inductor for a unit current round the inductor is greatly increased, and so the inductance of the inductor is greatly increased. However, magnetic circuits have an importance beyond that of increasing the inductance of the inductors through which they are threaded.

Suppose that a loop of wire carrying a steady current I produces a magnetic field as indicated in Fig. 6.15. Let the resulting magnetic flux threading the wire be Φ. Let us divide this magnetic flux into 10 tubes of flux each carrying a magnetic flux 0.1Φ. Each of these tubes could exist by itself if an appropriate current were applied round its curved surface. As described in Sec. 3.7 the current per unit length required at any point of the tube is given by the magnetic field strength H at that point, and in accordance with the circulation law for the magnetic vector the total current flowing round the tube is I. Now let one of the 10 tubes into which the magnetic flux has been divided be filled with soft iron of permeability 1,000, as shown in Fig. 8.4. In accordance with Eq. (8.5) this multiplies the magnetic flux threading this particular tube by 1,000 while leaving the magnetic flux threading all other tubes unchanged. The magnetic flux threading the selected tube therefore changes from 0.1Φ to 100Φ, while the total flux in the tubes outside the soft iron remains at the value 0.9Φ. The total magnetic flux threading the wire is now 100.9Φ, of which about 99 per cent is confined to the magnetic circuit formed by the soft iron. This illustrates the fact that introduction of a soft-iron circuit not only increases the magnetic flux threading the electric circuit but can produce a situation in which most of the magnetic flux is confined to the magnetic circuit.

The fact that, in the situation described in connection with Fig. 8.4, most of the magnetic flux passes through the soft-iron circuit can be explained in the following way. The current principally responsible for producing the magnetic flux through the magnetic circuit consists of spinning electrons in the soft iron. The main function of the current I round the electric circuit is therefore to produce sufficient alignment of the spinning electrons in the iron so that these can produce magnetic flux round the soft-iron circuit. A permeability of 1,000 implies that M in Eq. (8.3) is 999 times bigger than H. Thus the current I flowing round the electric circuit in Fig. 8.4 is only 0.1 per cent of the total current producing the magnetic field, the remaining 99.9 per cent of the current being in the form of spinning electrons in the soft iron. It is not surprising therefore that most of the magnetic flux passes through the soft-iron circuit.

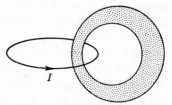

Fig. 8.4. A magnetic circuit threading an electric circuit.

Another feature of significance that is illustrated in Fig. 8.4 is the following: To produce the magnetic flux 100Φ passing round the magnetic circuit by itself, the current I should, strictly speaking, be applied round the surface of the magnetic circuit in the form of a toroidal inductor of nonuniform cross section, the current per unit length at each point being equal to the magnetic field strength at that point. If instead of using this toroidal current flowing over the surface of the magnetic circuit we use the current I flowing round the wire illustrated in Fig. 8.4, an additional magnetic flux 0.9Φ threads the current, but this is an increase of only about 1 per cent in the total magnetic flux threading the current. This illustrates the fact that drastic changes can be made in the way in which the current I threads the magnetic circuit without any major change occurring in the magnetic flux threading the current. Thus, with a properly designed magnetic circuit threaded by an electric current I, practically all the magnetic flux passes round the magnetic circuit, and the magnetic flux threading the current is largely independent of how the current threads the magnetic circuit. To pass magnetic flux round a properly designed magnetic circuit, the necessary electric current can be threaded through the magnetic circuit more or less in any way that may be convenient.

From what has been said, it may be seen that a magnetic circuit of soft iron is able to channel magnetic flux in much the same way that a metallic circuit is able to channel electric current.   The ability of a magnetic circuit to channel magnetic flux depends upon the contrast in inductivity between the soft iron of the circuit and the inductivity of the surrounding medium.   The medium surrounding a magnetic circuit normally has an inductivity close to that for a vacuum, and so the available contrast in inductivity between the soft iron and the surrounding medium is of the order of 10^3.   While the ability of a soft-iron magnetic circuit to channel magnetic flux is of great practical importance, the process does not achieve the tremendous efficiency with which an insulated metallic circuit channels electric current.   For an electric circuit the contrast in conductivity between the metal and the insulator is of the order of 20 powers of 10 greater than the contrast in inductivity available for a magnetic circuit.   Designing a magnetic circuit is rather like designing an electric circuit using a poorly conducting material such as carbon embedded in a poorly insulating medium such as salt water.   Thus to avoid serious leakage of magnetic flux from a magnetic circuit it is necessary to arrange for the circuit to be thick and short.   A typical magnetic circuit might have a cross-sectional area of 10 cm² and be formed into a square circuit of edge 10 cm in the manner indicated in Fig. 8.5.

Simple calculations concerning magnetic circuits are made on the assumption that there is no leakage of magnetic flux from the circuit and all the magnetic flux passes round the circuit.   The way in which the electric current threads the magnetic circuit is then of no importance and can be arranged on the basis of practical convenience.   Thus to thread a current of 10 amp through the magnetic circuit shown in Fig. 8.5 one can wind 1,000 turns of insulated wire round one edge of the magnetic circuit and pass a current of 10 ma through the wire.

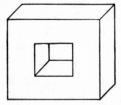

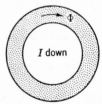

FIG. 8.5. Typical geometry of a magnetic circuit.

FIG. 8.6. Illustrating the calculation of the reluctance of a magnetic circuit.

8.6. Inductance and Reluctance of a Magnetic Circuit.   Consider the circular magnetic circuit of soft iron shown in Fig. 8.6.   Let S be the area of a normal cross section of the circuit and s be the perimeter of the circuit.   To avoid leakage of magnetic flux from the magnetic circuit the linear dimensions of S are not usually small compared with the size of the circuit.   It is necessary therefore to define the perimeter s of the circuit as the perimeter measured through the centroids of the normal cross sections, and this will be called the median length of the circuit. Let us suppose that a magnetic flux Φ passes round the magnetic circuit, and let us inquire how much current must thread through the circuit in order to maintain this magnetic flux.

Let us suppose first of all that the current I threading through the magnetic circuit is applied over the surface of the magnetic circuit in such a way as to avoid leakage completely. The magnetic circuit is then a toroidal inductor filled with soft iron. Let B be the magnetic flux density inside the magnetic circuit, and let the nonuniformity in the magnitude of B over a normal cross section of the circuit be neglected. Then

$$B = \frac{\Phi}{S} \qquad (8.7)$$

If μ is the inductivity of the soft iron, it follows from Eq. (8.5) that the current per unit length that must be applied round the surface of the magnetic circuit in order to maintain the flux Φ through the circuit is

$$H = \frac{1}{\mu} \frac{\Phi}{S} \qquad (8.8)$$

The total current I that must be applied round the curved surface of the magnetic circuit is obtained by multiplying the current per unit length H given by Eq. (8.8) by the median length s of the circuit. The total current I round the toroid is therefore

$$I = Hs \qquad (8.9)$$

Substituting for H from Eq. (8.8) into Eq. (8.9) we obtain

$$I = \frac{s}{\mu S} \Phi \qquad (8.10)$$

This equation can be written as

$$I = R\Phi \qquad (8.11)$$

where

$$R = \frac{s}{\mu S} \qquad (8.12)$$

Alternatively Eq. (8.10) can be written as

$$I = \frac{1}{L} \Phi \qquad (8.13)$$

where

$$L = \frac{\mu S}{s} \qquad (8.14)$$

Equation (8.14) is the same as Eq. (5.7) previously derived for a toroidal inductor. Expression (8.14) is simply the inductance of the inductor formed by wrapping the magnetic circuit tightly in a conducting sheet that covers the entire surface of the magnetic circuit. Equations (8.11) and (8.12) convey the same information as Eqs. (8.13) and (8.14) but make the statement in terms of the reciprocal of inductance. The reciprocal of inductance is known as reluctance and is measured in reciprocal henrys. Expression (8.12) is the reluctance of the inductor formed by wrapping the magnetic circuit tightly in a conducting sheet that covers the entire magnetic circuit. Expressions (8.12) and (8.14) will be called respectively the reluctance and inductance of the magnetic circuit.

So far we have not used the ability of the magnetic circuit under discussion to channel magnetic flux because we have applied the current to the surface of the magnetic circuit in such a way that no leakage of the magnetic flux from the magnetic circuit could take place. Let us now replace the current I round the curved surface of the magnetic circuit with a current I threading the magnetic circuit in some other way, and let us assume that leakage of magnetic flux from the magnetic circuit is negligible. In particular let the current I thread the magnetic circuit on a single loop of wire, and let the resulting magnetic flux passing round the magnetic circuit be Φ. The assumption of negligible leakage implies that the relation between I and Φ is still given by Eq. (8.11) or (8.13). Expression (8.14) therefore is the ratio of the magnetic flux threading the loop of wire to the current I flowing round the loop of wire and is therefore the inductance of the loop of wire in the presence of the threading magnetic circuit. Thus the inductance and reluctance of any one-turn loop of wire threading a magnetic circuit are simply the inductance and reluctance of the magnetic circuit itself provided that it can be assumed that the magnetic flux is substantially confined to the magnetic circuit.

The statements made in connection with Eqs. (8.11) and (8.13) can, if desired, be expressed in terms of magnetic scalar potential. Let us suppose that the current I is threaded through the magnetic circuit shown in Fig. 8.6 on a conducting sheet tightly wrapped round the magnetic circuit, the current being uniformly distributed along the length of the circuit. As described in connection with Fig. 7.9, the difference in magnetic scalar potential between any two normal cross sections of a toroidal inductor is the amperage flowing round the inductor between the cross sections. If we pass once round the magnetic circuit in the direction of the magnetic flux and return to the starting point, the drop in magnetic scalar potential is the total amperage I flowing round the inductor. Equation (8.11) can therefore be interpreted by saying that the drop in magnetic scalar potential I as we pass all the way round the magnetic circuit and return to the starting point is obtained by multiplying the magnetic flux Φ passing round the circuit by the reluctance R of the magnetic circuit.

It is not essential, and indeed it is not even usual, for a magnetic circuit to be constructed in the circular form indicated in Fig. 8.6. A construction more like that indicated in Fig. 8.5 is normally used. However, Eqs. (8.11) through (8.14) are applicable to a magnetic circuit such as that shown in Fig. 8.5 provided that the normal cross-sectional area of the circuit measured near the center of a side is S and the median length of the circuit is s. It is, of course, true that the appropriate cross-sectional area of the circuit near a corner is greater than S and that there is a tendency for the magnetic flux to leak across the inside corners of the circuit, but these effects are neglected in simple calculations.

In handling magnetic circuits it is convenient to draw circuit diagrams similar to those used in connection with electric circuits. An example of a magnetic-circuit diagram is shown in Fig. 8.7. The situation under discussion in this section is one in which a magnetic circuit of reluctance R given by Eq. (8.12) is threaded by a current I, as a result of which a magnetic flux Φ passes round the circuit. This information is conveniently depicted in the magnetic-circuit diagram shown in Fig. 8.7. To ensure that the direction of the magnetic flux Φ round the circuit is related by the right-hand-screw rule to the current I threading the circuit, it is convenient to adopt the convention that the gap in the arrow

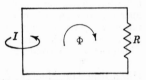

Fig. 8.7. Diagrammatic representation of a magnetic circuit of reluctance R threaded by a current I, as a result of which magnetic flux Φ passes round the circuit.

representing the current corresponds to the portion of the current on the underside of the sheet of paper. The relation among I, Φ, and R in Fig. 8.7 is described by Eq. (8.11). This is the equation for a magnetic circuit that corresponds to Ohm's Law for an electric circuit.

8.7. Multiturn Electric Circuit Threading a Magnetic Circuit. The electric circuits used in conjunction with magnetic circuits usually consist of multiturn coils wound round the magnetic circuit. In this case it is necessary to distinguish between the current flowing round the electric circuit and the total current threading the magnetic circuit. It is also necessary to distinguish between the magnetic flux passing round the magnetic circuit and the total magnetic flux threading the electric circuit. In consequence it is necessary also to distinguish between the inductance or reluctance of the magnetic circuit and the inductance or reluctance of the electric circuit.

Consider a magnetic circuit of cross-sectional area S and median length s made of soft iron of inductivity μ. Onto the magnetic circuit let there be wound an n-turn coil of insulated conducting wire through which a steady current I is passed. The electric circuit may then be thought of as a helix of wire such as that shown in Fig. 5.11, through which is threaded a magnetic circuit such as that shown in Fig. 8.6 or 8.5. In these circumstances the current flowing round the electric circuit is I while the current threading the magnetic circuit is nI. The diagram for the magnetic circuit is therefore as shown in Fig. 8.8. The reluctance R of the magnetic circuit is calculated from Eq. (8.12). The magnetic flux Φ passing round the magnetic circuit is calculated from Eq. (8.11) if we remember to replace I by nI in accordance with Fig. 8.8. The magnetic flux Φ passing round the magnetic circuit is therefore given by

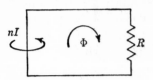

$$nI = R\Phi \qquad (8.15)$$

and is therefore

Fig. 8.8. Illustrating a magnetic flux Φ passing round a magnetic circuit of reluctance R threaded by an n-turn coil, each turn of which carries a current I.

$$\Phi = \frac{nI}{R} \qquad (8.16)$$

It is now necessary to be clear that the magnetic flux Φ passing round the magnetic circuit and given by Eq. (8.16) is not the magnetic flux threading the electric circuit. The magnetic flux threading an electric circuit is obtained by applying Eq. (2.48) to a geometrical surface spanning the electric circuit. For a multiturn coil a geometrical surface spanning the electric circuit is shown in Fig. 5.12. This consists of n normal cross sections of the coil, connected together by means of a narrow strip. The magnetic flux threading the electric circuit is therefore the magnetic flux crossing n normal cross sections of the magnetic circuit and is therefore

$$n\Phi \qquad (8.17)$$

Substituting into this expression from Eq. (8.16) we see that the magnetic flux threading the n-turn electric circuit is

$$n\Phi = \frac{n^2 I}{R} \qquad (8.18)$$

The inductance of the electric circuit is the ratio of the magnetic flux (8.18) threading the electric circuit to the current I flowing round the electric circuit and is therefore

$$\frac{n\Phi}{I} \qquad (8.19)$$

Substituting for $n\Phi$ from Eq. (8.18) into expression (8.19) we deduce that the inductance of the n-turn electric circuit threading a magnetic circuit of reluctance R is

$$\frac{n^2}{R} \qquad (8.20)$$

Since the reciprocal of the reluctance R of the magnetic circuit is the inductance of the magnetic circuit given by Eq. (8.14), the expression (8.20) can be interpreted by saying that the inductance of an n-turn electric circuit threading a magnetic circuit is n^2 times the inductance of the magnetic circuit. This is simply the result for the inductance of an n-turn inductor obtained in Eq. (5.39) restated for the situation when there is a magnetic circuit threading the inductor.

8.8. Reluctances Connected in Series. It is sometimes convenient for different sections of a magnetic circuit to have different cross-sectional areas as indicated in Fig. 8.9. Let the various sections be numbered 1, 2, ... Let $S_1, S_2, \ldots$ be the normal cross-sectional areas of the sections, and let their lengths be $s_1, s_2, \ldots$ respectively. Let the inductivities of the various sections be μ_1, μ_2, ...

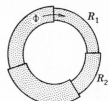

Fig. 8.9. A magnetic circuit consisting of several sections connected in series.

Suppose initially that the curved surfaces of the various sections of the magnetic circuit are wrapped tightly and completely with conducting sheets, thereby forming each section into an inductor. The inductances of the various sections are

$$L_1 = \frac{\mu_1 S_1}{s_1} \qquad L_2 = \frac{\mu_2 S_2}{s_2} \qquad \cdots \qquad (8.21)$$

and the corresponding reluctances are

$$R_1 = \frac{s_1}{\mu_1 S_1} \qquad R_2 = \frac{s_2}{\mu_2 S_2} \qquad \cdots \qquad (8.22)$$

Suppose that a magnetic flux Φ passes round the magnetic circuit, and let us neglect the distortions that occur at the joints between the various sections. To maintain this magnetic flux round the magnetic circuit, the amperages required round the various sections are

$$R_1 \Phi \qquad R_2 \Phi \qquad \cdots \qquad (8.23)$$

The total amperage required round the magnetic circuit in order to maintain the flux Φ through it is the sum of the amperages round the various sections and is therefore

$$I = R_1 \Phi + R_2 \Phi + \cdots \qquad (8.24)$$

This can be written as

$$I = R \Phi \qquad (8.25)$$

where

$$R = R_1 + R_2 + \cdots \qquad (8.26)$$

Equation (8.25) gives the total current I that must be threaded through the magnetic circuit shown in Fig. 8.9 in order to maintain the magnetic flux Φ round it.   Provided that leakage of magnetic flux from the magnetic circuit can be neglected, the current I need not flow round the surface of the magnetic circuit but instead can be threaded through the magnetic circuit in any way that may be convenient.

Equation (8.25) has the same form as Eq. (8.11).   The relation between the current threading the magnetic circuit shown in Fig. 8.9 and the magnetic flux Φ passing round it can therefore be calculated from a single reluctance R which, in accordance with Eq. (8.26), is the sum of the reluctances of the individual sections from which the complete magnetic circuit is formed.   An arrangement such as that shown in Fig. 8.9

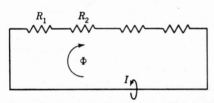

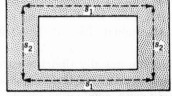

FIG. 8.10. A magnetic circuit consisting of a number of reluctances connected in series.

FIG. 8.11. A rectangular magnetic circuit.

is described as a magnetic circuit consisting of several reluctances connected in series.   Equations (8.25) and (8.26) show that the relation between the current I threading such a magnetic circuit and the magnetic flux Φ passing round it is the same as for a uniform magnetic circuit whose reluctance is the sum of the reluctances of the individual sections connected in series.   The magnetic circuit illustrated in Fig. 8.9 is represented diagrammatically as shown in Fig. 8.10.   A one-turn electric circuit threading this magnetic circuit has an inductance $1/R$, where R is given by Eq. (8.26).   An n-turn electric circuit threading a magnetic circuit consisting of a number of reluctances R_1, R_2, . . . connected in series has an inductance n^2/R, where R is given by Eq. (8.26).

As an example, suppose that a rectangular magnetic circuit has two sides of median length s_1 and cross-sectional area S_1 and two sides of median length s_2 and cross-sectional area S_2, as indicated in Fig. 8.11. Let the inductivity of the soft iron used be μ.   The four sides of the rectangle then constitute four reluctances connected in series, and their reluctances are

$$\frac{s_1}{\mu S_1} \qquad \frac{s_2}{\mu S_2} \qquad \frac{s_1}{\mu S_1} \qquad \frac{s_2}{\mu S_2} \tag{8.27}$$

The reluctance of the complete magnetic circuit is the sum of the reluctances (8.27) in accordance with Eq. (8.26) and is therefore

$$R = \frac{s_1}{\mu S_1} + \frac{s_2}{\mu S_2} + \frac{s_1}{\mu S_1} + \frac{s_2}{\mu S_2} \qquad (8.28)$$

or

$$R = \frac{2}{\mu}\left(\frac{s_1}{S_1} + \frac{s_2}{S_2}\right) \qquad (8.29)$$

If an n-turn electric circuit threads this magnetic circuit, its inductance, from Eqs. (8.20) and (8.29), is

$$\frac{n^2}{R} = \frac{\mu n^2}{2(s_1/S_1 + s_2/S_2)} \qquad (8.30)$$

Suppose that $s_1 = 10$ cm (10^{-1} m), $s_2 = 5$ cm (5×10^{-2} m), $S_1 = 10$ cm^2 (10^{-3} m^2), $S_2 = 5$ cm^2 (5×10^{-4} m^2), $\mu/\mu_v = 1,000$, and $n = 1,000$. From Eq. (8.29) the reluctance of the magnetic circuit evaluates to 3.2×10^5 henry^{-1}, and from Eq. (8.30) the inductance of the electric circuit evaluates to 3.1 henrys.

8.9. Gaps in Magnetic Circuits. Consider a magnetic circuit made of soft iron of inductivity μ surrounded by air whose inductivity may be taken to have the value μ_v for a vacuum. Let the normal cross-sectional area of the magnetic circuit be S and its length s. In this circuit cut a gap of width w normally across the circuit as shown in Fig. 8.12. Let the width w of the gap be small compared with the linear dimensions of the cross-sectional area S of the circuit. Let the magnetic circuit be threaded by an n-turn coil, each of whose turns carries a current I, and let us inquire concerning the magnetic flux density B produced in the gap. Such an arrangement is referred to as an electromagnet.

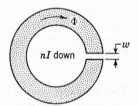

Fig. 8.12. A magnetic circuit possessing a gap.

If the width of the gap were large compared with the linear dimensions of a normal cross section of the circuit, magnetic flux would emerge from one open end of the soft iron and converge on the other end more or less as indicated in Fig. 4.3. If, however, the width of the gap is small compared with the linear dimensions of a normal cross section of the magnetic circuit, then the magnetic flux emerging from one face of the gap immediately enters the other face as indicated in Fig. 4.8. The lines of magnetic flux round the circuit are thus substantially the same as in the absence of the gap although some fringing does occur at the edge of the gap. Simple calculations concerning the effect of a narrow gap in a magnetic circuit are based upon the assumption that the lines of magnetic flux in the gap remain perpendicular to a normal cross section of the circuit, so that no fringing occurs. In these circumstances the gap is simply a section of a magnetic circuit as shown in Fig. 8.9, the length of the section being w, the cross-sectional area of the section being S, and the inductivity of the section being μ_v. The gap thus forms a reluctance in the magnetic circuit of magnitude

$$\frac{w}{\mu_v S} \qquad (8.31)$$

The remainder of the magnetic circuit forms a reluctance whose magnitude is

$$\frac{s}{\mu S} \qquad (8.32)$$

and the two reluctances given by expressions (8.31) and (8.32) are connected in series.

The appropriate magnetic-circuit diagram is therefore as shown in Fig. 8.13. The reluctance at the right in Fig. 8.13 corresponds to the gap in Fig. 8.12, and the reluctance at the top in Fig. 8.13 corresponds to the remainder of the magnetic circuit in Fig. 8.12. The total reluctance in the circuit is obtained by adding the expressions (8.31) and (8.32), thereby obtaining

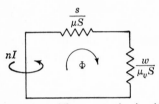

FIG. 8.13. The magnetic-circuit diagram for the magnetic circuit shown in Fig. 8.12.

$$R = \frac{1}{S}\left(\frac{w}{\mu_v} + \frac{s}{\mu}\right) \qquad (8.33)$$

The relation between the current nI threading the magnetic circuit and the magnetic flux Φ passing round the magnetic circuit is

$$nI = R\Phi \qquad (8.34)$$

and by substitution for R from Eq. (8.33) we obtain

$$I = \frac{1}{n}\frac{\Phi}{S}\left(\frac{w}{\mu_v} + \frac{s}{\mu}\right) \qquad (8.35)$$

The factor Φ/S appearing in Eq. (8.35) is the magnetic flux density in the magnetic circuit. Because of the assumption of no fringing at the gap, this is also the magnetic flux density B in the gap. Equation (8.35) can therefore be written as

$$I = \frac{1}{n}B\left(\frac{w}{\mu_v} + \frac{s}{\mu}\right) \qquad (8.36)$$

This equation gives the current I that must flow in the n-turn electric circuit threading the magnetic circuit in order to produce a magnetic flux density B in the gap.

Comparison of expression (8.31) with expression (8.32) shows that the two reluctances appearing in Fig. 8.13 are equal if the ratio of the length s of the soft-iron part of the magnetic circuit to the width w of the gap is equal to the permeability μ/μ_v of the soft iron. In practice, gaps are frequently sufficiently wide to make expression (8.31) large compared with expression (8.32). In these circumstances the reluctance associated with the gap in Fig. 8.13 is large compared with that associated with the rest of the magnetic circuit. Calculations concerning the magnetic field in the gap under these circumstances can be made on the assumption that the reluctance of the soft-iron part of the circuit is negligible. For this situation the second term in Eq. (8.36) disappears, and we obtain

$$I = \frac{1}{n} B \frac{w}{\mu_v} \tag{8.37}$$

Suppose, for example, that $s = 30$ cm (3×10^{-1} m), $w = 3$ mm (3×10^{-3} m), $\mu/\mu_v = 1,000$, $n = 1,000$, and $B = 1,000$ gauss (10^{-1} weber/m^2). From Eq. (8.37) we deduce that the required current I through the wire of the coil is 0.24 amp. If the more complete Eq. (8.36) is used, we obtain 0.26 amp.

8.10. Reluctances Connected in Parallel. It is possible for a magnetic circuit to be constructed in such a way that a magnetic flux Φ divides

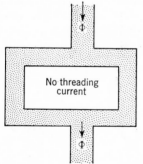

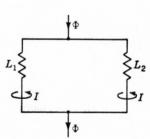

Fig. 8.14. Illustrating reluctances con-   Fig. 8.15. Circuit diagram showing two
nected in parallel.   sections of magnetic circuit of induct-
                                            ances L_1 and L_2 connected in parallel.

between two branches as shown in Fig. 8.14. Let the inductance of the left-hand branch of the magnetic circuit shown in Fig. 8.14, calculated in accordance with Eq. (8.14), be L_1. Let the inductance of the right-hand branch, calculated in the same way, be L_2. Figure 8.14 then represents the situation in which two sections of magnetic circuit of inductances L_1 and L_2 are connected in parallel. This is illustrated diagrammatically in Fig. 8.15.

It is supposed that there is no current threading the magnetic circuit formed by the two sections of magnetic circuit connected in parallel. On this assumption we have to calculate the way in which the magnetic flux Φ divides between the two branches. Let us suppose that a tightly fitting conducting surface is wrapped around the left-hand branch of the circuit shown in Fig. 8.14 and that a similar conductor is wrapped around the right-hand branch. Let the amperage that must be applied round the left-hand branch in order completely to prevent leakage of magnetic flux be I as shown in Fig. 8.15. Then the amperage that must be applied round the right-hand branch must also be I, so that no net current threads between the two branches. This can also be expressed by saying that, if I is the drop in magnetic scalar potential as we pass down the left-hand branch, the drop in magnetic scalar potential as we pass down the right-hand branch must also be I. In terms of I the magnetic flux passing through the left-hand branch is $L_1 I$ and that passing through the right-hand branch is $L_2 I$. Since these must add up to the magnetic flux Φ entering at the top and leaving at the bottom, we deduce that

$$\Phi = L_1 I + L_2 I \tag{8.38}$$

This can be written as

$$\Phi = LI \tag{8.39}$$

where

$$L = L_1 + L_2 \tag{8.40}$$

Equations (8.39) and (8.40) show that the pair of branches connected in parallel are equivalent to a single section of magnetic circuit whose inductance is the sum of the inductances of the two branches connected in parallel. Expressed in terms of the reluctances R_1 and R_2 of the two branches, Eq. (8.40) can be written as

$$\frac{1}{R} = \frac{1}{R_1} + \frac{1}{R_2} \tag{8.41}$$

If more than two branches are connected in parallel, then Eq. (8.41) is replaced by

$$\frac{1}{R} = \frac{1}{R_1} + \frac{1}{R_2} + \cdots \tag{8.42}$$

Hence if a number of sections of magnetic circuit of reluctances R_1, R_2, . . . are connected in parallel and no electric current threads between them, they are equivalent to a single section of magnetic circuit of reluctance R given by Eq. (8.42).

As an example, consider the two-mesh magnetic network shown in Fig. 8.16. Suppose that an n-turn coil is wound around the central arm and that it is required to calculate the inductance of the electric circuit so formed. Let the reluctance of the central section of the magnetic network between the points A and B be r. Let the reluctance of each of the outside arms of the magnetic network between the points A and B be R. The arrangement shown in Fig. 8.16 is therefore represented diagrammatically as shown in Fig. 8.17. In Fig. 8.17 we see that the two reluctances R are in parallel and are therefore equivalent to a single reluctance of magnitude $\frac{1}{2}R$. We therefore have an n-turn coil wound

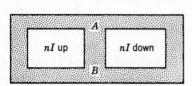

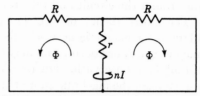

Fig. 8.16. A two-mesh magnetic network with an n-turn coil wound round the central arm, each turn carrying a current I.

Fig. 8.17. Magnetic-circuit diagram for the arrangement shown in Fig. 8.16.

upon a magnetic circuit of total reluctance $r + \frac{1}{2}R$, and the inductance of the coil is therefore

$$\frac{n^2}{r + \frac{1}{2}R} \tag{8.43}$$

8.11. Magnetic Networks. From what has been said it will be appreciated that there is a parallelism between magnetic circuits and the electric circuits studied in Part 2. Corresponding concepts are indicated in Table 8.1.

TABLE 8.1. RELATION BETWEEN ELECTRIC AND MAGNETIC CIRCUITS

Electric circuit	Magnetic circuit
Conductivity............	Inductivity
Conductance............	Inductance
Resistance..............	Reluctance
Electric current..........	Magnetic flux
Electric potential........	Magnetic scalar potential
Voltage.................	Amperage

One point of difference between the two cases should, however, be noted. In going round an electric circuit and returning to the starting point there is no net change of electric potential; the drop of potential in passing through the resistors is balanced by the rise of potential in passing through the batteries. For a magnetic circuit, however, there is in general a net drop in magnetic scalar potential in going round the circuit and returning to the starting point; the drop in magnetic scalar potential in passing round a magnetic circuit is equal to the current threading the magnetic circuit. The drop in magnetic scalar potential in passing through the reluctances forming the magnetic circuit is not balanced by a rise in magnetic scalar potential in passing through a coil threaded on the magnetic circuit. However, in the equations describing corresponding electric and magnetic circuits, the voltage connected in the electric circuit occupies the same position as the amperage threading the magnetic circuit. Thus the equations derived for the electric and magnetic circuits correspond, although care is necessary in making statements about magnetic scalar potential because it does not return to the initial value when we pass round the circuit and return to the starting point.

The entire theory of electric networks developed in Part 2 can be adapted for magnetic networks to any extent that may be required. A magnetic network of soft iron may have any number of meshes and nodes. Kirchhoff's conservation law for a magnetic network states that, neglecting leakage, the algebraic sum of the magnetic fluxes leaving any node is zero. Kirchhoff's circulation law for a magnetic network states that, in going round any mesh and returning to the starting point, the algebraic sum of the amperages associated with the various sections of the mesh is equal to the total current threading through the mesh in the direction related by the right-hand-screw rule. The amperage for each section of a mesh is calculated by multiplying the magnetic flux passing through that section by the reluctance of the section. Using Kirchhoff's laws, problems about magnetic networks can be solved in the same way as the corresponding problems about electric networks.

Suppose that, from ferromagnetic material obeying Eq. (8.5), there is constructed a magnetic network possessing a number of meshes numbered 1, 2, ... Let the total electric currents threading the various meshes be I_1, I_2, ... Let the resulting magnetic fluxes round the various meshes be Φ_1, Φ_2, ... It is supposed that the magnetic flux round each mesh is related by the right-hand-screw rule to the current threading that mesh. Application of Kirchhoff's laws leads to linear equations relating the currents threading the meshes with the magnetic fluxes round the meshes. These relations can be written either in the form

$$I_1 = r_{11}\Phi_1 + r_{12}\Phi_2 + \cdots$$
$$I_2 = r_{21}\Phi_1 + r_{22}\Phi_2 + \cdots \qquad (8.44)$$
$$\cdots \cdots \cdots \cdots \cdots \cdots$$

or in the form

$$\Phi_1 = l_{11}I_1 + l_{12}I_2 + \cdots$$
$$\Phi_2 = l_{21}I_1 + l_{22}I_2 + \cdots \qquad (8.45)$$
$$\cdots \cdots \cdots \cdots \cdots \cdots$$

The coefficients r_{11}, r_{22}, . . . appearing in Eqs. (8.44) are known as the coefficients of self-reluctance of the network, and the remaining coefficients in Eqs. (8.44) are known as the coefficients of mutual reluctance. These coefficients are such that

$$r_{mn} = r_{nm} \qquad (8.46)$$

and this arises from the fact that each side of this equation is the reluctance common to meshes m and n in the network. In Eqs. (8.45) the coefficients l_{11}, l_{22}, . . . may be called the coefficients of self-inductance of the magnetic network and the remaining coefficients may be called the coefficients of mutual inductance of the magnetic network. These coefficients are such that

$$l_{mn} = l_{nm} \tag{8.47}$$

Equation (8.47) follows from Eq. (8.46) when Eqs. (8.44) are solved for Φ_1, Φ_2, . . . in order to obtain Eqs. (8.45).

In practice, most of the elaboration used in handling electric networks is not required to handle magnetic networks. The reason is that, in order to avoid leakage of magnetic flux from magnetic networks, the circuits have to be thick and short. In consequence they are clumsy, and only simple networks are used. For the magnetic networks normally encountered, therefore, relatively simple calculations involving reluctances connected in series and in parallel are adequate. In some cases, however, use of the mesh-flux method is worthwhile.

As an example of the mesh-flux method, let us consider the magnetic network illustrated in Fig. 8.16. Using the symmetry of the network, mesh fluxes Φ can be introduced round the two meshes as shown in Fig. 8.17. There is then a magnetic flux Φ passing through each of the reluctances R, producing a magnetic flux 2Φ through the reluctance r. Application of Kirchhoff's circulation law to either of the meshes gives

$$R\Phi + r(2\Phi) = nI \tag{8.48}$$

where I is the current flowing round each of the n turns of the coil wound on the central arm of the network. Hence

$$\Phi = \frac{nI}{R + 2r} \tag{8.49}$$

The total magnetic flux threading each turn of the coil is 2Φ, and the corresponding magnetic flux threading the electric circuit associated with the coil is $2n\Phi$. The inductance of the coil is therefore

$$\frac{2n\Phi}{I} \tag{8.50}$$

and substitution for Φ from Eq. (8.49) into expression (8.50) verifies expression (8.43).

8.12. Magnetic Network of a Rotating Electrical Machine. An example of a more complicated magnetic network is provided by an electric motor or dynamo. In Fig. 8.18 the stippled areas indicate soft iron. The outer ring of soft iron forms what is known as the yoke of the machine, and to it are attached an even number of poles extending inward toward the axis of the machine. The inner ring of soft iron is what is known as the armature, which in practice is capable of rotating on its axis. The clearances between the armature and the pole faces are small. Round each pole is wound a multiturn coil of insulated copper wire known as a field coil, and the direction of winding on adjacent poles is opposite. Let

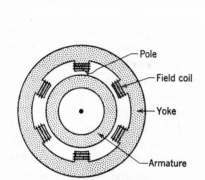

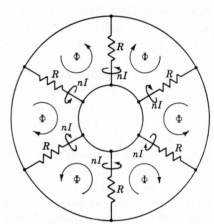

FIG. 8.18. Magnetic network of a rotating electrical machine.

FIG. 8.19. Magnetic-network diagram for the arrangement shown in Fig. 8.18.

n be the number of turns on each field coil and I the current flowing round each turn. Let w be the clearance between the armature and each pole face, and let w be small compared with the linear dimensions of the area S of a pole face. The reluctance of each gap between a pole face and the armature is therefore

$$R = \frac{w}{\mu_v S} \qquad (8.51)$$

Let us assume that, in comparison with the reluctance given by Eq. (8.51), the reluctance of other sections of the magnetic network is negligible. The magnetic-circuit diagram for the machine is then as shown in Fig. 8.19. Because the field coils on adjacent poles are wound in opposite directions, the magnetic fluxes round adjacent meshes of the network are in opposite directions; however, they all have the same magnitude Φ. To calculate Φ, we apply Kirchhoff's circulation law for magnetic networks to any one of the meshes. The total current threading each mesh is $2nI$, and the total magnetic flux through each reluctance R is 2Φ. In accordance with Eq. (8.11), the amperage required round each of these reluctances is $2R\Phi$, and therefore

$$2R\Phi + 2R\Phi = 2nI \qquad (8.52)$$

Solving for Φ we obtain

$$\Phi = \frac{nI}{2R} \qquad (8.53)$$

The total magnetic flux crossing each pole face is 2Φ, and this is distributed uniformly over an area S. Hence the magnetic flux density in each gap between a pole face and the armature is

$$B = \frac{2\Phi}{S} \qquad (8.54)$$

Substituting for Φ from Eq. (8.53) into Eq. (8.54) we obtain

$$B = \frac{nI}{RS} \qquad (8.55)$$

Using the value (8.51) for the reluctance of the gap, Eq. (8.55) becomes

$$B = \mu_v \frac{nI}{w} \qquad (8.56)$$

Equation (8.56) can also be derived as follows: Since the total current threading each mesh of the magnetic network is $2nI$, the drop in magnetic scalar potential in passing completely round a mesh is $2nI$. Neglecting all reluctances except those of the gaps, the drop in magnetic scalar potential $2nI$ in going round a mesh is developed entirely across the two gaps in the mesh. The drop in magnetic scalar potential across each gap is therefore nI, and the magnetic field strength in a gap is consequently nI/w. The magnetic flux density in a gap is therefore given by Eq. (8.56).

To use the magnetic network shown in Fig. 8.18 as a rotating electrical machine, slots are cut across the outer surface of the armature and insulated copper wires are wound onto the armature as indicated in Fig. 8.20. A wire carrying a current I' is passed back and forth across the surface of the armature, the distance between successive transits of the wire being equal to the distances between the centers of successive pole faces. Let the pole faces be rectangular with a width b parallel to the axis of the armature and a length a round the circumference of the armature as shown in Fig. 8.20. Let the axial width of the outer surface of the armature also be b. In accordance with Eq. (6.13), the force upon a wire traversing the armature opposite a pole face is

$$I'B \qquad (8.57)$$

per unit length, and the total force on such a wire is therefore

$$I'Bb \qquad (8.58)$$

This force is directed round the circumference of the armature and there-fore tends to turn it. During the interval of time in which the wires traversing the armature move from one pole face to the next, it is neces-sary to reverse the current in the wires in order that the forces on the armature are always directed the same way round the circumference. This reversal of current is accomplished by means of a switching mecha-nism known as a commutator attached to the spindle of the machine.

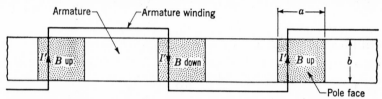

FIG. 8.20. A developed picture of a portion of the outer surface of an armature show-ing an armature winding.

Instead of using a single armature winding as shown in Fig. 8.20, a number of armature windings can be used so as to produce traverses across the armature spaced equally round the perimeter of the armature. If there are n' traverses per unit distance round the perimeter of the armature, there are $n'a$ traverses opposite a particular pole face. If there are p pole faces, there are altogether $pn'a$ traverses of the armature opposite the pole faces at a particular time. Each traverse results in a force round the circumference of the armature given by Eq. (8.58), and therefore the total force acting round the circumference of the armature is

$$pn'I'Bab \qquad (8.59)$$

In this expression Bab is the total magnetic flux crossing a pole face, and this is twice the flux Φ given by Eq. (8.53). Using this expression for the factor Bab in expression (8.59), we obtain for the total force acting round the perimeter of the armature

$$\frac{pnn'II'}{R} \qquad (8.60)$$

We see that the torque provided by the motor is increased by increasing the current round the poles and the current over the surface of the arma-ture. It is also increased by increasing the number of poles and by reduc-ing the reluctance of the gaps. The latter involves increasing the areas of the pole faces and reducing the clearance between them and the armature.

It should be noticed that the currents in the field coils and in the armature windings are only a small fraction of the total electric current involved in the operation of the machine.   Most of the current is in the form of spinning electrons in the yoke and in the armature.   Thus, while the forces that drive an electric motor are calculated from the currents in the field coils and in the armature windings, the forces are exerted predominantly between the spinning electrons in the yoke and those in the armature.

The design of a rotating electric machine in practice involves many considerations that have been elided in the above discussion.   In particular the ferromagnetic material used in the machine does not usually satisfy Eq. (8.5) because a more intense magnetic field in the gaps between the armature and the poles can be obtained by operating with the ferromagnetic material close to saturation.

8.13. Use of Permanent Magnets in Magnetic Circuits.   Instead of producing magnetic flux round a magnetic circuit by means of a threading electric current, it can also be produced by connecting in the magnetic circuit a piece of ferromagnetic material possessing permanent magnetic flux density as described in connection with the point P in Fig. 8.3 and in connection with the quantity B_0 in Eq. (8.6).   If the permanent magnet illustrated by the hatched section in Fig. 8.21 produces a magnetic flux

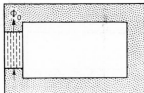

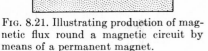

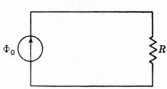

FIG. 8.21. Illustrating production of magnetic flux round a magnetic circuit by means of a permanent magnet.

FIG. 8.22. Diagrammatic representation of the situation illustrated in Fig. 8.21.

Φ_0 entering one end and leaving the other, and if the remainder of the magnetic circuit is made of soft iron and has a reluctance R, the situation can be represented diagrammatically as shown in Fig. 8.22.   We see that the permanent magnet produces through the soft iron the same magnetic flux that would be produced in the absence of the permanent magnet by a total threading current $R\Phi_0$.

It is usually necessary to make allowance for the fact that a permanent magnet has an internal reluctance R'.   This internal reluctance R' is to be thought of as in parallel with the flux generator Φ_0 in Fig. 8.22 and therefore in parallel with the external reluctance R.   This may be seen in the following way: The permanent magnet illustrated in Fig. 8.21 may be thought of as consisting of a bundle of magnetic needles aligned along the circuit.   Consider the magnetic flux entering the lower end of one of these needles and emerging from the upper end.   Some of the flux emanating from the upper end returns to the lower end via the soft-iron section of the circuit.   However, some of the magnetic flux emerging from the upper end of a magnetic needle returns to the lower end of the needle through the ferromagnetic material constituting the permanent magnet.

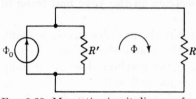

We thus see that a permanent magnet has an internal reluctance R' and that the arrangement shown in Fig. 8.21 is to be represented diagrammatically as shown in Fig. 8.23. Figure 8.23 reduces to Fig. 8.22 in circumstances when the internal reluctance R' of the permanent magnet is large compared with the external reluctance R.

FIG. 8.23. Magnetic-circuit diagram for the arrangement shown in Fig. 8.21 allowing for the internal reluctance R' of the permanent magnet.

The magnetic flux Φ_0 in Fig. 8.23 is the magnetic flux that would pass round the external circuit if the reluctance of the external circuit were zero.   Thus, if the permanent magnet were formed into a closed loop, as shown in Fig. 8.24, the magnetic flux passing round the loop would be

FIG. 8.24. A permanent magnet formed into a closed magnetic circuit.

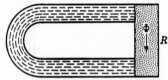

FIG. 8.25. A permanent magnet in the form of a horseshoe connected across a soft-iron armature.

Φ_0.   If, however, the permanent magnet does not form a closed magnetic circuit but has an external reluctance R connected between its pole faces as shown in Fig. 8.25, then it follows from Fig. 8.23 that the magnetic flux through the external reluctance is

$$\Phi = \frac{R'}{R + R'}\,\Phi_0 \tag{8.61}$$

This is the magnetic flux that emerges from one end of the permanent magnet in Fig. 8.25, passes through the external reluctance, and then enters the other end of the permanent magnet.   The magnetic flux Φ given by Eq. (8.61) is less than the magnetic flux existing when the permanent magnet is formed into a closed magnetic circuit as shown in Fig. 8.24 by the amount

$$\frac{R}{R + R'}\, \Phi \tag{8.62}$$

This is the magnetic flux which, as described in connection with Fig. 8.21, passes from upper ends of magnetic needles in the permanent magnet to the lower ends through the permanent magnet itself instead of through the external reluctance. This is the magnetic flux which, in Fig. 8.23, is represented as passing through the internal reluctance R' of the permanent magnet. The fact that the magnetic flux passing round the magnetic circuit shown in Fig. 8.25 is less than the magnetic flux passing round the magnetic circuit shown in Fig. 8.24 for the same permanent magnet is described by saying that the magnet is partially demagnetized as a result of insertion of soft iron into the magnetic circuit.

8.14. Calculation of the Internal Reluctance of a Permanent Magnet. Calculation of the internal reluctance of a permanent magnet brings in considerations beyond those involved in Eq. (8.12) because a permanent magnet consists of ferromagnetic material operated in the neighborhood of the point P in Fig. 8.3 instead of in the neighborhood of point O. Whereas the reluctance of a piece of soft iron is given by an application of Eq. (8.5) leading to Eq. (8.12), calculation of the internal reluctance of a permanent magnet must be deduced from Eq. (8.6). In Eq. (8.6) μ' is the slope at the point P in Fig. 8.3 of the magnetization curve passing through P. Furthermore B_0 in Eq. (8.6) is the

FIG. 8.26. A closed permanent magnet threaded by an electric current.

magnetic flux density produced by the ferromagnetic material when used as a permanent magnet on closed circuit as illustrated in Fig. 8.24 and when no current is applied round the magnet. If now a current per unit length H is applied round the surface of the permanent magnet in the direction related by the right-hand-screw rule to the direction of the permanent magnetic flux density B_0, the magnetic flux density B through the magnet when on closed circuit is given approximately by Eq. (8.6).

Let us suppose that a permanent magnet whose behavior is represented by Eq. (8.6) has a normal cross-sectional area S and a length s. Let us suppose that it is formed into a closed magnetic circuit as shown in Fig. 8.24 and that, with no current threading the magnetic circuit, the magnetic flux round the circuit is Φ_0. Let us now suppose that a current I threads the magnetic circuit as shown in Fig. 8.26 and that the modified flux round the magnetic circuit is Φ. In terms of the quantities appearing in Eq. (8.6) we have

$$\Phi_0 = B_0 S \qquad (8.63)$$

$$\Phi = BS \qquad (8.64)$$

$$I = Hs \qquad (8.65)$$

Equation (8.6) can therefore be rewritten as

$$\Phi = \Phi_0 + \frac{I}{R'} \qquad (8.66)$$

where

$$R' = \frac{s}{\mu' S} \qquad (8.67)$$

Equation (8.66) verifies the fact that the magnetic flux round the circuit shown in Fig. 8.26 is Φ_0 when there is no current I threading the magnetic

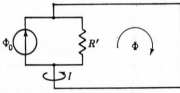 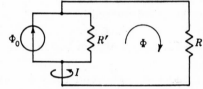

FIG. 8.27. Magnetic-circuit diagram representing a current I threading a closed permanent magnetic circuit of internal reluctance R' for which the magnetic flux in the absence of the current is Φ_0.

FIG. 8.28. Magnetic-circuit diagram for a permanent magnet of flux Φ_0 and internal reluctance R' connected across a piece of soft iron of reluctance R with a current I threading the circuit in the direction related by the right-hand-screw rule to the direction of the permanent magnetic flux.

circuit. Equation (8.66) shows in addition how the magnetic flux Φ passing round the circuit is modified when a current I threads the circuit. The first term on the left-hand side of Eq. (8.66) is the magnetic flux round the circuit due to the permanent magnetization, and the second term is the magnetic flux round the circuit due to the threading current. Equation (8.67) shows that the reluctance of a permanent magnet is calculated from the same formula (8.12) as for soft iron except that the μ appearing in Eq. (8.5) is replaced by μ' from Eq. (8.6). In other words the reluctance of a permanent magnet is calculated using the slope of the magnetization curve at the point P in Fig. 8.3 in place of the slope of the magnetization curve at the point O.

Equation (8.66) is the equation for the magnetic circuit shown in Fig. 8.27, which therefore represents the effect of threading a current I through a closed permanent magnet for which the internal reluctance is R' and the magnetic flux in the absence of current is Φ_0. If into this magnetic circuit we insert a piece of soft iron of reluctance R, Fig. 8.27 is replaced by Fig. 8.28. It is in fact unusual for a magnetic circuit containing a permanent magnet also to have electric current threaded through it. If I in Fig. 8.28 is made equal to zero, then Fig. 8.28 reduces to Fig. 8.23.

8.15. Permanent Magnet with Pole Pieces of Soft Iron.   In order to shape a magnetic field in a desired way it is quite common to use a horseshoe magnet as shown in Fig. 8.29 and to attach to the poles soft-iron pole pieces that can be used to shape the magnetic field.   An example of this occurs in the design of a moving-coil measuring instrument described in Sec. 6.5.   In Fig. 8.29 soft-iron pole pieces are attached to a permanent

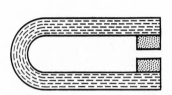

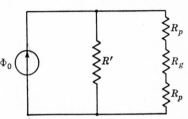

FIG. 8.29. Horseshoe magnet with soft-iron pole pieces producing a nearly uniform magnetic field in a narrow gap.

FIG. 8.30. Magnetic-circuit diagram for the arrangement shown in Fig. 8.29.

magnet in such a way as to produce a nearly uniform magnetic field in a gap.   To calculate the magnetic flux crossing the gap we can use the magnetic-circuit diagram shown in Fig. 8.30.   In this circuit diagram Φ_0 is obtained by multiplying the normal cross-sectional area of the permanent magnet by the magnetic flux density B_0 corresponding to the point P in Fig. 8.3.   The internal reluctance R' for the permanent magnet is evaluated using Eq. (8.67).   The reluctance R_p of each soft-iron pole piece is evaluated using Eq. (8.12), while the reluctance R_g of the gap is evaluated using expression (8.31).   The total reluctance connected across the permanent magnet is then

$$R = R_g + 2R_p   \qquad (8.68)$$

and the magnetic flux crossing the gap is obtained by substituting this value of R into Eq. (8.61).

8.16. The Equivalent Demagnetizing Current.   Suppose that a permanent magnet is connected across an external reluctance of magnitude

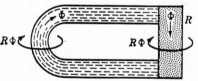

FIG. 8.31. Illustrating the equivalent demagnetizing current for a permanent magnet connected across an external reluctance.

R as shown in Fig. 8.31.   This external reluctance might be some combination of soft iron and air gaps.   The magnetic flux Φ through the external reluctance could be produced by means of a current wrapped round the reluctance and given by $R\Phi$ in accordance with Eq. (8.11). Since there is no net current threading the magnet circuit, the current applied to the external reluctance would have to be balanced by means of an equal and opposite current wrapped around the permanent magnet.

This current is related by the left-hand-screw rule to the magnetic flux Φ through the permanent magnet and may be regarded as the source of the demagnetization of the permanent magnet that is represented by the reluctance R' in Fig. 8.23. Thus a permanent magnet that is passing a magnetic flux Φ through an external reluctance R is demagnetized to the same extent as would occur if the magnet were on closed circuit and the circuit were threaded by a current I given by

$$I = -R\Phi \tag{8.69}$$

This current I must thread the magnetic circuit in the direction related by the right-hand-screw rule to the direction of the magnetic flux Φ passing round the circuit. The current I given by Eq. (8.69) is called the equivalent demagnetization current of the magnet when connected across an external reluctance R.

The truth of Eq. (8.69) does not depend upon the linear relation (8.66) between Φ and I and therefore does not depend upon the approximation (8.6) for ferromagnetic material producing a permanent magnetic flux. The concept of the equivalent demagnetization current expressed by Eq. (8.69) is therefore particularly useful when the nonlinear nature of the demagnetization curve PD in Fig. 8.3 must be taken into account.

Let the permanent magnet illustrated in Fig. 8.31 have a normal cross-sectional area S and a length s. Let the magnetic flux density within the permanent magnet be B, so that

$$BS = \Phi \tag{8.70}$$

Suppose that the demagnetization of the permanent magnet produced by the external reluctance R were instead produced by a demagnetization current I given by Eq. (8.69) applied to the magnet on closed circuit as indicated in Fig. 8.26. Let the demagnetization current be applied to the magnet uniformly over its surface and let the current per unit length be H. The total demagnetization current is then Hs, and Eq. (8.69) can be written as

$$Hs = -R\Phi \tag{8.71}$$

Neither Eq. (8.70) nor (8.71) depends upon the linear approximation (8.6) to the demagnetization curve of the magnet. Equations (8.70) and (8.71) can therefore be used in connection with an actual nonlinear demagnetization curve PD of the type illustrated in Fig. 8.3.

Let us suppose that the demagnetization curve for the ferromagnetic material of which the permanent magnet is manufactured is available and is as shown in Fig. 8.32. The relation between B and H represented by the curve PD shown in Fig. 8.32, together with Eqs. (8.70) and (8.71), constitute three relations to determine the magnetic flux Φ round the magnetic circuit, the magnetic flux density B in the magnet, and the equivalent demagnetization current H per unit length. These three quantities may be conveniently determined as follows: Between Eqs. (8.70) and (8.71) eliminate Φ, thereby obtaining

$$B = - \frac{s}{RS} H \qquad (8.72)$$

This relation between B and H can be represented in Fig. 8.32 by the dashed straight line through the origin.   The point Q where this straight line intersects the demagnetization curve PD then gives the required values of H and B, and the corresponding value of Φ is then given by Eq. (8.70).   The value of B corresponding to the point Q is therefore the magnetic flux density through the magnet when connected across an external reluctance R. If the resulting demagnetization of the magnet were produced by forming the magnet into a closed magnetic circuit and applying a current uniformly round its curved surface, the current per unit length would be the value of H corresponding to the point Q.

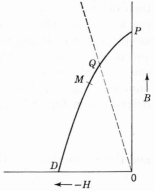

FIG. 8.32. Illustrating use of the demagnetization curve of a magnet.

The position of the point Q on the demagnetization curve in Fig. 8.32 is determined by the slope of the dashed straight line, and this is given by the coefficient of H on the right-hand side of Eq. (8.72).   If the length s of the permanent magnet is large and its normal cross section S is small, the point Q is close to the point P.   It is in these circumstances that the linear approximation represented by Eq. (8.6) is applicable.   On the other hand, for short thick magnets, the point Q is close to the point D, and the linear approximation represented by Eq. (8.6) is inapplicable. We also see from the coefficient of H on the right-hand side of Eq. (8.72) that the position of the point Q depends upon the magnitude of the external reluctance R.   For external reluctances of small value the point Q in Fig. 8.32 is near the point P, and the linear approximation represented by Eq. (8.6) is applicable.   On the other hand, for large values of R the point Q is near the point D, and the linear approximation (8.6) is inapplicable.

When designing a permanent magnet to pass a given magnetic flux Φ through a given external reluctance R, it is necessary to decide upon a normal cross-sectional area S for the magnet and a length s.   One of the considerations that enters into the design is a desire to make the volume

Ss of the permanent magnet as small as possible. By multiplying together Eqs. (8.70) and (8.71) we obtain

$$(-BH)(Ss) = R\Phi^2 \tag{8.73}$$

If the values of the external reluctance R and the magnetic flux Φ through it are specified, the right-hand side of Eq. (8.73) is specified. To minimize the volume Ss of the magnet it is therefore necessary to maximize the product $-BH$. Along the demagnetization curve PD in Fig. 8.32, H vanishes at the point P and B vanishes at the point D. As we move along the demagnetization curve from the point P to the point D, the product $-BH$ rises from zero to a maximum value at a point M and then decreases to zero again at the point D. Let us suppose that the point M has been located and that its coordinates are $(-H_M, B_M)$. These are the values of H and B that maximize the product $-BH$ in Eq. (8.73) and therefore minimize the volume Ss of the magnet for given values of the external reluctance R and of the magnetic flux Φ through it. For minimum volume, therefore, the appropriate cross-sectional area of the magnet, from Eq. (8.70), is

$$S = \frac{\Phi}{B_M} \tag{8.74}$$

and the appropriate length of the magnet, from Eq. (8.71), is

$$s = \frac{R\Phi}{H_M} \tag{8.75}$$

Suppose, for example, that the value of the external reluctance is controlled by an air gap of small width s_g and cross-sectional area S_g and that it is required to produce in the gap a magnetic flux density B_g. Then the appropriate value for the external reluctance is

$$R = \frac{s_g}{\mu_v S_g} \tag{8.76}$$

and for the magnetic flux through it is

$$\Phi = B_g S_g \tag{8.77}$$

Substituting these values for R and Φ into Eqs. (8.74) and (8.75) we obtain for the cross-sectional area and length of the permanent magnet of minimum volume

$$S = \frac{B_g}{B_M} S_g \tag{8.78}$$

$$s = \frac{B_g}{\mu_v H_M} s_g \tag{8.79}$$

A typical value for B_M is 1 weber/m², and a typical value for H_M is

40,000 amp/m.   If the magnetic flux density B_g to be produced in the gap is 1 weber/m², then it follows from Eq. (8.78) that the cross-sectional area of the magnet should be the same as that of the gap.   It further follows from Eq. (8.79) that the length of the magnet should be about 20 times the width of the gap.   It should be mentioned that Eqs. (8.78) and (8.79) are satisfactory estimates of the cross-sectional area and length of the permanent magnet of minimum volume only if the magnetic flux density B_g to be produced in the gap is of the same order of magnitude as B_M.   If this is not true, leakage from the magnetic circuit is important, and the accuracy of the equations is affected.

8.17. Application of the Concept of Magnetic Circuits to Any Magnetic Field.   The concept of a magnetic circuit as it has been developed in this chapter has involved the use of ferromagnetic material to channel the magnetic flux.   The accuracy of the methods involved depends upon the extent to which leakage of magnetic flux from the magnetic circuits is avoided.   It is, however, possible in principle to avoid leakage of magnetic flux completely.   Moreover it is not in principle necessary to use ferromagnetic material in order that the magnetic flux be channeled. Any magnetic field whatever can be divided into tubes of magnetic flux as described in Chaps. 2 to 4.   Moreover tubes of magnetic flux are always closed tubes carrying the same magnetic flux at all cross sections. Any tube of magnetic flux in any magnetic field therefore constitutes a magnetic circuit completely free of leakage.   The aggregate of tubes of magnetic flux constituting any magnetic field may therefore be regarded as an aggregate of ideal magnetic circuits.   The approximate methods used in this chapter are based upon the assumption that a ferromagnetic circuit constitutes a tube of magnetic flux and that tubes of magnetic flux outside the ferromagnetic material can be neglected.

SUMMARIZING EXERCISES

8.1. Describe the magnetization properties of ferromagnetic material, explaining what is meant by saturation and by hysteresis.

8.2. Explain the circumstances under which the magnetic flux density in ferromagnetic material may be regarded as proportional to the magnetic field strength. Mention typical numerical values for the permeability of ferromagnetic material.

8.3. Explain what is meant by a magnetic circuit of soft iron, describing the circumstances under which leakage of magnetic flux is likely to be small.

8.4. Explain what is meant by the reluctance of a magnetic circuit.   A magnetic circuit has length s and uniform cross-sectional area S.   The inductivity of the soft iron is μ, and leakage of magnetic flux from the magnetic circuit can be neglected. Calculate the reluctance of the magnetic circuit.

8.5. A magnetic circuit of soft iron has reluctance R, and leakage can be neglected. Prove that the inductance of a closed loop of wire threading the magnetic circuit is $1/R$.   Deduce the inductance of an n-turn coil wound on the magnetic circuit, and explain why the distribution of the turns round the magnetic circuit is comparatively unimportant.

8.6. If a magnetic circuit is composed of several sections of reluctances R_1, R_2, . . . , R_n connected in series, show that the reluctance of the complete circuit is $R_1 + R_2 + \cdots + R_n$, provided that leakage can be neglected. Prove also that, if the sections were connected in parallel, they could be used as a single reluctance of magnitude R, where $1/R$ is equal to the sum of the reciprocals of the reluctances of the individual sections.

8.7. A magnetic circuit has a gap of width w cut normally across it at a point where the cross-sectional area of the circuit is S. Explain under what circumstances the reluctance of the gap can be taken as $w/\mu_v S$, where μ_v is the vacuum inductivity. If the remainder of the magnetic circuit has length s, uniform cross-sectional area S, and inductivity μ, calculate the reluctance of the complete circuit including the gap. Describe the circumstances in which the reluctance of the complete circuit is given approximately by the reluctance of the gap.

8.8. Explain and justify Kirchhoff's laws for a magnetic network. Describe the parallelism that exists between electric and magnetic circuits. Explain the respect in which magnetic scalar potential behaves differently from electric potential.

8.9. Sketch the magnetic circuit of a rotating electrical machine having a circular armature concentric with a circular yoke to which are attached p pole pieces each carrying a field coil having n turns. The gaps between the pole faces and the armature are of width w, and the reluctance of the iron is negligible compared with that of the gaps. A steady current I flows in the wire of each field coil, the currents in adjacent coils being opposite in direction. Calculate the magnetic flux density in the gaps, neglecting fringing.

8.10. In terms of the phenomenon of magnetic hysteresis explain what is meant by a permanent magnet.

8.11. Explain to what extent a permanent magnet may be regarded as a source of magnetic flux in parallel with an internal reluctance. Describe how to estimate the strength of the source of flux and the magnitude of the internal reluctance.

8.12. Across the pole faces of a permanent magnet there exists a reluctance of magnitude R. Explain what is meant by the statement that the reluctance R partially demagnetizes the magnet, and define the equivalent demagnetizing current. If the permanent magnet is to produce through the reluctance R a given amount of magnetic flux, explain how to minimize the volume of the permanent magnet.

CHAPTER 9

TRANSFORMERS

9.1. Introduction. In mechanics considerable importance attaches to arrangements, such as gears, chains, etc., for coupling rotating spindles. There is a similar necessity in electrical science for coupling the motion of electrons round pairs of electric circuits. One of the means by which such coupling is achieved is known as a transformer.

9.2. Transformer with Negligible Magnetic Leakage. Consider a magnetic circuit of soft iron upon which are wound two electric circuits, one having n_1 turns and the other n_2 turns, as shown in Fig. 9.1. Let a current I_1 flow through one electric circuit and a current I_2 through the other electric circuit, and let Φ be the resulting magnetic flux passing round the magnetic circuit. Let the positive directions of the currents

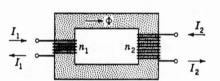

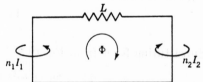

FIG. 9.1. An iron-core transformer. FIG. 9.2. Magnetic-circuit diagram for an iron-core transformer neglecting leakage.

I_1 and I_2 be defined so that they are related by the right-hand-screw rule to the positive direction of the magnetic flux Φ round the magnetic circuit. The magnetic-circuit diagram corresponding to the arrangement illustrated in Fig. 9.1 is shown in Fig. 9.2. It will be convenient to work in terms, not of the reluctance R of the magnetic circuit, but in terms of its reciprocal. This is the inductance L of the magnetic circuit defined by Eq. (8.14). As described in Sec. 8.6, this is the inductance of a one-turn loop of wire threading the magnetic circuit. An n-turn coil threading the magnetic circuit therefore has inductance n^2L. The coil on the left in Fig. 9.1 consequently has an inductance $n_1{}^2L$, and the coil on the right an inductance $n_2{}^2L$. The situation illustrated in Fig. 9.1 is one in which the magnetic flux threading one electric circuit also threads another. This involves what is known as magnetic coupling between the two electric circuits, and it is this magnetic coupling that we wish to study.

From Fig. 9.2 we see that the total current threading the magnetic circuit is

$$I = n_1 I_1 + n_2 I_2 \tag{9.1}$$

From Eq. (8.13) the relation between this current and the magnetic flux passing round the magnetic circuit is

$$\Phi = LI \tag{9.2}$$

Substituting for I from Eq. (9.1) into Eq. (9.2) we see that the expression for the magnetic flux Φ passing round the magnetic circuit in terms of the currents I_1 and I_2 flowing in the electric circuits is

$$\Phi = L(n_1 I_1 + n_2 I_2) \tag{9.3}$$

Let Φ_1 be the magnetic flux threading electric circuit 1 and Φ_2 be that threading electric circuit 2. Let the fluxes Φ_1 and Φ_2 thread the circuits in the directions related by the right-hand-screw rule to the directions of the currents I_1 and I_2. Φ_1 and Φ_2 are the magnetic fluxes crossing surfaces spanning the two electric circuits. As described in connection with Fig. 5.12, these surfaces may be taken respectively as n_1 and n_2 normal cross sections of the magnetic circuit. In terms of the magnetic flux Φ passing round the magnetic circuit, therefore, the magnetic fluxes threading the two electric circuits are

$$\Phi_1 = n_1 \Phi \tag{9.4}$$
$$\Phi_2 = n_2 \Phi \tag{9.5}$$

Substituting for Φ from Eq. (9.3) into Eqs. (9.4) and (9.5) we derive

$$\Phi_1 = n_1{}^2 L I_1 + n_1 n_2 L I_2 \tag{9.6}$$
$$\Phi_2 = n_1 n_2 L I_1 + n_2{}^2 L I_2 \tag{9.7}$$

These two equations can be written in the form

$$\Phi_1 = L_{11} I_1 + L_{12} I_2 \tag{9.8}$$
$$\Phi_2 = L_{21} I_1 + L_{22} I_2 \tag{9.9}$$
where
$$L_{11} = n_1{}^2 L \tag{9.10}$$
$$L_{22} = n_2{}^2 L \tag{9.11}$$
$$L_{12} = L_{21} = n_1 n_2 L \tag{9.12}$$

Equation (9.8) shows that the magnetic flux Φ_1 threading electric circuit 1 depends not only upon the current I_1 flowing in electric circuit 1 but also upon the current I_2 flowing in electric circuit 2. Likewise Eq. (9.9) shows that the magnetic flux Φ_2 threading electric circuit 2 depends not only upon the current I_2 in electric circuit 2 but also upon the current I_1 in electric circuit 1.

The coefficient L_{11} given by Eq. (9.10) is the inductance of electric circuit 1, and the first term of the right-hand side of Eq. (9.8) is the magnetic flux threading electric circuit 1 due to the current I_1 round electric circuit 1. Likewise the coefficient L_{22} given by Eq. (9.11) is the inductance of electric circuit 2, and the second term in Eq. (9.9) is the magnetic flux through electric circuit 2 due to the current I_2 in electric circuit 2. The second term in Eq. (9.8) is the magnetic flux through electric circuit 1 due to the current I_2 in electric circuit 2. This contribution to the magnetic flux through electric circuit 1 is proportional to the current I_2 in electric circuit 2; from Eq. (9.12) it is also proportional to the number n_1 of times that electric circuit 1 threads the magnetic circuit, to the number n_2 of times that electric circuit 2 threads the magnetic circuit, and to the inductance L of the magnetic circuit. Likewise the first term on the right-hand side of Eq. (9.9) represents the magnetic flux threading electric circuit 2 due to the current I_1 in electric circuit 1. This magnetic flux through electric circuit 2 is proportional to the current I_1 in electric circuit 1; from Eq. (9.12) it is also proportional to the number n_1 of times that electric circuit 1 threads the magnetic circuit, to the number n_2 of times that electric circuit 2 threads the magnetic circuit, and to the inductance L of the magnetic circuit. It is the presence of the second term on the right-hand side of Eq. (9.8) and the first term on the right-hand side of Eq. (9.9) that describes the magnetic coupling between the two electric circuits. This magnetic coupling is expressed by means of the coefficients L_{12} and L_{21}. In accordance with Eq. (9.12) these two coefficients are equal, and their common value is known as the coefficient of mutual inductance of the two electric circuits. The coefficients L_{11} and L_{22} are known as the coefficients of self-inductance of electric circuit 1 and electric circuit 2 respectively. The four coefficients L_{11}, L_{22}, L_{21}, and L_{21} are known as the coefficients of inductance of the pair of electric circuits.

If in Eqs. (9.8) and (9.9) we put

$$I_1 = 1 \qquad I_2 = 0 \tag{9.13}$$

it follows that

$$\Phi_1 = L_{11} \qquad \Phi_2 = L_{21} \tag{9.14}$$

Likewise if in Eqs. (9.8) and (9.9) we put

$$I_1 = 0 \qquad I_2 = 1 \tag{9.15}$$

it follows that

$$\Phi_1 = L_{12} \qquad \Phi_2 = L_{22} \tag{9.16}$$

Thus the coefficient of self-inductance L_{11} is numerically equal to the magnetic flux through electric circuit 1 when there is a unit current in electric circuit 1 and no current in electric circuit 2. Likewise the coefficient of self-inductance L_{22} is numerically equal to the magnetic flux through electric circuit 2 when there is a unit current in electric circuit 2 and no current in electric circuit 1.   The coefficient L_{12} is numerically equal to the magnetic flux through electric circuit 1 when there is a unit current in electric circuit 2 and no current in electric circuit 1.   This is identical in value with L_{21}, which is the magnetic flux through electric circuit 2 when there is unit current in electric circuit 1 and no current round electric circuit 2.   The equality of the coefficients L_{12} and L_{21} constitutes Green's reciprocal theorem for a transformer.   In words it states that the magnetic flux threading electric circuit 1 due to unit current in electric circuit 2, there being no current in electric current 1, is the same as the magnetic flux threading electric circuit 2 due to unit current in electric circuit 1, there being no current in electric circuit 2. In all these statements it is assumed that the relation between magnetic flux and electric current satisfies the right-hand-screw rule.

Equation (8.14) for the inductance L of the ferromagnetic circuit is based on the linear relation between magnetic flux density and magnetic field strength given in Eq. (8.5).   As described in Sec. 8.2, ferromagnetic material behaves in a linear manner only under certain restrictions. Subject to these restrictions, Eqs. (9.8) and (9.9) illustrate the applicability to magnetic flux of the principle of superposition.   The terms in the first column of the right-hand sides of Eqs. (9.8) and (9.9) are the magnetic fluxes through the two electric circuits of the transformer when there is a current I_1 in electric circuit 1 and no current in electric circuit 2. The terms in the second column on the right-hand sides of Eqs. (9.8) and (9.9) are the magnetic fluxes through the two electric circuits of the transformer when there is a current I_2 in electric circuit 2 and no current in electric circuit 1.   Equations (9.8) and (9.9) demonstrate the fact that, by superposing these two situations, we obtain the magnetic fluxes through the two electric circuits when there is simultaneously a current I_1 in electric circuit 1 and a current I_2 in electric circuit 2.

The transformer illustrated in Fig. 9.1 is idealized in the sense that all the magnetic flux threading either coil also threads the other.   This follows from the assumption of no leakage of magnetic flux from the magnetic circuit.   As a result of this assumption, the magnetic fluxes Φ_1 and Φ_2 threading the two electric circuits are respectively n_1 and n_2 times the same flux Φ, as described by Eqs. (9.4) and (9.5).   By dividing Eq. (9.5) by Eq. (9.4) we obtain

$$\frac{\Phi_2}{\Phi_1} = \frac{n_2}{n_1} \tag{9.17}$$

The assumption of no leakage of magnetic flux results, therefore, in a situation in which the magnetic fluxes threading the two electric circuits are in the ratio of the number of turns on the coils, regardless of the currents flowing in the electric circuits.   An idealized transformer is thus a device that keeps the magnetic fluxes threading the two electric circuits in a constant ratio.

9.3. Idealized Transformer with Multiple Windings. Suppose that an idealized transformer whose magnetic circuit has inductance L possesses a number of windings as indicated in Fig. 9.3. Let the numbers of turns upon the various windings be $n_1, n_2, n_3, \ldots$ Let the currents flowing through these windings be $I_1, I_2, I_3, \ldots$ respectively and let the resulting magnetic flux round the magnetic circuit be Φ. Let the currents $I_1, I_2, I_3, \ldots$ be related by the right-hand-screw rule to the direction of the magnetic flux Φ round the magnetic circuit. The total current threading the magnetic circuit is then

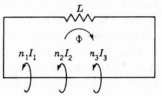

Fig. 9.3. Idealized transformer with multiple windings.

$$I = n_1 I_1 + n_2 I_2 + n_3 I_3 + \cdots \tag{9.18}$$

and substituting this value of I into Eq. (9.2) we obtain

$$\Phi = L(n_1 I_1 + n_2 I_2 + n_3 I_3 + \cdots) \tag{9.19}$$

The magnetic fluxes through the various electric circuits are

$$\begin{aligned} \Phi_1 &= n_1 \Phi \\ \Phi_2 &= n_2 \Phi \\ \Phi_3 &= n_3 \Phi \\ &\cdots\cdots \end{aligned} \tag{9.20}$$

and substitution into these equations for Φ from Eq. (9.19) gives

$$\begin{aligned} \Phi_1 &= L_{11} I_1 + L_{12} I_2 + L_{13} I_3 + \cdots \\ \Phi_2 &= L_{21} I_1 + L_{22} I_2 + L_{23} I_3 + \cdots \\ \Phi_3 &= L_{31} I_1 + L_{32} I_2 + L_{33} I_3 + \cdots \\ &\cdots\cdots\cdots\cdots\cdots \end{aligned} \tag{9.21}$$

where
$$\begin{aligned} L_{11} &= n_1{}^2 L & L_{12} &= n_1 n_2 L & L_{13} &= n_1 n_3 L \\ L_{21} &= n_2 n_1 L & L_{22} &= n_2{}^2 L & L_{23} &= n_2 n_3 L \\ L_{31} &= n_3 n_1 L & L_{32} &= n_3 n_2 L & L_{33} &= n_3{}^2 L \\ &\cdots\cdots\cdots\cdots\cdots\cdots\cdots\cdots \end{aligned} \tag{9.22}$$

The coefficient L_{11} is the inductance of winding 1 when no current flows in the other windings, and similar statements are true of the coefficients $L_{22}, L_{33}, \ldots$ These coefficients are known as the coefficients of self-inductance of the windings, and the remaining coefficients are known as the coefficients of mutual inductance. The coefficient L_{rs} is the magnetic flux threading electric circuit r when unit current flows round electric circuit s and there are no currents in the other windings. The coefficients of mutual inductance are such that

$$L_{rs} = L_{sr} \qquad (9.23)$$

Hence the magnetic flux threading electric circuit r due to unit current round electric circuit s, there being no current round the other circuits, is equal to the magnetic flux threading electric circuit s due to unit current in electric circuit r, there being no current in the other circuits.

Equations (9.20) show that multiple windings upon a magnetic circuit for which leakage of magnetic flux can be neglected produce a situation in which the magnetic fluxes threading the various electric circuits are maintained in the ratios of the number of times that the various electric circuits thread the magnetic circuit.

9.4. Transformer with Leakage of Magnetic Flux. In a practical transformer of the type illustrated in Fig. 9.1 some of the tubes of magnetic flux threading one coil complete their circuits between the coils

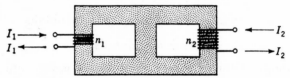

FIG. 9.4. A two-mesh magnetic circuit used as a transformer with leakage.

instead of through the other coil. Calculation of this leakage of magnetic flux is difficult, although its effect can be measured. Another situation involving leakage occurs with a transformer such as that shown in Fig. 9.4. Figure 9.4 illustrates a two-mesh magnetic network in which an n_1-turn coil threads one mesh and an n_2-turn coil threads the other mesh. In this situation, even if we neglect leakage of magnetic flux from the soft iron, part of the magnetic flux threading one coil fails to thread the other because it passes through the central arm of the magnetic network.

Let R_1 be the reluctance of the portion of the magnetic network to the left of the central arm. Let R_2 be the reluctance of the portion of the magnetic network to the right of the central arm. Let R_3 be the reluctance of the central arm. Let I_1 be the electric current flowing through the n_1-turn coil threading the left-hand mesh of the magnetic network, and let I_2 be the current flowing through the n_2-turn coil threading the right-hand mesh of the magnetic network. The total electric current threading the left-hand mesh of the magnetic network is then n_1I_1, and the total electric current threading the right-hand mesh of the magnetic network is n_2I_2. Let Φ_1 be the magnetic flux threading the n_1-turn electric circuit in the direction related by the right-hand-screw rule to the direction of the current I_1 round this circuit. The magnetic flux threading one turn of this electric circuit is then Φ_1/n_1, and this is therefore the magnetic flux passing round the left-hand mesh of the magnetic network. Let Φ_2 be the magnetic flux threading the n_2-turn electric circuit in the direction related by the right-hand-screw rule to the direction of the current I_2 round this circuit. The magnetic flux threading one turn of this circuit is then Φ_2/n_2, and this is therefore the magnetic flux passing round the right-hand mesh of the magnetic network. Let the positive directions of the currents I_1 and I_2 in the two electric circuits be chosen so that the mesh fluxes Φ_1/n_1 and Φ_2/n_2 round the meshes of the magnetic network pass through the common reluctance R_3 in opposite directions. The circuit diagram for the magnetic network is then as shown in Fig. 9.5.

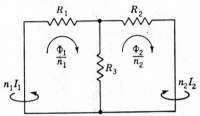

FIG. 9.5. Magnetic-circuit diagram for the arrangement shown in Fig. 9.4.

Application of Kirchhoff's circulation law to the left-hand mesh of the magnetic network shown in Fig. 9.5 gives

$$R_1 \frac{\Phi_1}{n_1} + R_3 \left(\frac{\Phi_1}{n_1} - \frac{\Phi_2}{n_2} \right) = n_1 I_1 \qquad (9.24)$$

and for the right-hand mesh we obtain in the same way

$$R_2 \frac{\Phi_2}{n_2} + R_3 \left(\frac{\Phi_2}{n_2} - \frac{\Phi_1}{n_1} \right) = n_2 I_2 \qquad (9.25)$$

Equations (9.24) and (9.25) can be rearranged in the form

$$I_1 = \frac{R_1 + R_3}{n_1{}^2} \Phi_1 - \frac{R_3}{n_1 n_2} \Phi_2 \qquad (9.26)$$

$$I_2 = - \frac{R_3}{n_1 n_2} \Phi_1 + \frac{R_2 + R_3}{n_2{}^2} \Phi_2 \qquad (9.27)$$

If these two equations are solved for Φ_1 and Φ_2 in terms of I_1 and I_2, we obtain

$$\Phi_1 = \frac{1}{R_2 R_3 + R_3 R_1 + R_1 R_2} [n_1{}^2 (R_2 + R_3) I_1 + n_1 n_2 R_3 I_2] \qquad (9.28)$$

$$\Phi_2 = \frac{1}{R_2 R_3 + R_3 R_1 + R_1 R_2} [n_1 n_2 R_3 I_1 + n_2{}^2 (R_1 + R_3)] \qquad (9.29)$$

Equations (9.28) and (9.29) can be written in the form of Eqs. (9.8) and (9.9) provided that

$$L_{11} = n_1{}^2 \frac{R_2 + R_3}{R_2 R_3 + R_3 R_1 + R_1 R_2} \tag{9.30}$$

$$L_{22} = n_2{}^2 \frac{R_1 + R_3}{R_2 R_3 + R_3 R_1 + R_1 R_2} \tag{9.31}$$

$$L_{12} = L_{21} = n_1 n_2 \frac{R_3}{R_2 R_3 + R_3 R_1 + R_1 R_2} \tag{9.32}$$

This calculation illustrates the fact that, provided that nonlinear behavior of ferromagnetic material is avoided, any two magnetically coupled electric circuits are such that the magnetic fluxes Φ_1 and Φ_2 through them are related to the currents I_1 and I_2 round them by linear equations of the forms (9.8) and (9.9).

For the arrangement shown in Fig. 9.4 the coefficients of self-inductance are given by Eqs. (9.30) and (9.31). In accordance with Eq. (9.8), Eq. (9.30) gives the ratio of the magnetic flux threading electric circuit 1 to the current in electric circuit 1 when there is no current in electric circuit 2. In other words the right-hand side of Eq. (9.30) is the inductance of coil 1 in Fig. 9.4 when coil 2 is on open circuit. In the same way Eq. (9.31) gives the inductance of coil 2 in Fig. 9.4 when coil 1 is on open circuit, while Eq. (9.32) gives the coefficient of mutual inductance for the two coils. We notice that the values of L_{12} and L_{21} are equal, so that the magnetic flux threading either electric circuit due to unit current in the other is the same.

If the value of the reluctance R_3 in Fig. 9.5 becomes indefinitely large, the transformer illustrated in Fig. 9.4 reverts to one of the type illustrated in Fig. 9.1. In these circumstances the terms in the numerators and denominators of Eqs. (9.30) to (9.32) not involving R_3 can be omitted, and these equations reduce to

$$L_{11} = \frac{n_1{}^2}{R_1 + R_2} \tag{9.33}$$

$$L_{22} = \frac{n_2{}^2}{R_1 + R_2} \tag{9.34}$$

$$L_{12} = L_{21} = \frac{n_1 n_2}{R_1 + R_2} \tag{9.35}$$

When the reluctance R_3 in Fig. 9.5 is made indefinitely large, the single magnetic circuit thereby formed has a total reluctance $R_1 + R_2$ and therefore an inductance equal to the reciprocal of $R_1 + R_2$. Equations (9.33) to (9.35) therefore convey the same information as Eqs. (9.10) to (9.12).

The presence of the reluctance R_3 in Fig. 9.5 reduces the magnetic coupling between the two coils, and it is convenient to introduce a coupling coefficient k to describe this fact. From Eqs. (9.10) to (9.12) it will be seen that the coefficient of mutual inductance L_{12} or L_{21} is equal to the geometric mean of the coefficients of self-inductance L_{11} and L_{22}. Introduction of the central arm in the transformer shown in Fig. 9.4 results in the coefficient of mutual inductance between the coils being less than the geometric mean of their coefficients of self-inductance. A convenient definition for the coupling coefficient k between the coils of a transformer is therefore

$$k = \frac{L_{12}}{(L_{11}L_{12})^{1/2}} = \frac{L_{21}}{(L_{11}L_{22})^{1/2}} \tag{9.36}$$

For an idealized transformer this coupling coefficient is unity in accordance with Eqs. (9.10) to (9.12) or alternatively in accordance with Eqs. (9.33) to (9.35). If there is no magnetic coupling between the coils, then L_{12} and L_{21} vanish, and therefore the coupling coefficient k defined by Eqs. (9.36) is zero. Thus, as we pass from a situation involving no magnetic coupling between the coils to a situation involving perfect magnetic coupling between the coils, the coupling coefficient k defined by Eqs. (9.36) varies from zero to unity. For the arrangement shown in Fig. 9.4, the coupling coefficient is calculated by substituting into Eqs. (9.36) the values of the coefficients of inductance given by Eqs. (9.30) to (9.32). The result is

$$k = \frac{R_3}{[(R_1 + R_3)(R_2 + R_3)]^{1/2}} \tag{9.37}$$

We notice that this coupling coefficient is independent of the number of turns on either coil. The coupling coefficient depends only upon the geometry of the magnetic network.

9.5. The Coefficients of Reluctance of a Transformer. Equations (9.8) and (9.9) employing the coefficients of inductance of a transformer are convenient in circumstances where it is the currents I_1 and I_2 in the electric circuits that are given and it is the magnetic fluxes Φ_1 and Φ_2 through the electric circuits that are to be calculated. Suppose, however, that it is the magnetic fluxes Φ_1 and Φ_2 through the electric circuits that are given and that it is the currents I_1 and I_2 in the electric circuits that are to be calculated. Then it is convenient to solve Eqs. (9.8) and (9.9) for I_1 and I_2, thereby obtaining

$$I_1 = R_{11}\Phi_1 + R_{12}\Phi_2 \tag{9.38}$$
$$I_2 = R_{21}\Phi_1 + R_{22}\Phi_2 \tag{9.39}$$

From the fact that

$$L_{12} = L_{21} \tag{9.40}$$

it follows that

$$R_{12} = R_{21} \tag{9.41}$$

The quantities R_{11} and R_{22} in Eqs. (9.38) and (9.39) may be called the coefficients of self-reluctance of the two coils, while the common value of R_{12} and R_{21} may be called the coefficient of mutual reluctance of the coils.   It should be noticed that the coefficients of reluctance for a transformer are not the reciprocals of the coefficients of inductance.   The coefficients of reluctance in Eqs. (9.38) and (9.39) must be obtained from the coefficients of inductance by algebraic solution of Eqs. (9.8) and (9.9) to obtain Eqs. (9.38) and (9.39).

The coefficients R_{11} and R_{21} are numerically equal to the currents round electric circuits 1 and 2 when there is a unit magnetic flux threading electric circuit 1 and no magnetic flux threading electric circuit 2.   In the same way the coefficients R_{12} and R_{22} are numerically equal to the currents round electric circuits 1 and 2 when there is a unit magnetic flux threading electric circuit 2 and no magnetic flux threading electric circuit 1.   Equation (9.41) states that the current in electric circuit 1 when there is a unit magnetic flux through electric circuit 2 and no magnetic flux through electric circuit 1 is the same as the current in electric circuit 2 when there is a unit magnetic flux through electric circuit 1 and no magnetic flux through electric circuit 2.   In all cases it is assumed that the relation between electric current and magnetic flux obeys the right-hand-screw rule.

Equations (9.26) and (9.27) are the Eqs. (9.38) and (9.39) for the arrangement shown in Fig. 9.4.   In this case therefore the coefficients of reluctance of the transformer are

$$R_{11} = \frac{R_1 + R_3}{n_1{}^2} \tag{9.42}$$

$$R_{22} = \frac{R_2 + R_3}{n_2{}^2} \tag{9.43}$$

$$R_{12} = R_{21} = -\frac{R_3}{n_1 n_2} \tag{9.44}$$

Notice that, provided that the currents round the two electric circuits are taken as positive when they are related by the right-hand-screw rule to the common magnetic flux threading both electric circuits, the coefficients of mutual reluctance of the coils are negative whereas the coefficients of mutual inductance are positive.   The coupling coefficient of the transformer, if expressed in terms of the coefficients of reluctance, is given by

$$k = -\frac{R_{12}}{(R_{11}R_{22})^{1/2}} = -\frac{R_{21}}{(R_{11}R_{22})^{1/2}} \tag{9.45}$$

This follows from the fact that substitution for the coefficients of reluctance from Eqs. (9.42) to (9.44) into Eqs. (9.45) gives Eq. (9.37).

The transformer indicated in Fig. 9.5 becomes a perfectly coupled transformer when the reluctance R_3 becomes indefinitely large, and we see from Eqs. (9.42) to (9.44) that this makes the coefficients of reluctance of the transformer indefinitely large. Hence the concept of coefficients of reluctance is not applicable to a perfectly coupled transformer. For an almost perfectly coupled transformer the value of R_3 in Eqs. (9.26) and (9.27) is large. This means that, in general, large currents I_1 and I_2 must flow around the electric circuits in order to produce specified magnetic fluxes Φ_1 and Φ_2 through the circuits. An exception to this statement occurs, however, if the pairs of terms on the right-hand sides of Eqs. (9.26) and (9.27) nearly cancel each other. This occurs when the specified magnetic fluxes Φ_1 and Φ_2 through the electric circuits satisfy, or nearly satisfy, the relation (9.17). As the reluctance R_3 tends to infinity, the currents I_1 and I_2 required to produce specified magnetic fluxes Φ_1 and Φ_2 tend to infinity unless the specified magnetic fluxes satisfy the relation (9.17). Thus for a perfectly coupled transformer finite currents through the windings are possible only if condition (9.17) is satisfied. If condition (9.17) is satisfied, then the prescribed values of Φ_1 and Φ_2 determine the magnetic flux Φ passing around the magnetic circuit in accordance with Eqs. (9.4) and (9.5). This determines in accordance with Eq. (9.3) the total current (9.1) threading the magnetic circuit, but the individual values of I_1 and I_2 are not determined. Thus the perfectly coupled transformer involves a peculiar situation in which the concept of coefficients of reluctance is inapplicable. Of course no transformer is perfectly coupled, and therefore, in practice, the coefficients of reluctance are always applicable. The inability to define coefficients of self- and mutual reluctance for a perfectly coupled transformer has made it customary to describe the properties of all transformers, whatever the degree of coupling, in terms of the coefficients of self- and mutual inductance. Nevertheless situations do occur in which it is simpler to use the coefficients of reluctance. For example, for the transformer shown in Fig. 9.4, the coefficients of reluctance given by Eqs. (9.42) to (9.44) are simpler than the coefficients of inductance given by Eqs. (9.30) to (9.32).

9.6. Any Number of Multiturn Coils Linked by a Magnetic Network.
Consider a magnetic network possessing a number of meshes labeled 1, 2, ... Suppose that there are electric currents threading the various meshes and that as a result there are magnetic fluxes passing round the various meshes. These mesh fluxes are related to the corresponding threading electric currents by Eqs. (8.45) in which the l coefficients are the coefficients of inductance of the magnetic network. Let us now suppose that mesh 1 of the magnetic network is threaded by an n_1-turn coil, each turn of which carries a current I_1. Let us assume likewise that mesh 2 of the magnetic network is threaded by an n_2-turn coil, each turn

of which carries a current I_2, and similarly for the other meshes of the magnetic network. Let the resulting magnetic flux threading electric circuit 1 be Φ_1, that threading electric circuit 2 be Φ_2, and so on. Then the total currents threading meshes 1, 2, . . . of the magnetic network are, respectively,

$$n_1 I_1, \ n_2 I_2, \ . \ . \ . \tag{9.46}$$

Moreover, the magnetic fluxes threading individual turns of electric circuits 1, 2, . . . are

$$\frac{\Phi_1}{n_1}, \frac{\Phi_2}{n_2}, \ . \ . \ . \tag{9.47}$$

and these are therefore the mesh fluxes round meshes 1, 2, . . . of the magnetic network. In all cases it is assumed that the positive directions of the magnetic fluxes and of the electric currents are related by the right-hand-screw rule. Application of Eqs. (8.45) to the mesh fluxes given by expressions (9.47) and the threading currents given by expressions (9.46) gives

$$\frac{\Phi_1}{n_1} = l_{11} n_1 I_1 + l_{12} n_2 I_2 + \ \cdot \ \cdot \ \cdot$$

$$\frac{\Phi_2}{n_2} = l_{21} n_2 I_1 + l_{22} n_2 I_2 + \ \cdot \ \cdot \ \cdot \tag{9.48}$$

$$. \ . \ . \ . \ . \ . \ . \ . \ . \ . \ . \ . \ . \ . \ .$$

These equations can be written in the form

$$\Phi_1 = L_{11} I_1 + L_{12} I_2 + \ \cdot \ \cdot \ \cdot$$

$$\Phi_2 = L_{21} I_1 + L_{22} I_2 + \ \cdot \ \cdot \ \cdot \tag{9.49}$$

$$. \ . \ . \ . \ . \ . \ . \ . \ . \ . \ . \ . \ . \ .$$

where
$$L_{11} = n_1{}^2 l_{11} \qquad L_{12} = n_1 n_2 l_{12} \qquad \cdot \ \cdot \ \cdot$$

$$L_{21} = n_1 n_2 l_{21} \qquad L_{22} = n_2{}^2 l_{22} \qquad \cdot \ \cdot \ \cdot \tag{9.50}$$

$$. \ . \ . \ . \ . \ . \ . \ . \ . \ . \ . \ . \ . \ . \ . \ . \ .$$

Equations (9.49) relate the magnetic fluxes threading electric circuits 1, 2, . . . with the electric currents flowing round these circuits and define the coefficients of inductance of the electric circuits. Equations (9.50) relate the coefficients of inductance of the electric circuits to the coefficients of inductance of the magnetic network. These equations show that the coefficients of inductance of the magnetic network are the coefficients of inductance of one-turn electric circuits threading the various meshes. From Eqs. (8.47) and (9.50) it follows that

$$L_{rs} = L_{sr} \tag{9.51}$$

Thus for any system of coils linked by a magnetic network of soft iron for which nonlinear effects are avoided, the magnetic flux threading electric circuit r due to unit current in electric circuit s, there being no current round the remaining circuits, is the same as the magnetic flux threading electric circuit s due to unit current round electric circuit r, there being no currents round the remaining circuits.

Instead of using the l coefficients of the magnetic network defined in Eqs. (8.45), we can use the r coefficients defined in Eqs. (8.44) to relate the mesh fluxes given by expressions (9.47) to the threading currents given by expressions (9.46). We then arrive at the equations

$$I_1 = R_{11}\Phi_1 + R_{12}\Phi_2 + \cdots$$
$$I_2 = R_{21}\Phi_1 + R_{22}\Phi_2 + \cdots \qquad (9.52)$$
$$\cdots \cdots \cdots \cdots \cdots \cdots$$

where
$$R_{11} = \frac{r_{11}}{n_1{}^2} \qquad R_{12} = \frac{r_{12}}{n_1 n_2} \qquad \cdots$$

$$R_{21} = \frac{r_{21}}{n_1 n_2} \qquad R_{22} = \frac{r_{22}}{n_2{}^2} \qquad \cdots \qquad (9.53)$$
$$\cdots \cdots \cdots \cdots \cdots \cdots \cdots \cdots \cdots$$

and
$$R_{mn} = R_{nm} \qquad (9.54)$$

Equations (9.52) define the coefficients of reluctance of electric circuits 1, 2, ... They are the equations that would be obtained by solving Eqs. (9.49) for I_1, I_2, ...

If more than one coil threads the same mesh of the magnetic network, the leakage flux between the coils can be used to subdivide the mesh into a pair of smaller meshes for each of which there is one threading coil. If desired, this leakage flux can be neglected when handling the coefficients of inductance of the coils but not when handling the coefficients of reluctance.

9.7. Coefficients of Inductance for a System of Inductors with No Ferromagnetic Network. Use of the coefficients of self- and mutual inductance for a system of coils does not depend upon the linkage of the coils by a ferromagnetic network. Absence of ferromagnetic material actually improves the linearity of the relationship between the currents through the coils and the magnetic fluxes threading them, since for soft iron the linear relation (8.5) is only an approximation. However, the absence of a magnetic network of soft iron threading the coils generally reduces the degree of magnetic coupling between them.

Let us suppose that we have a number of electric circuits numbered 1, 2, 3, . . . , some or all of which may be in the form of multiturn coils. Let the currents round the respective electric circuits be I_1, I_2, I_3, ... In the magnetic field of these currents let C be any closed geometrical curve, and let S be a surface spanning C. Let $d\mathbf{S}$ be a vector element of area of S at a point P. At P let the magnetic-flux-density vectors due to the various electric circuits be $\mathbf{B}_1$, $\mathbf{B}_2$, $\mathbf{B}_3$, ... Then, in accordance with Eq. (2.23), the resultant magnetic-flux-density vector $\mathbf{B}$ at P is

$$\mathbf{B} = \mathbf{B}_1 + \mathbf{B}_2 + \mathbf{B}_3 + \cdots \qquad (9.55)$$

If we multiply this equation scalarly by $d\mathbf{S}$ and integrate over the surface S spanning the closed curve C, we obtain

$$\int_S \mathbf{B} \cdot d\mathbf{S} = \int_S \mathbf{B}_1 \cdot d\mathbf{S} + \int_S \mathbf{B}_2 \cdot d\mathbf{S} + \int_S \mathbf{B}_3 \cdot d\mathbf{S} + \cdots \qquad (9.56)$$

This equation states that the magnetic flux threading any closed curve C due to the currents I_1, I_2, I_3, . . . round electric circuits 1, 2, 3, . . . is the algebraic sum of the magnetic fluxes threading the closed curve C due to the currents round the individual circuits. This is the principle of superposition for magnetic flux. In terms of this principle we can establish the coefficients of inductance for any system of electric circuits by allowing the rim C of the surface S to coincide with the various circuits in succession.

Consider a situation in which the currents round the circuits are

$$1, 0, 0, \ldots \qquad (9.57)$$

so that the current round circuit 1 is unity and round all the other circuits is zero. In these circumstances let the magnetic fluxes threading the circuits in the directions related by the right-hand-screw rule to the currents round them be

$$L_{11}, L_{21}, L_{31}, \ldots \qquad (9.58)$$

If alternatively the currents round the circuits are

$$0, 1, 0, \ldots \qquad (9.59)$$

let the magnetic fluxes threading the circuits be

$$L_{12}, L_{22}, L_{32}, \ldots \qquad (9.60)$$

In the same way if the currents round the circuits are

$$0, 0, 1, \ldots \qquad (9.61)$$

let the magnetic fluxes threading the circuits be

$$L_{31}, L_{32}, L_{33}, \ldots \qquad (9.62)$$

and so on. It follows from expressions (9.57) and (9.58) that if the currents round the circuits are

$$I_1, 0, 0, \ldots \qquad (9.63)$$

then the magnetic fluxes through the circuits are

$$L_{11}I_1, L_{21}I_1, L_{31}I_1, \ldots \qquad (9.64)$$

Likewise it follows from Eqs. (9.59) and (9.60) that if the currents round the circuits are

$$0, I_2, 0, \ldots \tag{9.65}$$

then the magnetic fluxes threading the circuits are

$$L_{12}I_2, L_{22}I_2, L_{32}I_2, \ldots \tag{9.66}$$

In the same way if the currents round the circuits are

$$0, 0, I_3, \ldots \tag{9.67}$$

then the magnetic fluxes through the circuits are

$$L_{13}I_3, L_{23}I_3, L_{33}I_3, \ldots \tag{9.68}$$

and so on. By addition of the corresponding magnetic fluxes in expressions (9.64), (9.66), (9.68), and so on, we obtain for the magnetic fluxes Φ_1, Φ_2, Φ_3, . . . through the electric circuits when the currents round them are I_1, I_2, I_3, . . . the equations

$$
\begin{aligned}
\Phi_1 &= L_{11}I_1 + L_{12}I_2 + L_{13}I_3 + \cdots \\
\Phi_2 &= L_{21}I_1 + L_{22}I_2 + L_{23}I_3 + \cdots \\
\Phi_3 &= L_{31}I_1 + L_{32}I_2 + L_{33}I_3 + \cdots \\
& \cdots\cdots\cdots\cdots\cdots\cdots\cdots\cdots\cdots
\end{aligned}
\tag{9.69}
$$

In the same way we may introduce coefficients of self- and mutual reluctance for any system of electric circuits. To produce through the electric circuits magnetic fluxes equal to

$$1, 0, 0, \ldots \tag{9.70}$$

let the currents required in the circuits be

$$R_{11}, R_{21}, R_{31}, \ldots \tag{9.71}$$

To produce through the electric circuits magnetic fluxes equal to

$$0, 1, 0, \ldots \tag{9.72}$$

let the currents required in the circuits be

$$R_{12}, R_{22}, R_{23}, \ldots \tag{9.73}$$

To produce through the electric circuits magnetic fluxes equal to

$$0, 0, 1, \ldots \tag{9.74}$$

let the currents required in the circuits be

$$R_{31}, R_{32}, R_{33}, \ldots \tag{9.75}$$

and so on. Then it follows by superposition that, to produce through the electric circuits magnetic fluxes equal to Φ_1, Φ_2, Φ_3, . . . the currents required round the circuits are

$$
\begin{aligned}
I_1 &= R_{11}\Phi_1 + R_{12}\Phi_2 + R_{13}\Phi_3 + \cdots \\
I_2 &= R_{21}\Phi_1 + R_{22}\Phi_2 + R_{23}\Phi_3 + \cdots \\
I_3 &= R_{31}\Phi_1 + R_{32}\Phi_2 + R_{33}\Phi_3 + \cdots
\end{aligned}
\tag{9.76}
$$

These equations are the ones obtained when Eqs. (9.69) are solved for $I_1, I_2, I_3, \ldots$. In all cases it is assumed that the fluxes threading electric circuits are related by the right-hand-screw rule to the currents round the electric circuits.

Comparison of Eqs. (9.69) with Eqs. (9.49) and of Eqs. (9.76) with Eqs. (9.52) shows that the coefficients of inductance and the coefficients of reluctance can be used for any system of electric circuits whether or not they are linked by a magnetic network.

Special importance attaches to the situation when there are only two electric circuits constituting a transformer. In this case Eqs. (9.69) reduce to Eqs. (9.8) and (9.9), while Eqs. (9.76) reduce to Eqs. (9.38) and (9.39). Even in the absence of a magnetic circuit, therefore, the behavior of a transformer is described by Eqs. (9.8) and (9.9), or alternatively by Eqs. (9.38) and (9.39). In terms of the coefficients in these equations we can define a coupling coefficient k, but in the absence of a magnetic circuit threading the two electric circuits the value of k is appreciably less than unity. For any transformer the coupling coefficient is defined by Eqs. (9.36) or equivalently by Eqs. (9.45).

It should be noticed that equality of the two expressions for the coupling coefficient in Eqs. (9.36) and of the two expressions for the coupling coefficient in Eqs. (9.45) depends upon the truth of Eqs. (9.40) and (9.41). Some discussion is, however, required to establish in the absence of a magnetic circuit the truth of Eqs. (9.40) and (9.41). Likewise for any system of coils Eqs. (9.51) and (9.54) are true, but their truth is more difficult to establish in the absence of a magnetic network coupling the coils. The procedure for establishing the truth of Eqs. (9.51) and (9.54) in the absence of a magnetic network is similar to that used for establishing the corresponding results in electrostatics for the coefficients of capacitance and elastance. An argument that is simple in principle is the following: In any magnetic field a tube of flux may be regarded as a magnetic circuit, and a complete magnetic field is an aggregate of tubes of magnetic flux. Hence any magnetic field may be regarded as constituting a complicated magnetic network. From this point of view the applicability of Eqs. (9.51) and (9.54) in the absence of a magnetic network is more or less obvious. As in electrostatics this argument may be stated more precisely in terms of Green's reciprocal theorem. Green's reciprocal theorem for a system of inductors will be discussed in Part 4, Sec. 8.4.

9.8. Calculation of the Coefficient of Mutual Inductance. In the absence of a ferromagnetic coupling circuit, calculation of the coefficient of mutual inductance between two electric circuits is liable to be difficult, although the value of the coefficient can usually be measured. There are, however, a number of simple situations in which the coefficients of mutual inductance can be satisfactorily calculated.

Let us calculate the coefficient of mutual inductance between two loops of wire whose linear dimensions are small compared with the distance r between them. The loops of wire may be of any shape. Let the areas of the loops be represented by vectors $\mathbf{S}_1$ and $\mathbf{S}_2$ as shown in Fig. 9.6. Let the loop of area S_1 be at the origin O and let that of area S_2 be at the point P. Let the vectors $\mathbf{S}_1$ and $\mathbf{S}_2$ be coplanar and make angles θ_1 and θ_2 with the direction OP as shown in Fig. 9.6. The point P may then be said to have polar coordinates (r,θ_1) with respect to the point O as origin. At the point P the radial direction is the direction from O to P, while

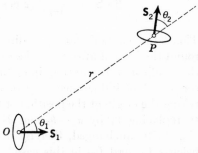

FIG. 9.6. Illustrating the calculation of the coefficient of mutual inductance between two loops of wire whose linear dimensions are small compared with the separation r between them.

the transverse direction is the direction in which the point P moves when θ_1 increases and r remains constant. The components of the vector area $\mathbf{S}_2$ in the radial and transverse directions at the point P are therefore given by

$$\mathbf{S}_2 = S_2(\cos \theta_2, \ \sin \theta_2) \tag{9.77}$$

To calculate the coefficient of mutual inductance between the two loops let us suppose that there flows round the loop of vector area $\mathbf{S}_1$ a unit current in the direction related by the right-hand-screw rule to the direction of the vector $\mathbf{S}_1$. This loop then produces at the point P a magnetic field for which the magnetic vector can be calculated by replacing I by unity and S by S_1 in Eqs. (7.32) and (7.33). The radial and transverse components of the magnetic vector at the point P due to unit current round the loop of area S_1 are therefore given by

$$\mathbf{H} = \frac{S_1}{4\pi r^3} (2 \cos \theta_1, \ \sin \theta_1) \tag{9.78}$$

If μ is the inductivity of the medium, it follows from Eq. (9.78) that the radial and transverse components of the magnetic-flux-density vector at the point P due to unit current round the loop of area S_1 are given by

$$\mathbf{B} = \frac{\mu S_1}{4\pi r^3} (2 \cos \theta_1, \sin \theta_1) \qquad (9.79)$$

The resulting magnetic flux threading the loop of area S_2 is obtained by taking the scalar product of the flux density vector given by Eq. (9.79) and the vector area given by Eq. (9.77). Evaluating this scalar product we obtain (see Part 3, Chap. 1, Prob. 3).

$$\mathbf{B} \cdot \mathbf{S}_2 = \frac{\mu S_1 S_2}{4\pi r^3} (2 \cos \theta_1 \cos \theta_2 + \sin \theta_1 \sin \theta_2) \qquad (9.80)$$

This is the magnetic flux threading the loop of area S_2 due to unit current round the loop of area S_1. The right-hand side of Eq. (9.80) is therefore the coefficient of mutual inductance L_{21} for the pair of loops. The coefficient of inductance L_{12} can be calculated by the same procedure, taking the origin at the position of the loop of area S_2. This is equivalent to replacing θ_1 by $\pi - \theta_2$ and θ_2 by $\pi - \theta_1$. This replacement leaves Eq. (9.80) unchanged, thereby demonstrating the equality of the coefficients L_{12} and L_{21} in this case. The coefficient of mutual inductance for the arrangement shown in Fig. 9.6 is therefore

$$L_{12} = L_{21} = \frac{\mu S_1 S_2}{4\pi r^3} (2 \cos \theta_1 \cos \theta_2 + \sin \theta_1 \sin \theta_2) \qquad (9.81)$$

If the loop of area S_1 possesses n_1 turns, the magnetic field that it produces is multiplied by n_1. Likewise if the electric circuit formed by the loop of area S_2 has n_2 turns, the magnetic flux threading this circuit is multiplied by n_2. In these circumstances the coefficient of mutual inductance given by Eq. (9.81) is replaced by

$$L_{12} = L_{21} = \frac{\mu n_1 n_2 S_1 S_2}{4\pi r^3} (2 \cos \theta_1 \cos \theta_2 + \sin \theta_1 \sin \theta_2) \qquad (9.82)$$

We notice that the coefficient of inductance of the coils is proportional to the inductivity of the medium and inversely proportional to the cube of the distance between them. It is also proportional to the product of the number of turns and the area of each coil, as well as depending upon the orientation of the coils. In the special case shown in Fig. 9.7 the vectors representing the areas of the loops are along the same line. For this case we have $\theta_1 = \theta_2 = 0$, and the coefficient of mutual inductance is

$$L_{12} = L_{21} = \frac{\mu n_1 n_2 S_1 S_2}{2\pi r^3} \qquad (9.83)$$

For the case shown in Fig. 9.8 the vectors representing the areas of the loops are perpendicular to the line joining them.   In this case we have $\theta_1 = \theta_2 = \frac{1}{2}\pi$, and the coefficient of mutual inductance is

$$L_{12} = L_{21} = \frac{\mu n_1 n_2 S_1 S_2}{4\pi r^3} \tag{9.84}$$

We notice from Eqs. (9.83) and (9.84) that the coefficient of mutual inductance in the case represented in Fig. 9.8 is one-half of that for the

FIG. 9.7. Illustrating the calculation of the coefficient of mutual inductance for two coaxial coils whose linear dimensions are small compared with their separation r.

FIG. 9.8. Illustrating the calculation of the coefficient of inductance of two coplanar coils whose linear dimensions are small compared with their separation r.

case represented in Fig. 9.7.   For the case illustrated in Fig. 9.9 the vectors representing the areas of the two coils are perpendicular, and one coil is located at a point on the line defined by the vector representing the area of the other.   In this case we have either $\theta_1 = 0$, $\theta_2 = \frac{1}{2}\pi$ or $\theta_1 = \frac{1}{2}\pi$, $\theta_2 = 0$.   In either case the coefficient of mutual inductance is zero in accordance with Eq. (9.82).   For circular loops it can easily be verified from Fig. 6.15 that the magnetic flux produced by a current in either coil in Fig. 9.9 threads no magnetic flux through the other.

Suppose that two coils each carrying 100 turns are arranged as shown in Fig. 9.7 in a medium for which the inductivity is substantially the same as that for a vacuum.   Let the area of each coil be 10 cm² (10^{-3} m²), and let the distance between the coils be 10 cm (10^{-1} m).   From Eq. (9.83) it follows that the coefficient of mutual inductance between the

FIG. 9.9. Illustrating a pair of coils for which the coefficient of mutual inductance is zero.

two coils evaluates to 2 μh.   This means that the magnetic flux threading either electric circuit due to 1 amp round the other is 2×10^{-6} weber.

Formulas (9.81) to (9.84) for the coefficient of mutual inductance of two electric circuits are based upon the assumption that the linear dimensions of these circuits are small compared with their distance apart. As an example of a situation in which the distance between the circuits need not be large compared with the linear dimensions of both, consider the arrangement shown in Fig. 9.10.   In Fig. 9.10 we have a circular loop of wire of radius a and center O.   The point P is located on the axis of the circle at a distance r from the wire.   At the point P there is a loop of wire whose linear dimensions are small compared with a but not necessarily small compared with the distance OP. The small loop need not be circular in shape. Let its area be represented by a vector $\mathbf{S}$ directed from O to P. Let the circular wire of radius a be electric circuit 1, and the small loop of area S be electric circuit 2. To calculate the coefficient of mutual inductance between the two circuits let there be a unit current in electric circuit 1 in the direction related by the right-hand-screw rule to the direction from O to P. If μ is the inductivity of the medium it follows from Eq. (6.53) that the magnetic flux density at P has magnitude

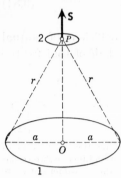

FIG. 9.10. Illustrating the calculation of the coefficient of mutual inductance between a small loop and a large circular loop in a parallel plane, the former loop being on the axis of the latter.

$$\frac{\mu a^2}{2r^3} \qquad (9.85)$$

and points in the direction from O to P. The magnetic flux threading electric circuit 2 is therefore

$$\frac{\mu a^2}{2r^3}S \qquad (9.86)$$

This is the magnetic flux threading electric circuit 2 due to unit current round electric circuit 1 and is therefore the coefficient of inductance L_{21}. Since the coefficients L_{21} and L_{12} are always equal, it follows that the coefficient of mutual inductance of the two circuits shown in Fig. 9.10 is

$$L_{12} = L_{21} = \frac{\mu a^2 S}{2r^3} \qquad (9.87)$$

If electric circuit 1 carries n_1 turns and electric circuit 2 carries n_2 turns, Eq. (9.87) is replaced by

$$L_{12} = L_{21} = \frac{\mu n_1 n_2 a^2 S}{2r^3} \qquad (9.88)$$

If the distance r in Fig. 9.10 is large compared with the radius a of electric current 1, the coefficient of mutual inductance of the arrangement can be calculated from Eq. (9.83). Putting $S_1 = \pi a^2$ and $S_2 = S$ in Eq. (9.83) we verify Eq. (9.88). Equation (9.88) is, however, applicable even when r in Fig. 9.10 is not large compared with a. Suppose, for example, that the electric circuit 2 is located at the center of electric circuit 1. Then we put $r = a$ in Eq. (9.88) and derive

$$L_{12} = L_{21} = \frac{\mu n_1 n_2 S}{2a} \qquad (9.89)$$

This expression is the coefficient of mutual inductance between a circular coil of radius a having n_1 turns and a small coplanar coil of area S having n_2 turns located at the center of the circle, the inductivity of the medium being μ.

9.9. The Sign of the Coefficient of Mutual Inductance. The coefficient of mutual inductance between a pair of electric circuits is an essentially positive quantity as we have defined it so far. In any magnetic field involving currents round a pair of electric circuits there is a certain amount of magnetic flux that threads both circuits. In the situation originally contemplated in Fig. 9.1, the magnetic flux threading both the circuits was essentially the whole of the magnetic flux. In the absence of a ferromagnetic circuit linking the two electric circuits, however, the magnetic flux common to both electric circuits is only a fraction of that threading either electric circuit. It has been our assumption that the positive direction of the electric currents round the two electric circuits is related by the right-hand-screw rule to the direction of the common magnetic flux threading both electric circuits. It is this convention as to sign that resulted in the coefficients of mutual inductance being positive and the coefficients of mutual reluctance being negative. It would have been equally possible to have taken the positive directions of the electric currents round the two electric circuits to have been related to the direction of the common magnetic flux threading both electric circuits by the left-hand-screw rule. With this convention as to sign the coefficients of mutual inductance would still have been positive and the coefficients of mutual reluctance negative. A third possibility would be to take the positive direction of current round one electric circuit to be related by the right-hand-screw rule to the direction of the common magnetic flux, and to take the positive direction of the electric current round the other electric circuit to be related by the left-hand-screw rule to the direction of the common magnetic flux. This convention as to sign would result in coefficients of mutual inductance being negative and coefficients of mutual reluctance positive. Although the last of these conventions as to sign sounds inconvenient, there are nevertheless occasions on which it is desirable to use it. This occurs when one of the coils has a variable orientation, as in the case of a coil rotating upon an axis.

Let us suppose that electric circuit 2 in Fig. 9.10 is able to rotate about an axis through P perpendicular to PO. Let the direction of the vector representing the area of the loop be turned through an angle θ as shown in Fig. 9.11. Consider first Fig. 9.11a, where θ is less than $\frac{1}{2}\pi$. Let the positive direction of the current round circuit 1 be related by the right-hand-screw rule to the direction from O to P. Then the magnetic flux due to unit current round circuit 1 threads circuit 2 in the direction from O to P. To obtain a positive coefficient of mutual inductance between the two circuits we therefore take the positive direction of the current round circuit 2 to be related by the right-hand-screw rule to the direction of the vector indicated by **S**. Since rotation of circuit 2 through an angle θ reduces the magnetic flux threading it by a factor $\cos \theta$, Eq. (9.88) is replaced by

$$L_{12} = L_{21} = \frac{\mu n_1 n_2 a^2 S}{2r^3} \cos \theta \qquad (9.90)$$

Now consider the situation indicated in Fig. 9.11b, where θ lies between $\frac{1}{2}\pi$ and π. Let us again take the positive direction of the current round circuit 1 to be related by the right-hand-screw rule to the direction from O to P. The magnetic flux again threads circuit 2 in the direction from O to P. To obtain a positive coefficient of mutual inductance between the two circuits the vector **S** representing the area of circuit 2 must be drawn in the direction opposite to that indicated in Fig. 9.11b, and the direction related to this by the right-hand-screw rule would be the direction of the positive current round circuit 2. If, however, the angle θ in Fig. 9.11 is variable and increases continuously, then the situation shown in Fig. 9.11a passes into the situation shown in Fig. 9.11b as θ increases through $\frac{1}{2}\pi$. At this point

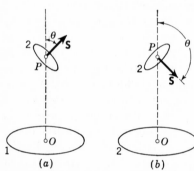

FIG. 9.11. Illustrating circumstances in which it is convenient for the coefficient of mutual inductance to be (a) positive, (b) negative.

it would be necessary to reverse the positive direction of the current in electric circuit 2 if a positive coefficient of mutual inductance between the circuits is to be retained.

In the case of continuous rotation of a coil it is usually more convenient to preserve the same positive direction for current round the electric circuit for all orientations of the coil. If we start with the convention described for Fig. 9.11a and then increase the magnitude of θ to the value indicated in Fig. 9.11b, we now have a situation in which the magnetic flux through electric circuit 2 due to unit current in electric circuit 1 passes through electric circuit 2 in the direction related by the left-hand-screw rule to the positive direction of current in electric circuit 2. This involves a negative value for the coefficient of mutual inductance between the two circuits in the situation indicated in Fig. 9.11b. In a situation when one of the coils rotates, a convenient procedure is therefore as follows: Decide upon a positive direction of the current round each of the circuits. When the magnetic flux through circuit 2 due to unit current round circuit 1 threads circuit 2 in the direction related by the right-hand-screw rule to the direction of the positive current round circuit 2 take the coefficient of mutual inductance as positive. When the magnetic flux through circuit 2 due to unit current in circuit 1 threads circuit 2 in the direction related by the left-hand-screw rule to the direction of a positive current round circuit 2, take the coefficient of mutual inductance as negative.

Application of this convention to the situation shown in Fig. 9.11 operates as follows. Take the positive direction round electric circuit 1 as the direction related by the right-hand-screw rule to the direction of O to P. Take the positive direction of the electric current in electric circuit 2 as that related by the right-hand-screw rule to the direction of the vector $\mathbf{S}$ representing the area of circuit 2. Then for all values of θ the coefficient of mutual inductance between the two circuits is given by Eq. (9.90). In this equation $\cos \theta$ is negative for the situation shown in Fig. 9.11b and positive for the situation shown in Fig. 9.11a.

9.10. The Coupling Coefficient of a Pair of Solenoids. Transformers not involving a ferromagnetic circuit frequently take the form of a pair of solenoids as indicated in Fig. 9.12 or 9.13. In each case let the longer

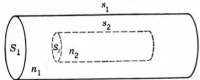

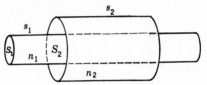

FIG. 9.12. Transformer consisting of a pair of solenoids, one completely inside the other.

FIG. 9.13. Transformer consisting of a pair of solenoids, with the shorter one wound on top of the longer one.

solenoid have cross-sectional area S_1 and length s_1 and be wound with n_1 equally spaced turns. In both cases let the shorter solenoid have cross-sectional area S_2 and length s_2 and be wound with n_2 equally spaced turns. Let the inductivity of the medium inside and outside the solenoids be μ. To make the calculation simple we shall suppose that each solenoid has a length large compared with the linear dimensions of its cross section. In these circumstances the coefficients of self-inductance of the two solenoids are given by Eq. (5.39) and are therefore

$$L_{11} = n_1{}^2 \frac{\mu S_1}{s_1} \tag{9.91}$$

$$L_{22} = n_2{}^2 \frac{\mu S_2}{s_2} \tag{9.92}$$

If we now calculate the coefficient of mutual inductance between the solenoids, we can substitute its value, together with the expressions

(9.91) and (9.92) for the self-inductances of the two solenoids, into Eqs. (9.36) and so derive the coupling coefficient of the transformer.

Take the positive directions of current round both solenoids as right-handed about a common direction threading the solenoids. A unit current round either solenoid then produces magnetic flux threading the other solenoid in the direction related by the right-hand-screw rule to the positive direction of current round this solenoid. With this convention the coefficient of mutual inductance between the solenoids is positive. To calculate the coefficient of mutual inductance for the situation illustrated in Fig. 9.12 let us pass a unit current round each turn of solenoid 1. The total current flowing round the curved surface of this solenoid is then n_1, and the magnetic field strength within the solenoid is n_1/s_1. The magnetic flux density within solenoid 1, assumed uniform, is therefore

$$\frac{\mu n_1}{s_1} \tag{9.93}$$

By multiplying this by the cross-sectional area S_2 of solenoid 2 we obtain the magnetic flux threading each turn of this solenoid, and by multiplying by the number of turns on solenoid 2 we obtain the magnetic flux threading the electric circuit associated with solenoid 2. Expression (9.93), multiplied by $S_2 n_2$, is therefore the magnetic flux threading electric circuit 2 due to unit current round electric circuit 1 and is therefore the coefficient of mutual inductance between the two circuits. We therefore obtain

$$L_{12} = L_{21} = n_1 n_2 \frac{\mu S_2}{s_1} \tag{9.94}$$

Substituting from Eqs. (9.91), (9.92), and (9.94) into Eqs. (9.36) we obtain for the coupling coefficient of the transformer illustrated in Fig. 9.12

$$k = \left(\frac{S_2 s_2}{S_1 s_1}\right)^{1/2} \tag{9.95}$$

The expression $S_2 s_2$ appearing in expression (9.95) is the volume of the smaller solenoid illustrated in Fig. 9.12. Likewise the expression $S_1 s_1$ appearing in expression (9.95) is the volume of the larger solenoid shown in Fig. 9.12. Equation (9.95) therefore shows that, to the degree of approximation of this calculation, the coupling coefficient between the two solenoids indicated in Fig. 9.12 is the square root of the ratio of the volume of the smaller solenoid to the volume of the larger solenoid. To make the coupling coefficient of the transformer as close to unity as possible, we therefore make the size and shape of the two solenoids coincide as closely as possible.

Now consider the transformer shown in Fig. 9.13. Unit current round circuit 1 again produces a magnetic flux density within solenoid 1 given by expression (9.93). The total magnetic flux threading solenoid 1 in these circumstances also threads solenoid 2. We assume that this magnetic flux is uniform within solenoid 1 and neglect the magnetic flux produced in the reverse direction between the two solenoids. The magnetic flux threading each turn of solenoid 2 is therefore obtained by multiplying expression (9.93) by the area S_1 of solenoid 1. The coefficient of mutual inductance of the two solenoids shown in Fig. 9.13 is therefore

$$L_{12} = L_{21} = n_1 n_2 \frac{\mu S_1}{s_1} \qquad (9.96)$$

Substitution from Eqs. (9.91), (9.92), and (9.96) into Eqs. (9.36) gives for the coupling coefficient of the transformer shown in Fig. 9.13

$$k = \left(\frac{S_1 s_2}{S_2 s_1}\right)^{\frac{1}{2}} \qquad (9.97)$$

The expression $S_1 s_2$ appearing in expression (9.97) is the volume common to the two solenoids shown in Fig. 9.13. The expression $S_2 s_1$ appearing in expression (9.97) is the volume of a cylinder formed by combining the larger cross-sectional area of the two solenoids with the greater length. The coupling coefficient given by Eq. (9.97) for the transformer shown in Fig. 9.13 can therefore be described as the square root of the ratio of the volume of the cylinder common to solenoids to the volume of the enveloping cylinder. We again see that, to make the coupling coefficient approach unity, we need to make the size and shape of the two solenoids as identical as possible.

For solenoids whose length is not large compared with the linear dimensions of the cross sections, Eqs. (9.95) and (9.97) for the coupling coefficient are inaccurate. These equations do, however, give a useful indication of the order of magnitude of the coupling coefficient and of the features of the geometry of the transformer upon which the coupling coefficient depends.

If occasion occurs to use a negative value for the coefficient of mutual inductance of a transformer, then we use a negative value for the coupling coefficient in accordance with Eqs. (9.36). For the transformer indicated in Fig. 9.12 let us suppose that the length of the smaller solenoid is sufficiently small so that this solenoid can rotate within the larger one about an axis perpendicular to the length of both solenoids. With the solenoids in the position indicated in Fig. 9.12, let us suppose that we have calculated the coupling coefficient in accordance with Eq. (9.95) and that the value is k_0. Let us now turn the smaller solenoid shown in Fig. 9.12 so that the angle between the lengths of the solenoids is θ. The magnetic flux threading the small solenoid due to unit current round the large solenoid is then reduced by a factor cos θ, and so the coupling coefficient between the two solenoids is

$$k = k_0 \cos \theta \qquad (9.98)$$

If θ increases to $\frac{1}{2}\pi$, the coupling coefficient given by Eq. (9.98) reduces to zero. If the value of θ increases beyond $\frac{1}{2}\pi$, the coupling coefficient given by Eq. (9.98) becomes negative. This indicates that the positive direction of the current round one solenoid is left-handed about the magnetic flux common to the two solenoids while the positive direction of the current round the other solenoid is right-handed about the common flux.

SUMMARIZING EXERCISES

9.1. Explain what is meant by an iron-core transformer. The transformer is constructed on a magnetic circuit for which the reciprocal of the reluctance is L, and leakage of magnetic flux can be neglected. The primary winding has n_1 turns, and the secondary winding n_2 turns. A generator delivering a steady current I_1 is connected across the primary winding, and a generator delivering a steady current I_2 is connected across the secondary winding. Assuming that the positive directions of the currents in the primary and secondary windings thread the magnetic circuit in the same direction, calculate the magnetic fluxes threading the primary and secondary electric circuits.

9.2. Explain what is meant by the coefficients of self-inductance L_{11} and L_{22} of a transformer and by the coefficients of mutual inductance L_{12} and L_{21}. Neglecting leakage, show that $L_{12} = L_{21}$.

9.3. A transformer with leakage is represented in the manner shown in Fig. 9.4. The reluctance of the central arm is R_3, the reluctance of that portion of the magnetic network on the left side of the central arm is R_1, and the reluctance of that portion of the magnetic network to the right of the central arm is R_2. If n_1 and n_2 are the numbers of turns on the primary and secondary windings respectively, calculate the coefficients of self- and mutual inductance L_{12} and L_{21} of the transformer, showing that $L_{12} = L_{21}$.

9.4. Explain what is meant by the coefficients of self- and mutual reluctance of a transformer, and explain why these coefficients are inapplicable for an idealized transformer involving no leakage.

9.5. Define the coefficients of self- and mutual inductance of any system of electric circuits carrying steady currents, whether linked by a magnetic network or not. By applying the principle of superposition, express the magnetic fluxes threading the circuits in terms of the currents round the circuits and the coefficients of self- and mutual inductance. By means of the coefficients of self- and mutual reluctance of the system, express the currents round the circuits in terms of the magnetic fluxes threading the circuits.

9.6. A circular coil of radius a possesses n_1 turns. A second planar coil of area S, whose linear dimensions are small compared with a, possesses n_2 turns. The second coil is mounted on the axis of the first coil at a distance r from the winding of the first coil, and the normal to the second coil makes an angle θ with the axis of the first coil. Calculate the coefficient of mutual inductance between the two coils.

9.7. Explain why it is sometimes convenient to take the coefficient of mutual inductance between two coils as positive and sometimes as negative. Describe a method for determining which sign to use.

9.8. Explain what is meant by the coupling coefficient of a transformer. Two long, thin solenoids have cross-sectional areas S_1 and S_2, and their lengths are s_1 and s_2 respectively. Their axes are parallel, and they are located in a nonmagnetic medium in such a way that the common volume is a maximum. Calculate the coupling coefficients between the solenoids (a) if $S_1 > S_2$, $s_1 > s_2$ and (b) if $S_1 < S_2$, $s_1 > s_2$. Describe any approximations used, and explain how to maximize the coupling coefficient.

CHAPTER 10

MAGNETIC VECTOR POTENTIAL

10.1. Introduction. Any closed geometrical curve C drawn in a magnetic field is threaded by a magnetic flux Φ. This magnetic flux is the sum of the magnetic fluxes associated with the various tubes of magnetic flux that thread C. To perform this summation it is convenient to draw a surface S spanning the closed curve C and to sum the magnetic fluxes of the tubes threading C by means of an integral over the surface S. In this way we arrived at Eq. (2.48) for the magnetic flux Φ threading a closed curve C. When evaluating in this way the magnetic flux threading a closed curve C, it does not matter what surface S is used to span C. Any surface spanning the closed curve C intercepts the tubes of magnetic flux threading C, and the integral on the right-hand side of Eq. (2.48) forms the sum of the magnetic fluxes associated with the tubes threading C and consequently gives the total magnetic flux Φ threading C.

The fact that the magnetic flux threading a closed curve C does not depend upon which surface S is used for spanning C suggests that it should be possible to evaluate the magnetic flux threading a closed curve C in terms of an integral taken around C. This can be done by a further development of the concept of a magnetic circuit discussed in Chap. 8. In Chap. 8 we saw that magnetic flux could be guided by a circuit of soft iron in much the same way that electric current is guided by a conducting circuit. In association with the electric current flowing round the electric circuit it is convenient to define at all points of space a magnetic vector field $\mathbf{H}$. In the same way it is possible for magnetic flux passing round a magnetic circuit to define at all points of space a vector field $\mathbf{A}$ known as the magnetic vector potential. The magnetic vector potential $\mathbf{A}$ is deduced from the magnetic flux Φ passing round a magnetic circuit by the same procedure that is used for deriving the magnetic vector $\mathbf{H}$ for a steady electric current I flowing round an electric circuit. With the aid of the magnetic vector potential $\mathbf{A}$ it is possible to express the magnetic flux threading a closed curve C in terms of an integral round C.

10.2. Definition of Magnetic Vector Potential. Suppose that we have a magnetic circuit whose center line follows a closed curve Γ as shown in Fig. 10.1. Let us suppose that, owing to a flow of steady current, a magnetic flux Φ passes round the magnetic circuit Γ and that we are interested in calculating the magnetic vector potential at a point O. The magnetic vector potential $\mathbf{A}$ at O is identical with the magnetic vector that would exist at O if Φ were a steady electric current flowing round an electric circuit Γ. In the formula that would be used to calculate the magnetic vector at O due to a steady electric current round the closed curve Γ we replace the current round Γ by Φ and the magnetic vector at O by $\mathbf{A}$. We then have an expression for the magnetic vector potential $\mathbf{A}$ at O due to the magnetic flux Φ passing round the magnetic circuit Γ.

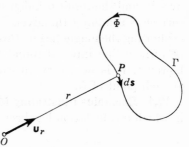

As an example, use can be made of Biot's formula (6.44). Let P be a point of the closed curve Γ in Fig. 10.1. Let r be the distance from O to P and let $\mathbf{u}_r$ be a unit vector pointing from O to P. Let $d\mathbf{s}$ be a vector element of

FIG. 10.1. Illustrating the calculation of the magnetic vector potential $\mathbf{A}$ at a point O due to a magnetic flux Φ passing round a closed magnetic circuit Γ.

length of Γ at P pointing round Γ in the direction of the magnetic flux Φ. In Eq. (6.44) we replace I by Φ and $\mathbf{H}$ by $\mathbf{A}$ and obtain the equation

$$\mathbf{A} = \frac{\Phi}{4\pi} \int_\Gamma \frac{\mathbf{u}_r \times d\mathbf{s}}{r^2} \qquad (10.1)$$

This equation gives the vector potential $\mathbf{A}$ at O due to the magnetic flux Φ passing round the closed magnetic circuit Γ. If there are a number of magnetic circuits Γ_1, Γ_2, . . . carrying magnetic fluxes Φ_1, Φ_2, . . . respectively, then the magnetic vector potential $\mathbf{A}$ at a point O is obtained by taking the vector sum of the contributions $\mathbf{A}_1$, $\mathbf{A}_2$, . . . from the respective magnetic circuits.

10.3. The Circulation Law for Magnetic Vector Potential. The most important property possessed by the magnetic vector $\mathbf{H}$ for a system of steady electric currents is the circulation law expressed by Eq. (4.6). If in this equation we replace $\mathbf{H}$ by $\mathbf{A}$ and I by Φ, we obtain

$$\int_C \mathbf{A} \cdot d\mathbf{s} = \Phi \qquad (10.2)$$

This equation states that the circulation of the magnetic vector potential $\mathbf{A}$ round any closed geometrical curve C in a magnetic field is equal to the magnetic flux Φ threading C. It is necessary that the direction of the vector element of length $d\mathbf{s}$ of C point round C in the direction related by the right-hand-screw rule to the direction of the magnetic flux Φ threading C.

Equation (10.2) is the equation that we seek expressing the magnetic flux Φ threading a closed curve C in terms of an integral taken round C. Equation (10.2) is alternative to Eq. (4.1) for calculating the magnetic flux threading a closed curve. If we use Eq. (4.1), we must choose a surface S spanning the closed curve C and then perform a surface integral over it, and the result is independent of the particular choice made of the surface S spanning the given closed curve C. If we use Eq. (10.2) for evaluating the magnetic flux threading the closed curve C, we have only to perform a line integral round C. Before evaluating this line integral, however, it is necessary to calculate the magnetic vector potential $\mathbf{A}$ at each point of C.

10.4. Examples Illustrating Magnetic Vector Potential. Any situation in which a calculation has been made of the magnetic vector $\mathbf{H}$ due to a

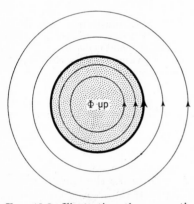

steady electric current I flowing round an electric circuit Γ can be converted to apply to a corresponding situation in which a magnetic flux Φ passes round a magnetic circuit Γ. We arrive at the magnetic scalar potential $\mathbf{A}$ for the magnetic circuit by replacing $\mathbf{H}$ and I by $\mathbf{A}$ and Φ respectively.

Consider, for example, a magnetic circuit with a circular cross section of radius a. Let us suppose that the magnetic circuit may be considered as straight and indefinitely long. The magnetic vector potential for this arrangement is to be compared with the magnetic field of a long, straight, solid wire carrying current uniformly

Fig. 10.2. Illustrating the magnetic vector potential for a long magnetic circuit having circular cross section and carrying magnetic flux Φ.

distributed over the cross section. This situation was discussed in Sec. 2.6. Making the necessary conversion to a magnetic circuit we see that the magnetic vector potential at each point is directed round a circle whose plane is perpendicular to the magnetic circuit and whose center lies on the axis of the magnetic circuit as shown in Fig. 10.2. To calculate the magnitude A of the magnetic vector potential at distance r from the axis of the magnetic circuit we apply Eq. (10.2) to a circle of radius r whose plane is perpendicular to the magnetic circuit and whose center lies on the axis of the magnetic circuit. For such a circle the left-hand side of Eq. (10.2) evaluates to

$$A2\pi r \qquad (10.3)$$

If r is greater than a, the magnetic flux threading the circle is the total magnetic flux

$$\Phi \tag{10.4}$$

passing along the magnetic circuit, but if r is less than a, then the magnetic flux threading the circle is

$$\frac{r^2}{a^2}\,\Phi \tag{10.5}$$

Application of Eq. (10.2) therefore involves equating expression (10.3) to expression (10.4) if r is greater than a but equating expression (10.3) to expression (10.5) if r is less than a. We therefore obtain for the magnitude A of the magnetic vector potential at distance r from the axis of the magnetic circuit shown in Fig. 10.2

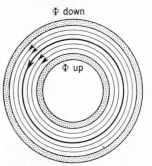

$$A = \frac{\Phi}{2\pi r} \qquad r > a \tag{10.6}$$

$$A = \frac{\Phi}{2\pi a^2}\,r \qquad r < a \tag{10.7}$$

For the magnetic vector potential **A** thus calculated, the circulation round any closed geometrical curve C gives the magnetic flux threading C in accordance with Eq. (10.2).

FIG. 10.3. Illustrating an electric circuit passing through a hollow toroid of soft iron.

If the straight magnetic circuit illustrated in Fig. 10.2 is bent round into circular form, the magnetic vector potential threads the circular magnetic circuit in the same way that the magnetic field threads through a circular electric circuit (see Fig. 6.15).

As another example to illustrate magnetic vector potential, let us consider a magnetic circuit in the form of what may be described as a magnetic toroid. Consider a hollow toroid of soft iron, for which a symmetrical plane section perpendicular to the axis of the toroid is illustrated in Fig. 10.3. Let us suppose that an electric circuit passes through the hollow toroid illustrated in Fig. 10.3 and that the current flowing along it produces a magnetic flux Φ round the toroid of soft iron uniformly distributed along its length. We suppose that the arrangement is such that there is no significant magnetic flux except through the soft iron. Magnetic flux passes round this toroid of soft iron in the same way that electric current flows round the conducting surface of a toroidal inductor. Calculation of the magnetic vector potential **A** due to the magnetic toroid is made in the same way as calculation of the magnetic vector **H** due to a toroidal inductor. It follows that there is no magnetic vector potential outside the magnetic toroid and that inside the toroid the magnetic vector potential is directed round the length of the toroid in closed circles. Moreover the magnitude A of the magnetic vector potential inside the toroid is equal to the magnetic flux flowing round the toroid per unit length. Hence if s is the perimeter of the toroid, assumed thin, the magnitude of the magnetic vector potential within the toroid is

$$A = \frac{\Phi}{s} \qquad (10.8)$$

While a magnetic toroid such as that illustrated in Fig. 10.3 is of no practical importance, it illustrates quite well the significance of magnetic vector potential. The magnetic flux threading the electric circuit shown in Fig. 10.3 is the magnetic flux passing round the magnetic toroid. This magnetic flux can be divided up into sections of unit length, each associated with a unit length of the electric circuit. We may thus speak of the magnetic flux threading the electric circuit per unit length, and this is the magnitude of the magnetic vector potential evaluated at the electric circuit in accordance with Eq. (10.8). A more general statement implied by Eq. (10.2) is the following. The magnetic flux threading any closed geometrical curve C can be evaluated per unit length of C. At a point P of C the magnetic flux per unit length is the component along C of the magnetic vector potential $\mathbf{A}$ at P. The component of $\mathbf{A}$ along C is to be taken in the direction related by the right-hand-screw rule to the direction in which the magnetic flux Φ threads C.

10.5. Unit of Magnetic Vector Potential. Since the dimensions of magnetic vector potential are those of magnetic flux per unit length, the unit in which magnetic vector potential is measured is the weber per meter. Magnetic vector potential can also be measured in volt-seconds per meter. We see therefore that magnetic vector potential has the property that its time rate of change is measured in volts per meter. In Part 4, Sec. 4.5, we shall see that it is no accident that the time rate of change of magnetic vector potential has the same dimensions as electric field strength.

10.6. Magnetic Vector Potential for Any Flow of Steady Current. Suppose that a steady electric current I flows round a closed electric circuit C. The current produces tubes of magnetic flux that thread through the electric circuit C. As discussed in Sec. 8.17, each of these tubes of magnetic flux may be considered as a magnetic circuit for which no soft iron is required. The aggregate of tubes of magnetic flux produced by the electric current may therefore be considered as a series of magnetic circuits Γ_1, Γ_2, . . . , and in principle we can calculate the magnetic fluxes Φ_1, Φ_2, . . . passing round these magnetic circuits. We can then calculate at any point the magnetic vector potentials $\mathbf{A}_1$, $\mathbf{A}_2$, . . . due to the various tubes of magnetic flux, and by forming the vector addition of these contributions we can evaluate the magnetic vector potential **A** due to the current I flowing round the electric circuit C. The process of adding up the contributions from the various tubes of magnetic flux requires a formula in vector calculus that it is not convenient to introduce at this point. The result of the summation is, however, a relatively simple formula that can be described as follows: Let $d\mathbf{s}$ be a vector element of length of the electric circuit C pointing round the circuit in the direction of the steady electric current I. Let r be the distance from the vector element of length $d\mathbf{s}$ to the point at which the magnetic vector potential **A** is to be evaluated. Then

$$\mathbf{A} = \frac{\mu I}{4\pi} \int_C \frac{d\mathbf{s}}{r} \tag{10.9}$$

The integral in this formula involves a vector addition of the vector elements of length $d\mathbf{s}$ of the electric circuit C, each weighted inversely proportional to its distance r from the point at which the magnetic vector potential **A** is being evaluated. Equation (10.9) can be used to evaluate the magnetic scalar potential due to a steady current I flowing round any closed circuit C. Moreover, if there are a number of steady electric currents flowing round various closed curves, Eq. (10.9) can be used to evaluate at any point the magnetic vector potential due to each of the circuits, and by vector addition of these contributions we can then form the magnetic vector potential at the point due to the system of electric currents.

Equation (10.9) can be used to evaluate the coefficient of mutual inductance between two electric circuits C_1 and C_2. Let $d\mathbf{s}_1$ be a vector element of length of the electric circuit C_1 and $d\mathbf{s}_2$ be a vector element of length of the electric circuit C_2. Let r be the distance between the elements of length of the two electric circuits, and let μ be the inductivity of the homogeneous medium surrounding the circuits. The coefficient of mutual inductance L_{21} is the magnetic flux through C_2 due to unit current round C_1. A unit current round C_1 produces at the position of the element of length $d\mathbf{s}_2$ of C_2 a vector potential given, in accordance with Eq. (10.9), by

$$\mathbf{A} = \frac{\mu}{4\pi} \int_{C_1} \frac{d\mathbf{s}_1}{r} \tag{10.10}$$

From Eq. (10.2) the resulting magnetic flux threading C_2 is

$$\int_{C_2} \mathbf{A} \cdot d\mathbf{s}_2 \tag{10.11}$$

Substituting for **A** from Eq. (10.10) into Eq. (10.11) we obtain

$$\frac{\mu}{4\pi} \int_{C_1} \int_{C_2} \frac{d\mathbf{s}_1 \cdot d\mathbf{s}_2}{r} \tag{10.12}$$

This is the magnetic flux through C_2 due to unit current round C_1 and is therefore the coefficient of mutual inductance L_{21}. If we put the unit current round C_2 and calculate the magnetic flux through C_1, we arrive at expression (10.12) with subscripts 1 and 2 interchanged, and as expected, this has the same value. It follows that

$$L_{12} = L_{21} = \frac{\mu}{4\pi} \int_{C_1} \int_{C_2} \frac{d\mathbf{s}_1 \cdot d\mathbf{s}_2}{r} \tag{10.13}$$

This equation can be used to calculate the coefficients of mutual inductance between any two electric circuits.

Equation (10.13) can in particular be used to calculate the coefficients of mutual inductance between a pair of circular loops of wire having a common axis. The radii of the loops may be unequal, and the separation between their planes may have any value. For this case Eq. (10.13) leads to an expression involving an elliptic integral, the values of which are, however, tabulated.

It is also possible to use expression (10.12) to calculate approximately the coefficient of self-inductance of a circular loop of wire of radius a. The procedure is to take C_1 as the circle formed by the centers of the normal cross sections of the wire and C_2 as a circle whose radius is less than that of the circle C_1 by an amount equal to the radius b of the wire. The result is

$$\mu \left(a \ln \frac{8a}{b} - 2 \right) \tag{10.14}$$

where μ is the inductivity of the medium surrounding the wire.

SUMMARIZING EXERCISES

10.1. Explain what is meant by magnetic vector potential. Adapt Biot's formula to calculate the magnetic vector potential due to a single tube of magnetic flux carrying a flux Φ.

10.2. Describe the circulation law for magnetic vector potential. Show that, using magnetic vector potential, the magnetic flux threading an electric circuit can be calculated by means of an integral round the circuit.

10.3. State the units in which magnetic vector potential is measured. Show that the time rate of change of magnetic vector potential is measured in the same units as electric field strength.

PART 4

RELATIONS BETWEEN ELECTRIC
AND MAGNETIC FIELDS

CHAPTER 1

FLOW OF ENERGY IN AN ELECTROMAGNETIC FIELD

1.1. Introduction. In previous parts study has been made of both electric and magnetic fields. These studies were so arranged that electric and magnetic fields could be examined almost independently. Thus in Part 2 study was made of the flow of steady electric current round resistive circuits under the influence of the electric field of batteries. However, in Part 2 no mention was made of the magnetic fields of the steady currents under investigation. In Part 3 study of the magnetic fields of steady electric currents was carried out in a manner largely independent of the electric fields required to drive the currents. This was done by the device of supposing that the circuits had negligible resistance so that substantially no electric field was required to maintain the currents. We have now reached a stage, however, when it is necessary to recognize explicitly the coexistence of electric and magnetic fields.

1.2. The Strip Transmission Line. In studying the relation between electric and magnetic fields it is repeatedly convenient to make use of what is known as the strip transmission line. A strip transmission line consists of a pair of perfectly conducting strips as shown in Fig. 1.1. The strips are mounted so as to be parallel and so as to have a separation a as shown in Fig. 1.1; each strip is supposed to be of width b and length l. As described in Part 3, Sec. 5.6, an arrangement such as that shown in Fig. 1.1 can be used as a capacitor, as an inductor, or as a resistor. In using the arrangement as a capacitor, we are concerned with the capacitivity ϵ of the medium between the strips. If fringing is neglected, the capacitance of the capacitor formed by the two strips is

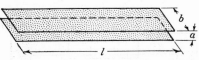

FIG. 1.1. A strip transmission line.

$$\epsilon \frac{bl}{a} \tag{1.1}$$

To use the arrangement shown in Fig. 1.1 as a resistor, the region between

the plates would be filled with a material of conductivity σ, and the conductance between the plates would then be

$$\sigma \frac{bl}{a} \tag{1.2}$$

To use the arrangement shown in Fig. 1.1 as an inductor, it is necessary to connect the strips together at the end by means of conducting rectangular plates of width b and length a. We then have an inductor of cross-sectional area al and length b. If μ is the inductivity of the medium, the inductance of the arrangement is

$$\mu \frac{al}{b} \tag{1.3}$$

provided that the magnetic field between the strips can be considered uniform and the magnetic field above and below the strips negligible.

When regarding the arrangement shown in Fig. 1.1 as a transmission line, it is usually convenient to think in terms of its capacitance C per unit length, its conductance G per unit length, and its inductance L per unit length. If in the calculation of these quantities all fringing is neglected we replace l by unity in Eqs. (1.1) to (1.3) and obtain

$$C = \epsilon \frac{b}{a} \tag{1.4}$$

$$G = \sigma \frac{b}{a} \tag{1.5}$$

$$L = \mu \frac{a}{b} \tag{1.6}$$

Neglect of all fringing implies that the distance a between the strips must be small compared with the linear dimensions of the strips. An arrangement in which Eqs. (1.4) to (1.6) are highly accurate could be constructed as shown in Fig. 1.2. Figure 1.2 is an end-on view of the strip transmission line, the hatched areas representing the strips of width b and separation a. Let us suppose that there exists between the plates a material whose dielectric constant is large compared with that existing in the

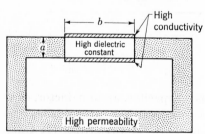

Fig. 1.2. Illustrating use of material of high dielectric constant and of a nonconducting ferromagnetic circuit to make the electric and magnetic fields in a strip transmission line uniform.

rest of space. As described in Part 1, Sec. 8.7, this produces a situation in which, when the transmission line is used as a capacitor, the charges on the strips are almost entirely upon the surfaces of the strips facing each other.   In these circumstances the electric field between the strips is nearly uniform, as shown in Fig. 1.3a.   The stippled region in Fig. 1.2 represents a magnetic circuit of high permeability that conveys magnetic flux emanating from one edge of the strip transmission line round to the opposite edge.   If a current I flows along one strip and back along the other, we obtain between the strips a practically uniform magnetic field as shown in Fig. 1.3b; moreover, there is practically no magnetic field above the upper strip or below the lower strip.   By picturing an

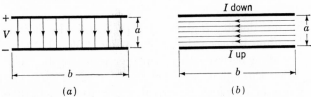

(a)   (b)

Fig. 1.3. Illustrating for a strip transmission line (a) the electric field between the strips and (b) the magnetic field between the strips.

arrangement such as that shown in Fig. 1.2, we may think of a voltage V between the strips as producing a uniform electric field as shown in Fig. 1.3a and a current I along one strip and back along the other as producing a uniform magnetic field between the strips as shown in Fig. 1.3b.

By simultaneously applying to the strip transmission line the voltage V shown in Fig. 1.3a and the current I shown in Fig. 1.3b, we produce in the region between the plates coexisting electric and magnetic fields. The electric field strength is given by

$$E = \frac{V}{a} \tag{1.7}$$

and the magnetic field strength by

$$H = \frac{I}{b} \tag{1.8}$$

Between these strips there is also a uniform electric flux density D and a uniform magnetic flux density B.   The electric flux density is related to the electric field strength by the equation

$$D = \epsilon E \tag{1.9}$$

and the magnetic flux density to the magnetic field strength by the equation

$$B = \mu H \tag{1.10}$$

The electric flux density D gives the positive charge per unit area on the positive strip; it also gives the equal and opposite negative charge per unit area on the negative strip. Let Q be the charge per unit length on the positive strip and $-Q$ the charge per unit length on the negative strip. Since the strips are of width b, the charge Q is spread over a rectangle whose dimensions are unity along the transmission line and b across the transmission line. The charge per unit area on the positive strip is therefore Q/b and that on the negative strip is equal and opposite to this. It follows that

$$D = \frac{Q}{b} \tag{1.11}$$

The magnetic flux density B given by Eq. (1.10) is the magnetic flux per unit area threading between the strips in Fig. 1.3b. Let Φ be the magnetic flux threading between the strips per unit length. This magnetic flux is threading through a section of the transmission line of unit length along the line and of width a perpendicular to the length of the line. The magnetic flux threading the line per unit area is therefore Φ/a, and it follows that

$$B = \frac{\Phi}{a} \tag{1.12}$$

By substituting for D and E from Eqs. (1.11) and (1.7) into Eq. (1.9) we obtain

$$Q = CV \tag{1.13}$$

where C is given by expression (1.4). Likewise by substituting for B and H from Eqs. (1.12) and (1.8) into Eq. (1.10) we obtain

$$\Phi = LI \tag{1.14}$$

where L is given by Eq. (1.6). Equation (1.13) verifies the fact that the ratio of the charge Q per unit length of the line to the voltage V between the strips is the capacitance C per unit length of the line. Likewise Eq. (1.14) verifies the fact that the ratio of the magnetic flux Φ threading unit length of the line to the current I flowing along one strip and back along the other is equal to the inductance L per unit length of the line.

Any transmission line can be used as a pair of conductors for connecting together a pair of electrical devices such as a battery and a resistor. For a strip transmission line such as we have described the associated electric and magnetic fields are particularly easy to visualize, as shown in Fig. 1.3.

1.3. Power Delivered from a Battery to a Resistor. In Part 2, Sec. 1.3, use was made of a strip transmission line to illustrate how the electric field of a battery can be applied to a resistor. The arrangement was illustrated in Part 2, Fig. 1.4, and is redrawn with modifications in Fig. 1.4 of this part. The details of the battery connection are not shown, but it is assumed that the voltage V is applied uniformly between the edges of length b of the transmission line at the left-hand end. It is supposed that there is no conductance between the strips of the transmission line except over a small length at the extreme right-hand end of the line. Here there is a resistor in the form of a rectangular piece of resistive sheet of length a and breadth b. The thickness of the sheet is τ and the conductivity is σ. The conductor connected across the line at the right-hand end of the

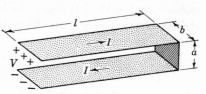

Fig. 1.4. Illustrating a battery of voltage V connected by a strip transmission line to a resistor.

transmission line therefore has a cross-sectional area τb and a length a. Being made of material of conductivity σ, the conductance of the resistor is

$$G = \sigma \frac{\tau b}{a} \qquad (1.15)$$

and its resistance is

$$R = \frac{1}{\sigma}\frac{a}{\tau b} \qquad (1.16)$$

In discussing a resistor in the form of a resistive sheet of conductivity σ and thickness τ, it is convenient to introduce a conductance g and a resistance r defined by the equations

$$g = \sigma\tau \qquad (1.17)$$

and

$$r = \frac{1}{\sigma\tau} \qquad (1.18)$$

By putting $a = b$ in Eqs. (1.15) and (1.16), we see that g and r are the conductance and resistance between opposite edges of a square of the resistive sheet of any size. The quantity g defined by Eq. (1.17) is called the surface conductance of the sheet, and the quantity r defined by Eq. (1.18) is called the surface resistance of the sheet. In terms of the quantities g and r defined by Eqs. (1.17) and (1.18), the conductance G and resistance R appearing in Eqs. (1.15) and (1.16) can be written as

$$G = g\frac{b}{a} \qquad (1.19)$$

$$R = r\frac{a}{b} \qquad (1.20)$$

Equations (1.19) and (1.20) give the conductance and resistance connected across the right-hand end of the transmission line shown in Fig.

1.4 in terms of the surface conductance g and the surface resistance r of the sheet of resistive material used.

Application of the voltage V to the left-hand end of the arrangement shown in Fig. 1.4 produces a steady current I passing upward through the battery, to the right along the upper strip, downward through the resistor, and to the left along the lower strip. Since we are assuming the strips to be perfectly conducting, the current I is related to the voltage V by the equation

$$\frac{I}{V} = G \tag{1.21}$$

where the conductance G is given by Eq. (1.19). Alternatively the relation between the current and the voltage can be written as

$$\frac{V}{I} = R \tag{1.22}$$

where the resistance R is given by Eq. (1.20). The power supplied by the battery and absorbed by the resistor is given by

$$VI = GV^2 = RI^2 \tag{1.23}$$

If we regard the two strips of the transmission line shown in Fig. 1.4 as forming a capacitor, the electric field between them is as shown in Fig. 1.3a and the electric field strength is given by Eq. (1.7). This is the electric field which, at the right-hand end of the transmission line, drives the electrons through the resistive sheet. If we regard the transmission line in Fig. 1.4 together with the battery at the left-hand end and the resistive sheet at the right-hand end as forming an inductor, a magnetic field threads the inductor as shown in Fig. 1.3b and the magnetic field strength is given by Eq. (1.8). Figures 1.3 and 1.4 thus illustrate the fact that, when a battery is joined to a resistor by a pair of leads, there coexists in the space between the leads both an electric and a magnetic field. Coexisting electric and magnetic fields form what is known as an electromagnetic field.

1.4. The Concept of Unit Channels. Let us consider a strip transmission line for which

$$a = 1 \qquad b = 1 \tag{1.24}$$

This is a strip transmission line with unit lateral dimensions, and we assume that precautions have been taken to preserve the uniformity of the electric and magnetic fields in the line between the strips as described in connection with Fig. 1.2. Such a transmission line is a useful device in analyzing electromagnetic fields and will be called a unit channel. To obtain the properties of a unit channel we substitute from Eqs. (1.24) into the equations of Sec. 1.2. We thus obtain the following results:

1. From Eqs. (1.4) and (1.6) the capacitance and inductance per unit length of a unit channel are simply the capacitivity ϵ and the inductivity μ of the medium within the channel. If the medium within the channel has a conductivity σ, Eq. (1.5) shows that σ is also the conductance per unit length of the unit channel.

2. From Eqs. (1.7) and (1.8), the voltage between the strips of a unit channel is the electric field strength E in the channel, and the current flowing along the strips is the magnetic field strength H in the channel.

3. From Eqs. (1.11) and (1.12), the charge per unit length on the strips of a unit channel is equal to the electric flux density D between the strips, while the magnetic flux threading between the strips of a unit channel per unit length is equal to the magnetic flux density B between the strips.

We can therefore say that a unit channel is a transmission line for which the capacitance and inductance per unit length are numerically equal to

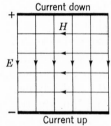

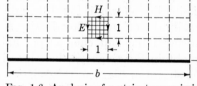

FIG. 1.5. The electromagnetic field of a unit channel.

FIG. 1.6. Analysis of a strip transmission line into unit channels.

the capacitivity and inductivity of the medium while the voltage and current are numerically equal to the electric field strength and magnetic field strength in the channel. A normal cross section of a unit channel is as shown in Fig. 1.5.

Now let us take a number of unit channels of the type indicated in Fig. 1.5 and fit them together side by side as indicated in Fig. 1.6. In Fig. 1.6 it is supposed that b unit channels of the type indicated in Fig. 1.5 are fitted together side by side so that the magnetic field of each unit channel fits on to that of the adjacent unit channels. This forms a strip transmission line in which the strips are of width b and the separation between them is unity. Now take a number a of such arrangements, and stack them above each other as shown in Fig. 1.6. If the intermediate conductors are removed, we then have a strip transmission line in which the strips are of width b and the separation between them is a. The unit channel shown in Fig. 1.5 may thus be regarded as the building block out of which we may construct the electromagnetic field shown in Fig. 1.3 in the manner indicated in Fig. 1.6.

A unit length of the transmission line whose normal cross section is shown in Fig. 1.6 involves a situation in which b capacitors, each of capacitance ϵ, are connected in parallel and then a arrangements of this type are connected in series. The resulting capacitance per unit length of the line is described by Eq. (1.4). Likewise a unit length of the transmission line whose normal cross section is shown in Fig. 1.6 consists of b reluctances, each of reluctance $1/\mu$, connected in series and then a arrangements of this type connected in parallel. The resulting inductance per unit length of the line is described by Eq. (1.6). Again, since E is the voltage associated with each unit channel in the transmission line illustrated in Fig. 1.6 and there are a such unit channels between the upper and lower strips, the total voltage V across the line is obtained by multiplying E by a, and this is described by Eq. (1.7). Likewise H in Fig. 1.6 is the current associated with each unit channel, and there are b unit channels across the transmission line. The total current I on a strip is therefore obtained by multiplying H by b, and this is described by Eq. (1.8). Furthermore the electric flux density D in a unit channel is the charge per unit length associated with the channel. By multiplying this by b we obtain the charge per unit length associated with the transmission line shown in Fig. 1.6, and this relation is exhibited in Eq. (1.11). Finally the magnetic flux density B in a unit channel is the magnetic flux threading the unit channel per unit length. By multiplying this by a we obtain the magnetic flux threading a unit length of the transmission line shown in Fig. 1.6; this relation is exhibited in Eq. (1.12).

The process of constructing the field of the transmission line shown in Fig. 1.6 out of unit channels may equally well be viewed as a process of dissecting the field of the transmission line into unit channels. Consider a geometrical plane drawn through the electromagnetic field parallel to the strips. Such a plane is perpendicular to the electric field and therefore coincides with an equipotential surface. As described in Part 1, Sec. 2.10, this surface can be replaced by a conducting sheet without upsetting the electric field. The plane surface under discussion is also composed entirely of lines of magnetic flux in the magnetic field and so does not intersect any tube of magnetic flux. As described in Part 3, Sec. 3.4, the surface can be replaced by a conducting sheet without upsetting the magnetic field. Hence the introduction of a perfectly conducting surface parallel to the strips does not affect either the electric field or the magnetic field. The electromagnetic field of a strip transmission line can therefore be dissected by conducting planes perpendicular to the electric field. Dissection of the electromagnetic field by means of planes perpendicular to the magnetic field is, however, more difficult and requires support of dissected portions of the field by some device such as that shown in Fig. 1.2. It should be noted, however, that the ideal support for the electromagnetic field in an individual unit channel consists of the rest of the electromagnetic field of the transmission line, as indicated in Fig. 1.6.   Thus, while the creation of the electromagnetic field of a single unit channel requires supporting devices such as those indicated in Fig. 1.2, a unit channel interior to the transmission line is automatically supported by the remainder of the electromagnetic field.

1.5. Use of Unit Channels to Describe Flow of Energy along a Transmission Line toward a Resistor.   Let us now examine the situation illustrated in Fig. 1.4 from the viewpoint of unit channels.   If in Fig. 1.4 conditions (1.24) were satisfied, the transmission line illustrated would be a unit channel, and the terminating resistor would consist of a unit square of a resistive sheet for which the surface conductance is given by Eq. (1.17) and the surface resistance by Eq. (1.18).   The voltage across the unit channel would be numerically equal to the electric field strength E, and the current along the strips would be numerically equal to the magnetic field strength H.   In these circumstances Eq. (1.21) would read

$$\frac{H}{E} = g \qquad (1.25)$$

and Eq. (1.22) would read

$$\frac{E}{H} = r \qquad (1.26)$$

We thus see that, if a unit channel is terminated with a unit square of a resistive sheet of surface resistance r, the ratio of the electric field strength in the unit channel to the magnetic field strength in the unit channel is equal to r.

For a unit channel, Eqs. (1.23) become

$$EH = gE^2 = rH^2 \qquad (1.27)$$

This equation gives three alternative expressions for the power supplied by the battery to the unit channel and delivered to the terminating resistor.   We see in particular from Eqs. (1.27) that the rate of flow of energy down a unit channel is the product of the electric field strength in the channel and the magnetic field strength in the channel, these two quantities being the voltage and current for the unit channel.

Now let us consider the situation illustrated in Fig. 1.4 under circumstances when conditions (1.24) are not satisfied.   The transmission line now consists of strips of width b and separation a and can be analyzed into unit channels as illustrated in Fig. 1.6.   The number of unit channels involved is ab, and each is conveying energy at the rate EH in accordance with Eqs. (1.27).   The total rate of flow of energy down the transmission line is therefore

$$(EH)(ab) \qquad (1.28)$$

However, in accordance with Eqs. (1.23), the total rate of flow of energy down the transmission line is also VI. Equating this to expression (1.28) we obtain

$$VI = (EH)(ab) \qquad (1.29)$$

We can verify this equation by substituting into the left-hand side the expressions for V and I in terms of E and H from Eqs. (1.7) and (1.8). We thus see that the total rate of flow of energy VI down the transmission

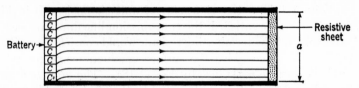

Fig. 1.7. Illustrating the flow of energy from a battery to a resistor.

line is distributed over the unit channels at the rate EH per channel. This is described by saying that energy is crossing each normal rectangular cross section of the transmission line at a rate EH per unit area per unit time.

The energy flowing down each unit channel is absorbed in the square of resistive material at the end of that channel. The terminating resistor is made up of ab such unit squares connected in parallel in the direction of the magnetic field and in series in the direction of the electric field. The power absorbed by each unit square of the terminating resistor is given by the second and third expressions in Eqs. (1.27). The total power absorbed by the terminating resistor is therefore given by either of the equivalent expressions

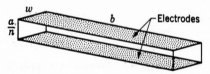

Fig. 1.8. An idealized voltaic cell used to construct the battery illustrated in Fig. 1.7.

$$(gE^2)(ab) = (rH^2)(ab) \qquad (1.30)$$

The total power absorbed in the terminating resistor is, however, given by the second and third expressions in Eqs. (1.23). By substituting into these expressions for V and I from Eqs. (1.7) and (1.8) and for G and R from Eqs. (1.19) and (1.20), we verify expressions (1.30).

The flow of energy across each rectangular normal cross section of the transmission line of amount EH per unit area per unit time from the battery toward the terminating resistor constitutes a flow of energy along the line between the strips as shown in Fig. 1.7. To simplify the geometry, an idealized battery has been shown, consisting of cells each of which is as indicated in Fig. 1.8. The voltaic cell shown in Fig. 1.8 has rectangular electrodes measuring w by b, the latter dimension being the same as the width of the strips of the transmission lines illustrated in Fig. 1.7. The separation between the electrodes of the cell shown in Fig. 1.8 is a/n, so that n such cells can be connected in series between the strips of the transmission line in the manner indicated in Fig. 1.7. As described in Part 2, Sec. 1.2, a voltaic cell may be thought of ideally as a self-charging parallel-plate capacitor of high capacitance; one plate is the negative electrode of the battery, and the other is the electrolyte, the separation between them being of atomic dimensions. A considerable amount of electric energy is stored in the battery near the active electrodes. Some additional electric energy is also stored between the strips of the transmission line, as described in Part 1, Chap. 8. There is also some energy associated with the motion of the electrons round the circuit to be discussed in Chap. 7 of this part. The system illustrated in Fig. 1.7 thus contains a considerable amount of electrical energy, most of which is stored close to the active electrodes in the battery. It is from the electrostatic energy stored close to the electrodes of the battery that the flow of energy down the line to the resistor originates as indicated in Fig. 1.7.

The process whereby energy is transferred from the battery to the resistor may be described as follows: The reservoir of energy close to the electrodes of the battery extends down the transmission line to the resistor. At the resistor energy is "dripping" out of the reservoir, each drip being used to accelerate an electron in the resistor between one collision and the next. The energy thus conveyed to the electrons is converted by collisions into the random motion associated with heat. At the battery energy drips into the reservoir each time that an electron is separated from a positive ion by the chemical process going on at an electrode. With energy dripping into the reservoir at the battery end and dripping out at the resistor end, there is a flow of energy through the system. At any normal rectangular cross section of the transmission line between the battery and the resistor the rate of this flow of energy amounts to EH per unit area per unit time, and the total rate of flow of energy over an entire cross section of the transmission line is VI. Thus, when an electron is separated from an ion by the chemical process going on at an electrode of the battery, electrical energy is emitted. It is the function of the transmission line to guide this energy between its conductors to the resistor, where the energy is used to accelerate an electron between one collision and the next. This picture of the process of energy transfer from a battery to a resistor is, of course, oversimplified. Not only has the operation of a battery been oversimplified, but it has been assumed that the resistance is entirely concentrated in the resistor at the end of the transmission line, whereas in fact there is some resistance associated with all parts of the circuit. The discussion has, however, brought out the vital fact that coexistence of electric and magnetic fields implies flow of energy.

1.6. The Poynting Vector. We have seen that the rate of flow of energy down the unit channel illustrated in Fig. 1.5 is the product of the electric field strength E and the magnetic field strength H. The direction of flow is from the battery toward the resistor and is therefore downward through the paper in Fig. 1.5. It follows therefore that the rate of flow of energy per unit area per unit time is represented by the vector

$$\mathbf{E} \times \mathbf{H} \tag{1.31}$$

where $\mathbf{E}$ is the electric vector in the unit channel and $\mathbf{H}$ is the magnetic vector in the unit channel. The direction of the vector (1.31) is along the

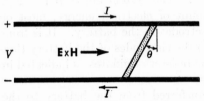

transmission line in the direction of energy flow. Since the directions of the electric and magnetic vectors are mutually perpendicular, the magnitude of the vector (1.31) is EH. Hence the vector (1.31) represents, in magnitude and direction, the rate of flow of energy along a unit channel. It therefore represents, in magnitude and direction, the rate of

FIG. 1.9. Illustrating the vector character of energy flow in an electromagnetic field.

flow of energy per unit area across a normal cross section of the strip transmission line illustrated in Fig. 1.6. The vector (1.31) is known as the power density vector, or the Poynting vector.

The vector character of the flow of energy in an electromagnetic field may be illustrated with the aid of Fig. 1.9. Figure 1.9 represents a strip transmission line of the type previously considered, with a battery connected at the left-hand end. A resistive sheet is connected across the line at an angle θ to a normal cross section. This resistive sheet is inserted in such a way as not to intersect any of the tubes of magnetic flux previously considered. The magnetic field to the right of the resistive sheet is then removed and that to the left retained. In these circumstances the electric current flows along one strip of the transmission line as far as a sloping resistive sheet, through the resistive sheet, and back to the battery along the other strip of the transmission line. There is a magnetic field between the strips to the left of the resistive sheet and no magnetic field to the right. The electric field, however, is the same as that previously considered and exists both to the left and to the right of the resistive sheet. To the right of the resistive sheet the Poynting vector given by expression (1.31) is zero because the magnetic vector is zero there. To the left of the resistive sheet, however, the Poynting vector given by expression (1.31) is directed parallel to the length of the transmission line from the battery toward the resistive sheet.   Let us calculate the power absorbed by the resistive sheet per unit area.   By definition of magnetic field strength, the current per unit width round the circuit, and in particular through the resistive sheet, is

$$H \qquad (1.32)$$

The voltage per unit distance in the direction of current flow in the resistive sheet is the component of the electric vector in this direction, namely,

$$E \cos \theta \qquad (1.33)$$

For a unit square of the resistive sheet with edges parallel to the edges of the sheet, therefore, the voltage acting across it is given by expression (1.33) and the current flowing through it is given by expression (1.32).   The power absorbed by unit area of the resistive sheet is therefore the product of these expressions, namely,

$$EH \cos \theta \qquad (1.34)$$

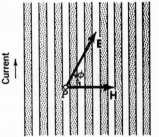

Fig. 1.10. Illustrating the property of the Poynting vector when the electric and magnetic vectors are not mutually perpendicular.

This, however, is the component of the Poynting vector (1.31) in the direction normally inward to the resistive sheet.   This illustrates the fact that, if an electromagnetic field is intersected by a surface which reduces the magnetic field on one side to zero, then the power absorbed by the intersecting surface per unit area is the inward normal component of the Poynting vector (1.31).

It is possible, for any electromagnetic field, to introduce a surface S so as to leave the electromagnetic field on one side of S (side 1) unaltered and to reduce the tangential component of the magnetic vector on the other side of S (side 2) to zero.   In these circumstances power is absorbed by the surface S per unit area equal to the normal component of the Poynting vector (1.31) evaluated close to S on side 1, the normal being directed from side 1 to side 2.   This is true even in situations where the directions of the electric vector $\mathbf{E}$ and the magnetic vector $\mathbf{H}$ are not mutually perpendicular.   This is illustrated in Fig. 1.10.   In this diagram $\mathbf{E}$ and $\mathbf{H}$ are the electric and magnetic vectors at a point P, and there is an angle ϕ between their directions.   Let us introduce a surface S passing through the point P and containing the directions of the electric and magnetic vectors at P.   Let the electrical properties of the surface be so designed as to reduce the tangential magnetic vector on the far side of the surface to zero.   In accordance with Part 3, expression (4.5), current must flow on the surface S in the direction shown in Fig. 1.10, and the current per unit width must be equal to the magnetic field strength

$$H \qquad (1.35)$$

at the point P. To reduce the tangential magnetic vector on the far side of the surface to zero, the surface must be designed with suitable resistive properties. The voltage per unit distance in the direction of the current is the component of the electric vector E in this direction. The voltage per unit distance in the direction of the current is therefore

$$E \sin \phi \qquad (1.36)$$

The surface resistance of S in the direction of current flow must therefore be equal to the ratio of expression (1.36) to expression (1.35). However, there is a component of the electric vector in the direction of the magnetic vector, namely,

$$E \cos \phi \qquad (1.37)$$

Since this voltage per unit distance acts in a direction perpendicular to the direction of current flow on S, the resistance of the sheet in the direction of the magnetic vector H must be infinite. The surface, therefore, would have to consist of a series of parallel wires possessing appropriate resistance and insulated from each other as indicated in Fig. 1.10. The power absorbed by this surface per unit area is obtained by multiplying the current per unit width given by expression (1.35) by the voltage per unit distance in the direction of current flow given by expression (1.36). The power absorbed by the surface per unit area is therefore

$$EH \sin \phi \qquad (1.38)$$

and this is the magnitude of the vector $E \times H$, even though the directions of E and H are not mutually perpendicular.

For any situation involving coexistence of an electric and magnetic field there is a flow of energy represented per unit area per unit time, in magnitude and direction, by the vector product of the electric vector E and the magnetic vector H. This vector gives the power that would be absorbed per unit area by a surface that intersects the electromagnetic field in such a way as to convert the tangential magnetic vector into current flowing over the surface. Design of such surfaces is not always easy. We shall, however, be principally concerned with situations in which the directions of the electric and magnetic vectors are mutually perpendicular and the intersecting surface is a resistive sheet or a simple adaptation thereof. The simplest situation is that shown in Fig. 1.7 where the power crossing a normal rectangular cross section of the strip transmission line per unit area is equal to the product of the electric field strength E and the magnetic field strength H, this power being absorbed in the resistive sheet at the end of the transmission line.

1.7. The Flow of Energy Involved in Charging a Capacitor. As a further example of flow of energy, let us consider the process whereby a capacitor is charged from a source delivering a constant current I_0. Let us take the capacitor in the form of a length l of strip transmission line as shown in Fig. 1.11.   Let a be the separation between the strips and b

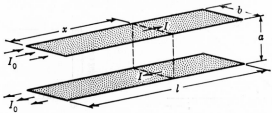

FIG. 1.11. Illustrating charging of a capacitor by means of a constant-current source I_0.

their width.   Let ϵ be the capacitivity of the medium between the strips and μ its inductivity.   We assume that the medium has no conductivity and that all fringing is avoided.   Let the source of constant current I_0 be applied at the left-hand end of the transmission line as shown in Fig. 1.11, and let the current be applied uniformly across the width of the strips.   As a result of this charging current the positive charge on the upper plate and the negative charge on the lower plate are increasing linearly with time at the rate I_0.   If we suppose that the charges on the plates are zero at time zero, the charge on the positive plate at time t is

$$I_0 t \tag{1.39}$$

The capacitance per unit length of the transmission line is given by Eq. (1.4) and the total capacitance of the capacitor by expression (1.1).   By dividing this capacitance into the charge given by expression (1.39), it follows that the voltage of the capacitor at time t is

$$V = \frac{a I_0}{\epsilon b l} t \tag{1.40}$$

The voltage between the plates of the capacitor therefore increases linearly with time t as shown in Fig. 1.12a, while the current transferring charge from the lower plate to the upper plate at the left-hand end of the capacitor remains constant as shown in Fig. 1.12b.

As described in Part 1, Chap. 8, electric energy is distributed uniformly throughout the volume between the plates of the capacitor.   At time t the electric energy stored per unit length of the transmission line is

$$W = \tfrac{1}{2} C V^2 \tag{1.41}$$

where the capacitance per unit length C of the line is given by Eq. (1.4) and the voltage V between the conductors is given by Eq. (1.40). Substituting these values into Eq. (1.41) we obtain

$$W = \frac{aI_0^2}{2\epsilon b l^2} t^2 \tag{1.42}$$

The length of the transmission line being l, the total energy stored in the

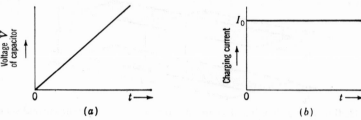

FIG. 1.12. Illustrating, for the capacitor shown in Fig. 1.11, the variation with time of (a) the voltage between the plates and (b) the charging current at the left-hand end.

capacitor is obtained by multiplying the expression on the right-hand side of Eq. (1.42) by l and is therefore

$$\frac{aI_0^2}{2\epsilon b l} t^2 \tag{1.43}$$

This expression for the total electric energy stored in the capacitor can also be obtained by taking one-half the product of the charge on the plates given by expression (1.39) and the voltage between the plates given by Eq. (1.40). Expression (1.43) shows that the electric energy stored in the capacitor is increasing proportional to the square of time. The rate at which it is increasing at time t is obtained by differentiating expression (1.43) with respect to t and is therefore

$$\frac{aI_0^2}{\epsilon b l} t \tag{1.44}$$

Thus the rate at which the capacitor is storing electric energy is itself increasing linearly with time.

The rate at which energy is flowing into the capacitor from the generator is

$$P_0 = VI_0 \tag{1.45}$$

Substitution into this equation for V from Eq. (1.40) gives

$$P_0 = \frac{aI_0^2}{\epsilon b l} t \tag{1.46}$$

The equality of expressions (1.44) and (1.46) verifies the fact that the rate at which the electric energy in the capacitor is increasing is equal to the rate at which it is flowing in from the generator.

While the current flowing along the strips of the transmission line at the left-hand end in Fig. 1.11 is I_0, that flowing along the strips at the right-hand end is clearly zero. The current along the strips therefore decreases from I_0 at the left-hand end to zero at the right-hand end. Let I be the current at distance x from the left-hand end. The current I has to charge only that part of the capacitor lying to the right of the normal cross section at position x. The positive and negative charges on the strips beyond this cross section are the fraction $(l - x)/l$ of the total positive and negative charges on the plates given by expression (1.39). The positive and negative charges on the plates beyond the normal cross section of the transmission line at position x are, therefore,

$$\frac{l - x}{l} I_0 t \tag{1.47}$$

It is the rate of increase of this charge that has to be provided by the current I flowing along the strips at position x. Hence

$$I = \frac{l - x}{l} I_0 \tag{1.48}$$

This equation shows that the current along the transmission line decreases linearly from I_0 at the left-hand end in Fig. 1.11 to zero at the right-hand

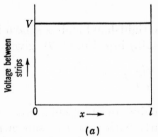
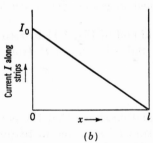

(a)   (b)

FIG. 1.13. Illustrating, for the strip transmission line shown in Fig. 1.11, the variation with distance x from the generator of (a) the voltage between the strips and (b) the current along the strips.

end as shown in Fig. 1.13b. The voltage between the conductors is, however, given by Eq. (1.40) and does not vary along the transmission line as shown in Fig. 1.13a. Comparison of Figs. 1.12 and 1.13 shows that, while the voltage between the strips is independent of distance along the transmission line, the voltage increases linearly with time as the capacitor is charged. On the other hand, while the charging current does not vary with time, it decreases linearly along the transmission line to zero at the far end.

The power supplied to the portion of the transmission line beyond the normal cross section at position x is

$$P = VI \qquad (1.49)$$

where the voltage V is given by Eq. (1.40) and the current I is given by Eq. (1.48). Substituting for I from Eq. (1.48) into Eq. (1.49), and using Eq. (1.45), we obtain

$$P = \frac{l - x}{l} P_0 \qquad (1.50)$$

This equation shows that the rate at which energy is passing a normal cross section of the transmission line decreases linearly from P_0 at the

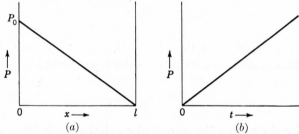

Fig. 1.14. Illustrating the variation of the rate of flow of energy past a normal cross section of the transmission line shown in Fig. 1.11 (a) as a function of distance x along the line and (b) as a function of time t.

left-hand end in Fig. 1.11 to zero at the right-hand end as shown in Fig. 1.14a. Substitution for P_0 from Eq. (1.46) into Eq. (1.50) gives

$$P = \frac{l - x}{l} \frac{aI_0^2}{\epsilon bl} t \qquad (1.51)$$

This equation shows that the power passing any particular cross section of the transmission line increases linearly with time t as shown in Fig. 1.14b. Thus the power passing a cross section of the transmission line increases linearly with time but decreases linearly with distance along the transmission line to zero at the far end.

The electric energy stored in the transmission line beyond the normal cross section at position x is the fraction $(l - x)/l$ of the total electric energy stored in the line given by expression (1.43). The electric energy stored in the transmission line beyond position x is therefore

$$\frac{l - x}{l} \frac{aI_0^2}{2\epsilon bl} t^2 \qquad (1.52)$$

and it increases with time at the rate

$$\frac{l - x}{l} \frac{aI_0^2}{\epsilon b l} t \tag{1.53}$$

Comparison of the right-hand side of Eq. (1.51) with expression (1.53) shows that the power passing any normal cross section of the transmission line is that required to provide the rate of increase of the electric energy stored in the transmission line beyond that normal cross section.

The relation between flow of energy and storage of energy can also be described as follows: Consider two closely spaced normal cross sections of the line at positions x and $x + dx$. At time t the electric energy stored per unit length of the line is W, given by Eq. (1.42). The differential electric energy stored between the cross sections at x and $x + dx$ is therefore $W \, dx$. The time rate of increase of the differential electric energy stored in the space between the two cross sections is therefore

$$dx \frac{dW}{dt} \tag{1.54}$$

This rate of increase of stored electric energy is occurring because the rate of flow of energy through the normal cross section at position $x + dx$ is less than that for the normal cross section at position x. Let the rate of flow of energy through the cross section at position $x + dx$ be less than that through the cross section at position x by the differential amount

$$-dP \tag{1.55}$$

Equating expression (1.55) for the net rate of inflow of energy to the portion of the transmission line between the normal cross sections at x and $x + dx$ to the net rate of increase of the stored electric energy in this portion of the transmission line, we obtain the equation

$$-dP = dx \frac{dW}{dt}$$

or

$$-\frac{\partial P}{\partial x} = \frac{dW}{dt} \tag{1.56}$$

A partial derivative has been shown on the left-hand side of this equation because, as shown in Fig. 1.14, P is a function of both x and t, and the derivative on the left-hand side of Eq. (1.56) implies the rate of change of P with x at constant t. On the right-hand side of Eq. (1.56) the electric energy per unit length W stored in the capacitor is a function of t only in accordance with Eq. (1.42). Equation (1.56) expresses the fact that the stored electric energy per unit length of the line is increasing with time because, in unit time, more energy is entering the unit length from the portion of the transmission line connecting it to the generator than is flowing out of the unit length to the remainder of the transmission line. We have already calculated the expression for P in Eq. (1.51) and for W in Eq. (1.42). By substituting these expressions for P and W into the left- and right-hand sides of Eq. (1.56), we can verify the truth of the equation.

1.8. Use of the Poynting Vector to Describe the Flow of Energy into a Capacitor. The total electric energy stored in the capacitor is given by expression (1.43), and this energy is to be thought of as distributed uniformly throughout the volume between the plates. The electric energy per unit volume w stored between the plates is therefore obtained by dividing expression (1.43) by the volume abl between the plates. The stored electric energy per unit volume is therefore

$$w = \frac{I_0{}^2}{2\epsilon b^2 l^2} t^2 \tag{1.57}$$

To visualize the way in which the electric energy becomes distributed throughout the volume in this way, we make use of the Poynting vector defined by expression (1.31).

At any normal cross section of the transmission line shown in Fig. 1.11, the electric field is as shown in Fig. 1.3a and the magnetic field as shown in Fig. 1.3b. These diagrams represent the electromagnetic field in the transmission line looking down the line away from the generator. It is in this direction therefore that the Poynting vector, defined by expression (1.31), is directed. In terms of the Poynting vector let us see how electric energy becomes stored in the capacitor uniformly throughout the volume between the plates.

The electromagnetic field between the strips of the transmission line shown in Fig. 1.11 can be calculated as follows: The electric flux density D is equal to the positive and negative charges per unit area of the strips and is therefore obtained by dividing expression (1.39) by the area bl of a strip. We deduce that

$$D = \frac{I_0}{bl} t \tag{1.58}$$

The electric field strength E and the magnetic field strength H between the strips are obtained by substituting for V and I from Eqs. (1.40) and (1.48) into Eqs. (1.7) and (1.8). We obtain

$$E = \frac{I_0}{\epsilon bl} t \tag{1.59}$$

$$H = \frac{l - x}{l} \frac{I_0}{b} \tag{1.60}$$

Equation (1.59) can also be obtained by dividing the expression for the electric flux density given in Eq. (1.58) by the capacitivity ϵ of the medium between the plates. Also, since the electric energy stored per unit volume is $\frac{1}{2}ED$, we can verify from Eqs. (1.58) and (1.59) the truth of Eq. (1.57). Equations (1.59) and (1.60) show that the electric and magnetic field strengths between the strips vary with time t as shown in Fig. 1.15 and with distance x along the transmission line as shown in

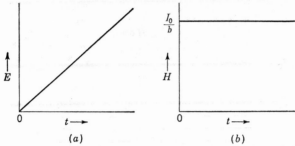

(a)   (b)

FIG. 1.15. Illustrating, for the arrangement shown in Fig. 1.11, the variation with time of (a) the electric field strength and (b) the magnetic field strength.

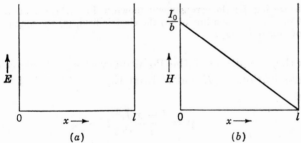

(a)   (b)

FIG. 1.16. Illustrating, for the arrangement shown in Fig. 1.11, the variation with distance along the transmission line of (a) the electric field strength and (b) the magnetic field strength.

Fig. 1.16.   Figures 1.15 and 1.16 are to be compared with Figs. 1.12 and 1.13 respectively in the light of Eqs. (1.7) and (1.8). The electric and magnetic fields between the strips are also illustrated in Fig. 1.17a and b respectively.

If we dissect the electromagnetic field of the transmission line shown in Fig. 1.11 into unit channels as described in connection with Fig. 1.6, the voltage and current associated with each unit channel are given by Eqs. (1.59) and (1.60) and vary with time t and distance x along the transmission line as shown in Figs. 1.15 and 1.16. The rate of flow of energy along each unit channel is given by

$$p = EH \qquad (1.61)$$

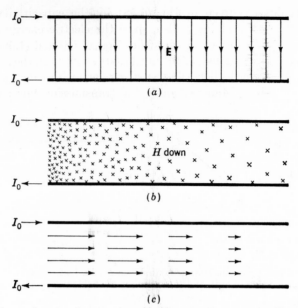

FIG. 1.17. Illustrating, for the arrangement shown in Fig. 1.11, the distribution along the length of the transmission line of (a) the electric field, (b) the magnetic field, and (c) the rate of flow of energy.

and this is the magnitude of the Poynting vector defined by expression (1.31). Substitution for E and H from Eqs. (1.59) and (1.60) into Eq. (1.61) gives

$$p = \frac{l - x}{l} \frac{I_0^2}{\epsilon b^2 l} t \qquad (1.62)$$

The variations of the rate of energy flow along a unit channel with distance x along the transmission line and with time t are therefore as shown in Fig. 1.18, which is to be compared with Fig. 1.14.

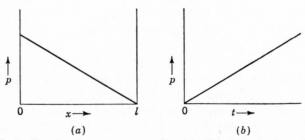

FIG. 1.18. Illustrating, for the arrangement shown in Fig. 1.11, the flow of energy per unit area per unit time across a normal cross section of the transmission line (a) as a function of distance along the line and (b) as a function of time.

We see from Fig. 1.18 that the flow of energy per unit area per unit time across any normal cross section of the transmission line shown in Fig. 1.11 decreases linearly as we move along the transmission line to zero at the far end.   For a unit channel Eq. (1.56) becomes

$$-\frac{\partial p}{\partial x} = \frac{dw}{dt} \tag{1.63}$$

In the space between the strips of the transmission line, consider a unit cube formed by taking unit length of a unit channel.   The electric energy stored in such a unit cube at time t is given by Eq. (1.57), and the right-hand side of Eq. (1.63) is the time rate of increase of this energy.   The left-hand side of Eq. (1.63) is the amount by which the rate of flow of energy along the unit channel decreases as we move a unit distance away from the source.   For the unit cube, therefore, the left-hand side of Eq. (1.63) is the excess of the rate of inflow of energy across the face nearest to the source over the rate of outflow of energy across the face farthest from the source.   Since there is no flow of energy over the other four faces of the cube, Eq. (1.63) expresses the fact that the net rate of inflow of energy into a unit cube in the field is equal to the rate of increase of the electric energy stored in the unit cube.   We thus see that, for the arrangement shown in Fig. 1.11, there is a flow of energy in the space between the strips that decreases to zero at the far end as indicated in Fig. 1.17c. The decreasing flow of energy as we move along the line results in accumulation of electric energy in the volume between the strips, and the energy per unit volume increases with time t in the manner described by Eq. (1.57).

The tubes of electric flux in the transmission line illustrated in Fig. 1.11 run perpendicularly across from the upper plate to the lower plate. Between these tubes of electric flux there is a sideways pressure as described in Part 1, Sec. 10.4.   The pressure is identical in value with the energy per unit volume and is, therefore, given by the right-hand side of Eq. (1.57).   The process of charging the capacitor consequently involves a situation in which the sideways pressure between the tubes of electric flux increases proportional to the square of time.   The process of charging the capacitor may be described by saying that the generator compresses the tubes of electric flux into the space between the plates. This increases the electric energy per unit volume between the plates and causes a flow of energy that decreases linearly to zero at the far end of the transmission line as shown in Fig. 1.17c.

It is to be noticed from Fig. 1.15 that, whereas the electric field strength in the capacitor increases linearly with time, the magnetic field strength remains constant.   It follows that the electric field soon becomes the dominant feature of the electromagnetic field between the plates.   If charging ceases at any time, the magnetic field strength between the plates completely disappears, leaving only the electric field. On the other hand it is to be noticed that presence of a magnetic field between the plates of the capacitor during the charging operation is essential to the process whereby electric energy is packed into the volume between the plates. Without a magnetic field, the Poynting vector would be zero and no flow of energy into the capacitor could take place. Thus it is an essential feature of the process of charging the capacitor that the generator providing the charging current should form a fringe of magnetic field extending between the plates of the capacitor as described by Fig. 1.16b and illustrated in Fig. 1.17b. This is associated with the fact that, in distributing over the plates of the capacitor the charge provided by the generator, a flow of current over the plates is required.

1.9. Flow of Energy in a Coaxial Transmission Line. In the preceding sections flow of energy along a transmission line has been discussed using a strip transmission line with a uniform electric field. Flow of energy may, however, be studied in a similar manner using any transmission line. Let us consider a coaxial transmission line for which the inner and outer conductors are thin, hollow, perfectly conducting circular cylinders of radii a and b respectively. Let ϵ and μ be the capacitivity and inductivity of the material between the conductors, and let us assume that this material is nonconducting.

The electric field of a coaxial transmission line carrying the charge Q per unit length on the inner conductor and $-Q$ per unit length on the inner surface of the outer conductor was discussed in Part 1, Sec. 11.3. The lines of electric force are radial as shown in Fig. 1.19, and the electric field strength at a point between the conductors distant r from the common axis is

$$E = \frac{Q}{2\pi\epsilon} \frac{1}{r} \tag{1.64}$$

The charge Q per unit length is related to the excess of voltage V of the inner conductor over the outer conductor by the equation

$$Q = CV \tag{1.65}$$

where C is the capacitance per unit length of the coaxial transmission line. From Part 1, Eq. (11.10), the capacitance per unit length of the transmission line is

$$C = \frac{2\pi\epsilon}{\ln (b/a)} \tag{1.66}$$

By substituting for C from Eq. (1.66) into Eq. (1.65) and then for Q

from Eq. (1.65) into Eq. (1.64) we obtain

$$E = \frac{V}{\ln{(b/a)}} \frac{1}{r} \qquad (1.67)$$

This equation expresses the electric field strength E at a point between the conductors distant r from the common axis in terms of the excess of voltage V of the inner conductor over the outer conductor and the dimensions of the conductors.

The magnetic field of a coaxial transmission line has been discussed in Part 3. If a steady current I flows along the inner conductor and back along the outer conductor, the lines of magnetic flux are circles whose planes are perpendicular to the length of the line and whose centers are on the common axis of the conductors as shown in Fig. 1.19.

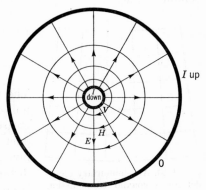

FIG. 1.19. The electromagnetic field of a coaxial transmission line.

At a point between the conductors distant r from the common axis the magnetic field strength is

$$H = \frac{I}{2\pi r} \qquad (1.68)$$

The electromagnetic field of a coaxial transmission line may be dissected by thin, conducting, circular cylinders coaxial with the bounding conductors. This does not affect either the electric or magnetic fields and corresponds to dissecting the electromagnetic field of a strip transmission line by means of conducting sheets parallel to the strips. The electromagnetic field of a coaxial transmission line may be thought of as made up of the electromagnetic fields of a series of coaxial transmission lines each fitting inside the other. By means of axial planes the electromagnetic field of a coaxial transmission line can be further subdivided into channels of the type indicated in Fig. 1.20. Moreover, if the subdivision is sufficiently fine, these channels may be considered rectangular in shape. If the channel shown in Fig. 1.20 is considered to be square and to have unit dimensions, it corresponds to the unit channel of a strip transmission line shown in Fig. 1.5. The voltage and current for the channel are given by Eqs. (1.67) and (1.68) respectively. The entire electromagnetic field of a coaxial transmission line may be thought of as made up of channels of the type indicated in Fig. 1.20, fitted together as shown in Fig. 1.19.

The flow of energy per unit area per unit time across a normal cross section of the transmission line is given by the Poynting vector $\mathbf{E} \times \mathbf{H}$. The direction of flow is downward through the paper in Fig. 1.19, and the magnitude of the flow is EH per unit area. Using the values of E and H given by Eqs. (1.67) and (1.68), we see that, at a point between the conductors distant r from the common axis, the flow of energy per unit area per unit time across a normal cross section of a coaxial transmission line is

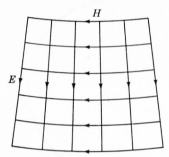

$$EH = \frac{VI}{2\pi \ln (b/a)} \frac{1}{r^2} \qquad (1.69)$$

FIG. 1.20. An elementary channel for a coaxial transmission line.

The power per unit area is not, therefore, uniform over the cross section. It decreases from the surface of the inner conductor to the surface of the outer conductor inversely proportional to the square of the distance r from the common axis. There is no flow of energy inside the hollow inner conductor, where there is no electromagnetic field, and the same applies to the region outside the outer conductor. We see, therefore, that the flow of energy between the conductors of a coaxial transmission line hugs the inner conductor, where the electromagnetic field is strongest.

From the flow of energy EH per unit area per unit time traversing a normal cross section of the transmission line, it is possible to calculate the total rate of flow of energy across the normal cross section, and the result must be the product of the voltage V between the conductors and the current I along the conductors. To demonstrate this, consider the portion of a normal cross section between radii r and $r + dr$. Let ds be an element of length of the ring thus formed. An element of area of the normal cross section at distance r from the common axis is therefore defined by $dr\, ds$, and the rate of flow of energy across this element is

$$EH\, dr\, ds \qquad (1.70)$$

Now $E\, dr$ in expression (1.70) is the voltage between the rings of radii r and $r + dr$. If we add up the contributions given by expression (1.70) for all elements of area between these rings, we obtain

$$E\, dr \int H\, ds \qquad (1.71)$$

where the integral is to be taken round the ring. From the circulation law for the magnetic field, the integral in expression (1.71) is the current I flowing along the inner conductor and back along the outer conductor.

Hence expression (1.71) becomes

$$IE \, dr \qquad (1.72)$$

This is the total rate of flow of energy across a normal cross section between a ring of radius r and one of radius $r + dr$. If we sum the contributions given by expression (1.72) for all rings constituting the normal cross section between the conductors of the transmission line, we obtain

$$I \int_a^b E \, dr \qquad (1.73)$$

The integral in this expression is the voltage V between the conductors, and it follows that the total rate of flow of energy across a normal cross section of the transmission line is

$$VI \qquad (1.74)$$

This total power is distributed over the normal cross section of the transmission line inversely proportional to the distance r from the common axis as described by Eq. (1.69).

The above analysis of the flow of energy between the conductors of a coaxial transmission line illustrates the fact that the electromagnetic fields of all transmission lines can be dissected into a large number of ideal strip transmission lines packed side by side as indicated in Fig. 1.19. No fringing is involved in the electromagnetic fields of the elementary channels, because each channel is supported by the channels around it. Thus, the ideal strip transmission line introduced in Sec. 1.2 is a useful tool in analyzing all transmission lines.

1.10. Flow of Energy along a Twin-wire Transmission Line. Consider a transmission line consisting of a pair of parallel, perfectly conducting circular wires. Figure 1.21 represents a normal cross section of the transmission line under circumstances when the left-hand wire is maintained at a positive potential with respect to the right-hand wire and a current flows down the left-hand wire and up the right-hand wire. This corresponds to a situation in which a source is connected across the transmission line above the plane of the paper and a load below the plane of the paper. The electric field of the twin-wire transmission line is discussed in Part 1, Sec. 11.4. The magnetic field of the twin-wire transmission line is discussed in Part 3, Sec. 2.8. The two fields form the electromagnetic field shown in Fig. 1.21.

The direction of the Poynting vector $\mathbf{E} \times \mathbf{H}$ is normally downward through the paper in Fig. 1.21. Outside the wires there is flow of energy across each unit area of a normal cross section. However, the flow of energy is strongest close to the wires where both the electric and magnetic fields are strongest. It is a disadvantage of a twin-wire transmission line that the flow of energy is not enclosed in any specific conduit as in the case of a coaxial transmission line. This advantage is mitigated, however, by the fact that the flow of energy hugs the two wires. The ease of construction of a twin-wire transmission line makes it the commonest arrangement used for connecting together electrical devices.

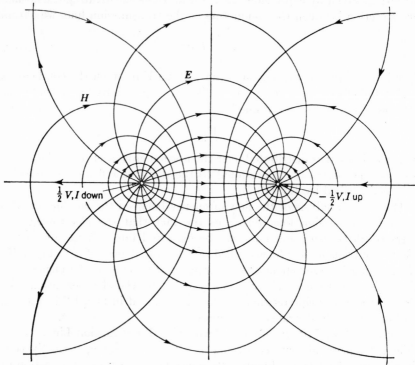

FIG. 1.21. The electromagnetic field of a twin-wire transmission line.

It should be particularly noticed that, while the currents on the two wires are flowing in opposite directions, the energy hugging the two wires is flowing in the same direction, namely, from the source toward the load. Near the positive wire the magnetic field is right-handed about the direction from the source to the load, and the electric field is radially outward from the wire. The direction of the Poynting vector $\mathbf{E} \times \mathbf{H}$ is therefore from the source to the load. Near the positive wire the flow of energy is in the same direction as the current on the wire. Near the negative wire the magnetic field is right-handed about the direction from the load to the source, but the electric field is directed radially inward toward the wire. The direction of the Poynting vector $\mathbf{E} \times \mathbf{H}$ is therefore from the source toward the load even close to the negative wire. For a twin-wire transmission line, therefore, the stream of energy leaving the source and flowing in the space surrounding the wires splits into two streams, one of which hugs the positive wire and the other the negative wire. These two streams of energy both flow into the load.

As in the case of a coaxial transmission line, a twin-wire transmission line may be analyzed into channels, each of which may be considered as a strip transmission line. The entire electromagnetic field of the twin-wire transmission line may be regarded as formed by strip transmission lines suitably packed together side by side. No fringing is involved in these elementary strip transmission lines because each is supported by the strip transmission lines by which it is surrounded. The argument associated with expressions (1.70) to (1.74) can be adapted to verify for a twin-wire transmission line, or indeed for any transmission line, the fact that the total rate of flow of energy across any normal cross section of the line is the product of voltage and current at that cross section.

1.11. Flow of Energy inside a Conducting Wire. For simplicity we have hitherto supposed that the conductors of the transmission lines under study were perfect conductors. In a perfect conductor no electric field is required to drive the current. In a place where there is no electric field, there can be no flow of energy in accordance with the Poynting vector $\mathbf{E} \times \mathbf{H}$. When the conductors of a transmission line are perfect conductors, therefore, the entire flow of energy is in the space surrounding the conductors. Thus, while the current flows in the wires, the energy flows in the space between the wires.

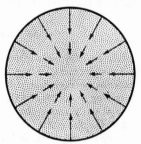

FIG. 1.22. Illustrating the radially inward flow of energy in a resistive wire.

In actual fact the conductors of a transmission line cannot be perfect conductors, and some flow of energy does therefore take place in the wires. Let us examine the nature of this flow of energy in a wire.

Consider a solid circular conducting wire carrying steady current uniformly distributed over the cross section. Figure 1.22 represents a normal cross section of such a wire, and the current is supposed to be downward through the paper. The magnetic field both inside and outside such a wire has been discussed in Part 3, Sec. 2.6. The lines of magnetic flux are in circles whose planes are perpendicular to the wire and whose centers lie on the axis of the wire. The magnetic field strength in the wire decreases linearly to zero at the center in accordance with Part 3, Eq. (2.27).

In a resistive wire the electric vector is in the direction of current flow. In Fig. 1.22, therefore, the electric vector is normally downward through the paper, and the electric field strength has the same value at all points of the normal cross section of the wire. The magnetic vector points round circles coaxial with the wire, and the magnetic field strength decreases linearly to zero at the center of the wire. If we form the Poynting vector **E** × **H**, we see that the direction of energy flow in the resistive wire is radially inward, and its magnitude decreases linearly to zero at the center. Thus the direction of energy flow in a resistive wire is not along the wire but is radially inward as shown in Fig. 1.22.

For a perfectly conducting wire the flow of energy is entirely outside the wire and is parallel to the length of the wire. If the wire is not perfectly conducting, some of this passing energy is abstracted by the wire and flows radially into the wire. The energy flowing into the wire is used to accelerate electrons between collisions and to maintain the steady drift of electrons. Thus the effect of resistance in the conductors of a transmission line is to abstract sideways some of the energy flowing along the line between the conductors. The energy abstracted sideways by the conductors is used to maintain the flow of current in the conductors against their resistance.

SUMMARIZING EXERCISES

1.1. Explain what is meant by a strip transmission line. A strip transmission line has perfectly conducting strips of width b with a separation a between them. The material between the strips has capacitivity ϵ, conductivity σ, and inductivity μ. Assuming uniformity of the fields, calculate the capacitance, conductance, and inductance of the transmission line per unit length.

1.2. To one end of the strip transmission line described in the previous exercise a battery is connected, and to the other end a resistor. The battery has a voltage V and delivers a current I. For the space between the strips calculate (a) the electric field strength, (b) the magnetic field strength, (c) the electric flux density, and (d) the magnetic flux density, assuming that the fields between the strips are uniform. Calculate also the charges per unit length on the strips and the magnetic flux threading between the strips per unit length of the line.

1.3. In the arrangement described in the previous exercise the terminating resistor consists of a uniform rectangular sheet of resistive material of edges a and b connected to the ends of the strips along the edges of length b. Explain what is meant by the surface resistance of the resistive sheet. In terms of the surface resistance and the linear dimensions of the rectangle, calculate the resistance connected between the conductors of the transmission line.

1.4. For the arrangement described in the previous two exercises, explain how the electromagnetic field between the strips can be dissected into unit channels. Show that, for each unit channel, the voltage is numerically equal to the electric field strength, the current is numerically equal to the magnetic field strength, the inductance per unit length is numerically equal to the inductivity of the medium, and the capacitance per unit length is numerically equal to the capacitivity of the medium. Explain why, for a unit channel, the phenomenon of fringing does not arise.

1.5. Explain what is meant by the statement that the rate of flow of energy along a unit channel is equal to the product of the electric field strength and the magnetic field strength. Define the Poynting vector.

1.6. If any electromagnetic field is bounded by a surface in such a way that the tangential component of the magnetic vector on the opposite side of the surface vanishes, show that the energy absorbed by the surface per unit area per unit time is equal to the inward normal component of the Poynting vector.

1.7. A length l of a strip transmission line composed of strips of width b and separation a is used as a capacitor and is charged by means of a current source delivering a constant current I_0 connected to one end of the line. Describe the process whereby the generator stores electric energy in the capacitor. Show that it is essential to the process that the magnetic field of the generator fringe into the electric field of the capacitor.

1.8. The space between the inner and outer conductors of a coaxial transmission line has an inner radius a and an outer radius b and is filled with a homogeneous nonconducting medium. The inner and outer surfaces of the transmission line are perfect conductors. To one end of the transmission line is connected a resistor, and to the other is connected a battery of voltage V delivering a current I. Neglecting fringing at the ends of the transmission line, calculate the electric and magnetic field strengths at any point between the conductors distant r from the common axis. Calculate the rate of flow of energy per unit area along the transmission line between the inner and outer conductors, showing that it is inversely proportional to r^2.

1.9. For the coaxial transmission line described in the previous exercise, verify that the integral of the power density over a normal cross section of the transmission line is equal to VI.

1.10. A section of twin-wire transmission line has a resistor connected at one end and a battery at the other. Explain why the flow of energy close to both wires is in the same direction while the currents are in opposite directions.

1.11. A solid circular wire is made of material of conductivity σ and carries a steady current I uniformly distributed over the cross section. Show that the flow of energy in the wire is radially inward, and explain the physical significance of this result.

CHAPTER 2

DISPLACEMENT CURRENT

2.1. Introduction. In Parts 2 and 3 we were concerned with steady flow of electric current round closed circuits. In general, however, it is not necessary for electric current to flow in closed circuits. Consider, for example, the process of charging a capacitor, studied in the previous chapter. In Fig. 1.11 the current generator causes electric current to flow from the lower plate to the upper plate. No closed electric circuit exists, however, and the flow of current results merely in increasing the charges on the plates of the capacitor. Flow of electric current in general results in transport of charge from one place to another, the positive charge increasing with time at the point of arrival and the negative charge increasing with time at the point of departure. These increasing positive and negative charges are avoided only in the special case of flow in closed circuits.

2.2. An Example of an Unclosed Flow of Electric Current. Let us examine the unclosed flow of electric current involved in charging the capacitor shown in Fig. 1.11. Figure 1.13b illustrates the fact that the current I along the strips decreases as we move from left to right in Fig. 1.11. In going from the normal cross section of the transmission line at distance x from the left-hand end to the normal cross section at distance $x + dx$, let the decrease in the current I flowing along the strips be $-dI$. For the upper strip this is the excess of the current flowing to the right at position x over the current flowing to the right at position $x + dx$. It is, therefore, the rate at which charge is accumulating on the upper strip between these two locations. If Q is the charge per unit length of the upper strip, the amount of charge on the upper strip between locations x and $x + dx$ is $Q\,dx$. The principle of conservation of charge therefore requires that

$$-dI = \frac{d}{dt}(Q\,dx) \tag{2.1}$$

This equation can be rewritten as

$$-\frac{dI}{dx} = \frac{dQ}{dt} \tag{2.2}$$

the truth of which can be verified from expressions (1.39) and (1.48). For the arrangement shown in Fig. 1.11, Eq. (2.2) expresses the relation that must exist between the current I along the strips and the charge Q per unit length on the strips in order to ensure that the principle of conservation of charge is satisfied.

Let us imagine that the arrangement shown in Fig. 1.11 is dissected into unit channels as indicated in Fig. 1.6, and let us apply Eq. (2.2) to a unit channel. For a unit channel the current I is identical with the magnetic field strength H between the strips, and the charge per unit length Q on the strips is identical with the electric flux density D between the strips. For a unit channel, therefore, Eq. (2.2) becomes

$$- \frac{dH}{dx} = \frac{dD}{dt} \qquad (2.3)$$

This equation illustrates the fact that there is a relation between the magnetic vector H and the electric-flux-density vector D. As described in Part 3, Chap. 3, the magnetic vector H gives a complete description of the geometry of the current flow associated with a magnetic field or any dissected portion thereof. Likewise, as described in Part 1, Chap. 3, the electric-flux-density vector D gives a complete description of the geometry of the charge distribution associated with an electric field or any dissected portion thereof. The relation between current flow and charge accumulation that is imposed by the principle of conservation of charge consequently implies a relation between the magnetic vector H and the electric-flux-density vector D in any electromagnetic field. Equation (2.3) is a statement of this relation for the arrangement shown in Fig. 1.11.

The existence of a relation between the magnetic vector H and the electric-flux-density vector D was discovered by James Clerk Maxwell in the middle of the nineteenth century. This discovery constituted a major advance in electrical science and permitted Maxwell to predict theoretically the existence of radio waves many years before their existence was demonstrated experimentally.

2.3. Relation between the Magnetic Vector H and the Electric-current-density Vector J. Before considering the relation that exists between the magnetic vector H and the electric-flux-density vector D, let us consider the relation that exists between the magnetic vector H and the current-density vector J for any closed, steady flow of current. The circulation law for the magnetic vector was described in Part 3, Sec. 4.2. The current-density vector J was first introduced in Part 2, Sec. 1.4, and further discussed in Part 3, Sec. 1.8.

Suppose that steady current flows round a closed circuit or system of closed circuits, thereby producing a magnetic field. Let C be a closed geometrical curve drawn in this magnetic field. At a point P of C let d**s**

be a vector element of length of C, and let the magnetic vector at C be
$\mathbf{H}$. From Part 3, Eq. (4.6), it follows that

$$\int_C \mathbf{H} \cdot d\mathbf{s} = I \tag{2.4}$$

where I is the total electric current threading the closed curve C in the
direction related by the right-hand-screw rule to the direction in which
$d\mathbf{s}$ points round C.

If the closed curve C is threaded by only one wire, then I in Eq. (2.4)
is the current along this wire taken in the appropriate direction.   If the
closed curve C is threaded by a number of wires, then I in Eq. (2.4) is
the algebraic sum of the currents on the various wires threading C, each
taken in the direction related by the right-hand-screw rule to the direction in which $d\mathbf{s}$ points round C.   If the closed curve C is drawn inside
conducting material, then I in Eq. (2.4) is the total current along those
tubes of flow threading C.   As described in Part 3, Sec. 1.8, the current I
threading C in this situation can be determined by drawing a surface S
spanning C.   Let $d\mathbf{S}$ be a vector element of area of S pointing in the
direction related by the right-hand-screw rule to the direction of $d\mathbf{s}$
round C.   At the element of area $d\mathbf{S}$ of S let $\mathbf{J}$ be the electric-current-
density vector.   It follows from Part 3, Eq. (1.20), that the total current
crossing the surface S is

$$I = \int_S \mathbf{J} \cdot d\mathbf{S} \tag{2.5}$$

Moreover this equation also evaluates the current I threading the closed
curve C when the current is flowing on individual wires.   In this case the
contributions to the integral on the right-hand side of Eq. (2.5) are zero
except where the spanning surface S intercepts the wires.   Thus Eq.
(2.5) gives, in all circumstances, the current I threading the closed curve
C spanned by the surface S.

Let us now substitute for I from Eq. (2.5) into Eq. (2.4), thereby
obtaining

$$\int_C \mathbf{H} \cdot d\mathbf{s} = \int_S \mathbf{J} \cdot d\mathbf{S} \tag{2.6}$$

This is a statement of the circulation law for the magnetic vector $\mathbf{H}$
associated with any closed, steady flow of current represented by a current-density vector $\mathbf{J}$.   Equation (2.6) states that the line integral of the
magnetic vector $\mathbf{H}$ round any closed geometrical curve C in the magnetic
field of any closed, steady flow of current is equal to the surface integral
of the current-density vector $\mathbf{J}$ over any surface S spanning C, it being
understood that the directions of the vectors $d\mathbf{s}$ and $d\mathbf{S}$ are related by the
right-hand-screw rule.

2.4. Electric Current round a Circuit Containing a Capacitor.   Let us consider an electric circuit in which the flow of current is interrupted by a capacitor as shown in Fig. 2.1.   For simplicity let us suppose for the time being that the region surrounding the conductor in Fig. 2.1 is a vacuum.   Let the generator deliver a current I, and let us not exclude the possibility that I may depend upon time t.   Let us suppose that, at time zero, no current is flowing and the capacitor is uncharged.   As a result of the current flowing subsequent to time zero, electrons are transferred from one plate of the capacitor to the other.   Let the resulting charges on the plates of the capacitor at time t be Q and $-Q$.   Let the signs be so chosen that the current I is flowing onto the plate carrying charge Q.   As a result of the current I flowing onto the upper plate of

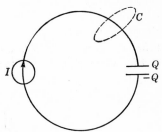

FIG. 2.1. An electric circuit in which the current is interrupted by a capacitor.

the capacitor in Fig. 2.1, the charge Q on this plate is increasing with time t.   From the principle of conservation of charge we have

$$I = \frac{dQ}{dt} \tag{2.7}$$

This equation states that the charge on the upper plate of the capacitor is increasing with time at the rate at which charge is being conveyed to the plate by the current.   Equation (2.7) also states that the negative charge on the lower plate of the capacitor in Fig. 2.1 is increasing at a rate equal to that at which charge is being removed by the current I.

In Fig. 2.1 there is a current I approaching the upper plate of the capacitor and an equal current I leaving the lower plate of the capacitor. This is sometimes described by saying that there is a current I "through" the capacitor.   In this sense one might say that the current I in Fig. 2.1 constitutes a closed flow of current and that the circulation of the magnetic vector round a geometrical closed curve C threading the circuit satisfies the circulation law expressed by Eq. (2.4).   However, in fact, there is no current passing from the upper plate of the capacitor to the lower plate through the intervening vacuum, and in consequence care is necessary in interpreting the circulation law (2.4).

Let us apply the circulation law in the form (2.6) to the situation illustrated in Fig. 2.1.   In the first instance let us draw the surface S spanning the closed curve C so that it intersects the wire carrying the current I. Contributions to the right-hand side of Eq. (2.6) then vanish except where the surface S crosses the wire, where the value of the integral is I.   However, let us now suppose that the surface S spanning the closed curve is drawn so as not to intersect the wire, but instead to pass between the plates of the capacitor. The current-density vector $\mathbf{J}$ then vanishes at all points of the surface S, and the right-hand side of Eq. (2.6) is zero. We thus have an absurd situation in which the circulation of the magnetic vector round the same closed curve C in the same magnetic field is I or zero according as the spanning surface S is drawn so as to intersect the wire or so as to pass between the capacitor plates. This impossible situation indicates that Eq. (2.6) requires modification for application to a flow of current other than a closed flow.

2.5. Maxwell's Displacement Current. Figure 2.2 shows in greater detail the part of the circuit in Fig. 2.1 in the neighborhood of the capaci-

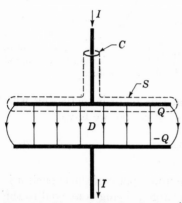

FIG. 2.2. The neighborhood of the capacitor in the circuit shown in Fig. 2.1.

tor. In Fig. 2.2 the current I flows in at the top and increases the charge Q on the upper plate of the capacitor, while an equal current I flows out at the bottom and increases the negative charge on the lower plate of the capacitor. In the neighborhood of the capacitor there is a field of electric flux density $\mathbf{D}$, which is nearly a parallel field passing from the upper plate to the lower plate. For the situation existing at any particular time t, the field of electric flux density represents, as described in Part 1, Chap. 3, a flux of charge that would discharge the system. In particular the outward normal electric flux density just outside a conductor is equal to the charge per unit area on the conductor near that point. The closed curve C of Fig. 2.1 is taken in Fig. 2.2 to coincide very nearly with the perimeter of a normal cross section of the wire connected to the positive plate of the capacitor. If the surface spanning the closed curve C is taken to be the normal cross section of the wire at C, evaluation of the right-hand side of Eq. (2.6) gives the current I flowing along the wire toward the positive plate of the capacitor as described by Eq. (2.5). Now let us suppose, however, that the surface S spanning C is taken to be that represented by the dashed line in Fig. 2.2. This surface is a surface that is wrapped tightly round the positive plate of the capacitor and the wire joining this plate to the closed curve C. This surface is therefore one that is open only enough to allow the wire carrying the electric current I to pass through the rim C. At all points of this surface S the current density J vanishes, and therefore the integral on the right-hand side of Eq. (2.5) is zero. However, it is possible to evaluate the current

I flowing through the closed curve C with the aid of the surface S in Fig. 2.2 in the following way: Let dS be an element of area of S, and let D be the electric flux density at the position of this element. Then D is also the charge per unit area on the conductor at the point adjacent to the element of area dS. It follows that the total charge on the conductor enveloped by the surface S is

$$Q = \int_S D \, dS \qquad (2.8)$$

Most of this charge is on the underside of the upper plate of the capacitor. If fringing is taken into account, however, a little of the charge exists on the top surface of the upper plate and even on the wire connected to this plate. If we now substitute from Eq. (2.8) into Eq. (2.7), we obtain

$$I = \frac{d}{dt} \int_S D \, dS \qquad (2.9)$$

This equation demonstrates the possibility of evaluating the current I flowing round the wire in Fig. 2.1 by means of an integral over a surface S that does not intersect the wire but instead passes between the plates of the capacitor; moreover, to achieve this objective, use must be made of the electric flux density D.

Let us, therefore, consider the field of electric flux density between the plates of the capacitor. The tubes of electric flux are as indicated in Fig. 2.2. At a point P between the plates let $\mathbf{D}$ be the electric-flux-density vector at time t. From the definition of the electric-flux-density vector given in Part 1, Chap. 3, it follows that, if at time t the capacitor were instantaneously discharged along the tubes of electric flux, then the flux, or displacement, of charge per unit area at the point P would be represented by the vector $\mathbf{D}$. Likewise, at time $t + dt$, instantaneous discharge of the capacitor along the tubes of electric flux would result in a displacement of charge per unit area past the point P represented by a vector $\mathbf{D} + d\mathbf{D}$. During the interval of time dt, therefore, there is an increase $d\mathbf{D}$ in the displacement of charge past the point P per unit area required in discharging the capacitor along tubes of electric flux. This may be expressed by saying that, if in the vacuum between the plates of the capacitor there existed a flow of current for which the current-density vector is

$$\frac{\partial \mathbf{D}}{\partial t} \qquad (2.10)$$

then there would be no accumulation of charge on the plates of the capacitor. The current flow implied by expression (2.10) would discharge the capacitor through the intervening vacuum as fast as the current I charged

it.   This means that the current density given by expression (2.10) forms
with the current I round the wire a closed flow of current as indicated in
Fig. 2.3.   It is the absence of the current represented by the current-
density vector (2.10) that results in the accumulation of positive and
negative charges on the plates of the capacitor.

The current that would correspond to the current-density vector (2.10)

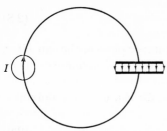

is known as Maxwell's displacement current.   The partial derivative with respect
to time is used in expression (2.10)
because the vector $\mathbf{D}$ is also a function of
position in space.   The most important
property of Maxwell's displacement current is that it does not flow.   It is the
absence of Maxwell's displacement current between the plates of capacitors that
results in the accumulation of charge on
the plates.   If Maxwell's displacement
current were added to the current actually

FIG. 2.3. Illustrating the fact that
a current density $\partial \mathbf{D}/\partial t$ between
the plates of the capacitor would
complete a closed electric current.

flowing through the conductors, a closed flow of current would result.
This may be expressed by saying that, if

$$\mathbf{J} \tag{2.11}$$

is the current-density vector representing the current actually flowing
through the conductors, then the combination of the flow (2.11) and the
flow (2.10) would form a closed flow.   In other words the flow of current
represented by the current-density vector

$$\mathbf{J} + \frac{\partial \mathbf{D}}{\partial t} \tag{2.12}$$

represents a closed flow of current.   The fact that the flow represented
by the second term in expression (2.12) does not in fact exist means that
the actual flow, represented by the first term in expression (2.12), is an
unclosed flow that leads to accumulation of charges in locations such as
the plates of capacitors.

2.6. Maxwell's Circulation Law for the Magnetic Vector.   We are
now in a position to see how to adapt the circulation law for the magnetic
vector, originally stated in the form (2.4) for a closed flow of current, to a
situation involving an unclosed flow as indicated in Fig. 2.1.   The procedure is to take the circulation law in the form of Eq. (2.6), but to replace
the unclosed flow of current represented by the current-density vector $\mathbf{J}$
by the closed flow represented by the current-density vector (2.12).
In this way we arrive at the equation

$$\int_C \mathbf{H} \cdot d\mathbf{s} = \int_S \left(\mathbf{J} + \frac{\partial \mathbf{D}}{\partial t} \right) \cdot d\mathbf{S} \tag{2.13}$$

This form of the circulation law for the magnetic vector applies to any geometrical closed curve C drawn in any electromagnetic field and spanned by any surface S. In Eq. (2.13) ds is a vector element of length of C and $d\mathbf{S}$ is a vector element of area of S, and it is assumed that the directions of these two vectors are related by the right-hand-screw rule. $\mathbf{H}$ is the magnetic vector at the position of the vector element of length ds of C. $\mathbf{J}$ is the current-density vector representing the flow of current at the position of the vector element of area $d\mathbf{S}$ of S. $\mathbf{D}$ is the electric-flux-density vector at the position of the vector element of area $d\mathbf{S}$ of S.

Let us apply the circulation law for the magnetic vector in the form given by Eq. (2.13) to the situation depicted in Fig. 2.1 using the closed curve C indicated by the dashed line. If a surface S is drawn spanning C, but not passing near the capacitor, then at all points of S the electric flux density $\mathbf{D}$ is negligible, as indicated in Fig. 2.2. With $\mathbf{D}$ negligible in Eq. (2.13), the circulation law for the magnetic vector reduces to Eq. (2.6) and so to Eq. (2.4). If, therefore, the closed curve C in Fig. 2.1 is spanned by a surface S that intersects the wire and does not pass near the capacitor, the circulation of the magnetic vector round C simply gives the current I flowing round the wire. Now suppose, however, that the closed curve C in Fig. 2.1 is spanned by a surface S that does not intersect the wire but, instead, passes between the plates of the capacitor. At all points of this surface the current-density vector $\mathbf{J}$ in Eq. (2.13) is zero. In these circumstances Eq. (2.13) reduces to

$$\int_C \mathbf{H} \cdot ds = \int_S \frac{\partial \mathbf{D}}{\partial t} \cdot d\mathbf{S} \qquad (2.14)$$

which can also be written as

$$\int_C \mathbf{H} \cdot ds = \frac{\partial}{\partial t} \int_S \mathbf{D} \cdot d\mathbf{S} \qquad (2.15)$$

If the closed curve C and the spanning surface S are drawn as indicated in Fig. 2.2, then the right-hand side of Eq. (2.15) becomes identical with the right-hand side of Eq. (2.9) and so is equal to the current I along the wire. The partial derivative with regard to time is retained in Eq. (2.15) in order to emphasize the fact that S is a surface fixed in space.

For the flow of steady current round closed circuits discussed in Parts 2 and 3, the electric field required to drive the current does not vary with time. In consequence, the associated electric-flux-density vector $\mathbf{D}$ at any point in the field does not vary with time. In these circumstances Eq. (2.13) reduces to Eq. (2.6) and, therefore, to Eq. (2.4). On the other hand, in the presence of an electric field that does vary with time, the circulation law for the magnetic vector $\mathbf{H}$ contains, on the right-hand side of Eq. (2.13), the quantity $\partial \mathbf{D}/\partial t$. Thus, in a time-varying electric field, the circulation law for the magnetic field constitutes a relation between the magnetic vector **H** and the electric-flux-density vector **D**. In a part of space where no current is flowing, this relation between the magnetic vector **H** and the electric-flux-density vector **D** reduces to the form given in Eq. (2.15). This equation can be expressed in words by saying that, in a part of space where no electric current is flowing, the circulation of the magnetic vector round any closed curve C is equal to the time rate of increase of the electric flux threading C. In a part of space where electric current is flowing, however, the current threading C must be added to the time rate of increase of the threading electric flux in accordance with Eq. (2.13). Both the electric current threading C and the electric flux threading C must be taken in the direction related by the right-hand-screw rule to the direction in which ds points round C.

2.7. The Significance of Maxwell's Displacement Current. If the region surrounding the conductors is a vacuum, then, as already described in Sec. 2.5, the most significant feature of Maxwell's displacement current given by expression (2.10) is that it does not flow. It is the absence of this flow that results in the actual flow of current leading to accumulation of charge on the surfaces of conductors. If, however, the space surrounding the conductors is filled with a dielectric material, then there is a portion of Maxwell's displacement current that does flow through the insulating material. Let us consider a piece of insulating material whose capacitivity is ϵ, and let there exist in the material an electric field that varies with time t. The relation between the electric vector **E** and the electric-flux-density vector **D** at any point in the material is given by

$$\mathbf{D} = \epsilon \mathbf{E} \qquad (2.16)$$

In terms of the vacuum capacitivity ϵ_v this equation can be written as

$$\mathbf{D} = \mathbf{D}_v + \mathbf{P} \qquad (2.17)$$
where
$$\mathbf{D}_v = \epsilon_v \mathbf{E} \qquad (2.18)$$
and
$$\mathbf{P} = (\epsilon - \epsilon_v)\mathbf{E} \qquad (2.19)$$

$\mathbf{D}_v$ given by Eq. (2.18) is the electric-flux-density vector that would exist in the absence of the insulating material. As explained in Part 1, Sec. 4.9, **P** is the correction to $\mathbf{D}_v$ arising from distortion, or polarization, of the electronic cloud associated with an atom or molecule of the insulating material. In circumstances when the electric vector **E** varies with time, the degree of distortion of the atoms or molecules of the insulating material varies with time. The varying distortion of the electronic clouds associated with the atoms or molecules of the material constitutes a current in the insulating material. This is not a current of free electrons as in a metal, but a current of bound electrons arising from a time variation in the distortion of the electronic clouds associated with the atoms or molecules of the insulating material. Substituting from Eq. (2.17) into expression (2.10) we see that Maxwell's displacement-current-density vector in a dielectric is given by

$$\frac{\partial \mathbf{D}}{\partial t} = \frac{\partial \mathbf{D}_v}{\partial t} + \frac{\partial \mathbf{P}}{\partial t} \tag{2.20}$$

The second term on the right-hand side of Eq. (2.20) is an actual current flowing in the insulating material and arising from a variation in the distortion of the electronic clouds associated with the atoms or molecules of the insulator. For a dielectric, therefore, it is only the current corresponding to the first term on the right-hand side in Eq. (2.20) that does not flow. This is the current that, in the absence of the insulating material, constitutes the whole contribution to Maxwell's displacement current.

2.8. An Application of the Circulation Law for the Magnetic Vector in an Electric Field That Varies with Time. As an example of the application of the circulation law for the magnetic vector under circumstances when Maxwell's displacement current must be taken into account, let us again consider the process of charging a capacitor illustrated in Fig. 1.11. Consider a cross section of the field of the capacitor by a plane between the strips and parallel to them. Figure 2.4 illustrates the situation in

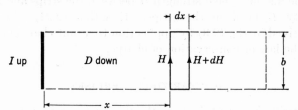

FIG. 2.4. Illustrating application of the circulation law for the magnetic vector to the arrangement shown in Fig. 1.11.

such a plane as seen from the positive plate of the capacitor, so that the direction of the electric-flux-density vector $\mathbf{D}$ is downward through the paper. In Fig. 2.4 a rectangle is drawn between two normal cross sections of the transmission line at distances x and $x + dx$ from the left-hand end of the line. The rectangle thus formed has a dimension dx along the line and b across the line. The direction of the magnetic vector $\mathbf{H}$ in the transmission line is parallel to the long sides of this rectangle as indicated in Fig. 2.4. Let H be the magnetic field strength along the side of the rectangle at position x, and let $H + dH$ be the magnetic field strength along the side at position $x + dx$. The circulation of the magnetic vector round the rectangle in the direction related by the right-hand-screw rule to the direction of the electric-flux-density vector is

$$\int \mathbf{H} \cdot ds = Hb - (H + dH)b$$

which simplifies to

$$\int \mathbf{H} \cdot ds = -b\, dH \tag{2.21}$$

The electric flux that is threading the rectangle in the downward direction in Fig. 2.4 is

$$\int \mathbf{D} \cdot d\mathbf{S} = Db\, dx \tag{2.22}$$

and consequently the Maxwellian displacement current threading the rectangle is

$$\frac{d}{dt} \int \mathbf{D} \cdot d\mathbf{S} = \frac{dD}{dt}\, b\, dx \tag{2.23}$$

Substituting from Eqs. (2.21) and (2.23) into Eq. (2.15) we obtain

$$-b\, dH = \frac{dD}{dt}\, b\, dx$$

which can be rewritten as

$$-\frac{dH}{dx} = \frac{dD}{dt} \tag{2.24}$$

This constitutes, for the arrangement shown in Fig. 1.11, a relation between the magnetic field strength H between the strips and the electric flux density D between the strips. Equation (2.24) is the relation already derived in Eq. (2.3) by application to a unit channel of Eq. (2.2) based on the law of conservation of charge.

SUMMARIZING EXERCISES

2.1. A capacitor is connected into an electric circuit carrying a current I. Show that, on the plate of the capacitor toward which the current is directed, charge is accumulating at a rate equal to I. Show also that, on the plate of the capacitor away from which the current is directed, negative charge is accumulating at the same rate. Explain why these accumulations of charge would not take place if at each point in the medium between the plates there existed a current-density vector equal to the time rate of increase of the electric-flux-density vector.

2.2. Explain what is meant by Maxwell's displacement current. In a dielectric, distinguish between the part of Maxwell's displacement current that exists and the part that does not exist.

2.3. A closed flow of steady current is described by means of a vector field of current density $\mathbf{J}$; write down the circulation law for the magnetic vector $\mathbf{H}$. Describe how the circulation law for the magnetic vector is modified in an electric field that varies with time. Write down the circulation law for the magnetic vector applicable in a part of space where no current flows but the electric field varies with time.

CHAPTER 3

MAGNETICALLY INDUCED VOLTAGE

3.1. Introduction. Another important relation between electric and magnetic fields arises from the fact that motion of a conductor in a magnetic field creates an electric field. It is this phenomenon that is used for generating electric power by means of rotating electrical machinery. The basic features of the electrical machine known as an electric motor were discussed in Part 3, Secs. 6.4 and 8.12. An electric motor is used to convert power supplied in electrical form into power delivered in mechanical form. The same machine can be used in reverse to convert power supplied in mechanical form into power delivered in electrical form. When used in this way, the machine is known as a dynamo, or generator.

3.2. Motion of a Conductor through a Steady Magnetic Field. Consider a magnetic circuit of rectangular cross section, one dimension of which is a as shown in Fig. 3.1. Let the magnetic flux passing round the circuit have uniform magnetic flux density B, and let the direction of this flux density be downward through the paper in Fig. 3.1. Let us suppose that there exists in the magnetic circuit a narrow gap between a pair of normal cross sections. In this gap place a piece of

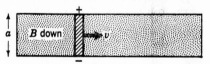

FIG. 3.1. Illustrating motion of a short piece of wire through a gap in a magnetic circuit.

metallic wire of length a as indicated in Fig. 3.1. Starting with the wire initially at rest, let us move the wire to the right across the magnetic field.

As described in Part 3, Chap. 2, an electron moving with velocity **v** across a magnetic field whose flux-density vector is **B** is subject to a force of magnetic origin, the force per unit charge being

$$\mathbf{v} \times \mathbf{B} \qquad (3.1)$$

In the arrangement shown in Fig. 3.1 the piece of wire of length a is supposed to be moved to the right with velocity v. The electrons in the wire are therefore moved with velocity v across a magnetic field of flux density B. These electrons are therefore subject to a force per unit

589

charge equal to

$$vB \tag{3.2}$$

parallel to the wire. The resulting displacement of electrons in the wire leads to a positive charge at the upper end of the wire and a negative charge at the lower end of the wire, as indicated in Fig. 3.1. These charges produce an electric field similar to that for a pair of equal and opposite point charges.

Let us suppose that the wire starts from rest and quickly acquires a steady velocity v across the magnetic field. The charges near the ends of the wire build up under the influence of the force of magnetic origin given by expression (3.2). As charges near the top and bottom of the wire build up, a downward electric field strength E is brought into play in the wire. This reduces the force tending to displace electrons along the wire, and a steady state is reached when the charges near the ends of the wire have built up to the stage where

$$E = vB \tag{3.3}$$

In this situation the upward force per unit charge of magnetic origin in the wire is balanced by the downward force of electric origin due to the charges that have built up near the upper and lower ends of the wire. This illustrates in a simple way how motion of a conductor across a magnetic field creates an electric field.

Let us now suppose that a portion of the strip transmission line shown in Fig. 1.1 is such that the separation between the plates is identical with the dimension a in Fig. 3.1. Let us connect the strip transmission line across the wire shown in Fig. 3.1 to form the arrangement shown in

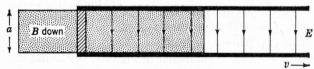

FIG. 3.2. Illustrating the charging of a capacitor by motion across a magnetic field of a wire connecting the plates.

Fig. 3.2.   Displacement of electrons along the wire traversing the magnetic field is now used to charge the capacitor formed by the strip transmission line.   The capacitor charges until the electric field strength between its plates is given by Eq. (3.3).   At this stage the combined forces of electric and magnetic origin on electrons in the vertical wire connecting the plates are zero, and no further increase takes place in the charges on the plates.   The separation between the plates of the capacitor being a, the voltage between the plates is obtained by multiplying

Eq. (3.3) by a and is, therefore,

$$V = vBa \qquad (3.4)$$

If motion of the vertical wire in Fig. 3.2 across the magnetic field ceases, the capacitor discharges through the wire.   In these circumstances both V and v in Eq. (3.4) become zero.   We see, therefore, that motion of the

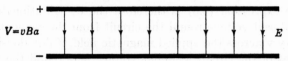

FIG. 3.3. Illustrating the voltage of a battery that would charge the capacitor shown in Fig. 3.2 to the same extent as that produced by motion in the presence of the magnetic field.

vertical wire across the magnetic field in Fig. 3.2 creates the same situation as would be created by connecting a battery of voltage V between the plates as indicated in Fig. 3.3, the voltage V being given by Eq. (3.4).

3.3. Magnetically Induced Voltage round Any Circuit Moving in a Steady Magnetic Field.   The voltage given by Eq. (3.4) is described as a magnetically induced voltage and arises from operation of the force of magnetic origin given, per unit charge, by expression (3.1).   For any electric circuit in motion in a steady magnetic field there is a magnetically induced voltage that can be calculated from the expression (3.1) as follows:

Let us suppose that C in Fig. 3.4 represents an electric circuit in motion; its motion may involve distortion.   Let a magnetic field that does not vary with time be applied to the circuit.   The magnetic field may, however, vary in magnitude and direction from point to point in space.   At a point P of the circuit C let $d\mathbf{s}$ be a vector element of length pointing round the circuit in the direction in which the magnetically induced voltage is to be regarded as acting.   Let the element of length $d\mathbf{s}$ be in motion with velocity $\mathbf{v}$, and let the applied magnetic-flux-density vector at P be $\mathbf{B}$.   Then the force of magnetic origin per unit charge acting upon electrons in the circuit at P is given, in accordance with expression (3.1), by $\mathbf{v} \times \mathbf{B}$.   The component of the force $\mathbf{v} \times \mathbf{B}$ per unit charge perpendicular to the circuit at P leads to a positive charge on one side of the wire and to a negative charge on the other, but does not contribute to a force tending to move electrons round the circuit.   The contribution of the element of length at P to the magnetically induced voltage round the circuit thus arises from the component of the vector $\mathbf{v} \times \mathbf{B}$ in the

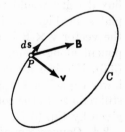

FIG. 3.4. Illustrating the calculation of magnetically induced voltage.

direction of the vector element of length ds. Let us consider the scalar product of the vector $\mathbf{v} \times \mathbf{B}$ and the vector $d\mathbf{s}$, namely,

$$(\mathbf{v} \times \mathbf{B}) \cdot d\mathbf{s} \tag{3.5}$$

This expression is the product of the component of the force per unit charge $\mathbf{v} \times \mathbf{B}$ round the circuit and the length ds of the element of circuit at P. The expression (3.5) is therefore the contribution to the magnetically induced voltage round the circuit from the element $d\mathbf{s}$ moving with velocity $\mathbf{v}$ across the applied magnetic field of flux density $\mathbf{B}$. For each element of the circuit a similar voltage acts round the circuit, and the total voltage is obtained by adding up the contributions from the various elements concerned. The total magnetically induced voltage is therefore

$$V = \int_C (\mathbf{v} \times \mathbf{B}) \cdot d\mathbf{s} \tag{3.6}$$

where the integral is taken round the electric circuit C or such part of it as may be under discussion. The magnetically induced voltage given by Eq. (3.6) is to be regarded as acting round the circuit in the direction defined by the vector element of length $d\mathbf{s}$.

Let us apply Eq. (3.6) to the situation illustrated in Fig. 3.2. Assuming that the magnetic field is confined to the magnetic circuit, the magnetic flux density vanishes at all points of the conductor except along the vertical wire. The component of the vector $\mathbf{v} \times \mathbf{B}$ along this wire is expression (3.2), and its value does not vary along the length a of the wire. The integral on the right-hand side of Eq. (3.6) therefore evaluates to the expression on the right-hand side of Eq. (3.4). If the magnetic field were not completely confined to the magnetic circuit, the magnetic flux density would not be negligible along those parts of the capacitor plates in Fig. 3.2 in contact with the magnetic circuit. However, the vector $\mathbf{v} \times \mathbf{B}$ is normal to the capacitor plates and so has no component along them. Hence, the integral on the right-hand side of Eq. (3.6), if taken along the entire conductor in Fig. 3.2 consisting of the lower capacitor plate, the vertical wire, and the upper capacitor plate, still reduces to the contribution associated with the vertical wire, which is given by Eq. (3.4).

3.4. Conversion of Energy from Mechanical to Electrical Form and Vice Versa. Equation (3.6) for the voltage induced in a circuit moving across a steady magnetic field forms the basis for the design of a dynamo. The principle may be illustrated with the aid of Fig. 3.2. Suppose that at the right-hand end of the transmission line we connect a resistor of resistance R between the conductors. The current I flowing round the circuit is then obtained by dividing the voltage given by Eq. (3.4) by

R and is therefore

$$I = \frac{vBa}{R} \tag{3.7}$$

Where this current flows through the vertical wire in Fig. 3.2, it is in the presence of a magnetic field of flux density B.   In accordance with Part 3, Eq. (6.13), the vertical wire is therefore acted upon by a force per unit length equal to IB.   To overcome this force and to maintain the motion to the right, we must apply a force to the right equal to

$$F = IBa \tag{3.8}$$

The rate at which this force is doing work is

$$Fv = IBav \tag{3.9}$$

Now power is being dissipated in the resistor connected at the right-hand end of the transmission.   This power is equal to the product of the voltage across the resistor given by Eq. (3.4) and the current I through it and is therefore

$$VI = vBaI \tag{3.10}$$

Comparison of Eqs. (3.9) and (3.10) shows that

$$Fv = VI \tag{3.11}$$

This equation states that, when a resistor is connected at the right-hand end of the transmission line shown in Fig. 3.2, work is required to move the electric circuit horizontally, and the rate of supply of energy is equal to the power dissipated in the resistor.   In other words, movement of the electric circuit in Fig. 3.2 to the right dissipates power in a load connected to the transmission line, and this power has to be supplied mechanically in moving the circuit.

The arrangement shown in Fig. 3.2 can also be used, in principle, as an electric motor.   Suppose that at the right-hand end of the transmission line a current I enters one conductor and leaves the other conductor. This current I, where it flows through the vertical wire, crosses a magnetic field of flux density B.   The wire is therefore acted upon by a force IB per unit length, and this amounts to a total force on the wire given by Eq. (3.8).   Thus, by applying a current I round the circuit, the conductor is subject to a force tending to move it.   If the circuit moves horizontally with velocity v, the work done by the force acting on the circuit is given by Eq. (3.9).   However, motion of the circuit across the magnetic field of flux density B causes an induced voltage given by Eq. (3.4). The direction of this voltage is such as to decrease the current I round the circuit unless a counteracting battery or other source of voltage is connected to the right-hand end of the transmission line.   When the circuit moves to the right, therefore, a voltage V given by Eq. (3.4) must be applied at the right-hand end of the transmission line.   Since this voltage is delivering a current I, the power that must be provided by the source of voltage is given by Eq. (3.10).   Comparison of Eqs. (3.9) and (3.10) again leads to Eq. (3.11).   Thus, if a voltage is applied at the right-hand end of the transmission line shown in Fig. 3.2, the circuit moves horizontally, and Eq. (3.11) shows that the rate at which mechanical work is done in the motion of the circuit is equal to the electrical power provided by the source of voltage.

The fact that Eqs. (3.9) and (3.10) apply to the arrangement shown in Fig. 3.2, whether it is used as a dynamo or as a motor, implies that in both cases the power conversion is the same, provided that the electric circuit carries the same current and moves with the same speed.

3.5. A Simple Dynamo.   While the arrangement shown in Fig. 3.2 illustrates in an elementary way the principle of operation of an electrical

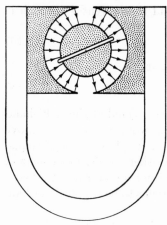

machine, a more practical arrangement would be that described in Part 3, Sec. 6.4 or 8.12.   Let us consider a simple dynamo of the type illustrated in Fig. 3.5.   Figure 3.5 illustrates a magnetic circuit possessing a cylindrical opening between a pair of pole faces, and this opening is nearly filled by a cylinder of soft iron.   The arrangement is so designed that the magnetic field is radially inward over the left half of the gap so formed and radially outward over the right half, while the magnetic flux density is substantially the same at all points in the gap and is equal to B.   In principle, the magnet could be either a permanent magnet or an electromagnet, but in all but the smallest machines an electromagnet would be used in practice.   The cylindrical piece of soft iron can rotate on its axis and carries in a diametral plane a rectangular coil of wire possessing n turns.   The rectangle has a dimension a perpendicular to the plane of the paper in Fig. 3.5 and a dimension b parallel to the plane of the paper. The area of each turn of the coil is, therefore,

Fig. 3.5. A simple dynamo.

$$S = ab \tag{3.12}$$

The cylindrical piece of soft iron upon which the coil is wound is known as the armature.

When the machine is used as a dynamo, the armature is driven with uniform angular velocity ω by means of a torque T, and a load is con-

nected in the armature coil. The peripheral velocity of the sides of
length a of the coil is

$$v = \tfrac{1}{2}b\omega \tag{3.13}$$

In accordance with either expression (3.1) or Eq. (3.6), each side of length
a of each turn of the coil is subject to a magnetically induced voltage per
unit length equal to vB, and there is no induced voltage in the sides of
length b. Allowing for the fact that there are n turns and that each turn
has two sides of length a, the total magnetically induced voltage in the
coil is

$$V = 2nvBa \tag{3.14}$$

Substituting for v from Eq. (3.13) into Eq. (3.14), and using Eq. (3.12),
we derive

$$V = nBS\omega \tag{3.15}$$

As the sides of the armature coil of length a shift from one pole face to
the other, the direction of the magnetic field reverses from radially outward to radially inward or vice versa. The magnetically induced voltage given by Eq. (3.15) therefore changes sign each half revolution of
the armature coil as shown in Fig. 3.6. However, if a commutator is
used to reverse the connections of the load as the sides of the armature

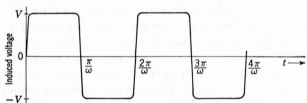

FIG. 3.6. Voltage induced round the armature coil for the dynamo shown in Fig. 3.5.

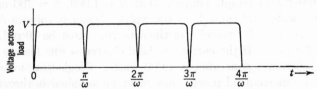

FIG. 3.7. Voltage developed across the load for the dynamo shown in Fig. 3.5, using a
commutator.

coil of length a move across from one pole face to the other, the voltage
developed across the load varies with time as shown in Fig. 3.7. With use
of a commutator, therefore, the dynamo applies to the load connected in
the armature coil a nearly uniform voltage given by Eq. (3.15). If the
load draws a current I, the electrical power generated by the dynamo is

$$VI = nBS\omega I \tag{3.16}$$

Along each side of length a the current I flowing round each turn of the armature coil runs perpendicular to a magnetic field of flux density B. Each such side is therefore subject to a force as described in Part 3, Sec. 6.3. The force per unit length is IB and acts in the direction opposing motion of the wire. The force on each side of length a of each turn is therefore IBa, and the forces on the two sides of length a of each turn constitute a torque of magnitude $IBab$. Using Eq. (3.12) and allowing for the n turns on the armature coil, the total torque tending to oppose rotation of the armature is

$$T = nIBS \qquad (3.17)$$

This is the magnitude of the torque that has to be applied to the armature in order to drive the dynamo. With the armature coil rotating with angular velocity ω, the mechanical power that has to be supplied to the armature is

$$T\omega = nIBS\omega \qquad (3.18)$$

Comparison of Eqs. (3.16) and (3.18) shows that

$$T\omega = VI \qquad (3.19)$$

and this equation states that the mechanical power supplied to the dynamo is equal to the electrical power delivered to the load. To allow for friction in the bearings it is, of course, necessary to supply somewhat more power to the dynamo than that given by Eq. (3.18). Likewise, because of resistance in the armature coil, somewhat less power than that given by Eq. (3.16) is delivered to the external load. Apart from these allowances for losses, however, the mechanical power supplied to the dynamo is equal to the electrical power delivered to the load.

As a numerical example suppose that $n = 1,000$, $S = 100$ cm² (10^{-2} m²), $B = 1$ weber/m², and $V = 100$ volts. Then it follows from Eq. (3.15) that the angular velocity of the armature must be 10 radians/sec, or about 100 rpm. If the current to be delivered to the load is 10 amp, the electrical power generated is 1,000 watts. Neglecting losses in the machine, the mechanical power that must be supplied is therefore also 1,000 watts, or about 1.3 horsepower. A somewhat greater horsepower would be required to overcome losses.

Use of the machine shown in Fig. 3.5 as an electric motor is discussed in Part 3, Sec. 6.4. It is there shown that, if a current I is made to flow round the armature coil, then the torque tending to turn the armature is given by Eq. (3.17) of this chapter. The variation of this torque with time is indicated in Part 3, Fig. 6.6, which should be compared with Fig. 3.7 of this chapter. From Eq. (3.17) it follows that the mechanical power delivered by the electric motor when its armature is rotating with angular velocity ω is given by Eq. (3.18). The current I round the armature coil must be maintained against a magnetically induced voltage given by Eq. (3.15). A battery or other source of voltage must, therefore, be connected into the armature coil. This source is providing the armature current I at the voltage V given by Eq. (3.15) and is therefore providing electrical power at the rate given by Eq. (3.16). Comparison of Eq. (3.16) with Eq. (3.18) shows that Eq. (3.19) is true whether the machine is used as an electric motor or as a dynamo. Moreover the fact that Eqs. (3.16) and (3.18) apply whether the machine is used as a dynamo or as an electric motor shows that the power converted is the same in both cases provided that the armature coil carries the same current and is rotating at the same speed.

3.6. A Simple Alternating-current Generator. Let us suppose that no commutator is used in association with the dynamo illustrated in Fig. 3.5, so that the induced voltage varies with time as shown in Fig. 3.6 instead of Fig. 3.7. Furthermore, let us suppose that the magnetic field applied to the armature is not specially shaped as shown in Fig. 3.5 but is simply a uniform magnetic field as illustrated in Fig. 3.8. We assume as before that the coil has n turns and is rectangular in shape, the dimension perpendicular to the paper in Fig. 3.8 being a and that parallel to the paper being b. The area S of each turn of the coil is therefore given by Eq. (3.12). Select a positive direction round the coil and draw a normal to the coil related by the right-hand-screw rule to the chosen positive direction round the coil. Let the direction of this normal make with the

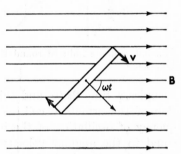

FIG. 3.8. Illustrating a simple a-c generator.

direction of the applied uniform magnetic field an angle ωt as shown in Fig. 3.8, so that with lapse of time t the coil rotates with uniform angular velocity ω. The peripheral velocity of the edges of the coil of length a is therefore given, as before, by Eq. (3.13).

It may be seen from Fig. 3.8 that the vector $\mathbf{v}$ representing the peripheral velocity of an edge of the coil of length a makes with the magnetic-flux-density vector $\mathbf{B}$ an angle ωt on one side of the coil and $\omega t + \pi$ on the other side of the coil. It follows from expression (3.1) that the magnetically induced voltage per unit length along a side of edge a of each turn of the coil has magnitude

$$vB \sin \omega t \tag{3.20}$$

Allowing for both edges of length a and for all n turns, the total induced voltage round the electric circuit is

$$V = 2navB \sin \omega t \tag{3.21}$$

Substituting for v from Eq. (3.13), and using Eq. (3.12), we obtain

$$V = nBS\omega \sin \omega t \tag{3.22}$$

This equation can be written as

$$V = V_0 \sin \omega t \tag{3.23}$$

where
$$V_0 = nBS\omega \tag{3.24}$$

Equation (3.23) shows that the induced voltage oscillates sinusoidally with time t as shown in Fig. 3.9. A complete cycle of the oscillation

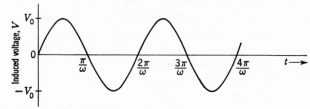

FIG. 3.9. Voltage induced round the rotating coil in the a-c generator illustrated in Fig. 3.8.

occupies a time $2\pi/\omega$, and this is the same as the time for one revolution of the armature coil. This is expressed by saying that the frequency of oscillation of the induced voltage in cycles per unit time is equal to the angular velocity of the armature coil in revolutions per unit time. Another convenient measure of the frequency of oscillation of the induced voltage is the angular velocity ω of the coil in radians per unit time. This is known as the angular frequency of oscillation of the induced voltage. Since there are 2π radians in a complete revolution, the angular frequency ω of oscillation in radians per unit time is related to the frequency of oscillation f in cycles per unit time by the equation

$$\omega = 2\pi f \tag{3.25}$$

The amplitude of oscillation of the induced voltage is V_0, given by Eq. (3.24). We notice that this equation is identical in form with Eq. (3.15). If the induced voltage is applied across a load of resistance R connected into the armature coil, the current through the load is obtained by dividing by R the voltage given by Eq. (3.23). The resulting current is described as an alternating current; strictly speaking, it is a sinusoidally alternating current.

The strength of oscillation of a sinusoidally alternating voltage is usually specified by what is known as the root-mean-square value of the voltage, V_{rms}.   The square of the voltage given by Eq. (3.23) is

$$V^2 = V_0^2 \sin^2 \omega t \tag{3.26}$$

and this can be written as

$$V^2 = \tfrac{1}{2} V_0^2 (1 - \cos 2\omega t) \tag{3.27}$$

The cosine term in this equation is as much positive as it is negative, and on the average its value is zero.   The mean value of the square of the voltage is therefore given by

$$\overline{V^2} = \tfrac{1}{2} V_0^2 \tag{3.28}$$

The root-mean-square value of the voltage is the square root of the expression on the left-hand side of this equation and is

$$V_{rms} = \frac{1}{\sqrt{2}} V_0 \tag{3.29}$$

The root-mean-square value of a sinusoidally alternating voltage is thus equal to the amplitude of the oscillatory voltage divided by $\sqrt{2}$.

As a numerical example, suppose that the root-mean-square voltage to be provided by the generator is 110 volts and that the frequency of oscillation is to be 60 cycles/sec.   The angular velocity of the armature coil must therefore be 60 rps, or 3,600 rpm.   From Eq. (3.25), this angular frequency may also be described as 377 radians/sec, and this is the value of ω to be substituted into Eq. (3.24).   From Eq. (3.29) it follows that a root-mean-square voltage of 110 volts implies an amplitude of oscillation of 156 volts, and this is the value of V_0 to be substituted into Eq. (3.24). If we also substitute into Eq. (3.24) the values $B = 1$ weber/m² and $S = 10^{-2}$ m², we deduce that 41 turns are required on the armature coil.

3.7. Relation between Induced Voltage and Rate of Change of Magnetic Flux.   Let us again consider the arrangement shown in Fig. 3.2. A normal cross section of the magnetic circuit is rectangular, and the vertical dimension is a.   Let the horizontal dimension be b, and let x denote the distance of the vertical wire from the left-hand edge of the magnetic circuit.   If a load is connected to the right-hand end of the transmission line, the electric circuit thereby completed is threaded by magnetic flux over an area $a(b - x)$.   The magnetic flux density being B, the magnetic flux threading the electric circuit is

$$\Phi = Ba(b - x) \tag{3.30}$$

This is the magnetic flux threading the electric circuit in the direction related by the right-hand-screw rule to the magnetically induced voltage given by Eq. (3.4).   As the electric circuit in Fig. 3.2 moves to the right with velocity v, the distance x of the vertical wire from the left-hand edge of the magnetic circuit increases, and the relation between v and x is

$$v = \frac{dx}{dt} \qquad (3.31)$$

As a result of the motion, the magnetic flux Φ threading the electric circuit is decreasing. By differentiating Eq. (3.30) with regard to time t, it follows that the rate of decrease of the magnetic flux threading the electric circuit is given by

$$-\frac{d\Phi}{dt} = Ba\frac{dx}{dt} \qquad (3.32)$$

On using Eq. (3.31), Eq. (3.32) can be written as

$$-\frac{d\Phi}{dt} = Bav \qquad (3.33)$$

Comparison of this equation with Eq. (3.4) shows that, for the arrangement shown in Fig. 3.2, the magnetically induced voltage round the electric circuit is equal to the time rate of decrease of the magnetic flux threading the electric circuit in the direction related by the right-hand-screw rule to the direction of the induced voltage. We shall show that this relation between magnetically induced voltage and the time rate of change of the threading magnetic flux applies to all situations in which an electric circuit is moving through a steady magnetic field.

Consider an electric circuit C in motion through a magnetic field as shown in Fig. 3.4. The motion of the electric circuit may include distortion. The magnetic field will be assumed to be independent of time, but it may vary in space from place to place both in magnitude and in direction. The resulting magnetically induced voltage round the circuit in the direction defined by the vector element of length $d\mathbf{s}$ is given by Eq. (3.6). Let us now calculate the rate at which the magnetic flux threading the circuit is changing owing to motion of the circuit.

During a small interval of time dt the electric circuit C moves to a slightly different position C', as shown in Fig. 3.10. The vector element of length $d\mathbf{s}$ of the circuit at the point P receives during the time dt a vector displacement $\mathbf{v}\,dt$. It therefore traces out an element of area represented by the vector

$$d\mathbf{s} \times \mathbf{v}\,dt \qquad (3.34)$$

The magnetic flux threading this element of area is

$$\mathbf{B} \cdot (d\mathbf{s} \times \mathbf{v}\,dt) \qquad (3.35)$$

The decrease $-d\Phi$ in magnetic flux threading the electric circuit during the time dt is obtained by adding up the contributions given by expression (3.35) for all the elements of area given by expression (3.34) between the closed curves C and C' in Fig. 3.10.   This implies integration of the expression (3.35) with respect to ds round the electric circuit.   We write the result as

$$-d\Phi = \int_C \mathbf{B} \cdot (ds \times \mathbf{v}\, dt)$$ (3.36)

from which it follows that

$$-\frac{d\Phi}{dt} = \int_C \mathbf{B} \cdot (ds \times \mathbf{v})$$ (3.37)

We wish to establish the identity of the expression on the right-hand side of Eq. (3.37) for the rate of decrease of the magnetic flux Φ threading the

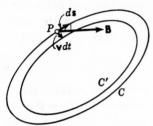

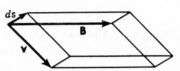

FIG. 3.10. Illustrating the calculation of the rate of change of the magnetic flux threading an electric circuit as a result of motion of the circuit through the magnetic field.

FIG. 3.11. Illustrating the proof of Eq. (3.38).

circuit with expression (3.6) for the magnetically induced voltage round the circuit.

The equality of expressions (3.6) and (3.37) is established if we prove that

$$(\mathbf{v} \times \mathbf{B}) \cdot ds = \mathbf{B} \cdot (ds \times \mathbf{v})$$ (3.38)

We can verify the truth of this equation by considering the parallelepiped defined by the vectors $\mathbf{v}$, $\mathbf{B}$, and ds and shown in Fig. 3.11.   One face of this parallelepiped has an area represented vectorially by $\mathbf{v} \times \mathbf{B}$, and the left-hand side of Eq. (3.38) is, therefore, the product of the area of the base and the height.   The left-hand side of Eq. (3.38) is thus the volume of the parallelepiped.   However, the right-hand side of this equation is also the volume of the parallelepiped evaluated by using as base a face defined by the two vectors ds and $\mathbf{v}$.   The left- and right-hand sides of Eq. (3.38) are therefore two equivalent expressions for the volume of the parallelepiped shown in Fig. 3.11.

By using Eq. (3.38) in relation to Eqs. (3.6) and (3.37) it now follows that

$$V = -\frac{d\Phi}{dt}$$ (3.39)

This equation states that, for any electric circuit moving in any steady magnetic field, the magnetically induced voltage round the circuit is equal to the time rate of decrease of the magnetic flux through the circuit. In the argument leading to Eq. (3.39), care is necessary with the signs. This care is exercised by taking the magnetic flux Φ threading the electric circuit to be related by the right-hand-screw rule to the direction of the magnetically induced voltage V round the circuit.

We now see that, instead of evaluating the magnetically induced voltage round an electric circuit from expression (3.1) by application of Eq. (3.6), we may as an alternative use Eq. (3.39). As an example, consider the a-c generator discussed in Sec. 3.6 and illustrated in Fig. 3.8. Let us evaluate the magnetic flux Φ threading the armature coil in the direction of the normal indicated in Fig. 3.8. The component of the magnetic-flux-density vector normal to the plane of the coil is

$$B \cos \omega t \qquad (3.40)$$

Each turn of the coil has area S, and therefore the n turns have total area nS. The magnetic flux threading the electric circuit is therefore

$$\Phi = nSB \cos \omega t \qquad (3.41)$$

Substitution of this value of Φ into Eq. (3.39) gives

$$V = nSB\omega \sin \omega t \qquad (3.42)$$

This is therefore the magnetically induced voltage round the electric circuit in the direction related by the right-hand-screw rule to the direction normal to the circuit illustrated in Fig. 3.8. Equation (3.42) verifies Eq. (3.22), previously derived by application of expression (3.1) in accordance with Eq. (3.6).

Great importance attaches to Eq. (3.39). This importance does not arise merely from the fact that it often provides the most convenient way of calculating the voltage induced round an electric circuit moving through a steady magnetic field. We shall see in Chap. 4 that, if a fixed electric circuit is in the presence of a magnetic field which varies with time, then voltage is also induced round the circuit, and it is again given by Eq. (3.39). The equality of the voltage induced round a circuit and the time rate of decrease of the magnetic flux threading the circuit is in fact a universally applicable law of electrical science, known as Faraday's law of induction.

Equation (3.39) makes it clear why the unit of magnetic flux known as the weber is also equal to a volt-second, as mentioned in Part 3, Sec. 2.11. A rate of change of 1 weber/sec in the magnetic flux threading an electric circuit induces 1 volt round the circuit.

3.8. Flow of Energy in an Electrical Machine. In Chap. 1 we saw that, when a battery is connected to a resistive load by means of a transmission line as shown in Fig. 1.4, the Poynting vector affords a description of the flow of energy from the battery to the load between the conductors of the transmission line. Charged particles located in the battery near the active electrodes are accelerated by the chemical process involved and emit energy. This energy is guided between the conductors of the transmission line as shown in Fig. 1.7 and is used in the resistor to accelerate electrons between collisions. A similar process is involved when electrical power is produced by a dynamo. We can illustrate this by the simple arrangement shown in Fig. 3.2.

Let us suppose that the arrangement shown in Fig. 3.2 is used as a dynamo and that a resistive load is connected to the right-hand end of the transmission line. When the electric circuit moves to the right, electrons in the vertical wire at the left-hand end are accelerated between collisions by force of magnetic origin given by expression (3.1). Acceleration of charges in the vertical wire by force of magnetic origin replaces acceleration of charges in a battery by the chemical process. The accelerated electrons in the vertical wire in the arrangement shown in Fig. 3.2 emit energy, which is guided to the resistor at the right-hand end of the transmission line, where the energy is used to accelerate electrons in the resistor between collisions.

If the arrangement shown in Fig. 3.2 is used as an electric motor, a battery is connected at the right-hand end of the transmission line. The energy emitted by the battery is guided to the vertical wire at the left-hand end of the transmission line, where it maintains the current through the vertical wire. Motions of the charges through this wire produce a force of magnetic origin on the wire in accordance with expression (3.1), and this is what moves the electric circuit.

The flow of energy between the conductors of the transmission line in the arrangement shown in Fig. 3.2 is, however, complicated by the following consideration. The rate of flow of energy is obtained in magnitude and direction by combining the electric vector $\mathbf{E}$ with the magnetic vector $\mathbf{H}$ in accordance with expression $\mathbf{E} \times \mathbf{H}$ for the Poynting vector. There are, however, two contributions to the magnetic vector in the arrangement shown in Fig. 3.2. One arises from the current round the electric circuit associated with a load or battery at the right-hand end of the transmission line. This magnetic field alone, combined with the electric field illustrated in Fig. 3.2, would produce a flow of energy along the transmission line that behaves as indicated in Fig. 1.7. However, besides the magnetic field that arises from the current round the electric circuit, there is an additional, and normally much stronger, magnetic field associated with the magnetic circuit. The electric field between the conductors of the transmission line combines with the magnetic field associated with the magnetic circuit to produce a closed flow of energy. This must be superposed upon a flow of the type shown in Fig. 1.7 in order to obtain the complete flow of energy associated with the machine. Thus a simple flow of energy from source to load is distorted in an electrical machine by superposition of a closed flow of energy associated with the magnetic flux passing round the magnetic circuit.

The way in which a closed flow of energy occurs in an electrical machine may be illustrated with the aid of Fig. 3.12. The stippled region represents a magnetic circuit in which there is a gap, magnetic flux passing along the circuit from right to left and producing in the gap a horizontal magnetic field with magnetic vector **H**. At the top and bottom of the gap

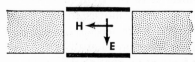

in the magnetic circuit are placed the plates of a capacitor which is charged to produce between the plates a vertical electric field with electric vector **E**. The plates of the capacitor, together with the pole faces of the magnetic circuit, form a rectangular chan-

FIG. 3.12. Illustrating production of a closed flow of energy.

nel. Such a situation is involved in the arrangement shown in Fig. 3.2. In the rectangular channel in Fig. 3.12 we have a crossed electric and magnetic field producing, in accordance with the Poynting vector **E × H**, a flow of energy downward through the channel. If allowance is made for fringing of the electric field at the edges of the capacitor and of the magnetic field at the edges of the gap, the energy flowing down the rectangular channel returns outside the channel and forms a closed flow of energy. It is such a closed flow of energy that must be superposed upon a flow of the type shown in Fig. 1.7 in order to obtain a complete picture of the flow of energy involved in an elementary electrical machine of the type shown in Fig. 3.2.

To examine the significance of the closed flow of energy described in connection with Fig. 3.12 we must intercept the flow of energy at two locations by means of surfaces of the type involved in the definition of the Poynting vector. The portion of the flow between the dissecting surfaces requires that energy be made available at one dissecting surface and absorbed at the other. For the closed flow of energy threading through the rectangular channel shown in Fig. 3.12, let us intercept the flow by means of two rectangular cross sections at opposite ends of the channel. The electromagnetic field in the channel is then substantially the same as that described in connection with Fig. 1.6. We see, therefore, that the intercepting surface at one end of the channel must involve a battery from which energy emerges, and the intercepting surface at the other end of the channel must be a resistive sheet in which the energy is absorbed. It follows that energy is in fact flowing through the rectangular channel in Fig. 3.12 in the sense that, if the flow is intercepted in the manner contemplated in the definition of the Poynting vector, then the flow is duly detected.

We thus see that an electrical machine involves closed flow of energy arising from the coexistence of the electric field associated with the induced voltage and the magnetic field associated with the magnetic circuit. This closed flow is superposed upon the flow arising from coexistence of the electric field associated with the induced voltage and the magnetic field associated with the current through the armature winding. It is, however, only the latter flow that is involved in the power conversion provided by the machine, and this is the only flow that is channeled into or out of the space round the conductors of the transmission line connected to the machine.

SUMMARIZING EXERCISES

3.1. Explain why an electric field is brought into existence when a conducting wire moves across the lines of magnetic flux of a steady magnetic field. Explain what is meant by magnetically induced voltage.

3.2. An electric circuit C is in motion in a steady magnetic field. A vector element of length ds of C is moving with velocity $\mathbf{v}$, and at the position of the element the applied magnetic-flux-density vector is $\mathbf{B}$. Derive the line integral that expresses the magnetically induced voltage round C in the direction defined by ds.

3.3. Describe the principle of operation of a simple dynamo. Prove that, neglecting losses, the electrical power generated by the dynamo when running steadily is equal to the mechanical power supplied to the armature.

3.4. A closed electric circuit C is in motion in a steady magnetic field. A vector element of length ds of C is moving with velocity $\mathbf{v}$, and at the position of the element the applied magnetic-flux-density vector is $\mathbf{B}$. Calculate the time rate of change of the magnetic flux threading C. Prove that the time rate of decrease of the magnetic flux threading C is equal to the magnetically induced voltage round C. Describe the relation that must exist between the direction of the magnetic flux through C and the direction of the induced voltage round C.

3.5. Describe the principle of operation of a simple a-c generator. Explain what is meant by root-mean-square voltage.

CHAPTER 4

FARADAY'S LAW OF INDUCTION

4.1. Introduction. At a point in an electromagnetic field where the electric vector is **E** and the magnetic-flux-density vector is **B**, a test charge moving with velocity **v** is subject to a force per unit charge equal to

$$\mathbf{E} + \mathbf{v} \times \mathbf{B} \qquad (4.1)$$

This statement, which was first introduced in Part 3, Sec. 2.2, involves a paradox to which reference has not previously been made. Elucidation of this paradox leads to a crucial advance in our understanding of electrical science.

4.2. The Paradox of Relative Motion. The velocity **v** appearing in expression (4.1) is the velocity of the test charge relative to the observer. However, different observers could be in motion relative to one another, and they would then form different assessments of the velocity **v** of the test charge. At first sight, therefore, it would appear that the different observers, on substituting into expression (4.1) the different velocities **v** that they observe, would obtain different assessments of the force per unit charge acting on the test charge. The force on the test charge does not, however, depend upon which observer is involved. All observers must in fact form the same estimate of the force on the test charge, and yet, if they are moving relative to one another, they clearly make different assessments of the velocity **v** of the test charge.

This paradox can be illustrated with the aid of a dynamo. Let us suppose that a wheel is mounted adjacent to the dynamo and that it is able to rotate on the same axis as the armature, but not necessarily at the same speed. Let us suppose that the observer is attached to this wheel and that he is able to operate the wheel at any speed that he chooses. If the observer keeps his wheel at rest relative to the frame of the dynamo, he sees a point of the armature winding moving with velocity **v** through a fixed magnetic field of flux density **B**, and he appreciates the fact that electrons are driven round the armature winding by the force **v** × **B** per unit charge. Let us now suppose that the observer's wheel rotates at the same speed as the armature. The observer then sees a fixed armature winding in the presence of a rotating magnetic field. Since the

606

observer now considers the armature winding to be at rest, he is bound to assess the force $\mathbf{v} \times \mathbf{B}$ on the electrons in the winding as zero. We must therefore ask how an observer rotating with the armature is to explain the operation of the dynamo.

Elucidation of this matter depends upon the fact that different observers moving with different velocities make different assessments of the electric vector $\mathbf{E}$ and different assessments of the magnetic-flux-density vector $\mathbf{B}$ at each point of space. Suppose that there are a number of observers in motion relative to one another and that they are numbered 1, 2, ... Suppose that each observer is observing a particular unit test charge. Let the estimates made by the various observers of the velocity of the test charge be $\mathbf{v}_1$, $\mathbf{v}_2$, ... Let the estimates made by the various observers of the electric vector applied to the test charge be $\mathbf{E}_1$, $\mathbf{E}_2$, ... Again, let the estimates made by the various observers of the magnetic-flux-density vector applied to the test charge be $\mathbf{B}_1$, $\mathbf{B}_2$, ... It follows from expression (4.1) that the estimates made by the various observers of the resultant force acting on the unit test charge are respectively

$$\mathbf{E}_1 + \mathbf{v}_1 \times \mathbf{B}_1, \ \mathbf{E}_2 + \mathbf{v}_2 \times \mathbf{B}_2, \ . \ . \ . \tag{4.2}$$

Thus, not only do different observers form different estimates of the velocity with which the test charge is moving, but they also form different assessments of the electromagnetic field through which the test charge is moving. Each observer therefore forms a different estimate of the force of electric origin acting on the test charge and a different estimate of the force of magnetic origin acting on the test charge. Each observer combines these two estimates to assess the total force acting on the test charge. This total force is, however, the same for all observers. Thus all the expressions (4.2) for the force acting on the unit test charge are identical, and we have

$$\mathbf{E}_1 + \mathbf{v}_1 \times \mathbf{B}_1 = \mathbf{E}_2 + \mathbf{v}_2 \times \mathbf{B}_2 = \ \cdot \ \cdot \ \cdot \tag{4.3}$$

What is different for the different observers is the way they regard this total force as split into a force of electric origin and a force of magnetic origin.

Let us again consider a dynamo fitted with an observer's wheel coaxial with the armature. If the observer is fixed relative to the frame of the machine, he sees an armature coil rotating in a fixed magnetic field and regards the force driving electrons round the armature winding as a force of magnetic origin. If, however, the observer rotates with the armature, he assesses the force of magnetic origin as zero and regards the force driving electrons through the armature winding as a force of electric origin. To an observer for whom the armature appears at rest, the magnetic field associated with the frame of the machine is rotating.   At points which this observer regards as fixed, therefore, the magnetic field is varying with time.   In association with the time variation of the magnetic field, this observer measures an electric field, and it is this electric field that he regards as the driving force for current in the armature winding.   This brings out the important point that, associated with a time-varying magnetic field, there exists an electric field.   From the viewpoint of the frame of the machine, the dynamo works because a force of magnetic origin is brought into play by motion of the armature winding through a fixed magnetic field.   From the viewpoint of the armature, however, the dynamo works because the time variation of the magnetic field at each point of the armature winding is associated with an electric field that drives current through the winding.

From the point of view of an observer fixed relative to the frame of the dynamo, the voltage induced round the armature winding C is given by Eq. (3.6) and is therefore

$$\int_C (\mathbf{v} \times \mathbf{B}) \cdot d\mathbf{s} \tag{4.4}$$

For a few simple arrangements this integral was evaluated in Chap. 3. From the point of view of an observer moving with the armature, the same induced voltage must be given by

$$\int_C \mathbf{E} \cdot d\mathbf{s} \tag{4.5}$$

where $\mathbf{E}$ is the electric vector that he observes at points along the armature winding.   Now let us consider the viewpoint of the observer when his wheel is rotating with a nonzero velocity different from that of the armature.   In this case he judges that both the armature and the frame of the machine are in motion.   As he sees the situation, the force tending to move electrons round the armature winding is neither purely of electric origin nor purely of magnetic origin.   At a point of the armature winding he evaluates the electric vector $\mathbf{E}$, the magnetic-flux-density vector $\mathbf{B}$, and the velocity $\mathbf{v}$ of the winding.   He combines these to form the force per unit charge on electrons in the armature winding at that point in accordance with the expression (4.1).   His evaluation of the voltage induced round the armature circuit is then

$$\int_C (\mathbf{E} + \mathbf{v} \times \mathbf{B}) \cdot d\mathbf{s} \tag{4.6}$$

Thus different observers in motion in different ways relative to the dynamo form different assessments of $\mathbf{E}$, $\mathbf{B}$, and $\mathbf{v}$, but when these are combined together in the expression (4.1), all observers form the same assessment of the force per unit charge acting on a test charge, and so all observers obtain the same value for the induced voltage acting round the armature winding in accordance with expression (4.6).   What is different for the different observers is the way in which the total induced voltage given by expression (4.6) divides between an induced voltage of electric origin given by expression (4.5) and an induced voltage of magnetic origin given by expression (4.4).

4.3. Faraday's Law of Induction.   We are now in a position to state one of the most important laws of electrical science.   Equation (3.39) shows that, when an electric circuit C is moving through a steady magnetic field, a voltage is induced round C equal to the time rate of decrease of the magnetic flux threading C.   Faraday's law of induction asserts the truth of this statement for any electric circuit C, fixed or moving, in any electromagnetic field, provided that the voltage induced round the electric circuit is defined by Eq. (4.6).   Moreover, Faraday's law of induction asserts the truth of the statement when C is not necessarily an electric circuit but is simply a closed geometrical curve drawn in any electromagnetic field.   Faraday's law of induction can therefore be described as follows:

Let C be any closed geometrical curve drawn in any electromagnetic field.   Let $d\mathbf{s}$ be a vector element of length of C pointing round C in a selected direction.   If the curve is in motion through the electromagnetic field, let $\mathbf{v}$ be the velocity of the element of length $d\mathbf{s}$.   Define the voltage induced round the closed curve C in the direction specified by $d\mathbf{s}$ to be

$$V = \int_C (\mathbf{E} + \mathbf{v} \times \mathbf{B}) \cdot d\mathbf{s} \qquad (4.7)$$

where $\mathbf{E}$ is the electric vector and $\mathbf{B}$ the magnetic-flux-density vector at the element of length $d\mathbf{s}$.   Let Φ be the total magnetic flux threading the closed curve C in the direction related by the right-hand-screw rule to the direction of $d\mathbf{s}$ round C.   If $d\mathbf{S}$ is a vector element of area of a surface S spanning C, and if the direction of $d\mathbf{S}$ is related by the right-hand-screw rule to the direction of $d\mathbf{s}$, then

$$\Phi = \int_S \mathbf{B} \cdot d\mathbf{S} \qquad (4.8)$$

where $\mathbf{B}$ is the magnetic-flux-density vector at the element of area $d\mathbf{S}$.   Faraday's law of induction asserts that, in all circumstances,

$$V = -\frac{d\Phi}{dt} \qquad (4.9)$$

This is expressed by saying that the voltage induced round any closed curve in any electromagnetic field is equal to the time rate of decrease of the magnetic flux threading the closed curve.   The induced voltage is defined by Eq. (4.7) and the threading magnetic flux by Eq. (4.8), and it is important that the direction of the vector element of length $d\mathbf{s}$ in Eq. (4.7) be related by the right-hand-screw rule to the direction of the vector element of area $d\mathbf{S}$ in Eq. (4.8).

When rotating electrical machinery is not involved, the commonest situation arising in practice is that in which the electric circuit is fixed in location. Equation (4.7) then reduces to

$$V = \int_C \mathbf{E} \cdot d\mathbf{s} \tag{4.10}$$

Substitution from Eqs. (4.10) and (4.8) into Eq. (4.9) then gives

$$\int_C \mathbf{E} \cdot d\mathbf{s} = -\frac{\partial}{\partial t} \int_S \mathbf{B} \cdot d\mathbf{S} \tag{4.11}$$

This equation applies to any fixed, closed curve C spanned by any surface S in any electromagnetic field. The partial form of the derivative with respect to time appearing on the right-hand side of Eq. (4.11) is used to emphasize the fact that the closed curve C under consideration is fixed in space. The version of Faraday's law of induction expressed by Eq. (4.11) can be described in the following words: For any fixed, closed curve in any electromagnetic field, the circulation of the electric vector round the curve is equal to the rate of decrease of the magnetic flux through the curve, the two directions being related by the right-hand-screw rule.

It is difficult to overemphasize the importance in electrical science of the law of induction. We shall see that Faraday's law of induction plays in electrical science the role played by Newton's law of motion in mechanical science.

4.4. Association of an Electric Field with a Time-varying Magnetic Field. As expressed in Eq. (4.11), Faraday's law of induction describes the fact that, in association with a time-varying magnetic field, there exists an electric field. Let us illustrate this relationship by considering the electromagnetic field of an inductor for which the current is increasing with time.

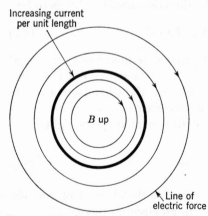

FIG. 4.1. The electric field of a long solenoid for which the current increases with time.

Let the inductor be an indefinitely long solenoid possessing a circular cross-sectional area of radius a. In Fig. 4.1 the heavy circle indicates a normal cross section of the solenoid.   Let the solenoid carry a current I per unit length uniformly distributed along its length, and let μ be the inductivity of the medium.   The magnetic field strength inside the solenoid is then I and the magnetic flux density is μI, while the magnetic field outside the solenoid is negligible.   In Fig. 4.1 the current round the solenoid is assumed to be flowing in the counterclockwise direction, so that the magnetic flux within the inductor is upward from the paper.   Now suppose that the current per unit length round the solenoid vanishes at time zero and increases steadily with time t at the rate $\dot{I}$.   Then

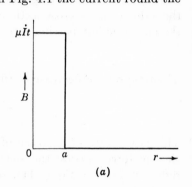

$$I = \dot{I}t \qquad (4.12)$$

and the magnetic flux density inside the solenoid is

$$B = \mu\dot{I}t \qquad (4.13)$$

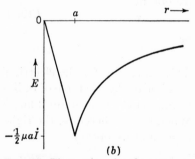

The variation of the magnetic flux density as a function of distance r from the axis of the solenoid is shown in Fig. 4.2a.

Equation (4.13) shows that the magnetic flux density within the solenoid increases with time.   In consequence there is an associated electric field, the circulation of which round any fixed, closed curve is given by Eq. (4.11).   From the axial symmetry of the arrangement it follows that

Fig. 4.2. Illustrating, for the arrangement shown in Fig. 4.1, the variation with radial distance of (a) the magnetic flux density and (b) the electric field strength.

the lines of electric force are circles whose planes are perpendicular to the length of the solenoid and whose centers lie on the axis of the solenoid as indicated in Fig. 4.1.   It further follows from symmetry that the electric field strength is a function only of radial distance r from the axis of the solenoid.   Let E be the electric field strength at distance r from the axis, and let E be taken as positive when it points round a line of electric force in the same direction that the current flows round the solenoid. The circulation of the electric vector round a line of electric force of radius r is

$$E(2\pi r) \qquad (4.14)$$

For each line of electric force, expression (4.14) is equal to the time rate of decrease of the magnetic flux threading the line in the upward direction in Fig. 4.1.

Let us consider first a line of electric force outside the solenoid, that is, one for which $r > a$. The magnetic flux threading the line of electric force is then the total magnetic flux passing through the inductor. Since the inductor has a cross-sectional area πa^2, it follows from Eq. (4.13) that the magnetic flux passing through it is

$$\Phi = \pi a^2 \mu \dot{I} t \qquad (4.15)$$

The time rate of decrease of this magnetic flux is

$$- \frac{d\Phi}{dt} = -\pi a^2 \mu \dot{I} \qquad (4.16)$$

This is the rate of decrease of the magnetic flux threading any line of electric force outside the solenoid. Using Eq. (4.16) to evaluate the right-hand side of Eq. (4.11), and expression (4.14) for the left-hand side, we obtain

$$E(2\pi r) = -\pi a^2 \mu \dot{I} \qquad (4.17)$$

or

$$E = -\frac{1}{2} \mu \dot{I} a^2 \frac{1}{r} \qquad (4.18)$$

This expression for the electric field strength applies when $r > a$.

A line of electric force of radius r inside the solenoid is threaded by only a fraction r^2/a^2 of the total magnetic flux Φ passing through the inductor. When $r < a$, therefore, the right-hand side of Eq. (4.17) is multiplied by r^2/a^2, and we obtain

$$E(2\pi r) = -\pi a^2 \mu \dot{I} \frac{r^2}{a^2} \qquad (4.19)$$

The electric field strength inside the solenoid is therefore given by

$$E = -\tfrac{1}{2}\mu \dot{I} r \qquad (4.20)$$

The complete electric field strength inside and outside the solenoid associated with the increasing current round the solenoid is consequently given by

$$E = \begin{cases} -\dfrac{1}{2}\,\mu\dot{I}r & r < a \\[2mm] -\dfrac{1}{2}\,\mu\dot{I}a^2\,\dfrac{1}{r} & r > a \end{cases} \qquad (4.21)$$

This variation of E with the distance r from the axis of the solenoid is illustrated in Fig. 4.2b.

The negative value of E indicated in Eqs. (4.21) and in Fig. 4.2b means that the electric vector is directed round the circular lines of electric force in the direction opposite to the flow of current round the solenoid in Fig. 4.1.   This is true in particular at the surface of the solenoid, where the value of E given by Eqs. (4.21) is

$$-\tfrac{1}{2}\mu a \dot{I} \tag{4.22}$$

The circulation of this electric field round the perimeter of a normal cross section of the solenoid is obtained by multiplying the expression (4.22) for E by the perimeter $2\pi a$ of the cross section.   We thereby derive the voltage

$$V = -\pi a^2 \mu \dot{I} \tag{4.23}$$

The electric field given by expression (4.22) acts on the electrons forming the current round the solenoid in the direction tending to oppose the current.   To maintain the linear increase of current with time assumed in Eq. (4.12) it is therefore necessary to apply round the solenoid not only the voltage required to overcome the effect of ohmic resistance but also a voltage required to overcome the effect of the electric field given by expression (4.22).   This additional voltage is equal and opposite to the voltage given by Eq. (4.23).

The complete electric field associated with the increasing current that flows round the solenoid is described by Eqs. (4.21).   However, it may be noticed that, if the voltage given by Eq. (4.23) is all that we need to know, it can be calculated directly from Eq. (4.16) by application of Faraday's law of induction in the form given in Eq. (4.9).

4.5. The Definition of Electric Potential.   Faraday's law of induction requires a modification in the definition of electric potential.   In electrostatics the relation between the electric vector $\mathbf{E}$ and the electric potential ϕ was expressed by the equation

$$\mathbf{E} = -\operatorname{grad} \phi \tag{4.24}$$

The drop in potential in going from a point P in an electrostatic field to a point Q was expressed by the equation

$$\phi_P - \phi_Q = \int_P^Q \mathbf{E} \cdot d\mathbf{s} \tag{4.25}$$

Moreover, for any closed geometrical curve C in an electrostatic field,

$$\int_C \mathbf{E} \cdot d\mathbf{s} = 0 \tag{4.26}$$

Equation (4.11) shows that, when the closed curve C is threaded by a time-varying magnetic flux, the circulation of the electric vector round C is no longer zero.   This upsets Eq. (4.26) and consequently upsets Eqs. (4.24) and (4.25).   A reconsideration of the definition of the electric potential is therefore required before it can be used in the presence of a time-varying magnetic field.

To define electric potential ϕ in the presence of a time-varying magnetic field, use is made of the magnetic vector potential $\mathbf{A}$ discussed in Part 3, Chap. 10. The magnetic vector potential $\mathbf{A}$ is related to the magnetic circuits formed by tubes of magnetic flux in the same way that the magnetic vector $\mathbf{H}$ is related to closed flow of steady electric current. Magnetic vector potential has the property that its circulation round any closed geometrical curve C is equal to the magnetic flux threading C. The direction of the circulation round C must be related to the direction in which the magnetic flux threads C by the right-hand-screw rule. Thus the magnetic flux Φ threading any closed geometrical curve C in a magnetic field can be expressed by the equation

$$\Phi = \int_C \mathbf{A} \cdot d\mathbf{s} \tag{4.27}$$

The vector element of length $d\mathbf{s}$ of C in Eq. (4.27) must point round C in the direction related by the right-hand-screw rule to the direction in which the magnetic flux Φ threads C. Equation (4.27) is alternative to Eq. (4.8) for evaluating the magnetic flux threading a closed curve.

To define the electric potential ϕ in the presence of a time-varying magnetic field we replace Eq. (4.8) for magnetic flux by Eq. (4.27). Equation (4.11) expressing Faraday's law of induction for any fixed geometrical closed curve C in any electromagnetic field then becomes

$$\int_C \mathbf{E} \cdot d\mathbf{s} = -\frac{\partial}{\partial t} \int_C \mathbf{A} \cdot d\mathbf{s} \tag{4.28}$$

This can be rewritten as

$$\int_C \mathbf{E} \cdot d\mathbf{s} = -\int_C \frac{\partial \mathbf{A}}{\partial t} \cdot d\mathbf{s} \tag{4.29}$$

or as

$$\int_C \left(\mathbf{E} + \frac{\partial \mathbf{A}}{\partial t} \right) \cdot d\mathbf{s} = 0 \tag{4.30}$$

In general the magnetic scalar potential $\mathbf{A}$ is a function of position in the field as well as a function of time. The partial derivative of $\mathbf{A}$ with respect to t in Eq. (4.30) implies a time derivative of $\mathbf{A}$ at a fixed point of the closed curve C. Faraday's law of induction thus implies that, in the presence of a time-varying magnetic field, Eq. (4.26) is replaced by Eq. (4.30). Thus to convert the electrostatic Eqs. (4.24) to (4.26) into equations applicable in any electromagnetic field we must replace $\mathbf{E}$ by

$$\mathbf{E} + \frac{\partial \mathbf{A}}{\partial t} \tag{4.31}$$

The drop in electric potential in going from a point P to a point Q in any electromagnetic field is therefore defined by the equation

$$\phi_P - \phi_Q = \int_P^Q \left(\mathbf{E} + \frac{\partial \mathbf{A}}{\partial t} \right) \cdot d\mathbf{s} \qquad (4.32)$$

where the integral is taken from the point P to the point Q along any curve joining the two points. Likewise, the downward gradient of the electric potential at any point in the field gives not $\mathbf{E}$, but the vector (4.31), and this result is written as

$$\mathbf{E} + \frac{\partial \mathbf{A}}{\partial t} = - \text{grad } \phi \qquad (4.33)$$

In electrostatics no magnetic field is involved, and so $\mathbf{A}$ is zero. Equations (4.33), (4.32), and (4.30) then reduce to Eqs. (4.24) to (4.26). For the flow of steady electric currents studied in Part 2, a magnetic field is involved as described in Part 3, but the magnetic field does not vary with time. For the flow of steady currents, therefore, $\mathbf{A}$ does not vanish, but its time derivative does vanish. Hence, in this case too Eqs. (4.33), (4.32), and (4.30) reduce to Eqs. (4.24) to (4.26). For an electromagnetic field that varies with time, however, the time derivative of the magnetic vector potential must be incorporated in the definition of electric potential as described by Eqs. (4.30), (4.32), and (4.33).

While a time-varying electromagnetic field normally involves a situation in which there is a time-varying electric field and a time-varying magnetic field at all points, situations frequently occur in electrical science in which, for some regions in the field, the effect of the electric field is predominant, while for other regions the effect of the magnetic field is predominant. Suppose, for example, that in a time-varying electromagnetic field, Eq. (4.32) is to be used to evaluate the difference of potential between the plates of a capacitor. In the space between the plates of the capacitor the time derivative of the magnetic vector potential $\mathbf{A}$ will not, in general, vanish. However, it will, in all probability, be small compared with the electric vector $\mathbf{E}$. In these circumstances Eq. (4.32) can be replaced by Eq. (4.25) and the calculation made as in electrostatics. Likewise, if the region between the plates of the capacitor is filled with a conducting medium, so that the capacitor is a resistor, the time derivative of $\mathbf{A}$ in Eq. (4.32) is frequently small compared with electric vector $\mathbf{E}$. In these circumstances Eq. (4.32) for calculating the difference of potential between the terminals of a resistor can be replaced by Eq. (4.25) and the calculation made in the same way as if the current through the resistor were steady.

A novel situation with respect to electric potential is presented, however, in the case of an inductor. Let us suppose that an inductor is wound with perfectly conducting wire and is provided with a pair of terminals P and Q. Let the inductor form part of an electric circuit, which may contain other inductors. Let us suppose that a time-varying current flows round the circuit. As a result, there is a time-varying magnetic flux threading the circuit, part of which is associated with the inductor whose terminals are P and Q. Let us suppose that, from the magnetic field, a calculation has been made of the magnetic vector potential at each point. Let us evaluate the difference of electric potential between the terminals P and Q of the given inductor by evaluating the integral on the right-hand side of Eq. (4.32) taken from one terminal to the other round the wire of the inductor. Since we are assuming the wire to be perfectly conducting, the electric field in it is negligibly small, and so $\mathbf{E}$ in Eq. (4.32) can be neglected. The drop in electric potential between terminal P and terminal Q of the inductor is therefore

$$\phi_P - \phi_Q = \int_P^Q \frac{\partial \mathbf{A}}{\partial t} \cdot d\mathbf{s} \qquad (4.34)$$

or

$$\phi_P - \phi_Q = \frac{\partial}{\partial t} \int_P^Q \mathbf{A} \cdot d\mathbf{s} \qquad (4.35)$$

The integral is taken from terminal P to terminal Q round the wire of the inductor. The integral on the right-hand side of Eq. (4.35) is the magnetic flux Φ threading that part of the electric circuit associated with the inductor. In terms of Φ, Eq. (4.35) can be written as

$$\phi_P - \phi_Q = \frac{\partial \Phi}{\partial t} \qquad (4.36)$$

The partial form of the time derivative in this equation emphasizes the fact that the inductor is supposed to be at rest. Equation (4.36) shows that, for an inductor wound with perfectly conducting wire, the difference of potential between its terminals is equal to the time rate of change of the magnetic flux threading that part of the electric circuit that is associated with the inductor. The direction in which the electric potential falls along the wire of the inductor is related by the right-hand-screw rule to the direction in which the magnetic flux threads the wire. The positive direction for fall of electric potential along the wire therefore coincides with the positive direction of current along the wire.

Since the electric vector in a perfectly conducting wire is negligibly small, Eq. (4.33) shows that the downward gradient of the electric potential along the wire of the inductor gives the component along the wire, not of the electric vector, but of the time derivative of the magnetic vector potential. A multiturn inductor can easily be provided with a series of terminals, or tapping points, at intervals along the wire as shown in Fig. 4.3. Equation (4.36) then shows that the difference of electric potential between any two tapping points is equal to the time rate of change of the magnetic flux threading that portion of the electric circuit between the two tapping points. For an inductor, therefore, the drop in electric potential along the wire is equal to the time rate of increase of the magnetic flux threading the portion of the circuit concerned, it being understood that the magnetic flux is measured in the direction related by the right-hand-screw rule to the direction in which potential falls.

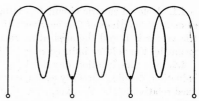

FIG. 4.3. An inductor provided with tapping points.

When the resistance of the wire is taken into account, part of the drop in potential along the wire is associated with resistance and the remainder of the drop in potential is equal to the time rate of change of the magnetic flux threading the portion of the circuit concerned.

4.6. Comparison between the Circulation Laws for the Electric and Magnetic Vectors. For a fixed closed curve C in any electromagnetic field the circulation law for the electric vector is given by Eq. (4.11) and the circulation law for the magnetic vector is given by Eq. (2.13). In a region of space free from electric current, the circulation law for the magnetic vector is expressed by Eq. (2.15). In these circumstances the two circulation laws are

$$\int_C \mathbf{H} \cdot d\mathbf{s} = \frac{\partial}{\partial t} \int_S \mathbf{D} \cdot d\mathbf{S} \qquad (4.37)$$

and

$$\int_C \mathbf{E} \cdot d\mathbf{s} = - \frac{\partial}{\partial t} \int_S \mathbf{B} \cdot d\mathbf{S} \qquad (4.38)$$

We notice the mathematical similarity that exists between the two laws in spite of their completely different physical interpretation.

In a time-varying magnetic field the existence of the expression on the right-hand side of Eq. (4.38) prevents the vanishing of the circulation of the electric vector. We saw in the previous section that this requires a modification in the definition of electric potential and that this is achieved by the use of magnetic vector potential. From Eq. (4.37) we see in a similar manner that, in a time-varying electric field, the circulation of the magnetic vector does not vanish even if no wire carrying current is encircled. It follows therefore that, in a time-varying electric field, a modification is required in the definition of magnetic scalar potential given in Part 3, Chap. 7. This modification is effected in a manner similar to that used for electric potential in the preceding section and involves the introduction of an electric vector potential. However, the situations in which magnetic scalar potential is normally used are not ones in which the corrections arising from time variation of the electric field are important. When magnetic scalar potential is required, therefore, it can normally be employed in the simple form given in Part 3, Chap. 7.

SUMMARIZING EXERCISES

4.1. A closed electric circuit C is in motion in any electromagnetic field. A vector element of length ds of C is moving with velocity $\mathbf{v}$. At this element the applied electric vector is $\mathbf{E}$ and the applied magnetic-flux-density vector is $\mathbf{B}$. Explain what is meant by the voltage induced round C in the direction defined by ds.

4.2. For the situation described in the previous exercise, state Faraday's law of induction, defining carefully each quantity involved. For an electric circuit C that is fixed relative to the observer, show that

$$\int_C \mathbf{E} \cdot ds = -\frac{\partial}{\partial t} \int_S \mathbf{B} \cdot d\mathbf{S}$$

where $d\mathbf{S}$ is a vector element of area of a surface S spanning C and $\mathbf{B}$ is the magnetic-flux-density vector at this element. Explain the relation that must exist between the direction of the vector element of length ds and the direction of the vector element of area $d\mathbf{S}$.

4.3. An indefinitely long solenoid of radius a exists in a homogeneous medium of inductivity μ. The current round the solenoid per unit length is I, and it increases with time at a uniform rate $\dot{I}$. Calculate the resulting electric field strength at a point distant r from the axis of the solenoid (a) when $r > a$ and (b) when $r < a$. Deduce the voltage that must be applied round the solenoid in order to maintain the linear increase of current with time.

4.4. An electric circuit C is located in a fixed position in an electromagnetic field that varies with time t. At a vector element of length ds of C the electric vector is $\mathbf{E}$ and the magnetic vector potential is $\mathbf{A}$. Show that Faraday's law of induction for the circuit can be written in the form

$$\int_C \left(\mathbf{E} + \frac{\partial \mathbf{A}}{\partial t} \right) \cdot ds = 0$$

4.5. Explain how to calculate the difference of electric potential between any two points of any electromagnetic field. Describe the approximate methods that may be used (a) in a part of the electromagnetic field that is predominantly electric and (b) in a part of the electromagnetic field that is predominantly magnetic. Give an example of each of these two special cases.

4.6. An inductor with closely spaced terminals at P and Q is wound with perfectly conducting wire and forms part of an electric circuit. Prove that the difference of potential between the terminals is equal to the time rate of change of the magnetic flux threading that part of the electric circuit that is associated with the inductor. Describe the relation that exists between the direction in which electric potential falls along the winding of the inductor and the direction of the magnetic flux threading the circuit. Deduce that the positive direction for fall of electric potential along the winding coincides with the positive direction of current in the winding.

4.7. Show that, if an inductor wound with perfectly conducting wire is provided with tapping points, the difference of electric potential between any two tapping points is equal to the time rate of change of the magnetic flux threading the part of the electric circuit between the tapping points.

CHAPTER 5

INERTIA AND MOMENTUM OF AN ELECTRIC CIRCUIT

5.1. Introduction. In Part 3, Chap. 1, reference was made to the fact that electrons moving round an electric circuit could be thought of as an electronic flywheel. The electrons possess inertia on account of their mass, but they possess far more inertia on account of their charge. The main reason for our interest in the magnetic flux threading an electric circuit arises from the fact that it is a measure of the momentum of the current associated with the charge of the electrons. From this point of view it is possible to present Faraday's law of induction simply as Newton's law of motion applied to a situation in which the inertia is electrical in origin.

5.2. A Battery Connected into a Perfectly Conducting Electric Circuit.
Let us consider a situation in which a piece of perfectly conducting wire is connected across the terminals of a battery that has a voltage V and negligible internal resistance. At time zero let the current flowing through the wire be zero. Subsequent to time zero there is current flowing round the wire under the influence of the electric field of the battery. This current, together with the magnetic flux threading the circuit, increases with time t. The time rate of increase of the magnetic flux threading the circuit can be derived from the voltage of the battery by an application of Faraday's law of induction.

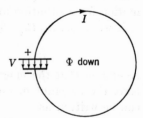

Fig. 5.1. Illustrating a battery of voltage V connected into a perfectly conducting electric circuit.

Figure 5.1 illustrates the relations between the voltage V of the battery, the current I round the perfectly conducting circuit, and the magnetic flux Φ threading the circuit. The positive direction of the current I is taken to be that flowing from the positive terminal of the battery round the circuit to the negative terminal of the battery. The magnetic flux Φ threading the circuit is taken to be in the direction related by the right-hand-screw rule to the direction of the current I round the circuit.

Since the electric field in a perfectly conducting wire is negligibly small, the circulation of the electric vector round the circuit shown in Fig. 5.1 arises solely from the electric field within the battery. It is important

619

to notice that the electric field within the battery is directed from the positive electrode to the negative electrode and therefore points round the electric circuit in the direction opposite to that of the current I. The circulation of the electric vector round the circuit in the direction of the current is therefore equal to $-V$, and it is this voltage that is equal to the time rate of decrease of Φ in accordance with Faraday's law of induction. It follows that the relation between the voltage V of the battery and the threading magnetic flux Φ in Fig. 5.1 is

$$V = \frac{d\Phi}{dt} \tag{5.1}$$

It is therefore a consequence of Faraday's law of induction that, when a battery is applied to a perfectly conducting electric circuit, the magnetic flux threading the circuit in the direction related by the right-hand-screw rule to the direction of the current is subject to a steady increase with time at a rate equal to the voltage of the battery.

The relation in mechanical science that corresponds to Eq. (5.1) states that the force applied to a system is equal to its time rate of increase of momentum. The voltage V in Eq. (5.1) is a measure of the force tending to accelerate electrons round the circuit, and Φ is a measure of the momentum developed by these electrons because of their charge. We thus see that Eq. (5.1) makes a statement equivalent to Newton's law of motion for a situation in which the inertia is electrical in origin.

If we integrate Eq. (5.1) with respect to time, we obtain

$$Vt = \Phi + \text{constant} \tag{5.2}$$

Assuming that the magnetic flux threading the circuit vanishes at time zero, the constant of integration in Eq. (5.2) is zero, and the equation can be written as

$$\Phi = Vt \tag{5.3}$$

Thus a constant voltage V applied to a perfectly conducting electric circuit results in the magnetic flux threading the circuit increasing steadily with time at the rate V. This corresponds to a mechanical situation in which the momentum of a body increases linearly with time as a result of the application of a constant force.

If nonlinear behavior of ferromagnetic material is avoided, we can calculate the inductance L of the circuit. The magnetic flux threading the circuit is then related to the current I round the circuit by the equation

$$\Phi = LI \tag{5.4}$$

Substituting this expression for Φ into Eq. (5.3), we obtain

$$I = \frac{V}{L}t \tag{5.5}$$

This equation states that application of a constant voltage V to a perfectly conducting circuit of inductance L results in the current I round the circuit increasing linearly with time at the rate V/L. This corresponds to a mechanical situation in which a constant force is applied to a body of given mass, and as a result the velocity of the body increases uniformly at a rate equal to the ratio of the applied force to the mass.

5.3. The Relative Importance of the Charge and Mass of Electrons for the Inertia Properties of Electric Circuits. In Part 3, Chap. 1, inertia of electrical origin was illustrated with the aid of a flywheel possessing a metal rim supported by light insulating spokes. The rim was supposed to have a mass M and to carry a charge per unit length equal to Q. It was stated that, for acceleration or deceleration of such a flywheel, the wheel would function as though it were uncharged and had a mass M' given by

$$M' = M + LQ^2 \qquad (5.6)$$

where L is the inductance of the metallic loop constituting the rim. In the light of Faraday's law of induction let us now investigate the truth of Eq. (5.6) and ascertain under what circumstances the inertia of the flywheel is due more to its charge Q per unit length than to its mass M.

Let us suppose that, at time t, the peripheral velocity of the rim is v and its acceleration is

$$\frac{dv}{dt} \qquad (5.7)$$

Since the rim of the wheel is charged, its motion produces an electric current I. The electric current is the amount of charge that passes a fixed point of the circle in unit time, and this is the amount of charge upon a section of the rim of length v. Since Q is the charge per unit length on the rim, it follows that

$$I = Qv \qquad (5.8)$$

Because the peripheral velocity v of the rim is increasing at the rate given by expression (5.7), it follows that the current I is increasing with time at a rate given by

$$\frac{dI}{dt} = Q\frac{dv}{dt} \qquad (5.9)$$

The magnetic flux threading the rim is therefore increasing at a rate given by

$$L\frac{dI}{dt} = LQ\frac{dv}{dt} \qquad (5.10)$$

In accordance with Faraday's law of induction this brings into play an electric field which tends to prevent acceleration of the wheel as described in Sec. 4.4. If E is the electric field strength at a point of the rim and l

is the perimeter of the rim, the circulation of the electric vector round the rim is

$$El \qquad (5.11)$$

Using expressions (5.10) and (5.11) in Faraday's law of induction, we deduce that

$$El = LQ \frac{dv}{dt} \qquad (5.12)$$

it being understood that the direction of the electric field round the rim is opposite to the direction of motion. The electric field strength E produces on the rim a retarding force QE per unit length, and the total peripheral retarding force is therefore QEl. Using Eq. (5.12), we see that the total force tending to oppose acceleration of the rim is

$$QEl = LQ^2 \frac{dv}{dt} \qquad (5.13)$$

To accelerate the rim, therefore, we have to apply a peripheral force F that exceeds the force given by Eq. (5.13) by the product of the mass M of the rim and its acceleration given by expression (5.7). The equation of motion of the rim is, therefore,

$$F - LQ^2 \frac{dv}{dt} = M \frac{dv}{dt} \qquad (5.14)$$

and this can be rewritten as

$$F = M' \frac{dv}{dt} \qquad (5.15)$$

where M' is given by Eq. (5.6). We thus see that, under the influence of a peripheral force F, the rim of the wheel accelerates as though its mass were M', given by Eq. (5.6). The presence of the charge Q per unit length therefore increases the inertia of the wheel, and the coefficient of Q^2 in Eq. (5.6) is the inductance L of the metal rim.

As already stated in Part 3, Chap. 1, flywheels met with in mechanical science are always such that the quantity M on the right-hand side of Eq. (5.6) is large compared with the quantity LQ^2. The reverse, however, is almost always true in electrical science. From Eq. (5.6) we see that the charge of the electrons controls the inertia properties of the circuit if

$$L > \frac{M}{Q^2} \qquad (5.16)$$

Let us investigate the truth of this inequality using an electric circuit whose perimeter is l and for which the cross-sectional area of the wire is A. Let N be the number of conduction electrons in the electric circuit per

unit volume.   The number of electrons per unit length of the wire is
then NA, and so the relevant charge per unit length is

$$Q = NAe \qquad (5.17)$$

where e is the charge on an electron.   Likewise, if m is the mass of an
electron, the mass of moving material per unit length is NAm, and therefore the total mass of the electronic flywheel is

$$M = NAml \qquad (5.18)$$

Substituting into the right-hand side of the inequality (5.16) the expressions for Q and M given by Eqs. (5.17) and (5.18), we obtain

$$\frac{M}{Q^2} = \frac{1}{N} \frac{l}{A} \frac{m}{e^2} \qquad (5.19)$$

To compare the expression on the right-hand side of Eq. (5.19) with
the inductance of the circuit in the manner indicated by the inequality
(5.16), let us consider an electric circuit in the form of a copper cylinder
of radius a and length b, the thickness of the wall being τ.   Such a cylindrical circuit constitutes a solenoid.   If we assume that the length of the
solenoid is large compared with its radius and take the surrounding
medium as having the inductivity μ_v of a vacuum, the inductance of the
circuit is

$$L = \mu_v \frac{\pi a^2}{b} \qquad (5.20)$$

Substituting from Eqs. (5.19) and (5.20) into the inequality (5.16), we
find that the inertia properties of the electric circuit are controlled by the
charge of the electrons rather than by their mass if

$$N > \frac{1}{2\pi a \tau r_e} \qquad (5.21)$$

where

$$r_e = \frac{\mu_v e^2}{4\pi m} \qquad (5.22)$$

The quantity r_e defined by Eq. (5.22) is often known as the "radius of
the electron" for the reason that the inertia properties of an electron
could be entirely explained in terms of its charge if the electron were a
hollow sphere of radius r_e carrying a charge e uniformly distributed over it.
The numerical value of r_e is obtained by substituting into the expression
on the right-hand side of Eq. (5.22) the known values for μ_v, e, and m.
We obtain

$$r_e = 2.8 \times 10^{-15} \text{ m} \qquad (5.23)$$

If we substitute this expression into the right-hand side of the inequality
(5.21) and in addition assume that the numerical values of $2\pi a$ and b

are both 10 cm ($= 10^{-1}$ m), we find that the inertia properties of the electric circuit are controlled by the charge of the electrons rather than by their mass if

$$N > 4 \times 10^{18} \text{ m}^{-3} \qquad (5.24)$$

In copper the number of conduction electrons per unit volume is about 8.5×10^{28} m^{-3}. Comparison of this figure with that on the right-hand side of the inequality (5.24) shows that, for a typical electronic circuit, the contribution of the charge of the electrons to the inertia properties of the circuit is some 10^{10} times greater than is the contribution of the mass of the electrons. To produce a situation in which a metallic electric circuit has inertia properties controlled by the mass of the electrons rather than by their charge, it would be necessary to consider an electric circuit whose linear dimensions were less than the wavelength of visible light.

Since it is clear that the inertia properties of practical electric circuits are entirely controlled by the charge of the electrons rather than by their mass, it may be wondered why, in our study of the diode vacuum tube in Part 2, Chap. 6, it was the inertia properties of the electrons arising from their mass that appeared in the calculation. The inertia properties of the electrons arising from their charges would indeed come into play if a time variation in the current through the tube were involved. Under the circumstances studied in Part 2, Chap. 6, the current through the tube was uniform between the cathode and the anode and was constant in time. If there is a time variation of the current through the tube, this implies a time variation of current round the electric circuit in which the tube is connected. In these circumstances the inductance of this circuit must be taken into account in accordance with Faraday's law of induction. The inductance of the circuit in which the tube is connected takes into account the inertia effect of electrons in the circuit arising from their charge, and these include the electrons between the cathode and anode of the tube.

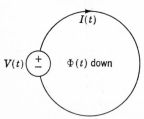

FIG. 5.2. Illustrating a time-varying voltage applied to a perfectly conducting electric circuit.

5.4. Time-varying Voltage Applied to a Perfectly Conducting Electric Circuit. Let us suppose that the battery in Fig. 5.1 is replaced by a dynamo or other device capable of generating a voltage that varies with time t. Let this generator be connected to a perfectly conducting electric circuit as shown in Fig. 5.2. Let $V(t)$ be the applied voltage, and let the resulting magnetic flux threading the electric circuit be $\Phi(t)$. It is assumed that this magnetic flux threads the electric circuit in the direction related by the right-hand-screw rule to the direction round the circuit in which the voltage acts.   By allowing V in Eq. (5.1) to become a function of time, we see that application of Faraday's law of induction to the circuit shown in Fig. 5.2 gives

$$\frac{d\Phi}{dt} = V(t) \qquad (5.25)$$

By integration of this equation with respect to time from t_0 to t we obtain

$$\Phi(t) = \int_{t_0}^{t} V(t) \, dt + \Phi_0 \qquad (5.26)$$

where Φ_0 is the magnetic flux threading the circuit at time t_0.   This equation permits us to calculate the time variation of the magnetic flux threading the circuit when the time variation of the applied voltage is known.

Since the magnetic flux Φ threading the electric circuit varies with time, so also does the current I round the circuit.   Let us assume that, at a particular time t, the current I round the circuit is the same at all points of the circuit.   Let us also assume that nonlinear behavior of ferromagnetic material is avoided.   The current $I(t)$ round the circuit is then related to the magnetic flux $\Phi(t)$ threading the electric circuit by means of the inductance L of the circuit in accordance with the equation

$$\Phi(t) = LI(t) \qquad (5.27)$$

Substitution for $\Phi(t)$ from this equation into Eq. (5.26) gives

$$I(t) = \frac{1}{L} \int_{t_0}^{t} V(t) \, dt + I_0 \qquad (5.28)$$

where I_0 is the current round the circuit at time t_0.   Equation (5.28) permits us to calculate the current round the circuit at any time in terms of the time variation of the applied voltage.

As an example let us suppose that the voltage is applied to the circuit by means of an a-c generator of angular frequency ω producing a voltage of amplitude V_0.   Let the applied voltage be

$$V = V_0 \cos \omega t \qquad (5.29)$$

Let us assume that at time zero the current round the circuit, and consequently the magnetic flux through it, are zero.   Then t_0, Φ_0, and I_0 in Eqs. (5.26) and (5.28) may all be replaced by zero.   Substituting into these equations the expression (5.29) for V, we obtain

$$\Phi = V_0 \frac{\sin \omega t}{\omega} \qquad (5.30)$$

and

$$I = \frac{V_0}{\omega L} \sin \omega t \qquad (5.31)$$

The variation with time t of the applied voltage V given by Eq. (5.29) is illustrated in Fig. 5.3a, and the resulting variation of the current I round the circuit given by Eq. (5.31) is illustrated in Fig. 5.3b. It will be observed that the current reaches its maximum positive values a quarter of a period after the voltage reaches its maximum positive values. Such a situation is described by saying that the current oscillation lags behind the voltage oscillation by a quarter of a period. A similar situation arises

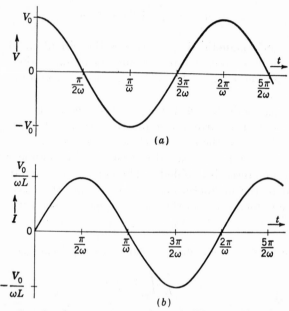

Fig. 5.3. Illustrating, for the arrangement shown in Fig. 5.2, (a) a sinusoidal applied voltage and (b) the resulting sinusoidal current.

when an oscillatory torque is applied to a flywheel mounted on smooth bearings; the flywheel executes an oscillatory motion and the torque reaches its maximum value at the instant when the direction of motion of the flywheel is being reversed.

5.5. Acceleration of Charge round an Electric Circuit Allowing for Resistance. In Sec. 5.2 we considered the application of a battery of voltage V to an electric circuit of negligible resistance and saw that the magnetic flux Φ threading the electric circuit increased at a rate equal to the applied voltage. Let us now consider the modification of this statement that occurs when the resistance R of the electric circuit is taken into account. We shall do this on the assumption that the current I round the electric circuit at any instant is the same at all points of the circuit. We shall also assume that, if the battery has an internal resistance, this is included in the total resistance R of the circuit.

For the situation discussed in connection with Fig. 5.1 we applied Faraday's law of induction to a closed curve C coinciding with the circuit and passing through the battery. With the resistance of the circuit taken into account we proceed in the same way, but it is convenient to divide the complete closed circuit C into two parts, C_1 and C_2. C_1 is that small part of the circuit where the closed curve C passes through the active surface of the battery. The remainder of the closed curve C is denoted by C_2. This is the part of the circuit that contains the resistance R. Electrons are driven through the resistance R by the fringe electric field of the battery. Let $d\mathbf{s}$ be a vector element of length of C pointing round the circuit in the direction of the current I, and let $\mathbf{E}$ be the electric vector at the element $d\mathbf{s}$. Then the voltage driving the current I through the resistance R is

$$\int_{C_2} \mathbf{E} \cdot d\mathbf{s} \qquad (5.32)$$

It follows from Ohm's law that

$$\int_{C_2} \mathbf{E} \cdot d\mathbf{s} = RI \qquad (5.33)$$

As in the case when the resistance of the circuit was neglected, the voltage of the battery is

$$-\int_{C_1} \mathbf{E} \cdot d\mathbf{s} \qquad (5.34)$$

the negative sign arising from the fact that the electric field at the active surface of the battery points round the circuit in the opposite direction to the current I as shown in Fig. 5.1. Hence

$$\int_{C_1} \mathbf{E} \cdot d\mathbf{s} = -V \qquad (5.35)$$

By adding Eqs. (5.33) and (5.35) we obtain

$$\int_{C} \mathbf{E} \cdot d\mathbf{s} = RI - V \qquad (5.36)$$

and the integral on the left-hand side of this equation is now the circulation of the electric vector round the complete closed circuit C. Application of Faraday's law of induction to this closed curve therefore gives

$$RI - V = -\frac{d\Phi}{dt} \qquad (5.37)$$

and this can be rewritten as

$$\frac{d\Phi}{dt} = V - RI \qquad (5.38)$$

Equation (5.38) reduces to Eq. (5.1) when the resistance R of the circuit is negligible.   Equation (5.38) shows that, when the resistance R of the circuit is not negligible, the rate of increase of the magnetic flux through the circuit is equal to the excess of the applied voltage over that required to overcome ohmic resistance.

Let us suppose that the current I round the circuit vanishes at time zero.   At this time, therefore, the current I in Eq. (5.38) is negligible, and the equation reduces to

$$\frac{d\Phi}{dt} = V \tag{5.39}$$

which is identical with Eq. (5.1).   We thus see that, even when the circuit has resistance, the initial rate of increase of the magnetic flux threading the circuit is the same as if the resistance were negligible.

As the current increases from zero, however, the term RI in Eq. (5.38) becomes important, and the rate of increase of the magnetic flux Φ threading the circuit becomes smaller.   Let us assume that the circuit has an inductance L, so that into Eq. (5.38) we can substitute

$$\Phi = LI \tag{5.40}$$

thereby obtaining

$$L\frac{dI}{dt} = V - RI \tag{5.41}$$

This equation shows that, as the current I through the circuit increases from zero, the right-hand side of Eq. (5.41) becomes smaller, and consequently the rate of increase of current round the circuit diminishes. When the current round the circuit ultimately becomes steady, the left-hand side of Eq. (5.41) vanishes, and we have

$$V = RI \tag{5.42}$$

In other words, after the current has settled down to a steady value, the relation between the applied steady voltage and the resulting steady current obeys Ohm's law.   All discussion of Ohm's law in Part 2 assumed that steady current had already been attained in this way.

To examine the details of the way in which the current rises from zero to the Ohm's-law value when a battery is switched into the circuit, we have to solve Eq. (5.41) for I under circumstances when V, L, and R are constants.   To do this we can rearrange Eq. (5.41) in the form

$$\frac{dI}{V - RI} = \frac{1}{L}\,dt \tag{5.43}$$

and then integrate to obtain

$$-\frac{1}{R}\ln\,(V - RI) = \frac{1}{L}\,t + \text{constant} \qquad (5.44)$$

or
$$\ln\,(V - RI) = -\frac{R}{L}\,t + \text{constant} \qquad (5.45)$$

The constant of integration is determined from the fact that, when $t = 0$, we have $I = 0$. Substituting these values into Eq. (5.45), we obtain

$$\ln V = \text{constant} \qquad (5.46)$$

Using this value for the constant of integration in Eq. (5.45), we derive

$$\ln\frac{V - RI}{V} = -\frac{R}{L}\,t \qquad (5.47)$$

which can be rewritten as

$$\frac{V - RI}{V} = e^{-(R/L)t} \qquad (5.48)$$

or
$$I = \frac{V}{R}\,(1 - e^{-(R/L)t}) \qquad (5.49)$$

This value of the current I round the circuit is plotted as a function of time t in Fig. 5.4. We see that, initially, the current increases linearly from zero as in the case when resistance is neglected. As the current builds up, however, the rate of increase of the current decreases, and ultimately the current reaches a steady value equal to that given by Ohm's law.

We see from Eq. (5.49) or from Fig. 5.4 that the time taken to approach the Ohm's-law value is two or three times the time

$$\frac{L}{R} \qquad (5.50)$$

This time is known as the time constant of the circuit. The larger the inductance of the circuit and the smaller its resistance, the longer does it take for a current to reach any stated fraction of the Ohm's-law value.

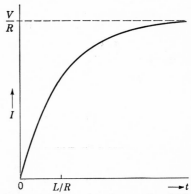

Fig. 5.4. Illustrating the way in which the current I round a circuit rises to the Ohm's-law value when a battery of voltage V is switched into the circuit.

For an inductance of 1 henry and a resistance of 1 ohm, the time constant given by expression (5.50) is equal to 1 sec. On the other hand, for an inductance of 1 μh and a resistance of 1 ohm, the time constant is equal to 1 μsec. We thus see that, while the time taken to reach the Ohm's-law current is usually small as measured by an ordinary clock, nevertheless the time can be long compared with times frequently of interest in electrical science.

As a further application of Eq. (5.41) and its integral given by Eq. (5.45), let us consider a situation in which the Ohm's-law current I_0 was reached some time prior to time zero, and let us suppose that at time zero the battery is short-circuited. After time zero we now have a situation in which there is no voltage acting round the circuit, and the current is being brought to rest under the influence of the resistance of the circuit. The quantity V in Eq. (5.41) therefore vanishes. Consequently V also vanishes in Eq. (5.43), which becomes

$$\frac{dI}{I} = -\frac{R}{L}\,dt \qquad (5.51)$$

and integration of this equation gives

$$\ln I = -\frac{R}{L}\,t + \text{constant} \qquad (5.52)$$

To determine the constant of integration under this new situation we use the fact that, when the time t is zero, I is equal to the Ohm's-law current I_0. Substituting these values into Eq. (5.52) we obtain

$$\ln I_0 = \text{constant} \qquad (5.53)$$

and on subtracting this equation from Eq. (5.52), we derive

$$\ln \frac{I}{I_0} = -\frac{R}{L}\,t \qquad (5.54)$$

This equation can be rewritten as

$$I = I_0 e^{-(R/L)t} \qquad (5.55)$$

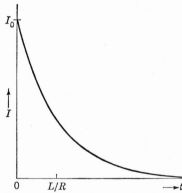

FIG. 5.5. Illustrating the deceleration of charge round an electric circuit after the driving voltage has been removed.

After the driving voltage round the circuit is cut off, therefore, the current decreases to zero exponentially as shown in Fig. 5.5. The time required for the current practically to disappear is two or three times the time constant given by expression (5.50).

Figures 5.4 and 5.5 illustrate the acceleration and deceleration of electric charge round an electric circuit, and they can be compared with similar information for the acceleration and deceleration of a flywheel in mechanics. If the resistive torque due to the bearings is proportional to the angular velocity of the wheel, application of a constant torque to the wheel accelerates it in the manner indicated in Fig. 5.4; after a while the wheel reaches a steady angular velocity and the applied torque is able to overcome only the resistance of the bearings. If, with the wheel turning, the applied torque is removed, the wheel then comes to rest as indicated in Fig. 5.5. This illustrates once again the fact that an electric circuit is an electronic flywheel for which the inertia properties are controlled by the charge of the electrons rather than by their mass.

5.6. Equivalent Circuit for a Loop of Resistive Wire. In the preceding section we considered a loop of resistive wire to which a fixed voltage V is applied. If the applied voltage varies with time, then V in Eq. (5.38) is a function of t. Substitution from Eq. (5.40) into Eq. (5.38) gives Eq. (5.41), which can be written as

$$V(t) = L\frac{dI}{dt} + RI(t) \qquad (5.56)$$

This is the equation for determining the current $I(t)$ round a circuit of inductance L and resistance R to which a time-varying voltage $V(t)$ is applied. It is supposed that, at a given instant, the current round the circuit is the same at all points of the circuit.

Let us examine Eq. (5.56) from a different point of view. Let us suppose that it is the current that is specified as a function of time and that it is the voltage required to maintain the current that has to be calculated. Then Eq. (5.56) expresses this voltage $V(t)$ in terms of the given current $I(t)$, the inductance L of the circuit, and the resistance R of the circuit. Equation (5.56) states that this voltage is the sum of two contributions. The first contribution is

$$L\frac{dI}{dt} \qquad (5.57)$$

and is associated with the inductance L of the circuit. The second contribution is

$$RI \qquad (5.58)$$

and is associated with the resistance R of the circuit. If the resistance of the circuit were negligible, then the applied voltage would be given entirely by expression (5.57). If the inductance were negligible, the applied voltage would be given entirely by expression (5.58). Taking account of both the inductance and the resistance of the circuit, Eq. (5.56) shows that the applied voltage is equal to the sum of the two voltages (5.57) and (5.58). This situation is conveniently represented by the equivalent circuit shown in Fig. 5.6. Figure 5.6 is drawn as though the inductance L of the loop were almost entirely controlled by a multiturn coil connected in the circuit. In practice this is very often the case. The coil indicated in Fig. 5.6 is assumed to endow the complete circuit with an inductance L but is assumed to have no resistance. Connected in series with the coil, however, there is a resistor of resistance R which is supposed to contribute nothing to the inductance of the loop. With a current $I(t)$ passing round the circuit indicated in Fig. 5.6, the

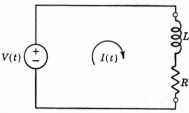

voltage developed across the coil is given by expression (5.57) and that across the resistor by expression (5.58). The combined voltage across the coil and the resistor is therefore given by the right-hand side of Eq. (5.56). Figure 5.6 is thus a diagrammatic representation of Eq. (5.56). The information contained in Eq. (5.56) can be expressed by saying that an electric circuit of inductance L and

FIG. 5.6. Equivalent circuit representing application of a voltage $V(t)$ to a circuit of inductance L and resistance R.

resistance R is equivalent to an inductor of inductance L but negligible resistance connected in series with a resistor of resistance R but negligible inductance.

If the electric circuit consists of a single turn of wire, then it is the inductance of this loop that is to be used as the inductance L in the equivalent circuit shown in Fig. 5.6. If, however, the electric circuit contains a multiturn coil, as is frequently the case in practice, then the inductance is likely to be controlled almost entirely by the geometry of the coil and hardly at all by the remainder of the electric circuit.

In terms of the equivalent circuit shown in Fig. 5.6 we can now recognize more clearly the significance of the discussion of resistive networks presented in Part 2. Each electric circuit discussed in Part 2 in fact had an inductance, although no mention was made of it. Each resistor should have been represented in a circuit diagram as having an inductor in series with it, as indicated in Fig. 5.6. However, in Part 2, we were concerned only with steady electric currents, that is, currents for which

$$\frac{dI}{dt} = 0 \qquad (5.59)$$

In these circumstances the voltage given by expression (5.57) vanishes, and only the Ohm's-law voltage given by expression (5.58) has to be taken into account.

5.7. Electromagnetic Waves. In Sec. 4.3 it is pointed out that the circulation law for the electric vector, in the form given by Faraday's law of induction, is applicable to any closed geometrical curve in any electromagnetic field.   Likewise, in Sec. 2.6 it is pointed out that, when Maxwell's displacement current is taken into account, the circulation law for the magnetic vector is applicable to any closed geometrical curve in any electromagnetic field.   The circulation laws for the electric and magnetic vectors in their general forms imply the existence of electromagnetic waves.   While it is not intended to discuss electromagnetic waves in detail at this time, certain statements made in this chapter are related to electromagnetic waves in a manner that should be mentioned.

The velocity of electromagnetic waves in free space, namely,

$$c = 2.998 \times 10^8 \text{ m/sec} \tag{5.60}$$

has already been encountered in Part 3, Eq. (2.33).   Information can never be transmitted with a speed in excess of the value given in Eq. (5.60).   Thus, if a battery is connected into an electric circuit at a particular instant, the reaction upon all electrons in the circuit is not immediate.   The information that the battery is connected is transmitted with the velocity c.   Thus, if l is a measure of the linear dimensions of the circuit, the time that elapses before all electrons of the circuit are aware that the battery is connected is of the order of magnitude

$$\frac{l}{c} \tag{5.61}$$

This results in a situation in which the current round the circuit at a particular instant is not in general the same at all points of the circuit. Now an assumption that the current round the circuit is the same everywhere was introduced in Sec. 5.4 between Eqs. (5.26) and (5.27).   This implies a restriction on the time of travel of an electromagnetic wave from one point of the circuit to another and therefore involves an upper limit to the size of the circuit under consideration.

To examine this limitation on the size of a circuit, let us now suppose that the source of voltage connected in the circuit varies continuously with time.   Furthermore, let us suppose that the time required for an appreciable variation of this voltage is

$$\tau \tag{5.62}$$

and let this time be called the time constant of the applied voltage.   If the time given by expression (5.61) is small compared with the time given by expression (5.62), then the time taken to transmit an electromagnetic wave from one point of the circuit to another is small compared with the time in which the voltage of the source changes.   Thus all electrons are more or less simultaneously aware of the voltage existing at the source. On the other hand let us consider a situation in which the transmission time l/c across the circuit is large compared with the time constant τ of the applied voltage.   In this case the voltage of the source changes substantially in less time than it takes to transmit to the distant electrons of the circuit the information concerning the value of the voltage existing at the source.   This leads to a situation in which the current existing in different parts of the circuit is different depending upon the time of transmission of information from the source.   Thus, when in Sec. 5.4 the assumption was introduced between Eqs. (5.26) and (5.27) that the current at all parts of the circuit is the same, there was an implied assumption that the size l of the circuit is such that the transmission line l/c across the circuit is small compared with the time constant τ of the applied voltage.   The size limitation on the circuit is therefore expressed by the inequality

$$l \ll c\tau \tag{5.63}$$

This assumption is not involved in Eq. (5.25), which is based on Faraday's law of induction, or in Eq. (5.26), which is simply obtained by integration of Eq. (5.25).   It is in the use of the inductance L of the circuit to relate the magnetic flux threading the circuit to the electric current round the circuit that the implication is introduced that the current is the same at all points of the circuit.   Thus, for a given rate of variation of the applied voltage, there is a limit to the size of circuit to which Eq. (5.27) is applicable and therefore for which Eq. (5.28) is true.   This size limitation is expressed by the inequality (5.63).

Let us illustrate the size limitation with the aid of the variation of applied voltage with time given by Eq. (5.29) and plotted in Fig. 5.3a. The frequency of oscillation is given by

$$f = \frac{\omega}{2\pi} \tag{5.64}$$

and the time for a complete oscillation is

$$T = \frac{1}{f} \tag{5.65}$$

During this time a wave advancing with the velocity c moves a distance

$$\lambda = cT \tag{5.66}$$

and this is known as the wavelength of an electromagnetic wave whose periodic time is T.   Substituting into Eq. (5.66) from Eq. (5.65) for T, we deduce that the relation between the frequency of oscillation f and the wavelength λ is

$$f\lambda = c \tag{5.67}$$

From Fig. 5.3a we see that an appropriate measure of the time constant of the oscillation is

$$\tau = \frac{T}{2\pi} \tag{5.68}$$

Multiplying this equation by c and using Eq. (5.66), we obtain

$$c\tau = \frac{\lambda}{2\pi} \tag{5.69}$$

Inequality (5.63) therefore reads

$$l \ll \frac{\lambda}{2\pi} \tag{5.70}$$

To estimate the size of the largest circuit to which Eq. (5.31) and Fig. 5.3b can be applied, we evaluate the wavelength λ from the frequency of oscillation f by means of Eq. (5.67), using the value given in Eq. (5.60) for c, and then use this value of λ in the inequality (5.70).   Calculations for frequencies of oscillation from zero to 10^{10} cycles/sec are summarized in Table 5.1.

TABLE 5.1. For Estimating the Maximum Circuit Size for Which Current round the Circuit Can Be Assumed Approximately the Same Everywhere

Frequency, cycles/sec	Angular frequency, radians/sec	Periodic time, sec	Time constant, sec	Wavelength, m	Size limit, m
0	0	∞	∞	∞	∞
10^2	6×10^2	10^{-2}	1.7×10^{-3}	3×10^6	5×10^5
10^4	6×10^4	10^{-4}	1.7×10^{-5}	3×10^4	5×10^3
10^6	6×10^6	10^{-6}	1.7×10^{-7}	3×10^2	50
10^8	6×10^8	10^{-8}	1.7×10^{-9}	3	0.5
10^{10}	6×10^{10}	10^{-10}	1.7×10^{-11}	3×10^{-2}	5×10^{-3}

In the table the second row corresponds to a frequency of 100 cycles/sec and therefore roughly to frequencies of the order of magnitude involved in the distribution of electric power.   From the last column we see that, at this frequency, circuits larger than about 500 km fail to satisfy the condition that the current round them may be considered uniform. The fourth row in the table corresponds to a frequency of 1 Mc/sec and therefore to a frequency of the order of magnitude used in radio broadcasting.   From the last column we see that, at this frequency, circuits larger than 50 m fail to satisfy the condition that the current round them may be considered the same at all points.   The next to last row in the table corresponds to a frequency of 100 Mc/sec and therefore to a frequency of the order of magnitude used in frequency-modulation broadcasting.   At this frequency we see from the last column in the table that circuits larger than 50 cm in size fail to satisfy the condition that the current round them is uniform.   At this frequency and at all lower frequencies, there is no difficulty in building equipment such that the circuits are small enough to satisfy the condition of current uniformity, and indeed this is usually the convenient practical procedure.   As we proceed upward in frequency from 100 Mc/sec to the highest radio frequencies in use, however, it becomes increasingly inconvenient to design circuits for which it may be assumed that the current round them is the same at all points.   The bottom row in the table corresponds to a frequency of 10,000 Mc/sec.   At this frequency it would be necessary to make circuits with a size small compared with 5 mm in order that the current round them may be taken to have the same value at all points, and circuits as small as this are not usually practical.   The table thus illustrates the fact that, at all but the highest radio frequencies in use, electric circuits can be made small enough so that the current round them may be assumed uniform.   A vast amount of electrical science is based upon the use of such circuits.

When an electric network is such that the transmission time of electromagnetic waves along any straight line drawn from one point of the network to another may be considered small compared with the time constant involved in the applied voltages and currents, the current round each mesh may be assumed to be the same at all points of the mesh. Analysis of the network is then considerably simplified, and the method of analysis is said to be based upon "electric-network theory."   When an electrical arrangement is too large for application of electric-network theory, the associated electromagnetic field must be dissected into building blocks in order to apply the theory.   However, for the remainder of this book, we shall assume that the electrical systems with which we are concerned are sufficiently small for application of electric-network theory to them without dissection.   In this way we postpone serious consideration of electromagnetic waves.

5.8. Skin Effect.   There is another respect in which electromagnetic waves are implicit in the considerations of this chapter.   In Sec. 5.5 a study was made of an electric circuit for which the current varies with time and for which resistance is taken into account.   The calculation of the resistance of a wire under these circumstances requires consideration. In Sec. 1.11, we saw that, for a resistive wire carrying steady current, the direction of flow of energy is radially inward.   For a nonsteady current, the direction of energy flow is still radially inward to a high degree of approximation.   However, the electromagnetic field inside the wire now takes the form of an electromagnetic wave.   The wavelength of an electromagnetic wave within a conducting wire is extremely small compared with the wavelength in free space and is usually comparable to or smaller than the radius of the wire.   The electromagnetic field in the wire thus involves an electromagnetic wave traveling radially inward from the surface of the wire toward the axis of the wire.   At sufficiently high frequencies of oscillation this wave is completely absorbed before it reaches the axis of the wire.   We then have a situation in which, even though the wire may be solid, the current through it exists only near the surface of the wire.   This phenomenon is known as "skin effect."

When skin effect exists, it is necessary to calculate the resistance of the wire by using, not the full cross-sectional area of the wire, but that fraction of the cross-sectional area in which substantial current is actually flowing.   When it is necessary to calculate the resistance of the wire in this way, the resistance depends somewhat upon the frequency of oscillation and is known as the high-frequency resistance of the wire.   It is not convenient to enter into the calculation of the high-frequency resistance of a wire prior to study of electromagnetic waves.   It will, however, be assumed henceforth that any resistance quoted for a wire has been calculated with due allowance for any skin effect that may be involved.

SUMMARIZING EXERCISES

5.1. A voltage V that varies with time t is applied round a perfectly conducting electric circuit.   The magnetic flux threading the electric circuit at time t in the direction related by the right-hand-screw rule to the direction round the circuit in which the voltage acts is Φ.   From Faraday's law of induction deduce that the time rate of increase of Φ is equal to V and explain why a negative sign is not involved.

5.2. The electric circuit in the previous exercise has inductance L, and the current in it at time t in the direction of the applied voltage is I.   It may be assumed that $\Phi = LI$.   If the current in the circuit at time t_0 is equal to I_0, and if V is specified as a function of t subsequent to time t_0, explain how to calculate the current I round the circuit at all times t subsequent to t_0.

5.3. Explain why the assumption that $\Phi = LI$ in the previous exercise implies a restriction in the size of the electric circuit.   Make a numerical estimate of the restriction in size for frequencies of oscillation of (a) 10^2 cycles/sec, (b) 10^6 cycles/sec, and (c) 10^{10} cycles/sec.

5.4. A voltage V that varies with time t is applied round an electric circuit of resistance R.   The resulting current in the circuit at time t in the direction of the applied voltage is I.   The associated magnetic flux threading the circuit in the direction related by the right-hand-screw rule to the direction of the current is Φ.   Explain why the time rate of increase of Φ is equal to $V - RI$.   Describe and justify an equivalent circuit for an inductor of inductance L and resistance R.

5.5. An inductor of inductance L and resistance R is on open circuit at time zero.   At this time a battery of voltage V is connected across the inductor.   Calculate the way in which the current through the inductor rises to the Ohm's-law value.

5.6. A constant-current source is passing a steady current I_0 through an inductor of inductance L and resistance R.   At time zero the source is short-circuited.   Calculate the way in which the current through the inductor decreases to zero.

5.7. An electric circuit has inductance L and resistance R.   Explain what is meant by its time constant.   Evaluate the time constant (a) if $L = 1$ henry, $R = 10$ ohms and (b) if $L = 1 \, \mu\text{h}$, $R = 1$ ohm.

CHAPTER 6

NETWORKS OF INDUCTORS

6.1. Introduction. Networks of capacitors were discussed in Part 1, and networks of resistors in Part 2. We now come to a discussion of networks of inductors.

An inductor has both an electric circuit round which the current flows and a magnetic circuit round which the magnetic flux passes, and the one threads the other. Connection between two inductors can be made

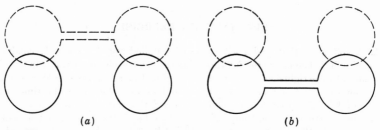

(a)   (b)

FIG. 6.1. Illustrating diagrammatically connection between two coils (a) in the magnetic circuits and (b) in the electric circuits.

either in the electric circuit or in the magnetic circuit. Figure 6.1 illustrates diagrammatically a pair of inductors, the continuous circles representing the electric circuits and the broken circles representing the threading magnetic circuits. In Fig. 6.1a the inductors are shown connected in their magnetic circuits, thereby forming a transformer. Connections in the magnetic circuits of inductors have already been discussed in Part 3, Chaps. 8 and 9. It is with connections in the electric circuits of inductors that we are now concerned.

Figure 6.1b illustrates a pair of inductors connected in their electric circuits but not in their magnetic circuits. To produce a situation of this type in practice special precautions are necessary. These precautions could take the form of a pair of soft-iron magnetic circuits independently threading the two inductors. If precautions are not taken, some of the magnetic flux threading the left-hand inductor in Fig. 6.1b also threads the right-hand inductor, and vice versa. This produces a situation in which the two inductors whose electric circuits are metallically connected are also magnetic-coupled. Such magnetic coupling is described with the aid of the coefficient of mutual inductance of the inductors discussed in Part 3, Chap. 9.

In discussing networks of inductors we shall assume that all connections are made in the electric circuits and that magnetic coupling between the inductors can be neglected unless the contrary is stated and coefficients of mutual inductance are quoted. We shall also assume that the sizes of the inductors and the lengths of the connecting wires are short enough to satisfy the conditions for application of network theory described in Sec. 5.7, so that the currents round each mesh of the network may be considered to be the same at all points of the mesh. Furthermore, we shall also assume that, if ferromagnetic material is involved, the associated nonlinear effects are avoided. We shall also assume, for the time being, that the resistances of the inductors are negligible. We are to discuss, therefore, what corresponds in electrical science to a machine composed of flywheels mounted on frictionless bearings and interconnected in various ways.

6.2. Inductors Connected in Series. A group of inductors connected by metallic wires as shown in Fig. 6.2 is said to be connected in series. Let a generator be connected across the inductors as shown, and let the dependence upon time t of the voltage of the generator be $V(t)$. As a result let a current $I(t)$ flow round the circuit in the direction indicated.

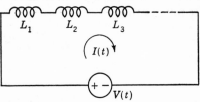

FIG. 6.2. Inductors connected in series.

Let L_1, L_2, . . . be the inductances of the various inductors, so that the associated magnetic fluxes threading the circuit are

$$L_1 I(t) \qquad L_2 I(t) \tag{6.1}$$

The corresponding voltages developed across the terminals of the inductors are, therefore,

$$L_1 \frac{dI}{dt} \qquad L_2 \frac{dI}{dt} \qquad \cdots \tag{6.2}$$

The sum of these voltages is the voltage $V(t)$ applied by the generator, so that

$$V(t) = L_1 \frac{dI}{dt} + L_2 \frac{dI}{dt} + \cdots \tag{6.3}$$

We now rewrite this equation in the form

$$V(t) = L \frac{dI}{dt} \tag{6.4}$$

where
$$L = L_1 + L_2 + \cdots \tag{6.5}$$

It follows that, when a number of noninteracting inductors are connected in series, they are equivalent to a single inductor whose inductance is the sum of the inductances of the individual inductors.

6.3. Inductors Connected in Parallel.   A group of inductors connected

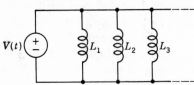

by metallic wires as shown in Fig. 6.3 is said to be connected in parallel, or in shunt.   Let a generator of voltage $V(t)$ be connected across the inductors as shown.   Let the resulting currents through the inductors whose inductances are L_1, L_2, . . .

FIG. 6.3. Inductors connected in parallel.

be $I_1(t)$, $I_2(t)$, . . . respectively.   The voltages that must be developed across the terminals of the various inductors are therefore

$$L_1 \frac{dI_1}{dt} \qquad L_2 \frac{dI_2}{dt} \qquad \cdots \tag{6.6}$$

Under the assumptions described in the introduction to this chapter, each of these voltages must be equal to the voltage $V(t)$ of the generator. It follows that

$$L_1 \frac{dI_1}{dt} = V(t)$$
$$L_2 \frac{dI_2}{dt} = V(t) \tag{6.7}$$
$$\cdots \cdots \cdots$$

If we integrate these equations with regard to time on the assumption that all currents start from zero at time zero, we obtain

$$I_1 = \frac{1}{L_1} \int_0^t V \, dt$$
$$I_2 = \frac{1}{L_2} \int_0^t V \, dt \tag{6.8}$$
$$\cdots \cdots \cdots \cdots$$

The total current supplied by the generator is the sum of the currents passing through the various inductors, and is therefore

$$I = I_1 + I_2 + \cdots \tag{6.9}$$

Substituting for I_1, I_2, . . . from Eqs. (6.8) into Eq. (6.9) we obtain

$$I = \left(\frac{1}{L_1} + \frac{1}{L_2} + \cdots \right) \int_0^t V \, dt \tag{6.10}$$

This equation can be written as

$$I = \frac{1}{L} \int_0^t V \, dt \qquad (6.11)$$

where

$$\frac{1}{L} = \frac{1}{L_1} + \frac{1}{L_2} + \cdots \qquad (6.12)$$

Equation (6.11) is the equation for the current delivered by the generator if it is connected across a single inductor of inductance L. We therefore see that, if a number of noninteracting inductors of inductances L_1, L_2, . . . are connected in parallel, they are equivalent to a single inductor of inductance L, given by Eq. (6.12). If desired, Eq. (6.12) can be described by saying that, when inductors are connected in parallel, it is the reluctances of the inductors that are additive.

It should be noted that, when capacitors are connected in parallel, it is the capacitances that are additive, but when inductors are connected in parallel, it is the reciprocals of the inductances that are additive. Likewise, when inductors are connected in series, it is the inductances that are additive, but when capacitors are connected in series, it is the reciprocals of the capacitances that are additive.

6.4. More Complicated Networks of Inductors. Any network of magnetically uncoupled inductors can be analyzed into arrangements of inductors connected in series and in parallel. The properties of the network can then be deduced from Eqs. (6.5) and (6.12). For more complicated networks, however, use may conveniently be made of Kirchhoff's network laws. Kirchhoff's conservation law for a network of inductors states as usual that the algebraic sum of the currents leaving any node of the network is zero. Kirchhoff's circulation law for a network of inductors requires, however, some consideration.

Kirchhoff's circulation law is based on the circulation law for the electric vector, and this now takes the form of Faraday's law of induction. The voltage applied round any mesh of a network is equal to the time rate of increase of the magnetic flux threading the mesh in the direction related by the right-hand-screw rule to the direction round the mesh in which the voltage acts. For an individual inductor of inductance L connected in the mesh and carrying a current I, the contribution to the time rate of increase of the magnetic flux threading the mesh is

$$L \frac{dI}{dt} \qquad (6.13)$$

This is therefore the voltage that exists across the terminals of the inductor and acts in the direction of the current I. As we move round a mesh in a network of inductors, therefore, the algebraic sum of the quantities given by expression (6.13) for the inductors in the mesh is equal to the total voltage acting round the mesh in the direction of the current. Using electric potential in the sense defined in Sec. 4.5, we may say that, for a coil of inductance L carrying a current I, expression (6.13) is the drop in potential as we pass through the coil from one terminal to the other in the direction of the current. Kirchhoff's circulation law for a network of inductors can therefore be expressed by saying that, as we pass completely round any mesh and return to the starting point, the algebraic sum of the drops in potential as we pass through the inductors is balanced by the algebraic sum of the increases in potential as we pass through the generators.

In using Kirchhoff's laws to analyze a network of inductors, there are two broad methods of attack. One is to introduce mathematical unknowns to describe the currents round the meshes. In this method Kirchhoff's conservation law is automatically satisfied, and the equations for the unknown mesh currents are obtained by applying Kirchhoff's circulation law to the various meshes. The other method is to introduce mathematical unknowns to describe the potentials of the nodes. In this method Kirchhoff's circulation law is automatically satisfied, and the equations to determine the unknown node potentials are obtained by applying Kirchhoff's conservation law to the various nodes.

6.5. The Mesh-current Method. To illustrate the mesh-current method, let us consider the arrangement of three inductors shown in

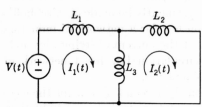

Fig. 6.4, and let a voltage $V(t)$ that varies with time t in a known manner be applied at the left. Let $I_1(t)$ and $I_2(t)$ be the resulting currents round the two meshes, so that the current through the common inductor of inductance L_3 is the difference between $I_1(t)$ and $I_2(t)$.

FIG. 6.4. Illustrating the mesh-current method applied to a network of inductors.

In the left-hand mesh in Fig. 6.4 we have an inductor of inductance L_1 carrying a current $I_1(t)$. The voltage that must exist across this inductor in the direction of the current in order to drive the current through it is

$$L_1 \frac{dI_1}{dt} \qquad (6.14)$$

Proceeding round the left-hand mesh to the inductor of inductance L_3, we observe that the current through this inductor in the direction of the current in the left-hand mesh is $I_1(t) - I_2(t)$. To drive this current through the inductor L_3 the voltage that must exist across the inductor in the direction of the mesh current round the left-hand mesh is

$$L_3 \frac{d}{dt}(I_1 - I_2) \tag{6.15}$$

By addition of expressions (6.14) and (6.15) we see that the total voltage that must be applied round the left-hand mesh to maintain the mesh current is

$$L_1 \frac{dI_1}{dt} + L_3 \frac{d}{dt}(I_1 - I_2) \tag{6.16}$$

It follows that

$$L_1 \frac{dI_1}{dt} + L_3 \frac{d}{dt}(I_1 - I_2) = V(t) \tag{6.17}$$

In the same way we obtain for the right-hand mesh in Fig. 6.4

$$L_2 \frac{dI_2}{dt} + L_3 \frac{d}{dt}(I_2 - I_1) = 0 \tag{6.18}$$

Equations (6.17) and (6.18) can be rewritten as

$$(L_1 + L_3)\frac{dI_1}{dt} - L_3 \frac{dI_2}{dt} = V(t) \tag{6.19}$$

$$-L_3 \frac{dI_1}{dt} + (L_2 + L_3)\frac{dI_2}{dt} = 0 \tag{6.20}$$

Equations (6.19) and (6.20) are a pair of algebraic equations for the time derivatives of I_1 and I_2. Solving this pair of equations we obtain

$$\frac{dI_1}{dt} = \frac{L_2 + L_3}{L_2 L_3 + L_3 L_1 + L_1 L_2} V(t) \tag{6.21}$$

$$\frac{dI_2}{dt} = \frac{L_3}{L_2 L_3 + L_3 L_1 + L_1 L_2} V(t) \tag{6.22}$$

We can now integrate Eqs. (6.21) and (6.22) with respect to time t from an initial instant t_0 at which the current round the left-hand mesh is I_{10} and the current round the right-hand mesh is I_{20}. We obtain

$$I_1 = \frac{L_2 + L_3}{L_2 L_3 + L_3 L_1 + L_1 L_2} \int_{t_0}^{t} V \, dt + I_{10} \tag{6.23}$$

$$I_2 = \frac{L_3}{L_2 L_3 + L_3 L_1 + L_1 L_2} \int_{t_0}^{t} V \, dt + I_{20} \tag{6.24}$$

As an example, let us suppose that the applied voltage in Fig. 6.4 is a sinusoidal oscillation of angular frequency ω and amplitude V_0 given by

$$V = V_0 \cos \omega t \tag{6.25}$$

and that the currents round the meshes vanish at time zero. In these circumstances Eqs. (6.23) and (6.24) become

$$I_1 = \frac{L_2 + L_3}{L_2 L_3 + L_3 L_1 + L_1 L_2} V_0 \frac{\sin \omega t}{\omega} \tag{6.26}$$

$$I_2 = \frac{L_3}{L_2 L_3 + L_3 L_1 + L_1 L_2} V_0 \frac{\sin \omega t}{\omega} \tag{6.27}$$

6.6. The Node-potential Method. To illustrate the node-potential method for analyzing a network of inductors let us again consider the

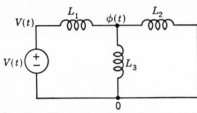

arrangement shown in Fig. 6.4. Choose the potential of the negative terminal of the generator to be zero so that the potential of the positive terminal is $V(t)$ as shown in Fig. 6.5. There is now only one node whose potential is unknown, namely, the node at which the three inductors meet. Let the potential of this node be $\phi(t)$, as indicated

FIG. 6.5. Illustrating the node-potential method for analyzing a network of inductors.

in Fig. 6.5. An equation to determine this unknown node potential is obtained by applying Kirchhoff's conservation law to this node.

The terminals of the inductor of inductance L_1 have potentials $V(t)$ and $\phi(t)$. The potential difference

$$\phi(t) - V(t) \tag{6.28}$$

is therefore equal to expression (6.13), where L is the inductance L_1 in Fig. 6.5 and I is the current from right to left through this inductor. The time rate of increase of the current leaving the node of potential $\phi(t)$ in Fig. 6.5 and flowing through the inductor of inductance L_1 is therefore

$$\frac{\phi(t) - V(t)}{L_1} \tag{6.29}$$

In the same way the current leaving this node and flowing through the inductor of inductance L_2 has a time rate of increase equal to

$$\frac{\phi(t) - 0}{L_2} \tag{6.30}$$

Likewise, the current leaving the node of potential $\phi(t)$ and flowing through the inductor of inductance L_3 has a time rate of increase equal to

$$\frac{\phi(t) - 0}{L_3} \tag{6.31}$$

The time rate of increase of the algebraic sum of the currents leaving the node of potential $\phi(t)$ is obtained by adding expressions (6.29) to (6.31) and is therefore

$$\frac{\phi(t) - V(t)}{L_1} + \frac{\phi(t) - 0}{L_2} + \frac{\phi(t) - 0}{L_3} \qquad (6.32)$$

By Kirchhoff's conservation law the algebraic sum of the currents leaving the node is zero. So also, therefore, is the time rate of increase of the algebraic sum of these currents. It consequently follows from expression (6.32) that

$$\frac{\phi(t) - V(t)}{L_1} + \frac{\phi(t) - 0}{L_2} + \frac{\phi(t) - 0}{L_3} = 0 \qquad (6.33)$$

This equation can be rewritten as

$$\left(\frac{1}{L_1} + \frac{1}{L_2} + \frac{1}{L_3}\right)\phi(t) = \frac{1}{L_1}V(t) \qquad (6.34)$$

from which it follows that the required node potential is

$$\phi(t) = \frac{L_2 L_3}{L_2 L_3 + L_3 L_1 + L_1 L_2}V(t) \qquad (6.35)$$

Equation (6.35) conveys the same information about the network of inductors under investigation as is conveyed by Eqs. (6.23) and (6.24). For example, the current I_1 given by Eq. (6.23) is the current from left to right through the inductor of inductance L_1 in Fig. 6.5. From Fig. 6.5 we see that the time rate of increase of the current I_1 is given by

$$\frac{dI_1}{dt} = \frac{V(t) - \phi(t)}{L_1} \qquad (6.36)$$

Substitution into this equation for $\phi(t)$ from Eq. (6.35) leads to Eq. (6.21) and, therefore, to Eq. (6.23).

6.7. A Two-mesh Network Involving Mutual Inductance. As a simple example of a network of inductors involving mutual inductance, let

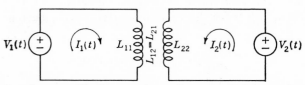

Fig. 6.6. A transformer with time-varying voltages applied across both windings.

us consider a transformer for which time-varying voltages are applied across the two windings, as illustrated in Fig. 6.6. Let L_{11} and L_{22} be the coefficients of self-inductance of the windings. Let L_{12} and L_{21} be the equal coefficients of mutual inductance between the windings. Let $V_1(t)$ and $V_2(t)$ be the voltages applied across windings 1 and 2, and let the resulting currents through the windings be $I_1(t)$ and $I_2(t)$ respectively. Let the voltages act round the circuits in the positive directions of the currents as indicated in Fig. 6.6.   Let $\Phi_1(t)$ and $\Phi_2(t)$ be the magnetic fluxes threading meshes 1 and 2 in the directions related by the right-hand rule to the directions of the corresponding currents $I_1(t)$ and $I_2(t)$. As described in Part 3, Sec. 9.9, the common value of L_{12} and L_{21} is positive or negative according as the currents $I_1(t)$ and $I_2(t)$ encircle the magnetic flux common to both windings in the same direction or in opposite directions.   The relations between the magnetic fluxes threading the meshes and the currents round the meshes are given by the equations

$$\Phi_1 = L_{11}I_1 + L_{12}I_2 \tag{6.37}$$
$$\Phi_2 = L_{21}I_1 + L_{22}I_2 \tag{6.38}$$

Application of Faraday's law of induction to closed curves coinciding with the electric circuits of meshes 1 and 2 gives

$$V_1(t) = \frac{d\Phi_1}{dt} \tag{6.39}$$

$$V_2(t) = \frac{d\Phi_2}{dt} \tag{6.40}$$

respectively.   If we substitute into these equations the values of Φ_1 and Φ_2 given by Eqs. (6.37) and (6.38), we obtain

$$V_1(t) = L_{11}\frac{dI_1}{dt} + L_{12}\frac{dI_2}{dt} \tag{6.41}$$

$$V_2(t) = L_{21}\frac{dI_1}{dt} + L_{22}\frac{dI_2}{dt} \tag{6.42}$$

If the currents round the windings are specified as functions of the time, these equations determine the voltages that must be applied to the windings to drive the currents.

If it is the voltages applied to the windings that are specified and the currents round the windings that have to be calculated, then we solve Eqs. (6.41) and (6.42) for the time derivatives of the currents, thereby obtaining

$$\frac{dI_1}{dt} = R_{11}V_1(t) + R_{12}V_2(t) \tag{6.43}$$

$$\frac{dI_2}{dt} = R_{21}V_1(t) + R_{22}V_2(t) \tag{6.44}$$

where $$R_{11} = \frac{L_{22}}{L_{11}L_{22} - L_{12}{}^2} \tag{6.45}$$

$$R_{22} = \frac{L_{11}}{L_{11}L_{22} - L_{12}{}^2} \tag{6.46}$$

$$R_{12} = R_{21} = -\frac{L_{12}}{L_{11}L_{22} - L_{12}{}^2} = -\frac{L_{21}}{L_{11}L_{22} - L_{21}{}^2} \tag{6.47}$$

The coefficients R_{11} and R_{22} are in fact the coefficients of self-reluctance of the transformer, while the common value of R_{12} and R_{21} is the coefficient of mutual reluctance for the transformer as described in Part 3, Sec. 9.5.   If the properties of the transformer are specified in terms of the coefficients of self- and mutual reluctance, we can write down at the start the equations

$$I_1 = R_{11}\Phi_1 + R_{12}\Phi_2 \tag{6.48}$$
$$I_2 = R_{21}\Phi_1 + R_{22}\Phi_2 \tag{6.49}$$

Differentiation of these equations with respect to time t then gives immediately Eqs. (6.43) and (6.44) on using Eqs. (6.39) and (6.40).   Integration of Eqs. (6.43) and (6.44) with respect to time gives

$$I_1(t) = R_{11}\int_{t_0}^{t} V_1\,dt + R_{12}\int_{t_0}^{t} V_2\,dt + I_{10} \tag{6.50}$$

$$I_2(t) = R_{21}\int_{t_0}^{t} V_1\,dt + R_{22}\int_{t_0}^{t} V_2\,dt + I_{20} \tag{6.51}$$

where I_{10} and I_{20} are the currents round meshes 1 and 2 at time t_0.

As an example, let us suppose that winding 2 of the transformer is short-circuited, so that

$$V_2 = 0 \tag{6.52}$$

Let us also assume that the currents in both windings start from zero at time zero.   Equations (6.50) and (6.51) then become

$$I_1(t) = R_{11}\int_{0}^{t} V_1\,dt \tag{6.53}$$

$$I_2(t) = R_{21}\int_{0}^{t} V_1\,dt \tag{6.54}$$

If the voltage applied to winding 1 is a sinusoidal voltage of angular frequency ω and amplitude V_0 given by

$$V_1(t) = V_0\cos\omega t \tag{6.55}$$

then Eqs. (6.53) and (6.54) yield

$$I_1(t) = R_{11}V_0\frac{\sin\omega t}{\omega} \tag{6.56}$$

$$I_2(t) = R_{21}V_0\frac{\sin\omega t}{\omega} \tag{6.57}$$

6.8. Equivalent T and π Networks for a Transformer.   The transformer shown in Fig. 6.6 may be represented by means of an equivalent T network as shown in Fig. 6.7 or alternatively by an equivalent π network as shown in Fig. 6.8.

Application of Kirchhoff's circulation law to meshes 1 and 2 in Fig. 6.7 in the manner described in Sec. 6.5 gives

$$V_1(t) = (L_{11} - L_{12})\frac{dI_1}{dt} + L_{12}\frac{d}{dt}(I_1 + I_2) \qquad (6.58)$$

$$V_2(t) = (L_{22} - L_{12})\frac{dI_2}{dt} + L_{12}\frac{d}{dt}(I_1 + I_2) \qquad (6.59)$$

Remembering that L_{12} and L_{21} are equal, we see that Eqs. (6.58) and (6.59) simplify to Eqs. (6.41) and (6.42) respectively. We thus see that the

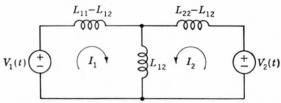

FIG. 6.7. Equivalent T network for the transformer shown in Fig. 6.6.

relation between the voltages applied to the windings in Fig. 6.6 and the resulting currents round the windings can, if desired, be calculated from the equivalent circuit shown in Fig. 6.7. It is frequently convenient to replace a transformer by the equivalent T network shown in Fig. 6.7. It should be noted, however, that this equivalent network implies a metallic connection between the two windings that does not exist for the actual transformer. The possibility that a steady difference of potential may exist between the windings of the transformer is not represented in the equivalent circuit shown in Fig. 6.7.

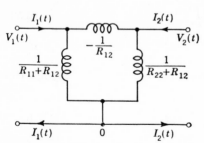

FIG. 6.8. Equivalent π network for the transformer shown in Fig. 6.6, described in terms of the coefficients of self- and mutual reluctance.

In the equivalent π network illustrated in Fig. 6.8 the inductances of the elements are stated in terms of the coefficients of self- and mutual reluctance of the transformer given by Eqs. (6.45) to (6.47). The equivalent π network assumes that the negative terminals of the transformer are connected together. Taking the potential of this node as zero, the potentials of the other two nodes are $V_1(t)$ and $V_2(t)$ as shown in Fig. 6.8. Application of Kirchhoff's conservation law to the nodes of potentials $V_1(t)$ and $V_2(t)$ in the manner described in Sec. 6.6 gives

$$\frac{dI_1}{dt} = (R_{11} + R_{12})(V_1 - 0) - R_{12}(V_1 - V_2) \qquad (6.60)$$

$$\frac{dI_2}{dt} = (R_{22} + R_{12})(V_2 - 0) - R_{12}(V_2 - V_1) \qquad (6.61)$$

These two equations simplify to Eqs. (6.43) and (6.44), thereby demonstrating that the network shown in Fig. 6.8 is equivalent to the transformer shown in Fig. 6.6 except for the fact that no metallic connection between the windings exists in the actual transformer.

6.9. Magnetic Coupling in Any Network of Inductors. Suppose that a network of inductors contains numerous inductors, numbered $1, 2, \ldots$, all of which are magnetically coupled with each other. Let the currents through the inductors be $I_1, I_2, \ldots$ and the magnetic fluxes threading these currents in the directions given by the right-hand-screw rule be $\Phi_1, \Phi_2, \ldots$. The relations between the currents and fluxes are described by means of a system of coefficients of self- and mutual inductance, or alternatively by means of a system of coefficients of self- and mutual reluctance, as described in Part 3, Sec. 9.7. The relations can be written as

$$\begin{aligned} \Phi_1 &= L_{11}I_1 + L_{12}I_2 + \cdots \\ \Phi_2 &= L_{21}I_1 + L_{22}I_2 + \cdots \\ &\;\cdots\cdots\cdots\cdots\cdots\cdots \end{aligned} \qquad (6.62)$$

or alternatively

$$\begin{aligned} I_1 &= R_{11}\Phi_1 + R_{12}\Phi_2 + \cdots \\ I_2 &= R_{21}\Phi_1 + R_{22}\Phi_2 + \cdots \\ &\;\cdots\cdots\cdots\cdots\cdots\cdots \end{aligned} \qquad (6.63)$$

The voltages $V_1(t)$, $V_2(t)$, $\ldots$ that must be applied to the various inductors in order to drive the currents $I_1(t)$, $I_2(t)$, $\ldots$ through them are given by the equations

$$\begin{aligned} V_1(t) &= \frac{d\Phi_1}{dt} \\ V_2(t) &= \frac{d\Phi_2}{dt} \\ &\;\cdots\cdots\cdots \end{aligned} \qquad (6.64)$$

Substitution for the magnetic fluxes from Eqs. (6.62) into Eqs. (6.64) gives

$$\begin{aligned} V_1(t) &= L_{11}\frac{dI_1}{dt} + L_{12}\frac{dI_2}{dt} + \cdots \\ V_2(t) &= L_{21}\frac{dI_1}{dt} + L_{22}\frac{dI_2}{dt} + \cdots \\ &\;\cdots\cdots\cdots\cdots\cdots\cdots\cdots\cdots \end{aligned} \qquad (6.65)$$

If the currents through the various inductors are specified as functions of time, these equations determine the voltages that must be applied in the various meshes in order to drive the currents. If it is the voltages that are specified, Eqs. (6.65) can be solved for the time derivatives of the currents. The result of this solution can be obtained by differentiating Eqs. (6.63) with respect to time and replacing the time derivatives of the magnetic fluxes in terms of the voltages from Eqs. (6.64). In this way we obtain

$$\frac{dI_1}{dt} = R_{11}V_1(t) + R_{12}V_2(t) + \cdots$$

$$\frac{dI_2}{dt} = R_{21}V_1(t) + R_{22}V_2(t) + \cdots$$

(6.66)

. . . .

If the voltages are specified as functions of time, these equations can immediately be integrated to obtain the currents through the various inductors.

As an example of the application of Eqs. (6.65), let us consider a situation in which n inductors are connected in series across a generator of

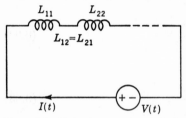

L_{11} L_{22}

$L_{12}=L_{21}$

$I(t)$ $V(t)$

FIG. 6.9. Inductors connected in series with allowance made for magnetic coupling.

voltage $V(t)$, as shown in Fig. 6.9. Let the coefficients of self-inductance of the inductors be L_{11}, L_{22}, ... Let us suppose, however, that it is necessary to take into account magnetic coupling between the various inductors. For this purpose it will be necessary to introduce, in addition to the coefficients of self-inductance, a system of coefficients of mutual inductance as indicated in Eqs. (6.65). With the inductors connected in series, the current through each inductor is the same. If this common current is $I(t)$, each current in Eqs. (6.65) must be replaced by $I(t)$. These equations then become

$$V_1(t) = (L_{11} + L_{12} + \cdots)\frac{dI}{dt}$$

$$V_2(t) = (L_{21} + L_{12} + \cdots)\frac{dI}{dt}$$

(6.67)

. . . .

We thus see that to the coefficient of self-inductance of each inductor must be added the coefficients of mutual inductance with respect to each of the other inductors in the series. The voltage $V(t)$ applied across the complete series of inductors is the sum of the voltages across the individual inductors.   By addition of Eqs. (6.67) we therefore obtain

$$V(t) = (\Sigma L_{mn}) \frac{dI}{dt} \tag{6.68}$$

where the coefficient of the time derivative of the current on the right-hand side of this equation denotes the sum of all the coefficients of self- and mutual inductance of the inductors.   It should be noted that, in this summation, each coefficient of mutual inductance is counted twice, first as L_{rs} and second as L_{sr}.   There are thus n^2 contributions to the summation.   It follows from Eq. (6.68) that the group of inductors connected in series is equivalent to a single inductor of inductance

$$\begin{aligned} \Sigma L_{mn} &= L_{11} + L_{22} + \cdots \\ &+ 2(L_{12} + \cdots) \end{aligned} \tag{6.69}$$

If magnetic coupling between the coils is disregarded, then the coefficients of mutual inductance disappear from Eq. (6.69), and the equivalent inductance of the group reduces to the value given by Eq. (6.5).

Equation (6.69) can be used for an accurate calculation of the inductance of a multiturn inductor.   Each turn of the inductor may be considered as an individual inductor, and the various turns as inductors connected in series.   In this case it is vital to allow for the mutual inductance between the various turns.   Let us suppose that each turn has an inductance L.   The mutual inductance between a pair of turns is somewhat less than L, by an amount depending upon the separation between the turns.   Let us, however, make the rough approximation that the coefficient of mutual inductance between any pair of turns is the same as the coefficient of self-inductance L of an individual turn.   Then all the coefficients of self- and mutual inductance involved in the summation given in Eq. (6.69) are equal to L.   As there are n^2 coefficients, the inductance of all n turns is

$$n^2 L \tag{6.70}$$

This may be compared with the expression for the inductance of an n-turn coil given in Part 3, Eq. (5.39).   We see that the expression (6.70) for the inductance of a multiturn coil is based upon the assumption of perfect magnetic coupling between every pair of turns.   With imperfect magnetic coupling between the various turns, the corresponding coefficients of mutual inductance are reduced and with them the inductance of the multiturn coil.   This reduction can in principle be estimated with the aid of expression (6.69) and the methods of calculating mutual inductance described in Part 3, Chaps. 9 and 10.

6.10. The Equivalent Transformer for a Network of Inductors.   Let us suppose that a network of inductors possesses a number of meshes

round which the currents are $I_1(t)$, $I_2(t)$, . . . and that the voltages
acting round these meshes in the directions of the currents are $V_1(t)$,
$V_2(t)$, ... Let us also suppose that the properties of the network of
inductors are described by means of a system of coefficients of self-
and mutual reluctance, so that the relations between the currents and
voltages round the meshes take the form given in Eqs. (6.66). Let us
now suppose that the network is enclosed in a box in such a way that only
two of the meshes protrude from the box by means of two pairs of terminals as shown in Fig. 6.10. Let the meshes accessible exterior to the
box be meshes 1 and 2, and let us suppose that it is only in these meshes
that voltages are applied to the net-
work. We then have a situation in
which the only nonzero voltages on
the right-hand side of Eqs. (6.66)

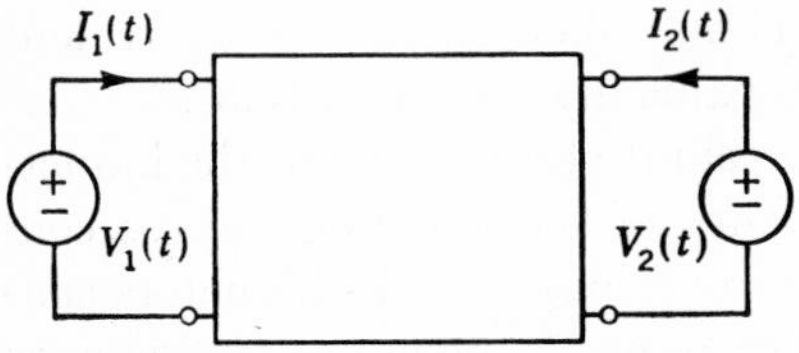

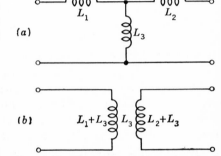

FIG. 6.10. Illustrating a network of
inductors with two pairs of accessible
terminals.

FIG. 6.11. Illustrating (a) a network of
inductors with two pairs of accessible
terminals and (b) the equivalent transformer.

are $V_1(t)$ and $V_2(t)$. On the right-hand side of these equations, therefore,
all columns disappear except the first two. Let us suppose, in addition,
that we are interested only in the currents $I_1(t)$ and $I_2(t)$ flowing in the
meshes accessible exterior to the box. Then it is only the first two of
Eqs. (6.66) that are of interest. With all voltages vanishing except
$V_1(t)$ and $V_2(t)$, these two equations reduce to Eqs. (6.43) and (6.44).
It follows, therefore, that the relations between the external voltages
and the time rates of change of the external currents for the network
indicated in Fig. 6.10 are the same as for a transformer for which the
coefficients of self-reluctance are the coefficients of self-reluctance of the
accessible meshes of the network and the coefficient of mutual reluctance
is the coefficient of mutual reluctance of the accessible meshes of the network. In this sense any network of inductors with two pairs of accessible
terminals is equivalent to an appropriately designed transformer.

As a simple example, let us consider the network of inductors shown in
Fig. 6.11a. By comparing the network with that shown in Fig. 6.7, we
see that the equivalent transformer has coefficients of self- and mutual

inductance L_{11}, L_{22}, and L_{12} such that

$$L_1 = L_{11} - L_{12} \tag{6.71}$$
$$L_2 = L_{22} - L_{12} \tag{6.72}$$
$$L_3 = L_{12} \tag{6.73}$$

Solution of these equations for the coefficients of self- and mutual inductance gives

$$L_{11} = L_1 + L_3 \tag{6.74}$$
$$L_{22} = L_2 + L_3 \tag{6.75}$$
$$L_{12} = L_3 \tag{6.76}$$

The equivalent transformer for the network of inductors shown in Fig. 6.11a is therefore as indicated in Fig. 6.11b.

A network of inductors having more than two accessible pairs of terminals can be represented in a similar way by means of a transformer having more than two windings.

The following point should, however, be noticed. From Eqs. (6.65) and (6.66) it follows that the equivalence existing between a transformer and a network of inductors involves the time rates of change of the currents rather than the currents themselves. This means that the equivalence does not in general hold for the steady currents that may be applied at the terminals. It is the time variation of the currents that is correctly related by the equivalent transformer of a network of inductors possessing pairs of accessible terminals.

6.11. The Thévenin and Norton Equivalent Circuits for a Network of Inductors. Consider a network of inductors possessing two pairs of accessible terminals. To one pair of terminals (terminals 1) let us connect a source for which either the voltage or the current varies with time t in a specified manner. To the other pair of terminals (terminals 2) let us suppose that a load is connected and that this load is an adjustable load. In this situation terminals 1 may be designated input terminals and terminals 2 output terminals. Let us suppose that, for the specified source connected at the input terminals, we are interested in considering a number of different loads connected at the output terminals. One procedure for handling this situation is to replace the network of inductors by its equivalent transformer as described in the previous section. However, it is possible to replace the equivalent transformer, together with the specified source connected at terminals 1, with simpler equivalent circuits. These circuits are the Thévenin equivalent circuit and the Norton equivalent circuit. It is convenient to employ an equivalent Thévenin or Norton circuit under circumstances when either the voltage or the current connected to terminals 1 is specified as a function of time t and when a number of different loads are to be connected to terminals 2.

Let us suppose that the given network of inductors has been replaced by an equivalent transformer and that this transformer is specified either by its coefficients of inductance L_{11}, L_{22}, and L_{12} (or L_{21}) or alternatively by its coefficients of reluctance R_{11}, R_{22}, and R_{12} (or R_{21}).   Figure 6.12a illustrates the two cases that occur.   In the one case it is the input voltage $V_1(t)$ that is specified as a function of time regardless of the load connected to the output terminals.   In the other case it is the current $I_1(t)$ at terminals 1 that is specified as a function of time regardless of the

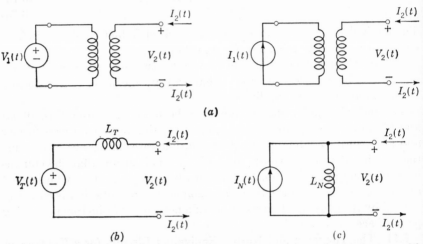

FIG. 6.12. Illustrating (a) a transformer equivalent to a network of inductors with two pairs of accessible terminals, (b) the equivalent Thévenin circuit, and (c) the equivalent Norton circuit.

load connected at the output terminals.   A change in the load would alter the input current as a function of time in the first case and the input voltage as a function of time in the second case.   In either case, however, it is possible to replace the transformer, together with the voltage or current applied at the input terminals, with a Thévenin equivalent circuit as shown in Fig. 6.12b or a Norton equivalent circuit as shown in Fig. 6.12c.   We have to establish the truth of these statements and to obtain expressions for the elements in the Thévenin and Norton equivalent circuits in terms of the coefficients describing the transformer in Fig. 6.12a and either the given applied voltage $V_1(t)$ or the given applied current $I_1(t)$.

In the case when it is the applied voltage that is specified, we shall need to make use of Eq. (6.44), which relates the input voltage $V_1(t)$, the output voltage $V_2(t)$, and the output current $I_2(t)$.   On the other hand, when it is the input current that is specified, we shall need to make use of Eq. (6.42), which relates the input current $I_1(t)$, the output current

$I_2(t)$, and the output voltage $V_2(t)$. We have to show that these relations between the output voltage and the output current can be reproduced by the circuit shown in Fig. 6.12b by suitable choice of the Thévenin voltage $V_T(t)$ and the Thévenin inductance L_T. Likewise, we must show that the relations between the output voltage and output current described by Eq. (6.42) or (6.44) can be described by the circuit shown in Fig. 6.12c with suitable choice of the Norton current $I_N(t)$ and the Norton inductance L_N.

For the Thévenin equivalent circuit shown in Fig. 6.12b the voltage that is acting round the circuit in the direction of the current $I_2(t)$ is $V_2(t) - V_T(t)$. It follows that

$$V_2(t) - V_T(t) = L_T \frac{dI_2}{dt} \tag{6.77}$$

This equation becomes identical with Eq. (6.44) if

$$V_T(t) = -\frac{R_{21}}{R_{22}} V_1(t) \tag{6.78}$$

and

$$L_T = \frac{1}{R_{22}} \tag{6.79}$$

It follows that, for a specified voltage $V_1(t)$ applied to the input terminals of the transformer in Fig. 6.12a, the Thévenin equivalent circuit shown in Fig. 6.12b reproduces the correct relation between the output voltage and the output current if the Thévenin voltage is given by Eq. (6.78) and the Thévenin inductance by Eq. (6.79).

In the same way Eq. (6.77) is identical with Eq. (6.42) if

$$V_T(t) = L_{21} \frac{dI_1}{dt} \tag{6.80}$$

and

$$L_T = L_{22} \tag{6.81}$$

It follows that, for a specified current $I_1(t)$ applied to the input terminals of the transformer in Fig. 6.12a, the relation between the output voltage and the output current is reproduced by the Thévenin equivalent circuit shown in Fig. 6.12b if the Thévenin voltage is given by Eq. (6.80) and the Thévenin inductance by Eq. (6.81).

For the Norton equivalent circuit shown in Fig. 6.12c, we notice that the total current flowing through the inductor of inductance L_N in the direction of the applied voltage $V_2(t)$ is $I_2(t) + I_N(t)$. It follows that

$$V_2(t) = L_N \frac{d}{dt} (I_2 + I_N) \tag{6.82}$$

This equation is identical with Eq. (6.44) if

$$\frac{dI_N}{dt} = -R_{21}V_1(t) \tag{6.83}$$

and

$$L_N = \frac{1}{R_{22}} \tag{6.84}$$

These equations show that, when it is the input voltage $V_1(t)$ to the transformer shown in Fig. 6.12a that is specified, the relation between the output voltage and the output current is represented correctly by the Norton equivalent circuit shown in Fig. 6.12c provided that the Norton current $I_N(t)$ is obtained by integrating Eq. (6.83) with respect to time and the Norton inductance L_N is given by Eq. (6.84).

Likewise, if it is the input current $I_1(t)$ to the transformer that is specified, we observe that Eq. (6.82) is identical with Eq. (6.42) provided that

$$\frac{dI_N}{dt} = \frac{L_{21}}{L_{22}}\frac{dI_1}{dt} \tag{6.85}$$

and

$$L_N = L_{22} \tag{6.86}$$

These equations show that, if the input current $I_1(t)$ to the transformer shown in Fig. 6.12a is specified, then the relation between the output voltage and the output current is correctly described by the Norton equivalent circuit shown in Fig. 6.12c provided that the Norton current $I_N(t)$ satisfies Eq. (6.85) and the Norton inductance L_N is given by Eq. (6.86). Equation (6.85) can be integrated in the form

$$I_N(t) = \frac{L_{21}}{L_{22}}I_1(t) + \text{constant} \tag{6.87}$$

where the constant is to be adjusted to reproduce correctly whatever steady current may be flowing in the output circuit. If it may be assumed that $I_1(t)$ vanishes prior to a certain instant and that no steady currents are then flowing, it follows that the constant in Eq. (6.87) vanishes, and we can write

$$I_N(t) = \frac{L_{21}}{L_{22}}I_1(t) \tag{6.88}$$

The above results concerning the Thévenin and Norton equivalent circuits for a transformer are summarized in Figs. 6.13 and 6.14. Figure 6.13 refers to the case in which it is the voltage $V_1(t)$ applied to the input terminals that is specified. If in this situation the transformer is described by means of its coefficients of reluctance, the Thévenin equivalent circuit is shown in Fig. 6.13b and the Norton equivalent circuit in Fig. 6.13c. Figure 6.14 refers to the case in which it is the input current

$I_1(t)$ that is specified. In this situation it is convenient to describe the transformer by means of its coefficients of inductance. The equivalent Thévenin circuit is shown in Fig. 6.14b and the equivalent Norton circuit in Fig. 6.14c.

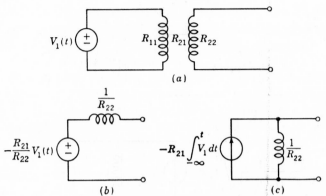

FIG. 6.13. Illustrating (a) a transformer whose input voltage is specified as a function of time, (b) the equivalent Thévenin circuit, and (c) the equivalent Norton circuit.

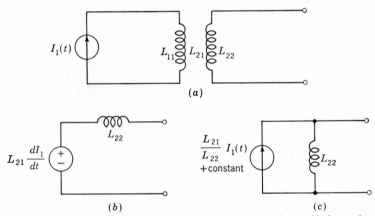

FIG. 6.14. Illustrating (a) a transformer whose input current is specified as a function of time, (b) the equivalent Thévenin circuit, and (c) the equivalent Norton circuit.

If in Fig. 6.13 it is desired to specify the transformer in terms of its coefficients of inductance, we substitute for the coefficients of reluctance in terms of the coefficients of inductance from Eqs. (6.45) to (6.47). If in addition we specify the coupling between the windings of the transformer by means of the coupling coefficient k defined in Part 3, Eqs. (9.36), instead of by means of the coefficient of mutual inductance, Fig. 6.13 is replaced by Fig. 6.15 and Fig. 6.14 by Fig. 6.16.

We notice that, in both Figs. 6.15 and 6.16, the Thévenin inductance is

identical in value with the Norton inductance. The common value of
this inductance is, however, different when it is the input voltage that is
specified (Fig. 6.15) from what it is when it is the input current that is
specified (Fig. 6.16). We also notice that, in Fig. 6.15b and c, the

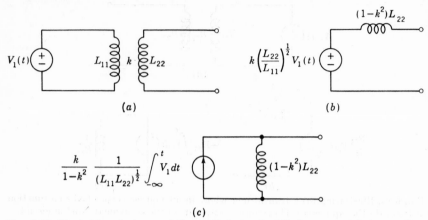

FIG. 6.15. Illustrating, in terms of the coefficients of self-inductance and the coupling
coefficient, the Thévenin and Norton equivalent circuits for a transformer with specified input voltage $V_1(t)$.

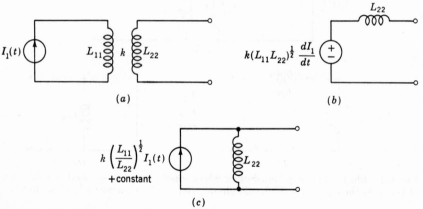

FIG. 6.16. Illustrating, in terms of the coefficients of self-inductance and the coupling
coefficient, the Thévenin and Norton equivalent circuits for a transformer with
specified input current $I_1(t)$.

Thévenin and Norton inductance is the inductance across the output
terminals when the given applied voltage $V_1(t)$ is set equal to zero.
Likewise, in Fig. 6.16b and c, the Thévenin and Norton inductance is the
inductance across the output terminals when the given applied current
$I_1(t)$ is set equal to zero. Moreover, in both cases the Thévenin voltage

is the voltage across the output terminals when on open circuit, and the Norton current is the current leaving the positive output terminal when the output terminals are on short circuit.

From the above equations we can verify that, between the elements of the Thévenin and Norton equivalent circuits, there exist the relations

$$L_T = L_N$$
$$L_T \frac{dI_N}{dt} = V_T(t) \tag{6.89}$$

6.12. The Voltage and Current Transformation Ratios for a Transformer. The input winding of a transformer is frequently known as the primary winding and the output winding as the secondary winding. By comparing Fig. 6.13a with Fig. 6.13b we see that a voltage $V_1(t)$ connected across the primary winding has the same effect as a voltage

$$-\frac{R_{21}}{R_{22}} V_1(t) \tag{6.90}$$

connected in series with an inductor of inductance $1/R_{22}$. From Eq. (6.44) we see that $1/R_{22}$ is the inductance of the secondary winding when the primary winding is short-circuited. We may thus say that the effect at the terminals of the secondary winding of a voltage $V_1(t)$ connected across the primary winding is the same as if this voltage were set equal to zero and a generator of voltage given by expression (6.90) were connected in series with the secondary winding.

The ratio of the voltage given by expression (6.90) to the voltage $V_1(t)$ applied across the primary winding is known as the voltage transformation ratio of the transformer. The voltage transformation ratio of the transformer is therefore

$$-\frac{R_{21}}{R_{22}} \tag{6.91}$$

Using Eqs. (6.46) and (6.47), the voltage transformation ratio given by expression (6.91) can be expressed in terms of the coefficients of inductance of the transformer as

$$\frac{L_{12}}{L_{11}} \tag{6.92}$$

Moreover if we express the coefficient of mutual inductance in terms of the coupling coefficient k of the transformer by means of Part 3, Eqs. (9.36), the voltage transformation ratio becomes

$$k \left(\frac{L_{22}}{L_{11}}\right)^{1/2} \tag{6.93}$$

in agreement with Fig. 6.15b. For a transformer wound upon a soft-iron magnetic circuit for which leakage is negligible, the coupling coefficient k is practically unity, and the inductances of the windings are in the ratio of the squares of the numbers of turns. In these circumstances, with n_1 turns on the primary winding and n_2 turns on the secondary winding, the voltage transformation ratio given by expression (6.93) becomes

$$\frac{n_2}{n_1} \tag{6.94}$$

and the Thévenin inductance in Fig. 6.15b vanishes. Thus a voltage connected across the primary winding is equivalent to a voltage across the load larger by the factor given by expression (6.94). If the voltage transformation ratio exceeds unity, the voltage is said to be "stepped up," and if the voltage transformation ratio is less than unity, the voltage is said to be "stepped down."

In the same way we see by comparing Fig. 6.14a with Fig. 6.14c that a current source $I_1(t)$ connected across the primary winding is equivalent to a current generator

$$\frac{L_{21}}{L_{22}} I_1(t) + \text{constant} \tag{6.95}$$

connected across an inductor of inductance L_{22}. From Eq. (6.42) we see that L_{22} is the inductance of the secondary winding when the primary winding is open-circuited or carries only a steady current. We may thus say that the effect at the terminals of the secondary winding of a current $I_1(t)$ flowing through the primary winding is the same as if this current were set equal to zero and a generator delivering a current given by expression (6.95) were connected in parallel with the secondary winding.

If steady currents are not involved as described in connection with Eq. (6.88), the current given by expression (6.95) can be written as

$$\frac{L_{21}}{L_{22}} I_1(t) \tag{6.96}$$

The ratio of this current to the current $I_1(t)$ applied in the primary winding is then known as the current transformation ratio of the transformer. The current transformation ratio is therefore

$$\frac{L_{21}}{L_{22}} \tag{6.97}$$

In terms of the coupling coefficient k of the transformer defined by Part 3, Eqs. (9.36), expression (6.97) can be written as

$$k \left(\frac{L_{11}}{L_{22}}\right)^{\frac{1}{2}} \tag{6.98}$$

in agreement with Fig. 6.16c. For a transformer wound upon a soft-iron magnetic circuit for which leakage is negligible, the current transformation ratio given by expression (6.98) reduces to

$$\frac{n_1}{n_2} \qquad (6.99)$$

where n_1 and n_2 are the numbers of turns on the primary and secondary windings respectively. Comparison of expression (6.94) for the voltage transformation ratio of a perfectly coupled transformer with expression (6.99) for the current transformation ratio shows that, when the voltage is stepped up by a perfectly coupled transformer, the current is stepped down in the same ratio, and vice versa.

SUMMARIZING EXERCISES

6.1. Prove that, if a number of magnetically uncoupled inductors whose inductances are L_1, L_2, . . . , L_n are connected in series, the system can be used as a single inductor of inductance $L_1 + L_2 + \cdots + L_n$. Prove also that, if the inductors are connected in parallel, the system can be used as a single inductor of inductance L where $1/L$ is equal to the sum of the reciprocals of the inductances of the individual inductors.

6.2. State and justify Kirchhoff's laws for networks of inductors.

6.3. A number of inductors of negligible resistance are formed into a network of inductors in such a way that magnetic coupling between the elements can be neglected. Sources of voltage that vary with time t are connected into the network. Explain how to calculate the voltages and currents in the network using (a) the method of analysis into parallel and series connections, (b) the mesh-current method, and (c) the node-potential method. Explain the advantages and disadvantages of the three methods.

6.4. Voltages V_1 and V_2 that vary with time t are applied to the primary and secondary windings of a transformer for which the coefficient of mutual inductance is L_{12}. The coefficient of self-inductance of the primary circuit is L_{11}, and the coefficient of self-inductance of the secondary circuit is L_{22}. Neglecting losses, write down equations to determine the currents I_1 and I_2 in the primary and secondary circuits respectively. Solve these equations for I_1 and I_2 on the assumption that the currents in the primary and secondary windings at time t_0 are I_{10} and I_{20} respectively. Describe how to carry out this calculation if the properties of the transformer are specified in terms of its coefficients of self- and mutual reluctance.

6.5. Explain what is meant by the equivalent T network of a transformer for which losses can be neglected. State the values of the elements in terms of the coefficients of self- and mutual inductance of the transformer. Justify the values stated, and mention a respect in which the two networks are not equivalent.

6.6. Explain what is meant by the equivalent π network of a loss-free transformer. State the values of the elements in terms of the coefficients of self- and mutual reluctance of the transformer. Justify the values stated, and mention a respect in which the two networks are not equivalent.

6.7. Explain how to allow for magnetic coupling between elements in a network of inductors. Inductors whose inductances are L_{11}, L_{22}, L_{33}, . . . are connected in series. Magnetic coupling exists between the inductors and is described by means of coefficients of mutual inductance L_{12}, L_{13}, L_{23}, ... If the arrangement is used as a single inductor, calculate its inductance.

6.8. Explain what is meant by the equivalent transformer for a network of loss-free inductors having a pair of input terminals and a pair of output terminals. Explain why the equivalent transformer correctly relates the input and output voltages to the time rates of change of the input and output current, but not necessarily to the input and output currents themselves.

6.9. To the primary winding of a loss-free transformer is applied a voltage V_1 that varies with time t and is independent of the load connected across the secondary winding. Calculate the Thévenin and Norton equivalent circuits for the arrangement, and explain what is meant by the voltage transformation ratio of the transformer. Describe the circumstances in which this is equal to the ratio of the number of turns on the secondary winding to the number of turns on the primary winding.

6.10. To the primary winding of a loss-free transformer is applied a generator delivering a current I_1 that depends upon time t and is independent of the load connected across the secondary winding. Evaluate the Thévenin and Norton equivalent circuits for the arrangement, and explain what is meant by the current transformation ratio of the transformer. Describe the circumstances in which this is equal to the ratio of the number of turns on the primary winding to the number of turns on the secondary winding.

CHAPTER 7

THE ELECTRICAL FORM OF KINETIC ENERGY

7.1. Introduction. We have seen that a current of electrons flowing round an electric circuit constitutes an electronic flywheel, the momentum of which is associated primarily with the charge on the electrons and is measured by the magnetic flux threading the circuit. Such a circuit also possesses energy on account of the motion of the electrons. If the inertia properties of the system were controlled by the mass of the electrons, the energy associated with their motion would be called kinetic energy. Since the inertia properties of the system are in fact controlled by the charge of the electrons, the energy associated with their motion is known as the magnetic energy of the circuit. Magnetic energy is thus the electrical form of kinetic energy.

In Part 1 we saw that electric energy stored in a capacitor is the electrical form of potential energy. The interplay that takes place in dynamics between kinetic energy and potential energy thus corresponds in electrical science to an interplay between magnetic and electric energy. In mechanical science considerable interest attaches to oscillatory systems, such as the balance wheel and hairspring of a clock, in which the energy of the system is being repeatedly transformed back and forth between the kinetic and potential forms. In electrical science even greater interest attaches to oscillatory systems in which the energy of the system is being repeatedly transformed back and forth between the magnetic and electric forms. The simplest such system involves an inductor connected in parallel with a capacitor. It is difficult to over-estimate the importance of oscillatory circuits of this type in electrical science.

In this chapter we are primarily concerned with introducing the concept of the magnetic energy of an electric circuit. Before doing so, however, it will be convenient to review the concept of the electric energy stored in a capacitor from a more dynamical standpoint than was adopted in Part 1, Chap. 8. However, considerable importance attaches to relating the concepts of electric and magnetic energy in electrical science to the concepts of potential and kinetic energy in mechanical science. We shall therefore begin by considering the concepts of potential and kinetic energy in mechanical science, writing the equations in the form subsequently used for discussing electric and magnetic energy in electrical science.   To facilitate comparison between corresponding concepts in mechanical and electrical science, the same equation numbers will be used in the two cases, with an affix m in the mechanical case.

7.2. Potential Energy in Mechanics.   Suppose that one end of a spring is fixed and that to the other end is applied a force F which in general is a function of time t.   Let the displacement of the movable end of the spring from its position when the spring is unstressed be x.   The displacement x is in the direction in which the force F acts and is in general a function of time t.   The velocity v of the movable end of the spring is given by

$$v = \frac{dx}{dt} \tag{7.1m}$$

The rate at which energy is being supplied to the spring is

$$P = Fv \tag{7.2m}$$

and by use of Eq. $(7.1m)$ this can be written as

$$P = F\frac{dx}{dt} \tag{7.3m}$$

We now assume that the displacement x of the movable end of the spring is proportional to the force F applied and write

$$x = CF \tag{7.4m}$$

where C is a constant known as the compliance of the spring.   Substitution for x from Eq. $(7.4m)$ into Eq. $(7.3m)$ gives

$$P = CF\frac{dF}{dt} \tag{7.5m}$$

This can be written as

$$P = \frac{dW_p}{dt} \tag{7.6m}$$

where

$$W_p = \tfrac{1}{2}CF^2 \tag{7.7m}$$

Alternatively we can substitute for F from Eq. $(7.4m)$ into Eq. $(7.3m)$ and obtain

$$P = \frac{1}{C}\,x\,\frac{dx}{dt} \tag{7.8m}$$

This equation can also be written in the form $(7.6m)$, where

$$W_p = \frac{1}{2C}\,x^2 \tag{7.9m}$$

The two equations (7.7m) and (7.9m) for W_p are identical with each other by virtue of Eq. (7.4m) and are also identical with the expression $\frac{1}{2}Fx$. We can thus write

$$W_p = \frac{1}{2}Fx = \frac{1}{2}CF^2 = \frac{1}{2C}x^2 \qquad (7.10m)$$

Equation (7.6m) states that the power delivered to the spring is the rate of increase of the quantity W_p given by Eqs. (7.10m). The quantity W_p is known as the potential energy of the spring, and Eq. (7.6m) states that the power delivered to the spring is equal to the time rate of increase of its potential energy.

If the velocity v of the movable end of the spring is specified as a function of time t, the corresponding displacement x is obtained as a function of time by integrating Eq. (7.1m), thereby obtaining

$$x = \int_{t_0}^{t} v\, dt + x_0 \qquad (7.11m)$$

where x_0 is the displacement at time t_0. The force that must be applied to the spring is then obtained as a function of time by substituting for x from Eq. (7.11m) into Eq. (7.4m), thereby obtaining

$$F = \frac{1}{C} \int_{t_0}^{t} v\, dt + F_0 \qquad (7.12m)$$

where F_0 is the force acting at time t_0. The potential energy W_p as a function of time is obtained by substituting for x and F from Eqs. (7.11m) and (7.12m) into one or other of the expressions given in Eqs. (7.10m).

7.3. Kinetic Energy in Mechanics. Consider a flywheel possessing a heavy rim supported by light spokes. Let a peripheral force F be applied to the rim, and let us suppose that in general this force is a function of time t. Let the resulting momentum of the rim be p, also a function of time. From Newton's law of motion we have

$$F = \frac{dp}{dt} \qquad (7.13m)$$

The rate at which energy is supplied to the rim by the force F is

$$P = Fv \qquad (7.14m)$$

where v is the peripheral velocity of the rim. Substitution for F from Eq. (7.13m) into Eq. (7.14m) gives for the power delivered to the rim

$$P = v\frac{dp}{dt} \qquad (7.15m)$$

We now assume that the momentum of the rim is proportional to its peripheral velocity and write

$$p = Mv \qquad (7.16m)$$

where M is the mass of the rim.   Substitution for p from Eq. (7.16m) into Eq. (7.15m) gives

$$P = Mv \frac{dv}{dt} \qquad (7.17m)$$

and this can be rewritten as

$$P = \frac{dW_k}{dt} \qquad (7.18m)$$

where

$$W_k = \frac{1}{2}Mv^2 \qquad (7.19m)$$

Alternatively we can substitute for v from Eq. (7.16m) into Eq. (7.15m) and obtain

$$P = \frac{1}{M} p \frac{dp}{dt} \qquad (7.20m)$$

This equation can then be written in the form of Eq. (7.18m), where

$$W_k = \frac{1}{2M} p^2 \qquad (7.21m)$$

The two expressions (7.19m) and (7.21m) for W_k are identical with each other by virtue of Eq. (7.16m), and also with the expression $\frac{1}{2}vp$.   We can therefore write

$$W_k = \frac{1}{2}vp = \frac{1}{2}Mv^2 = \frac{1}{2M} p^2 \qquad (7.22m)$$

Equation (7.18m) states that the power delivered to the wheel is equal to the time rate of increase of the expression W_k given by Eqs. (7.22m), and this quantity is known as the kinetic energy of the wheel.   Equation (7.18m) thus states that the power delivered to the wheel is equal to the time rate of increase of its kinetic energy.

If the force F applied to the rim of the wheel is specified as a function of time t, we can derive the momentum p of the wheel as a function of time by integrating Eq. (7.13m), thereby obtaining

$$p = \int_{t_0}^{t} F \, dt + p_0 \qquad (7.23m)$$

where p_0 is the momentum of the wheel at time t_0.   By substituting for p in terms of v from Eq. (7.16m) into Eq. (7.23m), we obtain for the peripheral velocity v of the rim at time t

$$v = \frac{1}{M} \int_{t_0}^{t} F \, dt + v_0 \qquad (7.24m)$$

where v_0 is the velocity of the rim at time t_0.   The kinetic energy W_k of the rim at time t is obtained by substituting for p and v from Eqs. $(7.23m)$ and $(7.24m)$ into one or another of the expressions in Eqs. $(7.22m)$.

7.4. An Oscillatory Mechanical System.   Let us consider an example of an oscillatory mechanical system in which there is repeated interchange of energy between the kinetic and potential forms.   A convenient system to consider is the balance wheel and hairspring of a clock.   Let the balance wheel be supposed to have a rim of mass M supported by light spokes.   Let C be the compliance of the hairspring, and let $F(t)$ be the peripheral restoring force exerted on the rim by the spring at time t. From Eq. $(7.4m)$ the peripheral displacement of the rim from the position where the hairspring is unstressed is $CF(t)$.   The time derivative of this displacement is the peripheral velocity v with which the rim is moving away from the position in which the spring is unstressed.   We therefore have

$$v = C \frac{dF}{dt} \qquad (7.25m)$$

Let us suppose that a peripheral force $F_0(t)$ is applied to the rim in the direction of the velocity v, so that the total peripheral force tending to move the rim is the excess of the applied force $F_0(t)$ over the restoring force $F(t)$ of the spring.   Newton's law of motion therefore gives

$$F_0 - F = M \frac{dv}{dt} \qquad (7.26m)$$

To study the relation between the kinetic energy of the wheel and the potential energy of the spring, multiply Eq. $(7.25m)$ by F and Eq. $(7.26m)$ by v, thereby obtaining

$$Fv = CF \frac{dF}{dt} \qquad (7.27m)$$

$$F_0 v - Fv = Mv \frac{dv}{dt} \qquad (7.28m)$$

Using the second expression in Eq. $(7.10m)$ for the potential energy W_p of the spring, Eq. $(7.27m)$ can be written as

$$Fv = \frac{dW_p}{dt} \qquad (7.29m)$$

Using the second expression in Eq. $(7.22m)$ for the kinetic energy W_k of the rim, Eq. $(7.28m)$ can be written as

$$F_0 v - Fv = \frac{dW_k}{dt} \qquad (7.30m)$$

Equation $(7.29m)$ states that the power supplied to the spring is equal to the time rate of increase of its potential energy. Equation (7.30m) states that the excess of the power supplied to the rim over that passed onto the spring is equal to the time rate of increase of the kinetic energy of the rim. If Eqs. (7.29m) and (7.30m) are added together, we obtain

$$F_0 v = \frac{dW}{dt} \qquad (7.31m)$$

where
$$W = W_k + W_p \qquad (7.32m)$$

The quantity W defined by Eq. (7.32m) is the sum of the kinetic energy of the rim and the potential energy of the spring and is therefore what is called the total energy of the mechanical system. Equation (7.31m) states that the power supplied to the system by the applied force $F_0(t)$ is equal to the time rate of increase of the total energy of the system.

Let us now suppose that a constant peripheral force F_0 is applied to the rim prior to time zero, so that the rim is at rest in a position displaced from that in which the spring is unstressed. Let us now suppose that, at time zero, the force F_0 is removed and the balance wheel and hairspring proceed to oscillate. Since we are neglecting friction, this oscillation continues indefinitely. After time zero, no external force is applied to the system, and therefore F_0 in the above equations is zero. Equations (7.25m) and (7.26m) therefore become

$$v = C \frac{dF}{dt}$$
$$-F = M \frac{dv}{dt} \qquad (7.33m)$$

while Eqs. (7.29m) and (7.30m) become

$$Fv = \frac{dW_p}{dt}$$
$$-Fv = \frac{dW_k}{dt} \qquad (7.34m)$$

Equations (7.34m) show that the power being delivered to the spring is the time rate of increase of its potential energy and is also the time rate of decrease of the kinetic energy of the rim. As the potential energy of the spring increases, the kinetic energy of the rim decreases, and vice versa. In Eq. (7.31m) the left-hand side is zero, so that the total energy W of the system is independent of time. Equation (7.32m) thus states that the sum of the kinetic energy of the rim and the potential energy of the spring remains constant and is equal to the potential energy of the spring at time zero.

To ascertain the way in which the velocity v of the rim varies with time, we eliminate F between Eqs. (7.33m) by differentiating the second with respect to t and substituting for the time derivative of F from one equation into the other.   We thereby obtain

$$MC \frac{d^2v}{dt^2} + v = 0 \qquad (7.35m)$$

and this equation can be rewritten as

$$\frac{d^2v}{dt^2} + \omega^2 v = 0 \qquad (7.36m)$$

where
$$\omega = \frac{1}{(MC)^{\frac{1}{2}}} \qquad (7.37m)$$

Equation (7.36m) is the equation of simple harmonic motion for angular frequency ω.   Its solution is

$$v = A \cos \omega t + B \sin \omega t \qquad (7.38m)$$

where A and B are constants to be determined from the conditions existing at time zero.   By substituting for v from Eq. (7.38m) into the second of Eqs. (7.33m), we obtain

$$F = \omega M (A \sin \omega t - B \cos \omega t) \qquad (7.39m)$$

The initial conditions that determine the constants A and B are

$$v = 0 \qquad F = F_0 \qquad \text{when } t = 0 \qquad (7.40m)$$

Substitution of these values into Eqs. (7.38m) and (7.39m) gives respectively

$$0 = A \qquad (7.41m)$$
$$F_0 = -\omega M B \qquad (7.42m)$$

Substitution for A and B from Eqs. (7.41m) and (7.42m) into Eq. (7.39m) gives

$$F = F_0 \cos \omega t \qquad (7.43m)$$

Substitution for A and B from Eqs. (7.41m) and (7.42m) into Eq. (7.38m) gives

$$v = -v_0 \sin \omega t \qquad (7.44m)$$

where
$$v_0 = \frac{F_0}{\omega M} \qquad (7.45m)$$

Equations (7.43m) and (7.44m) give, respectively, the oscillatory restoring force exerted by the hairspring on the rim of the balance wheel subsequent to time zero and the associated oscillatory velocity of the rim.

The periodic time of the oscillation is

$$T = \frac{2\pi}{\omega} \qquad (7.46m)$$

Substitution for ω from Eq. ($7.37m$) into Eq. ($7.46m$) gives

$$T = 2\pi (MC)^{\frac{1}{2}} \qquad (7.47m)$$

The number of complete oscillations executed per unit time is the reciprocal of the periodic time. The frequency of oscillation in cycles per unit time is therefore

$$f = \frac{\omega}{2\pi} \qquad (7.48m)$$

or

$$f = \frac{1}{2\pi (MC)^{\frac{1}{2}}} \qquad (7.49m)$$

The potential energy stored in the spring is obtained as a function of time by substituting for F from Eq. ($7.43m$) into the second of the three expressions for W_p in Eq. ($7.10m$). We obtain

$$W_p = W \cos^2 \omega t \qquad (7.52m)$$

where

$$W = \tfrac{1}{2} CF_0^2 \qquad (7.56m)$$

The quantity W is the potential energy of the spring at time zero. The kinetic energy of the rim is obtained as a function of time by substituting for v from Eq. ($7.44m$) into the second of the three expressions for W_k in Eqs. ($7.22m$). Using Eqs. ($7.45m$), ($7.37m$), and ($7.56m$), we obtain

$$W_k = W \sin^2 \omega t \qquad (7.58m)$$

From Eqs. ($7.52m$) and ($7.58m$), we observe that the sum of the potential and kinetic energies of the system is constant and equal to the potential energy of the spring at time zero given by Eq. ($7.56m$).

7.5. Electric Energy of a Capacitor Viewed Dynamically. Suppose that a capacitor of capacitance C is being charged with a current I, which may be a function of time t, as shown in Fig. 7.1. Let $Q(t)$ be the charge at time t on the plate of the capacitor onto which the current $I(t)$ flows, and let $-Q(t)$ be the charge on the other plate. Let the excess of potential of the former plate over the latter be $V(t)$. The relation between the current I and the charge Q is

FIG. 7.1. Illustrating charging of a capacitor with a time-varying current.

$$I = \frac{dQ}{dt} \qquad (7.1)$$

The power delivered to the capacitor is

$$P = VI \qquad (7.2)$$

and, on substituting for I from Eq. (7.1), this can be written as

$$P = V \frac{dQ}{dt} \qquad (7.3)$$

We now use the fact that the charge Q of the capacitor is related to the voltage V by the equation

$$Q = CV \qquad (7.4)$$

Substitution for Q from Eq. (7.4) into Eq. (7.3) gives for the power delivered to the capacitor

$$P = CV \frac{dV}{dt} \qquad (7.5)$$

and this can be written as

$$P = \frac{dW_e}{dt} \qquad (7.6)$$

where

$$W_e = \tfrac{1}{2}CV^2 \qquad (7.7)$$

Alternatively we can substitute for V from Eq. (7.4) into Eq. (7.3), thereby obtaining

$$P = \frac{1}{C} Q \frac{dQ}{dt} \qquad (7.8)$$

This can be written in the form of Eq. (7.6), where

$$W_e = \frac{1}{2C} Q^2 \qquad (7.9)$$

The expressions (7.7) and (7.9) for W_e are identical with each other by virtue of Eq. (7.4) and also with the expression $\tfrac{1}{2}VQ$. We can therefore write

$$W_e = \tfrac{1}{2}VQ = \tfrac{1}{2}CV^2 = \frac{1}{2C} Q^2 \qquad (7.10)$$

Equation (7.6) states that the power delivered to the capacitor is equal to the time rate of increase of the quantity W_e given by Eqs. (7.10). The quantity W_e is the electric energy stored in the capacitor already derived in Part 1, Eqs. (8.5). Equation (7.6) therefore states that the power delivered to the capacitor is equal to the time rate of increase of the electric energy stored in it.

To calculate the charge Q of the capacitor when the charging current I is known as a function of time, we integrate Eq. (7.1) with respect to t and obtain

$$Q(t) = \int_{t_0}^{t} I \, dt + Q_0 \qquad (7.11)$$

where Q_0 is the charge of the capacitor at time t_0. By substituting this value for Q into Eq. (7.4), we obtain for the voltage between the plates of the capacitor at time t

$$V(t) = \frac{1}{C} \int_{t_0}^{t} I\, dt + V_0 \qquad (7.12)$$

where V_0 is the voltage across the capacitor at time t_0. By substituting from Eqs. (7.11) and (7.12) for $Q(t)$ and $V(t)$ into Eqs. (7.10), we obtain the electric energy W_e stored in the capacitor as a function of time.

7.6. Magnetic Energy of an Inductor. Let us suppose that the magnetic flux $\Phi(t)$ threading an electric circuit is varying with time t as a result of a voltage $V(t)$ applied round the circuit as shown in Fig. 7.2. Let the resulting current round the circuit be $I(t)$. Let the positive direction of this current be in the direction round the circuit in which the voltage $V(t)$ acts, and let this direction be related by the right-hand-screw rule to the direction of the threading magnetic flux $\Phi(t)$.

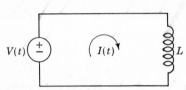

FIG. 7.2. Illustrating flow of current through an inductor as a result of an applied voltage.

From Faraday's law of induction we have

$$V = \frac{d\Phi}{dt} \qquad (7.13)$$

The power supplied to the inductor is given by

$$P = VI \qquad (7.14)$$

and on substituting for V from Eq. (7.13), Eq. (7.14) can be written as

$$P = I\frac{d\Phi}{dt} \qquad (7.15)$$

We now assume that the magnetic flux threading the circuit is related to the current round the circuit by the relation

$$\Phi = LI \qquad (7.16)$$

where L is the inductance of the circuit. If desired, the circuit may be pictured as including a multiturn coil, the geometry of which controls the inductance L of the circuit. Substitution for Φ from Eq. (7.16) into Eq. (7.15) gives

$$P = LI\frac{dI}{dt} \qquad (7.17)$$

and this can be written as

$$P = \frac{dW_m}{dt} \qquad (7.18)$$

where

$$W_m = \tfrac{1}{2}LI^2 \qquad (7.19)$$

Alternatively we can substitute for I from Eq. (7.16) into Eq. (7.15) and obtain

$$P = \frac{1}{L} \Phi \frac{d\Phi}{dt} \tag{7.20}$$

This equation can be written in the form of Eq. (7.18), where

$$W_m = \frac{1}{2L} \Phi^2 \tag{7.21}$$

The identity of expressions (7.19) and (7.21) for W_m with each other, and also with the expression $\frac{1}{2}I\Phi$, follows from Eq. (7.16). We can therefore write

$$W_m = \frac{1}{2}I\Phi = \frac{1}{2}LI^2 = \frac{1}{2L} \Phi^2 \tag{7.22}$$

Equation (7.18) shows that the power delivered to the inductor is equal to the time rate of increase of the quantity W_m defined by Eqs. (7.22). The quantity W_m is known as the magnetic energy of the circuit. It is the energy of the circuit associated with motion of the electrons round the circuit under circumstances when the inertia of the circuit is controlled by the charge of the electrons rather than by their mass. Magnetic energy is thus the electrical form of kinetic energy. Equation (7.18) states that the power delivered to the inductor is equal to the time rate of increase of the magnetic energy stored in the inductor.

To calculate the way in which the magnetic flux threading the circuit varies with time when the applied voltage V is specified as a function of time, we integrate Eq. (7.13) with respect to t, thereby obtaining

$$\Phi(t) = \int_{t_0}^{t} V \, dt + \Phi_0 \tag{7.23}$$

where Φ_0 is the magnetic flux threading the circuit at time t_0. By substituting this value of Φ into Eq. (7.16) we deduce that the current I flowing round the circuit at time t is

$$I(t) = \frac{1}{L} \int_{t_0}^{t} V \, dt + I_0 \tag{7.24}$$

where I_0 is the current round the circuit at time zero. By substituting expressions (7.23) and (7.24) into Eqs. (7.22), we can obtain the magnetic energy W_m of the circuit as a function of time.

Comparison should be made between (1) the equations developed in Sec. 7.5 and in this section for capacitors and inductors and (2) the corresponding equations developed in Secs. 7.2 and 7.3 for springs and flywheels. The comparison is particularly important between Eqs. (7.22) and (7.22m). This comparison illustrates the way in which the current I

flowing round an electric circuit corresponds to the peripheral velocity v of a flywheel. The inductance L of the circuit measures the inertia properties of the charges moving round the circuit in the same way that the mass M of the rim of the flywheel measures the inertia properties of the massive particles constituting the rim. The energy possessed by the circuit by virtue of the motion of the charges round it is measured by the magnetic energy W_m in the same way that the energy possessed by a flywheel by virtue of the peripheral motion of the massive rim is measured by the kinetic energy W_k. The total energy of motion of the electrons round the electric circuit in fact consists of a contribution of the type represented in Eqs. (7.22) associated with the charges of the electrons and a contribution of the type represented by Eqs. (7.22m) associated with the mass of the electrons. For the reasons stated in Sec. 5.3, however, the dimensions of electric circuits in practice are nearly always such that the contribution given by Eqs. (7.22) to the energy of motion of the electrons round the circuit completely dominates the contribution given by Eqs. (7.22m).

7.7. An Oscillatory Electric Circuit. Consider an electric circuit of inductance L in which is connected a capacitor of capacitance C as shown in Fig. 7.3. Let the generator pro-

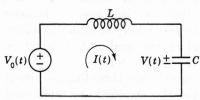

duce a time-varying voltage $V_0(t)$, and let $I(t)$ be the resulting current round the circuit at time t. Let the direction of the current I round the circuit be the direction in which the applied voltage V_0 acts, and let the positive plate of the capacitor be that onto which the current I flows. At time t let the voltage across the

FIG. 7.3. Illustrating an electric circuit of inductance L in which are connected a capacitor of capacitance C and a generator of voltage $V_0(t)$.

capacitor be $V(t)$, so that the charge on the positive plate of the capacitor is $CV(t)$. Since the time rate of increase of this charge is the current $I(t)$ round the circuit, it follows that

$$I = C \frac{dV}{dt} \tag{7.25}$$

The magnetic flux threading the electric circuit in the direction related by the right-hand-screw rule to the direction of the current is $LI(t)$. As shown in Fig. 7.3, the net voltage driving the current round the circuit is the voltage $V_0(t)$ of the generator less the voltage $V(t)$ across the capacitor. It follows from Faraday's law of induction that

$$V_0 - V = L \frac{dI}{dt} \tag{7.26}$$

To discuss the time variation of the magnetic energy stored in the inductor and of the electric energy stored in the capacitor we multiply Eq. (7.25) by V and Eq. (7.26) by I, thereby obtaining respectively

$$VI = CV \frac{dV}{dt} \tag{7.27}$$

$$V_0 I - VI = LI \frac{dI}{dt} \tag{7.28}$$

Equation (7.27) can be rewritten as

$$VI = \frac{dW_e}{dt} \tag{7.29}$$

where W_e is the electric energy stored in the capacitor given by the second of the three expressions for electric energy in Eqs. (7.10). Likewise Eq. (7.28) can be rewritten as

$$V_0 I - VI = \frac{dW_m}{dt} \tag{7.30}$$

where W_m is the magnetic energy stored in the inductor given by the second of the three expressions for magnetic energy in Eqs. (7.22). Equation (7.29) states that the power delivered to the capacitor is the time rate of increase of the electric energy stored in the capacitor. Equation (7.30) states that the excess of the power provided by the generator over the power delivered to the capacitor is the time rate of increase of the magnetic energy stored in the inductor. By addition of Eqs. (7.29) and (7.30) we obtain

$$V_0 I = \frac{dW}{dt} \tag{7.31}$$

where
$$W = W_m + W_e \tag{7.32}$$

The quantity W defined by Eq. (7.32) is the sum of the magnetic energy stored in the inductor and the electric energy stored in the capacitor. The quantity W is referred to as the total energy of the electrical system. Equation (7.31) states that the power delivered by the generator is equal to the time rate of increase of the total electrical energy of the system.

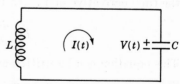

FIG. 7.4. An oscillatory electric circuit.

Let us now suppose that, prior to time zero, the generator consists of a battery having a steady voltage V_0. This results in a situation in which, at time zero, the voltage V across the capacitor is equal to V_0, while the current I round the circuit is zero. At time zero let the battery be short-circuited, so that the circuit then becomes that shown in Fig. 7.4. There is now no generator connected in the circuit, but the capacitor is charged at time zero to voltage V_0. Let us investigate the current $I(t)$ that flows round the circuit subsequent to time zero and the corresponding time variation in $V(t)$, the voltage across the capacitor.

Since, subsequent to time zero, the voltage V_0 of the generator vanishes, Eqs. (7.25) and (7.26) become

$$I = C\frac{dV}{dt}$$
$$-V = L\frac{dI}{dt} \tag{7.33}$$

while Eqs. (7.27) and (7.28) become

$$VI = \frac{dW_e}{dt}$$
$$-VI = \frac{dW_m}{dt} \tag{7.34}$$

Equations (7.34) show that the power being delivered to the capacitor is the time rate of increase of its electric energy and is also the time rate of decrease of the magnetic energy stored in the inductor. As the electric energy in the capacitor increases, the magnetic energy in the inductor decreases, and vice versa. Subsequent to time zero the left-hand side of Eq. (7.31) is zero, thereby showing that the total energy W of the electrical system is independent of time. Equation (7.32) thus states that the sum of the magnetic energy stored in the inductor and the electric energy stored in the capacitor remains constant and is equal to the energy stored in the capacitor at time zero.

To calculate the time variation of the current I round the circuit subsequent to time zero, we eliminate V between the two equations (7.33) by differentiating the second equation with respect to t and eliminating the time derivative of V. In this way we obtain

$$LC\frac{d^2I}{dt^2} + I = 0 \tag{7.35}$$

This equation can be written as

$$\frac{d^2I}{dt^2} + \omega^2 I = 0 \tag{7.36}$$

where

$$\omega = \frac{1}{(LC)^{\frac{1}{2}}} \tag{7.37}$$

Equation (7.36) is the equation of simple harmonic motion, and its solution is

$$I = A\cos\omega t + B\sin\omega t \tag{7.38}$$

where A and B are constants to be determined from the conditions specified at time zero.   By substituting from Eq. (7.38) for I into the second of Eqs. (7.33), we obtain for the voltage across the capacitor in Fig. 7.4 at time t

$$V = \omega L(A \sin \omega t - B \cos \omega t) \tag{7.39}$$

The initial conditions that determine the constants A and B in Eqs. (7.38) and (7.39) are

$$I = 0 \qquad V = V_0 \qquad \text{when } t = 0 \tag{7.40}$$

Substitution of these values into Eqs. (7.38) and (7.39) gives respectively

$$0 = A \tag{7.41}$$
$$V_0 = -\omega L B \tag{7.42}$$

Substitution for A and B from Eqs. (7.41) and (7.42) into Eq. (7.39) gives

$$V = V_0 \cos \omega t \tag{7.43}$$

Substitution for A and B from Eqs. (7.41) and (7.42) into Eq. (7.38) gives

$$I = -I_0 \sin \omega t \tag{7.44}$$

where
$$I_0 = \frac{V_0}{\omega L} \tag{7.45}$$

Equations (7.43) and (7.44) give the voltage across the capacitor and the current through the inductor subsequent to time zero.

Equation (7.43) shows that the voltage V across the capacitor varies sinusoidally with time with amplitude V_0 as shown in Fig. 7.5a.   The voltage across the capacitor oscillates sinusoidally with periodic time

$$T = \frac{2\pi}{\omega} \tag{7.46}$$

Substitution for ω from Eq. (7.37) into Eq. (7.46) shows that the periodic time of the oscillation is

$$T = 2\pi(LC)^{\frac{1}{2}} \tag{7.47}$$

The number of complete oscillations executed per unit time is the reciprocal of the periodic time.   The frequency of oscillation in cycles per unit time is therefore

$$f = \frac{\omega}{2\pi} \tag{7.48}$$

or
$$f = \frac{1}{2\pi(LC)^{\frac{1}{2}}} \tag{7.49}$$

This is known as the resonant frequency of the oscillatory circuit.

Equation (7.44) shows that the current through the inductor oscillates sinusoidally with time as shown in Fig. 7.5b.   The frequency of oscillation of the current is the same as that of the voltage.   The current starts from zero at time zero as a result of the assumed initial conditions expressed by Eqs. (7.40).   As t increases from zero, the current becomes negative because a capacitor charged initially as shown by the signs in Fig. 7.4

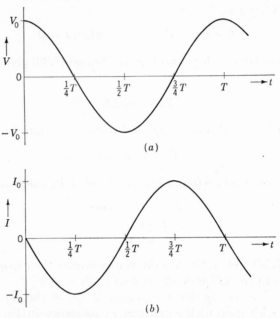

FIG. 7.5. Illustrating as a function of time, for the oscillatory circuit shown in Fig. 7.4, (a) the voltage across the capacitor and (b) the current through the inductor.

would involve an initial discharging current round the circuit in the direction opposite to that taken as the positive direction of I.   We observe that the current oscillation reaches its extreme values at the instants when the voltage oscillation vanishes, and vice versa.   Two oscillations related in this manner are said to be in quadrature.

The amplitude I_0 of the current oscillation through the inductor is expressed in terms of the amplitude V_0 of the voltage oscillation across the capacitor by means of Eq. (7.45).   This equation can be written as

$$I_0 = \frac{V_0}{R} \qquad (7.50)$$

where

$$R = \omega L = \frac{1}{\omega C} = \left(\frac{L}{C}\right)^{\frac{1}{2}} \qquad (7.51)$$

The two additional expressions for R given in Eqs. (7.51) follow from Eq.

(7.37).   Since R in Eq. (7.50) is the ratio of a voltage to a current, it is a resistance.   This resistance is known as the dynamic resistance of the oscillatory circuit, and from Eqs. (7.51) we see that the dynamic resistance of an oscillatory circuit is equal to the square root of the ratio of the inductance L of the inductor to the capacitance C of the capacitor.   The dynamic resistance R of an oscillatory circuit is the quantity by which the amplitude I_0 of the current through the inductor must be multiplied in order to obtain the amplitude V_0 of the voltage across the capacitor.   It must be noticed, however, that, as illustrated in Fig. 7.5, the instant at which the current through the inductor has the value I_0 differs from the instant at which the voltage across the capacitor has the value V_0 by a quarter of a period.

The electric energy stored in the capacitor is obtained as a function of time by substituting for V from Eq. (7.43) into the second of the three expressions for W_e given in Eqs. (7.10).   We obtain

$$W_e(t) = \tfrac{1}{2}CV_0^2 \cos^2 \omega t \tag{7.52}$$

Likewise the magnetic energy stored in the inductor is obtained as a function of time by substituting for I from Eq. (7.44) into the second of the expressions for W_m given in Eqs. (7.22).   We obtain

$$W_m(t) = \tfrac{1}{2}LI_0^2 \sin^2 \omega t \tag{7.53}$$

From Eq. (7.52) we see that the energy stored in the capacitor varies between zero and

$$\tfrac{1}{2}CV_0^2 \tag{7.54}$$

while from Eq. (7.53) we see that the magnetic energy stored in the inductor varies between zero and

$$\tfrac{1}{2}LI_0^2 \tag{7.55}$$

By substituting for I_0 into expression (7.55) from Eq. (7.50) and using the third of the expressions (7.51) for R, we see that expression (7.55) is identical in value with expression (7.54).   Moreover, expression (7.54) is the energy initially stored in the capacitor at time zero and is therefore the total energy W of the electrical system.   We can therefore write

$$W = \tfrac{1}{2}CV_0^2 = \tfrac{1}{2}LI_0^2 \tag{7.56}$$

Using these relations we can write Eqs. (7.52) and (7.53) in terms of the total energy W of the system, thereby obtaining

$$W_e(t) = W \cos^2 \omega t \tag{7.57}$$
$$W_m(t) = W \sin^2 \omega t \tag{7.58}$$

From these two equations we see that the electric energy stored in the capacitor and the magnetic energy stored in the inductor always add up to the initial energy W of the electrical system. This is illustrated in Fig. 7.6, where the electric energy stored in the capacitor is plotted vertically upward from the bottom of the diagram while the magnetic energy stored in the inductor is plotted vertically downward from the top of the diagram. Figure 7.6 describes the fact that the energy of the system oscillates back and forth between the capacitor and the inductor as time progresses, the total energy stored in the capacitor and in the inductor always adding up to the initial energy W given to the electrical system.

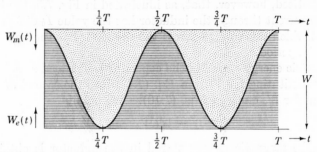

FIG. 7.6. Illustrating the oscillation of energy between the capacitor and the inductor in the oscillatory circuit shown in Fig. 7.4.

The energy stored in the capacitor reaches a maximum whenever the voltage across the capacitor reaches an extreme value, and this occurs every half period (see Fig. 7.5a). Likewise, the energy stored in the inductor reaches a maximum whenever the current through the inductor reaches an extreme value, and this occurs every half period (see Fig. 7.5b). The instants when the whole of the energy is stored in the inductor are separated from the instants when the whole of the energy is stored in the capacitor by a quarter of a period, as shown in Fig. 7.6.

Equations (7.34) show that the rate of flow of energy from the inductor to the capacitor is given by the product of the voltage V across the capacitor and the current I round the circuit or by the time rate of increase of the energy stored in the capacitor or by the time rate of decrease of the energy stored in the inductor. By differentiating Eq. (7.57) with respect to time, we see that, at time t, the rate of flow of energy from the inductor to the capacitor is given by

$$P(t) = -2\omega W \cos \omega t \sin \omega t \qquad (7.59)$$

and this can be rewritten as

$$P(t) = -\omega W \sin 2\omega t \qquad (7.60)$$

When this expression is positive, energy is flowing from the inductor to the capacitor; when it is negative, energy is flowing from the capacitor to the inductor. Using expression (7.60), the rate of flow of energy between the inductor and the capacitor is plotted as a function of time in Fig. 7.7. The rate of flow of energy from the inductor to the capacitor is plotted vertically upward, and the rate of flow of energy from the capacitor to the inductor is plotted vertically downward. At time zero we start with the voltage of the capacitor at its maximum value V_0, as shown in Fig. 7.5a, and with the current through the inductor zero, as shown in Fig. 7.5b. During the next eighth of a period energy flows into the inductor at an increasing rate, as shown in Fig. 7.7. After one-eighth of a cycle has

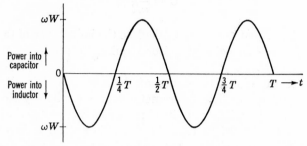

FIG. 7.7. Illustrating, as a function of time, the rate of flow of energy between the inductor and the capacitor for the oscillatory circuit shown in Fig. 7.4.

elapsed, the rate of flow of energy into the inductor becomes less and finally vanishes at $t = \frac{1}{4}T$. At this time all the energy has left the capacitor and is located in the inductor, as shown in Fig. 7.6; the current through the inductor is at an extreme value, as shown in Fig. 7.5b, while the voltage across the capacitor is zero, as shown in Fig. 7.5a. During the next quarter of a cycle energy flows from the inductor to the capacitor at a rate shown in Fig. 7.7. The rate of flow increases between $t = \frac{1}{4}T$ and $t = \frac{3}{8}T$ and then decreases to zero again at $t = \frac{1}{2}T$. At this time all the energy has left the inductor and returned to the capacitor, as shown in Fig. 7.6; the current through the inductor is zero, as shown in Fig. 7.5b, and the voltage across the capacitor is again at an extreme value, as shown in Fig. 7.5a. The extreme value of the voltage across the capacitor is now $-V_0$, however, instead of $+V_0$. During each succeeding half cycle the process of oscillation of energy between the capacitor and the inductor repeats as shown in Figs. 7.6 and 7.7. Successive half cycles are distinguished from each other, however, by reversals in the sign of the voltage across the capacitor and of the current through the inductor, as shown in Fig. 7.5.

Oscillatory circuits of the type shown in Fig. 7.4 are of tremendous importance in electrical science. We notice from Eq. (7.37) or (7.49) that the resonant frequency of the oscillatory circuit depends upon the product of the inductance of the inductor and the capacitance of the capacitor. We also notice from Eqs. (7.51) that the dynamic resistance of the oscillatory circuit depends upon the ratio of the inductance of the inductor to the capacitance of the capacitor. By suitable choice of L and C therefore, we can, in principle, obtain any assigned value for the resonant frequency of the oscillatory circuit and any assigned value for the dynamic resistance of the oscillatory circuit. Indeed from Eqs. (7.51) we can deduce that

$$L = \frac{R}{\omega} \tag{7.61}$$

and

$$C = \frac{1}{\omega R} \tag{7.62}$$

From these two equations we can calculate the inductance of the inductor and the capacitance of the capacitor required to produce any assigned values of ω and R.

In practice the ohmic resistance of the oscillatory circuit is also of importance and a significant parameter of the oscillatory circuit is the ratio of its dynamic resistance to its ohmic resistance. For the purpose of numerical illustration let us take the dynamic resistance R of the oscillatory circuit as 1,000 ohms. Let us further suppose that the resonant frequency of the circuit is to be 100 Mc/sec. This corresponds to an angular frequency of about 6×10^8 radians/sec. Substituting these values into Eqs. (7.61) and (7.62), we see that the required value of L is 1.6 μh and the required value of C is 1.6 $\mu\mu$f. If the desired resonant frequency were 100 cycles/sec, then the required value of inductance would be 1.6 henrys and of capacitance 1.6 μf. The wide range of inductance and capacitance available in practice permits the design of oscillatory circuits whose resonant frequencies can lie in a range from less than 10 cycles/sec to more than 1,000 Mc/sec.

SUMMARIZING EXERCISES

7.1. A capacitor of capacitance C is charged by means of a current source, and the voltage across the capacitor at time t is V. Prove that the power supplied by the source to the capacitor is equal to the time rate of increase of $\frac{1}{2}CV^2$. If the voltage across the capacitor is V_0 at time t_0 and the charging current thereafter is $I(t)$, calculate the voltage across the capacitor at any time t subsequent to t_0.

7.2. A generator whose voltage V depends upon time t is applied across a loss-free inductor of inductance L, and the resulting current through the inductor at time t is I. Show that the power supplied by the generator to the inductor is the time rate of increase of $\frac{1}{2}LI^2$. Explain what is meant by magnetic energy.

7.3. If in the preceding exercise the current through the inductor at time t_0 is I_0 and subsequent to this time the voltage applied across the inductor is $V(t)$, calculate the current through the inductor at any time t subsequent to t_0.

7.4. A generator whose voltage V_0 depends upon time t is connected in series with an inductor of inductance L and a capacitor of capacitance C. Resistance can be neglected. Write down equations to determine the voltage V across the capacitor at time t and the current I round the circuit at time t.   From these equations deduce that the power supplied by the generator is equal to the time rate of increase of W, where W is the sum of the magnetic energy stored in the inductor and the electric energy stored in the capacitor.

7.5. An inductor of inductance L is connected across a capacitor of capacitance C, and resistance can be neglected.   At time zero there is a voltage V_0 across the capacitor and no current in the inductor.   Calculate the voltage V across the capacitor and the current I in the inductor at any subsequent time t.   Draw diagrams to illustrate the variations of V and I with t.

7.6. Explain what is meant by an oscillatory electric circuit.   Calculate the frequency of oscillation of the circuit and the ratio of the maximum voltage across the capacitor to the maximum current through the inductor.

7.7. For an oscillatory electric circuit, describe the way in which energy oscillates back and forth between the inductor and the capacitor.   Illustrate the description with diagrams showing as a function of time (a) the energy stored in the capacitor, (b) the energy stored in the inductor, and (c) the rate of flow of energy between the capacitor and the inductor.

CHAPTER 8

MAGNETIC ENERGY OF A SYSTEM OF INDUCTORS

8.1. Introduction. It is shown in Part 1, Sec. 8.6, that the electric energy of an electrostatic field is to be considered as distributed throughout the field. At a point in the field where the electric field strength is E, the electric flux density is D, and the capacitivity is ϵ, the electric energy per unit volume is given by any of the following three equivalent expressions:

$$\tfrac{1}{2}ED = \tfrac{1}{2}\epsilon E^2 = \frac{1}{2\epsilon} D^2 \qquad (8.1)$$

Corresponding statements are true for the storage of magnetic energy in the magnetic field associated with any system of inductors. There is a close mathematical parallelism between the concept of storage of magnetic energy in a magnetic field and the concept of storage of electric energy in an electrostatic field. The development of this chapter and of the next chapter closely follows the corresponding development in connection with electric fields in Part 1, Chaps. 8 to 10. The close parallelism of the mathematical equations must not, however, obscure the fact that magnetic energy is kinetic in character, whereas electric energy is potential in character.

8.2. Magnetic Energy of a Circuit Carrying Current. Let us first establish Eqs. (7.22) for the magnetic energy stored in an inductor by an argument similar to that used in Part 1, Sec. 8.2, for establishing Eqs. (7.10) for the electric energy stored in a capacitor.

Consider an electric circuit carrying a current I and threaded by a magnetic flux Φ whose direction is related by the right-hand-screw rule to the direction of current flow. By multiplying Eq. (7.15) by dt we see that, to increase the magnetic flux threading the electric circuit by a small amount $d\Phi$, an amount of energy

$$I \, d\Phi \qquad (8.2)$$

must be supplied to the circuit from a source. It follows that, if a circuit carrying a current I has its threading magnetic flux increased by a small amount $d\Phi$, then the magnetic energy of the circuit increases by an amount $I \, d\Phi$. This statement is to be compared with the following statement concerning a capacitor. If a capacitor is charged to a voltage V

684

and a small amount of charge dQ is then transferred from the negative plate to the positive plate, the increase in the electric energy of the capacitor is $V\, dQ$.

Let us now use expression (8.2) to calculate the total magnetic energy required to establish a current I round a circuit and the associated magnetic flux Φ threading the circuit, starting from a situation in which both the current and the flux are zero.   In doing so we shall assume that, if ferromagnetic material is present, it is acting in a substantially linear manner.   Let us consider a stage in the process of supplying energy to the circuit at which the current is a fraction x of the final current I.   At this stage the current round the circuit is xI and the magnetic flux threading the circuit is $x\Phi$.   Now let us increase the threading magnetic flux by a small amount $dx\,\Phi$.   According to expression (8.2) the increment in the magnetic energy of the circuit is

$$(xI)(dx\,\Phi) \tag{8.3}$$

To create the final current I round the circuit and the final magnetic flux Φ through the circuit starting from a situation in which both current and flux are zero, we have to make increments in magnetic flux until the fraction x has increased from zero to unity.   The total magnetic energy supplied is therefore

$$W = \int_0^1 (xI)(dx\,\Phi) \tag{8.4}$$

In this equation I and Φ are constants, being the final current and flux associated with the circuit.   They can therefore be brought in front of the integral sign, and Eq. (8.4) can be written as

$$W = I\Phi \int_0^1 x\, dx \tag{8.5}$$

The value of the integral in this equation is $\frac{1}{2}$; consequently the formula for the magnetic energy of a circuit for which the current is I and the threading magnetic flux is Φ is

$$W = \tfrac{1}{2} I\Phi \tag{8.6}$$

Since the ratio of Φ to I is the inductance L of the circuit, formula (8.6) for the magnetic energy of the circuit can be written in any of the following equivalent forms:

$$W = \tfrac{1}{2}I\Phi = \tfrac{1}{2}LI^2 = \frac{1}{2L}\,\Phi^2 \tag{8.7}$$

These equations verify Eqs. (7.22).

If it is necessary to take into account nonlinear behavior of ferromagnetic material, then integration of expression (8.2) to obtain the total magnetic energy of the circuit is more difficult.   For the ferromagnetic material concerned, the relation between the magnetic field strength H and the magnetic flux density B must be ascertained as described in Part 3, Sec. 8.2. From this can be calculated the relation between the current I round the circuit and the magnetic flux Φ threading the circuit. We then use this relation in expression (8.2) and carry out the integration graphically or numerically.

8.3. Magnetic Energy of a System of Inductors.   Let us now consider how to calculate the magnetic energy stored in a system of inductors. Let the electric circuits associated with the inductors be numbered 1, 2, . . . , and let the currents flowing round these circuits be I_1, I_2, . . . , respectively. Let the magnetic fluxes threading the circuits in the directions related by the right-hand-screw rule to the corresponding currents be Φ_1, Φ_2, . . . , respectively. In terms of these currents and fluxes we wish to calculate the magnetic energy stored by the system of inductors, neglecting nonlinear effects of ferromagnetic material. At a certain stage during the process of creating the currents and fluxes, let the currents and fluxes be a fraction x of their final values. Now increase the fluxes threading the circuits by small fractions dx of their final values. This involves threading fluxes $dx\,\Phi_1$, $dx\,\Phi_2$, . . . through currents $x_1 I_1$, $x_2 I_2$, . . . , respectively. The corresponding increase in magnetic energy is

$$(x I_1)(dx\,\Phi_1) + (x I_2)(dx\,\Phi_2) + \cdots \qquad (8.8)$$

The total magnetic energy involved in creating the final currents and fluxes is obtained by integrating expression (8.8) with respect to x from zero to unity, and is therefore

$$W = \int_0^1 [(x I_1)(dx\,\Phi_1) + (x I_2)(dx\,\Phi_2) + \cdots] \qquad (8.9)$$

Since I_1, Φ_1, I_2, Φ_2, . . . are constants in this equation, it can be written as

$$W = (I_1\Phi_1 + I_2\Phi_2 + \cdots) \int_0^1 x\,dx \qquad (8.10)$$

thereby giving

$$W = \tfrac{1}{2}(I_1\Phi_1 + I_2\Phi_2 + \cdots) \qquad (8.11)$$

We thus see that the total magnetic energy stored in the system of inductors is obtained by multiplying each current by the threading magnetic flux, summing for all circuits, and dividing by 2.

Let us suppose that we are dealing with a system of inductors for which the coefficients of inductance L_{mn} and the coefficients of reluctance R_{mn} have been calculated. In terms of these coefficients it is possible to express the magnetic energy given by Eq. (8.11) for the system of inductors either entirely in terms of the currents round the circuits or entirely in terms of the magnetic fluxes threading the circuits. The magnetic fluxes threading the circuits are expressed in terms of the currents round them by means of the equations

$$\Phi_1 = L_{11}I_1 + L_{12}I_2 + \cdots$$
$$\Phi_2 = L_{21}I_1 + L_{22}I_2 + \cdots \qquad (8.12)$$
$$\cdots \cdots \cdots \cdots \cdots$$

Substituting for the magnetic fluxes in terms of the currents from Eqs. (8.12) into Eq. (8.11) and remembering that $L_{mn} = L_{nm}$, we obtain

$$W = \tfrac{1}{2}(L_{11}I_1{}^2 + L_{22}I_2{}^2 + \cdots$$
$$+ 2L_{12}I_1I_2 + \cdots) \qquad (8.13)$$

This equation expresses the magnetic energy of the system of inductors in terms of the currents round the circuits and the coefficients of inductance.

Alternatively, using the coefficients of reluctance, we can express the currents round the circuits in terms of the magnetic fluxes threading them by means of the equations

$$I_1 = R_{11}\Phi_1 + R_{12}\Phi_2 + \cdots$$
$$I_2 = R_{21}\Phi_1 + R_{22}\Phi_2 + \cdots \qquad (8.14)$$
$$\cdots \cdots \cdots \cdots \cdots$$

Substituting for the currents in terms of the magnetic fluxes from Eqs. (8.14) into Eq. (8.11) and remembering that $R_{mn} = R_{nm}$, we obtain

$$W = \tfrac{1}{2}(R_{11}\Phi_1{}^2 + R_{22}\Phi_2{}^2 + \cdots$$
$$+ 2R_{12}\Phi_1\Phi_2 + \cdots) \qquad (8.15)$$

This expresses the magnetic energy of the system of inductors in terms of the magnetic fluxes threading the circuits and the coefficients of reluctance of the system.   Equations (8.11), (8.13), and (8.15) for a system of inductors correspond to Eqs. (8.7) for a single inductor.

For a transformer there are only two magnetically coupled electric circuits, circuits 1 and 2.   From Eqs. (8.11), (8.13), and (8.15) we see therefore that the magnetic energy stored in a transformer can be expressed in any of the following three equivalent forms:

$$W = \tfrac{1}{2}(I_1\Phi_1 + I_2\Phi_2) \qquad (8.16)$$
$$W = \tfrac{1}{2}(L_{11}I_1{}^2 + 2L_{12}I_1I_2 + L_{22}I_2{}^2) \qquad (8.17)$$
$$W = \tfrac{1}{2}(R_{11}\Phi_1{}^2 + 2R_{12}\Phi_1\Phi_2 + R_{22}\Phi_2{}^2) \qquad (8.18)$$

8.4. Green's Reciprocal Theorem for Inductors.   In deriving Eqs. (8.13) and (8.15) from Eq. (8.11) it was assumed that

$$L_{mn} = L_{nm} \qquad (8.19)$$

and that

$$R_{mn} = R_{nm} \qquad (8.20)$$

These equations were discussed in Part 3, Secs. 9.6 and 9.7.   The truth of Eqs. (8.19) and (8.20) was obvious in circumstances where the magnetic coupling between the inductors is controlled by a ferromagnetic network which behaves in a linear manner and from which leakage of magnetic flux can be neglected.   When no magnetic network is involved, however, the truth of Eqs. (8.19) and (8.20) is not so obvious and depends upon Green's reciprocal theorem for inductors.   The proof of this theorem is based on an elaboration of the argument leading to Eq. (8.11).

Consider a given system of inductors for which the associated electric circuits are numbered 1, 2, ...   Let us first apply currents I_1, I_2, . . . round the circuits, and let the corresponding magnetic fluxes be Φ_1, Φ_2, . . . threading the circuits in the directions related by the right-hand-screw rule to the directions of the currents.   For the same system of inductors let currents I_1', I_2', . . . applied round the circuits give threading magnetic fluxes Φ_1', Φ_2', ...   Then Green's reciprocal theorem states that, neglecting nonlinear effects of ferromagnetic material,

$$I_1\Phi_1' + I_2\Phi_2' + \cdots = I_1'\Phi_1 + I_2'\Phi_2 + \cdots \qquad (8.21)$$

In writing down the result (8.21) it is convenient to list the currents and fluxes for the circuits according to the following scheme:

$$
\begin{array}{cc}
I_1 & I_2 \quad \cdots \\
\Phi_1 & \Phi_2 \quad \cdots \\
\hline
I_1' & I_2' \quad \cdots \\
\Phi_1' & \Phi_2' \quad \cdots
\end{array}
$$

One side of Eq. (8.21) is then formed by multiplying line 1 by line 4 and adding, while the other side of the equation is formed by multiplying line 2 by line 3 and adding.   It is frequently convenient to abbreviate Eq. (8.21) in the form

$$\Sigma I\Phi' = \Sigma I'\Phi \qquad (8.22)$$

where Σ denotes summation over the circuits.

Let us examine the implications of Green's reciprocal theorem for inductors before actually proving the theorem.

First let us consider a situation in which the current round circuit 1 is I and the currents round all other circuits are zero; let the magnetic fluxes threading the circuits under these circumstances be Φ_1, Φ_2, Φ_3, ...   Let us compare this with a situation in which the current round circuit 2 is I and the currents round all other circuits are zero; in this situation let the magnetic fluxes threading the circuits be Φ_1', Φ_2', Φ_3', ...   These currents and fluxes are summarized in the following table:

$$
\begin{array}{ccc}
I & 0 & 0 \quad \cdots \\
\Phi_1 & \Phi_2 & \Phi_3 \quad \cdots \\
\hline
0 & I & 0 \quad \cdots \\
\Phi_1' & \Phi_2' & \Phi_3' \quad \cdots
\end{array}
$$

To this pair of situations we now apply Green's reciprocal theorem for inductors. In Eq. (8.21) there is only one nonvanishing term on each side of the equation, and we derive

$$I\Phi_1' = I\Phi_2$$
or
$$\Phi_1' = \Phi_2 \tag{8.23}$$

This result states that the magnetic flux threading circuit 1 due to a current I round circuit 2 (the currents round the remaining circuits being zero) is equal to the magnetic flux threading circuit 2 when the current I flows round circuit 1 (the currents round the remaining circuits being zero).

In the result expressed by Eqs. (8.23) let us now put $I = 1$. Φ_1' is then the magnetic flux threading circuit 1 when unit current flows round circuit 2 and zero current round all other circuits. By definition of the coefficients of inductance we therefore have

$$\Phi_1' = L_{12} \tag{8.24}$$

In the same way we have

$$\Phi_2 = L_{21} \tag{8.25}$$

Green's reciprocal theorem in this case therefore gives

$$L_{12} = L_{21} \tag{8.26}$$

Since the numbers 1 and 2 could have been assigned to any pair of circuits of the system, the truth of Eq. (8.19) is established.

As another application of Green's reciprocal theorem for inductors let us thread a magnetic flux Φ through circuit 1 and arrange that no magnetic flux threads any of the other circuits; in these circumstances let the currents round the circuits be I_1, I_2, I_3, ... Let us compare this with a situation in which the magnetic flux Φ is threaded through circuit 2 and no magnetic flux is threaded through any of the other circuits; in these circumstances let the currents round the circuits be I_1', I_2', I_3', ... These currents and fluxes are shown in the following table:

I_1	I_2	I_3	$\cdot$ $\cdot$ $\cdot$
Φ	0	0	$\cdot$ $\cdot$ $\cdot$
I_1'	I_2'	I_3'	$\cdot$ $\cdot$ $\cdot$
0	Φ	0	$\cdot$ $\cdot$ $\cdot$

Applying Green's reciprocal theorem for inductors, Eq. (8.21) reduces to

$$I_2\Phi = I_1'\Phi$$
and so to
$$I_2 = I_1' \tag{8.27}$$

Hence the current round circuit 2 when a magnetic flux Φ is threaded through circuit 1 (there being no magnetic flux through the remaining circuits) is equal to the current round circuit 1 when the magnetic flux Φ is threaded through circuit 2 (there being no magnetic flux threading the remaining circuits).

We now consider the special case of the result expressed in Eqs. (8.27) that occurs when $\Phi = 1$. From the definitions of the coefficients of reluctance we have

$$I_2 = R_{21} \tag{8.28}$$

and
$$I_1' = R_{12} \tag{8.29}$$

It follows therefore that

$$R_{21} = R_{12} \tag{8.30}$$

and this establishes Eq. (8.20).

To prove Green's reciprocal theorem [Eq. (8.22)], let us consider a situation in which the currents round the circuits are

$$(1 - x)I_1 + xI_1' \qquad (1 - x)I_2 + xI_2' \qquad \cdots \tag{8.31}$$

where x is a fraction less than unity. Neglecting the nonlinear effects of any ferromagnetic material that may be present, it follows from the principle of superposition that the magnetic fluxes threading the circuits are

$$(1 - x)\Phi_1 + x\Phi_1' \qquad (1 - x)\Phi_2 + x\Phi_2' \qquad \cdots \tag{8.32}$$

These currents and fluxes have been chosen so that, when $x = 0$, they are identical with the first set of currents and fluxes contemplated in Green's reciprocal theorem; on the other hand, when $x = 1$, the currents and fluxes given by expressions (8.31) and (8.32) are identical with the second set of currents and fluxes contemplated in Green's reciprocal theorem. We can thus pass from the first set of currents and fluxes in the theorem to the second set by allowing x to go from zero to unity.

Let us calculate the work done in changing over from the first set of currents and fluxes to the second set. When x changes to $x + dx$, the flux threading circuit 1 increases by

$$d[(1 - x)\Phi_1 + x\Phi_1'] \tag{8.33}$$

and this is equal to

$$(\Phi_1' - \Phi_1)\, dx \tag{8.34}$$

In the process of increasing x to $x + dx$, therefore, an amount of flux given by expression (8.34) has to be threaded through the current

$$(1 - x)I_1 + xI_1' \tag{8.35}$$

In accordance with expression (8.2) this involves doing an amount of work

$$[(1 - x)I_1 + xI_1'](\Phi_1' - \Phi_1) \, dx \qquad (8.36)$$

This calculation must be carried for all the circuits and summed.   Hence the work done in increasing x to $x + dx$ is

$$\Sigma[(1 - x)I + xI'](\Phi' - \Phi) \, dx \qquad (8.37)$$

and this can be rearranged as

$$\Sigma[I(\Phi' - \Phi) \, dx + (I' - I)(\Phi' - \Phi)x \, dx] \qquad (8.38)$$

The total work done in changing over from the first system of currents and fluxes to the second system of currents and fluxes is obtained by integrating expression (8.38) with respect to x from zero to unity.   It is therefore

$$\sum I(\Phi' - \Phi) \int_0^1 dx + \sum (I' - I)(\Phi' - \Phi) \int_0^1 x \, dx \qquad (8.39)$$

On evaluating the integrals, expression (8.39) becomes

$$\Sigma[I(\Phi' - \Phi) + \tfrac{1}{2}(I' - I)(\Phi' - \Phi)]$$

and this can be rearranged as

$$(\tfrac{1}{2}\Sigma I'\Phi' - \tfrac{1}{2}\Sigma I\Phi) + \tfrac{1}{2}(\Sigma I\Phi' - \Sigma I'\Phi) \qquad (8.40)$$

Now the work done in changing over from the first system of currents and fluxes to the second system of currents and fluxes must be equal to the increase in the magnetic energy of the system.   But according to Eq. (8.11), the increase in magnetic energy of the system is the first expression in parentheses in expression (8.40).   It follows therefore that the second expression in parentheses in expression (8.40) must vanish, and this establishes the truth of Eq. (8.22).

8.5. Density of Magnetic Energy. Let us consider a region of space occupied by a magnetic field produced by steady electric currents. The region under consideration might be the interior of a toroidal

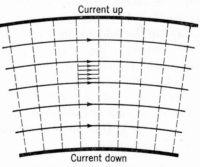

FIG. 8.1. Illustrating dissection of a magnetic field into building blocks each of which is an ideal solenoid.

or solenoidal inductor.   Such a region is illustrated in Fig. 8.1, where the continuous lines indicate lines of magnetic flux.   The broken lines in Fig. 8.1 represent surfaces of constant magnetic scalar potential intersecting the

lines of magnetic flux at right angles.   As described in Part 3, each tube of
magnetic flux could exist by itself if an appropriate current flows round its
curved surface.   At a point of a tube where the magnetic field strength is
H, the current per unit length that must flow round the tube is H.   Moreover, each tube of magnetic flux can be subdivided by a series of normal
cross sections into solenoidal inductors.   Each building block thus formed
may be regarded as an ideal solenoidal inductor for which the magnetic
field within it is uniform.   Nonuniformity of the magnetic field within
any particular solenoidal building block is prevented by the existence of
the remaining solenoidal building blocks that constitute the complete
magnetic field.

At a point in a magnetic field where the magnetic flux density is B
and the magnetic field strength is H, let us consider a solenoidal building
block bounded by the surface of a tube of magnetic flux of unit cross-
sectional area cut off by a pair of normal cross sections at unit distance
apart.   The volume of this solenoidal building block is unity.   If the
magnetic field in this building block is regarded as the field of an ideal
solenoidal inductor whose electric circuit is wrapped around the curved
surface of the building block, then the magnetic flux threading the inductor is B and the current round the inductor is H.   It follows from Eq.
(8.6) that the magnetic energy stored in the building block is $\frac{1}{2}HB$.
This energy is stored in a building block of unit volume, so that the magnetic energy stored per unit volume in the magnetic field at a place where
the magnetic field strength is H and the magnetic flux density is B is
$\frac{1}{2}HB$.   If each building block in the magnetic field is thought of as an
ideal solenoidal inductor, we see that magnetic energy is stored in each
building block.   Hence magnetic energy is distributed throughout the
magnetic field at the rate $\frac{1}{2}HB$ per unit volume.   The entire magnetic
energy of the field can be evaluated by calculating it at the rate $\frac{1}{2}HB$ per
unit volume, using for each element of volume the value of H and B at
the position of the element.

Taking the ratio of the magnetic flux density at a point in the field to
the magnetic field strength at the same point as equal to the inductivity
μ of the medium at that point, the expression for the magnetic energy per
unit volume at that point of the field can be written in any of the following equivalent forms:

$$w = \frac{1}{2}HB = \frac{1}{2}\mu H^2 = \frac{1}{2\mu} B^2 \qquad (8.41)$$

These expressions for the magnetic energy density at a point in a magnetic
field are to be compared with expressions (8.7) for the total magnetic
energy of an inductor.   They are also to be compared with expressions
(8.1) for the electric energy per unit volume in an electric field.

The way in which magnetic energy is distributed throughout a magnetic field tells us how much energy would be derived by abolishing any portion of the field. Suppose, for example, that the curved surface of any tube of magnetic flux were replaced by a conductor, leaving the field undisturbed as described in Part 3, Sec. 3.7. The portion of the magnetic field inside the tube could then be abolished, leaving the remainder of the magnetic field unchanged. The energy recovered from the field in this way can be obtained by calculating the energy within the tube of magnetic flux at the rate per unit volume given by Eqs. (8.41).

To illustrate numerically the order of magnitude of the energy density existing in a magnetic field, consider a toroidal inductor for which the cross-sectional area is 1 cm² and the perimeter is 10 cm.   Let the medium within the inductor have the inductivity of a vacuum. Let there be 1,000 turns of wire on the inductor, uniformly distributed round the perimeter, and let each turn carry a 1-ma current.   The inductance of the inductor evaluates to 1.26 mh.   Substituting $L = 1.26$ mh (1.26×10^{-3} henry) and $I = 1$ ma (10^{-3} amp) in the second of the three expressions for magnetic energy given in Eq. (8.7), we obtain for the total magnetic energy stored in the inductor 6.3×10^{-10} joule. The volume of the inductor is approximately the product of its length (10^{-1} m) and its cross-sectional area (10^{-4} m²) and is therefore 10^{-5} m³. Dividing the total energy in the inductor by the volume, we obtain for the magnetic energy per unit volume within the inductor 63 μj/m³.   This value for the energy density can also be derived by using the second of the three expressions for magnetic energy density given in Eqs. (8.41). The total current flowing round the curved surface of the toroid is 1 amp, and this is distributed uniformly over a length 10^{-1} m. The magnetic field strength within the inductor is therefore 10 amp/m. Using this value of H in the second of the three expressions for magnetic energy density given in Eqs. (8.41) together with the vacuum inductivity, we verify that the magnetic energy density within the toroid is 63 μj/m³.

SUMMARIZING EXERCISES

8.1. An electric circuit carries a steady current I.   Show that, if the magnetic flux threading the circuit in the direction related by the right-hand-screw rule to the direction of the current is increased by a differential amount $d\Phi$, then an amount of energy $I \, d\Phi$ must be supplied to the circuit from a source.

8.2. A system of electric circuits carries steady currents $I_1, I_2, \ldots$, and the circuits are threaded by magnetic fluxes $\Phi_1, \Phi_2, \ldots$ respectively.   Prove that the magnetic energy stored by the system is $\frac{1}{2}(I_1\Phi_1 + I_2\Phi_2 + \cdots)$.   By making use of the coefficients of inductance of the system, express the stored magnetic energy in terms of the currents in the circuits and not in terms of the magnetic fluxes threading the circuits.   By making use of the coefficients of reluctance of the system, express the stored magnetic energy in terms of the magnetic fluxes threading the circuits and not in terms of the currents.

8.3. State and prove Green's reciprocal theorem for a system of electric circuits carrying steady currents.   Use the theorem to deduce that the coefficients of inductance L_{mn} of the system of inductors are such that $L_{mn} = L_{nm}$ and the coefficients of reluctance R_{mn} of the system of inductors are such that $R_{mn} = R_{nm}$.

8.4. By using "building-block" analysis, show that the magnetic energy associated with a magnetic field is distributed throughout the field.   Neglecting nonlinear behavior of ferromagnetic material, explain why, at a point in the field where the magnetic field strength is H and the magnetic flux density is B, the magnetic energy density is $\frac{1}{2}HB$ per unit volume.   Show that the magnetic energy per unit volume can also be written as $\frac{1}{2}\mu H^2$ and as $\frac{1}{2}B^2/\mu$, where μ is the inductivity of the medium.

CHAPTER 9

THE RELATION BETWEEN FORCE AND ENERGY
IN A MAGNETIC FIELD

9.1. Introduction. The total force exerted upon an electric circuit carrying a current can, in principle, be calculated in the manner described in Part 3, Chap. 6. It was there shown that, if a magnetic field of flux density **B** is applied to a current represented vectorially by **I**, there is a force per unit length acting upon the current given by the vector

$$\mathbf{I} \times \mathbf{B} \tag{9.1}$$

When contributions of this kind are added up for the various elements of length of a circuit, the total force of magnetic origin acting upon the circuit can be calculated. In some cases, however, it is more convenient to make the calculation in a different way. Suppose, for example, that a transformer consists of two circular coils having a common axis and that the distance between the planes of the coils is x. Let us suppose that we wish to calculate the force F tending to increase the distance x between the coils. Consider a small increment dx in the distance x. In this displacement, the work done by the force F tending to increase x is

$$F \, dx \tag{9.2}$$

If the displacement is carried out in such a way that energy does not enter or leave the system as a whole, the work done during the displacement is equal to the decrement

$$-dW \tag{9.3}$$

in the energy of the system. By evaluating the energy of the system in the manner described in the preceding chapter, we can calculate expression (9.3), and by equating this to expression (9.2), we can derive the force F between the coils tending to increase the distance x between them.

It follows from expression (8.2) that the process of making the displacement dx in such a way that energy does not enter or leave the system implies making the displacement in such a way that the magnetic fluxes threading the electric circuits remain unchanged. As an alternative, it is possible to consider a displacement in which the currents round the coils remain constant.   In this case the magnetic fluxes threading the circuits change during the displacement, and energy either enters or leaves the system.   To maintain the constant currents, voltages have to be applied round the circuits, and the sources of these voltages either supply or receive energy.   If a calculation is made of the energy supplied by the sources maintaining the constant currents, then we can add this to expression (9.3) before equating to expression (9.2).   Thus the force tending to increase the distance x between the coils can be calculated by considering a small displacement in which the currents remain constant provided that due allowance is made for the energy supplied to the system by the voltages required to maintain the currents constant.

In this chapter we shall study the calculation of the forces between electric circuits carrying current by considering the work done during small displacements of the circuits.   This discussion is to be compared with that for forces on conductors in electrostatics given in Part 1, Chap. 10.

9.2. Calculation of Forces of Magnetic Origin from Changes in Magnetic Energy.   Consider a system of electric circuits round which there flow electric currents denoted by I_1, I_2, . . . and through which there thread magnetic fluxes denoted by Φ_1, Φ_2, ...   It is assumed that the magnetic fluxes are related to the electric currents by the right-hand-screw rule.   In accordance with Eq. (8.11) the magnetic energy of the system is

$$W = \tfrac{1}{2}\Sigma I\Phi \tag{9.4}$$

where Σ denotes summation over the circuits.   Consider a situation in which there are increments $d\Phi_1$, $d\Phi_2$, . . . in the magnetic fluxes threading the circuits and increments dI_1, dI_2, . . . in the electric currents round the circuits.   By taking differentials in Eq. (9.4), we deduce that the corresponding increase in the magnetic energy of the system is

$$dW = \tfrac{1}{2}\Sigma(I\,d\Phi + \Phi\,dI) \tag{9.5}$$

Now suppose that we are interested in calculating a certain force F. Consider a displacement of the system in which the point of application of this force moves through a distance dx and the points of application of other forces remain fixed.   The work done by the force is $F\,dx$ and would be equal to the decrement $-dW$ in the magnetic energy of the system if the magnetic fluxes through the circuits were kept constant.   However, when there is an increment $d\Phi_1$ in the magnetic flux threading the current I_1, an increment $d\Phi_2$ in the magnetic flux threading the current I_2, and so on, expression (8.2) shows that there is introduced into the system an amount of magnetic energy $\Sigma I\,d\Phi$.   This introduced energy must be allowed for in relating the work done $F\,dx$ and the decrement $-dW$ in the magnetic energy of the system.   We therefore arrive at the equation

$$F \, dx = -dW + \Sigma I \, d\Phi \qquad (9.6)$$

Substitution for dW from Eq. (9.5) into Eq. (9.6) gives

$$F \, dx = \tfrac{1}{2}\Sigma(I \, d\Phi - \Phi \, dI) \qquad (9.7)$$

Now compare expression (9.7) for the work done and expression (9.5) for the increment in the magnetic energy of the system.   By making the increments of magnetic flux vanish, we arrive at the equation

$$F \, dx = -dW \qquad \text{at constant } \Phi \qquad (9.8)$$

On the other hand by making the increments of current in Eqs. (9.5) and (9.7) vanish, we arrive at the equation

$$F \, dx = +dW \qquad \text{at constant } I \qquad (9.9)$$

We thus see that, whereas the work done in a displacement in which the magnetic fluxes are kept constant is the decrement in the energy of the system, the work done in the displacement in which the currents are kept constant is the increment in the energy of the system.   The difference in energy in the two cases is that supplied by the sources of voltage maintaining the currents constant in the situation corresponding to Eq. (9.9). Equations (9.8) and (9.9) can be rewritten as

$$F = -\frac{\partial W}{\partial x} \qquad \text{at constant } \Phi \qquad (9.10)$$

and

$$F = +\frac{\partial W}{\partial x} \qquad \text{at constant } I \qquad (9.11)$$

We see that the force tending to increase any coordinate of a system of electric circuits carrying current is equal to the rate of change of the magnetic energy of the system as this coordinate increases.   It is the rate of decrease of the magnetic energy of the system if it is supposed that the magnetic fluxes threading the circuits are kept constant but the rate of increase of the energy if it is supposed that the currents round the circuits are kept constant.

9.3. The Force between the Coils of a Transformer.   As an example of the application of Eqs. (9.10) and (9.11), let us consider the force acting between the coils of a transformer.   Let the two coils of the transformer exist in parallel planes whose distance apart is x, and let us calculate the force F tending to increase x.

Let us suppose first of all that the properties of the transformer are specified in terms of the coefficients of self- and mutual reluctance of the coils.   When there is a magnetic flux Φ_1 threading circuit 1 and a magnetic flux Φ_2 threading circuit 2, the magnetic energy of the transformer is given by Eq. (8.18). This expression for the magnetic energy of the transformer is convenient if we are to calculate the force F tending to increase x by means of Eq. (9.10). Application of Eq. (9.10) implies that, in evaluating the derivative with respect to x on the right-hand side of the equation, the magnetic fluxes Φ_1 and Φ_2 on the right-hand side of Eq. (8.18) remain constant. Furthermore, in the displacement, the self-reluctances R_{11} and R_{22} of the two coils do not change. The only quantity on the right-hand side of Eq. (8.18) that varies with x in the derivative occurring on the right-hand side of Eq. (9.10) is therefore the mutual reluctance R_{12}. Substitution for W from Eq. (8.18) into Eq. (9.10) therefore gives

$$ F = - \frac{\partial R_{12}}{\partial x} \Phi_1 \Phi_2 \qquad (9.12) $$

Provided that we can calculate the way in which the mutual reluctance of the coils varies with the distance x between their planes, we can immediately calculate from Eq. (9.12) the force tending to increase x when there is a magnetic flux Φ_1 through circuit 1 and a magnetic flux Φ_2 through circuit 2.

Alternatively let us suppose that the properties of the transformer are specified in terms of the coefficients of self- and mutual inductance. When the currents round the electric circuits 1 and 2 of the transformer are I_1 and I_2 respectively, the magnetic energy of the transformer is given by Eq. (8.17). This is the convenient form for the magnetic energy of a transformer when using Eq. (9.11). In the derivative occurring on the right-hand side of Eq. (9.11), the currents I_1 and I_2 appearing on the right-hand side of Eq. (8.17) are constants. Furthermore a variation in the distance x between the planes of the two coils does not vary the coefficients of self-inductance L_{11} and L_{22} of the coils. For the derivative with respect to x occurring on the right-hand side of Eq. (9.11), therefore, the only quantity on the right-hand side of Eq. (8.17) that varies is the coefficient of mutual inductance L_{12}. Substitution for W from Eq. (8.17) into Eq. (9.11) therefore gives

$$ F = \frac{\partial L_{12}}{\partial x} I_1 I_2 \qquad (9.13) $$

Provided that we know the way in which the coefficient of mutual inductance L_{12} of the transformer varies with the distance x between the planes of the coils, Eq. (9.13) gives the force F between the coils tending to increase x when the current round circuit 1 is I_1 and the current round circuit 2 is I_2.

In any particular case the force between the coils of the transformer can be calculated either from Eq. (9.12) or from Eq. (9.13). In practice it is more common to specify the behavior of the transformer by means of its coefficients of inductance and by means of the currents through the windings, and consequently Eq. (9.13) is more commonly used than Eq. (9.12).

As an example of the application of Eq. (9.13), let us consider a pair of coils of areas S_1 and S_2 at a distance r apart, large compared with the linear dimensions of either. Let the coils have n_1 and n_2 turns respectively, and let the currents round the two circuits be I_1 and I_2. Let us suppose that the planes of the two coils are perpendicular to the line joining them and that the currents flow the same way round the join of coil 1 to coil 2. For this situation the coefficient of mutual inductance between the coils has been calculated in Part 3, Eq. (9.83). The result is

$$L_{12} = \frac{\mu n_1 n_2 S_1 S_2}{2\pi r^3} \tag{9.14}$$

where μ is the inductivity of the medium. From Eq. (9.13) the force tending to increase the distance r between the coils is

$$F = \frac{\partial L_{12}}{\partial r} I_1 I_2 \tag{9.15}$$

and by substituting for L_{12} from Eq. (9.14) into Eq. (9.15) we obtain

$$F = -3 \frac{\mu n_1 n_2 S_1 S_2}{2\pi r^4} I_1 I_2 \tag{9.16}$$

The force between the coils is thus inversely proportional to the fourth power of the distance between them. If the currents flow the same way round the join of coil 1 to coil 2, the force is one of attraction, but if the currents flow opposite ways round the join of coil 1 to coil 2, then the force is one of repulsion.

It should be mentioned that, if the coordinate whose variation is being considered is not a distance but an angle, then Eqs. (9.10) to (9.13) give not a force but a torque. Suppose, for example, that one coil of a transformer can turn about an axis and that the position of this coil on its axis is specified by an angle θ. Then Eq. (9.13) shows that the torque tending to increase the angle θ is

$$T = \frac{\partial L_{12}}{\partial \theta} I_1 I_2 \tag{9.17}$$

As an illustration we may consider the arrangement shown in Part 3, Fig. 9.11. The torque acting upon coil 2 tending to increase the angle θ is given by

$$\frac{\partial L_{12}}{\partial \theta} I_1 I_2 \tag{9.18}$$

where L_{12} is given as a function of the angle θ by Part 3, Eq. (9.90).

9.4. The Centrifugal Force for Current round an Inductor.   If we think of the current round an electric circuit as an electronic flywheel, we see that there is a centrifugal force tending to expand the flywheel. However, this force has to be calculated allowing for the fact that the inertia properties of the electronic flywheel are controlled by the charge of the electrons rather than by their mass.   In the case of a solenoidal inductor in the form of a circular cylinder, the centrifugal force tends to increase the radius of the cylinder.   This is described as a pressure exerted on the solenoid by the magnetic field within the solenoid.

To calculate the pressure exerted upon an inductor by the magnetic field within the inductor let us consider a toroidal inductor of circular cross section.   Let r be the radius of a cross section and s the perimeter of the toroid, and let us assume that r is small compared with s.   If we regard the curved surface of the toroid as a continuous conductor and take the inductivity of the medium within to be μ, then the inductance of the toroid is

$$L = \mu \frac{\pi r^2}{s} \qquad (9.19)$$

Let p be the pressure exerted by the magnetic field within the toroid on the conducting surface.   The area of the conducting surface is $2\pi rs$.   If we consider a situation in which the radius r of the toroid increases to $r + dr$, the work done by the pressure of the field on the conductor is

$$p(2\pi rs)\, dr \qquad (9.20)$$

Let us suppose that this increment in the radius of the toroid is made without varying the current I flowing round the toroid.   Application of Eq. (9.11) then shows that

$$p(2\pi rs) = \frac{\partial W}{\partial r} \qquad \text{at constant } I \qquad (9.21)$$

Since the derivative on the right-hand side of this equation is to be carried out for a constant value of the current I flowing round the toroid, it is important to express the magnetic energy stored in the toroid entirely in terms of I and not in terms of the magnetic flux threading the toroid. We therefore select the second of the three expressions for the magnetic energy W in Eqs. (8.7) and write

$$W = \tfrac{1}{2}LI^2 \qquad (9.22)$$

Substituting for L from Eq. (9.19) into Eq. (9.22) we obtain

$$W = \tfrac{1}{2}\mu \frac{\pi r^2}{s} I^2 \qquad (9.23)$$

To evaluate the derivative of the right-hand side of Eq. (9.21) we must differentiate expression (9.23) with respect to r regarding I as a constant. Equation (9.21) therefore becomes

$$p(2\pi r s) = \mu \frac{\pi r}{s} I^2 \tag{9.24}$$

or

$$p = \tfrac{1}{2}\mu \left(\frac{I}{s}\right)^2 \tag{9.25}$$

The expression I/s appearing on the right-hand side of this equation is the current per unit length flowing round the toroid and is therefore equal to the magnetic field strength H within the toroid. Equation (9.25) can therefore be written as

$$p = \tfrac{1}{2}\mu H^2 \tag{9.26}$$

Moreover, since the inductivity μ of the medium is the ratio of the magnetic flux density B to the magnetic field strength H within the inductor, Eq. (9.26) can also be written as

$$p = \tfrac{1}{2}HB \tag{9.27}$$

We therefore see that the pressure exerted by the magnetic field within the toroid upon the conductor of the toroid is given by any of the equivalent expressions

$$\tfrac{1}{2}HB = \tfrac{1}{2}\mu H^2 = \frac{1}{2\mu} B^2 \tag{9.28}$$

As a numerical example, let us suppose that the inductivity of the medium within the toroid is that appropriate to a vacuum, that the perimeter of the toroid is 10 cm (10^{-1} m), and that the total current flowing round the curved surface of the toroid is 1 amp. The magnetic field strength within the toroid is then 10 amp/m, and the second of the expressions (9.28) shows that the pressure exerted by the magnetic field within the toroid upon the conducting surface of the toroid is 63 μnewtons/m^2.

The appearance of the factor $\tfrac{1}{2}$ in expression (9.27) is worthy of comment. Since H is the current per unit length flowing round the toroid and B is the magnetic flux density just inside the toroid, it might be asked why the force per unit area on the conductor cannot be calculated from expression (9.1), leading to a pressure HB. It should be noted, however, that, while B is the magnetic flux density just inside the toroid, the magnetic flux density just outside the toroid is zero. Expression (9.27) shows that, to obtain the force per unit area on the conductor, the current per unit length H has to be multiplied by the mean of the magnetic flux density B just inside the toroid and the zero magnetic flux density just outside the toroid.

9.5. Sideways Pressure of Tubes of Magnetic Flux. Expressions (9.28) have been shown to give the pressure on the wall of a toroidal inductor within which the magnetic field strength is H and the magnetic flux density is B. The same statement applies to a solenoidal inductor provided that steps are taken to avoid nonuniformity of the magnetic field within the solenoid, as illustrated in Part 3, Fig. 5.1. In fact, the solenoid may be regarded as a short section of a toroid of small curvature. We have seen that any magnetic field can be subdivided into building blocks, each of which may be thought of as an ideal solenoidal inductor. In this way we see that the pressure on the bounding conductor of any magnetic field can be calculated from expressions (9.28), where H and B are the magnetic field strength and the magnetic flux density close to the bounding surface. This follows from the fact that the pressure on the bounding surface is simply the pressure in the ideal solenoidal building blocks immediately adjacent to the bounding surface. We thus see that, when a conducting surface carrying current forms the boundary of a magnetic field, the surface is subject to pressure from the magnetic field. Moreover, at a point of the surface close to which the magnetic field strength is H and the magnetic flux density is B, the pressure on the bounding surface is given by any of the equivalent expressions (9.28). By evaluating this pressure all over the surface of the bounding conductor and summing the contributions vectorially, we arrive at the total force on the bounding conductor. This result is frequently expressed by saying that the tubes of magnetic flux lying along the bounding conductor are exerting a pressure on the conductor and that the total force on the bounding conductor is the vector sum of the pressures exerted by all the tubes of magnetic flux lying along the bounding conductor.

By use of Part 3, Sec. 3.7, the concept of tubes of magnetic flux exerting pressure on conductors may be extended by saying that tubes of magnetic flux exert a sideways pressure on each other given by expressions (9.28). The forces of magnetic origin exerted on electric circuits may then be regarded as the consequence of the sideways pressure exerted by the tubes of magnetic flux on each other.

9.6. Tension in Tubes of Magnetic Flux. Consider a toroidal inductor of normal cross-sectional area S and perimeter s, and let μ be the inductivity of the medium within the toroid. Let the curved surface of the toroid be a continuous conductor, so that the inductance of the toroid is

$$L = \frac{\mu S}{s} \qquad \text{`} \qquad (9.29)$$

Let us now consider a situation in which the perimeter of the toroid is increased from s to $s + ds$. We suppose that the conductor forming the toroid is sufficiently elastic to permit this displacement. Moreover, we neglect the force required to stress the conductor itself and concentrate our attention on the forces of magnetic origin that are associated with the current round the inductor.   To increase the perimeter from s to $s + ds$ let the required force of magnetic origin be F.   If W is the energy stored in the toroid, then it follows from Eq. (9.11) that

$$F = \frac{\partial W}{\partial s} \quad \text{at constant } I \tag{9.30}$$

To use this formula we express the energy W stored in the toroid entirely in terms of the current I flowing round the toroid and not in terms of the magnetic flux threading the toroid.   In other words, we write

$$W = \tfrac{1}{2}LI^2 \tag{9.31}$$

where the inductance L of the toroid is given by Eq. (9.29).   Substitution for L from Eq. (9.29) into Eq. (9.31) gives for the energy stored in the toroid

$$W = \frac{1}{2}\frac{\mu S}{s} I^2 \tag{9.32}$$

Substitution for W from Eq. (9.32) into Eq. (9.30) gives

$$F = -\frac{1}{2}\frac{\mu S}{s^2} I^2 \tag{9.33}$$

This equation can be rewritten in the form

$$\frac{F}{S} = -\tfrac{1}{2}\mu \left(\frac{I}{s}\right)^2 \tag{9.34}$$

The quantity I/s appearing on the right-hand side of this equation is the current per unit length flowing round the curved surface of the toroid and is consequently the magnetic field strength H within the toroid.   In terms of H, Eq. (9.34) can therefore be written as

$$\frac{F}{S} = -\tfrac{1}{2}\mu H^2 \tag{9.35}$$

This equation shows that, in expanding the perimeter of the toroid from s to $s + ds$, a force is required on account of the magnetic field associated with the toroid in addition to that required to stress the metal.   For a given magnetic field strength H within the toroid Eq. (9.35) shows that the force F is proportional to the cross-sectional area S of the toroid. Moreover, the negative sign in Eq. (9.35) shows that this force is in the nature of a tension.   The information contained in Eq. (9.35) is described by saying that the tubes of magnetic flux threading the toroid are in tension and the tension per unit area is $\tfrac{1}{2}\mu H^2$.   This tension per unit area can be expressed in any of the equivalent forms

$$\tfrac{1}{2}HB = \tfrac{1}{2}\mu H^2 = \frac{1}{2\mu} B^2 \qquad (9.36)$$

By dissecting any magnetic field into ideal solenoidal building blocks we see that tubes of magnetic flux are in tension and that, at a point in a magnetic field where the magnetic field strength is H and the magnetic flux density is B, the tension per unit area is given by any of the equivalent expressions (9.36).

We notice that expressions (9.36) for the tension per unit area of tubes of magnetic flux are identical with the expressions (9.28) for the sideways pressure exerted by tubes of magnetic flux and also with the expressions (8.41) for the magnetic energy stored per unit volume.

9.7. The Pull of a Magnet.   To illustrate the phenomenon of tension in tubes of magnetic flux, let us consider the pull exerted by a magnet.   Figure 9.1 illustrates a horseshoe magnet with an armature placed in close proximity to the pole faces.   The armature is supposed to be made of soft iron, while the horseshoe magnet may be either a permanent magnet or an electromagnet.   Let the pole faces of the magnet be of area S, large compared with the separation a between the pole faces and the armature.   The horseshoe magnet and the armature, together with the narrow gaps separating them, constitute a magnetic circuit, the properties of which may be discussed by the methods described in Part 3, Chap. 8.   In particular a calculation can be made of the total magnetic flux Φ passing round the magnetic circuit.

FIG. 9.1. A horseshoe magnet and soft-iron armature.

The tubes of magnetic flux passing round the magnetic circuit are in tension in the manner described in the preceding section.   This tension is a convenient way of visualizing the magnetic attraction that exists between the magnet and the armature.   Moreover, a calculation of the force of attraction between the horseshoe magnet and the armature is conveniently made by means of an application of the expressions (9.36) for the tension per unit area of the tubes.   If the total magnetic flux Φ passing round the magnetic circuit has been calculated by the methods described in Part 3, Chap. 8, the magnetic flux density in the gaps between the magnet and the armature is

$$B = \frac{\Phi}{S} \qquad (9.37)$$

Taking the inductivity in the gaps to be the vacuum inductivity μ_v, it follows from the third of expressions (9.36) that the tension per unit area of the tubes of magnetic flux crossing the gaps is

$$\frac{1}{2\mu_v}\left(\frac{\Phi}{S}\right)^2 \tag{9.38}$$

At each pole face this tension per unit area is applied across an area S, giving a total force between a pole face and the armature equal to

$$\frac{1}{2\mu_v}\left(\frac{\Phi}{S}\right)^2 S \tag{9.39}$$

Allowing for both pole faces, we see that the total force of attraction between the magnet and the armature is

$$F = \frac{\Phi^2}{\mu_v S} \tag{9.40}$$

Calculation of the force of attraction between the magnet and the armature therefore reduces to a calculation of the magnetic flux Φ passing round the magnetic circuit.

Let us suppose that the magnet is an electromagnet formed by a horseshoe of soft iron wound with n turns of wire each carrying a current I. The total reluctance R of the magnetic circuit is obtained by adding the reluctance of the magnet, the reluctance of the armature, and the reluctances of the two gaps. The magnetic flux passing round the magnetic circuit is then given by

$$\Phi = \frac{nI}{R} \tag{9.41}$$

Substituting this value for Φ into Eq. (9.40), we obtain for the force of attraction between the electromagnet and the armature

$$F = \frac{n^2 I^2}{\mu_v S R^2} \tag{9.42}$$

As described in Part 3, Sec. 8.9, the reluctance of either gap is

$$\frac{a}{\mu_v S} \tag{9.43}$$

If we assume that the reluctance of the soft iron is small compared with the reluctance of the two gaps, we can write for the total reluctance of the magnetic circuit

$$R = \frac{2a}{\mu_v S} \tag{9.44}$$

Substituting for R from Eq. (9.44) into Eq. (9.42), we obtain for the force of attraction between the electromagnet and the armature

$$F = \frac{\mu_v S n^2 I^2}{4a^2} \tag{9.45}$$

We can arrive at Eq. (9.45) alternatively as follows: The total current threading the magnetic circuit is nI, and this is therefore the total drop in magnetic scalar potential in passing round the magnetic circuit. If we neglect the reluctance of the soft iron in comparison with that of the gaps, the drop in magnetic scalar potential nI round the circuit is developed entirely across the gaps. The magnetic scalar potential across each gap is therefore $\frac{1}{2}nI$, and the magnetic field strength in each gap is

$$H = \frac{nI}{2a} \tag{9.46}$$

Using this value for H in the second of the expressions (9.36), we obtain for the tension per unit area of the tubes of magnetic flux crossing the gap

$$\tfrac{1}{2}\mu_v \left(\frac{nI}{2a}\right)^2 \tag{9.47}$$

Multiplying this tension per unit area by the area S of a pole face and multiplying by 2 to allow for both pole faces, we again arrive at Eq. (9.45).

Equation (9.45) shows that the force of attraction between the electromagnet and the armature is proportional to the square of the total current nI threading the magnetic circuit. The force is also proportional to the area S of a pole face and increases as the width a of the gaps decreases. The force of attraction does not, however, increase indefinitely as a decreases because Eq. (9.45) is based upon the assumption that the total reluctance of the magnetic circuit is controlled by the reluctance of the gaps. To the right-hand side of Eq. (9.44) should be added the reluctance of the soft iron, and this dominates the total reluctance of the magnetic circuit if the gap width a becomes extremely small. With the armature in contact with the electromagnet, the value of R in Eq. (9.42) is the reluctance of the soft iron.

If the coil of the electromagnet is wound with wire of resistance r per unit length and the length per turn is l, then it follows from Ohm's law that the voltage required to drive the current I through the winding is

$$V = nlrI \tag{9.48}$$

Substitution for I in terms of V from Eq. (9.48) into Eq. (9.45) gives

$$F = \frac{\mu_v S V^2}{4a^2 l^2 r^2} \tag{9.49}$$

We thus see that, for a wire possessing a given resistance r per unit length, the force of attraction between the electromagnet and the armature is proportional to the square of the voltage V applied to the winding and is independent of the number n of turns on the winding. As described in Part 3, Sec. 5.12, this is because an increase in the number of turns increases the resistance of the coil and therefore decreases the current round each turn; the total current threading the magnetic circuit is thus independent of the number of turns. However, the number of turns used in the winding affects the power P dissipated in the coil. The power is

$$P = \frac{V^2}{nlr} \tag{9.50}$$

This equation determines the minimum number of turns that can be used to keep the power dissipated in the winding less than a prescribed value.

Let us solve Eq. (9.49) for the resistance r of the wire per unit length and Eq. (9.50) for the number n of turns in the winding. We thus obtain

$$r = \frac{V}{2al}\left(\frac{\mu_v S}{F}\right)^{1/2} \tag{9.51}$$

$$n = \frac{V^2}{lrP} \tag{9.52}$$

If the force of attraction F, the voltage V, and the geometrical dimensions of the arrangement are specified, Eq. (9.51) gives the resistance per unit length that the wire must have and hence the size of the wire to be used. Moreover, if the maximum power P to be dissipated in the coil is specified, Eq. (9.52) gives the minimum number of turns that may be used.

As a numerical illustration, let us suppose that the gap width a between the electromagnet and the armature is 1 mm (10^{-3} m) and the area S of each pole face is 1 cm^2 (10^{-4} m^2). Let us suppose that the force F of attraction between the electromagnet and the armature is to be 1 newton and that this is to be provided with a voltage V of 10 volts applied in the winding of the electromagnet. If the length l of each turn of the winding is 5 cm (5×10^{-2} m), Eq. (9.51) shows that the resistance r per unit length of the wire must be about 1.1 ohms/m. From this information the wire size may be determined from a table of wire gauges. It then follows from Eq. (9.52) that, if the power dissipated in the winding is to be less than 1 watt, the number of turns must exceed about 1,800.

9.8. The Parallelism between Electric and Magnetic Energy. From the discussion of magnetic energy and of forces of magnetic origin given in this chapter and the preceding chapter it is clear that there is a close parallelism with the corresponding discussion of electric energy and of forces of electric origin in Part 1, Chaps. 8 to 10. As explained in Part 3, Sec. 4.5, the parallelism between electric and magnetic phenomena is of two types, one being a parallelism in physical significance and the other a parallelism in the manner in which the quantities handle mathematically. For example, the electric vector $\mathbf{E}$ corresponds to the magnetic-flux-density vector $\mathbf{B}$ in the sense that both describe the way in which force is exerted. On the other hand, the electric vector $\mathbf{E}$ corresponds to the magnetic vector $\mathbf{H}$ in the sense that the properties of both involve circulation laws. The parallelism that exists between the treatments of electric and magnetic energy is one that involves a parallelism of the way in which the quantities are handled mathematically. This parallelism is summarized in Table 9.1:

TABLE 9.1. PARALLELISM BETWEEN CONCEPTS INVOLVING ELECTRIC AND MAGNETIC ENERGY

Electric feature	Magnetic feature
Voltage V of conductor..................	Current I round circuit
Electric charge Q on conductor............	Magnetic flux Φ through circuit
Capacitance C..........................	Inductance L
Electric energy W_e......................	Magnetic energy W_m
$W_e = \tfrac{1}{2}VQ = \tfrac{1}{2}CV^2 = \dfrac{1}{2C}Q^2$...........	$W_m = \tfrac{1}{2}I\Phi = \tfrac{1}{2}LI^2 = \dfrac{1}{2L}\Phi^2$
Electric field strength E..................	Magnetic field strength H
Electric flux density D...................	Magnetic flux density B
Capacitivity ϵ..........................	Inductivity μ
Electric energy w_e per unit volume.........	Magnetic energy w_m per unit volume
$w_e = \tfrac{1}{2}ED = \tfrac{1}{2}\epsilon E^2 = \dfrac{1}{2\epsilon}D^2$..............	$w_m = \tfrac{1}{2}HB = \tfrac{1}{2}\mu H^2 = \dfrac{1}{2\mu}B^2$
Sideways pressure of tubes $= \tfrac{1}{2}ED$.......	Sideways pressure of tubes $= \tfrac{1}{2}HB$
Tension of tubes $= \tfrac{1}{2}ED$ per unit area.....	Tension of tubes $= \tfrac{1}{2}HB$ per unit area

The parallelism indicated in Table 9.1 between electric and magnetic energy should not obscure the fact that electric energy is potential in character whereas magnetic energy is kinetic in character, as discussed in Chap. 7.

SUMMARIZING EXERCISES

9.1. For a system of inductors carrying steady currents, explain how the principle of virtual work can be used for calculating the force acting on a particular inductor. If W is the magnetic energy of the system, show that the force tending to increase a coordinate x is $-dW/dx$ if the magnetic fluxes threading the circuits are kept constant but is $+dW/dx$ if the currents in the circuits are kept constant.

9.2. The primary and secondary windings of a transformer exist in parallel planes whose distance apart is x. The coefficient of mutual inductance between the windings is L_{12}. If there is a current I_1 in the primary winding and a current I_2 in the secondary winding, show that the force tending to increase x is

$$\frac{\partial L_{12}}{\partial x} I_1 I_2$$

9.3. In the previous exercise suppose that one of the windings is capable of rotating about an axis and that the position of the winding is specified by means of an angular coordinate θ measured round the axis. Explain how to calculate the torque tending to increase θ.

9.4. A thin toroidal inductor has perimeter of length s and an axial cross section that is circular. The radius of the cross section is r, and r is small compared with s. Current flows toroidally round the curved surface, uniformly distributed along the perimeter, and produces within the toroid a magnetic field strength H and a magnetic flux density B. Prove that the magnetic field within the toroid tends to increase r and that the sideways pressure exerted by the magnetic field in the toroid is equal to $\frac{1}{2}HB$.

9.5. Explain what is meant by the statement that tubes of magnetic flux exert sideways pressure on each other. Explain why, at a point where the magnetic field strength is H and the magnetic flux density is B, the sideways pressure exerted by a tube of magnetic flux is $\frac{1}{2}HB$.

9.6. Explain what is meant by the statement that tubes of magnetic flux are in tension. Show that, at a point where the magnetic field strength is H and the magnetic flux density is B, the tension in a tube of magnetic flux is $\frac{1}{2}HB$ per unit area.

9.7. A horseshoe magnet is provided with a soft-iron armature as shown in Fig. 9.1. Explain the force of attraction between the magnet and the armature in terms of the tension in the tubes of magnetic flux. Explain how to calculate this force of attraction by first calculating the tension per unit area in the tubes of magnetic flux.

9.8. It is sometimes said that there is an exact parallelism between the concepts of electric and magnetic energy. Discuss this statement.

CHAPTER 10

FLOW OF ENERGY INTO AND OUT OF INDUCTORS

10.1. Introduction. In Sec. 7.6 we saw that, if a battery is connected across an inductor, energy flows from the battery into the inductor. Furthermore we saw in Sec. 8.5 that the magnetic energy acquired by the inductor in this way is distributed throughout the magnetic field of the inductor. Let us now investigate how the energy flows from the battery into the inductor and becomes distributed throughout the magnetic field. A similar investigation of the flow of energy involved in charging a capacitor was made in Secs. 1.7 and 1.8.

10.2. Flow of Energy into an Inductor Formed by a Strip Transmission Line. Let us form an inductor by taking a length of strip transmission

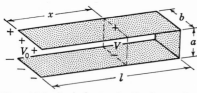

FIG. 10.1. An inductor in the form of a length of strip transmission line short-circuited at one end.

line as shown in Fig. 1.1 and short-circuiting one end as shown in Fig. 10.1. Such an inductor thus consists of a perfectly conducting strip of breadth b and total length $2l + a$, bent as shown in Fig. 10.1. A battery of voltage V_0 is connected across the inductor at the left-hand end, and we assume that the voltage V_0 is applied uniformly across the width of the strip. Nonuniformity of the magnetic field in the inductor is either neglected or avoided by a device such as that shown in Fig. 1.2.

Since resistance of the circuit is being neglected, Faraday's law of induction requires that application of a constant voltage V_0 to the inductor results in the magnetic flux threading the inductor increasing linearly with time t at the rate V_0. This situation was described in Sec. 5.2 and is represented by Eq. (5.1). If we suppose that the magnetic flux threading the inductor is zero at time zero, then the magnetic flux threading the inductor at time t is

$$V_0 t \tag{10.1}$$

For the strip transmission line formed by the upper and lower strips in Fig. 10.1, the inductance per unit length is given by Eq. (1.6) and the total inductance of the inductor by expression (1.3). By dividing this

710

inductance into the magnetic flux given in expression (10.1), it follows
that the current round the inductor at time t is

$$I = \frac{bV_0}{\mu a l} t \tag{10.2}$$

The current round the inductor therefore increases linearly with time t
as shown in Fig. 10.2a, while the voltage driving the current remains constant as shown in Fig. 10.2b.

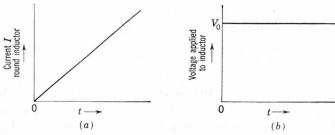

(a)   (b)

Fig. 10.2. Illustrating, for the inductor shown in Fig. 10.1, the variation with time of
(a) the current I round the inductor and (b) the voltage applied to the inductor at
the left-hand end.

Magnetic energy is stored by the inductor principally in the volume
between the strips.   At time t the magnetic energy stored per unit length
of the transmission line is

$$W = \tfrac{1}{2}LI^2 \tag{10.3}$$

where the inductance per unit length L of the line is given by Eq. (1.6)
and the current I round the inductor is given by Eq. (10.2).   Substitution
of these values into Eq. (10.3) gives

$$W = \frac{bV_0^2}{2\mu a l^2} t^2 \tag{10.4}$$

The length of the transmission line forming the inductor being l, the total
magnetic energy stored in the inductor is obtained by multiplying the
expression on the right-hand side of Eq. (10.4) by l and is therefore

$$\frac{bV_0^2}{2\mu a l} t^2 \tag{10.5}$$

This expression for the total magnetic energy stored in the inductor can
also be obtained by taking, in accordance with Eq. (8.6), one-half the
product of the current round the inductor given by Eq. (10.2) and the
magnetic flux threading the inductor given by expression (10.1).   Expression (10.5) shows that the magnetic energy stored in the inductor is
increasing proportionally to the square of time.   The rate at which it is

increasing at time t is obtained by differentiating expression (10.5) with respect to t and is therefore

$$\frac{bV_0^2}{\mu al}t \tag{10.6}$$

Thus the rate at which the inductor is storing magnetic energy is itself increasing linearly with time.

The rate at which energy is flowing into the inductor from the battery is

$$P_0 = V_0 I \tag{10.7}$$

Substitution into this equation for I from Eq. (10.2) gives

$$P_0 = \frac{bV_0^2}{\mu al}t \tag{10.8}$$

The equality of expression (10.6) and the expression on the right-hand side of Eq. (10.8) verifies the fact that the rate at which the magnetic energy in the inductor is increasing is equal to the rate at which it is flowing in from the battery.

While the voltage between the strips of the transmission line at the left-hand end in Fig. 10.1 is V_0, that between the strips at the right-hand end is zero. The voltage between the strips therefore decreases from V_0 at the left-hand end to zero at the right-hand end. Let V be the voltage between the strips at distance x from the left-hand end. The voltage V is associated with the supply of magnetic energy to that part of the inductor lying to the right of the normal cross section at position x. The magnetic flux threading that part of the inductor beyond this cross section is the fraction $(l - x)/l$ of the total magnetic flux threading the inductor and given by expression (10.1). The magnetic flux threading the inductor beyond the normal cross section of the transmission line at position x is therefore

$$\frac{l - x}{l}V_0 t \tag{10.9}$$

It is with the rate of increase of this magnetic flux that the voltage V between the strips at position x is associated. By Faraday's law of induction the time rate of increase of the magnetic flux given by expression (10.9) is equal to the voltage V between the strips at position x. Hence

$$V = \frac{l - x}{l}V_0 \tag{10.10}$$

This equation shows that the voltage between the strips of the transmission line decreases linearly from V_0 at the left-hand end in Fig. 10.1 to zero at the right-hand end as shown in Fig. 10.3b. The current along the strips is, however, given by Eq. (10.2) and remains constant along the transmission line as shown in Fig. 10.3a. Comparison of Figs. 10.2 and 10.3 shows that, while the current along the strips is independent of distance along the transmission line, the current increases linearly with time as the inductor receives magnetic energy. On the other hand, while the voltage existing between the strips does not vary with time, it decreases linearly along the transmission line to zero at the far end.

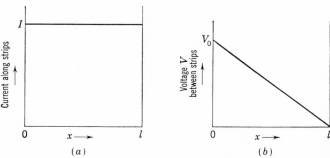

FIG. 10.3. Illustrating, for the strip transmission line shown in Fig. 10.1, the variation with distance x from the battery of (a) the current I along the strips and (b) the voltage V between the strips.

The power supplied to the portion of the transmission line beyond the normal cross section at position x is

$$P = VI \tag{10.11}$$

where the voltage V is given by Eq. (10.10) and the current I is given by Eq. (10.2). Substitution for V from Eq. (10.10) into Eq. (10.11) gives

$$P = \frac{l - x}{l} P_0 \tag{10.12}$$

where P_0 is the power supplied by the battery and given by Eq. (10.7). Equation (10.12) shows that the rate at which energy passes a normal cross section of the transmission line decreases linearly from P_0 at the left-hand end in Fig. 10.1 to zero at the right-hand end as shown in Fig. 10.4a. Substitution for P_0 from Eq. (10.8) into Eq. (10.12) gives

$$P = \frac{l - x}{l} \frac{b V_0^2}{\mu a l} t \tag{10.13}$$

This equation shows that the rate at which energy is passing any particular cross section of the transmission line increases linearly with time t as shown in Fig. 10.4b. Thus the power passing a cross section of the transmission line increases linearly with time, but decreases linearly with distance along the transmission line to zero at the far end.

The magnetic energy stored in the inductor beyond the normal cross section at position x is the fraction $(l - x)/l$ of the total magnetic energy stored in the inductor and given by expression (10.5). The magnetic energy stored in the inductor beyond position x is therefore

$$\frac{l - x}{l} \frac{bV_0^2}{2\mu al} t^2 \tag{10.14}$$

and it increases with time at the rate

$$\frac{l - x}{l} \frac{bV_0^2}{\mu al} t \tag{10.15}$$

Comparison of the expression on the right-hand side of Eq. (10.13) with expression (10.15) shows that the power passing any normal cross section

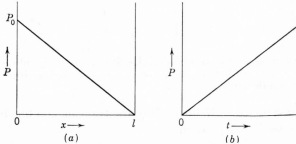

(a) (b)

Fig. 10.4. Illustrating, for the transmission line shown in Fig. 10.1, the variation in the rate of flow of energy past a normal cross section (a) as a function of distance x along the line and (b) as a function of time t.

of the transmission line is that required to provide the rate of increase of the magnetic energy stored in the inductor beyond that normal cross section.

The relation between the flow of energy and the storage of energy may also be described as follows. Consider two normal cross sections of the transmission line at positions x and $x + dx$. At time t the magnetic energy stored per unit length of the line is W, given by Eq. (10.4). The differential magnetic energy stored between the cross sections at x and $x + dx$ is therefore $W\, dx$. The time rate of increase of the differential magnetic energy stored in the space between the two cross sections is therefore

$$dx \frac{dW}{dt} \tag{10.16}$$

This rate of increase of the stored magnetic energy is occurring because the rate of flow of energy across the normal cross section at position $x + dx$ is less than that for the normal cross section at position x. Let the rate of flow of energy through the cross section at position $x + dx$ be less than that through the cross section at position x by the differential amount

$$-dP \qquad (10.17)$$

Equating expression (10.17) for the net rate of inflow of energy into the portion of the transmission line between the cross sections at x and $x + dx$ to the time rate of increase of the stored magnetic energy in this portion of the transmission line given by expression (10.16), we obtain

$$-dP = dx\,\frac{dW}{dt}$$

or

$$-\frac{\partial P}{\partial x} = \frac{dW}{dt} \qquad (10.18)$$

A partial derivative has been shown on the left-hand side of this equation because, as shown in Fig. 10.4, P is a function of both x and t, and the derivative on the left-hand side of Eq. (10.18) implies the rate of decrease of P with x at constant t.   On the right-hand side of Eq. (10.18) the magnetic energy per unit length W stored in the inductor is a function of t only in accordance with Eq. (10.4).   Equation (10.18) expresses the fact that the stored magnetic energy per unit length of the line is increasing with time because, in unit time, more energy is entering the unit length from the portion of the transmission line connecting it to the battery than is flowing out to the remainder of the inductor.   We have already calculated the expression for P in Eq. (10.13) and for W in Eq. (10.4).   By substituting these expressions for P and W into the left- and right-hand sides of Eq. (10.18), we can verify the truth of the equation.

10.3. Use of the Poynting Vector to Describe the Flow of Energy into an Inductor.   As described in Sec. 8.5, the total magnetic energy (10.5) stored in the inductor is to be thought of as distributed throughout the magnetic field, and this means primarily throughout the volume between the strips of the inductor shown in Fig. 10.1.   The magnetic energy per unit volume w stored within the inductor shown in Fig. 10.1 is therefore obtained by dividing expression (10.5) by the volume abl of the inductor.   The stored magnetic energy per unit volume is therefore

$$w = \frac{V_0{}^2}{2\mu a^2 l^2}\,t^2 \qquad (10.19)$$

To visualize the way in which the magnetic energy becomes distributed throughout the volume of the inductor in this way, we make use of the Poynting vector defined by expression (1.31).

At any normal cross section of the transmission line shown in Fig. 10.1, the electric vector **E** is as shown in Fig. 1.3a and the magnetic vector **H** is as shown in Fig. 1.3b. This figure represents the electromagnetic field in the transmission line looking along the line away from the battery. It is in this direction therefore that the Poynting vector **E** ⨯ **H** is directed. In terms of the Poynting vector, let us see how the magnetic energy becomes stored in the inductor throughout its magnetic field.

The electromagnetic field between the strips of the transmission line shown in Fig. 10.1 can be calculated as follows: The magnetic flux density B is obtained by dividing the total magnetic flux threading the inductor given by expression (10.1) by the cross-sectional area al of the inductor. We deduce that

$$B = \frac{V_0}{al} t \tag{10.20}$$

The electric field strength E and the magnetic field strength H between the strips are obtained by substituting for V and I from Eqs. (10.10) and (10.2) into Eqs. (1.7) and (1.8). We obtain

$$E = \frac{l - x}{l} \frac{V_0}{a} \tag{10.21}$$

$$H = \frac{V_0}{\mu al} t \tag{10.22}$$

Equation (10.22) can also be obtained by dividing the expression for the magnetic flux density given in Eq. (10.20) by the inductivity μ of the medium between the strips. Also, since the magnetic energy stored per

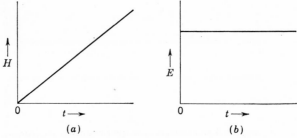

Fig. 10.5. Illustrating, for the arrangement shown in Fig. 10.1, the variation with time t of (a) the magnetic field strength and (b) the electric field strength.

unit volume is $\frac{1}{2}HB$, we can verify from Eqs. (10.22) and (10.20) the truth of Eq. (10.19). Equations (10.21) and (10.22) show that the electric and magnetic field strengths between the strips vary with time t as shown in Fig. 10.5 and with distance x along the transmission line as shown in Fig. 10.6. Figures 10.5 and 10.6 are to be compared with Figs. 10.2 and 10.3 respectively in the light of Eqs. (1.7) and (1.8). The magnetic and electric fields between the strips are also illustrated in Fig. 10.7a and b, respectively.

If we dissect the electromagnetic field of the transmission line into unit channels as described in connection with Fig. 1.6, the voltage and current associated with each unit channel are given by Eqs. (10.21) and (10.22), and they vary with time t and distance x along the transmission line as

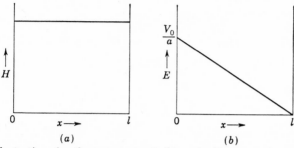

FIG. 10.6. Illustrating, for the arrangement shown in Fig. 10.1, the variation with distance x along the transmission line of (a) the magnetic field strength and (b) the electric field strength.

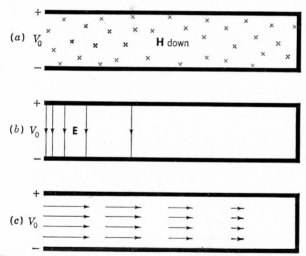

FIG. 10.7. Illustrating, for the arrangement shown in Fig. 10.1, (a) the magnetic field, (b) the electric field, and (c) the flow of energy along the transmission line.

shown in Figs. 10.5 and 10.6. The rate of flow of energy along each unit channel is

$$p = EH \qquad (10.23)$$

and this is the magnitude of the Poynting vector **E** ✕ **H**. Substituting for E and H from Eqs. (10.21) and (10.22) into Eq. (10.23), we obtain

$$p = \frac{l - x}{l} \frac{V_0{}^2}{\mu a^2 l} t \qquad (10.24)$$

The variations of the rate of flow of energy along a unit channel with distance x along the transmission line and with time t are therefore as shown in Fig. 10.8, which is to be compared with Fig. 10.4.

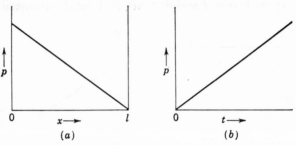

(a)   (b)

FIG. 10.8. Illustrating, for the arrangement shown in Fig. 10.1, the flow of energy per unit area per unit time across a normal cross section of the transmission line (a) as a function of distance x along the line and (b) as a function of time t.

We see from Fig. 10.8a that the flow of energy per unit area per unit time traversing any normal cross section of the transmission line decreases linearly as we move along the transmission line to zero at the far end. For a unit channel Eq. (10.18) becomes

$$-\frac{\partial p}{\partial x} = \frac{dw}{dt}$$ (10.25)

In the space between the strips of the transmission line, consider a unit cube formed by taking unit length of a unit channel. The magnetic energy stored in such a unit cube at time t is given by Eq. (10.19), and the right-hand side of Eq. (10.25) is the time rate of increase of this energy. The left-hand side of Eq. (10.25) is the amount by which the rate of flow of energy along the unit channel decreases as we move unit distance away from the source. For the unit cube, therefore, the left-hand side of Eq. (10.25) is the excess of the rate of inflow of energy across the face nearest to the battery over the rate of outflow of energy across the face farthest from the battery. Since there is no flow of energy over the other four faces of the cube, Eq. (10.25) expresses the fact that the net rate of inflow of energy into any unit cube between the strips of the transmission line is equal to the rate of increase of the magnetic energy stored in the unit cube. We thus see that, for the arrangement shown in Fig. 10.1, there is a flow of energy in the space between the strips that decreases to zero at the far end as indicated in Fig. 10.7c. The decreasing flow of energy as we move along the line results in accumulation of magnetic energy in the volume between the strips, and the energy per unit volume increases with time t in the manner described by Eq. (10.19).

The tubes of magnetic flux in the transmission line illustrated in Fig. 10.1 run perpendicularly across from one open edge of the line to the other.

Between these tubes of magnetic flux there is a sideways pressure as described in the previous chapter. The pressure is identical in value with the magnetic energy per unit volume and is therefore given by the right-hand side of Eq. (10.19). The process of storing energy in the inductor therefore involves a situation in which the sideways pressure between the tubes of magnetic flux increases proportionally to the square of time. The process may be described by saying that the battery compresses the tubes of magnetic flux into the space within the inductor. This increases the magnetic energy per unit volume in the inductor and causes a flow of energy that decreases linearly to zero at the far end of the inductor as shown in Fig. 10.7c.

It is to be noticed from Fig. 10.5 that, whereas the magnetic field strength in the inductor increases linearly with time, the electric field strength remains constant. It follows that the magnetic field soon becomes the dominant feature of the electromagnetic field in the inductor. If the process of storing energy in the inductor ceases at any time, the electric field strength in the inductor completely disappears, leaving only the magnetic field.   On the other hand it is to be noticed that the presence of an electric field in the inductor during the process of storing magnetic energy is essential to the process whereby energy is packed into the inductor.   Without an electric field, the Poynting vector would be zero and no flow of energy into the inductor could take place.   Thus it is an essential feature of the process of storing energy in the inductor that the battery providing the energy should form a fringe of electric field extending into the inductor as described by Fig. 10.6b and illustrated in Fig. 10.7b.

10.4. Flow of Energy into Inductors of Various Shapes.   The way in which the flow of energy along a strip transmission line is modified in the case of a coaxial transmission line has been described in Sec. 1.9. Figure 10.9 represents an axial cross section of a coaxial inductor, between the inner and outer conductors of which a battery of voltage V_0 is connected at the left-hand end. Storage of energy in this inductor involves considerations similar to those for the inductor shown

FIG. 10.9. An axial cross section of an inductor formed by short-circuiting a piece of coaxial transmission line at one end.

in Fig. 10.1. As described in Sec. 1.9, the flow of energy hugs the inner conductor, where the electromagnetic field is strong.

The nature of the flow of energy along a twin-wire transmission line has been described in Sec. 1.10.   Figure 10.10 represents a section of a twin-wire transmission line short-circuited at the right-hand end by means of a plate perpendicular to the wires.   If the separation between the wires is small compared with the length, then the short-circuiting plate can be replaced by a short-circuiting wire as described in Part 3, Sec. 5.8.   To an inductor formed by a section of twin-wire transmission line short-circuited at the right-hand end, let a battery of voltage V_0 be applied at the left-hand end.   The resulting flow of energy into the inductor hugs the two wires in the manner described in Sec. 1.10.   The flow of energy is away from the source in the neighborhood of both wires in spite of the fact that the current flows in opposite directions on the wires.

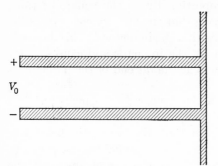

10.5. Flow of Energy into Solenoidal and Toroidal Inductors. Let us now consider a solenoidal inductor formed by taking a rectangular strip of a perfect conductor and bending it into a circular cylindrical form as indicated in

Fig. 10.10. An inductor formed by short-circuiting a piece of twin-wire transmission line at one end.

Fig. 10.11.   Across the unclosed gap of the strip let a steady voltage V_0 be applied uniformly along the gap by means of a battery.   In accordance with Faraday's law of induction, energy flows from the battery into the inductor and is stored in the magnetic field indicated in Fig. 10.11a.

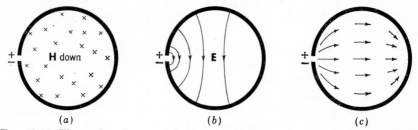

Fig. 10.11. Illustrating, for a continuously conducting solenoidal inductor, (a) the magnetic field within the inductor, (b) the fringing electric field of the voltage source connected to the inductor, and (c) the flow of energy into the inductor.

Analysis of this situation in detail is difficult, but its main features can be seen by regarding the solenoidal inductor illustrated in Fig. 10.11 as a distorted form of the inductor illustrated in Fig. 10.7.   The electric field of the battery fringes into the volume within the inductor as illustrated in Fig. 10.11b.   By combining the electric field illustrated in Fig. 10.11b with the magnetic field illustrated in Fig. 10.11a we can form the Poynting vector $\mathbf{E} \times \mathbf{H}$ and so arrive at the energy flow illustrated in Fig. 10.11c.

Similar statements apply to the perfectly conducting toroidal inductor whose axial cross section is as indicated in Fig. 10.12.   The electromagnetic field in Fig. 10.12 again demonstrates that the process whereby energy is fed into an inductor is one in which the source of voltage creates a fringing electric field extending into the inductor.   This electric field,

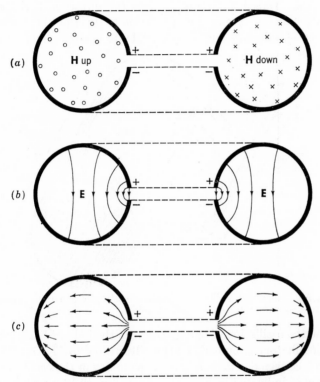

FIG. 10.12. Illustrating, for a continuously conducting toroidal inductor into which a source of voltage is connected, (a) the magnetic field, (b) the electric field, and (c) the energy flow.

combined with the magnetic field of the inductor, produces the flow of energy that packs magnetic energy into the volume within the inductor.

10.6. Flow of Energy in an Oscillatory Electric Circuit.   If the flow of energy into the inductor illustrated in Fig. 10.7 were stopped at a certain stage and the battery were replaced by a resistor, the energy stored in the inductor would flow out again and be converted into heat by the resistor.   In this process the direction of the current would be opposite to that associated with the storage process.   The direction of the magnetic field shown in Fig. 10.7a would therefore be reversed, and this would reverse the directions of the arrows in Fig. 10.7c.   We see therefore that the discussion of energy flow into an inductor given in Secs. 10.2 and 10.3

can easily be adapted to describe flow of energy out of an inductor.   In the same way the process of energy flow into a capacitor illustrated in Fig. 1.17 can easily be adapted to describe the process of energy flow out of a capacitor; if at a certain stage in the charging process the source is replaced by a resistor, the direction of the magnetic field illustrated in Fig. 1.17*b* is reversed, and this reverses the direction of the arrows in Fig. 1.17*c*.   Since we are now in a position to describe the flow of energy into and out of inductors and capacitors, let us combine the two situations

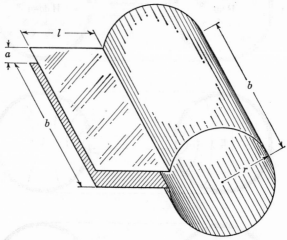

FIG. 10.13. An elementary oscillatory circuit consisting of a parallel-plate capacitor connected to a continuously conducting solenoid.

to describe the oscillation of energy between the inductor and the capacitor of an oscillatory circuit of the type illustrated in Fig. 7.4.

It will be convenient to simplify the geometry of the oscillatory circuit in the manner indicated in Fig. 10.13.   In Fig. 10.13 a rectangular strip of perfectly conducting material of breadth *b* has been bent in such a way as to constitute a solenoid in the form of a circular conducting cylinder to which is connected a parallel-plate capacitor.   To minimize irrelevant fringing phenomena we assume that the radius *r* of the inductor is small compared with its length *b* and that the separation *a* between the plates of the capacitor is small compared with the linear dimensions *b* and *l* of the plates.   Let the inductivity of the medium be μ and the capacitivity be ϵ.   Then the capacitance of the capacitor is

$$C = \epsilon \frac{bl}{a} \tag{10.26}$$

and the inductance of the inductor is

$$L = \mu \frac{\pi r^2}{b} \tag{10.27}$$

It follows from Eq. (7.47) that the periodic time for the oscillatory circuit is

$$T = 2\pi(\mu\epsilon)^{\frac{1}{2}} \left(\frac{\pi r^2 l}{a}\right)^{\frac{1}{2}} \tag{10.28}$$

We notice that, in forming the product of the expressions on the right-hand sides of Eqs. (10.26) and (10.27) to calculate the periodic time given by Eq. (10.28), the dimension b disappears. Thus the periodic time given by Eq. (10.28) does not depend upon the dimension b, provided that this is large compared with r and a. It is, of course, assumed that all the dimensions of the oscillatory circuit satisfy the size limitation discussed in Sec. 5.7 and summarized by the inequality (5.70.)

Let us suppose that, at time zero, there is a voltage across the capacitor and no current round the inductor. Then, as shown in Fig. 7.5, the current round the inductor builds up between time zero and time $\frac{1}{4}T$, while during the same interval the voltage across the capacitor drops to zero. Between time $\frac{1}{4}T$ and time $\frac{1}{2}T$ the flow of charge round the inductor slows down and the voltage of the capacitor builds up with the opposite sign from that existing between time zero and time $\frac{1}{4}T$. At time $\frac{1}{2}T$ the voltage across the capacitor is at an extreme value and the current round the inductor vanishes. Between time $\frac{1}{2}T$ and time $\frac{3}{4}T$ current again builds up round the inductor in the opposite direction from that flowing between time zero and time $\frac{1}{2}T$. The voltage across the capacitor again passes through zero at time $\frac{3}{4}T$, and the original state of affairs is regained at time T. During each succeeding period of duration T the above sequence of events repeats.

The electromagnetic field associated with the oscillatory circuit is obtained by combining that shown for the inductor in Fig. 10.11 with that shown for the capacitor in Fig. 1.17. We thus arrive at the sequence of events presented in Fig. 10.14. Diagrams are shown at intervals of one-eighth of a period. At time zero the electric field in the capacitor has a maximum value, and it fringes into the inductor as shown in Fig. 10.14a. The electric field decreases only slightly from the left-hand edge of the capacitor to the right-hand edge, but it decreases more quickly as we enter the inductor. The electric field vanishes, however, only at the extreme right-hand edge of the inductor. The strength of this electric field weakens between time zero and time $\frac{1}{4}T$ and then reverses direction. Between time $\frac{1}{4}T$ and time $\frac{1}{2}T$ the electric field increases in strength with the opposite direction and reaches a maximum strength at time $\frac{1}{2}T$. After time $\frac{1}{2}T$ the electric field weakens again and reverses direction at time $\frac{3}{4}T$. The electric field regains at time T the same magnitude and direction that it had at time zero.

The magnetic field in the inductor vanishes at time zero, since the current round the inductor vanishes at this time. After time zero the magnetic field increases and reaches a maximum value at time $\frac{1}{4}T$, as shown in Fig. 10.14c. The complete magnetic field is formed by fitting the magnetic field shown in Fig. 10.11a onto the magnetic field shown in Fig. 1.17b. The magnetic field in the inductor in Fig. 10.14c is almost

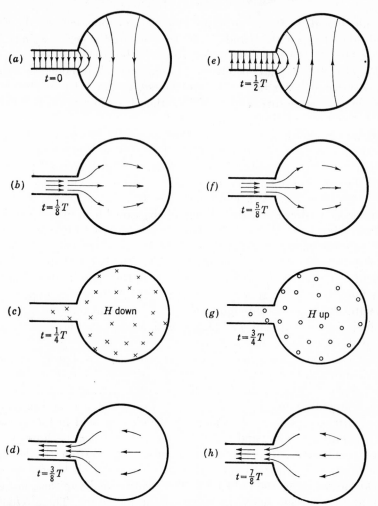

Fig. 10.14. Illustrating the process of oscillation of the oscillatory circuit shown in Fig. 10.13.

uniform; it fringes into the capacitor, vanishing at the left-hand edge of the capacitor. After time $\frac{1}{4}T$ the magnetic field decreases to zero at time $\frac{1}{2}T$, when it reverses in direction. The magnitude of the magnetic field again reaches a maximum value at time $\frac{3}{4}T$ and returns to zero at time T, when the situation is the same as it was at time zero.

At time $\frac{1}{8}T$ the inductor and capacitor contain an electric field of the type indicated in Fig. 10.14a and a magnetic field of the type indicated in Fig. 10.14c.   On forming the Poynting vector $\mathbf{E} \times \mathbf{H}$, we see that, at time $\frac{1}{8}T$, the flow of energy is as indicated in Fig. 10.14b.   The flow is from the capacitor to the inductor, and the maximum flow occurs at the junction between the two.   This flow describes the way in which the electric energy stored principally in the capacitor at time zero is converted into magnetic energy stored principally in the inductor at time $\frac{1}{4}T$.   Between time $\frac{1}{4}T$ and time $\frac{1}{2}T$ the flow of energy is reversed and describes the way in which the magnetic energy stored principally in the inductor at time $\frac{1}{4}T$ is converted into electric energy stored principally in the capacitor at time $\frac{1}{2}T$.   In each succeeding interval of $\frac{1}{2}T$ the oscillation of energy from the capacitor into the inductor and back is repeated.   In alternate half periods the directions of the electric and magnetic fields are reversed, but this does not affect the direction of the Poynting vector $\mathbf{E} \times \mathbf{H}$.

It is particularly to be noticed that the flow of energy back and forth between the capacitor and the inductor depends upon the fact that the electric field of the capacitor fringes into the inductor and the magnetic field of the inductor fringes into the capacitor.   At the junction between the capacitor and the inductor the electric field is substantially the electric field in the capacitor.   When V is the voltage across the capacitor, therefore, the electric field strength at the junction between the capacitor and the inductor may be taken as

$$E = \frac{V}{a} \qquad (10.29)$$

Likewise the magnetic field strength at the junction between the capacitor and the inductor is substantially the magnetic field strength in the inductor.   When I is the current round the inductor, the current per unit width round the inductor is I/b.   Hence the magnetic field strength at the junction between the inductor and the capacitor may be taken as

$$H = \frac{I}{b} \qquad (10.30)$$

From the Poynting vector, the rate of flow of energy per unit area at the junction between the capacitor and the inductor is EH, and this may be considered to be distributed uniformly over an area ab.   Hence the total rate of flow of energy between the capacitor and the inductor is

$$P = (EH)(ab) \qquad (10.31)$$

and substitution into this equation from Eqs. (10.29) and (10.30) gives

$$P = VI \qquad (10.32)$$

Thus the rate of flow of energy between the capacitor and the inductor is obtained by multiplying the voltage of the capacitor by the current through the inductor.   The variation of this power with time is given by Eq. (7.60) and is plotted in Fig. 7.7.

An oscillatory circuit such as that shown in Fig. 10.13 is usually represented in a circuit diagram as shown in Fig. 10.15.   The wires indicated in Fig. 10.15 joining the terminals of the capacitor to the terminals of the inductor correspond in the arrangement shown in Fig. 10.13 to the

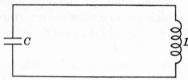

FIG. 10.15. Representation in a circuit diagram of the oscillatory circuit illustrated in Fig. 10.13.

junction between the capacitor and the inductor.   However, oscillatory circuits do not always, or even usually, possess the simple geometry illustrated in Fig. 10.13.   By substituting numerical values into Eq. (10.28) it can be seen that an inductor of the form shown in Fig. 10.13 becomes inconveniently large at frequencies less than about 1,000 Mc/sec, and a multiturn inductor is then required.   When a multiturn inductor is used, the actual physical structure is not radically different from that indicated in the circuit diagram of Fig. 10.15.   The pair of wires joining the terminals of the capacitor to the terminals of the inductor may then be thought of as a short piece of twin-wire transmission line that behaves in the manner described in Sec. 1.10.   It is the function of this short piece of twin-wire transmission line to permit the electric field of the capacitor to fringe into the inductor and the magnetic field of the inductor to fringe into the capacitor, thereby permitting an interchange of energy between the two devices in the manner described by the Poynting vector. As demonstrated in Sec. 1.10, the total rate of flow of energy along the transmission line at any instant is the product of the voltage between the wires and the current along them, and this corresponds to the product of the voltage across the capacitor and the current through the inductor in agreement with Eq. (10.32).

It is important to notice that, whereas the storage of energy in inductors and capacitors can usually be calculated with reasonable accuracy neglecting the effect of fringing, the opposite is true for energy flow.   Flow of energy between an inductor and a capacitor can be understood only by realizing that the electric field of the capacitor fringes into the magnetic field of the inductor and the magnetic field of the inductor fringes into the electric field of the capacitor.   The process of connecting circuit elements by means of conducting wires to form electric networks is a process of controlled fringing of the field of one element into the field of another. By this technique enormous numbers of practical problems in electrical science are solved, analysis of which constitutes what is known as electric network theory.

SUMMARIZING EXERCISES

10.1. A section of perfectly conducting strip transmission line is short-circuited at one end, thereby forming an inductor. Across the other end is connected a source of constant voltage. Describe the process whereby energy flows from the source into the inductor and is stored as magnetic energy. In particular, show that fringing of the electric field of the source into the inductor is essential to the process of inflow of energy into the inductor.

10.2. In terms of the Poynting vector, describe the process of energy flow in an oscillatory electric circuit. Show that the oscillation of energy between the inductor and the capacitor involves fringing of the magnetic field of the inductor into the capacitor and fringing of the electric field of the capacitor into the inductor.

10.3. Explain why, in an oscillatory electric circuit, storage of energy in the inductor and capacitor can be understood without allowing for fringing whereas flow of energy can be understood only by taking fringing into account.

TABLE OF NUMERICAL VALUES

Mass of proton.................... 1.67×10^{-27} kg
Mass of electron m................. 9.1×10^{-31} kg
Mass of proton/mass of electron..... 1,840
Charge on proton................. 1.60×10^{-19} coulomb
Charge on electron e................ -1.60×10^{-19} coulomb
Charge on proton/mass of proton.... 9.6×10^{7} coulombs/kg
Charge on electron/mass of electron.. -1.76×10^{11} coulombs/kg
Vacuum inductivity:
  μ_v............................. $4\pi \times 10^{-7}$ henry/m, or 1.257×10^{-6} henry/m
  $\mu_v/2\pi$......................... 2×10^{-7} henry/m
  $\mu_v/4\pi$......................... 10^{-7} henry/m
  $1/4\pi\mu_v$........................ 6.332×10^{4} m/henry
Velocity of light in vacuum $1/(\mu_v\epsilon_v)^{1/2}$ 2.998×10^{8} m/sec
Vacuum capacitivity:
  ϵ_v............................. 8.854×10^{-12} farad/m
  $2\pi\epsilon_v$.......................... 5.563×10^{-11} farad/m
  $1/2\pi\epsilon_v$........................ 1.798×10^{10} m/farad
  $4\pi\epsilon_v$.......................... 1.113×10^{-10} farad/m
Constant of electrostatics $1/4\pi\epsilon_v$..... 8.988×10^{9} m/farad
"Radius" of electron $\mu_v e^2/4\pi m$....... 2.8×10^{-15} m
Radius of a molecule............... $\sim 2 \times 10^{-10}$ m
Conductivity of copper............. 5.8×10^{7} mhos/m
Earth's magnetic moment/μ_v........ 8.1×10^{22} amp-m^2
Earth's radius.................... 6.37×10^{6} m

PROBLEMS*

Part 1, Chapter 1

★1. The Moon is at a distance r_1 from the Earth and r_2 from the Sun. Treating the Sun, Earth, and Moon as particles of masses S, E, and M, respectively, calculate the ratio of the Earth's pull on the Moon to the Sun's pull on the Moon. Evaluate this ratio assuming that $E = 6 \times 10^{24}$ kg, $S = 2 \times 10^{30}$ kg, $r_1 = 4 \times 10^5$ km, $r_2 = 1.5 \times 10^8$ km.

★2. Three particles of masses m_1, m_2, and m and charges Q, $-Q$, and zero, respectively, are located in free space at the vertices A, B, and C of an equilateral triangle. Calculate the ratio of the force between the particles at A and B to that between those at B and C. Evaluate this ratio numerically if the particles at A, B, and C are, respectively, a proton, an electron, and a neutron.

★3. A, B, C, D are four consecutive points on a straight line in free space such that $AB = BC = CD = a$. At A and D there are point charges each of strength Q, while at B and C there are point charges each of strength $-Q$. Calculate the electric field strength at C due to the charges at A, B, and D. Deduce the force on the charge at C in magnitude and direction. Evaluate the force in newtons if $a = 1$ m and $Q = 1,000$ $\mu\mu$coulombs.

★4. $ABCD$ is a square of edge a in free space, and point charges of strengths Q, $-Q$, Q, $-Q$ are placed at A, B, C, and D, respectively. Calculate the electric vector at B due to the charges at A, C, and D. Deduce the force on the charge at B in magnitude and direction. If $a = 1$ m and the force on the charge at B is to be 1 newton, find the required value of Q in coulombs.

★5. Two point charges, each of strength Q, are located at the points A and B, and N is the mid-point of AB. Show that N is a neutral point in the electric field at which the electric field strength vanishes and the direction of the electric vector is indeterminate. Sketch the lines of force of the field.

★6. Point charges of strengths Q and $-\frac{1}{4}Q$ are located at the points A and B, respectively, and N is a point on AB produced such that $AB = BN$. Show that N is a neutral point in the field, and sketch the lines of force.

Part 1, Chapter 2

★1. A coil spring is such that the force required to compress it is equal to the product of a constant λ with the distance x of compression. Prove that the work done in compressing the spring to the distance x equals $\frac{1}{2}\lambda x^2$. Describe what is meant by the potential energy W of the spring when compressed, and explain why differentiation of W with respect to x gives the force required to compress the spring to the distance x.

★2. A spring of unusual design is such that its uncompressed length is extremely large and the force required to compress it to length x is A/x^2, where A is a constant. If the spring has been compressed to length x and is now released, show that the energy made available is A/x.

* The simpler problems are indicated by stars.

731

★3. Three particles each carrying a charge Q are located at the vertices of an equilateral triangle of edge a. Calculate the work done in bringing a fourth particle carrying a charge Q' from infinity to the center of the triangle. Evaluate the work done in joules if $Q = Q' = 1$ μcoulomb and $a = 1$ cm.

★4. $ABCD$ is a square of edge a in free space, and there are point charges of strengths Q, $-Q$, and Q at the three corners A, B, and C, respectively. Calculate the work done in moving a point charge of strength Q' from the center of the square to the point D.

★5. A, B, C, D are four consecutive points on a straight line such that $AB = BC = CD = a$. At A and D there are point charges of strength Q, and at B there is a point charge of strength $-Q$. Calculate the electric potential at a point distant x $(<a)$ from C in the direction of D. Evaluate also the potential at points on the line such that (a) $x > a$, (b) $-a > x > -2a$, and (c) $x < -2a$. Plot the potential in volts as a function of x for $Q = 1{,}000$ $\mu\mu$coulombs and $a = 1$ m.

★6. In a system of rectangular cartesian coordinates, there are point charges of strength Q at the points $(-2a,0,0)$ and $(-a,0,0)$ while there is a point charge of strength $-Q$ at the point $(a,0,0)$. Calculate the electric potential at the point $(0,y,0)$. Plot the potential in volts as a function of y for $Q = 1{,}000$ $\mu\mu$coulombs and $a = 1$ m.

★7. $ABCD$ is a square of edge a, and there are point charges each of strength Q at the three corners A, B, and C. Calculate the amount by which the potential at D exceeds the potential at the center of the square.

★8. In a system of cartesian coordinates (x,y,z), a point charge of strength Q is located at $(a,0,0)$ and an equal point charge of strength Q is located at $(-a,0,0)$. Calculate the electric potential at a point on the y axis distant y from the origin. By differentiation with respect to y deduce the electric field strength at the point. Verify the result of this calculation of the electric field strength from the law of inverse squares without making use of electric potential.

9. A, M, B, N are points on a straight line such that $AM/MB = AN/BN = 1/k$, k being a positive constant less than unity. P is a variable point in space such that $AP/PB = 1/k$. Prove that the locus of P is a sphere on MN as diameter.

10. At two points A and B in free space are located two point charges of strengths Q and $-kQ$, respectively, k being a positive constant less than unity. Calculate the electric potential at a point P distant r_1 from A and r_2 from B. Prove that the potential at all points P such that $r_2/r_1 = k$ is the same as the potential at infinity. Show that the locus of these points is a sphere enveloping the point B, and find the points where the sphere intersects a straight line drawn through the point charges.

11. $ABCD$ are four consecutive points on a straight line such that $AB/BC = AD/CD = 4$ and $BD = 2a$. A sphere S, with center O, is drawn on BD as diameter. Point charges of strengths Q, $-\frac{1}{4}Q$, and $\frac{1}{4}Q$ are placed at A, C, and O, respectively. Show that the sphere S is an equipotential surface, and calculate its potential.

★12. ABC is an equilateral triangle of edge b in free space. Three spherical conductors of identical radii a, small compared with b, have their centers at A, B, and C, and each carries a charge Q. By considering the field of three point charges at A, B, and C, show that the potential of the spherical conductors is approximately

$$\gamma_e Q \left(\frac{1}{a} + \frac{2}{b} \right)$$

where γ_e is the constant of electrostatics. Evaluate the potential in volts if $a = 1$ cm, $b = 1$ m, and $Q = 1{,}000$ $\mu\mu$coulombs.

★13. The free space between the conductors of a spherical capacitor has internal radius a and external radius b. A charge $-Q$ is transferred from the inner conductor to the outer conductor. Taking the potential to be zero at infinity, calculate the potential of the inner conductor and show that it can be raised in the ratio $b/(b - a)$ by increasing the radius of the outer conductor to infinity. If $Q = 1,000$ $\mu\mu$coulombs and $a = 1$ cm, calculate the potential of the inner conductor in volts (*a*) if $b = 2$ cm and (*b*) if *b* is indefinitely large.

14. A large spherical capacitor is used as a Van de Graaff high-voltage generator for accelerating electrons. An electron of charge $-e$ and mass m leaves the inner conductor with negligible velocity and is accelerated through a vacuum until it arrives at the outer conductor. If the potential of the inner conductor is maintained at a voltage V below that of the outer conductor, calculate the velocity with which the electron reaches the outer conductor. Evaluate this velocity if $V = 10^4$ volts. Show that, if $V = 10^6$ volts, the effect of relativity on the mass of the electron must be taken into account. Taking the mass of the electron as $m(1 - v^2/c^2)^{-\frac{1}{2}}$, where $c = 3 \times 10^8$ m/sec, evaluate the velocity with which electrons reach the outer conductor when $V = 10^6$ volts.

15. Between the horizontal plates of a parallel-plate capacitor there exists air of density ρ_1 in which there is a uniform downward electric field. In the air there is a spherical drop of oil of radius a and density ρ_2 ($<\rho_1$) to which is conveyed a single electronic charge e. The strength of the electric field is adjusted to a value E such that the drop floats. Calculate the electronic charge e in terms of E, a, ρ_1, ρ_2, and the acceleration g due to gravity.

16. A cloud chamber contains a parallel-plate capacitor whose plates are horizontal. Between the plates there is a gas containing aqueous vapor, and the chamber is provided with arrangements to expand the gas and so condense vapor. An ionizing particle is shot through the gas between the plates, producing a line of ionized atoms upon which aqueous vapor is condensed by expansion. Each drop has radius a and density ρ and carries a single electronic charge. To prevent the drops from falling under gravity (acceleration g) a vertically electric field of field strength E is applied between the plates and adjusted so that the condensation track remains stationary. Calculate the value of the electronic charge.

Part 1, Chapter 3

★1. A spherical capacitor has inner conductor of radius a and outer conductor of radius b with free space between the conductors. The inner conductor carries a charge Q, and the outer conductor a charge $-Q$. A circular cone of semivertical angle θ is drawn with apex at the common center of the conductors. Prove that the fraction of the charge on either conductor located within the cone is $\sin^2 (\theta/2)$.

★2. In a system of cartesian coordinates two small spherical conductors are located at the points $(a,0,0)$ and $(-a,0,0)$. One carries a charge Q, and the other a charge $-Q$. If the system is discharged by moving the charge on one sphere to that on the other along the lines of force, calculate the charge per unit area that crosses the symmetrical plane at the point $(0,y,0)$.

★3. Two charged conductors in an electrostatic field are numbered 1 and 2. C_1 is a closed curve drawn on the surface of conductor 1. Lines of force leave conductor 1 along C_1 and arrive at conductor 2 along a closed curve C_2, forming an unclosed tubular surface denoted by S. By applying Gauss' theorem to a closed surface of which S is a part, show that the charge on conductor 2 enclosed by C_2 is equal and opposite to the charge on conductor 1 enclosed by C_1.

★4. A spherical conductor of area S in free space receives a charge Q. Calculate the electric field strength adjacent to its surface. The Earth has a charge that results in a vertical electric field, and the atmosphere in contact with the Earth may be taken as equivalent to free space. Assuming that the vertical electric field is 100 volts/m, calculate the total electrostatic charge on the Earth.

★**5.** An infinite plane conducting sheet in free space carries a total charge q per unit area uniformly distributed over the sheet. Calculate the electric vector at a point on either side of the sheet at distance d from it.

6. Explain why lines of force can begin only on positive charge and can end only on negative charge. Show that the electric potential cannot have a maximum or minimum at any point in space not occupied by electric charge. If the potential is maximum at any point, show that the point must be occupied by positive charge; if the potential is minimum at any point, show that the point must be occupied by negative charge.

7. A sphere is drawn in an electrostatic field in such a way that it does not enclose electric charge. Prove that the average value of the electric potential over the surface of the sphere is equal to the potential at the center.

Part 1, Chapter 4

★**1.** A parallel-plate capacitor has plates of area S and separation s. There is a homogeneous dielectric between the plates, and fringing may be neglected. It is observed that a voltage V maintained between the plates results in charges $\pm Q$ on the plates. Calculate the dielectric constant of the dielectric. If $V = 3$ volts, $Q = 1,000$ $\mu\mu$coulombs, $S = 100$ cm^2, and $s = 1$ mm, evaluate the dielectric constant.

★**2.** The space between the conductors of a spherical capacitor has inner radius a and outer radius b and is filled with a homogeneous dielectric of capacitivity ϵ. If s is the separation between the conductors and S is the area of a sphere whose radius is the geometric mean of a and b, prove that the capacitance of the capacitor can be written $\epsilon S/s$. Deduce that, if s is sufficiently small, a spherical capacitor may be regarded as a slightly bent parallel-plate capacitor with no fringing. Calculate the capacitance of a spherical capacitor for which $a = 9.9$ cm, $b = 10.1$ cm, and the dielectric constant is 2.

★**3.** A column of dielectric of capacitivity ϵ has a length l and a rectangular cross section of edges a and b. Conducting plates of area bl are attached to a pair of opposite rectangular faces, and the arrangement is used as a capacitor for which fringing may be neglected. Calculate the capacitance of the capacitor per unit length of the column. A strip transmission line is such that $a = 1$ cm, $b = 10$ cm, and the dielectric constant of the medium between the strips is 4. Calculate the capacitance per unit length of the line in microfarads per meter neglecting fringing.

★**4.** A capacitor with air as dielectric consists of $2n + 1$ parallel flat metal plates each of area S arranged vertically above one another. Alternate plates are connected to each terminal, so that one conductor of the capacitor consists of $n + 1$ of the plates and the other conductor of the n interleaved plates. The separation between all adjacent plates is initially s. One set of plates is now moved vertically a distance x ($<s$), so that alternate separations are now $s - x$ and $s + x$. Neglecting fringing, prove that the capacitance of the capacitor is

$$\frac{2n\epsilon Ss}{s^2 - x^2}$$

where ϵ is the capacitivity of air.

★**5.** A capacitor consists of $2n + 1$ parallel metal plates each of area S arranged vertically above one another. Alternate plates are connected to each terminal, so that one conductor of the capacitor consists of $n + 1$ of the plates and the other conductor of the n interleaved plates. The separation between all adjacent plates is s, and the capacitivity of the separating dielectric is ϵ. The dielectric is such that it will "break down" if the electric field in it exceeds E_{max}. Calculate the maximum charge that the capacitor can hold. If $n = 100$, $S = 10$ cm^2, and the dielectric is mica of dielectric constant 7 and dielectric strength 1.5×10^8 volts/m, evaluate the maximum charge that the capacitor can hold.

★6. The space between the conductors of a spherical capacitor has inner radius a and outer radius b and is filled with a homogeneous dielectric of capacitivity ϵ. The dielectric is such that it will break down if the electric field strength exceeds a value E_{max}. Calculate the maximum charge that the capacitor can hold. For air at normal temperature and pressure, $E_{max} = 3$ kv/mm and $\epsilon = \epsilon_v$ approximately. Evaluate the maximum charge possible if $a = 1$ cm.

★7. A capacitor is formed by taking a long strip of paper of length l, width b, and thickness a and attaching to the opposite faces strips of metal foil also of length l and width b. The composite strip is then rolled up so that, for substantially the whole length of the strip, there is paper in contact with both sides of each strip of foil. If ϵ is the capacitivity of the paper, calculate the capacitance between the two strips of foil neglecting fringing. If the capacitance is to be 1 μf, calculate the strip length required if $a = 0.1$ m, $b = 1$ cm, and the dielectric constant of the paper is 2.

★8. A variable capacitor with air dielectric (capacitivity ϵ) consists of $2n + 1$ parallel flat metal plates each in the form of a semicircle of radius a. At maximum capacitance the plates are arranged vertically above one another with the straight edges parallel, and the separation between adjacent plates is s. Alternate plates are connected to each terminal, so that one conductor consists of $n + 1$ of the plates and the other conductor consists of the n interleaved plates. The interleaved plates can be simultaneously turned on an axis running through the mid-point of the straight edge of each plate. These plates are first turned to the position of minimum capacitance and then turned through a further angle θ. For this position, calculate the capacitance of the capacitor neglecting fringing.

★9. In the previous problem the interleaved plates are pivoted on an axis, not through the common center of each plate, but through an extremity of the straight edge. These plates are turned from the position of maximum capacitance through an angle $\frac{1}{2}\pi - \theta$ as shown in the diagram. Neglecting fringing, calculate the capacitance of the capacitor as a function of the angle θ for values of θ between 0 and $\frac{1}{2}\pi$.

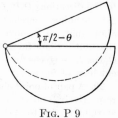

Fig. P 9

10. The solid angle contained by a cone of any shape is defined as the area intercepted on a sphere of unit radius with center at the vertex of the cone. Show that a circular cone of semivertical angle θ contains a solid angle $2\pi(1 - \cos\theta)$ and that the solid angle subtended at a point by all space is 4π.

11. C is a closed curve and O is a point in a homogeneous medium. The solid angle subtended by C at O is Ω. If a point charge of strength Q is placed at O, show that the electric flux threading C is $Q\Omega/4\pi$.

12. For the problem discussed in connection with Part 1, Fig. 4.2, a circle of radius h is drawn on the ground with its center vertically below the center of the small sphere. Calculate the charge on the ground within the circle.

★13. A thundercloud may be thought of as a point charge of strength Q at a height h_1 above the surface of the Earth together with a point charge of strength $-Q$ at a height h_2 above the surface of the Earth, the two point charges being on the same vertical line. The Earth is regarded as a flat conducting surface. An observer is situated at a point P on the surface of the Earth at a distance x from the vertical through the cloud.

Calculate the electric field strength at P and the rate at which it increases with time if the cloud moves horizontally toward the observer with uniform velocity v.

★**14.** Describe how to calculate the electric potential of a system of four point charges of strengths Q, $-Q$, Q, and $-Q$ located at the corners of a rectangle whose edges have lengths $2a$ and $2b$, the charges at the opposite ends of a diagonal being of the same sign. Show that the equipotential surfaces on which the potential is the same as that at infinity form a pair of symmetrical planes intersecting at right angles. Explain how to deduce the electric field of a point charge Q in the presence of a pair of metal sheets intersecting at right angles, the perpendicular distances of the point charge from one sheet being a and from the other sheet b.

★**15.** A large metal sheet in free space is bent along a straight line to form a corner having an angle $\frac{1}{2}\pi$. A point charge of strength Q is placed in this angle at a point whose perpendicular distance from both of the planes forming the corner is b. It may be assumed that the edges of the sheet are at a distance from the point charge large compared with b. Calculate the surface density of charge on the metal sheet at a point distant x from the corner in a plane through the point charge perpendicular to both halves of the sheet. Sketch the variation of the charge density with x.

16. Show that two planes intersecting with a plane angle θ between them contain a solid angle 2θ.

17. In Prob. 15 two lines are drawn on the metal sheet parallel to the corner, one through each of the feet of the perpendiculars from the point charge onto the sheet. Calculate the total charge on the sheet between these two lines.

★**18.** In Prob. 15 the point charge is replaced by a sphere of radius a, small compared with b. Calculate the capacitance of the capacitor formed by the sphere and the sheet.

19. Point charges of strengths Q_1, Q_2, . . . are located at points O_1, O_2, . . . on a straight line l. P is a point in the electric field, and the angles from the direction of l to the directions O_1P, O_2P, . . . are θ_1, θ_2, ... The point P is rotated round l as axis, forming a circle C whose plane is perpendicular to l and whose center is on l. Show that, as P moves along a line of force, the electric flux threading C remains constant. Show further that, as the point P moves along a line of force, the expression $Q_1 \cos \theta_1 + Q_2 \cos \theta_2 + \cdot \cdot \cdot$ remains constant, the constant being different for different lines of force.

20. A pair of point charges of strengths Q and $-Q$ are located at the points A and B, respectively, and the distance AB is $2a$. A line of force leaving either point charge at right angles to AB meets the plane bisecting AB at right angles in a point P. Calculate the angle PAB, and deduce the distance of P from the line AB.

21. A pair of point charges, each of strength Q, are located at the points A and B. A line of force leaving either point charge at right angles to AB passes to infinity at an angle α to the join of the charges. Calculate α.

22. A, B, and C are three equidistant points on a straight line. A charge of strength Q is placed at A, a charge of strength $-\frac{1}{4}Q$ is placed at B, and C is a neutral point. Calculate the angle with AB at which the critical line of force from A to C leaves A.

23. A, B, C, D are four consecutive points on a straight line such that $AB/BC = AD/CD = 1/k$ (>1), and S is a sphere on BD as diameter. A point charge of strength Q is placed at A, and a second point charge of strength $-kQ$ is placed at C. Show that the sphere S is an equipotential surface, and evaluate its potential. Deduce that, if S were a "grounded" spherical conductor and a point charge Q were placed at A, the resulting charge on the conductor would be $-kQ$.

24. A point charge of strength Q is placed at a point P distant d from the center O of a grounded spherical conductor of radius a ($a < d$). Prove that the field exterior to the sphere is the same as that existing in the absence of the conductor for a point charge of strength Q at P and a point charge of strength $-Qa/d$ at a point P' on PO such that $OP \times OP' = a^2$.

25. In a medium of capacitivity ϵ a small spherical conductor of radius b is placed at a distance d from the center of another spherical conductor of radius a. The radius a is small compared with the separation between the spheres, but the same is not necessarily true of the radius b. The sphere of radius b is grounded and forms one conductor of a capacitor of which the other conductor is the sphere of radius a. Calculate the capacitance.

26. In Prob. 24 the spherical conductor is disconnected from ground and possesses a charge Q'. Prove that the field exterior to the sphere is the same as that existing in the absence of the conductor for a point charge of strength Q at P, a point charge of strength $-Qa/d$ at P', and a point charge of strength $Q' + Qa/d$ at O. Deduce the potential of the sphere.

27. A point charge of strength Q is placed at a distance d from the center of an insulated, uncharged, spherical conductor of radius a $(a < d)$. Calculate the surface density of charge on the spherical conductor (a) at the point nearest to the point charge and (b) at the point farthest from the point charge. Calculate the ratio of the former to the latter when $d = 4a$.

28. A positive point charge of strength Q is placed at a distance d from the center of an insulated spherical conductor of radius a $(a < d)$. Calculate the least charge that must be given to the sphere in order that the surface density of charge on the sphere may be everywhere positive.

29. A point charge of strength Q is placed at a point P distant d from the center O of a grounded spherical conductor of radius a $(a < d)$. A geometrical plane is drawn through O perpendicular to OP, dividing the sphere into two halves. Calculate the charges induced on the two halves of the sphere.

30. Repeat the previous problem if the spherical conductor is insulated and uncharged.

31. Repeat Prob. 29 if the spherical conductor is insulated and carries a charge Q'.

32. A point charge of strength Q is placed at a point P distant d from the center of a grounded spherical conductor of radius a $(a < d)$. The tangent cone from P to the sphere is drawn, and the circle of contact divides the sphere into two portions. Calculate the charge on each portion of the sphere.

33. Repeat the previous problem if the spherical conductor is insulated and carries a charge Q'.

34. A point charge of strength Q is placed at a point P distant d from the center O of a hollow spherical conductor of internal radius a $(d < a)$. A geometrical plane p is drawn through O perpendicular to OP, dividing the sphere into two portions. Calculate the charges induced on the two portions of the sphere.

35. Repeat the previous problem if the plane p is drawn through P instead of O.

36. A hemispherical conducting dome of radius a rests on flat conducting ground, with which it is in electrical contact. At a height h $(<a)$ above the ground, a point charge of strength Q is placed on the axis of the hemisphere. Calculate the charge induced (a) on the hemisphere, (b) on the ground.

37. A conducting building erected on flat ground may be regarded as a hemisphere of radius a. A thundercloud above the building may be regarded as a point charge of strength Q at a height h $(>a)$ above ground level on the axis of the hemisphere. Sketch the lines of force, and calculate the electric field strength at the top of the building.

38. A pair of point charges of strengths Q and $-Q$ are placed at a distance $2d$ apart in air (capacitivity ϵ). They are surrounded by a metal sphere of radius a $(>d)$

with center at the mid-point between the charges. Calculate the force on either point charge.

39. A pair of equal and opposite point charges e and $-e$ form what is known as an electric dipole. If the position vector of the charge e with respect to the charge $-e$ is $\mathbf{d}$, the product $\mathbf{p} = e\mathbf{d}$ is known as the dipole moment. In a homogeneous medium of capacitivity ϵ it is required to calculate the electric potential ϕ at a point P whose position vector with respect to the center of the dipole is $\mathbf{r}$. If r is large compared with d and the angle from the direction of $\mathbf{d}$ to the direction of $\mathbf{r}$ is θ, show that

$$\phi = \frac{1}{4\pi\epsilon} \frac{p \cos\theta}{r^2}$$

40. In the previous problem calculate the electric vector at the distant point P due to the electric dipole. Sketch the lines of electric force for an electric dipole whose length d is indefinitely small but whose moment p is not small.

41. A conducting sphere of radius a is introduced into a uniform electric field in air (capacitivity ϵ). The undisturbed electric vector is $\mathbf{E}$, and this field may, if desired, be regarded as arising from a large, distant point charge. Prove that the disturbance in the uniform field produced by the spherical conductor is the same as would be produced in air by a small electric dipole at the center with dipole moment $4\pi a^3\epsilon\mathbf{E}$. Sketch the lines of force for the complete field.

42. A small electric dipole of moment p is placed at the center of a hollow spherical conductor of radius a. Sketch the lines of force, and deduce the maximum charge density induced on the sphere.

43. A, B, C are three consecutive points on a straight line in free space, and $AB = BC = a/\sqrt{2}$. A point charge Q is placed at A, a point charge $-Q/\sqrt{2}$ at B, and a point charge Q at C. Show that spheres of radius a, centers A and C, form an equipotential surface, and calculate the potential on this surface. If a conductor is formed by a pair of metal spheres of radius a intersecting at right angles, calculate the capacitance of the capacitor formed with the sphere at infinity.

44. Electric charge is distributed uniformly along a line AB, and P is a point in the field. Show that, as P moves along a line of force, the difference between the distances PA and PB remains constant. Deduce that the lines of force are hyperbolas with foci at A and B and that the equipotential surfaces are prolate spheroids with foci at A and B.

45. A parallel-plate capacitor has plates of area S with separation s, and fringing may be neglected. The dielectric between the plates has capacitivity ϵ, but there exist between the plates and the dielectric small gaps in which the capacitivity is ϵ_v. If a voltage V is maintained between the plates, calculate in magnitude and sign the charge per unit area on the surface of the dielectric close to the positive plate and compare it with the charge per unit area on the positive plate. Evaluate these quantities if $V = 1$ volt, $s = 1$ mm, and $\epsilon = 7\epsilon_v$.

46. A parallel-plate capacitor for which fringing may be neglected contains a dielectric possessing N atoms per unit volume. Each atom contains a bound electron (charge e, mass m) which, when displaced, suffers a restoring force equal to $m\omega_0^2$ times the magnitude of the displacement. If E is the electric field strength in the capacitor, calculate the displacement of the bound electrons and deduce the charge per unit area on the surfaces of the dielectric in contact with the plates. Show that the capacitivity of the dielectric is

$$\epsilon_v + \frac{Ne^2}{m\omega_0^2}$$

Evaluate the dielectric constant of the dielectric if $\omega_0 = 10^{16}$ radians/sec and $N = 10^{29}$ atoms/m^3. Give an interpretation of the angular frequency ω_0.

47. A surface S constitutes the interface between two dielectrics of capacitivities ϵ_1 and ϵ_2. Show that the component of the electric vector tangential to S has the same value on the two sides of S. Show also that the component of the electric-flux-density vector normal to S has the same value on the two sides of S. Deduce that lines of electric force are refracted at the interface and that, if θ_1, θ_2 are the angles made with the normal to S at the crossing point by the lines of force in the dielectrics of capacitivities ϵ_1, ϵ_2, respectively, then $\epsilon_1 \cot \theta_1 = \epsilon_2 \cot \theta_2$.

48. Show that there is no refraction of lines of electric force when they are parallel or perpendicular to an interface between two dielectrics.

49. In a dielectric of capacitivity ϵ there is a uniform electric field in which the electric field strength is E and the electric flux density is D. There exists in the dielectric a cylindrical cavity in which the axis is parallel to the field and the capacitivity is ϵ_v. The length of the cavity is s, and the normal cross-sectional area is S. If s is small compared with the linear dimensions of S, show that the electric field strength in the cavity is D/ϵ_v. If the linear dimensions of S are small compared with s, show that the electric field strength in the cavity is E.

50. Two homogeneous dielectrics have capacitivities ϵ_1 and ϵ_2 and are separated by a plane interface p. At a point O in the first dielectric distant d from p there is a point charge of strength Q, and it is required to calculate the electric vector at all points. Verify that continuity of the appropriate vector components of the field is satisfied at the interface in an electric field constructed as follows: In the second dielectric let the electric potential be that due to a point charge of strength $[2\epsilon_2/(\epsilon_1 + \epsilon_2)]Q$ at O in an infinite dielectric of capacitivity ϵ_2. In the first dielectric let the electric potential be that due to the given point charge at O together with a point charge of strength $[(\epsilon_1 - \epsilon_2)/(\epsilon_1 + \epsilon_2)]Q$ at the image of O in p, assuming an infinite homogeneous medium of capacitivity ϵ_1. Sketch the lines of force if $\epsilon_2 = 2\epsilon_1$.

51. In the previous problem calculate the force acting on the given point charge of strength Q, and explain the origin of the force.

52. A plane interface separates two dielectrics of capacitivities ϵ_1 and ϵ_2. A pair of point charges of strengths Q_1 and Q_2 are placed on a line perpendicular to the interface, one in each dielectric, the distance from either point charge to the interface being d. Calculate the force on each point charge, and explain why the forces do not balance.

53. A sphere of dielectric of radius a and capacitivity ϵ_2 is embedded in an infinite dielectric of capacitivity ϵ_1. There exists in the latter dielectric an electric field which, at a large distance from the sphere, is a uniform field for which the electric vector is **E**. Verify that the disturbance in this field produced by the sphere can be described as follows: Outside the sphere the disturbance has an electric potential equal to that produced in an infinite dielectric of capacitivity ϵ_1 by an electric dipole at the center of the sphere with dipole moment

$$-4\pi a^3 \epsilon_1 \frac{\epsilon_1 - \epsilon_2}{2\epsilon_1 + \epsilon_2} \mathbf{E}$$

Inside the sphere the complete field is a uniform one in which the electric vector is

$$\frac{3\epsilon_1}{2\epsilon_1 + \epsilon_2} \mathbf{E}$$

54. Show that the variation from place to place in the closeness of the lines of force in an electrostatic field is a measure of the variation in the strength of the electric flux density. Show that the variation in the closeness of the lines of force is not a measure of the variation in the electric field strength if there is a variation from place to place in the dielectric constant. In the previous problem sketch the lines of force if $\epsilon_2 = 2\epsilon_1$, and show that they are closer in the sphere than they are at a large distance from the sphere but that the electric field strength in the sphere is less than at a large distance from the sphere.

55. In a homogeneous medium of capacitivity ϵ electric charge is distributed along a curve C. P is a point of C distant s from a fixed point measured along the curve. At P the charge per unit length of C is q, and q may vary with s. At a point in the electric field distant r from P show that the electric potential is

$$\frac{1}{4\pi\epsilon} \int \frac{q}{r}\, ds$$

where the integral is taken along C.

56. A circular wire of radius a in air (capacitivity ϵ) carries a uniform charge q per unit length. At a point on the axis of the wire distant z from the center, calculate the electric vector. Sketch the lines of force.

57. In a homogeneous medium of capacitivity ϵ electric charge is distributed over a surface S. At a point P of S there is an element of area dS, and the charge per unit area is Q. At a point in the electric field distant r from P show that the electric potential is

$$\frac{1}{4\pi\epsilon} \int \frac{Q}{r}\, dS$$

where the integral is taken over S.

58. A circular disk of radius a in air (capacitivity ϵ) carries a uniform charge Q per unit area. At a point on the axis of the disk distant z from the center, calculate the electric vector. Sketch the lines of force.

59. A piece of dielectric in free space has the form of a circular cylinder of length l and radius a. It is permanently and uniformly polarized parallel to its axis so that there is a uniform charge P per unit area over one flat end and $-P$ per unit area over the other end. At a point on the axis distant z from the mid-point of the cylinder in the direction of polarization, calculate the electric potential (a) if $z > \frac{1}{2}l$ and (b) if $z < \frac{1}{2}l$. Sketch the lines of force.

60. In otherwise free space a geometrical sphere of radius a contains electric charge uniformly distributed at the rate ρ per unit volume. Calculate the electric flux density at distance r from the center (a) if $r > a$ and (b) if $r < a$. Deduce the electric potential as a function of r.

61. A sphere of dielectric of radius a in free space is permanently and uniformly polarized so that each element of volume dv is an electric dipole of moment $\mathbf{P}\, dv$. By analyzing separately the fields of the positive and negative charges of these dipoles, show that the external field of the sphere is the same as that produced in free space by a small dipole of moment $\frac{4}{3}\pi a^3 \mathbf{P}$ at the center.

Part 1, Chapter 5

★1. Five capacitors, each of capacitance C, are connected to form the network shown in the diagram. By analyzing the network into series and parallel connections, calculate the equivalent capacitance between the terminals.

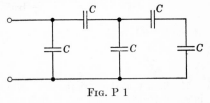

Fig. P 1

★2. In the network of the previous problem a battery of voltage V is connected between the terminals. By analyzing the network into series and parallel connections, calculate the voltages across all capacitors and the charges on all plates.

★3. If the previous problem is solved by the contracted charge method, show that three unknown charges must be introduced to specify the behavior of the network. Obtain three equations capable of determining the unknown charges. Solve these equations, and determine the charges on all plates and the voltages of all capacitors.

★**4.** If Prob. 2 is solved using the node-potential method, show that only two nodes have to be assigned unknown potentials in order to specify the behavior of the network. Obtain two equations capable of determining the unknown potentials. Solve these equations, and determine the voltages of all capacitors and the charges on all plates.

★**5.** In the network of Prob. 1 a charge Q is transferred from the lower terminal to the upper terminal. It is required to calculate the charges on all plates and the voltages of all capacitors. Decide whether it is simpler to use the contracted charge method or the node-potential method, and complete the solution.

★**6.** Four capacitors each of capacitance C are arranged in a network as shown in the diagram. All capacitors are initially uncharged, and a voltage is then connected across the terminals. If the insulation of the capacitors breaks down at a voltage V, calculate the maximum voltage that may be connected across the terminals.

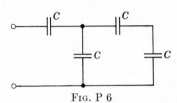

Fig. P 6

★**7.** Four capacitors each of capacitance C are arranged in a network as shown in the diagram. All capacitors are initially uncharged, and a charge Q is then transferred from one of the terminals to the other. Calculate the voltage developed across each capacitor.

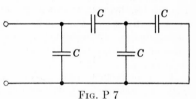

Fig. P 7

★**8.** A balanced network consists of five capacitors each of capacitance C as shown in the diagram. All capacitors are initially uncharged, and a charge Q is then transferred from one terminal to the other. Calculate the voltage developed across each capacitor.

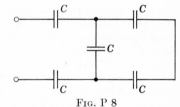

Fig. P 8

★**9.** A network consists of six capacitors each of capacitance C as shown in the diagram. All capacitors are initially uncharged, and a battery of voltage V is then connected across the terminals. Calculate the voltage developed across each capacitor.

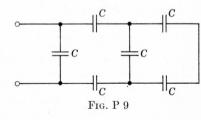

Fig. P 9

★**10.** Eight capacitors, each of capacitance C, are connected to form the network shown in the diagram, and a voltage V is maintained between the terminals. Calculate the charges on all plates.

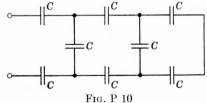

Fig. P 10

★**11.** Wires lie along all the edges of a geometrical cube and are soldered at the corners. Each wire is cut and a capacitor of capacitance C is inserted. Calculate the equivalent capacitance between any two adjacent corners.

★**12.** The bridge network shown in the diagram is such that, when a battery is connected across the terminals, the voltage across the "bridge" of capacitance C can be measured. If this voltage is zero, the bridge is said to be balanced. Prove that the condition for balance is $C_1/C_2 = C_3/C_4$.

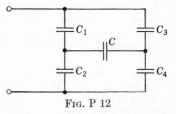

FIG. P 12

★**13.** If the bridge network of the previous problem is unbalanced, calculate the voltage developed across the capacitor of capacitance C when a voltage V is applied between the terminals.

★**14.** In the previous problem, C is a variable capacitor and $C_1 = 1$ μf, $C_2 = 2$ μf, $C_3 = 3$ μf, $C_4 = 4$ μf. If $V = 1$ volt, calculate the maximum voltage that can be developed across the variable capacitor. If C_4 is now short-circuited, recalculate the maximum voltage that can be developed across the variable capacitor.

★**15.** Two concentric, conducting, thin, spherical shells have radii a and b $(a < b)$. The medium between the shells has capacitivity ϵ_1, and that outside the larger shell has capacitivity ϵ_2. The smaller shell carries a charge Q, and the larger shell carries no net charge. By regarding the arrangement as a pair of capacitors connected in series or otherwise, calculate the potential of the smaller shell relative to zero at infinity.

16. In the previous problem a charge Q_1 is given to the smaller shell and a charge Q_2 to the larger shell. Calculate the charge on the outside surface of the larger shell and the potentials of both shells.

17. The space between the conductors of a spherical capacitor has internal radius a and external radius b. The space is divided into two halves by a geometrical plane through the common center of the spheres. One half is filled with a homogeneous dielectric of capacitivity ϵ_1, and the other half with a homogeneous dielectric of capacitivity ϵ_2. Calculate the capacitance of the capacitor. Evaluate the capacitance if $a = 1$ cm, $b = 2$ cm, and the dielectric constants are 7 and 1.

18. Three concentric spheres have radii a, b, and c $(a < b < c)$. Thin conducting shells coincide with the spheres of radii a and c. The space between the spheres of radii a and b is filled with a dielectric of capacitivity ϵ_1, while the space between the spheres of radii b and c is filled with a dielectric of capacitivity ϵ_2. Calculate the capacitance of the capacitor. Evaluate the capacitance if $a = 1$ cm, $b = 2$ cm, $c = 3$ cm, $\epsilon_1 = 7\epsilon_v$, and $\epsilon_2 = \epsilon_v$.

19. Two thin concentric spherical conductors of radii a and b $(a < b)$ exist in air, and the inner conductor is grounded. Calculate the capacitance of the capacitor so formed.

20. A parallel-plate capacitor in air (capacitivity ϵ) has plates of area S and separation s. A third parallel plate of thickness τ is introduced between the other two, all three being normal cross sections of the same cylinder. Calculate the increase in capacitance caused by introduction of the third plate. Explain why the modified capacitance does not vary as the third plate is moved in a direction normal to its plane.

21. Four normal cross sections of a cylinder are occupied by thin conducting plates of area S, and the separation between adjacent plates is s. The end plates are grounded, and charges Q_1 and Q_2 are given to the interior plates. If the capacitivity of the medium is ϵ, calculate the potentials of the interior plates.

22. A spherical capacitor in air has an inner conductor of radius a and a thin outer conductor of radius b. The inner conductor carries a charge Q_1 and the outer conductor a charge Q_2. If the inner conductor is now grounded, calculate the drop in potential of the outer conductor.

23. A distribution of electric charge in free space is surrounded by a pair of equipotential surfaces S_1 and S_2, of which S_1 surrounds S_2. If S_1 is replaced by a conductor, it forms with the sphere at infinity a capacitor of capacitance C_1. If instead S_2 is replaced by a conductor, it forms with the sphere at infinity a capacitor of capacitance C_2. If now both S_1 and S_2 are replaced by thin conducting shells, calculate the capacitance of the capacitor so formed.

24. A parallel-plate capacitor has plates of area S with a separation s between them. The dielectric between the plates has a capacitivity that increases linearly from ϵ_1 at one plate to ϵ_2 at the other plate. Neglecting fringing, calculate the capacitance of the capacitor.

Part 1, Chapter 6

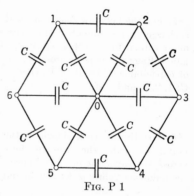

★**1.** In the network shown in the diagram, all capacitors have the same capacitance C and the central node is maintained at zero potential. Calculate the coefficients of self- and mutual capacitance of the network and the coefficients of self- and mutual elastance.

FIG. P 1

★**2.** For the network of the previous problem, calculate the equivalent capacitance between the central node and any other node.

★**3.** The bridge network shown in Chap. 5, Prob. 12, is balanced. If the capacitor of capacitance C is replaced by a battery of voltage V, calculate the voltage between the terminals.

★**4.** The bridge network shown in Chap. 5, Prob. 12, is balanced. A battery of voltage V_1 is applied across the terminals, and a second battery of voltage V_2 is inserted in the bridge in series with the capacitor of capacitance C. Calculate the voltage across this capacitor.

★**5.** In the network shown in the diagram, the lower two terminals are maintained at zero potential. Calculate the charges Q_1 and Q_2 that must be given to terminals 1 and 2 in order to raise them to potentials V_1 and V_2, respectively. Calculate for the network the coefficients of capacitance and the coefficients of elastance. Evaluate these coefficients numerically if $C_1 = 1$ μf, $C_2 = 2$ μf, and $C_3 = 3$ μf.

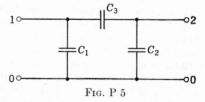

FIG. P 5

6. A network of capacitors has coefficients of capacitance c_{rs} $(r, s = 1, 2, \ldots, n)$. Prove that the coefficients of elastance are C_{rs}/C, where C is the determinant of the coefficients of capacitance and C_{rs} is the cofactor in this determinant of the element c_{rs}.

Part 1, Chapter 7

★1. Find the equivalent T network for the network shown in Chap. 6, Prob. 5. Evaluate the elements in the equivalent T network if $C_1 = 1$ μf, $C_2 = 2$ μf, and $C_3 = 3$ μf.

★2. Find the equivalent π network for the network in Part 1, Fig. 6.4. Evaluate the elements of the equivalent π network if $C_1 = 1$ μf, $C_2 = 2$ μf, and $C_3 = 3$ μf.

★3. A battery of voltage V is connected across the left-hand terminals of the network shown in Chap. 6, Prob. 5. Determine for the arrangement (a) the Thévenin equivalent circuit and (b) the Norton equivalent circuit. Evaluate the elements in these equivalent circuits if $C_1 = 1$ μf, $C_2 = 2$ μf, $C_3 = 3$ μf, and $V = 1$ volt.

★4. For the network shown in Chap. 6, Prob. 5, a charge Q is transferred from terminal 0 to terminal 1. Determine (a) the equivalent Thévenin circuit and (b) the equivalent Norton circuit. Evaluate the elements in these equivalent circuits if $C_1 = 1$ μf, $C_2 = 2$ μf, $C_3 = 3$ μf, and $Q = 1$ μcoulomb.

★5. For the network shown in the diagram a charge of 1 μcoulomb is transferred from one terminal to the other terminal. Calculate voltage developed across the capacitor of capacitance C for the following values of C: 1, 2, 3, and 4 μf.

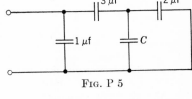

FIG. P 5

★6. For the network shown in the diagram, calculate the voltage developed across the capacitor of capacitance C for the following values of C: 1, 2, 3, and 4 μf.

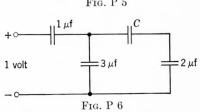

FIG. P 6

★7. A pair of capacitors of capacitances C_1 and C_2 carry charges Q_1 and Q_2, respectively, and the positive terminal of one is connected to the negative terminal of the other. The remaining pair of terminals are available for charging another network of capacitors. Prove that for this purpose the pair of capacitors are equivalent to a single capacitor of capacitance $C_1C_2/(C_1 + C_2)$ carrying a charge $(C_2Q_1 + C_1Q_2)/(C_1 + C_2)$.

Part 1, Chapter 8

★1. Two capacitors each of capacitance C are connected in series across a battery of voltage V. One capacitor is now short-circuited. Prove that the electric energy stored in the other capacitor after the short circuit is applied is double that stored in both capacitors together before the short circuit is applied.

★2. When an insulated charged capacitor is short-circuited, discuss what happens to the energy. In the previous problem, calculate the energy supplied by the battery when the short circuit is applied.

★3. A capacitor of capacitance 1 μf is charged to a potential difference of 1 volt in 1 sec, and the voltage increases at a uniform rate. Plot curves to show the variation with time of the power supplied to the capacitor and the energy stored in it.

★4. For the network of Chap. 6, Prob. 1, voltages V_1, V_2, V_3, V_4, V_5, and V_6 are applied to terminals 1, 2, 3, 4, 5, and 6, respectively. Calculate the energy stored in the network.

★5. For the network of Chap. 6, Prob. 1, charges Q_1, Q_2, Q_3, Q_4, Q_5, and Q_6 are conveyed to terminals 1, 2, 3, 4, 5, and 6, the network being initially uncharged. Calculate the energy stored in the network.

★6. For the network shown in Chap. 7, Prob. 5, a charge of 1 μcoulomb is transferred from the lower terminal to the upper terminal. If C is a capacitor of variable capacitance, calculate the value of C required to maximize the energy stored in this capacitor and evaluate the energy stored in the capacitor when so adjusted.

★7. If, for the network shown in Chap. 7, Prob. 6, C is a capacitor of variable capacitance, calculate the value of C required to maximize the energy stored in this capacitor and evaluate the energy stored in the capacitor when so adjusted.

★8. By using the formula for a parallel-plate capacitor, show that the capacitance of a spherical capacitor of inner radius r and outer radius $r + dr$, where dr is small compared with r, is the reciprocal of

$$\frac{dr}{4\pi\epsilon r^2}$$

where ϵ is the capacitivity of the medium. By placing a number of such capacitors in series, show that the capacitance of a spherical capacitor whose inner radius is a and whose outer radius is b is the reciprocal of

$$\frac{1}{4\pi\epsilon} \int_a^b \frac{dr}{r^2}$$

Evaluate this integral, and deduce the usual formula for the capacitance of a spherical capacitor.

★9. If v is the volume of a parallel-plate capacitor (product of plate area and separation), $E_{\max}$ is the maximum electric field that the dielectric can support without breaking down, ϵ is the capacitivity of the dielectric, and fringing is neglected, calculate the maximum energy that the capacitor can hold. For mica, $E_{\max} = 150 \text{ kv/mm}$ and the dielectric constant is 7. If the plate area is 100 cm² and the separation is 1 mm, calculate the maximum energy that the capacitor can hold in joules.

★10. A spherical capacitor has a homogeneous dielectric of capacitivity ϵ. It carries a charge Q on its inner conductor and a charge $-Q$ on its outer conductor. Calculate the energy density at a point between the conductors distant r from the common center. If $Q = 1$ μcoulomb and the radius of the inner conductor is 1 cm, find the maximum energy density in the field in joules per cubic meter, taking the dielectric constant of the medium as unity.

11. Two capacitors of capacitances C_1 and C_2 carry charges Q_1 and Q_2, respectively. If the capacitors are connected in parallel, calculate the loss in electric energy (a) if the positive plates are connected together and (b) if the positive plate of one capacitor is connected to the negative plate of the other.

12. Two capacitors of capacitances C_1 and C_2 are connected in series, and they are charged by connecting a voltage V between the extreme plates. Without loss of charge, the capacitors are now disconnected from the source and from each other. If the positive terminals of the capacitors are now connected together and the negative terminals are connected together, calculate the loss of electric energy.

★13. Three conducting spherical shells in air (capacitivity ϵ) have radii a, b, and c ($a < b < c$). The spheres of radii b and c are insulated, and the sphere of radius a receives a charge Q. Calculate the loss of energy if the spheres of radii b and c are connected by a wire.

★14. In a homogeneous medium of capacitivity ϵ there are four closed surfaces S_1, S_2, S_3, and S_4 each of which surrounds the preceding. S_1 and S_4 are replaced by conductors forming a capacitor, and S_1 carries a charge Q. S_2 and S_3 are equipotential surfaces on which the potentials are V_2 and V_3. Prove that the electric energy stored between S_2 and S_3 is $\frac{1}{2}Q(V_2 - V_3)$.

★15. In the previous problem the capacitivity between the surfaces S_2 and S_3 is increased from ϵ to ϵ'. Prove that the energy stored between the surfaces is increased in the ratio $(\epsilon' - \epsilon)/\epsilon'$.

Part 1, Chapter 9

★1. Two spherical conductors of radii a and b have their centers at a distance r apart in a homogeneous medium of capacitivity ϵ, and r is large compared with a and b. Prove that the coefficients of self- and mutual elastance of the system are approximately the reciprocals of $4\pi\epsilon a$, $4\pi\epsilon b$, and $4\pi\epsilon r$. Deduce that the coefficients of self- and mutual capacitance are approximately $4\pi\epsilon a$, $4\pi\epsilon b$, and $4\pi\epsilon ab/r$. Evaluate the coefficients of capacitance if $a = 1$ cm, $b = 10$ cm, $r = 1$ m, and the medium is free space.

★2. A capacitor consists of two conductors, numbered 1 and 2, of which 2 completely encloses 1, but otherwise the shapes are arbitrary. The capacitor is set up above conducting ground whose potential is taken to be zero. The capacitance of the capacitor formed by conductors 1 and 2 is C_i. The capacitance of the capacitor formed by conductor 2 and ground is C_0. Calculate the coefficients of self- and mutual capacitance of the system. Prove that the charge on conductor 1 depends on the difference of potential between conductors 1 and 2 and not on the difference of potential between conductor 2 and ground. Explain the significance of this result in connection with electrostatic screens.

3. Three concentric spherical conducting shells have radii a, b, and c $(a < b < c)$. The medium between the spheres of radii a and b has capacitivity ϵ_1, that between the spheres of radii b and c has capacitivity ϵ_2, and that outside the sphere of radius c has capacitivity ϵ_v. Calculate the coefficients of self- and mutual capacitance of the system of conductors.

★4. A pair of conductors numbered 1 and 2 have coefficients of self-capacitance c_{11} and c_{22} and a coefficient of mutual capacitance c_{12}. Relative to zero potential at infinity, the conductors are raised to potentials V_1 and V_2, respectively, and insulated. If the conductors are now joined by a wire, calculate their common potential.

★5. If conductors 1 and 2 of a system of conductors are joined by a wire, calculate the coefficients of capacitance of the new system in terms of those of the old system.

★6. The spherical conductors of radii a and b in Prob. 1 possess charges Q_1 and Q_2, respectively. Calculate the total energy stored in the electric field. Evaluate the energy for the dimensions given in Prob. 1 if $Q_1 = Q_2 = 1$ μcoulomb.

★7. The spherical conductors of radii a and b described in Prob. 1 are raised, respectively, to potentials V_1 and V_2 above ground potential. Calculate the total energy stored in the electric field. Evaluate the energy for the dimensions given in Prob. 1 if $V_1 = 100$ volts and $V_2 = 1,000$ volts.

★8. In Prob. 4 calculate the loss in energy of the field when the conductors are joined by the wire. Evaluate the loss of energy if the conductors are the spheres of Prob. 1.

★9. A system of conductors has given coefficients of capacitance. The conductors are charged, and the total charge involved is Q. If all the conductors are now joined by wires, calculate the common potential of the conductors.

10. A system of conductors numbered 1, 2, . . . carries charges Q_1, Q_2, . . . at potentials V_1, V_2, . . . , respectively. These are changed to charges Q_1', Q_2', . . . at potentials V_1', V_2', . . . , respectively. Using Green's reciprocal theorem, show that the excess in the energy of the system in the second case over that in the first case may be written either as $\frac{1}{2}\Sigma(V' - V)(Q' + Q)$ or as $\frac{1}{2}\Sigma(Q' - Q)(V' + V)$.

11. In a system of insulated charged conductors, a pair of conductors at potentials V_1, V_2 are joined by a wire, and a charge Q flows from the first to the second. Prove that the loss of energy is $\frac{1}{2}Q(V_1 - V_2)$. Discuss whether the potentials of the other conductors are affected.

12. Prove that the coefficients of elastance of a system of conductors are all positive.

13. Prove that the coefficient of self-elastance b_{11} of conductor 1 of a system of n conductors exceeds the coefficients of mutual elastance b_{12}, b_{13}, . . . , b_{1n}.

14. Prove that the coefficients of self-capacitance of a system of conductors are positive and the coefficients of mutual capacitance are negative.

15. If the algebraic sum of the charges on a system of conductors is positive, prove that there is at least one conductor on which the surface density of charge is everywhere positive.

16. A hollow conductor of any shape is divided into two parts that can be insulated from each other and are denoted by S and S'. The portion S' is permanently grounded. If S is also grounded and a point charge of strength Q_1 is placed at a point P outside the conductor, a charge Q_2 is induced on S. The point charge is now removed, and S is raised to potential V. By placing a small spherical conductor at P and applying Green's reciprocal theorem, show that the potential at P is $-(Q_2/Q_1)V$.

17. A hemispherical conducting dome of radius a rests on flat conducting ground, from which it is insulated. The dome is raised to a potential V above that of the ground. Calculate the potential on the axis of the dome at a height h above ground if $h < a$. (Compare Chap. 4, Prob. 36.)

18. In the previous problem calculate the potential on the axis of the dome at a height h above ground when $h > a$. Plot the variation of potential with height on the axis for values of h varying from zero to a value large compared with a.

19. A charged conductor has an equipotential surface S. The conductor is now grounded. A point charge of given strength is placed at a point of S and induces a charge on the conductor. Prove that the induced charge remains constant as the position of the point charge moves over the surface S.

Part 1, Chapter 10

★1. An attracted disk electrometer takes the form of a parallel-plate capacitor arranged with its plates (area S) horizontal, the lower plate being fixed and the dielectric being air (capacitivity ϵ). The upper plate forms one pan of a balance into the opposite pan of which weights may be placed. The capacitor is charged, and it is found that a weight w is required to produce balance. Neglecting fringing, calculate the magnitude of the charge on the capacitor. Evaluate the magnitude of the charge if $S = 100$ cm^2 and $w = 1$ g in weight.

★2. A spherical capacitor having an air dielectric (capacitivity ϵ) carries a charge Q on its inner conductor (radius a) and a charge $-Q$ on its outer conductor (radius b). Prove that each element of area of the inner conductor is subject to a force radially outward, and calculate the force per unit area. The inner conductor is now divided into two halves by a diametral plane. Calculate the force acting on either half tending to separate it from the other. Evaluate the force when $Q = 1$ μcoulomb and $a = 1$ cm.

★3. A spherical capacitor having air as dielectric (capacitivity ϵ) carries a charge Q on its inner conductor (radius a) and a charge $-Q$ on its outer conductor (radius b). The entire capacitor is divided into two halves by a plane through the common center. The inner and outer hemispheres of each half are held rigidly together, but the two halves of the capacitor are capable of moving apart. At distance r from the common center, calculate the pressure exerted by the field in one half of the capacitor on that in the other half. Deduce the force of repulsion between the two halves of the capacitor. Evaluate the force when $Q = 1$ μcoulomb, $a = 1$ cm, and $b = 2$ cm.

★**4.** In the previous problem calculate the force exerted separately on the two hemispheres forming one half of the capacitor. Verify that the resultant of these two forces is the force exerted on this half of the capacitor by the other half.

★**5.** Two spherical conductors of radii a and b have their centers at a large distance r apart in air (capacitivity ϵ). The conductors carry charges Q_1 and Q_2, respectively. Using the coefficients of elastance calculated in Chap. 9, Prob. 1, express the potential energy of the system in terms of the charges. By means of the principle of virtual work, deduce the force between the spheres tending to increase r.

★**6.** The conductors of the previous problem are maintained at potentials V_1 and V_2. By means of a displacement of the conductors in which r is increased but V_1 and V_2 are kept constant, calculate the force between the conductors. Verify the equivalence of the result to that obtained in the previous problem.

★**7.** In Chap. 4, Prob. 15, calculate the force exerted (a) on the point charge and (b) on the metal sheet.

8. In Chap. 4, Prob. 24, calculate the force exerted (a) on the point charge and (b) on the sphere.

9. In Chap. 4, Prob. 27, calculate the force exerted on the sphere.

10. In Chap. 4, Prob. 26, calculate the force exerted on the sphere. Discuss whether the force between the point charge and the sphere is an attraction or a repulsion.

11. In Chap. 4, Prob. 34, calculate the force exerted on the sphere.

12. Show that a point charge placed at the center of a hollow conducting sphere is in unstable equilibrium.

13. Three concentric spherical shells in air have radii a, b, and c ($a < b < c$), and the sphere of intermediate radius is divided along a diametral plane. If the inner and outer spheres are grounded and the intermediate sphere carries a charge Q, calculate the force between the two halves of this conductor. Discuss whether the force is an attraction or a repulsion.

14. A spherical capacitor in air has an inner conductor of radius a and an outer conductor in the form of a shell that can contract symmetrically. The outer conductor is grounded, and the inner conductor is insulated and carries a fixed charge Q. If the outer conductor is permitted to contract from radius b_1 to radius b_2 ($>a$), calculate the work done on the outer conductor by the electrical forces.

15. In the previous problem the outer conductor is again grounded and the inner conductor is maintained at a fixed potential V above the outer conductor by means of a battery. If the outer conductor is again allowed to contract from radius b_1 to radius b_2 ($>a$), calculate the work done on the outer conductor by the electrical forces. Calculate also the energy supplied by the battery.

16. A capacitor consists of three horizontal square conducting plates, each of edge a, arranged vertically above one another with corresponding edges parallel. Between adjacent plates there is a separation s small compared with a, and the medium is air (capacitivity ϵ). The top and bottom plates are connected by a wire, and between these plates and the central plate a voltage V is maintained. With the top and bottom plates fixed, the central plate is pulled horizontally parallel to an edge through a distance x appreciably less than a but large compared with s. Calculate the potential energy of the system, neglecting the effects of fringing. By differentiation with respect to x show that the force tending to restore the plate to its original position is approximately $\epsilon a V^2/s$. Explain the origin of this force in view of the fact that the lines of force meet the central plate at right angles and fringing was neglected in the calculation of potential energy. Evaluate the force if $s = 1$ mm, $a = 10$ cm, and $V = 100$ volts.

17. A quadrant electrometer is constructed as follows: A totally enclosed conducting circular cylinder has length small compared with its diameter and is arranged with its axis vertical. The cylinder is divided into four quadrants along a pair of mutually perpendicular axial planes. One terminal of the electrometer is connected to a pair of opposite quadrants, while the other terminal is connected to the other pair of opposite quadrants. By means of a torsion fiber hanging along the axis of the cylinder a conducting needle is suspended within the cylinder. The torsional properties of the fiber are such that, when there is no difference of potential between the terminals of the electrometer, the needle hangs in equilibrium with its center line in one of the diametral planes separating quadrants. Movement of the needle through an angle θ about a vertical axis from this position leads to a torsional restoring torque proportional to θ. The needle consists of a circular plate of radius slightly less than that of the cylinder with a pair of segments symmetrically removed. In conjunction with the quadrants the needle forms parallel-plate capacitors for which fringing is small. If the potentials of the terminals of the electrometer are V_1 and V_2 and the potential of the needle is V, prove that the angular deflection of the needle is proportional to $[V - \frac{1}{2}(V_1 + V_2)](V_1 - V_2)$ and is directed toward the pair of quadrants for which the potential is closest to that of the needle. Deduce that, if the potential of the needle is maintained sufficiently high, the deflection is proportional to the potential difference between the terminals.

18. A variable capacitor has a set of fixed plates known as a "stator" and a set of rotating plates known as a "rotor," and the angle θ denotes the angular position of the rotor. The capacitor has a maximum capacitance C_1 when $\theta = 0$ or π and a minimum capacitance C_2 when $\theta = \pi/2$ or $3\pi/2$. In other angular positions, the capacitance is

$$C_1 \cos^2 \theta + C_2 \sin^2 \theta$$

If a voltage V is maintained between the plates of the capacitor, calculate the torque tending to increase θ.

19. In the previous problem the applied voltage varies with time t sinusoidally and $V = V_0 \cos \omega t$. A flywheel is attached to the rotor, and it rotates with uniform angular velocity ω such that $\theta = \omega t - \delta$. Calculate the mean torque exerted on the rotor, and show that it is maximum if $\delta = \frac{1}{4}\pi$. If $C_1 = 100 \ \mu\mu f$, $C_2 = 10 \ \mu\mu f$, and the capacitor breaks down at 10,000 volts, evaluate the greatest torque that can be maintained on the average. If $\omega = 3,600$ rpm, calculate the horsepower of the motor. Discuss the suitability of such a synchronous motor for practical purposes.

20. A parallel-plate capacitor has square plates of edge a with a separation s small compared with a. The space between the plates is occupied by a dielectric of capacitivity ϵ, the rest of space being occupied by air (capacitivity ϵ_v). The dielectric is now withdrawn parallel to an edge through a distance x less than a. If the capacitor has a charge Q, calculate the electrical force tending to decrease x.

Part 1, Chapter 11

★1. A coaxial transmission line has inner conductor of external radius a and outer conductor of internal radius b. The dielectric has capacitivity ϵ and dielectric strength E_{max}. Calculate the maximum voltage that can be maintained between the conductors. Evaluate the maximum voltage if $a = 1$ cm, $b = 2$ cm, $\epsilon = \epsilon_v$, and $E_{max} = 3$ kv/mm.

★2. A capacitor consists of three thin coaxial metal circular cylinders of radii a, b, and c in air ($a < b < c$). Each cylinder is of length l, and the planes of the normal cross sections at each end of the three cylinders coincide. Calculate the capacitance of the capacitor, neglecting fringing. Recalculate the capacitance if the central cylinder is withdrawn axially through a distance z less than l.

★**3.** Two long parallel wires are embedded in a homogeneous medium of capacitivity ϵ, and each carries a uniform charge Q per unit length. The wires are separated by a distance d large compared with the radius of either. Calculate the force of repulsion between the wires per unit length. Evaluate the force per unit length if $Q = 1$ μcoulomb/m, $d = 10$ cm, and the dielectric constant of the medium is unity.

★**4.** A coaxial transmission line has an inner conductor of external radius a and an outer conductor of internal radius b, with a dielectric of capacitivity ϵ between them. If Q is the charge per unit length on the inner conductor, calculate the electric energy per unit volume at a point between the conductors distant r from the common axis. Deduce the total electric energy per unit length of the transmission line, and verify that it is equal to $Q^2/2C$, where C is the capacitance of the line per unit length.

★**5.** A long wire of radius a is suspended horizontally in air (capacitivity ϵ) above flat conducting ground at a height h large compared with a. Calculate the capacitance per unit length of the transmission line formed by the wire and the ground. Evaluate the capacitance per meter if $a = 1$ mm and $h = 10$ m.

★**6.** Two long parallel wires, each of radius a, are embedded in a medium of capacitivity ϵ. The wires have a separation d between their axes, and d is large compared with a. If the charge per unit length on each wire is Q, calculate the electric potential at a point distant r_1 from the axis of one wire and r_2 from the axis of the other. Sketch the equipotential surfaces and the lines of force.

7. A series of thin parallel wires intersect a perpendicular plane p in the points $O_1, O_2, \ldots$, and the wires carry uniform charges $Q_1, Q_2, \ldots$ per unit length. A point P in the plane p is such that the radii $O_1P, O_2P, \ldots$ make angles $\theta_1, \theta_2, \ldots$ with a fixed direction in p, all angles being measured the same way round. Show that, as P moves along a line of force, the expression $Q_1\theta_1 + Q_2\theta_2 + \cdots$ remains constant, the constant being different for different lines of force. (Compare Chap. 4, Prob. 19.)

8. In Prob. 6 a line of force leaving either wire perpendicular to the plane of the wires passes to infinity at an angle α with this plane. Calculate α.

★**9.** A triode vacuum tube makes use of a length l of a coaxial transmission line for which the inner radius is a and the outer radius is c. The inner conductor is used as the cathode, and the outer conductor as the anode. Between the cathode and the anode there is a grid in the form of a coaxial conducting cylinder of length l and radius b in which holes are cut so as to make the area of the grid a fraction α of the area of the complete cylinder. For purposes of rough calculation all electric fields are to be assumed strictly radial. Calculate (a) the coefficient of mutual capacitance between the cathode and the grid, (b) the coefficient of mutual capacitance between the cathode and the anode, and (c) the amplification factor of the tube. Evaluate these three quantities numerically if $l = 15$ mm, $a = 0.5$ mm, $b = 0.75$ mm, $c = 5$ mm, and $\alpha = 0.75$.

★**10.** A long thin straight wire is erected in air (capacitivity ϵ) at a distance d from an infinite conducting plane. If the wire carries a uniformly distributed charge Q per unit length, calculate the force per unit area on the plane at the foot of a perpendicular from the wire.

★**11.** A coaxial transmission line has an inner conductor of external radius a and an outer conductor of internal radius b. There is a dielectric of capacitivity ϵ between the conductors, and the charges on the conductors are Q and $-Q$ per unit length. Calculate the electrical force per unit area on the inner conductor tending to expand it. If the inner conductor is divided into two halves along a diametrical plane, calculate the force per unit length tending to separate the two halves.

★**12.** In a medium of capacitivity ϵ three parallel wires intersect a perpendicular plane in three collinear points whose separations are d. The radius of each wire is a, and a may be assumed small compared with d. The two outside wires are kept at the same potential and used as one conductor of a transmission line of which the other conductor is the central wire. Calculate the capacitance of the transmission line per unit length.

★13. In a medium of capacitivity ϵ four parallel wires intersect a perpendicular plane in the vertices and centroid of an equilateral triangle of edge d. The radius of each wire is a, and a may be assumed small compared with d. The three outside wires are kept at the same potential and used as one conductor of a transmission line of which the other conductor is the central wire. Calculate the capacitance of the transmission line per unit length.

★14. In a medium of capacitivity ϵ four parallel wires intersect a perpendicular plane in the corners of a square of edge d. The radius of each wire is a, and a may be assumed small compared with d. One adjacent pair of wires is maintained at one potential, and the other adjacent pair of wires is maintained at a different potential. Calculate the capacitance per unit length of the transmission line so formed.

★15. In the previous problem one pair of diagonally opposite wires is maintained at one potential and the other pair of diagonally opposite wires at a different potential. Calculate the capacitance per unit length of the transmission line so formed.

★16. The pair of wires of Prob. 6 is now located centrally in a conducting cylinder of internal radius b large compared with d. The arrangement is used as a transmission line for which the cylinder is one conductor and the pair of wires is the other conductor. Calculate the capacitance per unit length of the transmission line. Prove that this is the same capacitance per unit length as would be obtained for a coaxial transmission line whose outer radius is b and whose inner radius is the geometric mean of a and d.

17. In the arrangement described in the previous problem one wire now carries a charge Q_1 per unit length and the other wire a charge Q_2 per unit length, the large enclosing cylinder being at zero potential. Calculate the potentials of the two wires, and deduce the coefficients of self- and mutual elastance per unit length. Derive the coefficients of self- and mutual capacitance of the wires per unit length.

18. Repeat the previous problem if the arrangement of wires along the center of the cylinder of radius b is that described in Prob. 12 and b is large compared with d.

19. For the vacuum tube shown in Part 1, Fig. 11.5, it may be assumed that a and c are small compared with b while d is large compared with b; the value of n may be taken as 6. If the cathode is raised to unit potential while the grid and anode are grounded, calculate the charge on the grid and the charge on the anode. Deduce the amplification factor of the tube, and discuss means for increasing its value.

20. An infinite straight narrow slot of width $2a$ is cut in an infinite plane conducting sheet, and a steady voltage V is maintained between the two halves of the sheet. Assuming that the lines of force are circles coaxial with the slot, calculate the electric field strength at a distance r from the slot large compared with a. Sketch the equipotential surfaces. In a plane perpendicular to the length of the slot (r,θ) are polar coordinates such that the plane $\theta = 0$ contains the half of the sheet at zero potential and the plane $\theta = \pm\pi$ contains the half of the sheet at potential V. Calculate the electric potential at the point (r,θ), assuming that r is large compared with a.

21. Two geometrical planes p_1 and p_2 intersect in a horizontal line l in free space, each plane making an angle α with the vertical. A large conducting sheet is bent along a line so as to have an internal angle 2α and is placed so as to coincide with the upper halves of the planes p_1 and p_2 with the sharp edge along the line l. A second large conducting sheet is similarly bent and placed so as to coincide with the lower halves of the planes p_1 and p_2. The two sheets are not quite in contact along the line l, and a voltage V is maintained between the sheets. Assuming that the lines of force are circles coaxial with the line l, calculate the electric field strength at a point between the sheets at distance r from l. Deduce the surface density of charge on either sheet at distance r from l, showing that it becomes large at the sharp edges.

22. In a finite plane conducting sheet is cut a pair of infinitely long parallel narrow slots at a distance d apart. The two outer sections of the plane are maintained at zero potential, while the central section is maintained at potential V. Taking the capacitivity of the surrounding medium as ϵ, calculate the surface density of charge on the central section at a point distant x from one slot and $d - x$ from the other slot. Calculate also the surface density of charge at a point of one of the outer sections distant x from the nearer slot and $d + x$ from the farther slot.

23. A twin-wire transmission line has conducting wires of radius a at a distance d apart, d being large compared with a. The wires are joined by a strip of solid dielectric (capacitivity ϵ_2), the remainder of the dielectric being air (capacitivity ϵ_1). The normal cross section of the dielectric strip is bounded by the wires and by arcs of circles passing through the axes of the wires as shown in the diagram, a fraction x of the area of each wire being covered

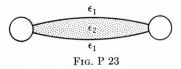

Fig. P 23

by the solid dielectric. If a steady voltage is maintained between the wires, show that the charge on each wire divides between the part of the wire covered by solid dielectric and the part covered by air in the ratio $x\epsilon_2$ to $(1 - x)\epsilon_1$. Calculate the capacitance per unit length of the transmission line.

24. A twin-wire transmission line in air (capacitivity ϵ) has wires of radius a with their axes at a distance d apart. The magnitude of a is less than $\frac{1}{2}d$ but is not necessarily small compared with $\frac{1}{2}d$. Calculate the capacitance per unit length by appropriately replacing equipotential surfaces by conductors in the electric field of a twin-wire transmission line with thin wires.

25. A coaxial transmission line in air (capacitivity ϵ) has an inner conductor of radius a and an outer conductor of radius b. The axis of the inner conductor is now displaced sideways through a distance d, less than $b - a$. Calculate the capacitance per unit length of the modified transmission line.

Part 2, Chapter 1

★1. A copper pipe has an internal radius a and an external radius b. It carries a current I distributed uniformly over its cross section. Calculate the current density in the conductor. Evaluate the current density if $a = 1$ cm, $b = 1.1$ cm, and $I = 1$ amp.

★2. A pipe has an internal radius a and an external radius b and is made of metal of conductivity σ. Calculate the resistance of a length l of the pipe. Evaluate the resistance if $l = 1$ m, $a = 1$ cm, $b = 1.1$ cm, and the metal is copper, for which $\sigma = 5.8 \times 10^7$ mhos/m.

★3. A wire of cross-sectional area S is made of metal possessing N electrons per unit volume capable of drifting along the wire to form an electric current. If each electron has a charge e and there is a steady current I through the wire uniformly distributed over the cross section, calculate the speed with which electrons are drifting through the wire. Evaluate the drift velocity if $N = 10^{29}$ electrons/m³, $I = 1$ amp, and the wire is circular with radius 1 mm.

★4. A rectangular column of material of low conductivity σ has dimensions a by b by l. Perfectly conducting strips of width b and length l are attached to a pair of opposite faces of area bl, and the arrangement is used as a transmission line. Calculate the conductance per unit length of the line. Evaluate the conductance per meter of line if $a = 1$ mm, $b = 1$ cm, and the insulating material has conductivity 10^{-15} mho/m.

★5. A coil is wound on a cylindrical form of radius r using wire of conductivity σ and radius a small compared with r. There are n turns of wire on the form, and the turns are nearly contiguous, so that the wire forms a helix of small pitch. Calculate the resistance of the coil. Evaluate the resistance if $a = 1$ mm, $r = 1$ cm, $n = 100$, and the metal is Nichrome, for which $\sigma = 10^6$ mhos/m.

★6. Power is supplied to an establishment at a fixed voltage V, but the current I used is a function of time t. Prove that, between times t_1 and t_2, the energy consumed is

$$V \int_{t_1}^{t_2} I \, dt$$

If the current I has a maximum value I_{max} at midday and a minimum value I_{min} at midnight and the curve of I against t is sinusoidal, show that the energy consumed per day is

$$\tfrac{1}{2} V (I_{max} + I_{min}) T$$

where T is the length of a day. If $V = 100$ volts, $I_{max} = 30$ amp, and $I_{min} = 2$ amp, calculate the energy consumed during a day (a) in kilowatthours and (b) in joules.

★7. A cable consists of n strands of wire each of radius a and conductivity σ. If the cable carries a steady current I, calculate the heat generated in the cable per unit length per unit time. If $a = 1$ mm, $n = 10$, $\sigma = 5.8 \times 10^7$ mhos/m, and $I = 1$ amp, evaluate the power consumed in heat per meter length of the cable.

★8. A voltaic cell has perfectly conducting electrodes in the form of parallel plates of area S with a separation s between them, and the volume Ss between the electrodes is filled with an electrolyte. The open-circuit voltage of the cell is V. When the cell is short-circuited, heat is generated in the electrolyte at a rate P. Deduce the conductivity of the electrolyte. Evaluate the conductivity of the electrolyte if $P = 10$ watts, $S = 100$ cm^2, $s = 1$ cm, and $V = 1.5$ volts.

9. A piece of material of conductivity σ has the form of a circular cone of small semivertical angle, truncated by two planes perpendicular to the axis at different distances from the vertex. The piece of material is used as a wire in air, the radius of the wire being a at one end and b at the other. If the wire is of length l, calculate the resistance between its ends.

10. A conducting medium possesses N electrons (charge e, mass m) per unit volume capable of drifting through the medium to form an electric current. Under the influence of a uniform electric field for which the electric vector is $\mathbf{E}$, the electrons drift through the medium with a mean drift velocity. An electron makes on the average ν collisions per unit time with atoms, and the resulting succession of impulses may be regarded as a retarding force equal to $m\nu$ times the mean drift speed. Calculate the mean drift velocity, and deduce that the conductivity of the medium is $Ne^2/m\nu$. Evaluate the conductivity (a) for a metal in which $N = 10^{29}$ electrons/m^3 and $\nu = 10^{13}$ collisions/sec and (b) for an ionized atmosphere in which $N = 10^{11}$ electrons/m^3 and $\nu = 10^4$ collisions/sec.

11. Between the plates of a parallel-plate capacitor there is an ionized gas possessing N free electrons (charge e, mass m) per unit volume. A voltage that varies sinusoidally with time t at an angular frequency ω is applied between the plates, and fringing is negligible, so that there is in the capacitor a uniform electric field of field strength $E_0 \cos \omega t$. It may be assumed that an individual electron in the medium oscillates with angular frequency ω under the influence of the applied electric field and that the collisional retarding force described in the previous problem is negligible. Show that the displacement of an electron at time t in the direction of positive applied electric field is

$$- \frac{e^2}{m\omega} E_0 \cos \omega t$$

and give a physical explanation of the negative sign. Calculate the contribution to the charge per unit area on the plates of the capacitor at time t due to oscillation of the electrons in the medium. Deduce that the capacitivity of the ionized gas is

$$\epsilon_v - \frac{Ne^2}{m\omega^2}$$

where ϵ_v is the vacuum capacitivity.

12. In the previous problem show that the capacitivity of an ionized medium containing N free electrons per unit volume vanishes for an angular frequency of oscillation equal to $(Ne^2/\epsilon_v m)^{\frac{1}{2}}$ and is negative for higher frequencies of oscillation. Deduce that it is possible for the capacitance of a capacitor to be negative. Give a physical explanation of the significance of this statement and the reason for its truth. If in the ionosphere $N = 10^{11}$ electrons/m³, evaluate the critical frequency in megacycles per second at which the capacitivity of the ionosphere changes sign.

Part 2, Chapter 2

★**1.** Five resistors, each of resistance R, are connected to form the network shown in the diagram. By analyzing the network into series and parallel connections, calculate the equivalent resistance between the terminals.

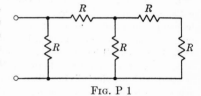

FIG. P 1

★**2.** In the network of the previous problem a battery of voltage V is connected between the terminals. By analyzing the network into series and parallel connections, calculate the voltage and current associated with each resistance.

★**3.** If the previous problem is solved by the mesh-current method, show that three unknown mesh currents must be introduced to specify the behavior of the network. Obtain three equations capable of determining the unknown mesh currents. Solve these equations, and determine the voltage and current associated with each resistor.

★**4.** If Prob. 2 is solved using the node-potential method, show that only two junctions have to be assigned unknown potentials in order to specify the behavior of the network. Obtain two equations capable of determining the unknown potentials. Solve these equations, and determine the voltage and current associated with each resistor.

★**5.** In the network of Prob. 1 a current I is led in at the upper terminal and out at the lower terminal. It is required to calculate the voltage and current associated with each resistor. Decide whether it is better to use the mesh-current method or the node-potential method, and complete the solution.

★**6.** Eight resistors, each of resistance R, are connected to form the network shown in the diagram, and a voltage V is maintained between the terminals. Calculate the current through each resistor.

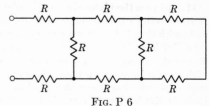

FIG. P 6

★7. The bridge network shown in the diagram is such that, when a battery is connected between the terminals, the current through the "bridge" of resistance R can be measured. If this current is zero, the bridge is said to be balanced. Prove that the condition for balance is $R_1/R_2 = R_3/R_4$.

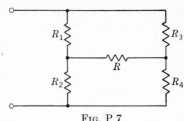

FIG. P 7

★8. A Wheatstone bridge is constructed by stretching a wire of uniform resistance per unit length between two points A and B. Between the point A and a point C is connected a resistor of known resistance R_0. Between C and B is connected a resistor whose resistance is to be determined. The point C is connected through a current-indicating device of resistance R to a sliding contact P on the wire AB. To determine the unknown resistance a battery is connected between A and B, and the sliding contact P is moved until the current through the indicator is zero. The distances of the sliding contact P from the ends A and B of the wire are then measured to be a and b, respectively. Prove that the required resistance is $(b/a)R_0$.

★9. If the bridge network of Prob. 7 is unbalanced, calculate the current through the bridge when a voltage V is applied between the terminals. If $V = 10$ volts, $R = 1$ ohm, $R_1 = 10$ ohms, $R_2 = 20$ ohms, and $R_3 = 30$ ohms, sketch a curve to show the way in which the current through the bridge depends on the value of R_4.

★10. Wires lie along the edges of a geometrical cube and are soldered together at the corners. The wire has a uniform resistance r per unit length, and the cube has edges of length a. If a battery of voltage V is connected between any two adjacent corners, calculate the rate at which heat is produced in the wires.

★11. A length of wire of radius a and conductivity σ is connected between the terminals of a battery having open-circuit voltage V and internal resistance r. Calculate the length of wire that must be used to maximize the power absorbed by the wire. Evaluate this length if $V = 1.5$ volts, $r = 0.1$ ohm, $a = 1$ mm, and $\sigma = 5.8 \times 10^7$ mhos/m.

★12. For the arrangement described in the previous problem it is desired to maximize, not the total power absorbed by the wire, but the power absorbed by the wire per unit volume. Show that the length of wire used must now be small compared with that calculated in the previous problem.

★13. Two resistors each of resistance R are connected in series across a battery of open-circuit voltage V and internal resistance r. One of the resistors is now short-circuited. Calculate the ratio by which the power absorbed by the other resistor is increased. Evaluate this ratio if $R = 1$ ohm and $r = 0.5$ ohm.

★14. Across a load of resistance R are connected (a) a storage battery of open-circuit voltage V_1 and internal resistance r_1 and (b) a d-c generator of open-circuit voltage V_2 and internal resistance r_2. Calculate the current supplied by each source and the power absorbed by the load.

★15. In the previous problem calculate the ratio of V_1 to V_2 at which the storage battery changes from charging to discharging. Evaluate this ratio if $r_1 = r_2 = 0.1$ ohm and $R = 0.5$ ohm.

16. For a network of capacitors the charge displaced round a mesh in the process of charging the network is known as the mesh charge. Devise a method for analyzing networks of capacitors using the mesh charges as mathematical unknowns, and apply it to the problems illustrated in Part 1, Figs. 5.7 and 5.3.

17. If the meshes in a network of capacitors can be chosen so that each mesh con-

tains a capacitor not included in any other mesh, show that the charge associated with the capacitor is the mesh charge for the mesh. Show that, if a mesh does not contain such a capacitor, one can be introduced without upsetting the behavior of the network provided that the capacitance of the introduced capacitor is regarded as infinite.

18. From a length of uniform wire having a resistance r per unit length is constructed a network in the form of a square of edge a together with the two diagonals. At each corner the three wires are soldered together, but at the intersection of the diagonals the two wires are insulated from each other. Calculate the equivalent resistance between the mid-points of the two diagonals.

★19. Electric power is supplied at a voltage V, center-tapped, and the three terminals of voltages $\frac{1}{2}V$, 0, and $-\frac{1}{2}V$ are connected by three wires each of resistance r to a pair of loads of resistances R_1 and R_2, one connected across each half of the line, as shown in the diagram. Calculate the current in the central wire, verifying that it vanishes if $R_1 = R_2$. Express the condition that the voltage across the load of resistance R_1 should exceed $\frac{1}{2}V$. Explain why it would be dangerous to connect a fuse in the central wire.

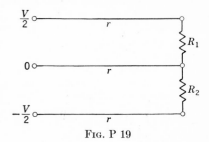

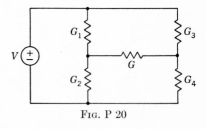

FIG. P 19

20. In the Wheatstone bridge shown in the diagram, G_1 and G_2 are the conductances of resistors known to a high degree of accuracy and G is the conductance of the current-indicating device in the bridge. G_4 is the conductance of a resistor whose resistance is to be determined, and a series of standard resistors are available to use as the remaining resistor. It is found that one of these, of conductance G_3, nearly balances the bridge. A much better balance is obtained, however, if a resistor of small conductance g_3 is connected in parallel with G_3 and a resistor of small conductance g_4 is connected in parallel with G_4. Show that the resistance of the unknown resistor is approximately

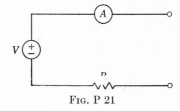

FIG. P 20

$$\frac{G_1}{G_2 G_3}\left(1 - \frac{1}{G_3}g_3 + \frac{G_1}{G_2 G_3}g_4\right)$$

★21. As shown in the diagram an ohmmeter is constructed by connecting in series a current-measuring meter A, a battery of fixed voltage V, and a resistor of fixed resistance. The resistor whose resistance is to be determined is connected across the terminals, and its resistance is deduced from the current I through the meter A. If full-scale deflection on the meter is produced by a current I_{max} and this is to correspond to zero external resistance, calculate the required internal resistance of the ohmmeter. Derive an expression for the external resistance in terms of the current through the meter, the current for full-scale deflection, and the voltage of the battery. If the scale of the meter is linear in current, show that, when the deflection of the needle is half of the full-scale deflection, the external resistance is equal to the internal resistance.

FIG. P 21

22. An instrument A for measuring current has a resistance R, and full-scale deflection corresponds to a current I_{max}. To adapt the instrument for measuring higher currents, it is used in conjunction with a pair of resistors of resistances R_1 and R_2 as shown in the diagram. Calculate the current through the meter due to (a) a current I entering at terminal 1 and leaving at terminal 3 and (b) a current I' entering at terminal 1 and leaving at terminal 2. For the same angular deflection of the needle, show that the ratio of I to I' is independent of the resistance R of the meter. Evaluate the ratio of R_1 to R_2 required to make the ratio of I' to I equal to 10.

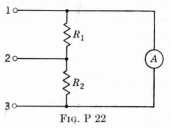

Fig. P 22

23. In the previous problem $R = 10$ ohms and $I_{max} = 10$ ma. Calculate the values of R_1 and R_2 required to use the meter for full-scale deflections of 100 ma and 1 amp.

24. A meter A for measuring current has resistance R_0 and is used in the network shown in the diagram to measure unknown high resistances connected either between terminals 1 and 2 or between terminals 2 and 3. The arrangement is to be such that the same meter deflection is obtained for a resistance $10R$ between terminals 1 and 2 as for a resistance R between terminals 2 and 3. Calculate the required ratio of R_1 to R_2 on the assumption that the resistances to be measured are all high compared with all other resistances involved.

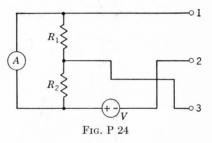

Fig. P 24

25. In the bridge network shown in the diagram V is the voltage of a battery and A is a current-measuring instrument. R_1 and R_2 are resistors of known resistance, and R_3 is a calibrated variable resistor. R is a resistor whose resistance at temperature T_0 is R_0 and whose resistance at temperature T is given by the equation

$$\frac{R - R_0}{R_0} = \alpha(T - T_0)$$

With the resistor R at temperature T_0, the variable resistor is adjusted to balance the bridge. The resistor R is now heated, and the resistance of the resistor R_3 has to be increased by an amount δR_3 to keep the bridge

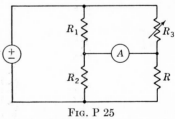

Fig. P 25

balanced. Calculate the temperature of the resistor R. Evaluate the temperature if $T_0 = 20°C$, $\alpha = 4 \times 10^{-3}$ deg^{-1}, $R_0 = R_1 = R_2 = 100$ ohms, and $\delta R_3 = 10$ ohms.

26. A telephone wire AB of length l and resistance r per unit length is erected above perfectly conducting ground. It develops a leak to ground of unknown resistance R at an unknown point distant x from the end A. Measurements of resistance are made between the end A and ground (a) when the end B is open-circuited and (b) when the end B is short-circuited to ground. If the measured values are R_1 and R_2, respectively, calculate the values of x and R.

27. A section AB of an electric railroad of length l is operated from two constant-voltage sources each of voltage V, one at each end. Current is supplied to the locomotives through an overhead wire of resistance R per unit length and is returned through the track whose resistance is r per unit length. At a particular moment a single locomotive drawing a constant current I is located at a distance x from the end A. Calculate the rates at which energy is being supplied by the sources at A and B and the rate at which it is being delivered to the locomotive.

28. In the ladder network shown in the diagram each element has the same resistance R and node 0 is at zero potential. The network extends indefinitely to the right, and initially no current flows in the network. A battery is now connected across the terminals at the left. The nodes are numbered as shown in the diagram, and the voltage of node number n is denoted by V_n. Show that for $n \geq 2$, the voltages of the nodes satisfy the linear difference equation

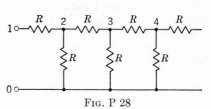

FIG. P 28

$$V_{n-1} - 3V_n + V_{n+1} = 0$$

By assuming that V_n is proportional to x^n, obtain an expression for V_n in terms of V_2. Deduce the equivalent resistance between the terminals.

Part 2, Chapter 3

★1. In the network shown in the diagram, all resistors have the same resistance R and the central node is maintained at zero potential. Calculate the coefficients of self- and mutual conductance of the network, and the coefficients of self- and mutual resistance.

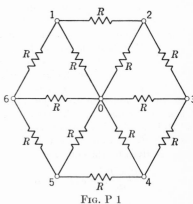

FIG. P 1

★2. For the network of the previous problem, calculate the equivalent resistance between the central node and any other node.

★3. The bridge network shown in Chap. 2, Prob. 7, is balanced. If a battery of voltage V is inserted in the bridge in series with the resistor of resistance R, calculate the voltage between the terminals of the network.

★4. The bridge network shown in Chap. 2, Prob. 7, is balanced. A battery of voltage V_1 is applied between the terminals, and a second battery of voltage V_2 is inserted in the bridge in series with the resistor of resistance R. Calculate the power delivered by the second battery.

★5. In the network shown in the diagram the lower two terminals are maintained at zero potential. The upper left-hand terminal is at steady potential V_1, and the upper right-hand terminal is at steady potential V_2. Calculate the current I_1 that enters terminal 1 and leaves terminal 0; calculate the current I_2 that

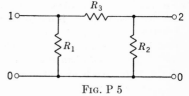

FIG. P 5

enters terminal 2 and leaves terminal 0. Derive for the network the coefficients of conductance and the coefficients of resistance. Evaluate these coefficients numerically if $R_1 = 1$ ohm, $R_2 = 2$ ohms, and $R_3 = 3$ ohms.

★6. For the network of Prob. 1, voltages V_1, V_2, V_3, V_4, V_5, and V_6 are applied to terminals 1, 2, 3, 4, 5, and 6, respectively. Calculate the rate of dissipation of energy in the network.

★7. For the network of Prob. 1, currents I_1, I_2, I_3, I_4, I_5, and I_6 are led in at terminals 1, 2, 3, 4, 5, and 6, respectively, and are led out at terminal 0. Calculate the rate of dissipation of energy in the network.

8. A network of resistors has a pair of input terminals at which the voltage and current are V_1 and I_1 and a pair of output terminals at which the voltage and current are V_2 and I_2. Relations between voltages and currents are given by Part 2, Eqs. (3.50) and (3.51). Show that the input voltage and current can be expressed in terms of the output voltage and current by equations of the form

$$V_1 = A V_2 - B I_2$$
$$I_1 = C V_2 - D I_2$$

Evaluate the coefficients A, B, C, and D in terms of the coefficients of resistance of the network, and find what relation among the coefficients A, B, C, and D expresses the fact that $r_{12} = r_{21}$. If the network is symmetrical with respect to the input and output terminals, show that $A = D$.

9. A network of resistors has a pair of input terminals at which the voltage and current are V_1 and I_1 and a pair of output terminals at which the voltage and current are V_2 and I_2. The sign conventions are such that the input current enters the network at the positive input terminal while the output current leaves the network at the positive output terminal. If the network is symmetrical with respect to the input and output terminals, show that the input voltage and current can be expressed in terms of the output voltage and current by means of equations of the form

$$V_1 = A V_2 + B I_2$$
$$I_1 = C V_2 + A I_2$$

It is required to connect across the output terminals a resistor whose resistance R is such that the corresponding equivalent resistance between the input terminals is also equal to R. Show that there is a unique resistance R (known as the image resistance of the network) that satisfies this condition, and evaluate it in terms of the coefficients A, B, and C.

10. In the previous problem calculate the equivalent resistance between the input terminals when the output terminals are (a) open-circuited and (b) short-circuited. Deduce that the geometric mean of these equivalent resistances is equal to the image resistance of the network.

11. A number of identical networks of resistances of the type described in Prob. 9 are connected in cascade, the output terminals of one network being connected to the input terminals of the next. Show that the network thus formed has an image resistance equal to that of each individual network.

12. The network shown in the diagram is composed of a series resistor of resistance R center-tapped as shown in the diagram, together with a shunt resistor of conductance G. Calculate the image resistance of the network.

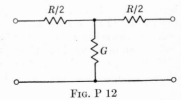

Fig. P 12

13. A network is composed of a pair of shunt resistors each of conductance $\tfrac{1}{2}G$ and a series resistor of resistance R as shown in the diagram. Calculate the image resistance of the network.

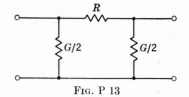

Fig. P 13

14. A section of an attenuator is constructed as shown in the diagram. Show that its image resistance is R. Show further that, if a resistor of resistance R is connected across the output terminals and a battery is connected across the input terminals, the ratio of the output voltage to the input voltage is $e^{-\gamma}$.

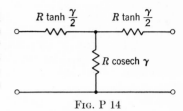

Fig. P 14

15. A section of an attenuator is constructed as shown in the diagram. Show that its image resistance is R. Show further that, if a resistor of resistance R is connected across the output terminals and a battery is connected across the input terminals, the ratio of the output voltage to the input voltage is $e^{-\gamma}$.

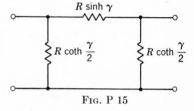

Fig. P 15

16. A network of resistors has coefficients of resistance r_{pq} $(p, q = 1, 2, \ldots, n)$. Prove that the coefficients of conductance are R_{pq}/R, where R is the determinant of the coefficients of resistance and R_{pq} is the cofactor in this determinant of the element r_{pq}.

17. The behavior of a network of resistors is described by means of mesh currents I_1, I_2, . . . , and the voltages applied round the meshes are V_1, V_2, . . . , respectively. Show that these voltages and currents are connected by linear equations, and explain the relation between these equations and those discussed in Sec. 3.1.

Part 2, Chapter 4

★1. Find the equivalent T network for the network shown in Chap. 3, Prob. 5. Evaluate the elements in the equivalent T network if $R_1 = 1$ ohm, $R_2 = 2$ ohms, and $R_3 = 3$ ohms.

★2. Find the equivalent π network for the network in Part 2, Fig. 3.4. Evaluate the elements in the equivalent π network if $R_1 = 1$ ohm, $R_2 = 2$ ohms, and $R_3 = 3$ ohms.

★3. A battery of voltage V is connected between terminals 1 and 0 in the network shown in Chap. 3, Prob. 5. Calculate for the arrangement (a) the Thévenin equivalent circuit and (b) the Norton equivalent circuit. Evaluate the elements in these equivalent circuits if $R_1 = 1$ ohm, $R_2 = 2$ ohms, $R_3 = 3$ ohms, and $V = 1$ volt.

★4. For the network shown in Chap. 3, Prob. 5, a current I is led in at terminal 1 and led out at terminal 0. Calculate (a) the equivalent Thévenin circuit and (b) the equivalent Norton circuit. Evaluate the elements in these equivalent circuits if $R_1 = 1$ ohm, $R_2 = 2$ ohms, $R_3 = 3$ ohms, and $I = 1$ amp.

★5. For the network shown in the diagram a current of 1 amp is led in at one terminal and out at the other. It is required to adjust the resistance R of the variable resistor to maximize the rate of dissipation of energy in this resistor. Calculate the value of R that must be used and the energy dissipated in the variable resistor when so adjusted.

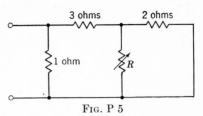

Fig. P 5

★6. For the network shown in the diagram it is required to adjust the resistance R of the variable resistor to maximize the rate of dissipation of energy in this resistor. Calculate the value of R that must be used and the energy dissipated in the variable resistor when so adjusted.

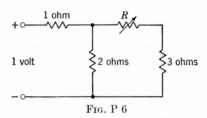

Fig. P 6

★7. For the network shown in the diagram the voltage V, the current I, and the resistance r are fixed and the resistance R is variable. Calculate the maximum rate at which it is possible to dissipate energy in the variable resistor.

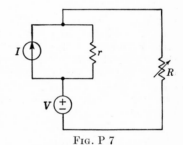

Fig. P 7

★8. A storage battery of open-circuit voltage V_1 and internal resistance r_1 is connected in parallel with a d-c generator of open-circuit voltage V_2 and internal resistance r_2. Show that the arrangement is equivalent to a single source of open-circuit voltage $(r_2V_1 + r_1V_2)/(r_1 + r_2)$ and internal resistance $r_1r_2/(r_1 + r_2)$.

★9. A balanced attenuator is constructed as shown in the diagram, and a battery of voltage V and internal resistance r is connected across the left-hand pair of terminals. Evaluate the Thévenin voltage and the Norton current for the arrangement. Calculate also the resistance involved in the Thévenin and Norton equivalent circuits.

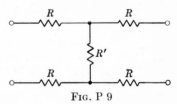

Fig. P 9

10. A battery of voltage V and internal resistance R is connected across the input terminals of the network shown in Chap. 3, Prob. 14. Show that the Thévenin equivalent circuit for the arrangement involves a Thévenin resistance R and a Thévenin voltage $Ve^{-\gamma}$.

11. Repeat the previous problem for the network shown in Chap. 3, Prob. 15.

Part 2, Chapter 5

★1. A perfectly conducting spherical electrode of radius a is embedded in a concentric perfectly conducting spherical tank containing a homogeneous medium of conductivity σ. A current I is led in at the electrode and out at the wall of the tank. At a point between the electrode and the wall distant r from the common center, calculate the dissipation of energy per unit volume. Evaluate the energy dissipated per cubic meter if $I = 1$ amp, $r = 1$ m, and $\sigma = 1$ mho/m.

★2. A pair of perfectly conducting spherical electrodes of radius a are maintained with their centers at a distance d apart near the center of a tank of radius b containing homogeneous fluid of conductivity σ. The dimension a is small compared with d, and d is small compared with b. Calculate the resistance between the electrodes on the assumption that b is infinite. Evaluate the resistance if $a = 1$ cm, $d = 10$ cm, and $\sigma = 1$ mho/m.

★3. A large tank with an open top is filled to a certain level with fluid of uniform conductivity σ, and the air above the surface of the fluid may be assumed non-conducting. A pair of perfectly conducting spherical electrodes are partly immersed in the fluid so that their centers lie in the plane of the surface at a distance d apart (d large compared with a). Calculate the resistance between the electrodes.

★4. A large perfectly conducting tank with an open top is filled to a certain level with a fluid of uniform conductivity σ. The tank may be idealized as a hemisphere of infinite radius. Near the center of the tank a perfectly conducting sphere of radius a is immersed in the fluid with its center at a depth d below the free surface, and it may be assumed that a is small compared with d. A voltage is maintained between the sphere of radius a and the wall of the tank. By suitably introducing an additional source of current, or otherwise, outline a method for calculating the lines of flow of the electric current in the fluid, and calculate the resistance between the sphere and the wall of the tank. Evaluate the resistance if $a = 1$ cm, $d = 10$ cm, and the fluid is sea water ($\sigma = 4$ mhos/m).

★5. It is required to calculate the capacitance of a capacitor of given dimensions having air as dielectric. The capacitor is immersed in a large electrolytic tank in which the fluid has a conductivity σ small compared with the conductivity of the plates. The resistance between the plates is found to be R. Calculate the capacitance of the capacitor.

6. A large perfectly conducting tank at zero potential is filled with a homogeneous medium of conductivity σ. Near the center of the tank there are three perfectly conducting spherical electrodes, each of radius a, at the vertices of an equilateral triangle of side d, large compared with a. Taking the radius of the tank as infinite, calculate the coefficients of self- and mutual resistance of the system and deduce the coefficients of self- and mutual conductance. Evaluate the coefficients if $a = 1$ cm, $d = 10$ cm, and $\sigma = 1$ mho/m.

7. In the arrangement described in the previous problem, currents I_1, I_2, and I_3 are led in at the three electrodes and out at the wall of the tank. Calculate the total rate of dissipation of energy in the medium. Evaluate the rate of dissipation of energy if $I_1 = I_2 = I_3 = 1$ amp, $a = 1$ cm, $d = 10$ cm, and $\sigma = 1$ mho/m.

8. In the arrangement described in Prob. 6, the electrodes are maintained at voltage V_1, V_2, and V_3. Calculate the total rate at which energy is dissipated in the medium. Evaluate the rate of dissipation if $V_1 = V_2 = V_3 = 1$ volt, $a = 1$ cm, $d = 10$ cm, and $\sigma = 1$ mho/m.

9. A large perfectly conducting rectangular tank contains fluid of conductivity σ. Near the center of one face of the tank a small perfectly conducting spherical electrode of radius a is mounted at a distance d from the face. It may be assumed that a is small compared with d and that d is small compared with the dimensions of the tank. Calculate the resistance between the electrode and the wall of the tank.

10. A coaxial transmission line is made of perfectly conducting cylinders, and the space between the conductors has internal radius a and external radius b. The transmission line terminates at a particular normal cross section, and in this cross

section there is stretched between the conductors a uniform sheet of resistive material for which the resistance between opposite edges of a square is r. Calculate the resistance connected across the end of the transmission line.

11. The transmission line described in Part 1, Chap. 11, Prob. 16, is made of material of perfect conductivity and terminates at a particular normal cross section. Stretched between the conductors in this normal cross section is a uniform sheet of resistive material for which the resistance between opposite edges of a square is r. Calculate the resistance connected across the end of the transmission line.

12. A large uniform resistive sheet is such that the resistance between opposite edges of a square is r. The sheet has a perfectly conducting rim round its outer edge, and this may be regarded as a circle of infinite radius. Point sources of current of strengths $I_1, I_2, \ldots$ are led into the sheet at points $O_1, O_2, \ldots$ in the sheet and out at the infinite rim. A point P in the field of flow is such that the radii $O_1P, O_2P, \ldots$ make angles $\theta_1, \theta_2, \ldots$ with a fixed direction in the sheet, all angles being measured the same way round. Show that, as the point P moves along a line of flow, the expression $I_1\theta_1 + I_2\theta_2 + \cdots$ remains constant, the constant being different for different lines of flow. (Compare Part 1, Chap. 11, Prob. 7.)

13. A, B, C are three collinear points on the resistive sheet described in the previous problem, and $AB = BC = d$. By means of small electrodes a current I is led in at B while $\frac{1}{2}I$ is led out at A and $\frac{1}{2}I$ at C. A line of flow leaves B at an angle α with BC. Calculate the angle at which the join of the electrodes at which this line of flow arrives at either A or C. Sketch the lines of flow.

14. A, B, C are three collinear points on the resistive sheet described in Prob. 12. By means of small electrodes a current I is led in at A and another current I at B while a current I is led out at C. A circle is drawn with center C and radius equal to the geometric mean of CA and CB. Show that the two semicircles into which the circle is divided by the line through the electrodes each form part of a line of flow. Sketch the lines of flow.

15. For the resistive sheet described in Prob. 12 a current I is led in by a small electrode at the point O and the current is led out at the rim. A circle of radius a is drawn on the sheet with its center at a distance d from O ($d > a$), and the portion of the sheet within this circle is removed. Describe a method for calculating the flow in the sheet. If the electrode at O has a radius b small compared with a and the rim has a radius R large compared with d, calculate the resistance between the electrode and the rim.

16. A pair of perfectly conducting electrodes is embedded in a homogeneous medium of capacitivity ϵ. The coefficients of self-elastance are b_{11} and b_{22}, while the coefficient of mutual elastance is b_{12}. If the medium is replaced by one having a homogeneous conductivity σ, calculate the resistance between the electrodes.

17. A large perfectly conducting tank contains a fluid of conductivity σ_1 up to the level of a plane p and a fluid of conductivity σ_2 above p, and the two fluids do not mix. A point source of steady current of strength I is introduced at a point distant d below the plane p and flows to the wall of the tank. It may be assumed that d is small compared with the dimensions of the tank and the depths of the fluids. Describe a method for calculating the current-density vector at any point, and sketch the lines of flow when $\sigma_1 > \sigma_2$. (Compare Part 1, Chap. 4, Prob. 50.)

18. A sphere of material of radius a and conductivity σ_2 is embedded in a large block of material of conductivity σ_1. There exists in the latter material an electric current which, at a large distance from the sphere, is a uniform flow represented by a current-density vector $\mathbf{J}$. Calculate the current-density vector in the sphere. (Compare Part 1, Chap. 4, Prob. 53.)

19. In the previous problem sketch the lines of flow (a) if σ_2 is large compared with σ_1, (b) if $\sigma_2 = 2\sigma_1$, (c) if $\sigma_2 = \sigma_1$, (d) if $\sigma_2 = \frac{1}{2}\sigma_1$, and (e) if σ_2 is small compared with σ_1.

Part 2, Chapter 6

★1. The cathode and anode of a triode vacuum tube are in the form of parallel metal plates with a parallel metal grid between them through which electrons can pass. Taking the potential of the cathode as zero, the grid is maintained at a potential V_g and the anode at a potential V_a. If V_g is positive and V_a is negative, show that an electron that is emitted from the cathode with negligible velocity and that passes the grid does not reach the anode. Calculate the fraction of the distance from the grid to the anode at which the electron is turned back.

★2. In the previous problem the electron (charge $-e$, mass m) leaves the cathode at right angles with a nonzero velocity u_0. Find how large u_0 must be in order that the electron can reach the anode.

★3. The cathode and anode of a diode vacuum tube are parallel metal plates at a distance s apart, and the anode is maintained at a potential V below that of the cathode. An electron (charge $-e$, mass m) leaves a point P of the cathode with a fixed velocity u_0 at a variable angle θ to the plane of the cathode. If the electron returns to the cathode at a point Q without striking the anode, calculate the distance PQ. Prove that PQ is greatest if $\theta = \pi/4$.

★4. A cathode-ray tube whose gun has an accelerating voltage V_a is equipped for electrostatic deflection of the spot in two perpendicular directions by passing the beam in succession through two identical sets of deflecting plates with their planes perpendicular. Explain why the deflection of the spot per unit deflecting voltage is different for the two perpendicular directions. For each set of deflecting plates the length parallel to the beam is L and the separation between the plates is s. Prove that the difference between the deflections per unit deflecting voltage for the two perpendicular directions cannot be less than $L^2/2V_a s$ approximately.

5. A voltaic cell on open circuit has a pair of plane electrodes at a distance d apart, and fringing may be neglected. In the electrolyte close to one of the electrodes there is space charge, and the charge per unit volume varies with distance x from the electrode proportionally to $e^{-x/a}$, where a is small compared with d. The difference of potential between this electrode and the middle of the electrolyte is V. Prove that the electric field strength at distance x from the electrode is approximately

$$\frac{V}{a} e^{-x/a}$$

Deduce the distribution of electric potential with x, taking the potential of the electrode as zero. Sketch a curve to show the distribution of the potential.

6. A diode vacuum tube possesses a pair of coaxial electrodes of which the inner is the cathode. If a steady current flows from the anode to the cathode, prove that the product of the radial velocity of the electrons and the density of space charge varies inversely as the distance from the axis of the cathode.

★7. The anode of a diode vacuum tube obeying Charles' law has a voltage that exceeds the voltage of the cathode by an amount V, and V has a saw-tooth variation with time t as shown in the diagram. Draw a sketch of the resulting current through the tube as a function of time. If I_0 is the maximum current through the tube, show that, during the interval $0 \leq t \leq \frac{1}{4}T$, the current I through the tube is given by

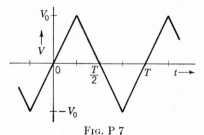

Fig. P 7

$$\frac{I}{I_0} = \left(\frac{4t}{T}\right)^{3/2}$$

Show that the mean current through the tube is

$$\frac{2}{T}\int_0^{T/4} I\, dt$$

and that this evaluates to $I_0/5$.

★**8.** The current I through a diode vacuum tube is related to the applied voltage V by the equation

$$\frac{I}{I_s} = \begin{cases} 0 & V \geq 0 \\ \left(\dfrac{V}{V_s}\right)^{3/2} & 0 \leq V \geq V_s \\ 1 & V \geq V_s \end{cases}$$

so that V_s is the voltage that must be applied to produce saturation and I_s is the saturation current. The saw-tooth voltage described in the previous problem is applied to the tube, and $V_0 > V_s$. Draw a sketch of the resulting current through the tube as a function of time t, and calculate the mean value of the current.

★**9.** Over a limited range of voltage and current the characteristic curve of the diode described in the previous problem can be represented by the tangent to the Child's-law curve at the point $V = V_s$, $I = I_s$. Calculate the elements in the Thévenin and Norton equivalent circuits for the tube. Evaluate these elements if $V_s = 150$ volts and $I_s = 50$ ma.

★**10.** The behavior of a diode vacuum tube can be idealized by stating that, when the voltage of the anode is negative with respect to the cathode, the tube is nonconducting but, when the anode is positive with respect to the cathode, the tube has a fixed resistance R. Across such an idealized diode is connected a voltage that varies with the time t sinusoidally with angular frequency ω and amplitude V_0, the voltage being $V_0 \sin \omega t$. Calculate the current through the tube as a function of time, and deduce the mean current through the tube.

★**11.** A full-wave rectifier consists of a pair of identical diodes used as shown in the diagram. The voltages at the top and bottom terminals at the left vary with time t

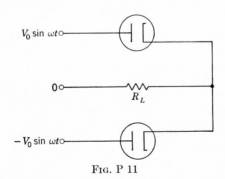

Fig. P 11

as shown, and the center terminal is at zero potential. If the behavior of each diode is idealized as described in the previous problem, calculate the voltage across the load resistor of resistance R_L as a function of time and deduce the mean voltage across the load. Evaluate the mean voltage if $V_0 = 100$ volts and $R = R_L = 1,000$ ohms.

★12. A bridge rectifier consists of four identical diodes used as shown in the diagram. The voltage between the terminals at the left varies with time t sinusoidally with angular frequency ω and amplitude V_0, the voltage being $V_0 \sin \omega t$. If the behavior of each diode is idealized as described in Prob. 10, calculate the voltage across the load resistor of resistance R_L as a function of time and deduce the mean voltage across the load. Evaluate the mean voltage if $V_0 = 100$ volts and $R = R_L = 1,000$ ohms.

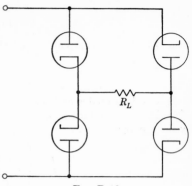

Fig. P 12

13. If a diode vacuum tube has a voltage V applied across it and a current I passing through it, the tube is absorbing energy at a rate VI. Explain what happens to this energy. In each of the two preceding problems, calculate (a) the mean power dissipated in the diodes and (b) the mean power delivered to the load. Express the second of these as a fraction of the mean power delivered by the source. Evaluate this ratio if $R = R_L = 1,000$ ohms.

14. The relation between the voltage V across a diode vacuum tube and the current I through the tube is given by Charles' law [Part 2, Eq. (6.45)]. If $V = V_0 \sin \omega t$, calculate the root-mean-square value of the current through the tube.

15. It may be assumed that the saturation current for a cathode is proportional to $T^2 e^{-T_0/T}$, where T is the absolute temperature of the cathode and T_0 is an absolute temperature characteristic of the substance of which the cathode is made. A small increase in the temperature of the cathode causes an increase in the saturation current. Calculate the ratio of the percentage increase in saturation current to the percentage increase in absolute temperature. Evaluate this ratio for tungsten ($T_0 = 5.2 \times 10^{4}°$K) operating at a temperature of $1000°$K.

16. For a planar diode, the separation between the cathode and the anode is s, and the current through the tube is limited by space charge. If electrons start from the cathode with negligible velocity and arrive at the anode with velocity u_a, prove that the transit time across the tube is $3s/u_a$. Evaluate the transit time if $s = 1$ mm and the potential of the anode exceeds that of the cathode by 100 volts.

17. A transistor diode is such that, when a voltage V is connected across its terminals, the current through the transistor is $I_T[\exp(V/V_T) - 1]$, where I_T and V_T are a current and a voltage characteristic of the transistor. If the saw-tooth voltage illustrated in Prob. 7 is applied across the transistor, calculate the mean current through the transistor.

18. In an electric field in which the space charge ρ per unit volume is a function of the three rectangular cartesian coordinates x, y, z, show that the components D_x, D_y, D_z of the electric-flux-density vector are also functions of x, y, z and that Part 2, Eq. (6.27), is replaced by

$$\frac{\partial D_x}{\partial x} + \frac{\partial D_y}{\partial y} + \frac{\partial D_z}{\partial z} = \rho$$

Deduce that the electric potential ϕ is a function of x, y, z and that Part 2, Eq. (6.31), is replaced by

$$\frac{\partial^2 \phi}{\partial x^2} + \frac{\partial^2 \phi}{\partial y^2} + \frac{\partial^2 \phi}{\partial z^2} = -\frac{1}{\epsilon_v}\rho$$

Part 2, Chapter 7

★1. For a triode vacuum tube whose cathode is maintained at zero potential, the relation among the anode current I, the anode voltage V_a, and the grid voltage V_g can be written as

$$I = \alpha \left(V_g + \frac{1}{\mu} V_a \right)^{\frac{3}{2}}$$

it being assumed that $V_g < 0$, $V_a > 0$, and α, μ are constants. Sketch curves showing the relation between I and V_a for a series of fixed negative values of V_g. The anode potential is maintained by an anode battery of voltage V whose negative terminal is connected to the cathode and whose positive terminal is connected through a load resistor of resistance R_L to the anode. Show that the anode potential is related to the anode current by the equation

$$V_a = V - IR_L$$

Describe a method of numerical solution of the above two equations so as to obtain the relation between I and V_g. Apply the method when $V = 300$ volts, $R_L = 50,000$ ohms, $\mu = 20$, and $\alpha = 2 \times 10^{-4}$ amp/volt$^{\frac{3}{2}}$.

★2. In the arrangement shown in the diagram it is required to choose the value of the bias resistor R_k so as to make the grid voltage have a prescribed negative value V_g. Calculate the value of R_k on the assumption that the tube behaves in accordance with the Thévenin equivalent circuit in Part 2, Fig. 7.8. Evaluate R_k if $V_g = -6$ volts, $\mu = 20$, $\mu R = 10,000$ ohms, $V_0 = 2$ volts, $V = 200$ volts, and $R_L = 20,000$ ohms. Evaluate also the resulting anode current.

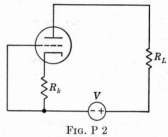

FIG. P 2

★3. To the input terminals of the amplifier shown in the diagram is applied a voltage $A \cos \omega t - B$, where A and B are positive constants $(A < B)$, t denotes time, and ω is an angular oscillation frequency. Assuming that the tube behaves in accordance

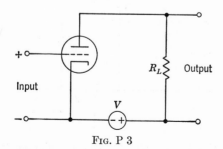

FIG. P 3

with the Thévenin equivalent circuit in Part 2, Fig. 7.8, calculate the oscillatory component of the voltage between the output terminals. Deduce the gain of the amplifier for oscillations of angular frequency ω. Evaluate the gain if the amplification factor of the tube is 20, the anode resistance of the tube is 10,000 ohms, and the value of the load resistance R_L is 20,000 ohms.

★**4.** A cathode-follower stage in an amplifier is arranged as shown in the diagram. The tube may be assumed to behave in accordance with the Thévenin equivalent circuit in Part 2, Fig. 7.8. If a voltage V_1 is applied between the input terminals, calculate the voltage V_2 produced between the output terminals. Evaluate the output voltage if $V_1 = 1$ volt, $V = 100$ volts, $R_k = 8,000$ ohms, $\mu = 20$, $\mu R = 10,000$ ohms, and $V_0 = 2$ volts.

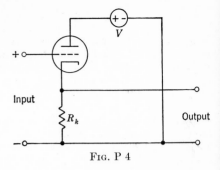
Fig. P 4

★**5.** In the previous problem a small variation δV_1 is made in the input voltage. Calculate the corresponding change δV_2 in the output voltage. Show that the magnitude of the ratio of δV_2 to δV_1 is always less than unity. Evaluate the ratio if the amplification factor of the tube is 20, the anode resistance of the tube is 10,000 ohms, and $R_k = 8,000$ ohms.

★**6.** In the arrangement shown in the diagram it may be assumed that the tube behaves in accordance with the Norton equivalent circuit in Part 2, Fig. 7.15, and that the anode resistance may be taken as indefinitely large. Calculate the grid voltage and the anode current. Evaluate these quantities if $G = 1,500$ μmhos, $\mu' = 20$, $V_s = 100$ volts, $V_0 = 2$ volts, and $R_k = 500$ ohms.

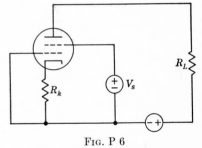
Fig. P 6

★**7.** A grounded-grid amplifier is arranged as shown in the diagram, and the tube behaves in accordance with the Thévenin equivalent circuit in Part 2, Fig. 7.8. If a voltage V_1 is applied at the input terminals, calculate (a) the voltage of the cathode relative to the grid and (b) the voltage V_2 between the output terminals. If V_1

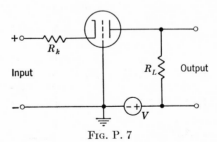
Fig. P. 7

receives a small variation δV_1, calculate the corresponding small variation δV_2 in V_2 and deduce the gain of the amplifier. Evaluate the gain if the amplification factor of the tube is 20, the anode resistance is 10,000 ohms, the load resistance R_L is 20,000 ohms, and the value R_k of the cathode resistor is small enough to be neglected.

★**8.** In the previous problem calculate the equivalent resistance between the input terminals when the output terminals are on open circuit. Evaluate the equivalent resistance for the numerical values quoted in the previous problem.

9. An arrangement for reducing variations in the voltage of a d-c power supply is constructed as indicated in the diagram. The supply voltage is V_1 and the load voltage is V_2, the load resistance being R_L. It may be assumed that the vacuum tube behaves in accordance with the Thévenin equivalent circuit in Part 2, Fig. 7.8. If a variation δV_1 in the supply voltage causes a variation δV_2 in the load voltage, calculate the ratio of δV_2 to δV_1. Evaluate the ratio if $\mu = 20$, $\mu R = 20{,}000$ ohms, and $R_L = 500$ ohms.

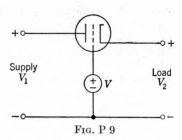

Fig. P 9

10. In the previous problem state what effect on the output voltage V_2 is produced by variations in the voltage V. Explain what happens if the voltage V is the output voltage of a vacuum-tube amplifier for which the input voltage is proportional to V_2.

11. A triode vacuum tube is provided with a feedback resistor connecting the anode to the grid, and the arrangement is used as shown in the diagram. It may be assumed that the behavior of the vacuum tube is described by the Thévenin equivalent circuit in Part, 2, Fig. 7.8, and that the anode resistance is negligible compared with

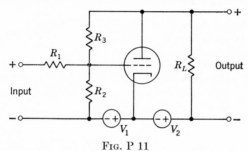

Fig. P 11

the other resistances involved. If an increment δV_i is made in the input voltage, calculate the corresponding increment in the output voltage. Show that, if the amplification factor of the tube is high and R_1, R_2, and R_3 are all of the same order of magnitude, the ratio of the increment in the output voltage to the increment in the input voltage is $-R_3/R_1$.

12. In the previous problem the feedback resistor is replaced by a diode for which the direction of conductance is from the anode terminal of the triode to the grid terminal of the triode. If the diode obeys Child's law, sketch the relation between the increment in output voltage and the corresponding increment in input voltage.

13. Because of nonlinearity in the characteristic curve of a vacuum tube, the relation between the output voltage V_2 and the input voltage V_1 of an amplifier is given by the equation

$$V_2 = a + bV_1 + cV_1{}^2$$

If the input voltage varies with time t in accordance with the equation $V_1 = V_0 \cos \omega t$, show that the output voltage contains contributions that vary with time proportionally to $\cos \omega t$ and $\cos 2\omega t$. Calculate the ratio of the amplitude of the output oscillation of angular frequency 2ω to the amplitude of the output oscillation of angular frequency ω.

14. A triode vacuum tube has a cathode at zero potential, a grid at a positive potential, and an anode at a negative potential, so that there is no current through the tube from the anode to the grid. There is now introduced into the tube a small amount of gas each of whose molecules is such that, if hit by an electron that has been accelerated through a voltage V or more, it separates into an electron and a positive ion. It is now found that current passes through the tube from the anode to the grid if the grid voltage exceeds V. Explain this phenomenon.

15. A transistor may be assumed to behave in accordance with the equivalent network shown in the diagram. If the relations between the input voltage and current

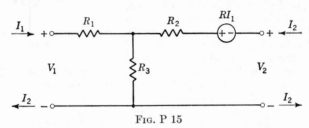

FIG. P 15

V_1, I_1 and the output voltage and current V_2, I_2 are written like Part 2, Eqs. (3.50) and (3.51), evaluate r_{11}, r_{22}, r_{12}, and r_{21}. Show that r_{12} and r_{21} are unequal, and explain why.

16. In the previous problem express the relations between V_1, I_1 and V_2, I_2 in the form described in Chap. 3, Prob. 8, calculating the values of the coefficients A, B, C, and D.

17. In Prob. 15 the terminals at the left are used as input terminals and the terminals at the right as output terminals. If a load resistor of resistance R_L is connected across the output terminals, calculate the ratio of the voltage V_2 across the load to the input voltage V_1. Plot this ratio as a function of R_L if $R_1 = 10^3$ ohms, $R_2 = 5 \times 10^4$ ohms, $R_3 = 10$ ohms, and $R = 2 \times 10^6$ ohms.

18. In the previous problem calculate the input resistance. Plot the input resistance as a function of the load resistance R_L if $R_1 = 10^3$ ohms, $R_2 = 5 \times 10^4$ ohms, $R_3 = 10$ ohms, and $R = 2 \times 10^6$ ohms.

Part 3, Chapter 1

1. Waves of water are produced at one end of a long tank. The crests and troughs are propagated along the length of the tank, and their velocity is v. Show that a particular crest intersects a vertical plane making an angle θ with the length of the tank in a point that moves horizontally with velocity $v \sec \theta$. Prove that the velocity of the waves does not constitute a vector but that the reciprocal of the velocity is a vector.

★2. An electron is moving with velocity represented in magnitude and direction by the vector **v**. If **v** varies with time t, explain why the acceleration of the electron is represented in magnitude and direction by the vector $d\mathbf{v}/dt$.

★3. In a system of rectangular cartesian coordinates a vector **A** has components (A_x, A_y, A_z) and a vector **B** has components (B_x, B_y, B_z). Prove that

$$\mathbf{A} \cdot \mathbf{B} = A_x B_x + A_y B_y + A_z B_z$$

★4. A cube has unit edges, three of which lie along the positive coordinate axes. Write down the components of the four vectors that coincide with the diagonals of the cube and start from the points $(0,0,0)$, $(1,0,0)$, $(0,1,0)$, and $(0,0,1)$. Evaluate the scalar product of the first and last of these vectors.

★5. Show that the area of a parallelogram for which two adjacent sides are represented by the vectors **A** and **B** is the magnitude of the vector $\mathbf{A} \times \mathbf{B}$.

★6. In a plane, three vectors **A**, **B**, and **C** are drawn from an origin, and their tips specify the vertices of a triangle. Prove that the area of the triangle is the magnitude of the vector $\frac{1}{2}(\mathbf{A} \times \mathbf{B} + \mathbf{B} \times \mathbf{C} + \mathbf{C} \times \mathbf{A})$.

★7. If **i**, **j**, and **k** are unit vectors along the x, y, and z axes in a system of right-handed rectangular cartesian coordinates, prove that

$$\mathbf{i} \times \mathbf{j} = \mathbf{k} = -\mathbf{j} \times \mathbf{i}$$
$$\mathbf{j} \times \mathbf{k} = \mathbf{i} = -\mathbf{k} \times \mathbf{j}$$
$$\mathbf{k} \times \mathbf{i} = \mathbf{j} = -\mathbf{i} \times \mathbf{k}$$

Deduce that, for a vector **A** having components (A_x, A_y, A_z) and a vector **B** having components (B_x, B_y, B_z),

$$\mathbf{A} \times \mathbf{B} = \begin{vmatrix} \mathbf{i} & \mathbf{j} & \mathbf{k} \\ A_x & A_y & A_z \\ B_x & B_y & B_z \end{vmatrix}$$

8. Repeat Prob. 6 when the three vectors **A**, **B**, and **C** are drawn from an origin in three-dimensional space. Calculate the area of a triangle whose vertices in a system of rectangular cartesian coordinates are located at the points $(1, -2, 3)$, $(3, 1, -2)$, and $(-2, 3, 1)$. Give the components of a unit vector normal to the triangle.

★9. Show that the volume of a parallelepiped for which three concurrent edges are represented by the vectors **A**, **B**, and **C** is equal to the magnitude of the quantity $(\mathbf{A} \times \mathbf{B}) \cdot \mathbf{C}$.

★10. For any three vectors **A**, **B**, and **C** show that

$$(\mathbf{A} \times \mathbf{B}) \cdot \mathbf{C} = (\mathbf{C} \times \mathbf{A}) \cdot \mathbf{B} = (\mathbf{B} \times \mathbf{C}) \cdot \mathbf{A} = \begin{vmatrix} A_x & A_y & A_z \\ B_x & B_y & B_z \\ C_x & C_y & C_z \end{vmatrix}$$

★11. AB is a diameter of a circle of radius a and there is a uniform electric field parallel to AB, the electric vector being **E**. The vector $d\mathbf{s}$ is a vector element of length of either semicircle joining A to B, and it points along the semicircle from A to B. Evaluate

$$\int \mathbf{E} \cdot d\mathbf{s}$$

taken along either semicircle from A to B.

★12. A spherical conducting tank contains water of conductivity σ, and at the center of the tank there is a small spherical conducting electrode. A steady current I follows symmetrically from the electrode to the wall of the tank. In the water is drawn an elliptical area S that subtends at the electrode a circular cone of semivertical angle θ. At a point P of S there is a vector element of area $d\mathbf{S}$ pointing away from the side of S on which the electrode exists. If the current-density vector at P is **J**, evaluate

$$\int_S \mathbf{J} \cdot d\mathbf{S}$$

taken over the elliptical area.

13. A point charge of strength Q is located at the origin O of a system of cartesian coordinates (x, y, z). A cylinder of radius a is drawn with its axis coinciding with the x coordinate axis, and the cylinder is intercepted by the plane $x = b$, b being positive. The normal cross section of the cylinder in this plane is denoted by S_1. The portion of the cylinder for which $0 < x < b$ is denoted by S_2, and the portion for which $x < 0$ is denoted by S_3. If $d\mathbf{S}$ is a vector element of area of S_1, directed parallel to the positive x axis, show that

$$\int_{S_1} \mathbf{D} \cdot d\mathbf{S} = \frac{Q}{2} \left[1 - \frac{b}{(a^2 + b^2)^{\frac{1}{2}}} \right]$$

the integral being taken over the circle S_1. If $d\mathbf{S}$ is a vector element of area of S_2, evaluate

$$\int_{S_2} \mathbf{D} \cdot d\mathbf{S}$$

If $d\mathbf{S}$ is a vector element of area of S_3, evaluate

$$\int_{S_3} \mathbf{D} \cdot d\mathbf{S}$$

Verify that the sum of these three integrals is Q, and give a physical reason for this result.

14. A conducting material is such that, when a uniform electric field represented by an electric vector $\mathbf{E}$ is applied in the conductor, there results a uniform electric current represented by the current-density vector $\mathbf{J}$. The conducting material is what is known as nonisotropic, so that the direction of $\mathbf{J}$ does not coincide with the direction of $\mathbf{E}$. Prove that the rate of production of heat per unit volume is given by the scalar product $\mathbf{E} \cdot \mathbf{J}$.

Part 3, Chapter 2

★1. The free space between the inner and outer conductors of a coaxial transmission line has inductivity μ_v and capacitivity ϵ_v. There is a steady current I along one conductor and back along the other. In the magnetic field between the conductors an electron (charge e) moves with uniform velocity v parallel to the current on the inner conductor. If r is the distance of the electron from the axis of the transmission line, calculate in magnitude and direction the force required to keep the particle moving in this way. Prove that the force could be applied by charges Q and $-Q$ per unit length on the inner and outer conductors, respectively, if $Q = (v/c^2)I$ and $c = 1/(\mu_v \epsilon_v)^{\frac{1}{2}}$. If the electron acquired its velocity by acceleration through 1,000 volts, and if $I = 1$ amp, calculate the required value of Q.

★2. In a system of cartesian coordinates (x,y,z) there is a pair of long, thin wires parallel to the z axis and passing through the points $(\frac{1}{2}d,0,0)$ and $(-\frac{1}{2}d,0,0)$. There is a steady current I along each wire in the direction of the positive z axis, and the inductivity of the medium is μ. Calculate the magnetic flux density at the point $(x,0,0)$ and plot it as a function of x. Calculate the magnetic flux density at the point $(0,y,0)$ and plot it as a function of y. Sketch the lines of magnetic flux.

★3. Four long thin straight wires are mounted in air with their lengths parallel and horizontal. They intersect a vertical plane perpendicular to their lengths in the vertices of a rectangle. One pair of sides of the rectangle is horizontal and of length a, while the other pair is vertical and of length b. The upper pair of wires is used as a twin-wire transmission line with a steady current I_1 along one wire and back along the other. The lower pair is used similarly, the current being I_2. Wires in the same vertical plane carry currents in opposite directions. Calculate the magnetic flux density at a point distant y vertically above the center of the rectangle. If $I_1 = I_2$, show that the magnetic flux density vanishes at the center of the rectangle, and sketch the lines of magnetic flux.

★4. In the previous problem the upper wires carry uniformly distributed charges Q and $-Q$ per unit length while the lower wires carry uniformly distributed charges $-Q$ and Q per unit length, wires in the same vertical plane having charges of opposite sign. Sketch the lines of electric force, and show how they are related to the lines of magnetic flux in the previous problem for the case $I_1 = I_2$.

5. A long straight conductor in air is in the form of a hollow circular cylinder of uniform wall thickness, the internal radius being a and the external radius being b. A current I flows along the conductor distributed uniformly over the cross section. Calculate the magnetic flux density at distance r from the axis of the conductor (a) when $r \geq b$, (b) when $a \leq r \leq b$, and (c) when $r \leq a$. On the assumption that $a = \frac{3}{4}b$, plot as a function of r the ratio of the magnetic flux density at distance r to the magnetic flux density at the outer surface of the conductor.

★6. In Prob. 3, $I_1 = I_2 = I$ and $a = b = d$. A plane at an angle $\frac{1}{4}\pi$ with the horizontal passes through a pair of wires, and a tube of magnetic flux intersects this plane in a small area dS at distance r ($< d/\sqrt{2}$) from the line of zero magnetic flux density. Calculate the magnetic flux associated with the tube. Evaluate the magnetic flux in webers if $I = 1$ amp, $d = 10$ cm, $r = 3$ cm, and $dS = 1$ cm².

★7. A long thin straight wire in free space is carrying a current I. In a plane through the wire an equilateral triangle of side a is drawn with a vertex on the wire and the opposite side parallel to the wire. Calculate the magnetic flux threading the triangle. If $I = 1$ amp and $a = 10$ cm, evaluate the magnetic flux threading the triangle in webers.

8. A solid circular wire of radius a carries a steady current I uniformly distributed over the cross section. A coaxial cylindrical surface is drawn within the wire having a radius such that half the magnetic flux within the wire is enclosed by the surface and the other half lies between the surface and the boundary of the wire. Calculate the radius of the cylindrical surface.

Part 3, Chapter 3

★1. The interior of a thin hollow spherical conductor has radius a. A thin wire of length $2a$ is fitted so as to run along a diameter of the sphere. A steady current I flows along the wire and returns uniformly through the conducting sphere. Calculate the magnetic field strength at any point inside the sphere a distance r from the axis of the wire. Explain why the result is independent of the radius of the sphere. Evaluate the magnetic field strength in amperes per meter if $I = 1$ amp and $r = 1$ cm.

2. Two hollow conducting circular cones are constructed one with semivertical angle α and the other with semivertical angle β. They are arranged coaxially with vertices in contact. A total current I flows symmetrically along the generators of one cone toward the common vertex and symmetrically away from the vertex on the other cone. Show that the magnetic field between the cones is the same as that due to a current I along the common axis in the absence of the cones. At a point distant R from the common vertex, calculate the current per unit width on the cone of angle α and that on the cone of angle β. If $I = 1$ amp, evaluate the current per unit width at a point on either cone distant 10 cm from the axis.

★3. A toroidal inductor is formed by selecting a tube of magnetic flux from the field of an infinite straight wire carrying a current in air and enveloping the tube by a current distributed appropriately round the length of the tube. The cross section of the toroid has area S, and its linear dimensions are small compared with its distance r from the axis of the toroid. Calculate the magnetic field strength within the inductor and the total solenoidal current round the toroid. Deduce the ratio of the total magnetic flux threading the inductor to the total current round it. Evaluate the ratio if $r = 10$ cm and $S = 3$ cm².

★4. An equilateral triangle of side a is rotated about a line in its plane that is parallel to one side and does not intersect the other two sides. The distance from the axis of rotation to the parallel side is b and to the opposite vertex of the triangle is

$b + a \sqrt{3}/2$. The toroidal surface thus formed is used as a toroidal inductor with an air core and with a total current I distributed uniformly round the toroid. Calculate the total magnetic flux threading the toroid.

★5. Repeat the previous problem if the distance from the axis of rotation to the parallel side of the triangle is b while that to the opposite vertex is $b - a \sqrt{3}/2$, assumed to be positive.

★6. An indefinitely thin straight wire carries steady current I. A system of cylindrical polar coordinates (r,θ,z) is introduced in which r denotes distance from the axis of the wire, θ denotes azimuth around the wire in the direction related by the right-hand-screw rule to the direction of the current, and z denotes distance measured parallel to the wire in the direction of current flow. On the cylinder $r = a$, a closed sinuous curve C is drawn for which $z = b \sin n\theta$, n being any positive integer. Evaluate

$$\int \mathbf{H} \cdot d\mathbf{s}$$

along the curve C from the point where $\theta = 0$ to the point where $\theta = \pi/n$, showing that it is independent of b. Deduce that

$$\int \mathbf{H} \cdot d\mathbf{s}$$

taken round the entire closed curve C from $\theta = 0$ to $\theta = 2\pi$ is equal to the current I threading the curve.

Part 3, Chapter 4

★1. Four coaxial circular cylinders have radii a, b, c, and d $(a < b < c < d)$. There is metal between the cylinders of radii a and b and also between the cylinders of radii c and d. The arrangement forms a coaxial transmission line, and the inductivity is everywhere the same. A steady current I flows along the inner conductor and back along the outer conductor, uniformly distributed over the cross section in each case. It may be assumed from symmetry that all lines of magnetic flux are circles with axis along the axis of the transmission line and that the magnetic field strength H is a function only of distance r from the common axis. From the circulation law for the magnetic vector deduce the magnetic field strength (a) for $r \leq a$, (b) for $r \geq d$, (c) for $b \leq r \leq c$, (d) for $a \leq r \leq b$, and (e) for $c \leq r \leq d$. Plot H as a function of r.

★2. A coaxial inductor made of thin metal has inner radius a and outer radius c, with flat ends at a distance l apart. A geometrical circular cylinder is drawn coaxial with the inductor and of radius b $(a < b < c)$. The part of the inductor within the cylinder of radius b is filled with a medium of inductivity μ, and the inductivity elsewhere is μ_v. If a steady current I flows round the inductor, uniformly distributed round the perimeter, calculate (a) the magnetic flux threading the inductor within the medium of inductivity μ_v and (b) the magnetic flux threading the inductor within the medium of inductivity μ. Evaluate the ratio of the latter flux to the total flux threading the inductor if $a = 1$ cm, $b = 2$ cm, $c = 10$ cm, and $\mu/\mu_v = 1,000$.

★3. The azimuthal angle round an axis l is denoted by θ. For $0 < \theta < \alpha$ the inductivity is μ_1, and for $\alpha < \theta < 2\pi$ the inductivity is μ_2. A thin wire lying along the axis l carries a steady current I. Assuming that the lines of magnetic flux are circular, calculate the magnetic field strength at distance r from the wire (a) in the medium of inductivity μ_1 and (b) in the medium of inductivity μ_2. If $I = 1$ amp, $\mu_1 = \mu_v$, $\mu_2 = 1,000\mu_v$, and $\alpha = \pi/6$, evaluate the magnetic flux density in the medium of inductivity μ_v at distance 1 cm from the wire.

★4. A long thin solenoid of length l, with open ends at A and B, carries a magnetic flux Φ internally from B to A. Calculate the magnetic flux density at a point on BA produced at a distance x beyond A. Calculate also the magnetic flux density at a point outside the solenoid equidistant from A and B, the common distance r being in excess of half of the length of the solenoid. Convert the calculated magnetic flux densities into magnetic field strengths, assuming that the medium is free space. Evaluate the magnetic field strengths if $\Phi = 1$ μweber and $l = x = r = 10$ cm. Explain how these magnetic field strengths can be interpreted as currents per unit length.

★5. A thin toroidal inductor conveys an amount of flux Φ round a circular path of radius r. A quadrant of the toroid is now removed without changing the magnetic flux threading the remainder of the inductor. Calculate the resulting magnetic-flux-density vector at the center of the circle in magnitude and direction. If the quadrant of the toroid is now replaced and the other three quadrants are removed, show that the magnetic-flux-density vector at the center of the circle is reversed.

★6. $ABCD$ is a square labeled cyclically. Along the edge AB there is a magnetic needle of pole strength Φ with the positive pole at A and the negative pole at B. Along the side CD there is a thin solenoid carrying a magnetic flux Φ from D to C. Prove that, of all the flux leaving the positive pole of the magnetic needle, one-half passes to the negative pole through the solenoid. Explain in what way the lines of magnetic flux of the system would be changed if the magnetic needle were along the edge AD with the positive pole at A and the solenoid were along the edge BC carrying magnetic flux from B to C.

★7. An electric point charge of strength Q executes a circular orbit of radius r with uniform speed v in air. Along the axis of the orbit there is a magnetic needle of length l whose poles are of strengths Φ and $-\Phi$. The mid-point of the magnet coincides with the center of the orbit, and the direction of motion in the orbit is right-handed about the direction from the negative to the positive pole of the magnet. Calculate in magnitude and direction the force exerted by the magnet on the point charge. Evaluate the force if $l = 10$ cm, $r = 1$ cm, $\Phi = 1$ μweber, $Q = 1$ μcoulomb, and $v = 1$ m/sec.

★8. A cylindrical bar magnet is uniformly magnetized parallel to its length. It is bent into a circle so that the flat ends are nearly in contact, and in the air gap between the ends a nearly uniform magnetic field is produced. If M is the intensity of magnetization of the magnet, calculate the magnetic flux density in the gap. Evaluate the magnetic flux density if $M = 10^5$ amp/m.

9. A thin iron ring of radius a in air has an inductivity μ and a cross-sectional area S whose linear dimensions are small compared with a. Closely spaced turns of thin insulated wire are wound onto the ring in such a way that there are n_1 uniformly spaced turns round one half of the ring and n_2 uniformly spaced turns round the other half of the ring. A steady current I is passed through the wire. Calculate the magnetic flux density at a point outside the iron on the axis of symmetry of the ring at its center (a) if $n_1 = n_2$ and (b) if $n_1 \neq n_2$. Evaluate the magnetic flux density if $n_1 = 495$, $n_2 = 505$, $I = 1$ amp, $a = 10$ cm, $S = 3$ cm^2, and $\mu = 1,000\mu_v$.

10. A uniform steady current I per unit width flows in a horizontal sheet in the ionosphere at a height h above the Earth's surface, which may be assumed flat. Taking the Earth and the intervening atmosphere to be nonconducting and nonmagnetic, calculate the magnetic field strength produced at the Earth's surface. If the magnetic flux density produced by the current at the Earth's surface is 10^{-4} gauss, deduce the current per unit width in the ionosphere.

11. A circular cylinder of soft iron of radius a has a small hole bored along its axis. Through the hole is threaded a long straight insulated wire carrying a steady current I. The inductivity of the soft iron is μ, and that outside the iron is μ_v. Calculate, for all points both inside and outside the cylinder, (a) the magnetic vector and (b) the magnetic-flux-density vector.

12. In a large piece of soft iron is cut a cavity in the form of a circular cylinder of radius a. The inductivity of the soft iron is μ, and that within the cavity is μ_v. A steady current I passes through a long straight insulated wire that runs through the iron and along the axis of the cavity. Calculate for all points inside and outside the cavity (a) the magnetic vector and (b) the magnetic-flux-density vector.

13. A thin solenoid of length s conveying a fixed magnetic flux Φ exists in air (inductivity μ) with its axis parallel to a distant perfectly conducting plane sheet of infinite dimensions. The solenoid is now moved toward the sheet until the separation between them is d. Assuming that there is no magnetic field on the opposite side of the sheet, calculate the current per unit width induced on the sheet at the foot of the perpendicular from the center of the solenoid.

14. A conducting sheet S separates a medium numbered 1 from a medium numbered 2 and at a point P carries a current per unit width represented vectorially by **I**. At a point in medium 1 close to P the component of the magnetic vector tangential to S is represented vectorially by $\mathbf{H}_{T1}$. At a point in medium 2 close to P the component of the magnetic vector tangential to S is represented vectorially by $\mathbf{H}_{T2}$. If **n** is a unit vector normal to S at P and pointing from medium 2 to medium 1, show that $\mathbf{H}_{T1} - \mathbf{H}_{T2} = \mathbf{I} \times \mathbf{n}$. Deduce that, at any interface over which there is no current, the tangential component of the magnetic vector is continuous.

15. A surface S carrying no current constitutes the interface between two media of inductivities μ_1 and μ_2. Show that the tangential component of the magnetic vector and the normal component of the magnetic-flux-density vector are continuous at the interface. Deduce that lines of magnetic flux are refracted at the interface and that, if θ_1, θ_2 are the angles made with the normal to S at the crossing point by the lines of flux in the media of inductivities μ_1, μ_2, respectively, then $\mu_1 \cot \theta_1 = \mu_2 \cot \theta_2$. (Compare Part 1, Chap. 4, Prob. 47.)

16. Show that there is no refraction of lines of magnetic flux when they are parallel or perpendicular to an interface between two media of different inductivities. (Compare Part 1, Chap. 4, Prob. 48.)

17. In a medium of inductivity μ there is a uniform magnetic field in which the magnetic field strength is H and the magnetic flux density is B. There exists in the medium a cylindrical cavity in which the axis is parallel to the field and the inductivity is μ_v. The length of the cavity is s, and the normal cross-sectional area is S. If s is small compared with the linear dimensions of S, show that the magnetic flux density in the cavity is B. If the linear dimensions of S are small compared with s, show that the magnetic flux density in the cavity is $\mu_v H$. (Compare Part 1, Chap. 4, Prob. 49.)

Part 3, Chapter 5

★1. A solenoid is formed from thin metal sheet, and a normal cross section is a regular hexagon of edge a. Its length s is large compared with a, and the inductivity of the medium is μ. Calculate the inductance of the solenoid, neglecting nonuniformity of the magnetic field.

★2. An open-ended circular cylinder of radius a has length l. The center point of the cylinder is joined to the rim existing at each end of the cylinder by a circular cone. The toroidal surface of triangular cross section thus formed is occupied by metal sheet and used as a toroidal inductor. Current flows symmetrically along one half of the cone toward the apex and then along the other half of the cone away from the apex, the circuit being completed through the cylinder. If the medium within the inductor has inductivity μ, calculate the inductance, showing that it is independent of the magnitude of a. Evaluate the inductance if $l = 10$ cm and the interior of the toroid is part of a vacuum tube.

★3. A strip transmission line consists of a pair of horizontal conducting strips of width b and separation a arranged one vertically above the other. The medium between the strips has inductivity μ, capacitivity ϵ, and conductivity σ. A unit length of the line is cut off by vertical planes perpendicular to the length of the line, and in these vertical planes rectangular conducting sheets of width b and height a are fitted so as to convert the section of line into a solenoid. Calculate the inductance of this unit length of the line, assuming that nonuniformity of the magnetic field is avoided. Calculate also the capacitance of the line per unit length (neglecting fringing) and the conductance of the line per unit length. Evaluate the inductance, capacitance, and conductance per unit length if $a = 1$ mm, $b = 1$ cm, $\mu = \mu_v$, $\epsilon = 7\epsilon_v$, and $\sigma = 10^{-15}$ mho/m.

★4. The form of a toroidal inductor is made of material of inductivity μ and is bounded by two coaxial cylinders of radii a and b $(a < b)$ and by a pair of planes perpendicular to the common axis at distance l apart. Thin insulated wire is wound closely and uniformly along the whole perimeter of the form so that each turn is nearly in a plane through the axis of symmetry of the toroid. If there are n turns of wire altogether, calculate the inductance of the inductor. Evaluate the inductance if $l = 10$ cm, $a = 2$ cm, $b = 5$ cm, $\mu = \mu_v$, and $n = 100$. Evaluate the inductance also if $\mu = 1,000\mu_v$, $n = 1,000$, and the geometrical dimensions are the same as those given before.

★5. A coaxial inductor made of thin metal sheet has an inner conductor of radius a and an outer conductor of radius c, the flat ends being at a distance l apart. A coaxial circular cylinder of radius b is drawn, the value of b being intermediate between a and c. With the cylinder of radius b the inductivity is μ_1, and outside this cylinder the inductivity is μ_2. Calculate the inductance of the coaxial inductor.

★6. In the previous problem a toroidal inductor is formed by replacing the metal sheet by n turns of wire uniformly wound round the perimeter. Calculate the inductance of the toroidal inductor. Evaluate the inductance if $\mu_1 = 1,000\mu_v$, $\mu_2 = \mu_v$, $n = 100$, $l = 10$ cm, $a = 2$ cm, $b = 4$ cm, and c has the values (a) 5 cm and (b) 10 cm.

7. A coaxial inductor made of thin metal sheet has an inner conductor of radius a and an outer conductor of radius b, the flat ends being at a distance l apart. A plane is drawn through the common axis, and the values of the inductivity on the two sides of the plane are μ_1 and μ_2. Calculate the inductance of the inductor.

8. In the previous problem the metal sheet is stripped from the core, which is then used as the form of a multiturn toroidal inductor producing the same magnetic field in the core. Calculate the ratio of the number of turns required on the section of inductivity μ_2 to the number required on the section of inductivity μ_1. Evaluate this ratio if $\mu_1 = 1,000\mu_v$ and $\mu_2 = \mu_v$.

9. On a cylindrical form of length s and cross-sectional area S is wound a solenoid having n turns uniformly distributed along the length. Over this solenoid is wound an almost identical solenoid also having n turns. Assuming that the inductivity of the form is μ, that the magnetic field in the form is uniform, and that no appreciable magnetic flux can pass between the two windings, calculate the inductance of the inductor when (a) the two wires at one end are connected to one terminal of the inductor and the two wires at the other end are connected to the other terminal, (b) when the wires at one end are connected together and the wires at the other end are connected to the terminals, and (c) when a wire at one end is connected to a wire at the other end and the remaining wires are connected to the terminals.

★10. A solenoidal inductor possesses n turns uniformly wound on a form of inductivity μ having the shape of a circular cylinder of length l and radius a. The wire is thin and has a resistance r per unit length. A battery of voltage V is connected between the terminals of the inductor, and it may be assumed that the magnetic field within the form is uniform. Calculate the magnetic flux threading the wire.

11. A solenoid is wound on a cylindrical form of length s and cross-sectional area S made of material of inductivity μ. Each turn of wire has resistance r, and the turns are distributed uniformly along the length of the form. A current is passed through the coil from a battery of voltage V, and it may be assumed that the magnetic field in the form is uniform. The coil is wound with a sufficient number of turns to prevent the rate of conversion of electrical energy into heat in the wire from exceeding P. Calculate the minimum possible inductance of the coil. Evaluate the minimum inductance if $s = 10$ cm, $S = 10$ cm^2, $\mu = \mu_v$, $r = 0.1$ ohm, $V = 10$ volts, and $P = 1$ watt.

12. Two vertical planes p_1 and p_2 are intercepted by a horizontal plane p_3. A conducting sheet occupies the portion of p_1 above p_3, the portion of p_3 between p_1 and p_2, and the portion of p_2 above p_3, thereby forming a conducting trough of width w. A horizontal wire of radius a runs perpendicularly across from one vertical side of the trough to the other at a height h above the bottom. It may be assumed that a is small compared with h and that the medium in the trough has inductivity μ. The arrangement is used as an inductor by passing current along the wire and completing the circuit through the trough. Calculate the inductance.

13. An inductor has the form of a cylindrical solenoid of length s with two layers of wires each carrying n turns. The inner and outer layers have normal cross-sectional areas S_1 and S_2, and the current flows round both layers in the same direction. The medium is air (inductivity μ), and the magnetic field in the coil may be assumed parallel. If I is the current in an individual turn, calculate (a) the magnetic flux threading each turn of the inner layer, (b) the magnetic flux threading between the layers, (c) the magnetic flux threading the wire, and (d) the inductance of the coil. Evaluate the inductance if the layers are wound on coaxial circular cylinders of radii 1 and 1.2 cm, each being of length 5 cm, and the total number of turns is 100.

Part 3, Chapter 6

★1. In a mass spectroscope a series of particles of masses m_1, m_2, . . . are projected vertically upward from a point O in a uniform horizontal magnetic field of flux density B, and gravity may be neglected. All particles carry the same charge e and have the same velocity of projection u. Calculate the distances from O at which the particles first return to the horizontal plane through O. Evaluate the distance for particles of mass equal to 32 times the mass of a proton if e is equal to the charge on a proton, the particles are accelerated from rest through a potential difference of 1,000 volts, and $B = 1,000$ gauss.

★2. In a cyclotron a particle of charge e and mass m is projected from a point O at right angles to a uniform magnetic field of flux density B. After describing a semi-circular path of radius a, the particle is subject to an accelerating voltage V that does not change the direction of motion but instantaneously increases the kinetic energy by an amount eV. Calculate the distance of the particle from the point O after describing a further semicircular path. Show that the time of traverse for the two semicircles is the same.

★3. In a system of rectangular cartesian coordinates (x,y,z) there is a uniform magnetic field in which the magnetic-flux-density vector is $(0,0,B)$. A particle of charge e is projected at time zero from the point $(a,0,0)$ with velocity $(0,v,w)$. Describe the trajectory of the particle, and calculate the coordinates of the particle at a time t after projection.

★4. A cathode-ray tube has gun voltage V, and the spot is capable of being deflected simultaneously in two directions at right angles. Deflection in one direction is by means of an electric field, and that in the other direction is by means of a magnetic field. The deflecting electric and magnetic fields influence the electron beam over the same path length and at the same distance from the screen. Both deflecting fields vary in strength with time t periodically. The periodic time is $2\pi/\omega$, the deflecting electric field strength being $E_0 \cos \omega t$ and the deflecting magnetic flux density $B_0 \sin \omega t$. With suitable approximations show that the spot on the screen describes an ellipse and calculate the axis ratio. If $V = 1{,}000$ volts, evaluate the ratio of E_0 to B_0 required to produce a circle on the screen.

5. In the previous problem the deflecting electric and magnetic fields are now maintained at steady values but the design of the gun is modified so that the electron beam contains electrons with a wide range of velocities. Prove that the trace on the screen is part of a parabola.

★6. A cathode-ray tube has a beam velocity v, and its deflecting field (electric or magnetic) influences the beam over a length L. The deflecting field oscillates sinusoidally with time, executing f complete oscillations per unit time. Prove that the deflection of the spot on the screen cannot follow the variation of the deflecting field faithfully unless f is small compared with $v/2\pi L$. Evaluate this limiting frequency if $L = 3$ cm and the gun potential is $1{,}000$ volts.

★7. In a homogeneous medium of inductivity μ four long thin parallel wires intersect a plane normal to them in the corners of a square of edge a. The current in each wire is of magnitude I, but the currents at the opposite ends of one diagonal of the square flow in the opposite direction to the currents at the opposite ends of the other diagonal. Calculate in magnitude and direction the force on each wire per unit length. Evaluate the force per unit length if $I = 1$ amp, $a = 10$ cm, and $\mu = \mu_v$.

★8. A rectangular coil is mounted so that it can turn on an axis running through the mid-points of opposite sides. There are n turns of wire on the coil, each carrying a steady current I and each of area S. There is a uniform magnetic field of flux density B perpendicular to the axis of rotation. If κ is the moment of inertia of the coil about its axis of rotation, show that the equation of motion of the coil (neglecting frictional effects) is

$$\kappa \frac{d^2\theta}{dt^2} = -nIBS \sin \theta$$

where θ is the angle measured from the direction of the magnetic field to the coil-normal whose direction is related to the current by the right-hand-screw rule. By multiplying the equation of motion by $2\, d\theta/dt$ and integrating, show how to calculate the angular velocity of the coil in terms of θ, assuming that the coil starts from rest at $\theta = \theta_0$. If the coil is slightly disturbed from its position of unstable equilibrium, calculate the angular velocity with which it reaches the position of stable equilibrium.

9. An electric motor of the type described in connection with Part 3, Fig. 6.5, is such that the break in torque when the winding passes from pole face to pole face may be neglected and the torque assumed to be independent of the angular position of the winding. The rectangular armature winding has n turns, each of area S, and the sides parallel to the axis of rotation are perpendicular to a magnetic field of flux density B. The motor is connected to machinery that exerts a resistive torque equal to k times the angular velocity ω of the motor. The armature, together with the machinery connected to it, has a moment of inertia κ. Show that the equation of motion for the armature is

$$\kappa \frac{d\omega}{dt} = nIBS - k\omega$$

With the machine stopped and no current in the armature winding, a current I is suddenly applied and then maintained steady. Calculate the initial angular acceleration of the machine and the steady angular velocity which it finally acquires. If $n = 1,000$, $S = 100$ cm^2, $B = 10,000$ gauss, and the initial angular acceleration is 10 radians/sec^2, evaluate the moment of inertia of the system. If the steady angular velocity of the machine is 1,000 rpm, evaluate the resistance constant k.

★10. The coil of a moving-coil instrument for measuring steady current is rectangular, with a pair of edges parallel to the axis of rotation and perpendicular to the magnetic field across which they move. The magnetic flux density at these edges is B, and the coil has n turns each of area S. At full-scale deflection the needle is turned from zero through an angle $\theta_{\max}$, and the current through the coil is then $I_{\max}$. Calculate the torque of the spring per unit angular deflection. Evaluate this quantity in newton-meters per radian if $I_{\max} = 100$ ma, $B = 1,000$ gauss, $S = 1$ cm^2, and $\theta_{\max} = 90°$.

11. The coil of the instrument described in the previous problem carries a steady current I. The movement has a moment of inertia κ about the axis of rotation, and the torque of the spring per unit angular deflection is k. If θ is the angular deflection of the needle from the equilibrium position for zero current, show that the equation of motion of the needle is

$$\kappa \frac{d^2\theta}{dt^2} + k\theta = nIBS$$

Show that the needle oscillates about its true reading with frequency $(k/\kappa)^{1/2}/2\pi$, and suggest a method for preventing this.

★12. In a medium of inductivity μ, $ABCD$ is a square of edge a labeled cyclically. Along the edge AB there lies a magnetic needle of pole strength Φ with the positive pole at A and the negative pole at B. Along the side CD there lies a thin solenoid carrying a magnetic flux Φ from D to C. Calculate the force between the solenoid and the magnetic needle. Evaluate the force if $\Phi = 10^{-5}$ weber, $a = 10$ cm, and $\mu = \mu_v$.

13. In Chap. 4, Prob. 13, calculate the force of repulsion between the solenoid and the conducting sheet.

★14. A magnetic needle is freely pivoted in a uniform magnetic field. The magnetic moment of the needle (product of pole strength and length) is m, and the moment of inertia of the magnet about an axis through the pivot perpendicular to its length is κ. The needle is slightly disturbed from its position of equilibrium and is found to oscillate with frequency f. Calculate the value of the magnetic field strength.

★15. Explain how to use a pivoted magnetic needle to explore a magnetic field. Show that the ratio of the magnetic field strengths at two points is equal to the square of the ratio of the corresponding frequencies of vibration of the needle.

16. A tangent galvanometer has a closely wound n-turn coil in the form of a vertical circle of radius a. At the center of the coil a small magnetic needle is pivoted about a vertical axis. With no current in the coil, the needle rests in stable equilibrium under the Earth's magnetic field, the horizontal component of the magnetic vector being H. The coil is turned about a vertical axis until its plane contains the direction of the magnetic needle. If a steady current I is now passed through the coil, calculate the angle θ through which the needle is deflected, showing that I is proportional to tan θ.

17. A tangent galvanometer is set up to measure a current I as described in the previous problem. The coil of the galvanometer is now turned slowly about a vertical axis until its plane overtakes the vertical plane through the magnetic needle. If ϕ is the angle through which the coil has been turned, evaluate I in terms of the constants of the galvanometer and the angle ϕ instead of the angle θ, showing that I is proportional to sin ϕ.

★18. A loop of wire in air has the form of a square of edge a and carries a steady current I. Calculate the magnetic field strength at the center of the square.

19. The moving-coil instrument described in Prob. 11 is used as a ballistic instrument to measure the total flux of charge Q involved in discharging a capacitor. It may be assumed that the charge Q passes through the winding of the instrument so quickly that the needle does not suffer any appreciable displacement until the discharge is practically complete. By integrating the equation of motion over this short interval of time, show that the initial angular velocity of the needle is $(nBS/\kappa)Q$. Calculate the total angular throw of the needle and show that it is proportional to Q.

20. A solenoid is wound with insulated wire on a circular cylindrical form of radius a and length l. The length l is not necessarily large or small compared with a. If there are n turns of thin wire closely and uniformly wound and there is a steady current I through the wire, calculate the magnetic field strength at the center of the coil.

★21. The moving-coil instrument described in Part 3, Sec. 6.5, is connected in series with a diode and a source of alternating voltage equal to $V_0 \cos \omega t$. The relation between the current I through the diode and the voltage V across the diode may be taken as $I = GV$ if $V > 0$ and $I = 0$ if $V < 0$. It may be assumed that the inductance and resistance of the instrument are negligible and that the moving parts of the instrument are too massive to oscillate at angular frequency ω. Show that the deflection of the needle is proportional to V_0.

22. A pair of thin soft-iron rods of length l are placed at a distance x apart, their extremities being at the corners of a rectangle. A uniform magnetic field of strength H is applied parallel to the rods so that each becomes a magnetic needle of pole strength αH, where α is a constant. Calculate the force of repulsion between the rods. The arrangement is placed at the center of a closely wound n-turn coil of radius a. The rods are parallel to the axis of the coil, and the dimensions l and x are small compared with a. Calculate the force of repulsion between the rods in terms of the current through the coil. On this principle devise an instrument for measuring (a) direct current and (b) alternating current.

23. A circular coil is wound with insulated wire on a bobbin just wide enough to accept a single turn. Each successive turn is wound on top of the preceding turn, the smallest turn being of radius a and the largest of radius b. There is a large number n of turns, and the diameter of the wire is small compared with both a and $b - a$. If a steady current I passes through the coil, calculate the magnetic field strength at the center of the coil.

24. A circular coil is wound with thin insulated wire on a bobbin just wide enough to accept n turns side by side, the axial width of the bobbin being l. A number m of such layers of turns are wound on the bobbin, the smallest being of radius a and the largest of radius b. If a steady current I passes through the wire, calculate the magnetic field strength at the center of the coil.

★25. A pair of identical closely wound n-turn circular coils of radius a are mounted in a medium of inductivity μ with a common diameter and with their planes perpendicular. The current in both coils oscillates sinusoidally with the same angular frequency ω and the same amplitude I_0. The current in one coil at time t is $I_0 \cos \omega t$, and that in the other coil is $I_0 \sin \omega t$. Calculate in magnitude and direction the magnetic-flux-density vector at the common center of the coils as a function of time.

26. Three identical circular coils are mounted with a common diameter and with angles of $\pi/3$ between their planes. The current in each coil oscillates sinusoidally with the same angular frequency ω and the same amplitude I_0. The currents in the three coils at time t are $I_0 \cos \omega t$, $I_0 \cos (\omega t + \frac{2}{3}\pi)$, and $I_0 \cos (\omega t - \frac{2}{3}\pi)$. Show that, if these currents are suitably arranged, the direction of the magnetic field at the common center rotates with uniform angular velocity ω.

27. Magnetic storms are thought to be associated with a ring current in the equatorial plane of the Earth, the center of the ring being at the center of the Earth and the radius of the ring being about six times that of the Earth. In a particular magnetic storm the axial disturbance in the Earth's magnetic field is found to be about 10^{-3} gauss. Estimate the strength of the ring current in amperes.

28. In a right-handed system of rectangular cartesian coordinates (x,y,z) in a vacuum there is a uniform electric field of field strength E parallel to the positive y axis and a uniform magnetic field of flux density B parallel to the positive z axis. A particle having charge e and mass m is released from rest at the origin at time zero. At time t the particle has a velocity whose components are $(u,v,0)$. If ω is the angular gyrofrequency associated with the magnetic field, show that

$$\frac{du}{dt} = \omega v$$

$$\frac{dv}{dt} = \frac{eE}{m} - \omega u$$

Calculate u and v at time t, and show that, on the average, the particle drifts with velocity E/B in a direction perpendicular to the electric and magnetic fields, the direction being related by the right-hand-screw rule to rotation from the direction of the electric field to the direction of the magnetic field through an angle $\frac{1}{2}\pi$.

29. In the previous problem calculate the coordinates of the particle at time t. Show that the motion of the particle can be generated by rolling a hoop along the x axis in the xy plane. Calculate the radius of the hoop and the speed with which it rolls. Evaluate these quantities for (a) an electron and (b) a proton if $E = 1$ volt/m and $B = 1$ gauss.

30. In Prob. 28 the strength of the uniform electric field now varies sinusoidally with time t, and the angular frequency ω is equal to the angular gyrofrequency of the uniform magnetic field. Taking the electric field as $E_0 \cos \omega t$, derive a differential equation for v and show that it has a solution of the form $t \cos \omega t$. Deduce that the speed of the particle increases indefinitely.

31. In an ionized atmosphere there are N electrons (charge $-e$, mass m) per unit volume capable of drifting through the medium to form an electric current. There is a uniform electric field of field strength E in the direction of the y axis and a uniform magnetic field of flux density B in the direction of the z axis. The effect on an electron of collisions with other particles is a retarding force equal to $m\nu$ times the mean drift velocity of the electrons. Calculate the cartesian components of the mean drift velocity of the electrons, and deduce the components of the electric-current-density vector.

32. In the previous problem explain physically why the direction of the current does not coincide with the direction of the applied electric field, and calculate the rate at which electrical energy is converted into heat per unit volume.

33. In an ionized atmosphere there are N free electrons (charge $-e$, mass m) per unit volume capable of drifting through the medium to form an electric current, and there is a uniform magnetic field of flux density B in the direction of the z axis. The particles other than the free electrons are given a uniform wind motion of velocity V in the direction of the y axis. Collisions between these particles and the free electrons cause drift of the electrons, and the impulses upon an electron may be regarded as a force equivalent to $m\nu$ times the vector excess of the wind velocity over the mean drift velocity of the electrons. Calculate the cartesian components of the mean drift velocity of the electrons.

34. In the previous problem each unit volume of the ionized atmosphere contains not only N free electrons (charge $-e$, mass m) but also N positive ions (charge e, mass m_i) capable of drifting through the medium to form an electric current. Collisions between the ions and the neutral molecules cause drift of the ions, and the consequent impulses upon an ion may be regarded as a force equal to $m_i\nu_i$ times the vector excess of the wind velocity over the mean drift velocity of the ions. If the effect of collisions between ions and electrons may be neglected, calculate the cartesian components of the mean drift velocities of both ions and electrons and deduce the components of the electric-current-density vector. Investigate the limiting case when the ions move with the wind.

35. The instrument described in Part 3, Sec. 6.5, is modified so that the width of the gaps in the magnetic circuit varies with angular position round the axis. The arrangement is such that, when the angular position of the coil is θ, the arms of the coil parallel to the axis of rotation are in a field of magnetic flux density $\beta\theta$, where β is a constant. Prove that, if a constant current flows through the coil, the torque on the coil in position θ is proportional to θ.

36. The moving-coil instrument described in Part 3, Sec. 6.5, is connected in series with a battery and a resistor of unknown resistance. However, the spring of the instrument is replaced by the device described in the preceding problem, and the current through this device is arranged to be proportional to the voltage across the resistor. Show that the angular displacement of the needle is proportional to the conductance of the unknown resistance.

37. A long straight wire in air (inductivity μ) carries a steady current I_1. In an axial plane of this wire there is a circular wire of radius a carrying a steady current I_2. The center of the circle is at a distance d from the straight wire $(d > a)$. Calculate the force between the two currents.

38. A long straight wire in air (inductivity μ) carries a steady current I. In a plane perpendicular to this wire there is a circular loop of radius a carrying a steady current I_2. If the center of the loop is at a distance d from the straight wire, calculate the torque on the loop (a) if $d > a$ and (b) if $d < a$.

39. A loop of wire has the shape of an ellipse of semimajor axis a and semiminor axis b. Calculate the magnetic field strength at the center of the ellipse. Verify that the result yields the appropriate values for the limiting cases of (a) a circular loop and (b) a twin-wire transmission line.

Part 3, Chapter 7

★1. The core of a toroidal inductor is divided into four quadrants in which the inductivities are μ_1, μ_2, μ_3, and μ_4. The core is tightly wrapped with metal foil, and a total current I flows round the inductor, producing in the core a magnetic field whose lines of magnetic flux are circles coaxial with the inductor. Calculate the change in magnetic scalar potential along each quadrant of the core. Evaluate these quantities if $I = 1$ amp, $\mu_1 = \mu_v$, $\mu_2 = 10\mu_v$, $\mu_3 = 100\mu_v$, and $\mu_4 = 1{,}000\mu_v$.

★2. A long straight thin wire is erected at a height h above a large perfectly conducting horizontal sheet. A steady current I flows through the wire and returns through the sheet. Calculate the magnetic scalar potential at a point on the sheet distant y from the vertical plane through the wire, stating what location has been chosen for the zero of potential. Deduce the potential along two lines on the sheet distant h from the vertical plane through the wire on opposite sides. Calculate the fraction of the return current that passes between these lines.

★3. A small magnet of moment m is placed in a uniform magnetic field of flux density B, and the direction of the magnetic flux through the magnet is opposite to the direction of the uniform field. Prove that in the combined magnetic field there is a pair of null points on the axis of the magnet, and calculate their distances from the magnet. Sketch the lines of magnetic flux.

★4. A small loop of wire of area S carrying a steady current I is placed in a uniform magnetic field of field strength H. The plane of the loop is perpendicular to the uniform field, which threads the loop in the direction related by the right-hand-screw rule to the direction of the current. Prove that there is a circle on which the combined magnetic field vanishes, and calculate its radius. Sketch the lines of magnetic flux.

★5. Assuming that the exterior magnetic field of the Earth is that of a small centrally located solenoid, prove that there is no variation with height in the magnetic dip (the angle of depression of the magnetic vector below the horizontal).

6. Assuming that the exterior magnetic field of the Earth is that of a small centrally located solenoid, calculate the strength of the Earth's magnetic field at a point in the atmosphere at height h as a ratio to the strength at the Earth's surface vertically below. Deduce that the strength of the Earth's magnetic field decreases with increasing height in the atmosphere by a fraction $3/a$ per unit height approximately. If the magnetic flux density at the surface is 0.5 gauss, calculate the magnetic flux density in the ionosphere at a height of 100 km, taking $a = 6,370$ km.

★7. A pair of closely wound circular coils each have n turns of radius a. They are arranged coaxially in air with their centers at a distance $2b$ apart, and a steady current I is passed through each coil. Calculate the magnetic scalar potential at a point on the common axis distant $z - b$ from the center of one coil and $z + b$ from the center of the other coil (a) if the currents in the coils are in the same direction and (b) if they are in opposite directions. In both cases deduce the magnetic field strength at the center of each coil and at the point midway between the centers.

8. A circular loop of wire of radius a in air carries a steady current I. At a point on the axis of the loop distant d from the center is placed a small magnet of moment m. The magnetic flux through the magnet is directed along the axis of the loop in the direction related by the right-hand-screw rule to the direction of the current I. Calculate in magnitude and direction the force exerted by the magnet on the loop.

9. A pair of closely wound circular coils having radii a and b possess m and n turns, respectively. The coils are arranged coaxially with a distance $\frac{1}{2}(a + b)$ between their centers, and a steady current I passes through each coil in the same sense. Calculate the magnetic field strength at the point O on the common axis distant $\frac{1}{2}a$ from the center of the coil of radius a and $\frac{1}{2}b$ from the center of the coil of radius b.

10. In the previous problem calculate the magnetic field strength H at a point on the axis of the coils distant z from the point O. Show that, at the point O, dH/dz and d^2H/dz^2 are zero if $m/a^2 = n/b^2$. Show that, in addition, d^3H/dz^3 is zero if $a = b$ and $m = n$. Explain how the arrangement can be used to produce a nearly uniform magnetic field over a specified volume.

11. It may be assumed that the Earth is a sphere of radius a in free space permanently and uniformly magnetized so that each element of volume dv of the sphere is a small magnet of moment $\mathbf{M}\,dv$. Show that the external magnetic field of the Earth is the same as that produced in free space by a small magnet of moment $\frac{4}{3}\pi a^3 \mathbf{M}$ at the center. (Compare Part 1, Chap. 4, Prob. 61.)

12. Two homogeneous media have inductivities μ_1 and μ_2 and are separated by a plane interface p. In the first medium there is a thin solenoid conveying a magnetic flux Φ from a point O_2 at a distance d_2 from p to a point O_1 at a distance d_1 from p. Describe a method for calculating the magnetic field at all points of both media. (Compare Part 1, Chap. 4, Prob. 50.)

13. In the previous problem calculate the force exerted on the solenoid if $d_1 = d_2 = d$ and the length of the solenoid is $2d$.

14. A sphere of soft iron of radius a and inductivity μ exists in air (inductivity μ_v). If a uniform magnetic field of flux density B is applied to the sphere, calculate the magnetic flux density interior to the sphere. (Compare Part 1, Chap. 4, Prob. 53.)

Part 3, Chapter 8

★1. An inductor has n turns of wire wound on a magnetic circuit of inductivity μ whose cross-sectional area is a rectangle of edges c and d. The circuit is in the form of a rectangle, the median length of one pair of sides being a and that of the other pair being b. If leakage is neglected, calculate the inductance of the coil. Evaluate the inductance if $\mu = 1{,}000\mu_v$, $n = 1{,}000$, $a = 10$ cm, $b = 20$ cm, $c = 2$ cm, and $d = 4$ cm.

★2. A choke coil has n turns of wire wound on a magnetic circuit of inductivity μ rectangular in shape. Two opposite sides of the rectangle have median length a with rectangular cross sections having edges of lengths c and d_1. The other two sides have median length b with rectangular cross sections having edges of lengths c and d_2. If leakage is neglected, calculate the inductance of the coil. All dimensions are specified except d_1 and d_2, and the geometric mean of d_1 and d_2 is specified to be d. Prove that the inductance of the coil is maximized if $d_1 = d(a/b)^{1/2}$ and $d_2 = d(b/a)^{1/2}$.

★3. A substantially uniform magnetic field is generated in an air gap of width w in a soft-iron magnetic circuit, and the reluctance of the iron may be assumed negligible compared with that of the gap. Round the iron are wound n turns of wire each of resistance r. If a battery of voltage V is connected across the coil, calculate the magnetic flux density in the gap. Evaluate the magnetic flux density if $V = 10$ volts, $r = 1$ ohm, and $w = 2$ mm. Calculate the number of turns that must be used if the power dissipated in the winding is to be less than 1 watt.

★4. A magnetic network of soft iron is constructed with the dimensions shown in the diagram. All arms of the network have a normal cross-sectional area A, and the

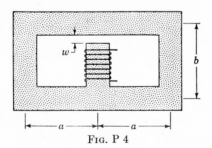

Fig. P 4

central arm contains a narrow gap of width w as indicated. The inductivity of the soft iron is μ, that of the surrounding air is μ_v, and leakage of magnetic flux may be neglected. Calculate the inductance of an n-turn coil wound on the central arm.

★5. In the electric motor described in connection with Part 3, Fig. 6.5, the permanent magnet is replaced by an electromagnet on which are wound n' turns of wire each carrying a steady current I'. The reluctance of the soft iron of the electromagnet, of the pole pieces, and of the armature may be neglected, and each of the two air gaps is to be regarded as having a width w and an area A. Calculate the magnetic flux density in the gaps, and deduce the torque on the armature. Evaluate the torque if $n = 100$, $n' = 1{,}000$, $I = 1$ amp, $I' = 100$ ma, $S = 100$ cm^2, and $w = 1$ cm.

★6. A rotating electrical machine has the
magnetic network shown in the diagram, and
the reluctance of the iron may be neglected.
The gaps are of width w, and the magnetic
field in them may be assumed uniform.
Each field coil has n turns carrying a steady
current I. Neglecting leakage, calculate the
magnetic flux density in the gaps.

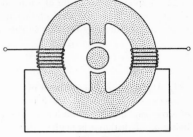

FIG. P 6

★7. A rotating electrical machine has the magnetic network shown in the diagram, and the reluctance of the iron
may be neglected. The gaps are of width w, and the magnetic field in them may be assumed uniform.   Each field
coil has n turns carrying a steady current I.   Neglecting
leakage, calculate the magnetic flux density in the gaps.
Show that, for the same number of turns on the field coils
and the same current in the field coils, the arrangement
given in this problem produces twice as much magnetic
flux density in the gaps as the arrangement given in the
previous problem.

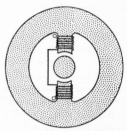

FIG. P 7

★8. In the moving-coil measuring instrument described in connection with Part 3,
Fig. 6.5, the permanent magnet may be regarded as a source of flux of strength Φ with
an internal reluctance R.   Each air gap may be regarded as having an area A and a
width w, while the reluctance of the soft-iron armature and pole pieces may be neglected.   Calculate the magnetic flux density in the gaps.   Evaluate the magnetic flux
density if $\Phi = 5 \times 10^{-5}$ weber, $R = 10^8$ henry^{-1}, $w = 1$ mm, and $A = 1$ cm^2.

9. A sample of ferromagnetic material is in the shape of a complete toroidal ring
and forms the core of a toroidal inductor.   Application of a current H per unit length
round the core produces a magnetic flux density B in the core.   The demagnetization
curve relating B with H is given by the equation

$$B = B_s \left(\coth \frac{H + H_1}{H_2} - \frac{H_2}{H + H_1} \right)$$

where B_s, H_1, and H_2 are constants.   Calculate (a) the magnetic flux density in the
core when no current is applied round it, (b) the current per unit length that must be
applied to reduce the magnetic flux density in the core to zero, (c) the value of $(1/\mu_v)$
(dB/dH) when $H = 0$, and (d) the value of $(1/\mu_v)(dB/dH)$ when $B = 0$.   Evaluate
these quantities if $B_s = 1$ weber/m^2, $H_1 = 50,000$ amp/m, and $H_2 = 10,000$ amp/m.

10. For the demagnetization curve described in the previous problem find a numerical method for locating the point for which the product $-BH$ is maximum.   Find the
values of B and H for which $-BH$ is maximum when $B_s = 1$ weber/m^2, $H_1 =$
50,000 amp/m, and $H_2 = 10,000$ amp/m.

11. The ferromagnetic ring described in Prob. 9 is broken at one section, and by
means of soft-iron pole pieces of negligible reluctance, the magnetic field is applied
across a gap of area A and width w.   The field in the gap is practically uniform and is
to have a magnetic flux density B_g.   It is required to calculate the cross-sectional
area S and length s of the ferromagnetic material that will minimize the volume of

this material. Find the values of S and s if $A = 1$ cm^2, $w = 1$ mm, $B_g = B_s = 1$ weber/m^2, $H_1 = 50,000$ amp/m, and $H_2 = 10,000$ amp/m.

12. A magnetic circuit of uniform cross-sectional area S and median length s is wound with an n-turn coil. Leakage of flux from the circuit may be neglected, but the relation between the magnetic flux density B and the magnetic field strength H for the ferromagnetic material used is

$$B = B_s \left(\coth \frac{3\mu H}{B_s} - \frac{B_s}{3\mu H} \right)$$

where B_s is the saturation flux density. Calculate the magnetic flux Φ threading the electric circuit when there is a steady current I round it, and evaluate $d\Phi/dI$ when $I = 0$. Sketch the relation between Φ and I when $\mu = 1,000\mu_v$ and $B_s = 1$ weber/m^2.

13. A magnet in air has the form of a circular cylinder of length l and radius a, and a is not necessarily small or large compared with l. The magnet is permanently and uniformly magnetized parallel to its axis, so that magnetic flux emanates from one flat end with a uniform distribution M per unit area and returns to the other flat end with the same uniform distribution. At a point on the axis distant z from the mid-point of the magnet, calculate (a) the magnetic field strength and (b) the magnetic flux density. (Compare Part 1, Chap. 4, Prob. 59.)

14. A solenoid in air has the form of a circular cylinder of length l and radius a, and a is not necessarily small or large compared with l (Part 3, Fig. 4.7). The solenoid carries a uniformly distributed current I per unit length round its curved surface. At a point on the axis distant z from the mid-point of the cylinder, calculate the magnetic flux density. Compare the result with that in the previous problem.

Part 3, Chapter 9

★1. A transformer is constructed by winding an n_1-turn electric circuit and an n_2-turn electric circuit on the central arm of the soft-iron magnetic network shown in the diagram. The inductivity of the iron is μ, and leakage may be neglected. The

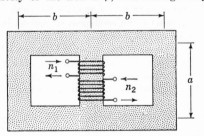

Fig. P 1

normal cross-sectional area of all arms of the magnetic network is S, and the other dimensions are shown in the diagram. Calculate the coefficients of self- and mutual inductance for the transformer. Evaluate the coefficients if $\mu = 1,000\mu_v$, $n_1 = 100$, $n_2 = 1,000$, $a = b = 10$ cm, and $S = 10$ cm^2. Calculate the magnetic fluxes threading the two electric circuits if there is a current of 1 amp in the 100-turn winding and a current of 100 ma in the 1,000-turn winding (a) if the currents have the directions indicated in the diagram and (b) if one of the currents is reversed.

★2. On the central arm of the magnetic network of the previous problem is wound a third coil having n_3 turns. Calculate the coefficients of self- and mutual inductance for the system of three electric circuits. Evaluate them if $n_3 = 2,000$ and other numerical values are as stated in the previous problem.

★3. A transformer is constructed by winding an n_1-turn electric circuit and an n_2-turn electric circuit round a soft-iron magnetic network as shown in the diagram. The inductivity of the iron is μ, and leakage from the iron may be neglected. The normal cross-sectional area of all arms of the magnetic network is S, and the other

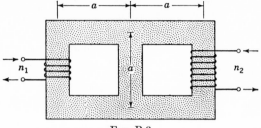

FIG. P 3

dimensions are shown in the diagram. Calculate for the transformer (a) the coefficients of self- and mutual reluctance, (b) the coefficients of self- and mutual inductance, and (c) the coupling coefficient. Evaluate these quantities if $\mu = 1{,}000\mu_v$, $n_1 = 100$, $n_2 = 1{,}000$, $a = 10$ cm, and $S = 10$ cm².

★4. In a homogeneous medium of inductivity μ two circular loops of wire of radii a and b are concentric and coplanar and b is small compared with a. At a point in the plane distant r from the common center ($r > a$), calculate the magnetic flux density due to a steady current I round the loop of radius b. By integration over the portion of the plane for which $r > b$ calculate the magnetic flux threading the large loop due to a current I round the small loop. Calculate independently the magnetic flux threading the small loop due to a current I round the large loop. Deduce the coefficient of mutual inductance for the two loops.

★5. In the previous problem the large loop is replaced by a closely wound circular coil of radius a having n_1 turns and the small loop is replaced by a closely wound circular coil of radius b having n_2 turns. Calculate the coefficient of mutual inductance between the coils. Evaluate the coefficient of mutual inductance if $n_1 = 100$, $n_2 = 10$, $a = 10$ cm, $b = 1$ cm, and $\mu = \mu_v$.

★6. A transformer has coefficients of self-inductance L_{11} and L_{22} and a coefficient of mutual inductance L_{12}. One terminal of the primary winding is connected to one terminal of the secondary winding, thereby converting the transformer into an inductor. Calculate the inductance of the inductor, distinguishing between the two cases that arise.

★7. Two multiturn solenoids are arranged in air with their central points coincident and one completely inside the other. The inner solenoid is such that it can rotate on an axis perpendicular to the axes of the solenoids. The two solenoids are connected in series, forming what is known as a variometer. The direction related by the right-hand-screw rule to current on the inner solenoid makes an angle θ with the direction related by the right-hand-screw rule to the direction of the current on the outer solenoid. The coefficients of self-induction of the solenoids are L_{11} and L_{22}, and the coefficient of mutual induction between them when $\theta = 0$ is L_{12}. Calculate the inductance of the variometer when set at angle θ.

★8. In the previous problem the large solenoid has cross-sectional area S_1, length s_1, and possesses n_1 turns, while the small solenoid has cross-sectional area S_2, length s_2, and possesses n_2 turns. Show that the inductance of the variometer when set at angle θ is approximately

$$\mu \left(n_1{}^2 \frac{S_1}{s_1} + n_2{}^2 \frac{S_2}{s_2} + 2 n_1 n_2 \frac{S_2}{s_1} \cos \theta \right)$$

where μ is the inductivity of the air. Evaluate the inductance as a function of θ if $n_1 = n_2 = 100$, $s_1 = 6$ cm, $s_2 = 4$ cm, the outer solenoid has the form of a circular cylinder of diameter 6 cm, and the inner solenoid one of diameter 4 cm.

★9. A pair of fixed inductors with an unknown coefficient of mutual inductance is connected in series in two ways, and the inductance of the inductors thereby formed is measured to be L_1 and L_2. Calculate the coefficient of mutual inductance of the original inductors.

10. The magnetic circuit described in Chap. 8, Prob. 12, is provided with two windings numbered 1 and 2 having n_1 and n_2 turns, respectively, forming a transformer. With a steady current I_1 in winding 1 and no current in winding 2, calculate the magnetic flux Φ_2 threading winding 2. With a current I_2 in winding 2 and no current in winding 1, calculate the magnetic flux Φ_1 threading winding 1. Explain why Φ_1 is not equal to Φ_2 when $I_1 = I_2$. Verify that Φ_1 is equal to Φ_2 if the common value of I_1 and I_2 is sufficiently small.

11. Four coplanar long straight thin wires in air (inductivity μ) intersect a perpendicular plane in the consecutive collinear points $ABCD$, and $AB = a$, $BC = b$, $CD = a$. The wires through the points A and B are used as one twin-wire transmission line, and the wires through the points C and D are used as a second twin-wire transmission line. Calculate the coefficient of mutual inductance per unit length between the two transmission lines.

12. Four coplanar long straight thin wires in air (inductivity μ) intersect a perpendicular plane in the corners of a rectangle of edges a and b. Each pair of wires with separation a is used as a twin-wire transmission line. Calculate the coefficient of mutual inductance per unit length between the two transmission lines.

Part 3, Chapter 10

1. Three coaxial circular cylinders have radii a, $a + \tau$, and b $(a < a + \tau < b)$, and the magnitude of τ is small compared with the magnitude of a. A coaxial transmission line has its inner conductor coinciding with the cylinder of radius a and its outer conductor coinciding with the cylinder of radius b. Between the cylinders of radii a and $a + \tau$ there is a homogeneous medium of inductivity μ and negligible conductivity, the remainder of the space between the inner and outer conductors being occupied by air. The inductivity μ is large compared with the inductivity of air, and it may be assumed that the magnetic flux between the conductors is confined to the region between the cylinders of radii a and $a + \tau$. If a steady uniformly distributed current I flows along the inner conductor and back along the outer conductor, calculate in magnitude and direction the magnetic vector potential at the surface of (a) the inner conductor and (b) the outer conductor. If A is the magnitude of the vector potential at the surface of the inner conductor, show that the inductance of the transmission line per unit length is A/I. Evaluate A in webers per meter if $\mu = 100\mu_v$, $a = 1$ cm, $b = 2$ cm, $\tau = 2$ mm, and $I = 1$ amp.

2. A coaxial transmission line is formed by a pair of thin coaxial circular metal cylinders of radii a and b $(a < b)$. The space between the conductors is filled with a homogeneous nonconducting medium of inductivity μ. A steady uniformly distributed current I flows along the inner conductor and back along the outer conductor. Calculate in magnitude and direction the magnetic vector potential at all locations between the conductors.

3. A long straight wire in air (inductivity μ) carries a steady current I. In an axial plane is drawn a geometrical circle of radius a with its center at a distance d from the wire. The distance d is greater than a but is not necessarily large compared with a. Calculate the magnetic flux threading the circle.

4. In the previous problem the geometrical circle is replaced by a circular loop of wire. Calculate the coefficient of mutual inductance between the two circuits.

5. In Prob. 3 the geometrical circle is rotated round the wire to form a toroidal surface. This surface is closely and uniformly wound with wire to form a toroidal inductor having n turns. Calculate the coefficient of self-inductance of the inductor.

6. A twin-wire transmission line in air (inductivity μ) has thin wires at a distance d apart. Between the wires there is a coplanar circular loop of wire of radius a with its center equidistant from the parallel wires. The radius a is less than $\frac{1}{2}d$ but is not necessarily small compared with $\frac{1}{2}d$. Calculate the coefficient of mutual inductance between the transmission line and the loop.

Part 4, Chapter 1

★1. A strip transmission line has perfectly conducting strips of length l and width b with a separation a between them, and fringing may be neglected. Across one end of the line is connected a battery of voltage V and across the other end a resistor consisting of a uniform rectangular sheet having uniform surface resistance r and edges of lengths a and b. A third perfectly conducting thin strip of width b and length less than l is now introduced between the other two strips at a distance d from one and $a - d$ from the other ($d < a$), and the introduced strip does not extend outside the electromagnetic field in the line. The intermediate strip is slid along the line until it makes firm contact with the terminating resistive sheet. Show that introduction of the third strip does not upset the electromagnetic field in the line and divides the flow of energy down the line in the ratio d to $a - d$. Calculate the total resistance terminating each section of the line, and deduce from Ohm's law the rate of dissipation of energy in each resistor. Verify that these rates are in the ratio d to $a - d$.

★2. A coaxial transmission line is made of a pair of perfectly conducting coaxial circular cylinders of radii a and b ($a < b$) with air between them. At the end of the line a resistive sheet of uniform surface resistance is connected between the inner and outer conductors. The plane of the sheet is perpendicular to the length of the line, and the sheet makes contact with each conductor along the entire perimeter. At the other end of the line is connected a battery of voltage V delivering a current I. At a point on the terminating resistive sheet at distance r from the axis of the transmission line, calculate the voltage per unit distance acting in the radial direction and the current per unit width flowing in the radial direction. Deduce the heat produced in the sheet per unit area per unit time, showing that it increases from the outer edge to the inner edge inversely proportionally to r^2. Explain this result in terms of the Poynting vector. Evaluate the heat produced per unit area per unit time as a function of r if $V = 1$ volt, $I = 1$ amp, $a = 1$ cm, and $b = 3$ cm.

★3. A twin-wire transmission line is composed of a pair of parallel wires each of radius a, at a distance d apart in air, and d may be assumed large compared with a. A steady current I flows down one wire and back along the other, and there is a steady voltage V between the wires. Calculate the energy flowing per unit time per unit area along the center line between the wires. If $d = 10$ cm, $a = 1$ mm, and the line is transmitting a power of 1 watt, evaluate the power density along the center line between the conductors in watts per square meter.

★4. In the previous problem calculate the power density close to either wire of the transmission line and express it as a ratio to the power density on the center line between the wires. Evaluate this ratio if $d = 10$ cm and $a = 1$ mm.

5. A solid circular wire of radius a is made of material of uniform conductivity σ and carries a steady current I uniformly distributed over the cross section. Calculate in magnitude and direction the Poynting vector at a point in the wire distant r from the axis ($r < a$). Evaluate the power density as a function of r if $I = 1$ amp, $\sigma = 5.8 \times 10^7$ mhos/m, and $a = 1$ mm.

6. A long straight conductor is in the form of a hollow, circular cylinder of uniform wall thickness, the internal radius being a and the external radius being b. The conductivity of the metal is σ. A current I flows along the conductor distributed uniformly over the cross section. Show that the flow of energy in the conductor is radially inward, and calculate the power density at a point distant r from the axis of the conductor $(a < r < b)$. Draw a sketch of the variation in the power density as a function of r, and evaluate the power density at the outer surface of the conductor if $I = 1$ amp, $\sigma = 5.8 \times 10^7$ mhos/m, $a = 0.9$ cm, and $b = 1.1$ cm.

7. A length l of coaxial transmission line consists of a pair of coaxial perfectly conducting cylinders, the inner being of radius a and the outer of radius b. The medium has a capacitivity ϵ and zero conductivity. The arrangement is used as a capacitor, and fringing at the ends may be neglected. With the capacitor uncharged at time zero, a generator delivering a constant current I_0 is connected across the line at one end, the other end being open-circuited. Calculate (a) the voltage between the conductors at time t, (b) the current along the conductors at distance x from the generator, (c) the power density at time t at a point between the conductors distant x from the generator and r from the axis, and (d) the electric energy per unit volume at time t at a point between the conductors distant r from the axis. Sketch curves to illustrate the results.

8. A pair of circular cylinders of radii a and b are drawn coaxial with a circular cone of semivertical angle θ. The cylinders are occupied by perfectly conducting metal sheets forming the inner and outer conductors of a coaxial transmission line. The portion of the cone between the conductors is occupied by a resistive sheet of uniform resistivity, and the sheet is connected to each conductor of the transmission line round the entire perimeter of a normal cross section. To one end of the transmission line is connected a battery of voltage V delivering a current I. Calculate the energy absorbed per unit area per unit time at a point on the resistance sheet distant r from the axis of the transmission line $(a < r < b)$.

9. Two planes p_1 and p_2 intersect in a horizontal line l in air, each plane making an angle θ with the vertical. A large conducting sheet is bent along a line so as to have an internal angle 2θ and is placed so as to coincide with the upper halves of the planes p_1 and p_2 with the sharp edge along the line l. A second large conducting sheet is similarly bent and is placed so as to coincide with the lower halves of the planes p_1 and p_2. The two sheets are not quite in contact along the line l. A voltage V is maintained between the sheets and results in a discharge between the sharp edges, the current per unit length of l being I. At a point between the sheets at distance r from l calculate (a) the electric field strength, (b) the magnetic field strength, and (c) the Poynting vector. Verify that the total rate at which energy is flowing into the discharge per unit length across a cylinder of radius r coaxial with l is equal to the rate at which energy is being dissipated in the discharge per unit length of l.

Part 4, Chapter 2

★1. A parallel-plate capacitor has plates of area S with separation s, and fringing may be neglected. The medium between the plates has capacitivity ϵ and conductivity σ. The voltage applied across the capacitor oscillates sinusoidally with time t, the angular frequency being ω and the amplitude V_0. Calculate (a) the amplitude of the conduction current per unit area between the plates of the capacitor and (b) the amplitude of the displacement current per unit area between the plates of the capacitor. Evaluate these quantities if $s = 1$ mm, $\sigma = 10^{-15}$ mho/m, $\epsilon = 7\epsilon_v$, the frequency of oscillation is 60 cycles/sec, and the root-mean-square voltage is 110.

★2. In the previous problem calculate the fraction of the displacement current that actually flows. If between the plates and the dielectric there are small gaps in which the capacitivity is ϵ_v, show that the part of the displacement current that actually flows is associated with charges on the surface of the dielectric. If the voltage across the capacitor is $V_0 \cos \omega t$, calculate in magnitude and sign the charge per unit area on the surface of the dielectric close to the positive plate of the capacitor at time zero. Calculate also the charge per unit area on the positive plate at time zero. Evaluate the above quantities if $s = 1$ mm, $\epsilon = 7\epsilon_v$, and the root-mean-square voltage is 110.

3. A long thin perfectly conducting straight wire in a homogeneous nonconducting medium of capacitivity ϵ is cut, and a parallel-plate capacitor is inserted. The capacitor has perfectly conducting circular plates of radius a and separation s, and the plates are coaxial with the wire. The current along the wire oscillates sinusoidally with time t, the angular frequency being ω and the amplitude I_0. Assuming that there is no fringing of the electric field at the edge of the capacitor, calculate (a) the amplitude of the displacement current density in the capacitor, (b) the amplitude of the magnetic field strength in the capacitor at distance r from the axis, and (c) the amplitude of the magnetic field strength outside the capacitor at distance r from the axis. Evaluate these quantities as functions of r if $I = 1$ amp, $a = 1$ cm, $s = 1$ mm, and $\epsilon = \epsilon_v$.

4. If in the previous problem it may be assumed that the magnetic field in the interior of a plate is negligible, show that current flows only on the surfaces of the plates and is different on the internal and external surfaces. If the current along the wire is $I_0 \cos \omega t$, calculate as a function of time the current per unit width at a distance r from the axis (a) on the internal surface of a plate and (b) on the external surface. Evaluate the amplitudes of these currents per unit width as functions of r if $I_0 = 1$ amp and $a = 1$ cm.

5. In Prob. 3 calculate the Poynting vector at a point between the plates of the capacitor at a distance r from the axis. Deduce the total rate of flow of energy at the edge of the capacitor, and discuss the source of this power. Show that, while the electric energy stored in the capacitor can be satisfactorily calculated neglecting fringing of the electric field at the edge, the flow of energy into and out of the capacitor can be explained only by taking fringing into account.

Part 4, Chapter 3

★1. The diagram shows an axial cross section of a permanent magnet possessing an annular gap in which the magnetic flux density is B. In the gap there is located coaxially with the magnet a circular coil possessing n turns each of radius a. The coil oscillates sinusoidally within the gap in the axial direction, the amplitude of the

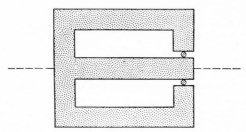

Fig. P 1

oscillation being b and the angular frequency of oscillation being ω. Calculate the amplitude of the voltage developed at the terminals of the coil. Evaluate the root-mean-square value of the voltage if $B = 1,000$ gauss, $a = 1$ cm, $b = 1$ mm, $n = 10$, and the frequency of oscillation is 256 cycles/sec.

★2. In the device described in the previous problem a sinusoidal current of amplitude I_0 and angular frequency ω is passed through the coil. Calculate the amplitude of the force tending to cause axial motion of the coil. Evaluate the amplitude of the force if $B = 1,000$ gauss, $a = 1$ cm, $n = 10$, the frequency of oscillation is 256 cycles/sec, and the root-mean-square value of the current is 1 amp.

★3. In a system of rectangular cartesian coordinates in a homogeneous medium of inductivity μ there is a steady current I along the x axis. A wire of length $2l$ is parallel to the z axis, and its mid-point M lies in the plane $z = 0$ at a fixed distance a from the current. If the point M moves with uniform velocity v parallel to the x axis, calculate the magnetically induced voltage between M and either end of the wire. Evaluate the voltage if $I = 1$ amp, $v = 1$ m/sec, $a = 10$ cm, $l = 10$ cm, and $\mu = \mu_v$.

★4. The dynamo described with Part 4, Fig. 3.5, is modified so that each pole subtends at the axis of rotation an angle α less than π. Assuming that fringing is neglected and that the machine is provided with a commutator, calculate the root-mean-square voltage generated. If $n = 1,000$, $S = 100$ cm², $B = 1$ weber/m², and $\alpha = 2\pi/3$, calculate the angular velocity of the armature required to generate a root-mean-square voltage of 100.

★5. The electric motor discussed in connection with Part 3, Fig. 6.5, draws energy from the electric power supply at a constant rate. Show that the torque exerted by the motor is greatest when the speed is least.

★6. In the machine described with Part 4, Fig. 3.5, the permanent magnet is replaced by an electromagnet for which the field coil has n' turns each carrying a steady current I'. The two gaps in the magnetic circuit are each of width w, and the reluctance of the rest of the magnetic circuit may be neglected. If the machine is used as a d-c generator, calculate the voltage induced in the armature winding. If the machine is used as an electric motor, calculate the torque exerted on the armature. Evaluate the voltage generated in the one case and the torque exerted in the other if $n = 100$, $n' = 1,000$, $S = 100$ cm², $w = 1$ cm, $\omega = 1,000$ rpm, $I = 10$ amp, $I' = 100$ ma.

★7. A coil on closed circuit having a resistance R is located in a steady magnetic field, and no current is flowing round it. The coil is now withdrawn from the field to a place where no magnetic flux threads the circuit. If, at a time t during the process of withdrawal, the magnetic flux threading the circuit is Φ and the current round it is I, show that

$$I = -\frac{1}{R}\frac{d\Phi}{dt}$$

assuming that the directions of Φ and I are related by the right-hand-screw rule. Deduce that the ratio of the original magnetic flux threading the circuit to the total charge that passes round the circuit during the entire process of withdrawal is equal to R.

★8. In the previous problem the coil possesses n turns each of area S. The coil is placed at a position P in a steady magnetic field with its plane perpendicular to the direction of the magnetic-flux-density vector, and it may be assumed that the field is uniform over the area of the coil. If withdrawal of the coil from the magnetic field causes a total charge Q to pass round the circuit, calculate the magnetic flux density at P. Evaluate the magnetic flux density if $n = 100$, $S = 1$ cm², $R = 10$ ohms, and $Q = 10$ μcoulombs.

★9. In the previous problem the coil remains at the point P, but its plane is rotated from the initial position perpendicular to the field to a final position parallel to the field. If during the process a total charge Q flows round the circuit, calculate the magnetic flux density at P.

★10. A fixed magnetic needle has pole strength Φ and length s. A closely wound circular coil of radius a has n turns, and its axis coincides with the axis of the magnetic needle. The coil moves with uniform velocity v along the axis, passing the mid-point of the magnetic needle at time zero. Calculate the voltage induced round the coil as a function of time t.

11. A homopolar generator consists of a circular conducting disk of radius a rotating on its axis with uniform angular velocity ω in a uniform magnetic field of flux density B parallel to the axis. Calculate the voltage induced between the rim and the axis. Evaluate the voltage if $a = 10$ cm, $\omega = 3{,}600$ rpm, and $B = 1{,}000$ gauss.

12. If in the previous problem the magnetic field covers only a quadrant of the disk, explain why the device acts as an electromagnetic brake for which the torque is proportional to the angular velocity of the disk and to the square of the applied magnetic flux density.

13. Two long coaxial perfectly conducting circular cylinders have a homogeneous nonconducting medium between them. The difference between the radii is s, and this may be assumed small compared with the radii themselves. There is a steady electric current I per unit length on the outer cylinder flowing circumferentially round the perimeters of normal cross sections. There is a steady current I per unit length on the inner conductor flowing in the opposite direction. In addition a steady voltage V is maintained between the conductors. At points between the conductors calculate (a) the electric vector, (b) the magnetic vector, and (c) the Poynting vector. Show that the Poynting vector represents a closed steady flow of energy between the conductors, and discuss the "reality" of the flow. Explain what action would be required to maintain in existence by itself the portion of the system between any two azimuthal planes through the axis.

Part 4, Chapter 4

★1. In the arrangement in Part 4, Fig. 3.2, calculate, neglecting fringing, (a) the electric vector $\mathbf{E}$ between the plates outside the magnetic circuit, (b) the electric vector $\mathbf{E}$ between the plates inside the magnetic circuit, (c) the vector $\mathbf{v} \times \mathbf{B}$ at a point between the plates inside the magnetic circuit and moving with the plates, (d) the vector $\mathbf{v} \times \mathbf{B}$ between the plates at a point outside the magnetic circuit and moving with the plates, and (e) the vector $\mathbf{E} + \mathbf{v} \times \mathbf{B}$ at all points between the plates. Sketch diagrams to illustrate the distribution between the plates of the vector fields $\mathbf{E}$, $\mathbf{v} \times \mathbf{B}$, and $\mathbf{E} + \mathbf{v} \times \mathbf{B}$.

★2. In the arrangement in Part 4, Fig. 3.2, the metal plates are now held fixed and the magnetic circuit is moved to the left with uniform velocity $\mathbf{v}$. Neglecting fringing, calculate (a) the voltage induced between the plates, (b) the electric vector $\mathbf{E}$ between the plates outside the magnetic circuit, (c) the vector $\mathbf{v} \times \mathbf{B}$ at a point between the plates inside the magnetic circuit and fixed relative to the plates, and (d) the electric vector $\mathbf{E}$ between the plates inside the magnetic circuit. Sketch diagrams to illustrate the distribution between the plates of the vector fields $\mathbf{E}$, $\mathbf{v} \times \mathbf{B}$, and $\mathbf{E} + \mathbf{v} \times \mathbf{B}$. Explain both the similarities and the differences between the answers to this problem and the answers to the previous problem.

★3. A circular coil of wire has n closely wound turns each of area S. At an angle θ to the axis of the coil there is a uniform magnetic field of flux density B. If the direction of the magnetic field turns with uniform angular velocity ω so that $\theta = \omega t$, calculate the voltage induced in the coil at time t. Deduce the root-mean-square voltage generated.

4. An a-c generator has the magnetic network shown in the diagram. The stator has an internal radius a and an axial width b. At the opposite ends of a diameter is cut a pair of shallow slots parallel to the axis, and a wire runs along one slot, round the stator at distance a from the axis, through the other slot, and then on round the stator back to the first slot. There are wound on the stator n such turns constituting the armature winding of the machine. The rotor carries the field coil, and this assembly is so designed that it produces at the internal surface of the stator an outward normal component of the magnetic-flux-density vector equal to $B \cos \theta$, where B is a constant and θ is an angle measured round the stator from the axis of the field coil. There is no component of the magnetic-flux-density vector parallel to the axis of rotation. If the rotor turns with uniform angular velocity ω, calculate the root-mean-square voltage induced in the armature winding. Evaluate the root-mean-square voltage if $n = 100$, $B = 1$ weber/m², $a = b = 1$ m, and the machine runs at 1,000 rpm.

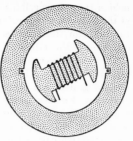

FIG. P 4

★5. A rectangular coil is pivoted about an axis through its center parallel to a pair of sides, and it is under the influence of a uniform magnetic field perpendicular to the axis. The direction of the magnetic field rotates round the axis with uniform angular velocity ω. If the coil is short-circuited, explain why it rotates.

★6. In the machine shown in Part 4, Fig. 3.5, the armature is wound with three identical coils whose planes pass through the axis of rotation and intersect at angles $\pi/3$. Show that any two of the coils can be connected in series in such a way that the voltage developed across the pair is at all times identical with the voltage developed across the third coil.

7. Between the pole faces of a large magnet there is an evacuated space in which there is a uniform magnetic field of flux density B. Into the evacuated space in a direction perpendicular to the magnetic field are shot electrons (charge $-e$, mass m) from a gun of voltage V. After the electrons have formed a closed loop, the magnetic field begins to increase at a rate $\dot{B}$ per unit time. During the ensuing revolution of the loop each electron is accelerated as though through a voltage δV. Calculate the radius of the loop, the time taken by an electron to describe one circuit of the loop, and the value of δV. Evaluate these quantities if $V = 10,000$ volts, $B = 30$ gauss, and $\dot{B} = 10^6$ gauss/sec. Estimate the number of circuits that an electron must perform to double its initial energy, and the time that elapses during the process.

★8. An autotransformer consists of a magnetic circuit of reluctance R upon which is wound an $(m + n)$-turn coil of negligible resistance. The ends of the winding are connected to terminals 1 and 3, while terminal 2 is connected to the point on the winding m turns from terminal 1 and n turns from terminal 2. If an alternating voltage $V_0 \cos \omega t$ is applied between terminals 1 and 3, calculate the voltage appearing between terminals 2 and 3. If the voltage $V_0 \cos \omega t$ is applied between terminals 2 and 3, calculate the voltage appearing between terminals 1 and 3.

9. A perfectly conducting plate of width b and length $2l + 2\pi r$ is bent into the form shown in Fig. 10.13 (page 722). The capacitor having plates of area bl with small separation a is provided with electrolyte and converted into a voltaic cell. The cylinder of radius r is used as an inductor in which the magnetic field may be assumed uniform. If the current round the inductor increases at a uniform rate $\dot{I}$, calculate the voltage of the voltaic cell.

10. Within the inductor of the previous problem draw the lines of magnetic vector potential, and calculate the magnetic vector potential at the surface of the inductor. Verify that the line integral of the time rate of increase of the magnetic vector potential round the inductor from one terminal of the voltaic cell to the other is equal to the voltage of the cell.

11. In the arrangement described in Prob. 9 sketch the way in which the electric field of the voltaic cell fringes into the inductor. In a plane perpendicular to the axis of the inductor a curve C is drawn from one terminal of the cell round a quadrant of the inductor, then across a diameter of the inductor, and finally round a further quadrant of the inductor to the other terminal of the cell. Calculate the line integral of the magnetic vector potential round C from the positive terminal of the cell to the negative terminal. For the fringing electric field of the cell, deduce the value of the line integral of the electric vector taken along the diameter of the inductor, and express it as a ratio to the voltage of the cell.

12. In the arrangement described in Prob. 9 a line of force of the fringing electric field of the cell in the inductor divides the magnetic flux threading the inductor so that a fraction k passes on the cell side of the line. Calculate, as a ratio to the voltage of the cell, the line integral of the electric vector along the line of force.

13. In the arrangement described in Prob. 9, θ denotes an azimuthal angle round the axis of the inductor. The plane $\theta = 0$ runs from the axis of the inductor in the direction opposite to the direction of the cell. The plane $\theta = \pi$ may be assumed to run to the positive terminal of the cell, and the plane $\theta = -\pi$ to run to the negative terminal of the cell. Taking the voltage of the cell as V and the electric potential on the plane $\theta = 0$ as zero, calculate the electric potential round the perimeter of the inductor as a function of θ. Explain why, round the perimeter of the inductor, there is a gradient of electric potential but no component of the electric vector. Draw a rough sketch of the equipotential surfaces for the electric potential within the inductor.

Part 4, Chapter 5

★1. A circuit of inductance L and negligible resistance has no current round it at time zero. At this time a voltage $V(t)$ that varies with time t is switched into the circuit. Calculate the current in the circuit at any subsequent time if $V(t) = V_0 e^{\sigma t}$ $(\sigma < 0)$. Draw sketches of the voltage and current as functions of time.

★2. Repeat the above problem if $V(t) = V_0 \cos \omega t$.

★3. Repeat Prob. 1 if $V(t) = V_0 \sin \omega t$.

★4. Repeat Prob. 1 if $V(t) = V_0 e^{\sigma t} \cos \omega t$ $(\sigma < 0)$.

★5. A solenoid of length s and radius a has n turns of wire closely and uniformly wound, and it may be assumed that the magnetic field within the solenoid is uniform. The inductivity of the medium is μ, and the resistance of the wire per unit length is r. If at time t_1 a steady voltage V is applied across the terminals of the solenoid, calculate the current through the wire at a later time t.

★6. In the previous problem it may be assumed that, at a certain time t_2 later than t_1, the current has become steady. At the time t_2 the applied voltage is short-circuited. Calculate the current through the solenoid at a later time t. Write down the time constant of the solenoid and evaluate it if $s = 5$ cm, $a = 1$ cm, $n = 100$, $r = 0.3$ ohm/m, and the permeability of the medium is unity.

★7. A coil has inductance L and resistance R, and there is no current through it prior to time zero. At time zero a steady voltage V is applied across the coil, and at time τ equal to the time constant of the coil the voltage is short-circuited. Calculate the current through the coil at a time t later than τ. Sketch the voltage across the coil and the current through it as functions of time.

8. A coil has inductance L and resistance R, and no current flows through it prior to time zero. At time zero a large voltage $V(t)$ is applied across the terminals of the coil for a short time τ, negligible compared with the time constant of the coil, and thereafter the coil is short-circuited. The value of $\int_0^\tau V(t)\, dt$ is Φ. Calculate the current through the coil at a subsequent time t not small compared with the time constant of the coil. Sketch the voltage across the coil and the current through it as functions of time.

9. The a-c generator in Part 4, Sec. 3.6, has a resistive load connected in series with the rotating coil, and the generator is used for producing in the load an alternating current of standard frequency f. The generator is driven by an engine that is not capable of delivering on the average a power greater than P. Calculate the minimum load resistance for which the standard frequency can be maintained.

10. The machine described with Part 4, Fig. 3.5, is used as an electric motor and operates from a power supply of constant voltage V. The armature winding has resistance R, and the machine is operating with steady angular velocity ω_0 against a mechanical load requiring a steady torque. The load is now gradually removed. When the load has been completely removed, calculate the uniform angular velocity of the machine. Plot a curve to show the relation between angular velocity and torque while the load is being removed.

11. A toroidal inductor has perimeter of length s and cross-sectional area S, and variation of the magnetic flux density over a cross section may be neglected. There are n turns of perfectly conducting wire, closely and uniformly wound, and each carries a current I that varies with time t. The toroid has a ferromagnetic core for which the relation between the magnetic flux density B and the magnetic field strength H is

$$B = B_s \left(\coth \frac{3\mu H}{B_s} - \frac{B_s}{3\mu H} \right)$$

B_s being the saturation flux density. Calculate as a function of I and dI/dt the voltage that must be applied across the terminals of the inductor in order to drive the current. If $I = I_0 \sin \omega t$ and I_0 is large enough to cause appreciable saturation, sketch a curve showing the voltage required as a function of time.

12. In the previous problem calculate the relation between B and H when H is small compared with B_s/μ, and deduce the significance of μ. If I is to start from zero and to increase steadily at the rate 1 amp/sec, calculate as a function of time the voltage that must be applied if $B_s = 1$ weber/m², $\mu = 1,000$, $n = 1,000$, $S = 1$ cm², and $s = 10$ cm. If, alternatively, a fixed voltage is applied across the inductor, sketch the variation of current with time and describe how this is modified when the resistance of the wire is taken into account.

Part 4, Chapter 6

★1. Five inductors, each of inductance L and negligible resistance, are connected together to form the network shown in the diagram, and a current I that depends on time t is to be passed in at one terminal and out at the other. Neglecting the mutual inductance of the inductors, calculate the voltage that must be applied between the terminals.

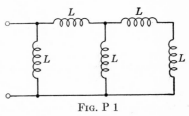

Fig. P 1

★2. In the previous problem the current entering one terminal and leaving the other oscillates sinusoidally with amplitude I_0 and angular frequency ω. If the current is given by $I = I_0 \cos \omega t$, calculate the voltage that must be applied between the terminals. Evaluate the root-mean-square value of the voltage if the root-mean-square current is 1 amp, the frequency of oscillation is 60 cycles/sec, and $L = 1$ henry.

★3. In the network of Prob. 1 there is no current prior to time zero. At time zero a generator delivering a current $I_0 \sin \omega t$ is applied across the terminals. Neglecting the mutual inductance of the inductors, calculate for every inductor the current through it and the voltage across it at time t.

★4. Five inductors, each of inductance L and negligible resistance, are connected together to form the network shown in the diagram, and mutual inductance between the inductors may be neglected. Prior to time zero there is no current in the network. At time zero a voltage V_0 sin ωt is applied across the terminals. Calculate for every inductor the voltage across it and the current through it at time t.

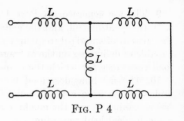

FIG. P 4

★5. In the network of the previous problem there is no current prior to time zero. At time zero a steady voltage V is applied across the terminals. At a subsequent time T the voltage is short-circuited. At a later time t calculate the current through the short circuit. Explain why the calculated current does not tend to zero as t tends to infinity.

★6. In the previous problem a resistor of resistance R is used in place of the short circuit. Calculate the current through the resistor at a time t later than T.

★7. A transformer has a primary winding whose coefficient of inductance is L_{11}, a secondary winding whose coefficient of inductance is L_{22}, and there is a coefficient of mutual inductance L_{12} between the windings. Across the secondary winding is connected a coil of inductance L. All losses are negligible, and no current exists at time zero. Thereafter a voltage $V(t)$ is applied across the primary winding. Calculate the current through the coil of inductance L at time t. Deduce the current if $V(t) = V_0$ sin ωt. Evaluate the root-mean-square current through the coil if $L = 0.5$ henry, $L_{11} = 1$ henry, $L_{22} = 0.25$ henry, the coupling coefficient of the transformer is 0.5, the frequency of oscillation is 60 cycles/sec, and the root-mean-square voltage applied is 100.

★8. A pair of identical transformers, for which losses may be neglected, each have coefficients of self-inductance L_{11} and L_{22} and coefficient of mutual inductance L_{12}. The primary winding of one transformer is connected across the secondary winding

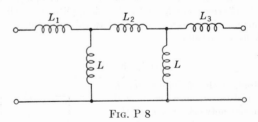

FIG. P 8

of the other transformer. Prove that the pair of transformers is equivalent to a network of the form shown in the diagram, and calculate the values of L_1, L_2, L_3, and L. Evaluate these quantities if $L_{11} = 1$ henry, $L_{22} = 4$ henrys, and the coupling coefficient of each transformer is unity.

★9. A pair of identical loss-free transformers (coefficients of inductance L_{11}, L_{22}, L_{12}) are connected in cascade as described in the previous problem. If a current generator delivering a current I that depends on time t is applied to the primary winding of the first transformer, calculate the open-circuit voltage appearing at the secondary terminals of the second transformer. Deduce the voltage if $I(t) = I_0$ cos ωt. Evaluate the root-mean-square voltage at the secondary terminals of the second transformer if $L_{11} = 1$ henry, $L_{22} = 4$ henrys, the coupling coefficient of each transformer is unity, the frequency of the applied current is 256 cycles/sec, and the root-mean-square value of the applied current is 1 ma.

★10. In the previous problem verify that the same open-circuit voltage would be obtained at the terminals of the primary winding of the first transformer if the current $I(t)$ were applied in the secondary winding of the second transformer.

11. In the audio-frequency amplifier shown in the diagram the two vacuum tubes are coupled by means of an iron-core transformer for which the coefficients of inductance are L_{11}, L_{22}, and L_{12}. Four batteries are involved having negligible internal resistances and voltages V_1, V_2, V_3, and V_4. A sinusoidal voltage of angular frequency ω is applied across the terminals. The associated current in the primary

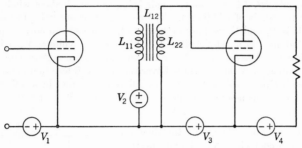

FIG. P 11

winding of the transformer is $I_1 \cos \omega t$, and the steady current through the winding is I_0. For time t calculate the voltage at the grid of the second tube relative to the cathode on the assumption that this tube is equivalent to an open circuit. Explain to what extent the transformer can be replaced by an equivalent T network. If $L_{11} = 10$ henrys, $L_{22} = 100$ henrys, the coupling coefficient of the transformer is unity, $V_3 = 50$ volts, and the frequency of oscillation is 256 cycles/sec, calculate the maximum permissible value of I_1 if the grid of the second tube must always have a negative potential relative to the cathode.

★12. The windings of a transformer are numbered 1 and 2. Their resistances are R_1 and R_2, respectively, and other losses may be neglected. The coefficients of self-inductance of the transformer are L_{11} and L_{22}, respectively, while the coefficient of mutual inductance is L_{12}. One terminal of winding 1 is connected to one terminal of winding 2, and across the remaining pair of terminals a steady voltage V is connected at time t_1. Calculate the current through the windings of the transformer at a later time t. Distinguish between the two cases that arise.

★13. In the previous problem it may be assumed that, at a certain time t_2 later than t_1, the current through the windings has become steady. At the time t_2 the voltage is short-circuited. Calculate the current through the windings at a later time t. Evaluate the two possible time constants of the arrangement if $R_1 = R_2 = 1$ ohm, $L_{11} = L_{22} = 1$ mh, and the coupling coefficient of the transformer is $\frac{1}{4}$.

14. Three coils are wound on a cylindrical form side by side, each constituting a right-handed helix. The windings are numbered 1, 2, and 3, number 2 being the middle winding. The coefficients of inductance of the system of inductors are L_{mn} (m, $n = 1$, 2, 3). The adjacent terminals of windings 2 and 3 are connected together by a wire, and the arrangement is used as a transformer. Calculate the coefficients of inductance of the transformer. Evaluate them if the coefficient of self-inductance of each of the original windings is L, the coefficient of mutual inductance between adjacent windings is $\frac{1}{2}L$, and that of the extreme windings is $\frac{1}{10}L$.

15. In the previous problem the remaining terminals of windings 2 and 3 are connected together by a wire, and losses may be neglected. No current exists prior to time zero, and at this time a voltage $V_0 \sin \omega t$ is applied across the terminals of winding 1. Calculate the current in the other two windings at a later time t. Evaluate the current when the coefficients of self- and mutual inductance of the three original windings have the values stated at the end of the previous problem.

16. Repeat Probs. 14 and 15 (*a*) if the connections of winding 3 are reversed, (*b*) if the connections of winding 2 are reversed, and (*c*) if the connections of both windings 2 and 3 are reversed.

17. Three coils are wound on a cylindrical form side by side, each constituting a right-handed helix. The terminals are numbered in order along the length of the form 1*A*, 1*B*, 2*A*, 2*B*, 3*A*, 3*B*, the first pair being the terminals of winding 1 and the last pair the terminals of winding 3. The coefficient of mutual reluctance between adjacent coils is R, and losses may be neglected. There is no current prior to time zero, and winding 2 is short-circuited. At time zero a voltage $V_1(t)$ is connected across winding 1 and a voltage $V_3(t)$ across winding 3, the voltage stated being the excess of the potential of the A terminal over that at the B terminal in both cases. If $V_1(t) = V_0 \cos \omega t$ and $V_3(t) = V_0 \sin \omega t$, calculate the current in winding 2 at time t. Evaluate the root-mean-square value of the current if $V_0 = 1$ volt and $R = -1$ henry^{-1}.

★18. For the network shown in the diagram calculate (*a*) the coefficients of self- and mutual reluctance for the equivalent transformer and (*b*) the coefficients of self- and mutual inductance for the equivalent transformer. Evaluate the coefficients if $L_1 = 1$ henry, $L_2 = 2$ henrys, and $L_3 = 3$ henrys.

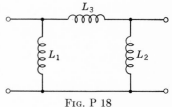

FIG. P 18

★19. For the network of the previous problem a voltage $V_0 \sin \omega t$ is applied across the left-hand terminals subsequent to time zero, the voltage prior to this time being zero. Calculate the Thévenin and Norton equivalent circuits for the arrangement.

★20. For the network of Prob. 18 a current $I_0 \sin \omega t$ is applied at the terminals on the left. Calculate the Thévenin and Norton equivalent circuits for the arrangement.

21. For the transformer described in Prob. 14 calculate the voltage and current transformation ratios. Evaluate these ratios for the coefficients of inductance stated at the end of Prob. 14.

22. A pair of coils numbered 1 and 2 have unknown coefficients of self- and mutual inductance. To measure the coefficient of mutual inductance, a ballistic galvanometer is connected across coil 2, and the resistance in this circuit is then R. When a battery of unknown voltage and unknown internal resistance is connected across coil 1, it is found that (*a*) the current in coil 1 settles down to a steady value I and (*b*) the total charge that passes through the galvanometer is Q. By applying the law of induction to coil 2 and integrating with respect to time, show that the coefficient of mutual inductance between the coils is RQ/I.

23. In the d-c generator described in connection with Part 4, Fig. 3.5, the permanent magnet is replaced by an electromagnet for which nonlinear behavior of the ferromagnetic material may be neglected. The coefficient of mutual inductance between the windings at the epoch of commutation is L_{12}. If I_1 is the current in the field winding, show that the voltage induced in the armature winding by its motion in the presence of the field winding is $\omega L_{12} I_1$.

24. For the generator described in the previous problem the coefficients of self-inductance of the field and armature windings are L_{11} and L_{22}. It may be assumed that L_{11} is large compared with L_{12} and that L_{12} is large compared with L_{22}. The field winding is connected across the armature winding through a variable resistor of resistance R, in comparison with which the resistances of the windings may be neglected. The machine is driven at constant angular velocity ω, and there is no electrical load connected to it. Show that the equation satisfied by the current I through either winding is

$$L_{11} \frac{dI}{dt} + RI = \omega L_{12} I$$

If $R > \omega L_{12}$, show that any current that may exist in the windings decays exponentially with the time constant $L/(R - \omega L_{12})$. Explain what happens if $R < \omega L_{12}$.

25. In the previous problem the ferromagnetic material possesses some residual magnetism, so that there is a fixed magnetic flux Φ_0 round the magnetic circuit in addition to that due to electric current. If $R > \omega L_{12}$, show that the current through the windings acquires a steady value, and calculate this value. If $R < \omega L_{12}$, show that the current increases until saturation of the ferromagnetic material comes into play.

26. For the d-c generator described in Prob. 23 there are n_1 turns on the field winding and n_2 turns on the armature winding. The magnetic circuit may be assumed to have uniform cross-sectional area S, with a length s in the ferromagnetic material and a length w in each of the gaps. The relation between the magnetic flux density B and the magnetic field strength H in the ferromagnetic material is now to be taken as

$$B = B_s \left(\coth \frac{3\mu H}{B_s} - \frac{B_s}{3\mu H} \right)$$

where B_s is the saturation flux density. Devise a numerical method for evaluating the voltage V induced in the armature winding as a function of the current I_1 in the field winding. Sketch the form of this function, and evaluate dV/dI_1 when $I_1 = 0$.

27. In the previous problem the relation between the voltage V induced in the armature winding and the current I_1 in the field winding is written $V = f(I_1)$. The generator is now connected as described in Prob. 24. Show that, when the current in the windings has acquired a steady value I, this value is a solution of the equation $f(I) = RI$. Devise a numerical method for solving this equation, showing that the solution is $I = 0$ if the value of R is greater than a certain value. If R is less than this value, show that there are two solutions and that it is the nonzero solution that corresponds to stable operation. Describe how the voltage between the armature terminals varies with the value of R.

28. In Prob. 26 the relation between the voltage V induced in the armature winding and the current I_1 in the field winding can be written $V = V_0 + rI_1$ over limited range of V and of I_1. The field winding is connected across the armature winding through a variable resistor of resistance R ($R > r$), and the resistances of the windings may be neglected. The generator delivers power into a load resistor of resistance R_L connected across the armature terminals. Calculate the voltage developed across the load and the power delivered to the load. If $V_0 = 200$ volts, $r = 10$ ohms, $R_L = 5$ ohms, and R can vary from 40 to 60 ohms, plot the variation with R of (a) the voltage across the load and (b) the power delivered to the load. If R is adjusted to produce 250 volts across the load, evaluate the power delivered to the load in kilowatts.

Part 4, Chapter 7

★1. The current through an inductor of 1 henry is increased uniformly from zero to 1 amp in 1 sec. Plot curves to show the variation with time of the power supplied to the inductor and the energy stored in it.

★2. A number of inductors of inductances $L_1, L_2, \ldots$ are connected in series with one another and with a generator delivering a current $I(t)$. Neglecting mutual inductance and losses, calculate the rate at which the generator is delivering energy at time t, and show that it is the same as if the generator were connected across a single inductor of inductance $L_1 + L_2 + \cdots$.

★3. In the previous problem calculate the magnetic energy stored in the system of inductors at time t and show that it is the same as that which would be stored by the same generator during the same time in a single inductor of inductance $L_1 + L_2 + \cdots$. Prove that the rate of increase of the magnetic energy stored in the network is equal to the rate at which energy is delivered by the generator.

★4. A steady current is passed through a number of inductors connected in series. Neglecting mutual inductance and resistance, prove that the magnetic energy stored in the system is divided between the inductors in the ratio of their inductances.

★5. A number of inductors of inductances L_1, L_2, . . . are connected in parallel with one another and with a generator of voltage $V(t)$. Mutual inductance and losses may be neglected, and no current exists at time zero. Calculate the rate at which the generator is delivering energy at time t, and show that it is the same if the generator were connected across a single inductor whose inductance is the reciprocal of $1/L_1 + 1/L_2 + \cdots$.

★6. In the previous problem calculate the magnetic energy stored in the system of inductors at time t and show that it is the same as that which would be stored by the same generator during the same time in a single inductor whose inductance is the reciprocal $1/L_1 + 1/L_2 + \cdots$. Prove that the rate of increase of the magnetic energy stored in the network is equal to the rate at which energy is delivered by the generator.

★7. A system of loss-free inductors possesses a pair of terminals, and application of a voltage V across the terminals causes the current at the terminals to increase at a rate V/L. With all currents initially zero, a current generator delivering a current $I(t)$ is connected across the terminals. Prove that the magnetic energy stored in the system at time t is $\frac{1}{2}LI^2(t)$ and that the time rate of increase of this is the power delivered by the generator.

★8. For the network shown in Chap. 6, Prob. 1, no current exists initially, and a generator delivering a constant current I is then applied across the terminals. Calculate the total magnetic energy stored in the network. Evaluate the magnetic energy if $L = 1$ henry and $I = 1$ amp.

9. A number of inductors are connected in parallel with one another and with a current generator. Mutual inductance and losses may be neglected, and initially no current exists. The current delivered by the generator is now increased to a steady value. Prove that the magnetic energy stored in the system is divided between the inductors in the ratio of the reciprocals of the inductances.

10. A number of inductors whose inductances are L_1, L_2, . . . and resistances R_1, R_2, . . . are connected in parallel. A steady voltage is applied across the inductors, and the currents through them acquire steady values. Show that the magnetic energy stored in the system is divided between the inductors in the ratios L_1/R_1^2, L_2/R_2^2, ... Since the currents through the inductors become steady both in this problem and in the previous problem, explain why the results are different.

11. In Prob. 8 calculate the magnetic energy stored in each inductor.

★12. A generator of voltage $V(t)$ is connected across a coil of inductance L and resistance R. Prove that the time rate of increase of the magnetic energy stored in the coil is equal to the excess of the power supplied by the generator over the power dissipated in the resistor.

★13. A generator delivering a current $I(t)$ is connected across a capacitor of capacitance C and leakage conductance G. Prove that the time rate of increase of the electric energy stored in the capacitor is equal to the excess of the power supplied by the generator over the power dissipated in the leakage conductance.

★14. A capacitor of capacitance C is connected in parallel with a resistor of conductance G. The capacitor is charged to a voltage V_0 at time zero and then discharges through the resistor. If V is the voltage of the capacitor at time t show that

$$C \frac{dV}{dt} + GV = 0$$

and deduce the dependence of V on t.

★15. The material between the plates of a capacitor has capacitivity ϵ and conductivity σ. The capacitor is charged to a certain voltage and is then allowed to discharge through its leakage conductance. Show that the voltage decreases by a factor e^{-1} in time ϵ/σ, where e is the base of Napierian logarithms. Evaluate the time constant ϵ/σ if $\epsilon = 7\epsilon_v$ and $\sigma = 10^{-15}$ mho/m.

★16. A capacitor of capacitance C is connected in parallel with a resistor of conductance G. At time zero the capacitor is uncharged, and a generator developing a constant current I_0 is connected across the capacitor. Calculate the voltage across the capacitor at time t.

★17. An oscillatory current of angular frequency ω, amplitude I_0, and phase β is written $I_0 \cos{(\omega t + \beta)}$. The current is passed through an inductor of inductance L and resistance R. Calculate the voltage developed across the terminals of the coil. Deduce the mean energy stored in the coil and the mean rate of dissipation of energy in the coil.

★18. An oscillatory voltage of angular frequency ω, amplitude V_0, and phase α is written $V_0 \cos{(\omega t + \alpha)}$. The voltage is applied across a capacitor of capacitance C and leakage conductance G. Calculate the current supplied to the capacitor. Deduce the mean energy stored in the capacitor and the mean rate of dissipation of energy in the capacitor.

★19. An inductor of inductance L carries a current that oscillates sinusoidally with period T and has a root-mean-square value I_0. Calculate the mean magnetic energy stored in the inductor at any time t, and show that successive maxima of the stored magnetic energy are separated by intervals of $\frac{1}{2}T$. Draw sketches showing (a) the variation with time of the magnetic energy stored in the inductor and (b) the variation with time in the rate of increase of the stored magnetic energy.

★20. Between the plates of a capacitor of capacitance C there is a voltage that oscillates sinusoidally with period T and has a root-mean-square value of V_0. Calculate the mean electric energy stored in the capacitor at any time t, and show that successive maxima of the stored electric energy are separated by intervals of $\frac{1}{2}T$. Draw sketches showing (a) the variation with time of the electric energy stored in the capacitor and (b) the variation with time in the rate of increase of the stored electric energy.

★21. A nonconducting anchor ring made of material of inductivity μ has perimeter s and cross-sectional area S, the linear dimensions of S being small compared with s. If the anchor ring is wrapped with metal foil and used as a toroidal inductor, calculate the magnetic energy stored in the inductor (a) if the total current round the curved surface is I and (b) if the magnetic flux through the inductor is Φ.

★22. If in the previous problem the foil is replaced by an electric circuit having n turns of wire closely and uniformly spaced, calculate the magnetic energy stored in the inductor (a) if the current round the electric circuit is I and (b) if the magnetic flux threading the electric circuit is Φ. Evaluate the stored energy if $s = 20$ cm, $S = 1$ cm^2, $\mu = 1,000\ \mu_v$, $n = 1,000$, and (a) $I = 1$ amp, (b) $\Phi = 10^{-5}$ weber.

★23. From a strip of perfectly conducting metal of width b and length $2l + 2\pi r$ an oscillatory electric circuit is constructed as shown in Fig. 10.13 (page 722). The capacitor is composed of plates of area bl and separation a, while the inductor is a cylinder of length b and radius r. The inductivity and capacitivity of the medium are μ and ϵ, respectively, and both the electric field in the capacitor and the magnetic field in the inductor may be considered uniform. Calculate the resonant frequency and the dynamic resistance. Evaluate these quantities if $a = 1$ mm, $b = 2$ cm, $l = 1$ cm, $r = 1$ cm, $\mu = \mu_v$, and $\epsilon = \epsilon_v$.

★24. For the oscillatory electric circuit of the previous problem, calculate the resonant wavelength. Examine how well the inequality (5.70) in Part 4 is satisfied for the numerical values given in the previous problem.

★25. The electric circuit described in Prob. 23 is oscillating at its resonant frequency, and the root-mean-square voltage across the capacitor is V_0. Calculate (a) the root-mean-square current round the inductor, (b) the mean magnetic energy stored in the inductor, (c) the mean electric energy stored in the capacitor, and (d) the maximum rate of flow of energy between the inductor and the capacitor. Evaluate these quantities if $V_0 = 1$ volt, $a = 1$ mm, $b = 2$ cm, $l = 1$ cm, $r = 1$ cm, $\mu = \mu_v$, and $\epsilon = \epsilon_v$.

★26. An oscillatory electric circuit consists of a multiturn inductor connected in parallel with a multiplate capacitor. The inductor has n_1 turns, each of area S_1 on a cylinder of length s_1 large compared with the linear dimensions of S_1. The capacitor has n_2 spaces between plates, the plates being of area S_2 with separations s_2 small compared with the linear dimensions of S_2. Every other plate of the capacitor is connected to one terminal of the inductor, while the remaining plates are connected to the other terminal of the inductor. The inductivity and capacitivity of the medium are μ and ϵ, respectively. Calculate the resonant frequency and the dynamic resistance. Evaluate these quantities if $n_1 = 100$, $S_1 = 1$ cm², $s_1 = 3$ cm, $n_2 = 10$, $S_2 = 1$ cm², $s_2 = 1$ mm, $\mu = \mu_v$, and $\epsilon = \epsilon_v$.

★27. The electric circuit described in the previous problem is oscillating at its resonant frequency, and the root-mean-square voltage across the capacitor is V_0. Calculate (a) the root-mean-square current through the inductor, (b) the mean magnetic energy stored in the inductor, (c) the mean electric energy stored in the capacitor, and (d) the maximum rate of flow of energy between the inductor and the capacitor. Evaluate these quantities for the numerical values stated at the end of the previous problem.

★28. An oscillatory circuit consists of a toroidal inductor made of metal sheet, split round the inner perimeter and connected to an annular parallel-plate capacitor as indicated in Part 3, Fig. 5.8. The radius of an axial cross section of the inductor is r, the radii of the inner and outer edges of the capacitor plates are a and b, and the separation between the plates of the capacitor is s. It may be assumed that s is small compared with r and that r is small compared with b. The inductivity and capacitivity of the medium are μ and ϵ, respectively. Calculate the resonant frequency and the dynamic resistance. Evaluate these quantities if $r = 1$ cm, $a = 1$ cm, $b = 2$ cm, $s = 1$ mm, $\mu = \mu_v$, and $\epsilon = \epsilon_v$.

29. In the network shown in the diagram a voltage $V_1(t)$ is applied at the left-hand terminals and the resulting open-circuit voltage appearing at the right-hand terminals is $V_2(t)$. Show that the variations with time t of the two voltages are related by the equation

$$V_1(t) = V_2(t) + LC \frac{d^2 V_2}{dt^2}$$

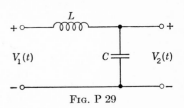

Fig. P 29

30. In the network of the previous problem it is required to produce an output voltage $V_2(t)$ equal to $V_0e^{-t^2/\tau^2}$, where τ is a constant. Calculate the necessary input voltage $V_1(t)$. Draw sketches of the input and output voltages as functions of time if $V_0 = 1$ volt and if (a) $\tau = \frac14(LC)^{1/2}$, (b) $\tau = (LC)^{1/2}$, and (c) $\tau = 4(LC)^{1/2}$.

31. In the network of Prob. 29, show that an output voltage of the form

$$V_2(t) = A\cos\omega t + B\sin\omega t$$

where $\omega = 1/(LC)^{1/2}$, requires no input voltage $V_1(t)$ no matter what the values of the constants A and B. Give a physical interpretation of this result.

32. In the network of Prob. 29, the output voltage is

$$V_2(t) = V_0 + A\cos\omega t + B\sin\omega t$$

where V_0, A, and B are constants, and $\omega = 1/(LC)^{1/2}$. Calculate the input voltage $V_1(t)$ and the current through the inductor at time t.

33. For the network of Prob. 29 a battery of voltage V_0 is applied at the left-hand terminals at time zero, and at this time there is no current through the inductor. Calculate the output voltage at any subsequent time t. Plot the output voltage as a function of time if $V_0 = 1$ volt, $L = 1$ henry, and $C = 1$ µf.

34. In the previous problem deduce the current through the inductor at time t. Plot it as a function of time if $V_0 = 1$ volt, $L = 1$ henry, and $C = 1$ µf.

35. In Prob. 33, calculate as functions of time (a) the electric energy stored in the capacitor and (b) the magnetic energy stored in the inductor. Plot the stored energies as functions of time if $V_0 = 1$ volt, $L = 1$ henry, and $C = 1$ µf.

36. In Prob. 33 calculate as functions of time (a) the rate of flow of energy into the capacitor, (b) the rate of flow of energy into the inductor, and (c) the rate of flow of energy out of the battery. Verify that the third of these quantities is equal to the sum of the other two. Plot the three rates of flow of energy as functions of time if $V_0 = 1$ volt, $L = 1$ henry, and $C = 1$ µf.

37. In the network shown in Prob. 29 the inductor has a resistance R in addition to an inductance L. For a given open-circuit output voltage $V_2(t)$ as a function of time t, calculate the required input voltage $V_1(t)$. Evaluate the input voltage when the output voltage is equal to $V_0e^{-t^2/\tau^2}$, where τ is a constant. Draw sketches of the input voltage as a function of time if $V_0 = 1$ volt, $\tau = (LC)^{1/2}$, and (a) $R = \frac{1}{16}(LC)^{1/2}$, (b) $R = \frac14(L/C)^{1/2}$, (c) $R = (L/C)^{1/2}$.

38. A voltage V_0e^{st}, where V_0 and s are real constants and t denotes time, is applied across a capacitor of capacitance C and negligible leakage. Calculate the ratio of the current supplied to the capacitor to the voltage across it. Show that the electric energy stored in the capacitor increases with time at the rate sCV^2.

39. A current I_0e^{st}, where I_0 and s are real constants and t denotes time, is applied to an inductor of inductance L and negligible resistance. Calculate the ratio of the voltage developed across the inductor to the current through it. Show that the magnetic energy stored in the inductor increases with time at the rate sLI^2.

40. A voltage V_0e^{st}, where V_0 and s are real constants and t denotes time, is applied across a capacitor of capacitance C and leakage conductance G. Show that the ratio of the current supplied to the capacitor to the voltage across it is $C(s - s_0)$, where $s_0 = -G/C$. Explain what happens when $s = s_0$.

41. A current I_0e^{st}, where I_0 and s are real constants and t denotes time, is applied to an inductor of inductance L and resistance R. Show that the ratio of the voltage developed across the inductor to the current through it is $L(s - s_0)$, where $s_0 = -R/L$. Explain what happens when $s = s_0$.

42. A generator has a voltage that varies with time t proportionally to e^{st}, where s is a real constant. The generator is connected in series with a resistor, an inductor, and a capacitor, the four elements forming a closed circuit. The resistance, inductance, and capacitance are R, L, and C, respectively. If the current round the circuit varies with time proportionally to e^{st}, show that the ratio of the voltage of the generator to the current that it delivers is $R + Ls + 1/Cs$.

43. In the previous problem show that the ratio of the current delivered by the generator to the voltage of the generator can be written in the form

$$\frac{1}{L}\frac{1}{s_1 - s_2}\left(\frac{s_1}{s - s_1} - \frac{s_2}{s - s_2}\right)$$

where s_1 and s_2 are the roots of the quadratic equation

$$LCs^2 + RCs + 1 = 0$$

Sketch the variation of the current-voltage ratio with s (*a*) if $R > 2(L/C)^{\frac{1}{2}}$ and (*b*) if $R < 2(L/C)^{\frac{1}{2}}$.

44. A coil has inductance L and resistance R, and the quantity $-R/L$ is denoted by s_0. If V_0 and s are real constants, show that the voltage across the terminals of the coil when there is a current

$$\frac{V_0}{L(s - s_0)}e^{st} + Ae^{s_0 t}$$

through the coil is independent of the value of the constant A. If there is no current through the coil at time zero and a generator of voltage $V_0 e^{st}$ is then connected across the coil, calculate the current at time t. Sketch curves to illustrate the variations of the voltage and current with time (*a*) if $s > 0$, (*b*) if $s = 0$, (*c*) if $s_0 < s < 0$, (*d*) if $s = s_0$, and (*e*) if $s < s_0$.

45. A capacitor has capacitance C and leakage conductance G, and the quantity $-G/C$ is denoted by s_0. If I_0 and s are constants, show that the current supplied to the capacitor when there is a voltage

$$\frac{I_0}{C(s - s_0)}e^{st} + Ae^{s_0 t}$$

across the capacitor is independent of the value of the constant A. If there is no voltage across the capacitor at time zero and a generator delivering a current $I_0 e^{st}$ is then connected across the capacitor, calculate the voltage at time t. Sketch curves to illustrate the variations of the voltage and current with time (*a*) if $s > 0$, (*b*) if $s = 0$, (*c*) if $s_0 < s < 0$, (*d*) if $s = s_0$, and (*e*) if $s < s_0$.

46. The following table lists in pairs what are known as dual concepts in electric network theory:

Voltage V.................	Current I
Resistance R...............	Conductance G
Inductance L...............	Capacitance C
Magnetic flux Φ.............	Electric charge Q
Magnetic energy W_m.........	Electric energy W_e
Series connection...........	Parallel connection
Short circuit................	Open circuit
Node......................	Mesh
Power VI..................	Power IV

Suppose that we have a given network of inductors, capacitors, and resistors and that from it we derive a "dual network" by replacing each element of the given network by the corresponding paired element listed in the table. It is asserted that any statement concerning the given network involving the quantities listed becomes a statement concerning the dual network by substituting everywhere the paired concept listed in the table. Discuss the truth of this statement by means of examples from the text and problems of this chapter or elsewhere.

47. Prior to time zero the capacitors in the network shown in the diagram have batteries connected across them. At time zero the batteries are suddenly removed and currents I_1 and I_2 flow round the meshes. Assuming that both of these currents vary with time t proportionally to e^{st}, where s is a negative real number, write down Kirchhoff's equations for the mesh currents. By eliminating I_1 and I_2 show that there are two possible values for s and evaluate them. Prove that, for one value of s, $I_1 = I_2$ and, for the other value of s, $I_1 = -I_2$. Deduce the relations between the initial charging voltages on the capacitors in the two cases.

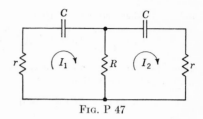

FIG. P 47

48. By taking the initial charging voltages on the capacitors in the previous problem as $\frac{1}{2}V_0$ for each value of s and superposing the two solutions, show that a solution can be obtained to the problem in which initially one capacitor is charged to voltage V_0 and the other capacitor is uncharged. Calculate the voltage across the latter capacitor as a function of time. Sketch the variation of this voltage with time if $V_0 = 1$ volt, $C = 1$ μf, $r = 1,000$ ohms, and $R = 1$ megohm. Give a physical explanation for the drastic difference between the two time constants involved.

49. A charged capacitor of capacitance C is connected in parallel with an inductor of inductance L and resistance R. If at time t the voltage across the capacitor is V and the current through the inductor from the negative plate of the capacitor to the positive plate is I, show that

$$C\frac{dV}{dt} - I = 0 \qquad L\frac{dI}{dt} + RI + V = 0$$

50. In the previous problem show that if V and I are both constant multiples of e^{st}, where e is the base of Napierian logarithms, then s is a solution of the quadratic equation

$$LCs^2 + RCs + 1 = 0$$

Show that the equation has real roots if $R > 2(L/C)^{\frac{1}{2}}$ and obtain the roots.

51. If s_1 and s_2 are the solutions of the quadratic equation in the previous problem, show that a solution of the differential equations in Prob. 49 is given by

$$V(t) = A_1e^{s_1t} + A_2e^{s_2t}$$
$$I(t) = C(s_1A_1e^{s_1t} + s_2A_2e^{s_2t})$$

where A_1 and A_2 are constants. Determine the values of A_1 and A_2 so that $V = V_0$ and $I = 0$ when $t = 0$.

52. If at time zero the capacitor in Prob. 49 is charged to voltage V_0 and there is no current through the inductor, describe the process of discharge of the capacitor through the inductor if $R > 2(L/C)^{\frac{1}{2}}$. Sketch curves showing the variation with time in the voltage across the capacitor and the current through the inductor.

53. Repeat the previous problem if $R < 2(L/C)^{\frac{1}{2}}$, showing that the discharge of the capacitor is oscillatory. Verify the results shown in Part 4, Fig. 7.5, in the limiting case when R is negligible.

54. In the network shown in the diagram all voltages and currents are zero at time zero, and at this time a battery of voltage V_0 is connected across the terminals. Show that, at time t, the current through the inductor can be written as

$$A_1 e^{s_1 t} + A_2 e^{s_2 t}$$

and the voltage across the capacitor as

$$V_0 + \frac{1}{C}\left(\frac{1}{s_1} A_1 e^{s_1 t} + \frac{1}{s_2} A_2 e^{s_2 t}\right)$$

where A_1, A_2 are constants and s_1, s_2 are the roots of the quadratic equation

$$LCs^2 + RCs + 1 = 0$$

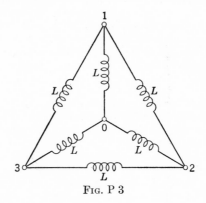

Fig. P 54

Determine the values of A_1, A_2 required to satisfy the conditions at time zero.

55. In the previous problem sketch the variation with time of the voltage across the capacitor and the current through the inductor (a) if $R > 2(L/C)^{\frac{1}{2}}$, (b) if $R = 2(L/C)^{\frac{1}{2}}$, and (c) if $R < 2(L/C)^{\frac{1}{2}}$.

Part 4, Chapter 8

★1. Two inductors each of inductance L and resistance R are connected in parallel across a generator delivering a steady current, and mutual inductance may be neglected. One inductor is disconnected. Prove that the magnetic energy now stored in the other inductor is double that originally stored in both inductors.

★2. Three coils are wound on a cylindrical form side by side. The coefficient of self-inductance of each coil is L, the coefficient of mutual inductance of adjacent windings is $\frac{1}{2}L$, and that of the extreme windings is $\frac{1}{10}L$. Identical currents I are passed through each winding, all right-handed about a common direction. Calculate the magnetic energy stored in the system. Recalculate the energy if the connections to the central winding are reversed.

★3. In the network of equal inductors shown in the diagram, a current I_1 is led in at terminal 1, a current I_2 at terminal 2, and a current I_3 at terminal 3, all three currents

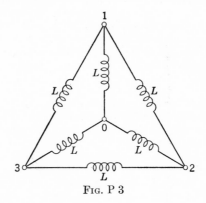

Fig. P 3

being led out at terminal 0. Neglecting magnetic coupling between the coils, calculate the magnetic energy stored in the network.

★4. A two-mesh magnetic network has magnetic fluxes Φ_1 and Φ_2 round the meshes as shown in the diagram. The reluctance common to the two meshes is R_3, and the additional reluctances in the meshes are R_1 and R_2 as shown. Calculate the magnetic energy stored in the system.

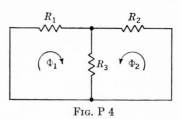

FIG. P 4

★5. Two coaxial circular loops of wire have radii a and b, and their centers are at a distance d apart. The radius a is small compared with the radius b, and a current I that depends on time t flows round the loop of radius a. Using Green's reciprocal theorem, or otherwise, calculate the voltage induced in the wire of radius b.

6. A small circular loop of wire of radius a is mounted with its center in the symmetrical plane of a long twin-wire transmission line composed of thin wires at a distance b apart, large compared with a. The plane of the loop is parallel to the plane of the transmission line, and the two planes are at a distance d apart. The transmission line is short-circuited at both ends at positions whose distances from the loop are large compared with both b and d. At a particular instant the current round the loop is steady and the current in the transmission line is increasing at the rate $\dot{I}$. Calculate the voltage that exists in the loop at this instant in terms of a, b, d, and $\dot{I}$.

★7. For the arrangement shown in Part 4, Fig. 6.6, losses in the transformer may be neglected. Calculate the time rate of increase of the magnetic energy stored in the transformer, and verify that it is equal to the sum of the rates at which energy is being supplied by the two generators. If the generator of voltage $V_2(t)$ is replaced by a resistor of resistance R, show that the rate at which energy is supplied by the generator of voltage $V_1(t)$ exceeds the rate at which energy is dissipated in the resistor by an amount equal to the time rate of increase of the magnetic energy stored in the transformer. If on the average there is no increase in the magnetic energy stored in the transformer, verify that the mean power delivered by the generator is equal to the mean power dissipated in the resistor.

★8. The space between the inner and outer conductors of a coaxial transmission line has internal radius a and external radius b and is filled with a homogeneous medium of inductivity μ. A steady current I passes uniformly along the inner conductor and back along the outer conductor. At a point between the conductors distant r from the axis, calculate the magnetic energy per unit volume. If $I = 1$ amp and the radius of the inner conductor is 1 cm, find the maximum energy density in the field in joules per cubic meter, taking the permeability of the medium as unity.

★9. In the previous problem the part of the magnetic field between circular cylinders of radii r_1 and r_2 coaxial with the transmission line ($a < r_1 < r_2 < b$) is isolated by the introduction of thin conducting cylinders of radii r_1 and r_2. A current I is passed along one of these cylinders and back along the other in such a way as to abolish the magnetic field between them. Calculate the resulting loss in magnetic energy per unit length of the transmission line.

10. A toroidal form of ferromagnetic material constitutes the core of a toroidal inductor, and the relation between the current per unit length H round the toroid and the magnetic flux density B within the toroid is of the form shown in Part 3, Fig. 8.3. The current applied round the inductor varies with time in such a way that a complete hysteresis loop $SPDS'P'D'S$ is described. Show that the energy consumed per unit volume of the ferromagnetic core is numerically equal to the area enclosed by the hysteresis loop.

Part 4, Chapter 9

★1. An electric motor has a field winding carrying a current I_1 and an armature winding carrying a current I_2. The angular position of the armature is specified by means of an angle θ, and the coefficient of mutual inductance between the two windings is $L \cos \theta$. Assuming that the coefficients of self-inductance of the windings are independent of θ, calculate the torque exerted on the armature at the angular position θ.

★2. In the previous problem the armature rotates with uniform angular velocity ω and a commutator reverses the sign of the coefficient of mutual inductance whenever it reaches an extreme value. Plot the torque on the armature as a function of time.

★3. The machine described in Part 4, Chap. 3, Prob. 6, is used as an electric motor. Calculate the coefficient of mutual inductance between the field winding and the armature winding as a function of the angular position θ of the armature. If the armature rotates with uniform angular velocity ω, deduce the torque on the armature as a function of time.

★4. A variable-reluctance motor has a magnetic circuit of the form shown in the diagram, and the winding produces a magnetic flux Φ round the circuit. A portion of the magnetic circuit forms an armature that can rotate on an axis perpendicular to the length of the circuit. The reluctance of the circuit varies between a maximum value R_1 when $\theta = \frac{1}{2}\pi$ and a minimum value R_2 when $\theta = 0$. With the rotor in angular position θ it may be assumed that the reluctance of the magnetic circuit is

$$R_1 \sin^2 \theta + R_2 \cos^2 \theta$$

Calculate the torque on the armature when in angular position θ.

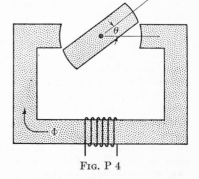

FIG. P 4

5. In the previous problem the magnetic flux Φ oscillates sinusoidally with angular frequency ω and the armature rotates uniformly with angular velocity ω. If $\Phi = \Phi_0 \cos \omega t$ and $\theta = \omega t - \delta$, calculate the torque on the armature at time t. Calculate the mean torque on the armature, and show that it is maximum if $\delta = \pi/4$. Evaluate the maximum value if $\Phi_0 = 10^{-4}$ weber, $R_1 = 10^7$ henry^{-1}, and $R_2 = 5 \times 10^6$ henry^{-1}.

6. A magnetic field is created by a system of coils carrying fixed currents. At a point in the field where the magnetic-flux-density vector is **B**, there is introduced a small loop of wire carrying a fixed current I. The vector area of the loop is **S**, pointing in the direction related by the right-hand-screw rule to the direction of the current I. Show that the magnetic energy of the system is $I\mathbf{S} \cdot \mathbf{B} + K$, where K is a constant as long as the currents producing the magnetic field remain constant.

7. In the previous problem deduce from the expression for the magnetic energy that the torque on the loop is represented vectorially by $I\mathbf{S} \times \mathbf{B}$.

8. In Prob. 6 the loop is held so that there is a fixed angle between the vectors **S** and **B**, but the loop is capable of linear displacement in the direction of a coordinate x. In this direction the rate of increase of the magnetic-flux-density vector is $\partial \mathbf{B}/\partial x$. Show that the force tending to move the loop in the specified direction is $I\mathbf{S} \cdot \partial \mathbf{B}/\partial x$.

9. If in Prob. 6 the loop is capable of movement, show that it seeks a location in the field where the magnetic flux density is greatest and aligns itself so that the vectors **S** and **B** are in the same direction.

10. In a homogeneous medium of inductivity μ there exist two small loops of wire of vector areas S_1 and S_2 carrying fixed currents I_1 and I_2, respectively. The directions of the vector areas are related by the right-hand-screw rule to the directions of the corresponding currents. The position vector of the loop of area S_2 with respect to the loop of area S_1 is r, and r is large compared with the linear dimensions of S_1 and S_2. The three vectors S_1, S_2, and r are coplanar. The angle from the direction of S_1 to the direction of r is θ_1, and the angle from the direction of r to the direction of S_2 is θ_2. Prove that the magnetic energy of the system is

$$\frac{\mu S_1 S_2}{4\pi r^3} I_1 I_2 (2 \cos \theta_1 \cos \theta_2 + \sin \theta_1 \sin \theta_2) + K$$

where K is a constant as long as I_1 and I_2 are constant.

11. For the pair of loops described in the previous problem calculate (a) the force between them tending to increase r, (b) the torque on the loop of area S_1 tending to increase θ_1, (c) the torque on the loop of area S_2 tending to increase θ_2, and (d) the force on either loop transverse to the vector r. Evaluate these quantities if $I_1 = I_2 = 1$ amp, $S_1 = S_2 = 10$ cm^2, $r = 30$ cm, $\theta_1 = \theta_2 = \pi/4$, and $\mu = \mu_v$.

12. Explain why the torques on the loops calculated in the previous problem do not balance. Show that the total mechanical action on each loop reduces to a force whose line of action does not pass through the loop. Verify that the total mechanical actions on the two loops do balance.

13. A magnetic field is created by a system of magnets with fixed pole strengths. At a point in the field where the magnetic vector is H, there is introduced a small magnetic needle of pole strength Φ, and the position vector of the positive pole with respect to the negative pole is s. Show that the magnetic energy of the system is $-\Phi s \cdot H + K$, where K is a constant as long as the pole strengths of the magnets producing the magnetic field remain constant.

14. In the previous problem deduce from the expression for magnetic energy that the torque on the needle is represented vectorially by $\Phi s \times H$.

15. In Prob. 13 the needle is held so that there is a fixed angle between the vectors s and H, but the needle is capable of a linear displacement in the direction of a coordinate x. In this direction the rate of increase of the magnetic vector is $\partial H / \partial x$. Show that the force tending to move the loop in the specified direction is $\Phi s \cdot \partial H / \partial x$.

16. If in Prob. 13 the needle is capable of movement, show that it seeks a location in the field where the magnetic field strength is greatest and aligns itself so that the vectors s and H are in the same direction.

17. In a homogeneous medium there exist two small magnetic needles whose pole strengths are Φ_1 and Φ_2. For the first magnet the position vector of the positive pole with respect to the negative pole is s_1, and for the second magnet it is s_2. The position vector of the magnet of length s_2 with respect to the magnet of length s_1 is r, and r is large compared with s_1 and s_2. The three vectors s_1, s_2, and r are coplanar. The angle from the direction of s_1 to the direction of r is θ_1, and the angle from the direction of r to the direction of s_2 is θ_2. Prove that the magnetic energy of the system is

$$-\frac{s_1 s_2}{4\pi r^3} \Phi_1 \Phi_2 (2 \cos \theta_1 \cos \theta_2 + \sin \theta_1 \sin \theta_2) + K$$

where K is a constant as long as Φ_1 and Φ_2 are constant.

18. For the pair of magnetic needles described in the previous problem calculate the mechanical action between them and compare the results with those obtained for a pair of small loops of current in Probs. 11 and 12. Evaluate the mechanical action if $\Phi_1 = \Phi_2 = 10^{-6}$ weber, $s_1 = s_2 = 1$ cm, $r = 10$ cm, $\theta_1 = \theta_2 = \pi/4$, and $\mu = \mu_v$.

★19. A coaxial transmission line has an inner conductor of radius a and an outer conductor of radius b between which there is air of inductivity μ. There is a steady current I flowing along the inner conductor and back along the outer. The outer conductor is now divided into two conductors along a diametrical plane. Calculate the force per unit length that must be applied to each half to keep it in place. Evaluate the force per meter length if $I = 1$ amp and $b = 1$ cm, assuming that the permeability of the medium between the conductors is unity.

★20. A horseshoe electromagnet of negligible reluctance in air is wound with n turns of wire each having resistance r. A flat soft-iron armature of negligible reluctance covers both pole faces, each of which is a square of edge a. The armature can rotate about an axis in the plane of the pole faces as indicated in the diagram. The armature

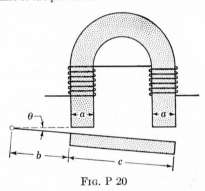

Fig. P 20

is pulled away from the pole faces and held at a small angle θ while a voltage V is connected across the winding. Show that the lines of magnetic flux in the air gaps are approximately circles coaxial with the pivot, and calculate the torque about the pivot tending to restore the armature to its original position. Evaluate the torque when $\theta = 1°$, $a = 1$ cm, $b = c = 4$ cm, $V = 10$ volts, and $r = 10^{-2}$ ohm. If the power dissipation in the winding is to be less than 1 watt, calculate the minimum number of turns of wire that can be used.

★21. An electric train is provided with magnetic brakes each consisting of a horseshoe electromagnet which, when energized by an n-turn coil carrying a steady current I, is attracted to the steel rail. The area of contact of a brake shoe with the rail is S, and the reluctance of the magnetic circuit so formed is R. If η is the coefficient of friction between the shoe and the rail, calculate the braking force. Evaluate the braking force if $n = 1,000$, $I = 1$ amp, $S = 100$ cm², $R = 10^5$ henry^{-1}, and $\eta = 0.1$.

★22. A magnetic field in air is found to exert a sideways pressure equal to the atmospheric pressure at sea level (10^5 newtons/m²). Calculate the magnetic flux density in gauss.

23. In Part 3, Chap. 4, Prob. 13, calculate the force per unit area on the sheet at the foot of the perpendicular from the center of the solenoid.

24. A beam of charged particles is emitted from the Sun, and the axis of the beam rotates with the Sun in the plane of the Earth's orbit. As the beam approaches the Earth, it is influenced by the Earth's magnetic field. The approaching beam may be regarded as a semi-infinite conducting medium with an infinite plane face into which the Earth's magnetic field cannot penetrate. The Earth's magnetic field may be regarded as arising from a small loop of wire whose axis is parallel to the face of the

advancing beam and for which Part 3, Eq. (7.35), is applicable. Show that, at the foot of the perpendicular from the center of the Earth onto the face of the beam, the strength of the Earth's magnetic field is doubled by the presence of the beam. If the advance of the beam at the foot of the perpendicular from the Earth is stopped when the length of the perpendicular is equal to six Earth's radii, calculate the pressure exerted by the beam.

25. In the previous problem estimate the modification in the magnetic field at the surface of the Earth caused by the presence of the beam of electrons from the Sun when the perpendicular from the center of the Earth onto the plane face of the beam is equal to 10 Earth's radii.

★26. In the d-c generator described with Part 4, Fig. 3.5, the permanent magnet is replaced by an electromagnet for which nonlinear behavior of the ferromagnetic material may be neglected. The coefficient of mutual inductance between the windings at the epoch of commutation is L_{12}. If I_1 is the current in the field winding and I_2 is the current in the armature winding, show that the torque required on the armature is $L_{12}I_1I_2$.

★27. Two coils have vertical planes with an angle $\frac{1}{2}\pi - \theta$ between them, and the coefficient of mutual inductance between the coils is $L \sin \theta$. The coils are connected in series, and a sinusoidal current $I_0 \cos \omega t$ is passed through. Calculate the mean torque between the two coils.

★28. In the previous problem one coil is fixed and the other can rotate on a vertical axis. This coil is too heavy to oscillate at an angular frequency ω and is provided with a spring that exerts a torque proportional to angular deviation from the position $\theta = 0$. Show that the deflection of the coil is proportional to the mean-square current through the coils provided that this current is sufficiently small.

★29. The voltage and current of a transmission line oscillate with angular frequency ω, the voltage being $V_0 \cos (\omega t + \alpha)$ and the current $I_0 \cos (\omega t + \beta)$. To measure the rate at which energy is flowing along the transmission line the current is passed through a fixed coil and a current proportional to the line voltage is passed through a pivoted coil. When the planes of the coils have an angle $\frac{1}{2}\pi - \theta$ between them, the coefficient of mutual inductance is $L \sin \theta$. Show that the mean torque on the pivoted coil is proportional to the mean rate of energy flow along the transmission line. If the pivoted coil has sufficient inertia and is restrained by a spring that exerts a torque proportional to angular deviation from the position $\theta = 0$, show that the device can be used as a wattmeter.

30. In the previous problem the restraining spring is replaced by an electromagnetic brake of the type described in Chap. 3, Prob. 12. The brake is on the same spindle as the pivoted coil, and the two coils operate as a motor. Show that, if the mechanism has sufficient inertia, the speed of rotation is proportional to the rate at which energy is flowing along the transmission line. Explain how the device can be used as a watt-hour meter.

Part 4, Chapter 10

1. A coaxial inductor consists of a pair of perfectly conducting thin coaxial cylinders short-circuited at one end. The space between the cylinders has inner radius a, outer radius b, and length l, and it is filled with a homogeneous nonconducting medium of inductivity μ and capacitivity ϵ. At the open end of the transmission line a battery of voltage V_0 is connected between the inner and outer conductors at time zero. Fringing of the electromagnetic field outside the space between the conductors may be neglected. At a point between the conductors distant x from the battery end and r from the axis, calculate for time t (a) the magnitude and direction of the Poynting vector, (b) the stored magnetic energy per unit volume, and (c) the stored electric energy per unit volume. Draw sketches to illustrate the variations of these quantities in space and time.

2. In the charging capacitor described in Part 4, Secs. 1.7 and 1.8, calculate the stored magnetic energy per unit volume at a distance x from the generator and show that it does not vary with time.

3. An oscillatory electric circuit is of the type in Part 4, Fig. 10.13. Three geometrical planes p_1, p_2, p_3 are drawn, of which the first passes through the lines where the capacitor joins the inductor. The plane p_2 is perpendicular to the plates of the capacitor and bisects the edges of length l. The plane p_3 is a diametrical plane of the inductor perpendicular to the plates of the capacitor. Show that the maximum rate of flow of energy across the planes p_2 and p_3 is approximately half that across the plane p_1. Describe the approximations involved.

★4. The diagram indicates an oscillatory electric circuit consisting of a length l of coaxial transmission line (inner radius a, outer radius b) connected across a parallel-plate capacitor whose plates are of area πa^2 and separation s, small compared with a and l. The homogeneous medium enclosed by the device has inductivity μ and

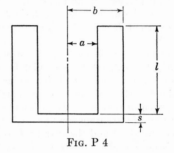

FIG. P 4

capacitivity ϵ, and losses may be neglected. Calculate approximately (a) the resonant frequency and (b) the dynamic resistance. Find how small s must be in order to satisfy Part 4, condition (5.70). Provided this condition is satisfied, plot a curve relating the resonant wavelength to the value of s if $a = 1$ cm, $b = 3$ cm, $l = 5$ cm, $\mu = \mu_v$, and $\epsilon = \epsilon_v$.

★5. If in the preceding problem the resonant angular frequency is ω and the voltage across the capacitor is $V_0 \cos \omega t$, calculate as a function of time t (a) the electric energy stored in the capacitor, (b) the magnetic energy stored in the inductor, and (c) the rate of flow of energy at the junction between the capacitor and the inductor. Draw curves to illustrate these results.

★6. In the oscillatory electric circuit described in Prob. 4 draw sketches to illustrate, at various stages during the oscillation cycle, (a) the electromagnetic field and (b) the flow of energy.

INDEX

Boldface numbers shown in parentheses refer to problems on the pages indicated

815